SOURCE BOOK ON SELECTION AND FABRICATION OF ALUMINUM ALLOYS

A comprehensive collection of
outstanding articles from the
industrial and reference literature

Compiled by
Publications Development
American Society for Metals

AMERICAN SOCIETY FOR METALS
Metals Park, Ohio 44073

Library of Congress Cataloging in Publication Data

American Society for Metals. Publications
    Development.
    Source book on selection and fabrication of
aluminum alloys.

    Includes bibliographical references and index.
    1. Aluminum alloys—Handbooks, manuals, etc.
I. Title.
TS555.A76 1978   673'.722   78-18869
ISBN 0-87170-003-4

PRINTED IN THE UNITED STATES OF AMERICA

Preface

During World War II, aluminum production facilities in the United States expanded sevenfold, and there was understandable speculation, if not concern, about declining consumption of aluminum in the postwar economy. What concern there may have been proved unwarranted as public acceptance of aluminum products continued to increase. Concurrently, new applications encouraged the development of new alloys, heat treatments and fabricating techniques — a trend that has by no means abated.

Impelled by the trend, there arose in the engineering and manufacturing communities a continuing need for reliable information on the selection of aluminum alloys and all aspects of their fabrication. Comprehensive, authoritative coverage in fully six volumes of the 8th Edition of Metals Handbook, as well as that issuing from other accredited publications, served to fulfill this need. SOURCE BOOK ON SELECTION AND FABRICATION OF ALUMINUM ALLOYS follows in this tradition by assembling for ready and convenient reference in a single book information that otherwise would entail a sizable assortment. The contents of the book, a brief summary of which follows, have been arranged in thirteen principal sections.

Introduction. The opening section presents an article containing a brief history of aluminum, the physical properties and characteristics of the unalloyed metal, and chemical composition limits and typical mechanical properties of wrought alloys.

Selection. The article "Selection of Aluminum Alloys" provides information basic to the selection of wrought and cast alloys. It explains the designation system for wrought alloys and compares key characteristics, such as corrosion resistance, workability, machinability, brazeability and weldability of the wrought alloys in standard tempers. Coverage is also provided on effects of alloying elements, standard heat treatments and temper designations. The designation system for castings and ingot is explained, and the chemical composition limits and mechanical properties of cast alloys are tabulated.

Forming. A definitive article from Vol. 4 of Metals Handbook covers all aspects of commercial forming, including equipment and tools, lubricants, blanking and piercing, press-brake forming, contour roll forming, deep drawing, hot drawing, spinning, stretch forming, rubber-pad and hydraulic forming, forming by shot peening, drop hammer forming, explosive forming, and electrohydraulic and electromagnetic forming. The section concludes with an article on forming aluminum prepared by the Aluminum Association.

Cold Extrusion. A Metals Handbook article discusses the fundamentals of cold extrusion, including presses, tooling, stock for slugs, surface preparation, extrusion of shallow and deep cuplike parts and parts with complex shapes, and dimensional accuracy. A second article, "Extruding Aluminum," serves as a supplement.

Forging and Forging Design. This section comprises four articles — the first on forging of aluminum alloys from Vol. 5 of Metals Handbook, and the remaining three on die forging design, forging tolerances, and drafting conventions for forging. Forging methods, alloys and temperatures, forgeability, hammers and presses, dies, preparation of stock, heating for forging, heating of dies, lubricants, trimming and cleaning are among the basic subjects covered. The forging design articles are among the most authoritative available.

Melting and Casting. "Foundry Melting of Aluminum Alloys" and "Production of Aluminum Alloy Castings" are articles from Vol. 5 of Metals Handbook. The article on melting covers types of furnaces, materials of construction, charging practice, control of composition and impurities, and transferring molten aluminum. The article on production of castings discusses casting processes, including sand, plaster mold, investment, permanent mold, and die casting. It is supplemented by an article on casting aluminum prepared by the Aluminum Association.

Machining. Two articles on machining of aluminum alloys are contained in this section. Among the subjects accorded broad coverage are cutting force and power, selection of alloy and temper, general machining conditions, tool design, tool material, cutting fluid, and distortion and dimensional variation. The machining processes discussed include turning, boring, planing and shaping, broaching, drilling, reaming, burnishing, tapping, multiple-operation machining, grinding, lapping, and chemical machining.

Heat Treating. "Heat Treating of Aluminum Alloys," an article from Vol. 2 of Metals Handbook, covers all aspects of the subject, including solution treating, quenching, treatments prior to precipitation hardening, hardening cast alloys, effects of reheating, annealing, furnace equipment and accessories, temperature control, grain growth, and effect of heat treatment on corrosion resistance.

Cleaning and Finishing. A 24-page Metals Handbook article covers all of the methods and equipment employed in cleaning and finishing of aluminum alloys. Among them are abrasive blast cleaning, barrel finishing,

polishing and buffing, chemical cleaning, chemical and electrolytic polishing, alkaline and acid etching, anodizing processes, chemical conversion coating, immersion and chemical plating, and painting. The section concludes with the Aluminum Association designation system for aluminum finishes.

Welding. Two arc welding processes — gas metal-arc and gas tungsten-arc — are widely used for welding aluminum alloys and are covered in the lead article of this section. This comprehensive article from Vol. 6 of Metals Handbook discusses all aspects of these key processes, including base metals, filler metals, joint design and edge preparation, cleaning, preheating, fixtures, shielding gases, arc characteristics, electrode wires, weld backing, multiple-pass and automatic welding, weld soundness, and repair and spot welding. Comparable coverage of basic subject matter is given resistance welding of aluminum alloys in the second article of the section.

Brazing. This section and the section on soldering are the largest in the book, because it is felt that expanded coverage in these subject areas is warranted in terms of future technological requirements. The lead article is from Vol. 6 of Metals Handbook and covers current brazing methods. It is supplemented by an introduction to aluminum brazing and individual articles on joint and jig design; base metals, brazing filler metals and fluxes; pre-cleaning, oxide removal, post-cleaning and finishing; torch brazing; flux-dip brazing; furnace brazing; vacuum and controlled atmosphere brazing; other brazing methods; brazing aluminum to other metals; joint inspection, testing and performance; and safety — all of which are from the Aluminum Brazing Handbook.

Soldering. An introduction to aluminum soldering is followed by separate articles covering material for soldering; pre-cleaning, oxide removal and surface preparation; post-cleaning and finishing; jig and joint design; torch, iron and hot-plate soldering; abrasion and ultrasonic soldering; furnace soldering; other soldering techniques — reaction, wipe, induction, dip and radiant heat; soldering castings; soldering aluminum to other metals and non-metallics; joint inspection, testing and performance; and safety measures.

Mechanical and Adhesive Joining. The first article in the final section of the book covers the mechanical joining methods — riveting, stitching, stapling, and the use of standard and special fasteners — and adhesive bonding. The second article on evaluation of adhesives for joining aluminum originally appeared in Metals Engineering Quarterly.

The American Society for Metals extends its grateful appreciation to The Aluminum Association, Inc., for permission to include in this book a selection of outstanding articles that have appeared in their handbooks. Grateful acknowledgment is also extended to the many contributors to ASM publications, notably Metals Handbook, on whose work the value of this book to the engineering community so largely depends.

Paul M. Unterweiser
Staff Editor
Manager, Publications Development
American Society for Metals

William H. Cubberly
Director of Reference Publications
American Society for Metals

Cover photo: Aluminum Company of America

Contributors to This Source Book*

C. H. AVERY
Douglas Aircraft Co.

F. R. BAYSINGER
Kaiser Aluminum & Chemical Corp.

B. W. BISCHOF
Aluminum Co. of Canada, Ltd.

H. H. BLOCK
AiResearch Mfg. Co.

ALFRED A. BOULD
Grumman Aircraft Engineering Corp.

A. B. BRADLEY
Warwick Industrial Furnace and
  Engineering Co.

CARSON L. BROOKS
Reynolds Metals Co.

JACK CARROLL
Amchem Products, Inc.

CHARLES E. CATALDO
NASA

VERNE CLAIRE, JR.
Kelsey-Hayes Co.

JOHN W. CLARKE
General Electric Co.

CHARLES C. COHN
Colonial Alloys Co.

ELDON COOPERRIDER
Lennox Industries Inc.

R. COUCHMAN
Aluminum Co. of America

JOHN H. DEN BOER
Reynolds Metals Co.

R. W. DIVELY
Goodyear Aerospace Corp.

J. R. DOUSLIN
Wyman-Gordon Co.

WALTER O. DOW, JR.
Sunbeam Corp.

V. E. DRESS
Lockheed Aircraft Corp.

EDWARD A. DURAND
International Business
  Machines Corp.

ALLAN ENIS
Union Carbide Corp.

GEORGE F. FARLEY
Spincraft, Inc.

DON R. FYLLING
FMC Corp.

J. E. GAROL
Douglas Aircraft Co.

R. H. GASSNER
Douglas Aircraft Co.

JAMES C. HERR
General Dynamics/Fort Worth

JOHN J. HOFFER
Eastman Kodak Co.

G. O. HOGLUND
Aluminum Co. of America

R. E. HUFFAKER
Ladish Co.

R. HUMPHREYS
North American Aviation, Inc.

FRANK W. HUSSEY
Frankford Arsenal

H. A. JAMES
Sciaky Bros., Inc.

W. R. JEBSON
Westinghouse Electric Corp.

DONALD A. JOHNSON
Bendix Corp.

A. J. KAISER
Brunswick Corp.

RICHARD T. KENNEDY
Sunbeam Corp.

R. D. KESLER
General Dynamics/Astronautics

G. V. KINGSLEY
Bohn Aluminum and Brass Corp.

A. J. KISH
ACF Industries Inc.

G. H. KISSIN
Kaiser Aluminum and
  Chemical Corp.

VIRGIL J. KNIERIM
Aeroquip Corp.

JOSEPH KOCHANEK
Chandler Evans Corp.

T. E. KRAMER
Ross Pattern & Foundry, Inc.

WILL LADD
Globe Industries, Inc.

* Affiliations given were applicable at date of contribution.

E. R. LOEBACH
Studebaker Corp.

JOHN LONGABAUGH
Outboard Marine Corp.

WILLIAM A. MADER
Oberdorfer Foundries, Inc.

LAWSON E. MARSH
Morris Bean & Co.

T. I. McCLINTOCK
Aluminum Co. of America

MATTIE F. McFADDEN
Raytheon Co.

C. E. McHAN
Lockheed Aircraft Corp.

F. G. McKEE
Aluminum Co. of America

FLORENCE R. MEYER
Aeroprojects, Inc.

J. DEAN MINFORD
Aluminum Co. of America

A. M. MONTGOMERY
Aluminum Co. of America

G. R. MOUDRY
Harvey Aluminum, Inc.

CARL H. MUTH
Universal Castings Corp.

G. D. NELSON
Monsanto Chemical Co.

PAUL R. O'BRIEN
Reynolds Metals Co.

WILLIAM OBERNDORFER
Chrysler Corp.

ARTHUR L. PAGE
Talon, Inc.

VITO PALOMBELLA
Grumman Aircraft Engineering Corp.

WALTER PAJERSKI
Mine Safety Appliances Co.

CHARLES PELLEGRINI
Arwood Corp.

JACK W. PETERSEN
Adams & Westlake Co.

SCOTT F. REEKIE
Tektronix, Inc.

CARL REXER
Eastman Kodak Co.

R. A. RIDOUT
Kaiser Aluminum & Chemical
Sales, Inc.

EARL J. ROBERTS
Lockheed Aircraft Corp.

C. A. ROSELLEN
Hughes Aircraft Co.

W. C. RUDD
AMF Thermatool, Inc.

Z. P. SAPERSTEIN
American Welding and
Manufacturing Co.

H. L. SAUNDERS
Alcan Research and
Development Limited

WARREN F. SAVAGE
Rensselaer Polytechnic Institute

R. SCHMIDT
United States Department
of the Navy

WILLIAM C. SCHULTE
Curtiss-Wright Corp.

E. R. SEAY
Lockheed Aircraft Corp.

HARRY SOSSON
Artcraft Plating, Inc.

ALFRED SPOLIDORO
Western Electric Co., Inc.

ELLIS STAIR
Boeing Co.

JACK H. THOMPSON
Bodine Foundry Co.

M. M. TILLEY
Kaiser Aluminum & Chemical
Sales, Inc.

R. A. TITLOW
General Motors Corp.

ELMER P. TORKE
Mirro Aluminum Co.

E. S. TYMINSKI
Air Products and Chemicals Inc.

R. V. VANDEN BERG
Aluminum Co. of America

ANTHONY V. VECCHIOTTI
Monroe Forgings, Inc.

N. L. WARD
Consultant

GILBERT G. WARREN
Bendix Corp.

N. E. WHEELER
General Motors Corp.

J. C. WHITE
North American Aviation, Inc.

F. R. WIEHL
Singer Co.

GEORGE R. WLODYGA
Ford Motor Co.

JOHN A. WYMAN
Permold Inc.

and

THE ALUMINUM ASSOCIATION, INC.

CONTENTS

Section I:
Introduction

Aluminum

Today man chooses aluminum for more than a thousand kinds of applications either because its ease of fabrication makes product costs competitive, or because the properties and performance of the pure metal and its many alloys are superior as compared with other materials. Many buildings are now largely aluminum, as are trucks, trains, airplanes, boats and spaceships. Principal aluminum mill products and the industries that use them are shown in the accompanying chart. (See Figure 1-1.)

Unknown to the world as an available shop material until the beginning of this century, aluminum is now the most widely used of all metals except iron. Its ready availability today and for the future is assured by the fact that aluminum is the most abundant metal in the earth's crust.

Because extraction of the metal from its ore requires several chemical steps, plus electrolytic reduction, the initial cost of a product made of aluminum is often not lower than that of similar products made of competitive materials.

However, many aluminum products end up costing less than their counterparts made of other materials because aluminum is easier to cut and form, requires less maintenance, is lighter at comparable strength, reflects radiant energy more efficiently, or is a better conductor of heat and electricity than other commercial materials. Also, some products which have to be assembled from several shapes when made of other materials can be made in a single piece at lower cost by extruding, forging or casting aluminum.

For electrical power transmission and distribution, even the original cost of aluminum is significantly lower than its chief competitor, copper, which was used for this purpose almost exclusively, prior to the development of aluminum. On a pound-for-pound basis, aluminum can conduct twice as much electricity as can copper.

History

In nature, aluminum is found in the earth where it was firmly combined with other elements, principally oxygen and silicon, in the beginning of the world billions of years ago. As man developed his arts, crafts and tools, he began to utilize the earth's elements in the materials at hand. He employed aluminum for about 7,000 years in the form of fine pottery clay, without even knowing he was using a material that contained a metal.

Much later, but for still several hundred years prior to the discovery of the metal itself, he used it in the form of alum for dying cloth and making certain medicines and other chemical compounds.

Finally in 1782, the great French chemist Lavoisier reported, "It is highly probable that alumine is the oxide of a metal whose affinity for oxygen is so strong that it cannot be overcome either by carbon or any other known reducing agent." But it was not until 1825 that a scientist named H. C. Oersted reported to the Royal Danish Academy of Sciences in Copenhagen that he had "found the metal of clay."

Oersted had obtained a small lump of aluminum by heating potassium amalgam with aluminum chloride.

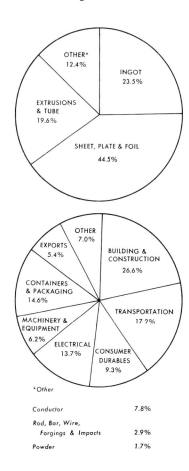

SOURCE: Estimated by the Statistical and Commercial Research Policy Committee of The Aluminum Association

Fig. 1-1. Charts show percentage of mill products (top) purchased by U.S. fabricators to make thousands of consumer products for markets shown in bottom chart.

TABLE 1-1
Physical Properties of Aluminum
(99.95% Minimum Purity)

Properties	British Units	Metric Units
Density at 20 C	0.0975 lb per cu in.	2.70 grams per cc
Melting Point	1220 F	660 C
Boiling Point at 760 mm Mercury	4221 F	2327 C
Thermal Conductivity at 25 C	1540 Btu per hr per sq ft per in. thickness per deg F	0.53 g cal per sec per sq cm per cm thickness per deg C
Mean Specific Heat (0 C to 100 C)	0.225 Btu per lb per deg F	0.225 cal per gram per deg C
Coefficient of Linear Thermal Expansion (20 C to 100 C)	0.00001322 per deg F	0.0000239 per deg C
Latent Heat of Fusion	167 Btu per lb	93 cal per gram
Crystal Structure	Face-centered cubic	Face-centered cubic
Modulus of Elasticity (Young's)	10,000,000 psi	703,000 kg per sq cm
Modulus of Rigidity (Shear)	3,790,000 psi	267,000 kg per sq cm
Poisson's Ratio	0.33	0.33
Electrical Resistivity at 20 C	15.8 ohms circular mil per ft	0.00000263 ohm-cm
Temperature Coefficient of Electrical Resistivity at 20 C	0.00238 per deg F	0.00429 per deg C
Magnetic Susceptibility at 18 C		+0.00000065/gram

During the next several decades improved chemical processes for obtaining aluminum were discovered and developed by others, but the best of them was slow and relatively unproductive; the metal was rare and expensive and therefore found little practical use.

Then, in early 1886, working independently and each unaware of the other's activities, Charles Martin Hall in Oberlin, Ohio, and Paul L. T. Héroult in Paris, France, discovered almost simultaneously the electrolytic process which was developed into that now used for the volume production of aluminum.

Today aluminum is produced from fine, white granules of pure aluminum oxide (alumina). Alumina is obtained chemically from bauxite, which is mined from deposits generally lying near the surface of the earth.

The alumina (Al_2O_3) is dissolved in molten cryolite in large, carbon-lined cells. Low voltage, high amperage, direct electrical current separates the aluminum and oxygen. The lining of a cell is the cathode (negative) and the carbon electrode suspended in the center of the cell is the anode (positive). A series of these cells, electrically connected together by large aluminum bus bars, is called a "potline."

A more detailed account of how aluminum is made is given in the booklet, *The Story of Aluminum,* available upon request from the *Aluminum Association.*

Characteristics

As it comes direct from a reduction cell in the potline, aluminum content of the molten metal is from 99.5 to 99.79%. This is called "commercial purity" aluminum, and has many decorative and electrical applications.

The physical properties of unalloyed aluminum are given in Table 1-1. Aluminum alone is quite soft, but the addition of small amounts of certain other elements produces aluminum alloys of remarkable strength without adding appreciably to weight.

Consequently, the largest use of commercial purity aluminum is to produce alloys, which are the "many metals of aluminum." (Chemical compositions of the principal aluminum alloys are given on Table 1-2). Following are the principal characteristics of aluminum.

Light—Aluminum is the lightest (0.1 pound per cubic inch) of all usual structural metals, except magnesium. Because it weighs only about one-third as much as either copper or iron, aluminum sheet equal in weight and thickness to copper will cover about three times as much area.

Depending upon section thickness necessary to meet the strength required by the application, an average of two to three times the number of products made of aluminum may be shipped and less transportation-fuel consumed.

Strong—Cold working increases the strength and hardness of aluminum and all of its alloys. For example, the tensile strength of commercially pure aluminum is about 13,000 psi. Made "full hard" by rolling, its strength is approximately doubled. Greatly increased strengths are further obtained by alloying aluminum with various combinations of manganese, silicon, copper, magnesium and zinc.

Some, but not all, of the alloys can be additionally strengthened by heat treatments; alloys with strengths approaching 100,000 psi are now available. For further details, see the *How Aluminum Is Strengthened* and *Aluminum Alloy and Temper Designation Systems* sections of Chapter 2, entitled *Aluminum Alloys.*

The strength of aluminum increases at subzero temperatures, as does the ductility of most of its alloys; whereas, many other materials become brittle. While increasing ambient temperatures generally de-

TABLE 1-2
Chemical Composition Limits of Wrought Aluminum Alloys [1][2]

AA DESIGNATION	SILICON	IRON	COPPER	MANGANESE	MAGNESIUM	CHROMIUM	NICKEL	ZINC	TITANIUM	OTHERS Each	OTHERS Total	ALUMINUM Min. [4]
1050	0.25	0.40	0.05	0.05	0.05			0.05	0.03	0.03		99.50
1060	0.25	0.35	0.05	0.03	0.03			0.05	0.03	0.03[17]		99.60
1100	1.0 Si+Fe		0.05-0.20	0.05				0.10		0.05[17]	0.15	99.00
1145[8]	0.55 Si+Fe		0.05	0.05						0.03		99.45
1175[9]	0.15 Si+Fe		0.10					0.03		0.02[20]		99.75
1200	1.0 Si+Fe		0.05	0.05				0.10	0.05	0.05	0.15	99.00
1230[7]	0.7 Si+Fe		0.10	0.05				0.10		0.05		99.30
1235	0.65 Si+Fe		0.05							0.05		99.35
1345	0.30	0.40	0.10							0.05		99.45
2011	0.40	0.7	5.0-6.0					0.30		0.05[10]	0.15	Remainder
2014	0.50-1.2	0.7	3.9-5.0	0.40-1.2	0.20-0.8	0.10		0.25	0.15[21]	0.05[17]	0.15	Remainder
2017	0.20-0.8	0.7	3.5-4.5	0.40-1.0	0.40-0.8	0.10		0.25	0.15[21]	0.05	0.15	Remainder
2018	0.9	1.0	3.5-4.5	0.20	0.45-0.9	0.10	1.7-2.3	0.25		0.05	0.15	Remainder
2024	0.50	0.50	3.8-4.9	0.30-0.9	1.2-1.8	0.10		0.25	0.15[21]	0.05	0.15	Remainder
2025	0.50-1.2	1.0	3.9-5.0	0.40-1.2	0.05	0.10		0.25	0.15	0.05	0.15	Remainder
2117	0.8	0.7	2.2-3.0	0.20	0.20-0.50	0.10		0.25		0.05	0.15	Remainder
2124	0.20	0.30	3.8-4.9	0.30-0.9	1.2-1.8	0.10		0.25	0.15[21]	0.05	0.15	Remainder
2218	0.9	1.0	3.5-4.5	0.20	1.2-1.8	0.10	1.7-2.3	0.25		0.05	0.15	Remainder
2219	0.20	0.30	5.8-6.8	0.20-0.40	0.02			0.10	0.02-0.10	0.05[19]	0.15	Remainder
2618	0.10-0.25	0.9-1.3	1.9-2.7		1.3-1.8		0.9-1.2	0.10	0.04-0.10	0.05	0.15	Remainder
3003	0.6	0.7	0.05-0.20	1.0-1.5				0.10		0.05[17]	0.15	Remainder
3004	0.30	0.7	0.25	1.0-1.5	0.8-1.3			0.25		0.05[17]	0.15	Remainder
3005	0.6	0.7	0.30	1.0-1.5	0.20-0.6	0.10		0.25	0.10	0.05	0.15	Remainder
3105	0.6	0.7	0.30	0.30-0.8	0.20-0.8	0.20		0.40	0.10	0.05	0.15	Remainder
4032	11.0-13.5	1.0	0.50-1.3		0.8-1.3	0.10	0.50-1.3	0.25		0.05	0.15	Remainder
4043	4.5-6.0	0.8	0.30	0.05	0.05			0.10	0.20	0.05[17]	0.15	Remainder
4045[11]	9.0-11.0	0.8	0.30	0.05	0.05			0.10	0.20	0.05	0.15	Remainder
4343[11]	6.8-8.2	0.8	0.25	0.10				0.20		0.05	0.15	Remainder
5005	0.30	0.7	0.20	0.20	0.50-1.1	0.10		0.25		0.05	0.15	Remainder
5050	0.40	0.7	0.20	0.10	1.1-1.8	0.10		0.25		0.05[17]	0.15	Remainder
5052	0.45 Si+Fe		0.10	0.10	2.2-2.8	0.15-0.35		0.10		0.05[17]	0.15	Remainder
5056	0.30	0.40	0.10	0.05-0.20	4.5-5.6	0.05-0.20		0.10		0.05[17]	0.15	Remainder
5083	0.40	0.40	0.10	0.40-1.0	4.0-4.9	0.05-0.25		0.25	0.15	0.05	0.15	Remainder
5086	0.40	0.50	0.10	0.20-0.7	3.5-4.5	0.05-0.25		0.25	0.15	0.05	0.15	Remainder
5154	0.45 Si+Fe		0.10	0.10	3.1-3.9	0.15-0.35		0.20	0.20	0.05[17]	0.15	Remainder
5252	0.08	0.10	0.10	0.10	2.2-2.8					0.03	0.10	Remainder
5254	0.45 Si+Fe		0.05	0.01	3.1-3.9	0.15-0.35		0.20	0.05	0.05	0.15	Remainder
5356	0.50 Si+Fe		0.10	0.05-0.20	4.5-5.5	0.05-0.20		0.10	0.06-0.20	0.05[17]	0.15	Remainder
5454	0.40 Si+Fe		0.10	0.50-1.0	2.4-3.0	0.05-0.20		0.25	0.20	0.05	0.15	Remainder
5456	0.40 Si+Fe		0.10	0.50-1.0	4.7-5.5	0.05-0.20		0.25	0.20	0.05	0.15	Remainder
5457	0.08	0.10	0.20	0.15-0.45	0.8-1.2			0.03		0.03	0.10	Remainder
5652	0.40 Si+Fe		0.04	0.01	2.2-2.8	0.15-0.35		0.10		0.05[17]	0.15	Remainder
5657	0.08	0.10	0.10	0.03	0.6-1.0			0.03		0.02[20]	0.05	Remainder
6003[13]	0.35-1.0	0.6	0.10	0.8	0.8-1.5	0.35		0.20	0.10	0.05	0.15	Remainder
6005	0.6-0.9	0.35	0.10	0.10	0.40-0.6	0.10		0.10	0.10	0.05	0.15	Remainder
6053	[16]	0.35	0.10		1.1-1.4	0.15-0.35		0.10		0.05	0.15	Remainder
6061	0.40-0.8	0.7	0.15-0.40	0.15	0.8-1.2	0.04-0.35		0.25	0.15	0.05	0.15	Remainder
6063	0.20-0.6	0.35	0.10	0.10	0.45-0.9	0.10		0.10	0.10	0.05	0.15	Remainder
6066	0.9-1.8	0.50	0.7-1.2	0.6-1.1	0.8-1.4	0.40		0.25	0.20	0.05	0.15	Remainder
6070	1.0-1.7	0.50	0.15-0.40	0.40-1.0	0.50-1.2	0.10		0.25	0.15	0.05	0.15	Remainder
6101[12]	0.30-0.7	0.50	0.10	0.03	0.35-0.8	0.03		0.10		0.03[18]	0.10	Remainder
6151	0.6-1.2	1.0	0.35	0.20	0.45-0.8	0.15-0.35		0.25	0.15	0.05	0.15	Remainder
6162	0.40-0.8	0.50	0.20	0.10	0.7-1.1	0.10		0.25	0.10	0.05	0.15	Remainder
6201	0.50-0.9	0.50	0.10	0.03	0.6-0.9	0.03		0.10		0.03[18]	0.10	Remainder
6253[14]	[16]	0.50	0.10		1.0-1.5	0.15-0.35		1.6-2.4		0.05	0.15	Remainder
6262	0.40-0.8	0.7	0.15-0.40	0.15	0.8-1.2	0.04-0.14		0.25	0.15	0.05[5]	0.15	Remainder
6351	0.7-1.3	0.50	0.10	0.40-0.8	0.40-0.8			0.20	0.20	0.05	0.15	Remainder
6463	0.20-0.6	0.15	0.20	0.05	0.45-0.9					0.05	0.15	Remainder
6951	0.20-0.50	0.8	0.15-0.40	0.10	0.40-0.8			0.20		0.05	0.15	Remainder
7001	0.35	0.40	1.6-2.6	0.20	2.6-3.4	0.18-0.35		6.8-8.0	0.20	0.05	0.15	Remainder
7005	0.35	0.40	0.10	0.20-0.7	1.0-1.8	0.06-0.20		4.0-5.0	0.01-0.06	0.05[23]	0.15	Remainder
7011[24]	0.15	0.20	0.05	0.10-0.30	1.0-1.6	0.05-0.20		4.0-5.5	0.05	0.05	0.15	Remainder
7072[15]	0.7 Si+Fe		0.10	0.10	0.10			0.8-1.3		0.05	0.15	Remainder
7075	0.40	0.50	1.2-2.0	0.30	2.1-2.9	0.18-0.35		5.1-6.1	0.20[22]	0.05	0.15	Remainder
7079	0.30	0.40	0.40-0.8	0.10-0.30	2.9-3.7	0.10-0.25		3.8-4.8	0.10	0.05	0.15	Remainder
7178	0.40	0.50	1.6-2.4	0.30	2.4-3.1	0.18-0.35		6.3-7.3	0.20	0.05	0.15	Remainder

[1] Composition in percent maximum unless shown as a range or a minimum.

[2] For purposes of determining conformance to these limits, an observed value or a calculated value obtained from analysis is rounded off to the nearest unit in the last right-hand place of figures used in expressing the specified limit, in accordance with AN Standard Rules for Rounding Off Numerical Values (ANSI Z25.1).

[3] Analysis is regularly made only for the elements for which specific limits are shown, except for unalloyed aluminum. If, however, the presence of other elements is suspected to be, or in the course of routine analysis is indicated to be in excess of the specified limits, further analysis is made to determine that these other elements are not in excess of the amount specified.

[4] The aluminum content for unalloyed aluminum not made by a refining process is the difference between 100.00 percent and the sum of all other metallic elements present in amounts of 0.010 percent or more each, expressed to the second decimal.

[5] Also contains 0.40-0.7 percent each of lead and bismuth.

[6] Alloy 1350 formerly designated as EC.

[7] Cladding on alclad 2024.

[8] Foil.

[9] Cladding on clad 1100 and clad 3003 reflector sheet.

[10] Also contains 0.20-0.6 percent each of lead and bismuth.

[11] Brazing alloy.

[12] Bus conductor.

[13] Cladding on alclad 2014.

[14] Cladding on alclad 5056.

[15] Cladding on alclad 2219, 3003, 3004, 6061, 7075, 7079 and 7178.

[16] Silicon 45 to 65 percent of magnesium content.

[17] Beryllium 0.0008 maximum for welding electrode and filler wire only.

[18] Boron 0.06 percent maximum.

[19] Vanadium 0.05-0.15; zirconium 0.10-0.25.

[20] Gallium 0.03 maximum.

[21] Zirconium plus titanium 0.20 percent maximum.

[22] Zirconium plus titanium 0.25 percent maximum.

[23] Zirconium 0.08-0.20.

[24] High strength cladding alloy.

TABLE 1-3
Typical Mechanical Properties of Wrought Aluminum Alloys [1][2]

| ALLOY AND TEMPER | TENSION | | | | HARDNESS | SHEAR | FATIGUE | MODULUS [4] |
| | STRENGTH ksi (MPa) | | ELONGATION percent in 2 in. | | BRINELL NUMBER | ULTIMATE SHEARING STRENGTH | ENDURANCE LIMIT [3] | MODULUS OF ELASTICITY |
	ULTIMATE	YIELD	1/16 in. Thick Specimen	1/2 in. Diameter Specimen	500 kg load 10 mm ball	ksi (MPa)	ksi (MPa)	ksi (MPa) x 10³
1060-0	10 (69)	4 (28)	43		19	7 (48)	3 (21)	10.0 (69)
1060-H12	12 (83)	11 (76)	16		23	8 (55)	4 (28)	10.0 (69)
1060-H14	14 (97)	13 (90)	12		26	9 (62)	5 (34)	10.0 (69)
1060-H16	16 (110)	15 (103)	8		30	10 (69)	6.5 (45)	10.0 (69)
1060-H18	19 (131)	18 (124)	6		35	11 (76)	6.5 (45)	10.0 (69)
1100-0	13 (90)	5 (34)	35	45	23	9 (62)	5 (34)	10.0 (69)
1100-H12	16 (110)	15 (103)	12	25	28	10 (69)	6 (41)	10.0 (69)
1100-H14	18 (124)	17 (117)	9	20	32	11 (76)	7 (48)	10.0 (69)
1100-H16	21 (145)	20 (138)	6	17	38	12 (83)	9 (62)	10.0 (69)
1100-H18	24 (165)	22 (152)	5	15	44	13 (90)	9 (62)	10.0 (69)
1350-0 [5]	12 (83)	4 (28)	..	.. [6]	..	8 (55)	....	10.0 (69)
1350-H12 [5]	14 (97)	12 (83)	..	..	..	9 (62)	....	10.0 (69)
1350-H14 [5]	16 (110)	14 (97)	..	..	..	10 (69)	....	10.0 (69)
1350-H16 [5]	18 (124)	16 (110)	..	..	..	11 (76)	....	10.0 (69)
1350-H19 [5]	27 (186)	24 (165)	..	.. [7]	..	15 (103)	7 (48)	10.0 (69)
2011-T3	55 (379)	43 (296)		15	95	32 (221)	18 (124)	10.2 (70)
2011-T8	59 (407)	45 (310)		12	100	35 (241)	18 (124)	10.2 (70)
2014-0	27 (186)	14 (97)		18	45	18 (124)	13 (90)	10.6 (73)
2014-T4, T451	62 (427)	42 (290)		20	105	38 (262)	20 (138)	10.6 (73)
2014-T6, T651	70 (483)	60 (414)		13	135	42 (290)	18 (124)	10.6 (73)
Alclad 2014-0	25 (172)	10 (69)	21			18 (124)	....	10.5 (75)
Alclad 2014-T3	63 (434)	40 (276)	20			37 (255)	....	10.5 (75)
Alclad 2014-T4, T451	61 (421)	37 (255)	22			37 (255)	....	10.5 (75)
Alclad 2014-T6, T651	68 (469)	60 (414)	10			41 (283)	....	10.5 (75)
2017-0	26 (179)	10 (69)		22	45	18 (124)	13 (90)	10.5 (75)
2017-T4, T451	62 (427)	40 (276)		22	105	38 (262)	18 (124)	10.5 (75)
2018-T61	61 (421)	46 (317)		12	120	39 (269)	17 (117)	10.8 (74)
2024-0	27 (186)	11 (76)	20	22	47	18 (124)	13 (90)	10.6 (73)
2024-T3	70 (483)	50 (345)	18		120	41 (283)	20 (138)	10.6 (73)
2024-T4, T351	68 (469)	47 (324)	20	19	120	41 (283)	20 (138)	10.6 (73)
2024-T361 [8]	72 (496)	57 (393)	13		130	42 (290)	18 (124)	10.6 (73)
Alclad 2024-0	26 (179)	11 (76)	20			18 (124)	....	10.6 (73)
Alclad 2024-T3	65 (448)	45 (310)	18			40 (276)	....	10.6 (73)
Alclad 2024-T4, T351	64 (441)	42 (290)	19			40 (276)	....	10.6 (73)
Alclad 2024-T361 [8]	67 (462)	53 (365)	11			41 (283)	....	10.6 (73)
Alclad 2024-T81, T851	65 (448)	60 (414)	6			40 (276)	....	10.6 (73)
Alclad 2024-T861 [8]	70 (483)	66 (455)	6			42 (290)	....	10.6 (73)
2025-T6	58 (400)	37 (255)		19	110	35 (241)	18 (124)	10.4 (72)
2117-T4	43 (296)	24 (165)		27	70	28 (193)	14 (97)	10.3 (71)
2218-T72	48 (331)	37 (255)		11	95	30 (207)	....	10.8 (74)
2219-0	25 (172)	11 (76)	18	..	..	....	....	10.6 (73)
2219-T42	52 (359)	27 (186)	20	..	..	....	....	10.6 (73)
2219-T31, T351	52 (359)	36 (248)	17	..	..	....	....	10.6 (73)
2219-T37	57 (393)	46 (317)	11	..	..	....	....	10.6 (73)
2219-T62	60 (414)	42 (290)	10	..	..	....	15 (103)	10.6 (73)
2219-T81, T851	66 (455)	51 (352)	10	..	..	....	15 (103)	10.6 (73)
2219-T87	69 (476)	57 (393)	10	..	..	....	15 (103)	10.6 (73)
3003-0	16 (110)	6 (41)	30	40	28	11 (76)	7 (48)	10.0 (69)
3003-H12	19 (131)	18 (124)	10	20	35	12 (83)	8 (55)	10.0 (69)
3003-H14	22 (152)	21 (145)	8	16	40	14 (97)	9 (62)	10.0 (69)
3003-H16	26 (179)	25 (172)	5	14	47	15 (103)	10 (69)	10.0 (69)
3003-H18	29 (200)	27 (186)	4	10	55	16 (110)	10 (69)	10.0 (69)
Alclad 3003-0	16 (110)	6 (41)	30	40		11 (76)	....	10.0 (69)
Alclad 3003-H12	19 (131)	18 (124)	10	20		12 (83)	....	10.0 (69)
Alclad 3003-H14	22 (152)	21 (145)	8	16		14 (97)	....	10.0 (69)
Alclad 3003-H16	26 (179)	25 (172)	5	14		15 (103)	....	10.0 (69)
Alclad 3003-H18	29 (200)	27 (186)	4	10		16 (110)	....	10.0 (69)
3004-0	26 (179)	10 (69)	20	25	45	16 (110)	14 (97)	10.0 (69)
3004-H32	31 (214)	25 (172)	10	17	52	17 (117)	15 (103)	10.0 (69)
3004-H34	35 (241)	29 (200)	9	12	63	18 (124)	15 (103)	10.0 (69)
3004-H36	38 (262)	33 (228)	5	9	70	20 (138)	16 (110)	10.0 (69)
3004-H38	41 (283)	36 (248)	5	6	77	21 (145)	16 (110)	10.0 (69)
Alclad 3004-0	26 (179)	10 (69)	20	25		16 (110)	....	10.0 (69)
Alclad 3004-H32	31 (214)	25 (172)	10	17		17 (117)	....	10.0 (69)
Alclad 3004-H34	35 (241)	29 (200)	9	12		18 (124)	....	10.0 (69)
Alclad 3004-H36	38 (262)	33 (228)	5	9		20 (138)	....	10.0 (69)
Alclad 3004-H38	41 (283)	36 (248)	5	6		21 (145)	....	10.0 (69)

For numbered footnotes see page 6.

TABLE 1-3 (Continued)
Typical Mechanical Properties

| ALLOY AND TEMPER | TENSION | | | | HARDNESS | SHEAR | FATIGUE | MODULUS |
| | STRENGTH ksi (MPa) | | ELONGATION percent in 2 in. | | BRINELL NUMBER | ULTIMATE SHEARING STRENGTH | ENDURANCE[3] LIMIT | MODULUS[4] OF ELASTICITY |
	ULTIMATE	YIELD	1/16 in. Thick Specimen	1/2 in. Diameter Specimen	500 kg load 10 mm ball	ksi (MPa)	ksi (MPa)	ksi (MPa) x 10^3
3105-0	17 (117)	8 (55)	24	. . .	. . .	12 (83)	. . . . . .	10.0 (69)
3105-H12	22 (152)	19 (131)	7	. . .	. . .	14 (97)	. . . . . .	10.0 (69)
3105-H14	25 (172)	22 (152)	5	. . .	. . .	15 (103)	. . . . . .	10.0 (69)
3105-H16	28 (193)	25 (172)	4	. . .	. . .	16 (110)	. . . . . .	10.0 (69)
3105-H18	31 (214)	28 (193)	3	. . .	. . .	17 (117)	. . . . . .	10.0 (69)
3105-H25	26 (179)	23 (159)	8	. . .	. . .	15 (103)	. . . . . .	10.0 (69)
4032-T6	55 (379)	46 (317)	. . .	9	120	38 (262)	16 (110)	11.4 (79)
5005-0	18 (124)	6 (41)	25	. . .	28	11 (76)	. . . . . .	10.0 (69)
5005-H12	20 (138)	19 (131)	10	. . .	. . .	14 (97)	. . . . . .	10.0 (69)
5005-H14	23 (159)	22 (152)	6	. . .	. . .	14 (97)	. . . . . .	10.0 (69)
5005-H16	26 (179)	25 (172)	5	. . .	. . .	15 (103)	. . . . . .	10.0 (69)
5005-H18	29 (200)	28 (193)	4	. . .	. . .	16 (110)	. . . . . .	10.0 (69)
5005-H32	20 (138)	17 (117)	11	. . .	36	14 (97)	. . . . . .	10.0 (69)
5005-H34	23 (159)	20 (138)	8	. . .	41	14 (97)	. . . . . .	10.0 (69)
5005-H36	26 (179)	24 (165)	6	. . .	46	15 (103)	. . . . . .	10.0 (69)
5005-H38	29 (200)	27 (186)	5	. . .	51	16 (110)	. . . . . .	10.0 (69)
5050-0	21 (145)	8 (55)	24	. . .	36	15 (103)	12 (83)	10.0 (69)
5050-H32	25 (172)	21 (145)	9	. . .	46	17 (117)	13 (90)	10.0 (69)
5050-H34	28 (193)	24 (165)	8	. . .	53	18 (124)	13 (90)	10.0 (69)
5050-H36	30 (207)	26 (179)	7	. . .	58	19 (131)	14 (97)	10.0 (69)
5050-H38	32 (221)	29 (200)	6	. . .	63	20 (138)	14 (97)	10.0 (69)
5052-0	28 (193)	13 (90)	25	30	47	18 (124)	16 (110)	10.2 (70)
5052-H32	33 (228)	28 (193)	12	18	60	20 (138)	17 (117)	10.2 (70)
5052-H34	38 (262)	31 (214)	10	14	68	21 (145)	18 (124)	10.2 (70)
5052-H36	40 (276)	35 (241)	8	10	73	23 (159)	19 (131)	10.2 (70)
5052-H38	42 (290)	37 (255)	7	8	77	24 (165)	20 (138)	10.2 (70)
5056-0	42 (290)	22 (152)	. . .	35	65	26 (179)	20 (138)	10.3 (71)
5056-H18	63 (434)	59 (407)	. . .	10	105	34 (234)	22 (152)	10.3 (71)
5056-H38	60 (414)	50 (345)	. . .	15	100	32 (221)	22 (152)	10.3 (71)
5083-0	42 (290)	21 (145)	. . .	22	. . .	25 (172)	. . . . . .	10.3 (71)
5083-H321	46 (317)	33 (228)	. . .	16	. . .	. . . . . .	23 (159)	10.3 (71)
5086-0	38 (262)	17 (117)	22	. . .	. . .	23 (159)	. . . . . .	10.3 (71)
5086-H32, H116, H117	42 (290)	30 (207)	12	. . .	. . .	. . . . . .	. . . . . .	10.3 (71)
5086-H34	47 (324)	37 (255)	10	. . .	. . .	27 (186)	. . . . . .	10.3 (71)
5086-H112	39 (269)	19 (131)	14	. . .	. . .	. . . . . .	. . . . . .	10.3 (71)
5154-0	35 (241)	17 (117)	27	. . .	58	22 (152)	17 (117)	10.2 (70)
5154-H32	39 (269)	30 (207)	15	. . .	67	22 (152)	18 (124)	10.2 (70)
5154-H34	42 (290)	33 (228)	13	. . .	73	24 (165)	19 (131)	10.2 (70)
5154-H36	45 (310)	36 (248)	12	. . .	78	26 (179)	20 (138)	10.2 (70)
5154-H38	48 (331)	39 (269)	10	. . .	80	28 (193)	21 (145)	10.2 (70)
5154-H112	35 (241)	17 (117)	25	. . .	63	. . . . . .	17 (117)	10.2 (70)
5252-H25	34 (234)	25 (172)	11	. . .	68	21 (145)	. . . . . .	10.0 (69)
5252-H38, H28	41 (283)	35 (241)	5	. . .	75	23 (159)	. . . . . .	10.0 (69)
5254-0	35 (241)	17 (117)	27	. . .	58	22 (152)	17 (117)	10.2 (70)
5254-H32	39 (269)	30 (207)	15	. . .	67	22 (152)	18 (124)	10.2 (70)
5254-H34	42 (290)	33 (228)	13	. . .	73	24 (165)	19 (131)	10.2 (70)
5254-H36	45 (310)	36 (248)	12	. . .	78	26 (179)	20 (138)	10.2 (70)
5254-H38	48 (331)	39 (269)	10	. . .	80	28 (193)	21 (145)	10.2 (70)
5254-H112	35 (241)	17 (117)	25	. . .	63	. . . . . .	17 (117)	10.2 (70)
5454-0	36 (248)	17 (117)	22	. . .	62	23 (159)	. . . . . .	10.2 (70)
5454-H32	40 (276)	30 (207)	10	. . .	73	24 (165)	. . . . . .	10.2 (70)
5454-H34	44 (303)	35 (241)	10	. . .	81	26 (179)	. . . . . .	10.2 (70)
5454-H111	38 (262)	26 (179)	14	. . .	70	23 (159)	. . . . . .	10.2 (70)
5454-H112	36 (248)	18 (124)	18	. . .	62	23 (159)	. . . . . .	10.2 (70)
5456-0	45 (310)	23 (159)	. . .	24	. . .	. . . . . .	. . . . . .	10.3 (71)
5456-H111	47 (324)	33 (228)	. . .	18	. . .	. . . . . .	. . . . . .	10.3 (71)
5456-H112	45 (310)	24 (165)	. . .	22	. . .	. . . . . .	. . . . . .	10.3 (71)
5456-H321[11], H116, H117	51 (352)	37 (255)	. . .	16	90	30 (207)	. . . . . .	10.3 (71)
5457-0	19 (131)	7 (48)	22	. . .	32	12 (83)	. . . . . .	10.0 (69)
5457-H25	26 (179)	23 (159)	12	. . .	48	16 (110)	. . . . . .	10.0 (69)
5457-H38, H28	30 (207)	27 (186)	6	. . .	55	18 (124)	. . . . . .	10.0 (69)
5652-0	28 (193)	13 (90)	25	30	47	18 (124)	16 (110)	10.2 (70)
5652-H32	33 (228)	28 (193)	12	18	60	20 (138)	17 (117)	10.2 (70)
5652-H34	38 (262)	31 (214)	10	14	68	21 (145)	18 (124)	10.2 (70)
5652-H36	40 (276)	35 (241)	8	10	73	23 (159)	19 (131)	10.2 (70)
5652-H38	42 (290)	37 (255)	7	8	77	24 (165)	20 (138)	10.2 (70)
5657-H25	23 (159)	20 (138)	12	. . .	40	14 (97)	. . . . . .	10.0 (69)
5657-H38, H28	28 (193)	24 (165)	7	. . .	50	15 (103)	. . . . . .	10.0 (69)

For numbered footnotes see page 6.

TABLE 1-3 (Concluded)
Typical Mechanical Properties

| ALLOY AND TEMPER | TENSION | | | | HARDNESS | SHEAR | FATIGUE | MODULUS |
| | STRENGTH ksi (MPa) | | ELONGATION percent in 2 in. | | BRINELL NUMBER | ULTIMATE SHEARING STRENGTH | ENDUR-ANCE[3] LIMIT | MODULUS[4] OF ELASTICITY |
	ULTIMATE	YIELD	1/16 in. Thick Specimen	1/2 in. Diameter Specimen	500 kg load 10 mm ball	ksi (MPa)	ksi (MPa)	ksi (MPa) x 10³
6005-T5	45 (310)	40 (276)	12	17	95	30 (207)	14 (97)	10.0 (69)
6061-0	18 (124)	8 (55)	25	30	30	12 (83)	9 (62)	10.0 (69)
6061-T4, T451	35 (241)	21 (145)	22	25	65	24 (165)	14 (97)	10.0 (69)
6061-T6, T651	45 (310)	40 (276)	12	17	95	30 (207)	14 (97)	10.0 (69)
Alclad 6061-0	17 (117)	7 (48)	25	..	..	11 (76)	......	10.0 (69)
Alclad 6061-T4, T451	33 (228)	19 (131)	22	..	..	22 (152)	......	10.0 (69)
Alclad 6061-T6, T651	42 (290)	37 (255)	12	..	..	27 (186)	......	10.0 (69)
6063-0	13 (90)	7 (48)	..	..	25	10 (69)	8 (55)	10.0 (69)
6063-T1[10]	22 (152)	13 (90)	20	..	42	14 (97)	9 (62)	10.0 (69)
6063-T4	25 (172)	13 (90)	22	..	..	......	......	10.0 (69)
6063-T5	27 (186)	21 (145)	12	..	60	17 (117)	10 (69)	10.0 (69)
6063-T6	35 (241)	31 (214)	12	..	73	22 (152)	10 (69)	10.0 (69)
6063-T83	37 (255)	35 (241)	9	..	82	22 (152)	......	10.0 (69)
6063-T831	30 (207)	27 (186)	10	..	70	18 (124)	......	10.0 (69)
6063-T832	42 (290)	39 (269)	12	..	95	27 (186)	......	10.0 (69)
6066-0	22 (152)	12 (83)	..	18	43	14 (97)	......	10.0 (69)
6066-T4, T451	52 (359)	30 (207)	..	18	90	29 (200)	......	10.0 (69)
6066-T6, T651	57 (393)	52 (359)	..	12	120	34 (234)	16 (110)	10.0 (69)
6070-T6	55 (379)	51 (352)	10	..	....	34 (234)	14 (97)	10.0 (69)
6101-H111	14 (97)	11 (76)	..	..	...	......	......	10.0 (69)
6101-T6	32 (221)	28 (193)	15[9]	..	71	20 (138)	......	10.0 (69)
6262-T9	58 (400)	55 (379)	..	10	120	35 (241)	13 (90)	10.0 (69)
6463-T1[10]	22 (152)	13 (90)	20	..	42	14 (97)	10 (69)	10.0 (69)
6463-T5	27 (186)	21 (145)	12	..	60	17 (117)	10 (69)	10.0 (69)
6463-T6	35 (241)	31 (214)	12	..	74	22 (152)	10 (69)	10.0 (69)
7001-0	37 (255)	22 (152)	..	14	60	......	......	10.3 (71)
7001-T6, T651	98 (676)	91 (627)	..	9	160	......	22 (152)	10.3 (71)
7005-T53	57 (393)	50 (345)	15	..	....	......	......	......
7075-0	33 (228)	15 (103)	17	16	60	22 (152)	......	10.4 (72)
7075-T6, T651	83 (572)	73 (503)	11	11	150	48 (331)	23 (159)	10.4 (72)
Alclad 7075-0	32 (221)	14 (97)	17	..	..	22 (152)	......	10.4 (72)
Alclad 7075-T6, T-651	76 (524)	67 (462)	11	..	..	46 (317)	......	10.4 (72)
7079-0	33 (228)	15 (103)	17	16	..	......	......	10.4 (72)
7079-T6, T651	78 (538)	68 (469)	..	14	145	45 (310)	23 (159)	10.4 (72)
Alclad 7079-0	32 (221)	14 (97)	16	..	..	......	......	10.4 (72)
Alclad 7079-T6	71 (490)	62 (427)	10	..	..	42 (290)	......	10.4 (72)
7178-0	33 (228)	15 (103)	15	16	...	......	......	10.4 (72)
7178-T6, T651	88 (607)	78 (538)	10	11	...	......	......	10.4 (72)
7178-T76, T7651	83 (572)	73 (503)	..	11	...	......	......	10.3 (71)
Alclad 7178-0	32 (221)	14 (97)	16	..	...	......	......	10.4 (72)
Alclad 7178-T6, T651	81 (558)	71 (490)	10	..	...	......	......	10.4 (72)

[1] The mechanical property limits are listed by major product in the "Standards Section" of this manual.

[2] The indicated typical mechanical properties for all except 0 temper material are higher than the specified minimum properties. For 0 temper products typical ultimate and yield values are slightly lower than specified (maximum) values.

[3] Based on 500,000,000 cycles of completely reversed stress using the R. R. Moore type of machine and specimen.

[4] Average of tension and compression moduli. Compression modulus is about 2% greater than tension modulus.

[5] Electrical conductor grade, 99.50% minimum aluminum.

[6] Alloy 1350-0 wire will have an elongation of approximately 23% in 10 inches.

[7] Alloy 1350-H19 wire will have an elongation of approximately 11½% in 10 inches.

[8] Tempers T361 and T861 were formerly designated T36 and T86, respectively.

[9] Based on ¼ in. thick specimen.

[10] Temper T1 was formerly designated T42.

[11] Material in this temper is not recommended for and should not be used in applications requiring exposure to sea water.

crease aluminum's strength, some alloys can withstand temperatures of 500°F (260°C) and retain satisfactory strengths for some applications.

Mechanical properties of the principal wrought aluminum alloys are given on Table 1-3.

Corrosion Resistant—Proper alloy selection and proper care can result in corrosion-free service for aluminum products in a wide range of applications on land, sea and in the air.

Actually, aluminum reacts with oxygen much more rapidly than do most other metals, but the action is self-limiting with aluminum, whereas it is usually progressive with other metals.

Aluminum's corrosion-resistance is due to the fact that in air a rapid growth of a thin, invisible but hard, protective film of aluminum oxide occurs. This film has some of the qualities of glass and is naturally strongly bonded to the aluminum surface permanently excluding oxygen unless the film is damaged. But as soon as the bare metal is exposed to air the protective oxide film begins immediately to reform to prevent further oxidation.

Conducts Electricity—Aluminum alloys are the most economical conductors of electricity available because they handle over twice as much current as does copper on a weight basis. High strength with high conductivity is obtained in the familiar large over-land power transmission cables by stranding 1350 alloy with a "core" of stronger aluminum alloy, such as 6201, which still conducts much more current than does copper on a weight-for-weight basis.

Conducts Heat—Heating and cooling applications both benefit from the fact that aluminum conducts heat three times as well as iron. Refrigerator evaporator coils, cooking utensils, engine components and heat exchangers of various types now are usually made of aluminum.

Reflects Radiant Energy—Aluminum is an excellent reflector of radiant energy. Polished surfaces are most efficient through the entire range of wavelengths, from ultra-violet through infra-red and the electromagnetic waves of radio and radar. Heater and lamp reflectors, roofing and siding sheet, and building insulation are principal applications of aluminum sheet and foil.

Non-Magnetic—For practical purposes, aluminum is non-magnetic, which makes it one of the few metals suitable for certain electrical and electronic shielding applications. It is also essentially non-sparking.

Non-Toxic—It has been used for cooking utensils and foil wraps for decades and is widely employed for industrial food-processing equipment.

Selection of Aluminum Alloys

In most applications for which the metalworker today uses "aluminum" he actually is using an aluminum alloy. Similarly, the "copper, iron or steel," or other metals with which he works also are alloys.

In fact, the usefulness of nearly every metal is greatly extended by combining the pure metal with precise amounts of other elements. In this manner, "new metals" which are better for various applications than the pure metals, are created.

Often, these alloys are still referred to by the name of the principal metal only. An aluminum alloy often is simply called "aluminum" in general shop conversation. But each alloy has a number, which is always specified when it is important to use only that alloy.

The wide range and many combinations of desirable properties which are obtained by alloying aluminum with other elements have made aluminum one of man's most versatile materials.

Aluminum is available in every shape of mill product. Table 2-1 is representative of alloy availabilities and applications. The principal benefits obtained by alloying aluminum are increased strength, better machinability, and excellent workability and weldability. Different alloys have these characteristics in varying combinations and degrees. But most aluminum alloys still retain pure aluminum's long-lasting attractive appearance and remarkably light weight.

Know Your Aluminum

Having a good knowledge of materials, how they are best worked and for what applications they should be used are important parts of becoming a good metalworker, in much the same way as knowing how to select and use metalworking tools for different kinds of jobs. In each instance, some of this knowledge can be gained only through practice and actual experience, but much valuable basic knowledge can, of course, also be provided by books.

In discussing what we need to know about aluminum alloys, we will start by considering what elements are most frequently added to aluminum, and what effects they have in terms of creating several "new aluminums," each having its own specifics or characteristics. As with most metals, there are two main classes of alloys of aluminum: *wrought alloys* and *casting alloys*.

Wrought Aluminum Alloys

Silicon, iron, copper, manganese, magnesium, nickel and zinc are the principal elements used for wrought aluminum alloys. None of these is used in large percentage; a few other elements, not mentioned in this list, are sometimes also added, but in smaller amounts.

For convenience, two similar "series numbering" systems (one for wrought and one for casting alloys) have been established to identify the principal elements in a given alloy. The wrought series and their major alloying elements are as follows:

Designations for Wrought Aluminum Alloy Groups

	Alloy No.
Aluminum—99.00% minimum and greater	1xxx

Major Alloying Element

		Alloy No.
Aluminum alloys grouped by major alloying elements	Copper	2xxx
	Manganese	3xxx
	Silicon	4xxx
	Magnesium	5xxx
	Magnesium and Silicon	6xxx
	Zinc	7xxx
	Other elements	8xxx
Unused Series		9xxx

This system of four-digit numerical designation is used to identify wrought aluminum and wrought aluminum alloys.

The first digit indicates the alloy group as shown in the table: the 1xxx series is for minimum aluminum purities of 99.00 percent and greater, and the 2xxx through 8xxx series group aluminum alloys by major alloying elements.

The last two digits identify the aluminum alloy or indicate the aluminum purity. The second digit indicates modifications of the original alloy or impurity limits.

Aluminum—In the 1xxx group for minimum aluminum purities of 99.00 percent and greater, the last two of the four digits in the designation indicate the minimum aluminum percentage.

These digits are the same as the two digits to the right of the decimal point in the minimum aluminum percentage when it is expressed to the nearest 0.01 percent. The second digit in the designation indicates modifications in impurity limits.

If the second digit in the designation is zero, it indicates that there is no special control on individual impurities; integers 1 through 9, which are assigned consecutively as needed, indicate special con-

TABLE 2-1
Comparative Characteristics and Applications of Aluminum

ALLOY AND TEMPER	RESISTANCE TO CORROSION		Workability (Cold) ⑤	Machineability ⑤	Brazeability ⑥	WELDABILITY ⑥			SOME APPLICATIONS OF ALLOYS
	General ①	Stress-Corrosion Cracking ②				Gas	Arc	Resistance Spot and Seam	
1060–0	A	A	A	E	A	A	A	B	Chemical equipment, railroad tank cars
H12	A	A	A	E	A	A	A	A	
H14	A	A	A	D	A	A	A	A	
H16	A	A	B	D	A	A	A	A	
H18	A	A	B	D	A	A	A	A	
1100–0	A	A	A	E	A	A	A	B	Sheet metal work, spun hollowware, fin stock
H12	A	A	A	E	A	A	A	A	
H14	A	A	A	D	A	A	A	A	
H16	A	A	B	D	A	A	A	A	
H18	A	A	C	D	A	A	A	A	
1350–0	A	A	A	E	A	A	A	B	Electrical conductors
H12, H111	A	A	A	E	A	A	A	A	
H14, H24	A	A	A	D	A	A	A	A	
H16, H26	A	A	B	D	A	A	A	A	
H18	A	A	B	D	A	A	A	A	
2011–T3	D③	D	C	A	D	D	D	D	Screw machine products
T4, T451	D③	D	B	A	D	D	D	D	
T8	D	B	D	A	D	D	D	D	
2014–0				D	D	D	D	B	Truck frames, aircraft structures
T3, T4, T451	D③	C	C	B	D	D	B	B	
T6, T651, T6510, T6511	D	C	D	B	D	D	B	B	
2017–T4, T451	D③	C	C	B	D	D	B	B	Screw machine products, fittings
2018–T61				B					Aircraft engine cylinders, heads and pistons
2024–0				D	D	D	D	D	Truck wheels, screw machine products, aircraft structures
T4, T3, T351, T3510, T3511	D③	C	C	B	D	C	B	B	
T361	D③	C	D	B	D	D	C	B	
T6	D	B	C	B	D	D	C	B	
T861, T81, T851, T8510, T8511	D	B	D	B	D	D	C	B	
T72				B					
2025–T6	D	C		B	D	D	B	B	Forgings, aircraft propellers
2117–T4	C	A	B	C	D	D	B	B	Rivets
2218–T61	D	C						C	Jet engine impellers and rings
T72	D	C		B	D	D	C	B	
2219–0					D	D	A	B	Structural uses at high temperatures (to 600 F, 316 C), high strength weldments
T31, T351, T3510, T3511	D③	C	C	B	D	A	A	A	
T37	D③	C	D	B	D	A	A	A	
T81, T851, T8510, T8511	D	B	D	B	D	A	A	A	
T87	D	B	D	B	D	A	A	A	
2618–T61	D	C		B	D	D	C	B	Aircraft engines
3003–0	A	A	A	E	A	A	A	A	Cooking utensils, chemical equipment, pressure vessels, sheet metal work, builder's hardware, storage tanks
H12	A	A	A	E	A	A	A	A	
H14	A	A	B	D	A	A	A	A	
H16	A	A	C	D	A	A	A	A	
H18	A	A	C	D	A	A	A	A	
H25	A	A	B	D	A	A	A	A	
3004–0	A	A	A	D	B	B	A	B	Sheet metal work, storage tanks
H32	A	A	B	D	B	B	A	A	
H34	A	A	B	C	B	B	A	A	
H36	A	A	C	C	B	B	A	A	
H38	A	A	C	C	B	B	A	A	
3105–0	A	A	A	E	B	B	A	B	Residential siding, mobile homes, rain carrying goods, sheet metal work
H12	A	A	B	E	B	B	A	A	
H14	A	A	B	D	B	B	A	A	
H16	A	A	C	D	B	B	A	A	
H18	A	A	C	D	B	B	A	A	
H25	A	A	B	D	B	B	A	A	
4032–T6	C	B		B	D	D	B	C	Pistons

For numbered footnotes see page 11.

Source: Metalworking With Aluminum, 2nd Ed., Aluminum Assn., Inc.

TABLE 2-1 (Continued)
Comparative Characteristics and Applications of Aluminum

ALLOY AND TEMPER	RESISTANCE TO CORROSION		Workability (Cold) [5]	Machineability [5]	Brazeability [6]	WELDABILITY [6]			SOME APPLICATIONS OF ALLOY
	General [1]	Stress-Corrosion Cracking [2]				Gas	Arc	Resistance Spot and Seam	
5005–0	A	A	A	E	B	A	A	B	Appliances, utensils, architectural, electrical conductor
H12	A	A	A	E	B	A	A	A	
H14	A	A	B	D	B	A	A	A	
H16	A	A	C	D	B	A	A	A	
H18	A	A	C	D	B	A	A	A	
H32	A	A	A	E	B	A	A	A	
H34	A	A	B	D	B	A	A	A	
H36	A	A	C	D	B	A	A	A	
H38	A	A	C	D	B	A	A	A	
5050–0	A	A	A	E	B	A	A	B	Builder's hardware, refrigerator trim, coiled tubes
H32	A	A	A	D	B	A	A	A	
H34	A	A	B	D	B	A	A	A	
H36	A	A	C	C	B	A	A	A	
H38	A	A	C	C	B	A	A	A	
5052–0	A	A	A	D	C	A	A	B	Sheet metal work, hydraulic tube, appliances
H32	A	A	B	D	C	A	A	A	
H34	A	A	B	C	C	A	A	A	
H36	A	A	C	C	C	A	A	A	
H38	A	A	C	C	C	A	A	A	
5056–0	A[4]	B[4]	A	D	D	C	A	B	Cable sheathing, rivets for magnesium, screen wire, zippers
H111	A[4]	B[4]	A	D	D	C	A	A	
H12, H32	A[4]	B[4]	B	D	D	C	A	A	
H14, H34	A[4]	B[4]	B	C	D	C	A	A	
H18, H38	A[4]	C[4]	C	C	D	C	A	A	
H192	B[4]	D[4]	D	B	D	C	A	A	
H392	B[4]	D[4]	D	B	D	C	A	A	
5083–0	A[4]	B[4]	B	D	D	C	A	B	Unfired, welded pressure vessels, marine, auto aircraft cryogenics, TV towers, drilling rigs, transportation equip., missile components
H321	A[4]	B[4]	C	D	D	C	A	A	
H323	A[4]	B[4]	C	D	D	C	A	A	
H343	A[4]	B[4]	C	C	D	C	A	A	
H111	A[4]	B[4]	C	D	D	C	A	A	
5086–0	A[4]	A[4]	A	D	D	C	A	B	
H32, H16, H117	A[4]	A[4]	B	D	D	C	A	A	
H34	A[4]	B[4]	B	C	D	C	A	A	
H36	A[4]	B[4]	C	C	D	C	A	A	
H38	A[4]	B[4]	C	C	D	C	A	A	
H111	A[4]	A[4]	B	D	D	C	A	A	
5154–0	A[4]	A[4]	A	D	D	C	A	B	Welded structures, storage tanks, pressure vessels, salt water service
H32	A[4]	A[4]	B	D	D	C	A	A	
H34	A[4]	A[4]	B	C	D	C	A	A	
H36	A[4]	A[4]	C	C	D	C	A	A	
H38	A[4]	A[4]	C	C	D	C	A	A	
5252–H24	A	A	B	D	C	A	A	A	Automotive and appliance trim
H25	A	A	B	C	C	A	A	A	
H28	A	A	C	C	C	A	A	A	
5254–0	A[4]	A[4]	A	D	D	C	A	B	Hydrogen peroxide and chemical storage vessels
H32	A[4]	A[4]	B	D	D	C	A	A	
H34	A[4]	A[4]	B	C	D	C	A	A	
H36	A[4]	A[4]	C	C	D	C	A	A	
H38	A[4]	A[4]	C	C	D	C	A	A	
5454–0	A	A	A	D	D	C	A	B	Welded structures, pressure vessels, marine service
H32	A	A	B	D	D	C	A	A	
H34	A	A	B	C	D	C	A	A	
H111	A	A	B	D	D	C	A	A	
5456–0	A[4]	B[4]	B	D	D	C	A	B	High strength welded structures, storage tanks, pressure vessels, marine applications
H111	A[4]	B[4]	C	D	D	C	A	A	
H321[7], H116, H117	A[4]	B[4]	C	D	D	C	A	A	
H323	A[4]	B[4]	C	D	D	C	A	A	
H343	A[4]	B[4]	C	C	D	C	A	A	
5457–0	A	A	A	E	B	A	A	B	Anodized auto and appliance trim
5652–0	A	A	A	D	C	A	A	B	Hydrogen peroxide and chemical storage vessels
H32	A	A	B	D	C	A	A	A	
H34	A	A	B	C	C	A	A	A	
H36	A	A	C	C	C	A	A	A	
H38	A	A	C	C	C	A	A	A	

For numbered footnotes see facing page.

TABLE 2-1 (Concluded)

Comparative Characteristics and Applications of Aluminum

ALLOY AND TEMPER	RESISTANCE TO CORROSION General ①	RESISTANCE TO CORROSION Stress-Corrosion Cracking ②	Workability (Cold) ⑤	Machineability ⑤	Brazeability ⑥	WELDABILITY ⑥ Gas	WELDABILITY ⑥ Arc	WELDABILITY ⑥ Resistance Spot and Seam	SOME APPLICATIONS OF ALLOY
5657–H241	A	A	A	D	B	A	A	A	Anodized auto and appliance trim
H25	A	A	B	D	B	A	A	A	
H26	A	A	B	D	B	A	A	A	
H28	A	A	C	D	B	A	A	A	
6005–T5	B	A	C	C	A	A	A	A	Heavy-duty structures requiring good corrosion-resistance, truck and marine, railroad cars, furniture, pipelines
6053–0	..	..	..	E	A	A	A	B	Wire and rod for rivets
T6, T61	A	A	..	C	A	A	A	A	
6061–0	B	A	A	D	A	A	A	B	Heavy-duty structures requiring good corrosion resistance, truck and marine, railroad cars, furniture, pipelines
T4, T451, T4510, T4511	B	B	B	C	A	A	A	A	
T6, T651, T652, T6510, T6511	B	A	C	C	A	A	A	A	
6063–T1	A	A	B	D	A	A	A	A	Pipe railing, furniture, architectural extrusions
T4	A	A	B	D	A	A	A	A	
T5, T52	A	A	B	C	A	A	A	A	
T6	A	A	C	C	A	A	A	A	
T83, T831, T832	A	A	C	C	A	A	A	A	
6066–0	C	A	B	D	D	D	B	B	Forgings and extrusions for welded structures
T4, T4510, T4511	C	B	C	C	D	D	B	B	
T6, T6510, T6511	C	B	C	B	D	D	B	B	
6070–T4, T4511	B	B	B	C	B	A	A	A	Heavy duty welded structures, pipelines
T6	B	B	C	C	B	A	A	A	
6101–T6, T63	A	A	C	C	A	A	A	A	High strength bus conductors
T61, T64	A	A	B	D	A	A	A	A	
6151–T6, T652	..	..	..	..	..	..	..	..	Moderate strength intricate forgings for machine and auto parts
6201–T81	A	A	..	C	A	A	A	A	High strength electric conductor wire
6262–T6, T651, T6510, T6511	B	A	C	B	A	A	A	A	Screw machine products
T9	B	A	D	B	A	A	A	A	
6463–T1	A	A	B	D	A	A	A	A	Extruded architectural and trim sections
T5	A	A	B	C	A	A	A	A	
T6	A	A	C	C	A	A	A	A	
7001–0	C③	C	D	B	D	D	D	B	High strength structures
T6, T6510, T6511									
7075–0	..	..	..	D	D	D	C	B	Aircraft and other structures
T6, T651, T652, T6510, T6511	C③	C	D	B	D	D	C	B	
T73, T7351	C	B	D	B	D	D	C	B	
7079–0	..	..	..	..	D	D	C	B	Structural parts for aircraft
T6, T651, T652, T6510, T6511	C③	C	D	B	D	D	C	B	
7178–0	..	..	..	..	D	D	C	B	Aircraft and other structures
T6, T651, T6510, T6511	C③	C	D	B	D	D	C	B	

① Ratings A through E are relative ratings in decreasing order of merit, based on exposures to sodium chloride solution by intermittent spraying or immersion. Alloys with A and B ratings can be used in industrial and seacoast atmospheres without protection. Alloys with C, D and E ratings generally should be protected at least on faying surfaces.

② Stress-corrosion cracking ratings are based on service experience and on laboratory tests of specimens exposed to the 3.5% sodium chloride alternate immersion test.

  A = No known instance of failure in service or in laboratory tests.

  B = No known instance of failure in service; limited failures in laboratory tests of short transverse specimens.

  C = Service failures with sustained tension stress acting in short transverse direction relative to grain structure; limited failures in laboratory tests of long transverse specimens.

  D = Limited service failures with sustained longitudinal or long transverse stress.

③ In relatively thick sections the rating would be E.

④ This rating may be different for material held at elevated temperature for long periods.

⑤ Ratings A through D for Workability (cold), and A through C for Machinability, are relative ratings in decreasing order of merit.

⑥ Ratings A through D for Weldability and Brazeability are relative ratings defined as follows:

  A = Generally weldable by all commercial procedures and methods.

  B = Weldable with special techniques or for specific applications which justify preliminary trials or testing to develop welding procedure and weld performance.

  C = Limited Weldability because of crack sensitivity or loss in resistance to corrosion and mechanical properties.

  D = No commonly used welding methods have been developed.

⑦ Material in this temper is not recommended for and should not be used in applications requiring exposure to sea water.

Source: Metalworking With Aluminum, 2nd Ed., Aluminum Assn., Inc.

trol of one or more individual impurities.
(Example: alloy 1345 = 99.45% Aluminum)

Aluminum Alloys—In the 2xxx through 8xxx alloy groups the last two of the four digits in the designation have no special significance but serve only to identify the different aluminum alloys in the group. The second digit in the alloy designation indicates alloy modifications. If the second digit in the designation is zero, it indicates the original alloy; integers 1 through 9, which are assigned consecutively, indicates alloy modifications.

Experimental Alloys—Experimental alloys also are designed in accordance with this system but they are indicated by the prefix X. The prefix is dropped when the alloy is no longer experimental. During development and before they are designated as experimental, new alloys are identified by serial numbers assigned by their originators. Use of the serial number is discontinued when the X number is assigned.

Principal Effects of Alloying Elements

Pure aluminum is not heat-treatable but it "work hardens" or gains strength when bent, hammered or otherwise worked. The addition of alloying elements does not eliminate this characteristic and all aluminum alloys also gain strength when cold worked. However, adding elements to aluminum affects the metal in many other respects, chief among which is that some alloys are heat treatable.

The principal effects of alloying elements for each group of wrought aluminum alloys are as follows:

1000 Series—Aluminum of 99 percent or higher purity has many applications, especially in the electrical and chemical fields. These alloys are characterized by excellent corrosion resistance, high thermal and electrical conductivity, low mechanical properties and excellent workability. Moderate increases in strength may be obtained by strain-hardening. Iron and silicon are the major impurities.

2000 Series—Copper is the principal alloying element in this group. These alloys require solution heat-treatment to obtain optimum properties; in the heat-treated condition mechanical properties are similar to, and sometimes exceed, those of mild steel.

In some instances, artificial aging is employed to further increase the mechanical properties. This treatment increases yield strength, with attendant loss in elongation; its effect on tensile (ultimate) strength is not as great.

The alloys in the 2000 series do not have as good corrosion resistance as most other aluminum alloys and under certain conditions they may be subject to intergranular corrosion. Therefore, these alloys in the form of sheet are often clad with an alloy which provides galvanic protection to the core material and thus greatly increases resistance to corrosion. Alloy 2024 is perhaps the best known and most widely used aircraft alloy.

3000 Series—Manganese is the major alloying element of alloys in this group, which are generally non-heat-treatable. Because only a limited percentage of manganese, up to about 1.5 percent, can be effectively added to aluminum, it is used as a major element in only a few instances. One of these, however, is the popular 3003, which is widely used as a general-purpose alloy for moderate-strength applications requiring good workability.

4000 Series—Major alloying element of this group is silicon, which can be added in sufficient quantities to cause substantial lowering of the melting point without producing brittleness in the resulting alloys. For these reasons aluminum-silicon alloys are used in welding wire and as brazing alloys where a lower melting point than that of the parent metal is required.

Most alloys in this series are non-heat-treatable, but when used in welding heat-treatable alloys they will pick up some of the alloying constituents of the latter and so respond to heat treatment to a limited extent. The alloys containing appreciable amounts of silicon become dark gray when anodic oxide finishes are applied, and hence are also used for architectural applications.

5000 Series—Magnesium is one of the most effective and widely used alloying elements for aluminum. When it is used as the major alloying element or with manganese, the result is a moderate to high strength non-heat-treatable alloy.

Magnesium is considerably more effective than manganese as a hardener, about 0.8 percent magnesium being equal to 1.25 percent manganese, and it can be added in considerably higher quantities.

Alloys in this series possess good welding characteristics and good resistance to corrosion in marine atmosphere. However, limitations on temper and operating temperatures should be placed on the higher magnesium content alloys (over about 3.5 percent) to avoid susceptibility to stress corrosion.

6000 Series—Alloys in this group contain silicon and magnesium in appropriate proportions to form magnesium silicide, thus making them heat-treatable. Major alloy in this series is 6061, one of the most versatile of the heat-treatable alloys.

Though not as strong as most of the 2000 or 7000 alloys, the magnesium-silicon (or magnesium-silicide) alloys possess good formability and corrosion resistance. with medium strength. Alloys in this heat-treatable group may be formed in the T4 temper (solution heat-treated but not artificially aged) and then reach full T6 properties by artificial aging.

7000 Series—Zinc is the major alloying element in this group, and when coupled with a small percentage of magnesium results in heat-treatable alloys of very high strength. Usually other elements such as copper and chromium are also added in small quantities. Outstanding member of this group is 7075, which is among the highest strength alloys available and is used in air-frame structures and for highly stressed parts.

Non-heat-treatable alloys—As indicated, the initial strength of alloys in this group depends upon the hardening effect of elements such as manganese, silicon, iron and magnesium, singly or in various combinations.

All four of the following hardening processes are effective strengtheners; all "stiffen" or "toughen" the alloy by advantageously distorting the invisible (submicroscopic) crystalline structure of the metal.

Work Hardening—As previously mentioned, cold working (work hardening) increases strength of both non-heat-treatable and heat-treatable alloys. The work may be applied in any manner, including rolling, bending, drawing, forging, stretching, or extruding. However, such work must be carried out at temperatures below the recrystallization range for the particular alloy (650-800°F).

Dispersion Hardening—Certain alloying elements form insoluble chemical compounds when added to molten aluminum. These add strength because they provide uniformly distributed microscopic particles which distort the metallurgical structure. A similar strengthening effect may be obtained in aluminum by mixing finely divided particles of a suitable material or compound, such as aluminum oxide, with powdered aluminum, then forcing the mixture into a solid mass under high pressure, but this method has only specialized use.

Aluminum Heat Treatments

Solid-Solution Hardening—Alloys are made by dissolving other metals in aluminum to form solid solutions. Some atoms of the alloying metals replace certain aluminum atoms in the metallurgical structure; this is called substitutional solid solution.

Other atoms of alloying elements occupy spaces between the base metal atoms in its metallurgical structure (lattice); this is termed interstitial solid solution. In both cases, the metallurgical structure is usually distorted by the new atoms in the structure, thus increasing strength. These alloys may then be further strengthened by heat treating and/or work hardening.

Precipitation Hardening—Heat-treatable aluminum alloys contain alloying elements that are more soluble at elevated temperatures than at room temperatures. When these alloys are solution-heated treated to put these elements back into solid solution and then rapidly quenched, a supersaturated condition is produced.

The strength of the alloy is developed as the alloying elements precipitate out of the solution with the passage of time. This effect is referred to as precipitation or age hardening.

Varying degrees of age hardening occur at room temperature, but artificial aging (or precipitation heat treatment at higher temperatures) usually is employed to develop maximum strengths as quickly as possible. Close control is essential to assure the correct metallurgical structure which will produce the desired properties.

Other thermal treatments used to prepare various aluminum alloys for optimum workability and application requirements include annealing, stabilizing, stress-relieving, homogenizing and refrigeration.

Annealing—Aluminum and all of its alloys may be annealed to remove the hardening or strengthening effects of cold working or heat-treatment described above. Annealing is accomplished by heating the metal above its recrystallization temperature 650-800°F (345-425°C), depending upon the alloy, and maintaining the required level until recrystallization is complete in work-hardened alloys. For heat-treatable alloys either a controlled cooling rate or a low temperature soaking treatment is necessary in order to precipitate particles of the alloying elements.

Annealing is used to restore ductility to make the alloy easier to work, at intermediate stages of fabrication in which extensive metal deformation (work hardening) has taken place, or whenever metalworking procedures or end-use requirements call for maximum ductility.

Stabilizing—Certain non-heat-treatable, work-hardening alloys containing magnesium, such as 5052, gain ductility but lose strength upon room temperature aging. Such age-softening alloys often are stabilized by heating to 225°F to 350°F (110°C to 180°C) to accelerate the softening to its ultimate limit.

Stress-relieving—Internal stresses built up by temperature gradients in aluminum either during quenching (rapid cooling) after heat treatment, or cooling after welding or casting, or from distortion of rolling, forging, extruding, bending, or drawing operations, can be reduced by either thermal or mechanical treatments.

Thermal treatments employing temperatures below those required for annealing often are used for non-heat-treatable wrought alloys, with some loss of strength and an increase in ductility.

Where applicable, the metallurgically superior procedure of stressing or compressing the metal *mechanically* to produce a small, controlled amount of plastic deformation (1-3%) to effect stress relief is employed, with no resultant loss of strength.

This treatment aligns the residual stress in the direction of working and also reduces the differences between compressive stresses in the outer layer of the metal and the interior tensile stresses. Mechanical stress-relieving is accomplished by stretching or compressing the metal in hydraulic machines.

Homogenizing—The workability of aluminum ingot often can be improved by controlled heating and cooling of the as-cast metal. Heat treatable alloy ingots usually have relatively large crystals of intermetallic compounds randomly distributed in the as-cast metal. Fabricating qualities are improved when more uniform distribution of these hardening constituents is achieved by heating the ingot alloy to near its solution-heat-treat temperature, holding it at that level for several hours, then cooling at a controlled rate.

Similar homogenization of non-heat-treatable alloy ingots to improve working qualities and grain size is achieved by "soaking" (holding at temperature) at a point close to the solidus temperature (approxi-

TABLE 2-2

Non-Heat-Treatable Alloys

Series	Examples	Major Alloying Elements	Typical %	Typical Uses
1000	1060			Chemical equipment
	1100			Deep-drawn parts
3000	3003	Mn	1.2	General purpose
	3004	Mn, Mg	1.2, 1.0	Eyelets, pressure vessels, can stock
4000	4032	Si	12.0	Pistons
	4043	Si	5.0	Brazing sheet
5000	5005	Mg	0.8	Anodized trays, etc.
	5052	Mg	2.5	Appliances, bus, truck
	5083	Mg	4.5	Boats, armor
8000	8001	Ni	1.0	Nuclear
	8280	Sn	6.5	Bearings

mately 830-1125°F, depending upon alloy), followed by cooling in still air.

Refrigeration—Hardening of naturally aging heat-treatable alloys can be retarded significantly by refrigeration immediately after solution heat treatment. the lower the temperature the longer the "workable life," within limits. Some applications of this practice are quite sophisticated, particularly where aerospace components, for example, are being fabricated. However, a typical simple use of refrigeration is for storage of alloy 2024 wire or rod to gain maximum workability when cold-heading rivets are produced from this alloy.

Temper Designation System

The temper designation system is used for all forms of wrought and cast aluminum and aluminum alloys except ingot. It is based on the sequences of basic treatments used to produce the various tempers. The temper designation follows the alloy designation, the two being separated by a hyphen.

Basic temper designations consist of letters. Subdivisions of the basic tempers, where required, are indicated by one or more digits following the letter. These designate specific sequences of basic treatments, but only operations recognized as significantly influencing the characteristics of the product are indicated. Should some other variation of the same sequence of basic operations be applied to the same alloy, resulting in different characteristics, then additional digits are added to the designation.

Tempers of Non-Heat-Treatable Aluminum Alloys

Some non-heat-treatable aluminum alloys are described in Table 2-2.

The basic temper designations and subdivisions for the non-heat-treatable alloys are as follows:

F as fabricated. Applies to products of shaping processes in which no special control over thermal conditions or strain-hardening is employed. For wrought products, there are no mechanical property limits.

O annealed (wrought products only). Applies to wrought products which are fully annealed to obtain the lowest strength condition.

H strain-hardened (wrought products only). Applies to products which have their strength increased by strain-hardening with or without supplementary thermal treatments to produce some reduction in strength. The H is always followed by two or more digits.

The first digit following the H indicates the specific combination of basic operations, as follows:

H1 strain-hardened only. Applies to products which are strain-hardened to obtain the desired strength without supplementary thermal treatment. The number following this designation indicates the degree of strain-hardening.

H2 strain-hardened and partially annealed. Applies to products which are strain-hardened more than the desired final amount and then reduced in strength to the desired level by partial annealing. For alloys that age-soften at room temperature, the H2 tempers have the same minimum ultimate tensile strength as the corresponding H3 tempers.

For other alloys, the H2 tempers have the same minimum ultimate tensile strength as the corresponding H1 tempers and slightly higher elongation. The number following this designation indicates the degree of strain-hardening remaining after the product has been partially annealed.

H3 strain-hardened and stabilized. Applies to products which are strain-hardened and whose mechanical properties are stabilized by a low temperature thermal treatment which results in slightly lowered tensile strength and improved ductility. This designation is applicable only to those alloys which, unless stabilized, gradually age-soften at room temperature. The number following this designation indicates the degree of strain-hardening before the stabilization treatment.

The digit following the designations H1, H2, and H3 indicates the degree of strain-hardening. Numeral 8 has been assigned to indicate tempers having an ultimate tensile strength equivalent to that achieved by a cold reduction (temperature during reduction not to exceed 120°F) of approximately 75 percent following a full anneal.

Tempers between 0 (annealed) and 8 are designated by numerals 1 through 7. Material having an ultimate tensile strength about midway between that of the 0 temper and that of the 8 temper is designated by the numeral 4; about midway between the 0 and 4 tempers by the numeral 2; and about midway between the 4 and 8 tempers by the numeral 6. Numeral 9 designates tempers whose minimum ultimate tensile strength exceeds that of the 8 temper by 2.0 ksi or more.

For two-digit H tempers whose second digit is odd, the standard limits for ultimate tensile strength are exactly midway between those of the adjacent two digit H tempers whose second digits are even.

NOTE: For alloys which cannot be cold reduced an amount sufficient to establish an ultimate tensile strength applicable to the 8 temper (75 percent cold reduction after full anneal), the 6 temper tensile strength may be established by a cold reduction of approximately 55 percent following a full anneal, or the 4 temper tensile strength may be established by a cold reduction of approximately 35 percent after a full anneal.

The third digit, when used, indicates a variation of a two-digit temper. It is used when the degree of control of temper or the mechanical properties are different from but close to those for the two-digit H temper designation to which it is added, or when some other characteristic is significantly affected.

NOTE: The minimum ultimate tensile strength of a three-digit H temper is at least as close to that of the corresponding two-digit H temper as it is to the adjacent two-digit H tempers.

Three-Digit H Tempers

The following three-digit H temper designations have been assigned for wrought products in all alloys:

H111 Applies to products which are strain-hardened less than the amount required for a controlled H11 temper.

H112 Applies to products which acquire some temper from shaping processes not having special control over the amount of strain-hardening or thermal treatment, but for which there are mechanical property limits.

The following three-digit H temper designations have been assigned for wrought products in alloys containing over a nominal 4 percent magnesium.

H311 Applies to products which are strain-hardened

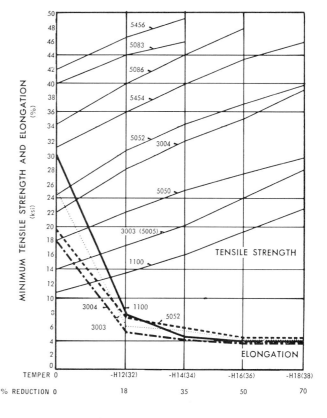

Fig. 2-1. Strain hardening curves non-heat-treatable alloys.

less than the amount required for a controlled H31 temper.

H321 Applies to products which are strain-hardened less than the amount required for a controlled H32 temper.

H323 ⎧Applies to products which are specially fabricated to have acceptable resistance to stress
H343 ⎩corrosion cracking

Mechanical Properties of Some Non-Heat-Treatable Alloys

Figure 2-1 shows strain-hardening curves for various popular non-heat-treatable alloys. The percent of reduction and corresponding tempers are shown at the bottom of the graph with the tensile strength shown along the left.

TABLE 2-3
Heat-Treatable Alloys

Series	Examples	Major Elements	Typical %	Typical Uses
2000	2014	Cu	4.4	Aircraft extrusions
	2024	Cu(+ Mg)	4.4(1.5)	Aircraft sheet
6000	6063	Mg(+ Si)	0.7(0.40)	Architectural extrusions
	6061	Mg(+ Si)	1.0(0.6)	General purpose medium strength
7000	7075	Zn(+ Mg)	5.6(2.5)	Aircraft uses high strength
	7178	Zn(+ Mg)	6.8(2.7)	Aircraft uses high strength

A few elongation curves are shown on the graph to portray the general trends. It can be noted that the ductility (elongation) decreases with increased amounts of cold work but tends to level out at the same value, regardless of alloy. Yield strengths are not plotted—they start lower (much lower than the tensile strengths at 0 reduction) and approach 1 to 2 ksi of the ultimate strengths at the H16 to H18 level. (Note that *minimum* values are shown rather than typical since the latter can be very misleading.)

Temper Designation System for Heat-Treatable Alloys

Some of the heat-treatable aluminum alloys are shown in Table 2-3.

The basic temper designations and subdivisions for the heat-treatable alloys are as follows:

F as fabricated. Applies to the products of shaping processes in which no special control over thermal conditions or strain-hardening is employed. For wrought products, there are no mechanical property limits.

O annealed (wrought products only). Applies to wrought products which are fully annealed to obtain the lowest strength condition

H strain-hardened (wrought products only). Applies to products which have their strength increased by strain-hardening, with or without supplementary thermal treatments to produce some reduction in strength. The H is always followed by two or more digits.

W solution heat-treated. An unstable temper applicable only to alloys which spontaneously age at room temperature for a long period of time after solution heat-treatment. This designation is specific only when the period of natural aging is indicated: for example, W ½ hr.

T thermally treated to produce stable tempers other than F, O, or H. Applies to products which are thermally treated with or without supplementary strain-hardening, to produce stable tempers. The T is always followed by one or more digits.

Subdivisions of T Temper; Thermally Treated

Numerals 1 through 10 following the T indicate specific sequences of basic treatments, as follows:

T1 cooled from an elevated temperature shaping process and naturally aged to a substantially stable condition. Applies to products for which the rate of cooling from an elevated temperature shaping process, such as casting or extrusion, is such that their strength is increased by room temperature aging.

T2 annealed (cast products only). Applies to cast products which are annealed to improve ductility and dimensional stability.

T3 solution heat-treated and then cold worked. Applies to products which are cold worked to improve① strength, or in which the effect of cold work in flattening or straightening is recognized in mechanical property limits.

T4 solution heat-treated and naturally aged to a substantially stable condition. Applies to products which are not cold worked after solution heat-treatment, or in which the effect of cold work in flattening or straightening may not be recognized in mechanical property limits.

T5 cooled from an elevated temperature shaping process and then artificially aged. Applies to products which are cooled from an elevated temperature shaping process, such as casting or extrusion, and then artificially aged to improve mechanical properties or dimensional stability or both.

T6 solution heat-treated and then artificially aged. Applies to products which are not cold worked after solution heat-treatment, or in which the effect of cold work in flattening or straightening may not be recognized in mechanical property limits.

T7 solution heat-treated and then stabilized. Applies to products which are stabilized to carry them beyond the point of maximum strength to provide control of some special characteristics.

T8 solution heat-treated, cold worked, and then artificially aged. Applies to products which are cold

---

1 A period of natural aging at room temperature may occur between or after the operations listed for tempers T3 through T10. Control of this period is exercised when it is metallurgically important.

worked to improve strength, or in which the effect of cold work in flattening or straightening is recognized in mechanical property limits.

T9 solution heat-treated, artificially aged, and then cold worked. Applies to products which are cold worked to improve strength.

T10 cooled from an elevated temperature shaping process, artificially aged and then cold worked. Applies to products which are artificially aged after cooling from an elevated temperature shaping process, such as casting or extrusion, and then cold worked to further improve strength.

Additional digits, the first of which shall not be zero, may be added to designations T1 through T10 to indicate a variation in treatment which significantly alters the characteristics of the product.

Additional Digits for T Tempers

The following additional digits have been assigned for stress-relieved tempers of wrought products:

T_51 Stress-relieved by stretching. Applies to the following products when stretched the indicated amounts after solution heat-treatment, or cooling, from an elevated temperature shaping process.

    Plate—1.5 to 3% permanent set
    Rod, bar, shapes, extruded tube—1 to 3% permanent set

Applies directly to plate and rolled or cold-finished rod and bar. These products receive no further straightening after stretching.

Applies to extruded rod, bar, shapes and tube when designated as follows:

T_510—Products that receive no further straightening after stretching.

T_511—Products that may receive minor straightening after stretching to comply with standard tolerances.

T_52 Stress-relieved by compressing. Applies to products which are stress-relieved by compressing after solution heat-treatment, to produce a permanent set of 1 to 5 percent.

T_54 Stress-relieved by combined stretching and compressing. Applies to die forgings which are stress relieved by restriking cold in the finish die.

The following temper designations have been assigned for variations of T4 and T6 tempers of wrought products.

T42 solution heat-treated from the 0 to F temper by the user, or by the producer to demonstrate response to heat-treatment, and naturally aged to a substantially stable condition.

T62 solution heat-treated from 0 or F temper by the user, or by the producer to demonstrate response to heat-treatment, and artificially aged.
Apply when available data indicate that any characteristic such as corrosion resistance, fatigue, or a mechanical property is significantly different from that for the T4 or T6 temper, respectively.

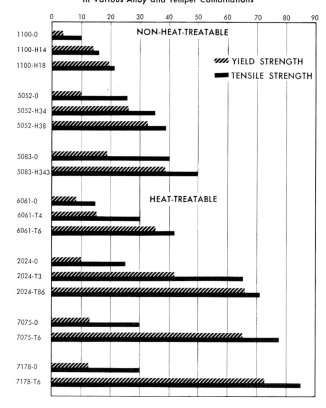

Fig. 2-2. *Mechanical properties of representative aluminum alloys.*

The solution heat-treatment practice used is the same as that for the T4 temper of the same alloy and product, and the artificial aging practice used is usually the same as that for the T6 temper of the same alloy and product. Material which is formed or cold worked by the user prior to solution heat-treatment may not attain the mechanical properties applicable to these tempers.

Mechanical Properties of Some Heat-Treatable Alloys

Figure 2-2 shows the tensile and yield strengths for some of the heat-treatable alloys in various tempers. Strengths for some non-heat-treatable alloys and combinations are shown for comparison.

Cladding

The heat-treatable (and in some cases the non-heat-treatable) alloys in sheet or plate form are sometimes clad with a layer of a corrosion-resistant alloy to improve corrosion resistance of a stronger alloy. The cladding is usually a layer on each side of the core alloy and usually comprises 2.5 to 5% of the total thickness. The cladding is pressure-welded to the core during the rolling operation. The original percentage thickness of cladding is retained, regardless of final gage.

The cladding not only protects because it is more resistant to corrosion than the core alloy, but it

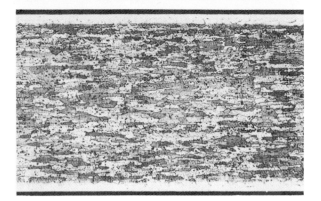

Fig. 2-3. Alclad 2024-T3 sheet; the clad portions are at top and bottom (100X, photographically enlarged 50%).

offers electrolytic or anodic protection as well. It establishes a galvanic cell since it is anodic to the core alloy and, therefore, it will have to be completely corroded away before the core is attacked. Since it is corrosion resistant, this usually takes a long time.

When an alloy is clad for corrosion resistance purposes, the combination is termed alclad, such as alclad 2024, etc. (See Figure 2-3).

Various combinations of core and cladding alloys can be combined for other purposes. For example, brazing sheet is made by cladding low-melting 4343 to high-melting 3003. This combination is termed brazing sheet number 12.

Aluminum Casting and Ingot Alloy Designation System

Elements which make up the major metal additions to produce aluminum casting alloys are generally similar to the groups of wrought alloys. A major difference is that the 6000 series is unused to date for casting and ingot alloys. Several important differences also are found in the use of silicon, tin and manganese, and, of course, in the fact that proportions of elements used in casting alloys frequently are quite different from those employed in the (roughly) similar wrought alloys.

The casting and ingot series and their major alloying elements are as follows.

Designations for Aluminum Casting Alloy Groups

	Designation No.
Aluminum—99.00% minimum and greater	1xx.x
Major Alloying Element	
Aluminum alloys grouped by major alloying element { Copper	2xx.x
Silicon, with added Copper and/or Magnesium	3xx.x
Silicon	4xx.x
Magnesium	5xx.x
Zinc	7xx.x
Tin	8xx.x
Unused Series	6xx.x
Other Major Alloying Elements	9xx.x

Casting and Ingot Alloy Designation System

This standard provides a system for designating aluminum and aluminum alloys in the form of castings and foundry ingot. The basic system consists of four digits; the first identifies the alloy group and the last identifies the product form, i.e., castings or ingot. A letter prefix is sometimes added to the four digits. Castings are designated by a suffix zero (0) which is separated from the first three digits by a decimal point.

Aluminum Castings and Ingot

The 1xx.x series indicates aluminum in the form of ingot or castings having a minimum aluminum percent of 99.00. The second two digits indicate the minimum aluminum content and are the same as the two digits to the right of the decimal in the minimum aluminum percentage when it is expressed to the nearest 0.01 percent.

Special control of one or more individual elements is indicated by a letter prefix to the basic four-digit designation.

Ingot is designated by a suffix one (1) which is separated from the first three digits by a decimal point.

Aluminum Alloy Castings and Ingot

The first digit in the basic four-digit designation identifies the alloy group. The second two digits are assigned when the alloy is registered.

A modification of the original alloy is indicated by a letter prefix before the numerical designation.

Ingot, which has chemical composition limits almost identical to those assigned to castings, is identified by the fourth digit one or two (1 or 2) which is separated from the first three digits by a decimal point.

Experimental Alloys

Experimental alloys also are designated in accordance with this system but are identified by the prefix x. The prefix is dropped when the alloy is no longer experimental. During development and before being designated as experimental, new alloys are identified by serial numbers assigned by their originators. Use of these serial numbers is discontinued when an x or standard designation number is assigned.

Standard Limits for Alloying Elements

Standard limits for alloying elements and impurities are expressed to the following places:

Less than 1/1000 percent	0.000x
1/1000 to 1/100 percent	0.00x
1/100 to 1/10 percent	
Unalloyed aluminum made by a refining process	0.0xx
Alloys and unalloyed aluminum not made by a refining process	0.0x
1/10 through ½ percent	0.xx
Over ½ percent	0.x, x.x, etc.

TABLE 2-4
Chemical Composition Limits for Sand and Permanent Mold Aluminum Casting Alloys

AA Number	Former Designation	Product ③	Silicon	Iron	Copper	Manganese	Magnesium	Chromium	Nickel	Zinc	Titanium	Tin	Others Each	Others Total
208.0	108	S	2.5-3.5	1.2	3.5-4.5	0.50	0.10		0.35	1.0	0.25			0.50
213.0	C113	S&P	1.0-3.0	1.2	6.0-8.0	0.6	0.10		0.35	2.5	0.25			0.50
222.0	122	S&P	2.0	1.5	9.2-10.7	0.50	0.15-0.35		0.50	0.8	0.25			0.35
242.0	142	S&P	0.7	1.0	3.5-4.5	0.35	1.2-1.8	0.25	1.7-2.3	0.35	0.25		0.05	0.15
295.0	195	S	0.7-1.5	1.0	4.0-5.0	0.35	0.03			0.35	0.25		0.05	0.15
B295.0	B195	P	2.0-3.0	1.2	4.0-5.0	0.35	0.05		0.35	0.50	0.25			0.35
308.0	A108	S&P	5.0-6.0	1.0	4.0-5.0	0.50	0.10		0.35	1.0	0.25			0.50
319.0	319, Allcast	S&P	5.5-6.5	1.0	3.0-4.0	0.50	0.10		0.25	1.0	0.25			0.50
328.0	Red X-8	S	7.5-8.5	1.0	1.0-2.0	0.20-0.6	0.20-0.6		2.0-3.0	1.5	0.25			0.50
A332.0	A132	P	11.0-13.0	1.2	0.50-1.5	0.35	0.7-1.3		0.50	0.35	0.25		0.05	0.50
F332.0	F132	P	8.5-10.5	1.2	2.0-4.0	0.50	0.50-1.5		0.50	1.0	0.25			0.50
333.0	333	P	8.0-10.0	1.0	3.0-4.0	0.50	0.05-0.50		0.50	1.0	0.25			0.50
355.0	355	S&P	4.5-5.5	0.6 ④	1.0-1.5	0.50 ④	0.40-0.6	0.25		0.35	0.25		0.05	0.15
C355.0	C355	S&P	4.5-5.5	0.20	1.0-1.5	0.10	0.40-0.6			0.10	0.20		0.05	0.15
356.0	356	S&P	6.5-7.5	0.6	0.25	0.35	0.20-0.40			0.35	0.20		0.05	0.15
A356.0	A356	S&P	6.5-7.5	0.20	0.20	0.10	0.20-0.40			0.05	0.20		0.05	0.15
357.0	357	S&P	6.5-7.5	0.15	0.05	0.03	0.45-0.6			0.05	0.20	0.15	0.05	0.15
360.0	360	D	9.0-10.0	2.0	0.6	0.35	0.40-0.6		0.50	0.50		0.15		0.25
A360.0	A360	D	9.0-10.0	1.3	0.6	0.35	0.40-0.6		0.50	0.50		0.15		0.25
380.0	380	D	7.5-9.5	2.0	3.0-4.0	0.50	0.10		0.50	3.0		0.35		0.50
A380.0	A380	D	7.5-9.5	1.3	3.0-4.0	0.50	0.10		0.50	3.0		0.35		0.50
384.0	384	D	10.5-12.0	1.3	3.0-4.5	0.50	0.10		0.50	1.0		0.15		0.25
413.0	13	D	11.0-13.0	2.0	0.6	0.35	0.10		0.50	0.50		0.15		0.25
A413.0	A13	D	11.0-13.0	1.3	0.6	0.35	0.10		0.50	0.50				0.25
B443.0	43 (0.15 max cu)	S&P	4.5-6.0	0.8	0.15	0.35	0.05			0.35	0.25		0.05	0.15
C443.0	A43	D	4.5-6.0	2.0	0.6	0.35	0.10		0.50	0.50		0.15		0.25
514.0	214	S	0.35	0.50	0.15	0.35	3.5-4.5			0.15	0.25		0.05	0.15
A514.0	A214	P	0.30	0.40	0.10	0.30	3.5-4.5			1.4-2.2	0.20		0.05	0.15
B514.0	B214	S	1.4-2.2	0.6	0.35	0.8	3.5-4.5	0.25		0.35	0.25		0.05	0.15
518.0	218	D	0.35	1.8	0.25	0.35	7.5-8.5		0.15	0.15		0.15		0.25
520.0	220	S	0.25	0.30	0.25	0.15	9.5-10.6			0.15	0.25		0.05	0.15
535.0	Almag 35	S&P	0.15	0.30	0.05	0.10-0.25	6.2-7.5				0.10-0.25		0.05 ⑤	0.15
705.0	603, Ternalloy 5	S&P	0.20	0.8	0.20	0.40-0.6	1.4-1.8	0.20-0.40		2.7-3.3	0.25		0.05	0.15
707.0	607, Ternalloy 7	S&P	0.20	0.8	0.20	0.40-0.6	1.8-2.4	0.20-0.40		4.0-4.5	0.25		0.05	0.15
A712.0	A612	S	0.15	0.50	0.35-0.65	0.05	0.6-0.8	0.40-0.6		6.0-7.0	0.25		0.05	0.25
D712.0	D612, 40E	S&P	0.30	0.50	0.25	0.10	0.50-0.65	0.35		5.0-6.5	0.15-0.25		0.05	0.20
713.0	613, Tenzaloy	S&P	0.25	1.1	0.40-1.0	0.6	0.20-0.50		0.15	7.0-8.0	0.25		0.10	0.25
771.0	Precedent 71A	S	0.15	0.15	0.10	0.10	0.8-1.0	0.06-0.20		6.5-7.5	0.10-0.20		0.05	0.15
750.0	750	S&P	0.7	0.7	0.7-1.3	0.10	0.10		0.7-1.3		0.20	5.5-7.0		0.30
A850.0	A750	S&P	2.0-3.0	0.7	0.7-1.3	0.10	0.10		0.30-0.7		0.20	5.5-7.0		0.30
B850.0	B750	S&P	0.40	0.7	1.7-2.3	0.10	0.6-0.9		0.9-1.5		0.20	5.5-7.0		0.30

① The alloys listed are those which have been included in Federal Specifications QQ-A-591d, ALUMINUM ALLOY DIE CASTINGS, QQ-A-596d, ALUMINUM ALLOY PERMANENT AND SEMI-PERMANENT MOLD CASTINGS, QQ-A-601d, ALUMINUM ALLOY SAND CASTINGS, and Military Specification MIL-A-21180C, ALUMINUM ALLOY CASTINGS, HIGH STRENGTH. Other alloys are registered with The Aluminum Association and are available. Information on these should be requested from individual foundries or ingot suppliers.

② Analysis is regularly made only for the elements for which specific limits are shown. If, however, the presence of other elements is suspected to be, or in the course of routine analysis is indicated to be, in excess of the specified limits, further analysis is made to determine that those other elements are not in excess of the amount specified. Composition in percent maximum unless shown as a range; aluminum is the remainder.

③ S = Sand Cast. P = Permanent Mold Cast. D = Die Cast.

④ If iron exceeds 0.45 percent, manganese content shall not be less than one-half the iron content.

⑤ Also contains 0.003-0.007 percent beryllium, boron 0.002 percent maximum.

TABLE 2-5
Mechanical Property Limits of Sand and Permanent Mold Aluminum Casting Alloys

ALLOY AA Number	ALLOY Former Designation	Product [2]	Temper	Tensile Strength ksi (MPa) min Ultimate	Yield	Elongation in 2 Inches percent min	ALLOY AA Number	ALLOY Former Designation	Product [2]	Temper	Tensile Strength ksi (MPa) min Ultimate	Yield	Elongation in 2 Inches percent min
208.0	108	S	F	19.0 (131)		1.5	355.0	355	S	T71	30.0 (207)		
208.0	108	S	T55	21.0 (145)			355.0	355	P	T51	27.0 (136)		
213.0	113	S	F	19.0 (131)			355.0	355	P	T6	37.0 (255)		1.5
213.0	113	P	F	23.0 (159)			355.0	355	P	T62	42.0 (290)		
222.0	122	S	T2	23.0 (159)			355.0	355	P	T71	34.0 (234)		
222.0	122	S	T61	30.0 (207)			C355.0	C355	P	T61	40.0 (276)		3.0
222.0	122	P	T551	30.0 (207)			356.0	356	S	T51	23.0 (159)		
222.0	122	P	T65	40.0 (276)			356.0	356	S	T6	30.0 (207)	20.0 (138)	3.0
242.0	142	S	T21	23.0 (159)			356.0	356	S	T7	31.0 (214)	29.0 (200)	
242.0	142	S	T571	29.0 (200)			356.0	356	P	T51	25.0 (172)		
242.0	142	P	T571	34.0 (234)			356.0	356	P	T6	33.0 (228)		3.0
242.0	142	P	T61	40.0 (276)			356.0	356	P	T7	29.0 (200)		4.0
295.0	195	S	T4	29.0 (200)		6.0	A356.0	A356	P	T61	37.0 (255)		5.0
295.0	195	S	T6	32.0 (221)	20.0 (138)	3.0	357.0	357	P	T6	45.0 (310)		3.0
295.0	195	S	T62	36.0 (248)			B443.0	43 (0.15 max cu)	S	F	17.0 (117)		3.0
295.0	195	S	T7	29.0 (200)		3.0	B443.0	43 (0.15 max cu)	P	F	21.0 (145)		5.0
B295.0	B195	P	T4	33.0 (228)		4.5	514.0	214	S	F	22.0 (152)		6.0
B295.0	B195	P	T6	35.0 (241)		2.0	A514.0	A214	P	F	22.0 (152)		2.5
B295.0	B195	P	T7	33.0 (228)		3.0	B514.0	B214	S	F	17.0 (117)	10.0 (69)	
308.0	A108	P	F	24.0 (165)			520.0	220	S	T4	42.0 (290)	22.0 (152)	12.0
319.0	319, Allcast	S	F	23.0 (159)			535.0	Almag 35	S	F	35.0 (241)	18.0 (124)	9.0
319.0	319, Allcast	S	T5	25.0 (172)			535.0	Almag 35	S	T2	35.0 (241)	18.0 (124)	9.0
319.0	319, Allcast	S	T6	31.0 (214)		1.5	705.0	603, Ternalloy 5	S	F or T5	30.0 (207)	17.0 (117)	5.0
319.0	319, Allcast	P	F	28.0 (193)		1.5	705.0	603, Ternalloy 5	P	T5	37.0 (255)		10.0
319.0	319, Allcast	P	T6	34.0 (234)		2.0	707.0	607, Ternalloy 7	S	F or T5	33.0 (228)	22.0 (152)	2.0
328.0	Red X-8	S	F	25.0 (172)		1.0	707.0	607, Ternalloy 7	P	T5	42.0 (290)		4.0
328.0	Red X-8	S	T6	34.0 (234)		1.0	707.0	607, Ternalloy 7	P	T7	45.0 (310)		3.0
A332.0	A132	P	T551	31.0 (214)			A712.0	A612	S	F	32.0 (221)	20.0 (138)	2.0
A332.0	A132	P	T65	40.0 (276)			D712.0	D612, 40E	S	F or T5	34.0 (234)	25.0 (172)	4.0
F332.0	F132	P	T5	31.0 (214)			713.0	613, Tenzaloy	S	F or T5	32.0 (221)	22.0 (152)	3.0
333.0	333	P	F	28.0 (193)			713.0	613, Tenzaloy	P	T5	32.0 (221)		4.0
333.0	333	P	T5	30.0 (207)			771.0	Precedent 71A	S	T6	45.0 (310)	37.0 (255)	5.0
333.0	333	P	T6	35.0 (241)			850.0	750	S	T5	16.0 (110)		5.0
333.0	333	P	T7	31.0 (214)			850.0	750	P	T5	18.0 (124)		8.0
355.0	355	S	T51	25.0 (172)			A850.0	A750	S	T5	17.0 (117)		3.0
355.0	355	S	T6	32.0 (221)	20.0 (138)	2.0	A850.0	A750	P	T5	17.0 (117)		3.0
355.0	355	S	T7	35.0 (241)			B850.0	B750	S	T5	24.0 (165)	18.0 (124)	
							B850.0	B750	P	T5	27.0 (186)		3.0

[1] Values represent properties obtained from separately cast test bars. The customer should keep in mind that (1) some foundries may offer additional tempers for the above alloys, and (2) foundries are constantly improving casting technique and, as a result, some may guarantee minimum properties in excess of the above.

[2] S = Sand Cast. P = Permanent Mold Cast.

Standard limits for alloying elements and impurities for casting alloy in ingot form (Ingot Designation xxx.1) are the same as for the alloy in the form of castings, except for the following:

Maximum Iron Percentage:

for Sand and Permanent Mold Castings — for Ingot
- Up thru 0.15 — 0.03 less than castings
- Over 0.15 thru 0.25 — 0.05 less than castings
- Over 0.25 thru 0.6 — 0.10 less than castings
- Over 0.6 thru 1.0 — 0.2 less than castings
- Over 1.0 — 0.3 less than castings

for Die Castings — for Ingot
- Up thru 1.3 — 0.3 less than castings
- Over 1.3 — 1.1 maximum

Minimum Magnesium Percentage:

for all Castings — for Ingot
- Less than 0.50 — 0.05 more than castings[a]
- 0.5 and greater — 0.1 more than castings[a]

Maximum Zinc Percentage:

for Die Castings — for Ingot
- Over 0.25 thru 0.6 — 0.10 less than castings
- Over 0.6 — 0.1 less thas castings

[a] Applicable only when the specified magnesium range for castings is greater than 0.15%.

Chemical composition limits for sand and permanent mold aluminum casting alloys are given in Table 2-4. Mechanical property limits of these alloys are in Table 2-5.

Section III:
Forming

Forming of Aluminum Alloys

*By the ASM Committee on Forming of Aluminum Alloys**

ALUMINUM and its alloys are among the most readily formable of the commonly fabricated metals. There are, of course, differences between aluminum alloys and other metals in the amount of permissible deformation, in some aspects of tool design, and in details of procedure. These differences stem primarily from the lower tensile and yield strengths of aluminum alloys, and from their comparatively slow rate of work hardening. The compositions and tempers of aluminum alloys also affect their formability. This article emphasizes those aspects of commercial forming processes and equipment that apply specifically to aluminum alloys. Basic information on the forming of metals in general is given in other articles in this volume.

Alloy Selection

The factors involved in selecting an alloy for a specific manufacturing application are discussed in detail in the article "The Selection and Application of Aluminum and Aluminum Alloys", on pages 866 to 888 in Volume 1 of this Handbook.

Ratings of general formability or workability of the commercially available alloys in the various tempers, and comparative ratings of alloys and tempers for specific types of forming, are tabulated under specific forming processes in this article. Such ratings provide generally reliable comparisons of work metals, but at best are only an approximate guide to forming limits in any specific application. Trial runs and evaluative techniques developed for specialized applications are needed in borderline or critical situations.

Choice of temper may depend on the severity of the forming operations. The annealed temper may be required for severe forming operations such as deep drawing, or for roll forming or bending to exceptionally small radii. Usually, the strongest temper that can be formed consistently is selected. For less severe forming operations, the intermediate tempers, or even full-hard work metal, can be used.

Non-Heat-Treatable Alloys. Alloys 1100 and 3003 are frequently used in forming applications, because of their excellent workability and low cost. If somewhat higher strength is required, alloys containing magnesium are commonly used (for example, in order of increasing strength, alloys 3004, 5052, 5154 and 5086).

If superior finishing characteristics are needed in addition to higher strength, an alloy containing a small amount of manganese in addition to magnesium (alloy 5053, 5252 or 5457) can be used. Holding impurities at a low level in alloys used for decorative and finishing purposes also helps in developing bright, uniform finish.

Heat treatable alloys are used in applications for which a high strength-to-weight ratio is required. These include alloys 6061, 2014, 2024, 7075 and 7178, in approximate order of increasing strength.

The annealed temper (O) is the most workable condition for forming, but it entails the greatest expense in subsequent heat treating and straightening. Alloys that have been freshly solution heat treated and quenched (W temper) are nearly as formable as when annealed, and can be given increased strength after forming by natural or artificial aging, without reheating and consequent exposure of the finished part to warping. Alloys can be stored in the W temper for a reasonable period at a low temperature. (Almost no aging occurs in most alloys at −20 F.)

Material that has been solution heat treated at the mill, but not artificially aged (T3, T4 or W temper), is generally suitable only for mild forming operations such as bending, mild drawing, or moderate stretch forming.

Solution heat treated and artificially aged (T6 temper) alloys are seldom used for forming, other than bending to standard radii and forming of very shallow shapes. Although alloys in the T6 temper are much stronger, they have lost so much ductility in hardening that they are apt to fracture in even moderately severe forming.

Equipment and Tools

Most of the equipment used in the forming of steel and other metals is suitable for use with aluminum alloys. Because of the generally lower yield strength of aluminum alloys, however, press tonnage requirements are usually lower than for comparable operations on steel, and higher press speeds can be used. Similarly, equipment for roll forming, spinning, stretch forming, and other forming operations on aluminum

*JAMES C. HERR, *Chairman,* Chief of Process Control, General Dynamics/Fort Worth; ELDON COOPERRIDER, Chief Plant Engineer, Lennox Industries Inc.

GEORGE F. FARLEY, President (retired), Spincraft Inc.; RICHARD T. KENNEDY, Product Engineering Manager, Sunbeam Corp.; C. E. MCHAN, Group Engineer, Manufacturing Research, Lockheed-Georgia Co. Div., Lockheed Aircraft Corp.; F. G. MCKEE, Manager of Metal Working Div.,

Alcoa Process Development Laboratories, Aluminum Company of America; PAUL R. O'BRIEN, Director of Automotive Section, Reynolds Metals Co.; ARTHUR L. PAGE, Engineer, Talon, Inc.

WALTER PAJERSKI, Manufacturing Process Engineer, Mine Safety Appliances Co.; SCOTT F. REEKIE, Manager of Metals and Plastics Plant, Tektronix, Inc.; R. A. RIDOUT, Director of Technical Services, Kaiser Aluminum & Chemical Sales, Inc.

need not be so massive or rated for such heavy loading as for comparable operations on steel.

Tools. Total wear on tools used in forming aluminum is somewhat less than with steel. This results in part from the lower force levels involved, and in part from the smoother surface condition that is characteristic of aluminum alloys. Accordingly, tools can sometimes be made from less expensive materials, even for relatively long runs.

However, a higher-quality surface finish is generally required on tools used with aluminum alloys, to avoid marking. The oxide film on the surface of aluminum alloys is highly abrasive, and for this reason many forming tools are made of hardened tool steels. As a rule, these tools, even if otherwise suitable, should not be used interchangeably to form steel parts, because this could destroy the high finish on the tools.

Most aluminum alloys require smaller clearances between punches and dies in blanking and piercing than do steels. They require larger clearances but about the same radii on drawing tools, to allow free flow of metal and avoid excessive stretching.

The amount of springback in forming aluminum alloys is generally less than in forming low-carbon steel, and this must be considered in tool design. The amount of springback is roughly proportional to the yield strength of the metal.

The slower rate of work hardening of aluminum alloys permits a greater number of successive draws than is possible with steel.

Lubricants

Lubricants must be selected specifically for their compatibility with aluminum alloys and their suitability for the particular forming operation. A lubricant suitable for use on a steel part will not necessarily be suitable for use in the forming of a similar aluminum alloy part.

Properly formulated lubricants take into account the special requirements of regulation of moisture content in nonaqueous systems, corrosion inhibitors, and pH control, in order to prevent staining or corrosion of aluminum alloys and to make duration of contact with the workpiece less critical.

The lubricants most widely used in the forming of aluminum alloys are listed in Table 1 in approximate order of increasing effectiveness. The use of various special-purpose lubricants is discussed in sections of this article that deal with individual forming processes.

The kerosine used as a lubricant is less irritating to the hands than the one used as a fuel.

Blanking and Piercing

Blanking and piercing of aluminum alloy flat stock are ordinarily done in punch presses, because of their high production rates and ability to maintain close tolerances. Press brakes are sometimes used, particularly for experimental or short-run production.

Because of the generally lower shear strength of aluminum alloys, lower-tonnage presses or press brakes are

Table 1. Typical Lubricants Used in the Forming of Aluminum Alloys

(Listed in approximate order of increasing effectiveness) (a)

1 Kerosine
2 Mineral oil (viscosity, 40 to 300 sus at 100 F)
3 Petroleum jelly
4 Mineral oil plus 10 to 20% fatty oil
5 Tallow plus 50% paraffin
6 Tallow plus 70% paraffin
7 Mineral oil plus 10 to 15% sulfurized fatty oil plus 10% fatty oil
8 Dried soap films or wax films(a)
9 Fat emulsions in aqueous soap solutions plus finely divided fillers(b)
10 Mineral oil plus sulfurized fatty oil plus fatty oil plus finely divided fillers(b)

(a) For some applications, dried soap or wax films (lubricant No. 8) are less effective than lubricants No. 5, 6 and 7. (b) Typical fillers are chalk, lithopone, white lead, talc, mica, zinc oxide, clay, sulfur and graphite.

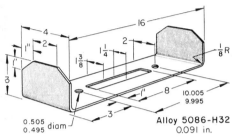

Fig. 1. Bracket produced in quantities of 100 to 500 by shearing, piercing, and forming. Piercing was done with tooling normally used for high production, to obtain dimensional accuracy. (Example 510)

usually required than for comparable operations with steel. Total shearing force needed can be calculated as the product of shear strength, total length of cut, and metal thickness, but allowance must be made for different alloys, for dulling of the cutting edges of punches and dies, and for variation in clearance between punch and die. The shear strength of the commonly used aluminum alloys ranges from 9000 to 49,000 psi, whereas that of low-carbon steel is from 35,000 to 67,000 psi.

Tool Materials. A discussion of materials for blanking and piercing dies is given on pages 69 to 77 in this volume. Aluminum alloys are classed with other soft materials, such as copper and magnesium alloys. In general, for a given tool material, tool life will be longer for blanking and piercing aluminum alloys than for steel.

In some applications, a less expensive die can be used than with steel parts, particularly for relatively short runs. Cast zinc dies, which cost only about one-fifth as much as tool steel dies, are used for runs of up to about 2000 parts. Steel-rule dies and template dies also reduce tooling costs for short runs or moderate-length runs. For example, an aluminum alloy blank 19.5 by 12 in. by 0.040 in. thick was made in a steel-rule die having an expected life of 150 pieces. For the production quantity, the burr height did not exceed 0.005 in. Punches and die buttons for seven pierced holes of $\frac{5}{32}$, $\frac{3}{16}$ and $\frac{1}{4}$-in. diameter were incorporated in the die.

Low-carbon steel or cast iron dies sometimes replace hardened tool steel dies, even for long runs.

Punches are usually made from annealed or hardened tool steel, depend-

ing on the size and complexity of the part and on the length of the run.

Carbide tools are seldom required, even for extremely long runs.

Tolerances. A tolerance of ±0.005 in. is normal in the blanking and piercing of aluminum alloy parts in a punch press. Using a press brake, it is possible to blank and pierce to a location tolerance of ±0.010 in. or less, although tolerances for general press-brake operations usually range from ±0.020 to ±0.030 in.

For economy in tool cost, specified tolerance should be no less than is actually necessary for the particular part. A tolerance of ±0.005 in. would probably require that the punch and die be jig-ground, adding 30 to 40% to their cost. A tolerance of ±0.002 in. may require the addition of a shaving operation. Besides the cost of an extra die, labor costs would be increased by the additional operation.

For extremely accurate work, an allowance must be made for the shrinkage of holes and expansion of blanks resulting from the elasticity of the stock. This allowance, made to both punch and die, does not change the clearance between them, and is primarily a function of stock thickness:

Stock thickness, in.	Allowance per side, in.
0.010 to 0.030	0.00050
0.030 to 0.060	0.00075
0.060 to 0.135	0.00100

For large sizes and for normal tolerances, this correction is not very important.

Unacceptable distortion or mislocation of existing holes in a part by subsequent operations must be avoided. In the following example, special tooling was used to maintain close tolerances between a large pierced opening and adjacent holes.

Example 510. Use of a Compound Die for Accurate Piercing of a Low-Production Part (Fig. 1)

The mounting bracket shown in Fig. 1 was produced in quantities of 100 to 500 pieces by shearing, piercing and forming, as follows:

1 Shear blank to size in a square shear (1200 pieces per hour)
2 Miter shear four corners in a square shear (650 pieces per hour)
3 Pierce rectangular opening and two round holes, in one stroke in a punch press, using a compound die (850 pieces per hour)
4 Form two flanges in two strokes in a press brake, using a standard 90° V-die (550 pieces per hour)

Dimensional tolerances (±$\frac{1}{32}$ in.) could be met by using low-production utility tooling for shearing and forming. However, it was necessary to pierce the rectangular opening and the two round holes in a single press stroke with a compound die, rather than to punch these openings successively in separate dies (normal low-production procedure), to maintain the accurate hole location shown in Fig. 1.

For lot sizes of up to 10,000 brackets, trimming the four corners of the sheared blank was incorporated into the compound die for the two holes and rectangular cutout. Another die bent both flanges in one press stroke. Maximum production rate was 850 pieces per hour. A three-station progressive die was estimated capable of producing 1600 pieces per hour.

Special requirements on press construction and maintenance, and on tool material and design, are sometimes imposed by tolerances and other workpiece specifications, as shown in the example that follows.

Example 511. Blanking, Drawing and Piercing a Gas-Mask Spacer to Close Tolerances (Fig. 2)

A spacer for a gas-mask filter can (Fig. 2) had to be produced to close tolerances on outside dimensions, and without burrs or sharp edges that could cut through the mineral wool that was wrapped over the outer edge of the spacer, as filter material, before it was inserted in the can.

To save the cost of an extra trimming or edge-turndown operation, the spacers were produced by blanking, drawing and piercing in a compound die. As the blanking sections of the die dulled, however, objectionably large burrs were produced, resulting in sharp outside edges and oversize parts.

To eliminate these problems, the blanking sections of the die were made from high-carbon high-chromium tool steel. Also, a four-post die set was used, and the operation was done in a press with minimum clearance in the gibs. The parts were checked regularly throughout the run for dimensional accuracy and burred edges.

The extreme outer dimensions were maintained satisfactorily by controlling the inside dimensions to the tolerances shown in Fig. 2.

Originally, aluminum alloy 3003-O was used, because of its drawability. A change was made to 3003-H14 because of its ability to hold closer tolerances, although scrap loss was higher because of fractures. The spacer also was successfully produced from aluminum alloy 5052-O.

For notching and piercing to close tolerances, an alternative to the use of a precision die in a punch press is the use of a tape-controlled turret punch press equipped with standard utility punches and dies, as described in the following example. Where such equipment is available, this technique is usually less expensive for relatively short runs, and is capable of maintaining tolerances of ±0.005 in.

Example 512. Cost of Close-Tolerance Piercing and Notching in a Punch Press vs a Tape-Controlled Turret Press (Fig. 3)

A cost comparison of two methods of piercing and notching a part to hole-location tolerance of ±0.008 in. is given in Fig. 3. The graph in Fig. 3 shows that a tape-controlled turret punch press with standard tooling produced parts more economically than a conventional punch press and precision compound die, for up to about 4000 pieces.

If the part design had been modified, the cost of a new tape for the tape-controlled press would have been only $43, compared with about $200 or more for modifying the precision die. Therefore, limited quantities of the modified part would have been produced at a lower unit cost by the tape-controlled press, but for large quantities, parts would be produced more economically by the conventional press method.

Production data applicable to both methods are given in the table with Fig. 3. They show the costs used in plotting the graph.

Sheared blanks 5.75 by 9.75 in. were used in both methods. The compound die was capable of holding dimensional tolerances within ±0.002 in., and the turret punch press within ±0.005 in.

If tolerances permit, holes in the sidewalls of formed parts can sometimes be pierced before forming. This can reduce costs by eliminating the need for one or more horn dies or cam-actuated dies and the resultant slow handling of parts.

An initial blank layout can be calculated from formulas used for determining bend allowance (see "Blank Size" on page 109 in "Press-Brake Forming"). The final blank layout is usually developed by successive trials and modifications. Trial blanks can be marked with a grid pattern to determine accurately the pattern and the dimensions of met-

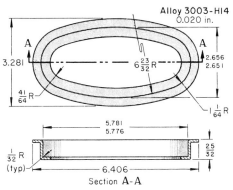

Fig. 2. Spacer for a gas mask produced to close tolerances by blanking, drawing and piercing in a compound die (Example 511)

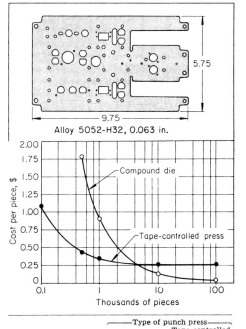

	— Type of punch press —	
Item	Conventional, with precision compound die	Tape-controlled turret type, with standard tooling
Die cost	$850	...
Tape cost	...	$ 43.30(a)
Labor costs (1000 pcs):		
Setup(b)	$18.32(c)	$ 38.44(d)
Production	30.23(e)	269.08(f)
Total (labor)	$48.55	$307.52

(a) Cost of 10 hr for production of tape, at $4.33 per hour for labor and overhead. (b) Four setups; 250 pieces per setup. (c) Based on ½ hr for each setup, at $9.16 per hr for labor and overhead. (d) Based on 1 hr for each setup, at $9.61 per hour for labor and overhead. (e) Based on 0.0033 hr per piece, at $9.16 per hour for labor and overhead. (f) Based on 0.028 hr per piece, at $9.61 per hour for labor and overhead.

Fig. 3. Cost comparison of two methods used to produce a flat part by blanking, piercing and notching (Example 512)

al movement. (No holes should be pierced in areas of metal movement if the hole shape is important.) The part described in the following example was produced by using a bend-allowance formula to determine flat pattern dimensions, and to determine flange hole locations on the blank.

Example 513. Rectangular Box Produced From a Flat Pierced Blank (Fig. 4)

The shallow rectangular box shown in Fig. 4 was produced by drawing a flat blank that had previously been blanked and pierced in a compound die.

The blank layout, also shown in Fig. 4, was developed to meet a tolerance of ±0.008 in. on the hole locations and length, width and height dimensions of the box, except at the corners, where compound metal movement took place during forming. Variations in metal thickness and hardness made it necessary to trim the four corners after forming to assure a uniform height. By using the conventional bend-allowance formula to determine the stock to allow for the flat blank, the flange widths and hole locations (after forming) were within the ±0.008-in. tolerance allowed.

The shape of the blank (as shown in Fig. 4) satisfied the requirement for a simple blanking-die contour and a minimum of trimming after forming. The areas of metal movement during the drawing operation are also shown on the blank layout in Fig. 4.

Clearance between punch and die must be controlled in blanking and piercing, in order to obtain a uniform shearing action. Clearance is usually expressed as the distance between mating surfaces of punch and die (per side) in percentage of work thickness.

Correct clearance between punch and die depends on the alloy as well as the sheet thickness. Suggested punch-to-die clearances for blanking and piercing the common alloys are listed in Table 2.

The character of the shearing action also depends on the sharpness of the tools. Dull cutting edges on punch and die have effects similar to those of excessive clearance, with the effect on burr size being particularly pronounced.

With proper clearance, the fractures proceeding from the punch surface and from the die surface of the work meet cleanly without secondary shearing and excessive plastic deformation. Secondary shearing indicates that the clearance is too small; a large radius or dished contour at the sheared edge and a stringy burr indicate that the clearance is too great.

For additional information on punch-to-die clearances, see the article "Piercing of Low-Carbon Steel", which begins on page 44 in this volume.

Die Taper. The walls of die openings in blanking or piercing dies are often tapered ½° from the vertical to minimize sticking of the blank or slug in

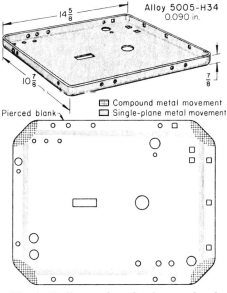

Fig. 4. Shallow rectangular box produced by drawing a flat blank that had been blanked and pierced in a compound die (Example 513)

the die. A straight vertical section of at least ⅛ in. (or equal to the metal thickness for stock thicker than ⅛ in.) is usually left at the upper end of the die opening, to provide for sharpening without changing the clearance. Tapered die relief is usually more suitable for piercing aluminum than counterbore design relief.

Stripping force of 3 to 20% of the total blanking and piercing tonnage is used for aluminum alloys. The force needed depends on the alloy, temper and stock thickness. Sharpness of cutting edges on punch and die, clearance between punch and die, lubrication, and uniformity of application of stripperplate pressure also affect stripping force.

Lubricants are normally used in blanking or piercing aluminum alloy parts, to reduce sticking of slugs or blanks in the die opening, and to facilitate clean stripping from the punch without buckling. Lower tool-maintenance costs and smoother edges on blanks or holes can be obtained with suitable lubrication. The lubricants most commonly used include the first four types listed in Table 1, or proprietary compounds based on them.

Press-Brake Forming

The press-brake forming techniques used with aluminum alloys are similar to those used with steel and other metals, differing only in some details of tool design.

Tolerances in press-brake forming are larger than those in punch-press operations. For simple shapes that are relatively long and narrow, a tolerance of ±1/32 in. can usually be maintained. On larger parts of more complex cross section, the tolerance may be as much as ±1/16 in.

Springback, or partial return to the original shape upon removal of the bending forces, occurs in most bending operations. (For a detailed discussion of springback, see page 108 in the article "Press-Brake Forming".)

The amount of springback depends on the yield strength, the bend radius, and the thickness of the stock. Table 3 shows the effects of these variables, giving springback allowances in degrees of overbending that have been used for high-strength aluminum alloys 2024 and 7075.

The springback allowance, or number of degrees of overbending required, ranges from 1° to 12° for 2024 and 7075-O (yield strength of 11,000 psi min), and from 7¼° to 33½° for 2024-T3 (yield strength of 50,000 psi). The allowance increases with increasing yield strength and bend radius, but varies inversely with stock thickness. The allowance for bends of other than 90° can be estimated on a proportional basis. For bend angles of less than 90°, the springback may be greater unless the bend radius is decreased, because the metal in the bend area may not have been stressed beyond its yield point.

Radii to which bends can be made depend on the properties of the metal, and on the design, dimensions and condition of tools. For most metals, the ratio of minimum bend radius to thickness is approximately constant, because

ductility is the primary limiting factor on minimum bend radius. This is not true of aluminum alloys, for which the ratio increases with the thickness.

Table 4 shows the experimentally determined variation of minimum bend radius with alloy, temper and thickness for most of the commonly used aluminum alloys, in conventional bending operations with rigid dies.

Table 5 lists the common aluminum alloys and tempers that are capable of 180° cold bends over zero radius, and shows the maximum sheet thickness at which such bends can be made.

Minimum bend radii recommended for several groups of aluminum alloys in press-brake and hydraulic forming are given in Tables 6 and 7 on page 872 of Volume 1 of this Handbook.

With special tooling, aluminum alloys can be bent to smaller radii than indicated in standard tables. Bottoming dies, and dies that combine bottoming with air bending, are used for this purpose. Hydraulic forming, forming with rubber-pad dies, and high-energy-rate forming also produce good small-radius bends.

Sometimes it is possible to take advantage of the grain direction in the work metal: The most severe bends can be made across the direction of rolling. If similar bends are made in two or

more directions, it is recommended that all bends be made at an angle to the direction of rolling, if possible.

Local heating along the bend lines can sometimes be used to produce small bend radii without fracture; this is particularly useful in bending plate.

The maximum temperature that can be used without serious loss in mechanical properties is 300 to 400 F for cold worked material. Reheating of naturally aged aluminum alloys 2014 and 2024 is not recommended unless the part will be artificially aged. Generally, any reheating sufficient to improve formability will lower the resistance to corrosion to an undesirable degree, except with alclad sheet.

Blank Development. For relatively simple parts, particularly where close tolerances are not required, the blank layout can be developed directly by using bend-allowance tables or mathematical formulas (see page 109, and Table 2 on page 110, in the article "Press-Brake Forming"). As a general rule, the initial calculated blank layout and die design are developed into final form by successive trial and modification.

Lubricants are needed for nearly all press-brake forming of aluminum alloys. The light protective film of oil sometimes present on mill stock is often adequate for mild bending opera-

Table 2. Punch-to-Die Clearances for Blanking and Piercing Aluminum Alloys

Alloy	Temper	Clearance per side, %t(a)	Alloy	Temper	Clearance per side, %t(a)
1100	O	5.0	5083	O	7.0
	H12, H14	6.0		H323, H343	7.5
	H16, H18	7.0	5086	O, H112	7.0
2014	O	6.5		H32, H34, H36	7.5
	T4, T6	8.0	5154	O, H112	7.0
2024	O	6.5		H32, H34, H36, H38	7.5
	T3, T36, T4	8.0	5257(b)	O	5.0
3003	O	5.0		H25	6.0
	H12, H14	6.0		H28	7.0
	H16, H18	7.0	5454	O, H112	7.0
3004	O	6.5		H32, H34	7.5
	H32, H34	7.0	6061	O	5.5
	H36, H38	7.5		T4	6.0
5005	O	5.0		T6	7.0
	H12, H14, H32, H34	6.0	7075	O	6.5
	H36, H38	7.0		W, T6	8.0
5050	O	5.0	7178	O	6.5
	H32, H34	6.0		W, T6	8.0
	H36, H38	7.0			
5052	O	6.5			
	H32, H34	7.0			
	H36, H38	7.5			

(a) t = thickness of sheet. (b) Also alloys 5357, 5457, 5557 and 5657.

Table 3. Springback Allowances for 90° Bends in 2024 and 7075 Aluminum Alloy Sheet

Sheet thickness, in.	*Springback allowance, in degrees, for bend radius, in., of:*							
	3/32	⅛	3/16	¼	5/16	⅜	7/16	½
2024-O and 7075-O								
0.020	3	4	5½	7½	8½	9	9½	12
0.025	2¾	3¾	5½	6½	8	8¼	8¾	10¾
0.032	2¼	3	4¾	6	6¾	7	7½	9½
0.040	2	3	4	5	6	6¼	6¾	8¾
0.051	2	2½	3½	4	5	5¼	5¾	7½
0.064	1½	2	2¾	3¾	4½	5	5½	6¾
0.081	1	1½	2	2½	3¼	3½	4	4¾
0.094	...	...	1¾	2½	3	3¼	3¾	4½
0.125	...	...	1½	2	2¼	2¾	3	3¾
2024-T3								
0.020	10	12	15½	19	22½	24	27¼	33½
0.025	8¾	10½	14	16¾	17¾	21	23	28½
0.032	7¾	8¾	12	14¼	16¾	17¾	19¼	24
0.040	7¼	8¼	10¾	12¾	14½	15¼	17	20½
0.051	...	...	9	10½	12¼	13	14½	16¾
0.064	...	...	8	9¾	11¼	12	12¾	15
0.081	...	...	...	...	9½	10½	11¼	13
0.094	...	...	...	...	8¾	9¾	10½	12

SOURCE: "Die Design Handbook", 2nd Edition, ASTME, McGraw-Hill, 1965

Table 4. Minimum Recommended Radii for 90° Cold Bends in Aluminum Alloy Sheet(a)

Alloy	Temper	0.016	0.025	0.032	0.040	0.050	0.063	0.090	0.125	0.190	0.250
		Minimum bend radius in 1/32 in., for sheet thickness, in., of:									
1100	O	0	0	0	0	0	0	0	0	0	0
	H12	0	0	0	0	0	0	0	0	3	6
	H14	0	0	0	0	0	0	0	0	3	6
	H16	0	0	0	0	1	2	3	4	8	16
	H18	1	1	2	2	3	4	6	8	16	24
2014	O	0	0	0	0	0	0	0	0	3	6
	T6	2	4	4	5	7	8	15	20	36	64
2024 & alclad 2024	O	0	0	0	0	0	0	0	0	3	6
	T3	2	3	4	5	7	8	15	20	30	48
3003, 5005, 5357 and 5457, at tempers listed at right	O	0	0	0	0	0	0	0	0	0	0
	H12 or H32	0	0	0	0	0	0	0	0	3	6
	H14 or H34	0	0	0	0	0	0	1	2	4	8
	H16 or H36	0	0	1	2	2	3	5	6	12	24
	H18 or H38	1	1	2	2	3	5	9	12	24	40
3004, alclad 3004, 5154, 5254 and 5454, at tempers listed at right	O	0	0	0	0	0	0	0	2	3	8
	H32	0	0	0	1	1	2	3	4	9	18
	H34	1	1	1	2	2	3	5	6	12	24
	H36	1	1	1	2	3	4	6	9	18	24
	H38	1	1	2	3	4	6	9	16	30	40
5050	O	0	0	0	0	0	0	0	0	0	0
	H32	0	0	0	0	0	0	0	2	3	8
	H34	0	0	0	0	0	1	2	4	6	12
	H36	1	1	1	2	2	3	6	8	16	24
	H38	1	1	2	3	4	6	9	12	24	40
5052 and 5652	O	0	0	0	0	0	0	0	2	3	4
	H32	0	0	0	0	1	2	3	4	6	12
	H34	0	0	0	1	1	2	4	5	9	16
	H36	1	1	1	2	3	4	5	8	18	24
	H38	1	1	2	3	4	6	9	12	24	40
5086 and 5155	O	0	0	0	0	0	1	2	3	6	8
	H32	1	1	1	2	2	3	5	6	12	16
	H34	1	1	2	2	3	3	6	8	18	24
6061 & alclad 6061	O	0	0	0	0	0	0	0	2	3	4
	T6	1	1	2	2	3	4	6	9	18	28
7075 & alclad 7075	O	0	0	0	1	1	2	3	5	9	18
	T6	2	2	4	8	10	12	18	24	36	64
7178 & alclad 7178	O	0	0	0	1	1	2	3	5	9	18
	T6	2	3	4	8	10	12	21	28	42	80

(a) These radii represent average values for forming in conventional equipment with tools of good design and condition. The minimum permissible radii in a forming operation on a specific part are subject to several variables and can be determined only by forming under shop conditions.

Table 5. Maximum Thicknesses of Aluminum Alloy Sheet That Can Be Cold Bent 180° Over Zero Radius

Alloy	Temper	Max sheet thickness, in.	Alloy	Temper	Max sheet thickness, in.
1100	O	1/8	5005	H34	1/32
	H12	1/16	5050	O	1/8
	H14	1/16		H32	1/16
	H16	1/64		H34	1/32
Alclad 2014 ..	O	1/16	5052	O	1/8
2024	O	1/16		H32	1/32
3003	O	1/8		H34	1/64
	H12	1/16	5086	O	1/8
	H14	1/16	5154	O	1/8
3004	O	1/8		H32	1/32
	H32	1/32	5457	O	1/8
	H34	1/64		H25	1/32
5005	O	1/8	6061	O	1/16
	H12	1/16		T4	1/32
	H14	1/16	7075	O	1/32
	H32	1/8			

tions, but when this is not sufficient, a lubricant is usually applied to the working surfaces of the tools and to the bend area of the workpiece to prevent scoring and metal pickup.

Depending on the severity of forming, the lubricant would generally be one of the first seven given in Table 1, or a proprietary compound based on one of these materials.

Tools. The bending, forming, piercing and notching dies used in press brakes for aluminum alloys are much the same as those used for low-carbon steel. To prevent marring or scratching of the workpiece, tools used for bending steel should be carefully cleaned and pol-ished before being used for aluminum alloys. Rubber pads used in press-brake dies, when clean, will not scratch the surface of an aluminum sheet.

Because of the differences in tensile strength and springback, shut-height settings for aluminum alloys may be different from those for low-carbon steel.

Examples of Applications. The versatility of press brakes is shown in the following six examples.

Example 514. Forming a Curtain-Wall Panel in a Press Brake (Fig. 5)

The curtain-wall panel shown in Fig. 5 was formed by joggling 1/8-in. and 3/16-in.-thick clad aluminum sheets (5005 core and 6061 cladding) in a press brake. Panels ranged in width from 10 to 54 in., and in length from 118 to 200 in.

Joggling was done in a 200-ton press brake with 16-ft span between columns, using a standard joggle die. To prevent ram deflection from causing the joggle line to bow across the sheet, guide posts were attached to each end of the joggle-die shoes, and two heel blocks were fastened along the back edge.

The flanges were formed in the same press brake used for joggling, with a V-bending punch and die 18 ft long.

The ram was adjusted for the 1/8-in. and 3/16-in. sheets when joggling and flanging.

The joggle-relief notch also shown in Fig. 5 was made in the part to facilitate bending the flanges after the sheet had been joggled. The centerline of the notch corresponded to the bend line of the flange. Two notches were pierced in one stroke of a 25-ton press brake having a 60-in. bed. The punch had a 5° shear angle to reduce shock to the ram. The same punch and die were used for both the 1/8-in. and 3/16-in.-thick sheets.

After joggling and bending, the gap in the corner at the joggle was welded, and the panel was anodized. The 6061 cladding was used because of its ability to be anodized to the black tone specified.

Example 515. Use of Cast Plastic Blankets for Bending Corrugated Sheet (Fig. 6)

A top of an aircraft cargo container was formed from corrugated sheet of aluminum alloy 6061-T4 by making two 45° bends across the corrugations (Fig. 6). Bending in air or in a rubber-pad die caused the corrugations (which also had been formed when the metal was in the T4 temper) to flatten excessively.

To keep the corrugations from flattening, 18-in.-wide plastic blankets were cast to fit on each side of the sheet. The plastic, which

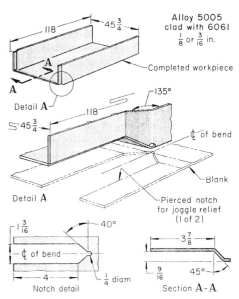

Fig. 5. Curtain-wall panel produced from clad aluminum sheet by joggling and bending in a press brake (Example 514)

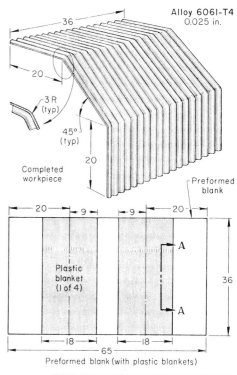

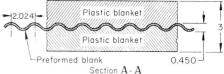

Fig. 6. Top of an aircraft cargo container formed from a corrugated aluminum blank that was encased in plastic blankets for bending in a standard V-die (Example 515)

was formulated from a polyamid resin and a plasticizer, had enough body to support the corrugations, but was flexible enough to follow the bend. The blankets were reusable, because they returned to the flattened condition after being removed from the formed workpiece.

The 45° bends were press-brake formed in air with a standard V-die and a punch with a 2-in. radius. The outside radius on the bends was 3 in., and the bent portions were held within an over-all total tolerance of 0.030 in. Springback was controlled to keep the bend angle within 1°.

Production rate was four containers per hour, and lot size was about 300 a month. Larger widths of corrugated stock (to 72 in.) also were formed, depending on the dimensions of the container needed.

The next example illustrates a technique to produce bend radii that are too small to be obtained satisfactorily with normal practice.

Example 516. Change in Punch Design That Eliminated Fracture in Forming a Small-Radius 90° Bend (Fig. 7)

In producing a bracket for an electronics application (Fig. 7), 5005-H34 alloy sheet 0.090 in. thick had to be bent 90° to an inside radius not to exceed 0.060 in. When the bracket was formed in a press-brake V-punch or with a punch of conventional design (Fig. 7) in a punch press, fracture occurred along the bend line. No significant improvement was obtained by increasing the punch radius.

Fracturing was eliminated by providing the wall of the punch with a 15° lead angle, as shown in Fig. 7. Springback as well as fracturing decreased progressively as the lead angle was lengthened from ⅛ in. to the ⁷⁄₁₆ in. shown in Fig. 7. Beyond that length, no further improvement was obtained.

Quantity often determines whether a press brake or punch press will be used for bending operations. The press brake is usually preferred for short runs and experimental or pilot operations, because of its versatility, ability to get into production quickly, and low tooling costs. The punch press offers higher production rates and lower unit labor costs, and therefore is better suited for long runs. The following example compares two methods in the production of a part requiring a simple bend.

Example 517. Press Brake vs Punch Press for a Simple Bending Operation (Fig. 8)

Only simple bending was required for producing the reinforcing member shown in Fig. 8. Standard dies in a press brake were used for small quantities; a specially designed forming die in a punch press was used for large quantities.

The press-brake method required three operations, with adjustment of ram and gage for each operation; the punch-press method required only one operation, with no need for gage setting.

The minimum number of pieces that would justify the higher tooling costs for the punch-press method was 20,000, as shown by the break-even chart in Fig. 8.

Tools for both methods were made of 4130 or 4140 steel at Rockwell C 32; tool wear was negligible after many thousands of pieces. No lubrication was required in forming.

The number of pieces per setup depends on various factors. For example, determining factors can be the length of time for which a punch press or a press brake is needed on one production schedule, or a possible need for a continuous flow of parts to a subsequent operation, or factors that control work flow to the forming operation.

Other production considerations may override the cost factor. In Example 517, close dimensional tolerances on the finished parts could have required the use of the punch-press method, even

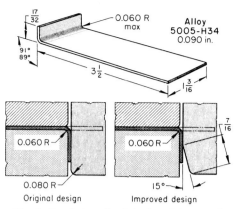

Fig. 7. Bracket, and original and improved design of punch for forming the small-radius bend without fracture (Example 516)

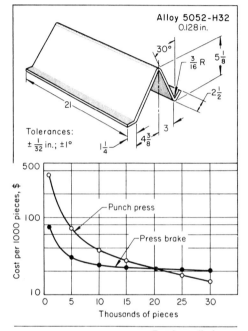

Fig. 8. Reinforcing member that was formed in small quantities (up to 20,000 pieces) in a press brake, and in large quantities (20,000 pieces or more) in a punch press (Example 517)

Item	Forming method	
	Press brake	Punch press
Production, pcs/hr	200	900
Number of setups	3(a)	1
Total setup cost	$3	$1.75
Pieces per setup	1000	5000
Setup cost per piece	$0.003	$0.00035
Labor cost per piece	$0.015	$0.0033
Die cost	$60	$350

(a) One setup for each of the three operations that were required for press-brake forming.

for fewer than 20,000 pieces, because the press-brake method, with three setups and three stock-gage changes, provided a greater likelihood of variation in dimensions.

Immediate availability of equipment capable of handling parts of an extreme size or requiring a length of stroke greater than average will sometimes be of prime importance. The small quantity of parts required in the following example was produced more economically in a press brake, but it was necessary to do one bending operation in a gap-frame press, because of the need for an unusual depth of stroke to form a channel.

Example 518. Three-Operation Short-Run Forming of a Housing in a Press Brake and a Gap-Frame Press (Fig. 9)

Because the total quantity required was relatively low (fewer than 2000 pieces), the housing shown in Fig. 9 was formed most economically by making maximum use of available general-purpose equipment and tooling. As shown in Fig. 9, the first two of the three operations were done in a press brake using standard dies, which met the specified tolerance of ±⅛₂ in. Because of the depth of the channel, however, it was necessary to use a gap-frame press for making the U-bend. As shown in Fig. 9, a simple forming punch was mounted on a plate, with a stripper plate in the upper portion of the die.

Maintaining the ⅟₁₆-in. radius specified for the bends presented no problem as long as the stock was sheared so that the bends were made across the grain. No lubrication was needed for any of the forming operations. Tool wear was negligible throughout the production run.

The following example illustrates the accuracy to which parts can be formed in a press brake by using special equipment and techniques.

Example 519. Production of Aluminum Cabinet Tops in Seven Bends in a Press Brake (Fig. 10)

The cabinet top shown in Fig. 10 was completed by bending previously notched blanks (Fig. 10, detail A) in a press brake. Blanks were cut in a power shear, then notched and pierced in a punch press. After the press-brake operations, corners were completed by shielded-arc welding and grinding.

Although the side flanges were simple to bend, their accuracy influenced the front lip enclosure; consequently, all bends had to be closely controlled. When standard tooling and normal shop practice were employed, the product lacked the required accuracy. The problem was solved by developing a special gage that allowed control of each bend within ±0.005 in. (±0.020 in. over-all). This gage used adjustable stops that were positioned by operating dials, which were placed at the front of the die for the operator's convenience. Ten positions on the dials enabled the operator to set the stops quickly to the required position. Press-brake operations and time required for each are tabulated with Fig. 10.

Contour Roll Forming

Aluminum alloys are readily shaped by contour roll forming, using equipment and techniques similar to those used for steel (see the article "Contour Roll Forming", page 224 in this volume). Operating speeds can be higher for the more ductile aluminum alloys than for most other metals. Speeds as high as 800 ft per min have been used in mild roll forming sections 50 to 100 ft long made of ⅟₃₂-in.-thick alloy 1100-O coil stock.

Power requirements for roll forming of aluminum alloys are generally lower than for comparable operations on steel, because of the lower yield strength of most aluminum alloys.

Tooling. The design of rolls and related equipment, as well as the selection of tool materials, is discussed in the article "Contour Roll Forming", page 224 in this volume. The most commonly used material is L6 tool steel, a low-alloy nickel-chromium grade with excellent toughness, wear resistance, and hardenability. For extremely severe forming operations or exceptionally long runs, a high-carbon high-chromium grade such as D2 is preferred because it has superior resistance to galling and wear. These tool steels are hardened to Rockwell C 60 to 63. The tools are highly polished, and are sometimes chromium plated to prevent scratching and to minimize the pickup of chips when surface finish of the work is critical.

For short runs and mild forming operations, rolls can be made of turned and polished gray cast iron (class 30 or better) or low-carbon steel. For light-gage metals, tools made of plastics reinforced with metal powder, or made of specially treated hardwood, have occasionally been used.

For some applications in the roll forming of light-gage alloys where quality of surface finish is the primary concern, use has been made of cast zinc tools, at the cost of shorter tool life.

Extremely close tolerances are required on tool dimensions. Allowance for springback must be varied with alloy and temper, as well as with material thickness and radius of forming, as indicated in Table 3. Final adjustments must be made on the basis of production trials.

Layout and tool dimensions incorporate bending allowances, as described on page 228 in the article "Contour Roll Forming" in this volume.

The final strip width must be established on the basis of production trials if tolerances are close or if the curved segments constitute a substantial portion of the strip width.

Severity of Forming. Limits on severity of forming are similar to those for press-brake forming discussed in the previous section. However, minimum bend radii can be approximately half the values shown in Table 4. This is possible because of the combined effects of: (a) a restricted amount of forming in each stage, (b) the use of biaxial working of the metal on the outside of the bends, (c) edge compression, (d) highly polished rolls, and (e) suitable lubrication.

Similarly, the capability of forming 180° cold bends over zero radius can be extended beyond the limits given in Table 5.

Non-heat-treatable alloys are preferred for economy, and the hardest temper that will meet the forming requirements with a satisfactory yield is usually selected.

Tolerances of ±0.005 in. are common, and ±0.002 in. can be maintained on small, simple shapes formed from light-gage metals. One or two final sizing stations may be required where the contour is intricate or where spring back effects are large. Several techniques for maintaining tolerances in difficult situations are described in the article "Contour Roll Forming", page 224 in this volume.

Lubricants are required in nearly all contour roll forming of aluminum alloys, as discussed in the article "Contour Roll Forming" in this volume.

For high-speed or severe forming operations, the rolls and the work may be flooded with a liquid that functions both as a lubricant and as a coolant. A soluble oil in water is preferred for this type of operation. When a more effective lubricant is required, a 10% soap solution or an extreme-pressure (EP) compound may be used. These are better suited for minimizing tool wear and producing a high finish, but are more difficult to remove. Lubricants like

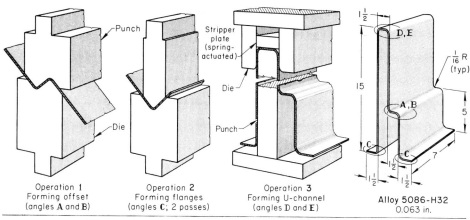

Operation	Machine	Setup time, minutes	Production, pieces/hr	Cost per piece(a)
1 Form offset	Press brake(b)	8	900	$0.0038
2 Form flanges (2 passes)	Press brake(b)	8	550	0.0059
3 Form U-channel	Punch press(c)	16	420	0.0072
Total forming cost per piece				$0.0169

(a) Direct labor cost for setup (amortized over 1000 pieces) plus production cost. (b) 30-ton mechanical press brake with 2-in. stroke and 6 ft between frame members, using standard 90° dies with 1/16-in. radius (tool material, 4130 or 4140 steel at Rockwell C 32). (c) 75-ton mechanical gap-frame press with 5-in. stroke and shut height of 15 to 18 in., using a special channel-form die and a 1/16-in.-radius punch (tool material, 4130 or 4140 steel at Rockwell C 32).

Fig. 9. *Use of a press brake and a gap-frame press for low-cost forming of a housing in small quantities* (Example 518)

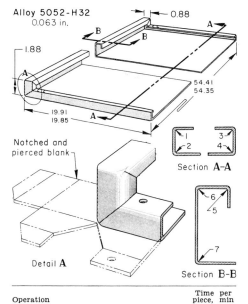

Operation	Time per piece, min
First Handling	
Remove formed piece; position blank	0.2079
Make 1st bend, one side (3 hits)	0.0880
Shift workpiece	0.0433
Make 2nd bend, one side (3 hits)	0.0880
Turn workpiece 180°	0.0856
Make 3rd bend (3 hits)	0.0880
Shift workpiece	0.0433
Make 4th bend (3 hits)	0.0880
Second Handling	
Transport and reposition piece	0.2079
Make 5th bend (2 hits)	0.0748
Shift workpiece	0.0433
Make 6th bend (2 hits)	0.0748
Shift workpiece	0.0433
Make 7th bend (2 hits)	0.0748
Net total	1.2510
Plus allowance of 5%	0.0626
Total production time	1.3136

A special adjustable gage controlled by dials on the front of the machine (so that it could be set quickly by the operator) was used to obtain the necessary degree of accuracy for producing a good closure on the front lip.

Fig. 10. *Cabinet top formed in seven bends in a press brake* (Example 519)

those numbered 1, 2, 4 and 7 in Table 1 are also used to some extent.

Applications. Roll formed aluminum alloy parts made from sheet or coiled strip include furniture parts, architectural moldings, window and door frames, gutters and downspouts, automotive trim, roofing and siding panels, and shelving.

Tubing, in sizes ranging from ¾ in. to 8 in. in outside diameter, and from 0.025 to 0.156 in. in wall thickness, is made in a combined roll-forming and welding process. Linear speeds of 30 to 200 ft per min are used in this process. Applications are irrigation pipe, condenser tubing, and furniture parts.

A modification of the roll-forming and welding process is used to make cable sheathing. Cable and strip are fed into the machine simultaneously; the strip is formed into a tube surrounding the cable, and then welded. The assembly is next passed through a sizing mill, which reduces the tubing slightly in size, and produces a waterproof and gastight sheath.

Other applications of contour roll forming include the forming of patterned, anodized or pre-enameled material. Such applications impose stringent requirements on tool design and maintenance, and lubrication sometimes cannot be used because of the nature of the coating or because of end-use requirements.

Deep Drawing

Equipment, tools and techniques used for deep drawing aluminum are similar to those used for other metals, and are described in detail in the article "Deep Drawing", which begins on page 162.

This section deals with those aspects of deep drawing that are peculiar to aluminum alloys. It is restricted to procedures using a rigid punch and die. Other procedures are described in subsequent sections of this article.

Equipment. Punch presses are used for nearly all deep drawing; press brakes are sometimes used for experimental or very short runs. Presses used for steel are also suitable for aluminum.

Tonnage requirements, determined by the same method as used for steel, are generally lower for comparable operations because of the lower tensile strength of aluminum alloys.

Press speeds are ordinarily higher than for steel. For mild draws, single-action presses are usually operated at 90 to 140 ft per min. Double-action presses are operated at 40 to 100 ft per min for mild draws, and at less than 50 ft per min for deeper draws, with low and medium-strength alloys. Drawing speeds on double-action presses are about 20 to 40 ft per min with high-strength alloys.

Tool Design. Tools for deep drawing are the same in general construction as those used with steel, but there are some significant differences. Aluminum alloy stock must be allowed to flow without undue restraint or excessive stretching. The original thickness of the metal is changed very little. This differs from deep drawing of stainless steel or brass sheet, which may be reduced as much as 25% in thickness in a single draw.

Clearances between punch and die are usually equal to the metal thickness plus about 10% per side for drawing alloys of low or intermediate strength. An additional 5 to 10% clearance may be needed for the higher-strength alloys and harder tempers. Typical clearances for multiple operations in drawing cylindrical and rectangular shells are given in Table 6.

Table 6. Typical Clearances Between Punch and Die for Successive Drawing Operations

Draw	Clearance per side, % of stock thickness
Cylindrical Shells	
First	110
Second	115
Third and subsequent	120
Final (tapered shells only)	100
Rectangular Shells	
First and subsequent	110
Final	100

With circular shells, clearance is usually increased with each successive draw, because of the metal thickening that occurred in the previous operation. The restrictions imposed on the drawing of rectangular shells by metal flow at the corners make equal clearances for each draw satisfactory. The final operation with tapered and with rectangular shells serves primarily to straighten walls, sharpen radii, and size the part accurately. Therefore, the clearance for these operations is equal to the thickness of the stock.

Excessive clearance may result in wrinkling of the sidewalls of the drawn shell; insufficient clearance will burnish the sidewalls and increase the force required for drawing.

Radii on Tools. Tools used for drawing aluminum alloys are ordinarily provided with draw radii equal to four to eight times the stock thickness. Punch nose radius is sometimes as large as ten times the stock thickness.

Table 7. Effect of Drawing on Mechanical Properties of Aluminum Alloys 3003 and 5052

Number of draws	Tensile strength, psi	Yield strength, psi	Elongation in 2 in., %
Alloy 3003			
0	16,000	6,000	30
1	19,000	17,000	11
2	22,000	21,000	9
3	23,500	22,000	8
4	24,500	22,500	8
(a)	(29,000)	(27,000)	(4)
Alloy 5052			
0	28,000	13,000	25
1	34,500	32,000	6
2	39,500	36,000	6
3	43,000	37,000	6
4	44,000	38,000	6
(a)	(42,000)	(37,000)	(7)

(a) Values in parentheses are typical values for these alloys in the full-hard condition.

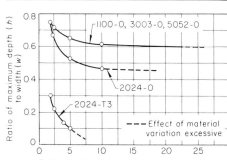

For cylindrical cups, width w equals the diameter, and vertical corner radius r equals half the diameter. Thus, the w/r ratio is 2, and values for h/w can be obtained from the graph.

For rectangular boxes, width w equals the square root of the projected bottom area (width times length). If length is more than three times the width, drawing limits will be more severe than limits shown in the above graph. For flanged boxes, the width of the flange must be included in depth h.

Fig. 11. Drawing limits for one-operation forming of cylindrical cups or rectangular boxes from aluminum alloy sheet 0.026 to 0.064 in. thick

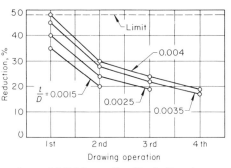

t = metal thickness. D = blank diameter.

Fig. 12. Effect of the relation of metal thickness to blank diameter on percentage reduction for successive drawing operations without intermediate annealing, for low-strength alloys such as 3003-O

A die radius that is too large may lead to wrinkling. A punch nose radius that is too sharp will increase the probability of fracture, or may leave objectionable circular shock lines that can be removed only by costly polishing.

Failure by fracture can sometimes be eliminated by increasing the die radius, or by making the drawing edge an elliptic form instead of a circular arc (see the section on Restraint of Metal Flow, on pages 172 to 175 in the article "Deep Drawing").

Surface Finish on Tools. Draw dies and punches should have a surface finish of 16 micro-in. or less for most applications. A finish of 3 or 4 micro-in. is often specified on high-production tooling for drawing light-gage or pre-coated stock. Chromium plating may also be specified to minimize friction and prevent pickup of dirt or other particles that could damage the finish on the part.

Tool Materials. The selection of materials for deep drawing tools is discussed in the article beginning on page 194 in this volume. Materials for small dies are chosen almost entirely on the basis of performance, but cost becomes a significant factor for large dies. Local variation in wear on tools is an important factor in tool life. A twentyfold variation in rate of wear can be observed on the die radius.

Lubricants for deep drawing aluminum alloys are usually commercial products based on the compositions listed in Table 1. Lubricants for deep drawing must allow the blank to slip readily and uniformly between the blankholder and the die, and must prevent stretching and galling while this movement takes place.

The drawing compounds can be applied only to the areas that will be subjected to a significant amount of cold working, unless local application interferes with the requirements of high-speed operation. Uniformity of application is critical, especially to enable the maintenance of correct blankholder pressure all around the periphery of the die.

Shallow drawing operations can usually be carried out with the use of lubricants 2, 3, or 4 in Table 1, in order of increasing severity of draw. Viscosity of mineral oil is increased as drawing severity increases. Lubricants 5, 6 and 7 in Table 1 are generally adequate for medium-depth draws, and for drawing operations of maximum severity.

Other factors besides percentage reduction in diameter (or depth of draw) and sharpness of radii must be considered in assessing the relative severity of deep drawing operations. Heavy-gage material necessitates higher deformation forces and therefore requires more effective lubrication. High-strength alloys exert a similar effect, and the more highly alloyed materials may also need a heavier, more effective type of lubricant, because of their generally thicker oxide coatings. To prevent scratching, heavier lubricants must be used with cast iron or low-carbon steel tools than with hardened, highly polished tools.

Drawing Limits. The reduction in diameter in a single operation possible with aluminum alloys is about the same as with drawing-quality steel. For deep drawn cylindrical shells, the following approximate reductions in diameter can be obtained with good practice.

First draw	Reduction, 40%
Second draw	20%
Third and subsequent draws	15%

The part can usually be completely formed without intermediate annealing. Four or more successive draws without annealing can be performed on such alloys as 1100, 3003 and 5005, with proper die design and effective lubrication. The amount of reduction is decreased in successive draws because of the loss in workability due to strain hardening. The total depth of draw thus obtainable without intermediate annealing exceeds that obtainable from steel, copper, brass or other common metals.

For high-strength aluminum alloys, the approximate amount of permissible reduction in a single draw is:

First draw .... Reduction, 30%
Second draw 15%
Third draw 10%

Local or complete annealing is usually necessary on alloys such as 2014 and 2024 after the third draw, before further operations can be performed. Alloys 3004, 5052 and 6061 are intermediate in behavior.

The rate of strain hardening is greatest for the high-strength alloys and least for the low-strength alloys. Table 7 shows the changes in mechanical properties that result from successive draws with alloys 3003 and 5052. The major portion of the change is accomplished in the first draw. The rate of strain hardening is more rapid with high-strength, heat treatable alloys such as 2014 and 2024.

Practical limits for single-operation deep drawing of cylindrical cups and rectangular boxes have been expressed in terms of dimensional ratios as shown in Fig. 11. (Reverse redrawing can be used to obtain a deeper shell than indicated by the limits in Fig. 11 for conventional drawing methods.)

The relation of the metal thickness (*t*) to the blank diameter (*D*) is an important factor in determining the percentage reduction for each drawing operation. As this ratio decreases, the probability of wrinkling increases, requiring more blankholding pressure to control metal flow and prevent wrinkles from starting. Figure 12 shows the effect of this ratio on percentage reduction of successive draws, without intermediate annealing, for low-strength alloys such as 3003-O.

Multiple-Draw Operations. The following four examples describe production procedures designed to take advantage of the formability of aluminum alloys. In all four examples, several deep draws were performed in succession without intermediate annealing.

If annealing were required, cleaning to remove drawing lubricant would be necessary before annealing, and descaling might also be needed, depending on the annealing procedure. In some applications the savings possible by the elimination of annealing and related operations can result in a lower overall cost with an aluminum alloy than with steel, even though the cost of the raw material is higher.

Example 520. Two-Draw Forming (Fig. 13)

Figure 13 shows the tooling setups used for two-operation deep drawing of shells, pairs of which were butt welded together to make 55-gal drums. The shells were drawn in long-stroke double-action presses of 300-ton to 400-ton capacity. Reduction was 40% in the first draw and 15% in the second.

Tools were of fine-grain cast iron hardened to Rockwell C 45 to 48 and were highly polished. This tooling and the application of a suitable grade of drawing lubricant (mineral oil base with sulfurized fatty oil and finely divided fillers) made possible a good surface finish and a low rejection rate.

After each shell was drawn, reinforcing beads were formed in the sidewalls with a

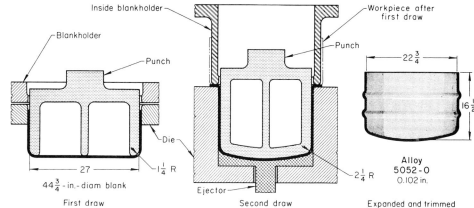

Fig. 13. Two-draw forming of a drum shell half. After being expanded and trimmed, matching halves were butt welded to make a 55-gal drum. (Example 520)

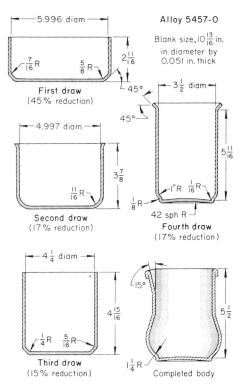

Fig. 14. Water-pitcher body formed from a 10¹³⁄₁₆-in.-diam blank in four draws without intermediate annealing (Example 521)

segmented expanding tool, and the edges were trimmed for butt welding (see Fig. 13).

Example 521. Four-Draw Forming Without Intermediate Annealing (Fig. 14)

The water-pitcher body shown in Fig. 14 was formed from an alloy 5457-O blank, 0.051 in. thick and 10¹³⁄₁₆ in. in diameter, in four successive draws in double-action presses, without intermediate annealing.

The steel tools were made with generous radii, and a medium-weight mineral oil that contained 10 to 20% fatty oil was used as the lubricant. The drawing operations were designed to allow the metal to flow with a minimum of restraint and without excessive stretching.

After drawing, the workpiece was trimmed and flanged in a lathe with a curling tool. The flange was subsequently flattened in a lathe with a roll flattening tool.

The bulge in the lower portion of the pitcher was produced by a rubber punch and split die in a single-action press, and the pouring lip was formed with male and female tools in a horn press. Finally, the exterior of the pitcher was polished and the handle was riveted to the shell.

Example 522. Six-Draw Forming Without Intermediate Annealing (Fig. 15)

Figure 15 shows the sequence of shapes in the eight-operation production of a seamless angel-cake pan for commercial bakeries. Despite the severity of some of the six draws required, the use of alloy 5052-O for the pans permitted successful production without intermediate annealing.

Before the first draw, blanks were coated with a heavy, clinging drawing compound similar to No. 10 in Table 1. For each operation, production rate was 350 pieces per

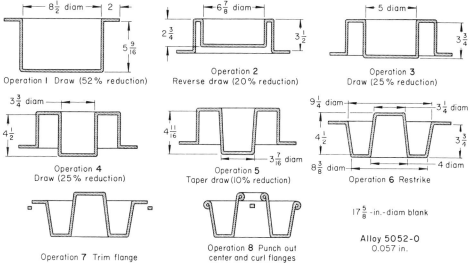

Fig. 15. Production of a seamless angel-cake pan in six draws without intermediate annealing (Example 522)

hour and direct-labor cost per 1000 pieces was $6.50. After the final operation, the pans were degreased by hot spray washing.

All tooling was made of D2 tool steel, hardened to Rockwell C 60 to 64 and chromium plated. Conventional draw rings and holddowns were used in the draw operations. The relatively low production, 15,000 pieces per year, was most economically reached by using successive operations in presses equipped with simple dies.

Originally, the pans were made by spinning, but the sidewalls thinned to the extent that the pans were not suited to heavy-duty commercial service.

Example 523. Reverse Redrawing vs Direct Redrawing (Fig. 16)

The steps used for drawing a coffee percolator shell are shown in Fig. 16; details of the drawing and two reverse redrawing operations are given below the illustration. By reverse redrawing, it is possible to effect reductions of 19.4% and 22%, respectively, whereas it was estimated that only 15% could have been obtained by direct drawing.

Dies and blankholders were made of gray iron. Clearance between the punches and dies was 1¼ times the work-metal thickness. Radii of the dies and blankholders were kept to the minimum that would not result in tearing of the workpiece. Corner radius on the die, over which the metal flowed, was ³⁄₁₆ in. for the final redraw. Tallow, lard oil or kerosine was used as the lubricant.

Blank development is of particular importance in the deep drawing of large rectangular and irregular shapes. Excessive stock at the corners must be avoided, because it hinders the uniform flow of metal under the blankholder and thus leads to wrinkles or fractures.

With suitable tooling and careful blank development, large rectangular and irregular shapes can often be produced economically in large quantities by deep drawing. Smaller quantities are made in sections with inexpensive tooling, and then assembled by welding.

Both the welding operation and the subsequent grinding and polishing of the weld areas are time-consuming and costly.

The two examples that follow describe the use of deep drawing for the production of large rectangular boxes. In the second of these examples, the boxes were originally produced by drawing, press-brake forming, and welding, but as the production quantity increased, the method was changed to deep drawing.

Example 524. Deep Drawing of Large Rectangular Boxes (Fig. 17)

A large rectangular tote box was produced by two deep drawing operations from a developed blank of 0.072-in.-thick aluminum alloy 5052-O, as shown in Fig. 17. Final operations were trimming and beading.

The punch and die for the first draw were designed with radii of ten times the metal thickness, or more, to avoid overstressing. The additional stretching in the second draw was helpful in wiping out buckles and sharpening corner radii. Hardened and polished (16 micro-in. max) tool steel was required for the punches and dies to produce a high-quality finish on the boxes.

The lubricant, a mineral oil that contained 10 to 15% sulfurized fatty oil and 10% fatty oil, and that was specially compounded for use on aluminum, also was helpful in minimizing drawing difficulty.

The rectangular boxes described in Example 524 could have been formed in sections by press-brake forming and the sections welded together. This method would be economical if only 4000 boxes were required in a two-year period, or if presses capable of forming the complete box were not available.

Example 525. Deep Drawing vs Drawing, Press-Brake Forming, and Welding of Rectangular Bins (Fig. 18)

A large rectangular bin was originally made in small quantities at a minimum of tooling cost, by drawing a rectangular pan 20⅝ in. long by 18⅝ in. wide by 6⅛ in. deep, trimming it to 5-in. depth, and welding it to a 17½-in.-high sidewall that was formed in a press brake. The bottom pan was drawn from alloy 3004-O, and the sidewall was formed from 3004-H32; sheet thickness was 0.102 in. This method entailed expensive hand operations, particularly in welding and in the finishing of welds. Consequently, when production volume was increased, tools were designed for making the bins entirely by drawing.

A round-cornered blank was developed from the more formable alloy 3003-O, and tools and a drawing procedure were perfected to change the workpiece gradually from a circular to a rectangular shape in three draws, as shown in Fig. 18. For the one-piece drawn bin, larger radii at the bottom, corner and flange were required than for the welded bin (see Fig. 18).

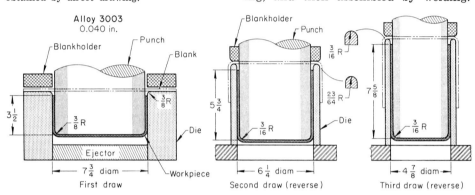

First draw — Load lubricated 12-in.-diam blank into die. Draw to cup as shown (35.4% reduction). Lift with ejector pad. **Second draw** — Turn cup upside down and place on die. Reverse redraw to cup as shown (19.4% reduction). Push through die. **Third draw** — Turn cup upside down and place on die. Reverse redraw to cup as shown (22% reduction). Push through die.

Fig. 16. Use of two reverse redraws in the production of a percolator shell (Example 523)

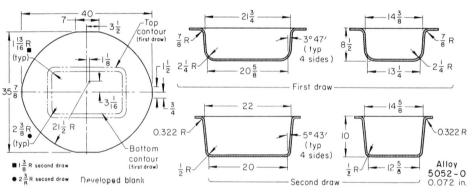

Fig. 17. Forming a large box from a developed blank in two draws (Example 524)

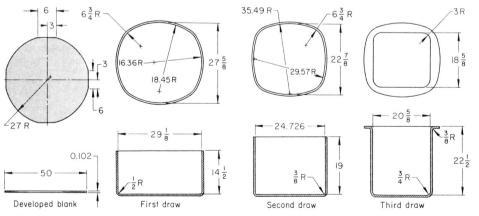
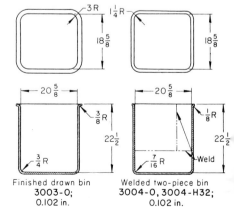

Fig. 18. Three-draw production of a rectangular bin (near right) that previously had been made as a welded assembly of a drawn base and a press-brake-formed sidewall (far right) (Example 525)

The tools were made from close-grain cast iron, and were polished to a 16 micro-in. finish. They required regular maintenance, and a heavy oil-base drawing compound was used, to prevent galling and high scrap losses.

The three dies were mounted on three separate presses so that as soon as one operation was finished, the part could be moved to the next operation and any variations in procedures or tooling that adversely affected the other operation or the part could be discovered immediately and corrected. For instance, excessively severe working in the first or second draw could have led to fractures in the third draw.

Tooling costs for deep drawing were amortized in less than three years by savings in labor costs over the previous method.

Warping. The nonuniformity of stress distribution in the drawing of rectangular or irregular shapes increases the tendency toward warping. Bowing or oil-can effects on the major surfaces become more pronounced with increasing size of the part.

Changes can sometimes be made in dimensional details of the drawing tools to eliminate these defects without the need for extra forming operations, as is demonstrated in the example that follows.

Example 526. Redesign of Punch, Pressure Pad and Subplate That Prevented Distortion of a Shallow Drawn Panel (Fig. 19)

A shallow drawn panel, shown in Fig. 19, was produced with warped, out-of-vertical sidewalls and with oil-can effect on the large flat surface.

Recessing the face of the punch to a depth of 0.030 in. (except for the outermost 0.062 in. on the periphery of the face), as shown in Fig. 19, produced straight, vertical sidewalls, but only partly corrected the oil-can effect on the face of the panel.

To correct the remaining curvature of the face, grooves were milled in a diamond pattern in the underside of the pressure pad to provide the effect of hinged corners, and the four corners were forced upward by a contoured subplate (machined with raised corners) under the pressure pad, as shown in Fig. 19. The subplate was 1 in. thick at the corners and 0.015 in. thinner in the central flat diamond-shape area. The high corners caused the pressure pad to flex sufficiently to apply an increased force on the part. The die was made of tool steel; the pressure pad was heat treated to a spring temper.

The same technique was applied to similar parts. The amount of corner elevation on the subplate varied, being developed on the basis of the part size.

The drawing of lithographed parts requires that the parts be accurately formed, with no marks or scratches on the finished surface. Drawing with a rubber die preserved the metal surface, in the following example.

Example 527. Mar-Free Drawing With a Rubber Die (Fig. 20)

The graduated-scale indicator dial shown in Fig. 20 was drawn from photoprinted and grained blanks. Accurate drawing and freedom from marring were necessary to maintain the calibrations and legibility of the scale.

The tooling consisted of a conventional punch made of soft steel, a pilot pin, a blankholder, and a rubber die 10 in. square by ¾ in. thick, machined to an inside diameter slightly smaller than the outside diameter of the punch. A rubber pressure pad, 2⅛ in. high with walls ¾ in. thick, was used under the blankholder. Inverted construction was used for the die. With the rubber tooling, accurate register of the scale was maintained and surface marring, which had occurred in conventional drawing, was eliminated. Drawing time with rubber tooling was reduced 50%, compared with conventional drawing. Also, various thicknesses of metal could be handled in the same die.

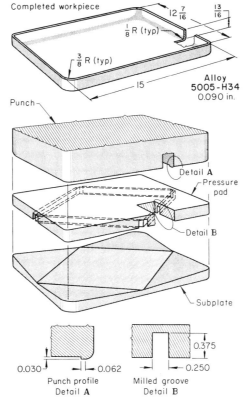

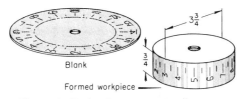

Fig. 19. Shallow panel that was drawn without distortion by using a recessed punch, grooved pressure pad, and contoured subplate (Example 526)

Punch profile Detail A — 0.030, 0.062
Milled groove Detail B — 0.250, 0.375

Fig. 20. Indicator dial that was drawn from a photoprinted and grained flat aluminum blank using a rubber die (Example 527)

Miscellaneous Shapes. Other shapes often produced by deep drawing (besides cylindrical and rectangular shells) include hemispherical shells, flat-bottomed hemispherical shells, and tapered shells.

Hemispherical shells with a final inside diameter less than about 150 times the original metal thickness can be drawn in one operation. For inside diameters of more than 150 times thickness, two draws will usually be required, to avoid wrinkles. Local thinning must be avoided in the first draw if the second draw is to be successful.

Flat-bottom hemispherical shells, unless very shallow, require at least two draws. The first draw produces a rounded shape, with a larger radius in the bottom area than on the side areas. The final draw flattens the bottom and gives the sides a uniform curvature of the radius required.

Tapered shells require more drawing operations for a given depth of draw than most other symmetrical shapes. The number of steps required increases with the taper angle. The bottom edges, except for the final operation, do not have the contour of a circular arc. The profile consists of essentially flat sections at an angle of about 40° to 50° from the horizontal. Stepwise reductions are made along the line of final contour as shown in Fig. 21, and the final draw straightens out the sidewalls to the desired shape.

Each operation after the first is restricted to a shallow draw to minimize strain hardening. With alloys of low and intermediate strength,

this procedure makes it possible to complete the series of draws without annealing. Contrary to normal practice, the amount of reduction per draw need not be lowered after the second draw.

Polishing or burnishing is often required on the completed shell to obtain a good-quality finish on the sidewalls.

Ironing is avoided in most deep drawing applications with aluminum alloys, but can be used to produce a shell with a heavy bottom and thin sidewalls.

The shell is first drawn to approximately the final diameter. The drawing lubricant is then removed, and the shell is annealed, bringing it to temperature rapidly to minimize the formation of coarse grains in areas that have been only slightly cold worked.

The sidewalls can then be reduced in thickness by 30 to 40% in an ironing operation. By repeating the cleaning, annealing and ironing steps, an additional reduction of 20 to 25% can be obtained, with good control over wall thickness.

A typical use of ironing is shown in Fig. 22. Here a cylindrical shell is produced with a thick bottom and thin sidewalls by a single deep draw and two successive ironing operations. The approximate final diameter and about half the final depth are obtained in the drawing operation. Wall thickness is reduced 33% in the first ironing step and 19% in the second.

Supplementary Forming. Various supplementary beading, bulging, necking and other forming operations are performed on drawn shells (see Examples 520, 521 and 522). In the following example, the use of a strong alloy (5154) not well suited to forming a radius equal to the sheet thickness necessitated annealing the drawn shell before subsequent offset forming of a bead on the circular edge.

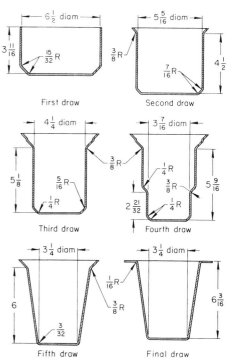

Fig. 21. Typical progression of shapes in multiple-draw forming of a tapered shell from an aluminum alloy blank 0.064 in. thick and 11½ in. in diameter

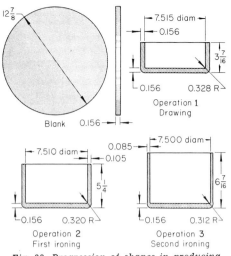

Fig. 22. Progression of shapes in producing a shell with a thick bottom and thin sides in one draw and two ironing operations

Example 528. Drawing and Supplementary Offset Forming of a Pressure Vessel (Fig. 23)

The pressure vessel shown in Fig. 23 was produced from alloy 5154-O sheet by blanking, deep drawing, annealing and forming.

The blank, 25 in. in diameter, was produced by a steel blanking die in a 600-ton mechanical press. The hemispherical shape of the workpiece (see Fig. 23) was drawn from the blank by a lubricated draw die in one operation in a 600-ton mechanical press.

After drawing, the workpiece was annealed for 2 hr at 650 F. Annealing was necessary to prevent cracking or excessive springback during subsequent forming of the circular edge between offset rolls.

The part was then trimmed by standard roll cutters to 9½ in. and formed between rolls, to produce an offset with an inside radius equal to the work-metal thickness. Both trimming and final forming were done in a bead-and-trim machine using interchangeable rolls.

Hot Drawing

Severe drawing operations are often impossible to perform at room temperature on large and relatively thick shapes made from high-strength aluminum alloys. However, the lower strength and increased ductility at temperatures above the recrystallization point of the alloy make it possible to produce large and relatively thick shapes by hot drawing. There is little or no advantage when stock is less than 0.125 in. thick.

Alloys frequently used in applications of this type include non-heat-treatable alloys 5083, 5086 and 5456, and heat treatable alloys 2024, 2219, 6061, 7075 and 7178.

Heavy-duty presses and related equipment are required. Drawing temperatures range from 350 to 600 F. The length of time the workpiece is held at temperature is controlled to avoid excessive grain growth in areas with little strain hardening.

Ordinary drawing compounds break down or burn at elevated temperature, and are not suitable for hot drawing operations.

Graphited tallow and hard yellow naphtha soap have sometimes been used as lubricants at intermediate elevated temperature. Lubricants that remain stable above 500 F include graphite and molybdenum disulfide. These materials can be used in the colloidal

form with a volatile vehicle, they can be mixed with other lubricants, or they can be applied to the die as powders.

Examples of Applications. The two examples that follow describe production applications of hot drawing.

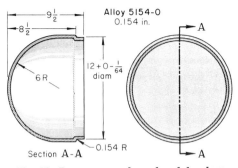

Fig. 23. Pressure vessel produced by deep drawing and forming with intermediate annealing (Example 528)

Table 8. Sequence of Operations and Manufacturing Details for Hot Drawing of a Flanged Circular Base for a Container (Example 529)

Sequence of Operations

1 – Shear. 2 – Cut circular blanks. 3 – Preheat blanks to 500 F. 4 – Preheat dies to 350 F. 5 – Lubricate blank and dies(a). 6 – Hot draw. 7 – Spin flange flat. 8 – Trim.

Manufacturing Details

Press .... 400-ton hydraulic(b)
Material for drawing tools(c) ...... Cast iron
Setup time .... 20 hr total
Production rate, drawing(d) ...6 pcs per hour
Labor cost, all operations ...... $20 per piece

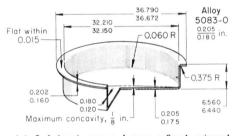

(a) Lubricant was a heavy refined mineral oil plus 10% acidless tallow. Dies were lubricated after each two parts. (b) Having a bed 60 by 48 in. (c) Die, punch and blankholder. (d) Includes time for reheating and lubricating dies.

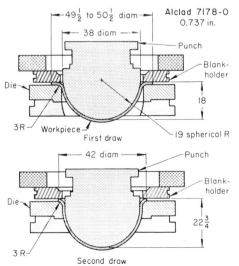

Fig. 24. Two-draw forming of a hemispherical shell. Workpiece was heated to 450 F for second draw. (Example 530)

Example 529. Hot Drawing a Large Circular Base for a Container (Table 8)

A large flanged circular base for a shipping container (see illustration in Table 8) was produced in quantities of 150 to 750 pieces by hot drawing alloy 5083-O blanks 45½ in. in diameter and 0.190 in. thick.

The sequence of operations and other manufacturing details are given in Table 8. As drawn, the flange was uneven and required flattening. This was done by spinning, using a hollow hardwood mandrel with a steel ring; larger quantities would have warranted the cost of additional press dies for flattening.

Originally, the base had been produced in 6-to-10-piece lots by spinning, but specified minimum wall thicknesses (see Table 8) were difficult to maintain.

Example 530. Use of Hot Drawing in Two-Draw Production of a Large Hemispherical Shell (Fig. 24)

A hemispherical shell was formed in two draws from a 60-in.-diam blank cut from alclad 7178-O plate 0.737 in. thick, as shown in Fig. 24. This shell was half of an underwater sonobuoy sphere designed to withstand external pressure of at least 4000 psi.

Both draws were made in a 1300-ton double-action hydraulic press with one set of tools. Die clearance was about 15% greater than work-metal thickness, and die radius was four times work-metal thickness.

For the first drawing, or preforming operation, the blank was at room temperature. The blank was lubricated with an aluminum drawing compound. The partly formed shell was then degreased and heated in a circulating-air furnace for about 20 min to 450 F, removed from the furnace, coated with a high-temperature lubricant, and drawn to full depth at 400 to 450 F. Wall thickness ranged from 115% of the nominal value at the top of the drawn shell to 90% at the bottom.

After forming, the shells were solution heat treated and artificially aged to the T6 temper to meet strength requirements.

Spinning

Spinning is often used for forming of aluminum alloy shapes that are surfaces of revolution. The manual lathes, automatic spinning machines, chucks and tools used for aluminum alloys are essentially the same as those used for steel and the other metals commonly formed by spinning (see the article "Spinning", which begins on page 201 in this volume).

Hand spinning lathes and simple tools are suitable for forming aluminum alloy blanks 0.020 to 0.081 in. thick; stock as thin as 0.004 in. can be spun with careful operation. For thicker and larger blanks, auxiliary equipment is used to apply pressure to the workpiece. This equipment varies from a simple scissors arrangement to feed screws to control tool advance, and air or hydraulic cylinders to provide pressure against the work.

Blanks up to ¼ in. thick can usually be spun at room temperature. For greater thicknesses, semimechanical to fully mechanical equipment is used, and the work metal is heated. Work metal 1 in. or more in thickness requires special heavy-duty machines and hot spinning.

Aluminum alloy parts 3 in. thick have been spun experimentally. Equipment is available for the spinning of parts as large as 16 ft in diameter.

Tolerances for spinning of aluminum alloys are essentially the same as for other common metals.

Alloys. A number of aluminum alloys are widely used in spinning applications. Desirable properties are ductility, relatively low ratio of yield strength to ultimate strength, slow rate of work hardening, and small grain size.

The alloys of low and intermediate strength that are spun most frequently include 1100, 2219, 3003, 3004, 5052, 5086 and 5154. Annealed blanks are generally used for severe forming; however, a harder temper is sometimes preferred, if it is sufficiently formable, to avoid a tendency to ball up ahead of the tool. A harder temper also may be used when forming is not severe enough to give the product its necessary strength by work hardening.

Heat treatable alloys used for high strength in the finished part are 2014, 2024 and 6061. If the forming is extensive, these alloys often must be annealed several times during spinning, or they may be spun hot.

One method used frequently for spinning heat treatable alloys is:

1 Spin annealed blank to approximate form.
2 Solution heat treat and quench.
3 Spin to final form at once, before appreciable age hardening.

If spinning to the final form cannot be done after solution heat treating and quenching, the quenched parts should be placed in a refrigerator, or packed in dry ice, and held as close to 0 F as possible until they can be spun. The parts are aged to the T6 temper after spinning has been completed.

Speeds. Typical spindle speeds for spinning flat blanks and drawn shells of various diameters are listed in Table 9. Rotational speed is decreased as blank diameter increases, so that peripheral speed is maintained in the same range regardless of the size of the workpiece. Peripheral speed ordinarily averages about 3000 ft per min for aluminum alloys. This is somewhat faster than the speeds normally used in spinning copper, brass, stainless steel and low-carbon steel.

Lubricants are needed in nearly all spinning operations. Beeswax, tallow, and petroleum jelly are suitable for most small parts. Hard yellow naphtha soap is an effective lubricant for larger workpieces. Colloidal graphite in kerosine, or compounds containing molybdenum disulfide, are used in hot spinning. Lubricating compounds used must be easily removable from the finished part without costly treatments.

Applications. Parts produced from aluminum alloys by spinning include tumblers, pitchers, bowls, cooking utensils, ring molds, milk cans, processing kettles, reflectors, aircraft and aerospace parts, architectural sections, tank heads, and streetlight standards.

Spinning is often selected in preference to drawing when quick delivery of small quantities is important, because the spun parts can usually be delivered before drawing tools have been made. Cones, hemispheres, tapered shapes, and parts with complex or re-entrant contours (if surfaces of revolution are) are often more readily formed by spinning than by other methods. Spinning is also used for very large parts when suitable press equipment and tools are not readily available or are too costly.

Spinning is not usually economical for quantities of more than 5000 to 10,000 pieces, because of comparatively low production rates and resulting high unit labor costs. There are exceptions, especially in the power spinning of truncated cone-shape parts having included angles of 40° or more. Spinning is capable of producing such parts at lower cost than deep drawing and gives a uniform wall thickness and a surface free from wrinkles, and increases the tensile strength of the work metal as much as 100%.

Examples 553 and 557 illustrate the relationship between quantity and cost in forming aluminum alloy parts by spinning versus deep drawing.

Example 531, which follows, describes the use of hot power spinning of 1¼-in.-thick plate to produce small quantities of a 4-ft-diam shell. Large presses and costly tools would be required to make these parts by deep drawing.

Table 9. Typical Spindle Speeds for Spinning of Aluminum Alloy Flat Blanks and Drawn Shells of Various Diameters

Diameter of blank, in.	Spindle speed, rpm
Flat Blanks	
Up to 12	600 to 1100
12 to 24	400 to 700
24 to 36	250 to 550
36 to 72	50 to 250
72 to 120	25 to 50
120 to 180	12 to 25
180 to 210	12
Drawn Shells	
10 to 14	1000 to 1200
14 to 20	650 to 800
20 to 30	475 to 550
30 to 40	325 to 375
40 to 50	250 to 300
50 to 70	200 to 210
70 to 90	150 to 175

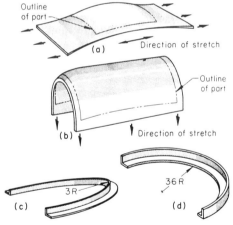

(a) Longitudinal stretching. (b) Transverse stretching. (c) Compound bend from extrusion. (d) Long sweeping bend from extrusion.

Fig. 25. Typical stretch formed shapes

Example 531. Hot Power Spinning of 48-In.-Diam Halves of a Spherical Buoy From 1¼-In.-Thick Plate

Hot power spinning was used to form the two halves of a 48-in.-diam spherical buoy from 1¼-in.-thick alloy 6061-O plate. The sequence of operations was as follows:

1 Cut 65-in.-diam circles from 66-in.-square plate stock with a band saw.
2 Lay out and drill 1-in.-diam center hole.
3 Rotate spinning mandrel at 24 rpm; heat mandrel with torches to 450 F, checking with temperature-sensitive crayons.
4 Clamp blank to mandrel with steel follower; rotate at 24 rpm.
5 Heat rotating blank with torches to 600 F; check with temperature-sensitive crayons. Continue to heat mandrel while blank is brought to temperature.
6 Increase speed to 78 rpm. Spin blank down against mandrel, making multiple forward and backward passes with hydraulic power-assist tool with 1½-in.-radius roller. Maintain temperature with torches.
7 Rough trim by hand while hot.
8 Allow to cool to 250 F.
9 Finish trim to depth.
10 Machine edge for welding.
11 Contour-machine outside surface, to wall thickness of ¾ to 1 in.
12 Weld required fittings in place. Weld two hemispheres together.
13 Heat treat to T6 temper.

The mandrel was a ribbed hemisphere made of gray iron, which was stress relieved and then machined to approximately 46 in. in diameter. It had a 1-in.-diam center pin for holding the blank.

The procedure described in Example 531 was used for low-quantity production. For quantities of 25 or more buoys, time would be saved by performing a preliminary breakdown operation over another cast mandrel, and cost could be reduced by the use of templates and tracer-machining fixtures.

Stretch Forming

Almost all of the aluminum alloys can be shaped by stretch forming. In this process, the work metal is stretched over a form and stressed beyond its yield point to produce the desired contour. (For a detailed description of this process see the article "Stretch Forming", which begins on page 239 in this volume.)

Typical shapes produced by stretch forming are shown in Fig. 25. These include large shapes with compound curvature formed by longitudinal and by transverse stretching of sheet, and compound bends or long sweeping bends formed from extrusions.

Alloys. Properties desirable for stretch forming are high elongation, wide forming range (spread between yield strength and tensile strength), toughness, and fine grain structure.

Table 10 shows the effect of elongation and forming range on stretch-

Table 10. Mechanical Properties and Stretchability Ratings for Aluminum Alloys Most Commonly Used in Stretch Forming

Alloy	Tensile strength, psi	Yield strength, psi	Forming range, psi(a)	Elongation in 2 in., %	Stretchability rating(b)
7075-W(c)	48,000	20,000	28,000	19	100
2024-W(c)	46,000	18,000	28,000	20	98
2024-T3	64,000	44,000	20,000	18	95
6061-W(c)	35,000	21,000	14,000	22	90
7075-O	32,000	14,000	18,000	17	80
2024-O	27,000	11,000	16,000	19	80
6061-O	18,000	8,000	10,000	22	75
3003-O	16,000	6,000	10,000	30	75
1100-O	13,000	5,000	8,000	35	70
7075-T6	76,000	67,000	9,000	11	10

(a) Tensile strength minus yield strength. (b) Relative amount of stretch permissible in stretch forming, based on 7075-W as 100. (c) Freshly quenched after solution heat treatment. (SOURCE: ASME Handbook, Metals Engineering Processes, 1st Edition, 1958, page 135)

Table 11. Practical Elongation Limits for Several Aluminum Alloys in Stretch Forming

Alloy	Maximum elongation, %(a)
2014-O, 2014-T3, 2024-O, 2024-T3 and 7075-O	8 to 10
2014-W, 2024-W, 7075-W and 7178-W(b)	10 to 14
6061-W(b)	15

(a) Measured over total length subject to stretch. (b) In the W temper, alloy is freshly quenched after solution heat treatment.

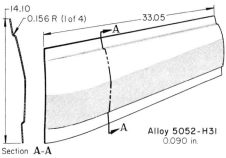

Fig. 26. Motor-coach body panel with formed features in both the horizontal and the vertical planes that was stretch drawn with shaped grippers (Example 532)

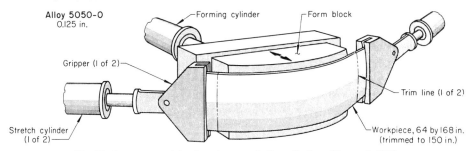

Fig. 27. Arrangement for forming parabolic reflectors (Example 533)

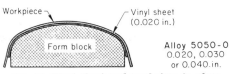

Fig. 28. Vinyl sheet and workpiece in place on form block after forming a parabolic microwave reflector (Example 534)

ability ratings for the alloys most commonly used in stretch forming. The stretchability rating varies directly with the forming range, except for 6061-W (which has somewhat higher elongation than adjacent alloys) and 7075-T6 (which has by far the lowest elongation listed). Alloys 1100-O and 3003-O, with the highest elongation shown, nevertheless are less desirable for stretch forming than the alloys above them in the list. Their low strength and the narrow spread between yield strength and tensile strength make them particularly susceptible to local necking and premature failure in stretch forming.

Table 11 gives percentage elongation limits for some alloys in stretch forming, based on industrial practice. Actual elongation in local areas can be much higher than the average over the entire stretched area; the limits in Table 11 are about 40 to 70% of the tensile elongation in a 2-in. gage length.

On the basis of the data in Tables 10 and 11, the following conclusions can be drawn:

1 Stretch-forming capability is influenced by tensile strength and the spread between yield strength and tensile strength, as well as by elongation.
2 Non-heat-treatable alloys perform best in the annealed temper, but many have good workability in the intermediate tempers.
3 The heat treatable alloys are most suitable for stretch forming when in the fresh W temper. This has the added advantage of producing high strength without the exposure to warping that would accompany heat treatment after forming.
4 Although the low-strength alloys 1100 and 3003 excel for most forming operations, they are inferior to the O, W and T3 tempers of the high-strength, heat treatable alloys in stretchability.
5 The artificially aged tempers of all alloys can be stretch formed less severely than the W tempers.

Tools. The materials used for the form block or die depend on the production quantities required, the severity of local stress and wear on the die, and the thickness and wear properties of the alloy to be formed. Materials include wood, plastics, faced concrete, cast zinc alloys, aluminum tool and jig plate, cast iron, and (rarely) steel or chromium-plated steel.

Lubricants are recommended in the stretch forming of aluminum alloys. Water-soluble oils are commonly used, with viscosity dependent on the severity of forming. Lubricants of types 9 and 10 in Table 1 are also used, along with calcium-base greases, paraffin, beeswax and commercial waxes. The application of too much lubricant can result in buckling of the workpiece. Sometimes a layer of sheet rubber, glass cloth, or plastic between die and workpiece serves as a lubricant. Be- cause of their inherent lubricity, dies made of zinc alloys require only a minimum of lubrication. Smooth-surfaced plastic dies may require no lubrication, because of their low coefficient of friction against aluminum.

Applications. The various stretch-forming techniques (including stretch drawing, stretch wrapping, and compression and radial drawing) are used extensively in the aerospace industry. Typical parts produced include wing-skin and fuselage panels, engine cowlings, window and door frames, and trim panels used in aerospace, automotive, architectural and appliance industries.

Stretch draw forming of aluminum is done using both the matched-die and form-block techniques. The matched-die method uses a single-action hydraulic press equipped with a means of closing and moving the jaws that grip each end of the blank. The punch is attached to the bed of the press and the die is attached to the ram.

The other method uses a form block that is attached to a stationary bed or to a hydraulic cylinder. With this method, the blank is gripped with jaws that hold it in tension or draw it over the form block.

The part in the following example was formed with matched dies in a stretch draw press.

Example 532. Use of Shaped Jaws for Two-Way Forming of a Coach Body Panel (Fig. 26)

The body panel for a motor coach shown in Fig. 26 was formed in a stretch draw press using matched dies. The part had contour features in both the horizontal and the vertical planes. The alloy 5052-H31 blank was 33.05 by 15 in. by 0.090 in. thick. Jaws that followed the faired contour of the coach panel gripped the blank and drew it over the punch to form the contour of the panel as well as the feature lines at the sides. The blank was stretched 1 to 1½% before forming. After the contour was formed, the press closed, striking the panel with the mating die to set the contours. The punch and die were made of cast iron.

Cost of the stretch draw die was about one-third that of a conventional press die. Production rate was approximately equal to that of a conventional process. Yearly production was 25,000 panels for each side of the coach.

The blanks were loaded into the jaws and the formed parts removed from the press with automatic material-handling equipment.

The formed panels were bright dipped and anodized by a sulfuric acid process.

Stretch drawing with form blocks was used for forming the parts for large parabolic reflectors described in the three examples that follow. No wrinkles, scratches or blemishes were permitted in the formed panels.

In the first example, the blank was held in a vertical position while a thoroughly cleaned moving form block shaped the part. A polyvinyl chloride sheet acted as lubricant between the blank and form block in the second example. In the third example, a support sheet was used during forming and for carrying the formed, unbonded honeycomb workpiece to the assembly area.

Example 533. Stretch Drawing a Parabolic Microwave Reflector (Fig. 27)

By stretch drawing, a three-dimensional parabolic curve was imposed on an alloy 5050-O sheet 64 by 168 in. by 0.125 in. thick, as shown in Fig. 27. A 196-ton horizontal stretch press with a form block actuated by a hydraulic cylinder was used. The crown of the curve was 9 in. high. Because the finished part was a microwave reflector, extreme care was used in handling and forming the sheet to keep it free of dust particles that might mar its mirror-smooth finish. Care also was necessary to prevent kinking or bending of the sheet while the press was being loaded.

The form block was epoxy-fiberglass molded on a steel frame. The contour was swept on with a form template.

All forming was done dry so that lubricant would not attract dust particles to the form block or workpiece. The form block was cleaned and inspected for imperfections before each piece was formed.

A prestretch of 3 or 4 tons was applied to the workpiece before the main ram of the press forced the form block into the sheet. Time for forming was 7 min floor-to-floor. Additional time was needed to prepare the blank and clean the form block. Setup time was 2 hr. A typical production lot was 150 to 200 pieces.

Example 534. Use of a Vinyl Sheet as Lubricant in Stretch Drawing a Parabolic Reflector (Fig. 28)

A parabolic microwave reflector was formed in a horizontal stretch draw press using a stationary form block, as shown in Fig. 28. The alloy 5050-O blanks were 50 in. wide by 220 in. long by 0.020, 0.030, or 0.040 in. thick.

A thin sheet of polyvinyl chloride was placed between the form block and the blank to act as a lubricant and to prevent dust particles that settled on the surface of the form block from being imbedded in the mirror-smooth surface of the workpiece.

The zone, or over-all, tolerance for the formed panel was ±0.030 in. The contour of the form block was accurate within 0.020 in. No allowance was made for springback. The time needed to form each part was 7 min, plus die and blank preparation time. Production-lot sizes were 150 to 200 pieces, but only about 70 panels were needed each month.

Example 535. Stretch Draw Forming of Skins for a Honeycomb Panel (Fig. 29)

A parabolic microwave reflector 30 ft in diameter was made of honeycomb panel with 0.003-in.-thick alloy 5050-O skins on each surface of the honeycomb. For ease in fabrication, the reflector was made in pie-shape sections 24 in. wide at the heel. Rectangular sheets 0.003 in. thick by 24 in. wide by 17 ft long for the reflecting surface were stretch draw formed in a 150-ton vertical stretch press, as shown in Fig. 29. First, a carrying sheet of 0.060-in.-thick alloy 5050-O was stretch drawn on the form block, and became the forming surface for the foil sheet. The workpiece foil was delivered on a roll. The end was unrolled, doubled, and inserted into the grippers at one end. The foil was unrolled over the forming surface; the other end was doubled and inserted into the grippers at the other end.

After the workpiece was formed, it was delivered on the carrying sheet to the assembly area, where it was trimmed to the tapering pie-shape form of the reflector section. Later, the honeycomb was bonded to it.

Outer skin sections were stretch formed in the same way as the reflector sections. After each outer section had been formed, it was taped to a preformed carrier sheet for transport to the honeycomb panel for bonding. The undersheet used as the forming surface for outer sections remained on the form block.

Even in a dust-free room, constant vigilance had to be maintained to keep surfaces of form blocks and carrying sheets free of dust. Receiving surfaces were cleaned before forming, before trimming and before assembly. Because of the cleaning and inspection involved, the extreme care needed to handle the sheets, and the high scrap rate (80 to 85%), production rates varied considerably.

Extruded or roll formed structural shapes, rods and bars are usually stretch formed in a radial draw former, but they can be stretch formed in a stretch draw press, as in the following two examples.

Example 536. Use of a Stretch Draw Press to Edge Bend Frame Members (Fig. 30)

Reinforcing frames for microwave reflectors (see Fig. 30) were made from alloy 6061-T4, ¾ in. thick by 11¹⁄₁₆ in. wide by 150 in. long. They were edge bent to conform to the parabolic contour. Before bending, each strip was trimmed in an arbor saw to the varying angle at which the frame member would meet the parabola of the reflector. Since the curve was parabolic, the radius of curvature varied continuously, but greatest distance from arc to chord was 9 in.

The frame member was stretch formed in a horizontal stretch draw press equipped with a low-carbon steel form block with an 11-in.-deep by ¾-in.-wide groove for the framing member. No lubricant was used. Life of the form block was indefinitely long. Setup time was 2 hr. Forming time for each part was 7 min, using three operators. There was no particular limit to the production-lot size that could have been run, but to match the skin production, lots were usually 700 pieces or less.

Example 537. Stretch Draw Forming of an Extruded Section (Fig. 31)

An extruded Z-bar of alloy 6063-T5, 1½ by 1½ by ³⁄₁₆ in., was annealed and then stretch drawn to make the roof stiffener shown in Fig. 31. The form block was machined to match the cross-sectional shape of the Z-bar so that it could support the flanges during forming.

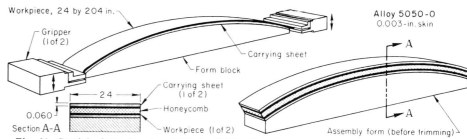

Fig. 29. Stretch draw forming 0.003-in.-thick skins for a honeycomb panel (Example 535)

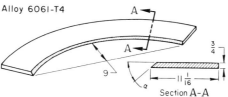

Fig. 30. Reinforcing frame member for a microwave reflector that was edge bent in a stretch draw press (Example 536)

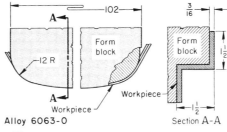

Fig. 31. Roof stiffener produced from an extruded Z-bar by stretch draw forming (Example 537)

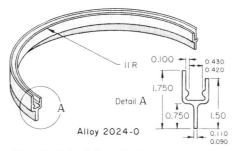

Fig. 32. Extruded section that was stretch wrapped with both a shaped form block and a segmented filler (Example 538)

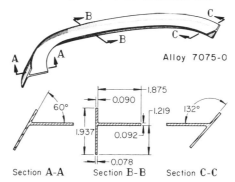

Fig. 33. Radial-draw formed T-section with radical changes in angle between leg and flange (Example 539)

The metal was stretched beyond its yield point and took a permanent set to the contour of the form block with little or no springback. The blank was cut 8 in. longer than the required length to provide stock for gripping in the jaws. After the workpiece was stretch formed, 4 in. was trimmed from each end.

The bar could have been roll formed, using a template, and then trimmed to length. Man-

hours for producing the stiffener by stretch forming and roll forming are compared below.

	Stretch forming	Roll forming
Setup time, man-hr	4.0	0.5
Time per piece, man-hr	0.1	0.5

Stretch wrapping uses a form block that is bolted to a rotary table. One end of the blank is clamped to the form block or to a table-mounted gripper. A hydraulic cylinder or a gripper applies tension to the other end of the blank while the form block revolves into it with the turning of the table. Sheets and extruded or rolled shapes are formed by this method. The forming of an aluminum panel is described in Example 325 in the article on Stretch Forming, page 242 in this volume.

Shaped form blocks that match the contour of extruded or rolled sections are used for support during forming. Filler strips, either segmented or made of low-melting alloys or strips of aluminum, are used to prevent the collapse of sections. In the following example, an extruded section was stretch wrapped using a shaped form block and a segmented filler.

Example 538. Support of Extruded Section During Stretch Wrapping (Fig. 32)

The extruded section shown in Fig. 32 was stretch wrapped into an arch that was used as the front frame member for an aircraft cockpit canopy. The material was alloy 2024-O, which was stretch wrapped using a segmented filler and a contoured form block to support the extruded section around the bend. After solution heat treating to the W temper, the workpiece was stretch wrapped again and checked in a fixture. Formed contour and changes in shape of the cross section were held within ±0.010 in.

The form block was made of zinc alloy for ease in machining the contour, and between 5000 and 6000 pieces were made on it with no signs of deterioration. Lubrication was residual mill oil. Setup time was 1 hr. Production time was 9 min per piece with two operators working. A 250-piece lot was processed every three months.

Radial-draw forming is a combination of stretch wrapping and compression forming. The workpiece is pressed against the form block by a roller or shoe while being wrapped around the turning form block. This method can be used to form a flange to a compound curvature while forming a leg, as in the following example:

Example 539. Radial-Draw Forming a T-Section Having Angular Changes Between Flange and Leg (Fig. 33)

As shown in Fig. 33, the canopy part made of a T-section varied in shape throughout its length. Originally, it was assembled and welded from three separately formed pieces. However, using radial-draw forming, the part was made from one piece of a T-shape extrusion of alloy 7075-O. The flange was given the compound curvature by a swiveled compression shoe. The leg of the T-section was stretch wrapped into a

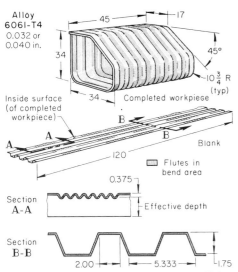

Fig. 34. Cargo container that was radial-draw formed from a commercial V-beam by fluting crests of corrugations to reduce stress in the bend zones (Example 540)

slot in the form block. Thus, the bending and twisting of the T-section were set at the same time by the combination of stretch wrapping and compression forming. Production rate was 15 pieces per hour.

Stretch forming is practical as long as the stresses on the inner and outer surfaces of the formed workpieces are kept below the tensile strength. Generally, difficulty arises when forming deep structural shapes or edge-bending pieces in one operation. Preformed sheet metal pieces with sections that are deep in relation to stock thickness may also be difficult to form. The parts can be formed in two or more steps with an intermediate anneal, or by altering the cross section to reduce the depth and nature of the bending zone, as in the following example.

**Example 540. Use of Fluted Corrugations
to Reduce Depth of Bend Zone
(Fig. 34)**

Corrugated 6061-T4 sheet was radial-draw formed to 90° and 45° bends to make the aircraft cargo container shown in Fig. 34. The stock was a commercial V-beam 120 in. long by 45 in. wide and 0.032 or 0.040 in. thick, with corrugations 1¾ in. deep repeated every 5.333 in. The 45° bend was formed successfully by radial-draw forming, but attempts to make the 90° bend failed, either by collapse of the inner ridges or, if enough stretch was applied to support them, by tearing of the outer crests.

To eliminate collapsing of the inner ridges at the 90° bends, a series of ⅜-in.-deep flutes was formed on each inner ridge in the bend zone. These flutes changed the nature of the bend and reduced the effective depth of the cross section by ⅜ in. As the 90° bends were made, the tension in the outer ridge was reduced and the flutes in the inner ridge were closed by compression. For the sake of appearance, flutes were also added to the 45° bends. The blanks were wiped as clean and free of lubricant and dust as possible, because lubrication had a deleterious effect on stretch forming of this piece.

The form block was made of epoxy-fiberglass on a steel base. The form was wiped into the epoxy with a template cut to the basic dimensions of the commercial V-beam contour. Wiping shoes and clamps of epoxy-fiberglass were cast against the form block. The epoxy-fiberglass form block had a life of 5000 pieces.

Inside radius of all bends was 9 in.; outside radius it had to fit to the contour of the aircraft fuselage. The 90° bends were overwrapped 20° to allow for springback; angular variation on bends was kept within 1°. Produc-

tion time was 15 min floor-to-floor with three men working — one operator and two handlers. Setup time was 1½ hr, and production rate was 300 pieces per month.

Rubber-Pad Forming

Aluminum alloys are formed by several techniques that can be classified as rubber-pad forming. A general description of processes, equipment, tools and applications is given in the article "Rubber-Pad Forming", which begins on page 209 in this volume.

Alloys for rubber-pad forming are selected on the same basis as for similar bending or deep drawing operations. With non-heat-treatable aluminum alloys, the temper that will meet the forming requirements and give the maximum strength in unworked areas is usually chosen.

Heat treatable aluminum alloys ordinarily are either formed in the annealed temper and then solution heat treated, or formed in the freshly quenched W temper.

Tool materials are usually masonite for short runs and aluminum alloy, zinc alloy, or steel for longer runs.

Several different types of rubber have been used as the pad material. Certain grades of rubber have particularly good resistance to oils and forming lubricants, and are available in a range of

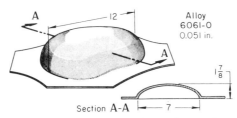

Fig. 35. Shallow part that was drawn with a rubber pad and a rigid female steel die in one operation

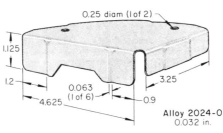

Fig. 36. Rubber-pad formed bulkhead with three flanges (one at rear, not shown) in which joggles had to set by hand after forming (Example 541)

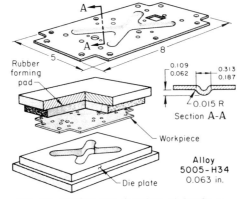

Fig. 37. Rubber-pad forming of beads in a pierced flat part (Example 542)

hardness, tensile strength, and deflection characteristics to meet different forming requirements.

Capabilities. A given alloy and temper can sometimes be formed more severely by rubber-pad forming than with conventional tools, because of the multidirectional nature of the force exerted against the workpiece. Also, the variable radius of the forming pad assists in producing a more uniform elongation of the workpiece than in conventional forming operations.

Forming the shallow part shown in Fig. 35 with a rubber pad and a rigid female die used the variable radius to an advantage. The development of wrinkles was almost eliminated, because the rubber acted as a blankholder and kept the work in contact with the flat and contoured die surfaces as the drawing progressed. A drawing compound was used on the blank.

Limitations. The simpler types of rubber-pad forming have relatively low production rates and correspondingly high unit labor costs, compared with punch-press operations. However, the rubber-diaphragm process is adaptable to automatic loading equipment and thus has fairly high production rates.

Applications. Rubber-pad forming is widely used in the aerospace industry, especially for structural parts and skin components. Products made in other industries include appliance parts, license plates, numerals, lighting reflectors, skin panels for buildings, moldings, utensils, and parts drawn from prefinished sheet.

Most rubber-pad forming is done on material 1/16 in. or less in thickness, with only a small percentage being thicker than ¼ in. However, aluminum alloy parts ⅝ in. thick have been formed in special heavy-duty equipment of the rubber-diaphragm type.

Some bulkheads and brackets have both straight and curved flanges with joggles at both ends. The form blocks for such parts are sometimes interchangeable between the Guerin and Verson-Wheelon rubber-pad processes (see pages 209 and 212 in the article "Rubber-Pad Forming", in this volume). Handwork is usually necessary to set the joggles and to smooth small buckles in the shrink flanges:

**Example 541. Use of Handwork to Finish
Rubber-Pad Formed Pieces (Fig. 36)**

Joggles at the ends of the three flanges in the aluminum alloy bulkhead shown in Fig. 36 had to be set by hand after the part was formed by the Verson-Wheelon process. The part was made of 0.032-in.-thick alloy 2024-O from a developed blank that was cut with a high-speed router and deburred by hand.

The form block was made of aluminum alloy 1⅞ in. thick, and had two ¼-in.-diam locating pins. A ¼-in.-thick cover plate was used to keep the web flat during forming. The cover plate was beveled and rounded on the edges to aid the flow of the rubber around the flanges. The rubber pad of the fluid cell was protected by a 1-in.-thick throw sheet. Forming pressure was 3000 psi. Cycle time was 2 min per piece. Production lots were 25 pieces.

The same part was formed by the Guerin process using the same tooling with a forming pressure of 600 psi. In the Guerin process, a ½-in.-thick throw sheet protected the rubber pad. The only significant difference in quality between the two processes was the forming of larger compression buckles in the shrink flange with the Guerin process. The joggles also had to be finished by hand, as in the Verson-Wheelon process.

The simultaneous blanking and piercing of flat stock can also be done with rubber-pad tooling. This type of operation is limited to aluminum alloy sheet no thicker than about 0.064 in.

The control of metal movement that can be obtained with rubber-pad forming not only permits more severe forming than with conventional tools, but also is applicable to beading operations. Beads are frequently used to obtain rigidity on large surfaces without increasing the metal thickness.

With a conventional steel punch, die and blankholder, metal is moved from the edges of the workpiece toward the bead, making the edges somewhat concave, and sometimes producing warping or oil-can effects. Some movement of metal toward the formed area is usually desirable, in order to prevent excessive thinning or cracking of the beads. In the forming of some parts, however, it may be necessary that metal movement be restricted to the immediate vicinity of the beads:

Example 542. Change From Conventional to Rubber-Pad Forming for Accuracy in Producing Beads in a Pierced Sheet (Fig. 37)

Figure 37 shows a beaded part in which the holes, produced to close tolerances on location and dimensions, had to be pierced before the beads were formed. When the part was formed conventionally with steel punch, die and blankholder, the holes distorted out of location, and the relatively large, flat surface warped. Also, irregular movement of the blank interfered with the accuracy of a subsequent press-brake flanging operation, which depended on the over-all dimensions of the part and the squareness of the edges.

Roughening the steel blankholder or otherwise restricting metal movement did not correct the problem.

Finally, the use of a rubber forming pad (Fig. 37) localized the forming operation to the immediate area of the beads, thereby solving the problem. It was not necessary to confine the rubber pad. Tooling costs were lowered by more than 80%, and rejections were reduced to a minimum.

With this improved method, it was only necessary to machine straight-sided grooves in a steel die and to provide two pilot pins for locating the workpiece. A female die restricted metal movement more effectively than a male die, and was used for this operation. Length of press stroke was not critical, and stock of various thicknesses could be formed on the one die.

A rubber slab of controlled properties, 1½ in. thick and with a hardness of Durometer A 90, was used for both the punch and blankholder. (This thickness and hardness combination is suitable for most beading operations on the more ductile aluminum alloys.) No lubrication was required. Tool life was about 100,000 pieces.

The deep drawing capabilities of rubber-pad processes vary with the different types of equipment. The severity of drawing possible with heavy-duty rubber-pad drawing by the Marform process (see page 213 in "Rubber-Pad Forming") is compared below with that possible in conventional drawing. The comparison is based on the drawing of alloys 1100-O and 3003-O.

Drawing severity	Reduction in diameter, %	Ratio of depth to diameter
Rubber-Pad Drawing		
Typical	57	1.1
Maximum	72	3.0
Conventional Drawing		
Maximum	40	0.45

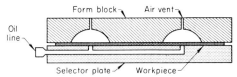

Fig. 38. Typical tooling setup for hydraulic forming of multiple beads in flat stock

Hydraulic Forming

True hydraulic forming by direct oil pressure against the surface of the workpiece has been applied to aluminum alloy flat stock. The process has been used mainly for the drawing of multiple beads on small quantities of large, flat sheets of thin material for aerospace applications. As shown in Fig. 38, a form block attached to the ram of the press holds the workpiece tightly against a selector plate, through which oil is introduced into channels at the bead locations.

In typical applications, up to 20 beads have been drawn in parts 20 to 30 in. wide by 60 to 80 in. long and about 0.012 in. thick, made from alloy 2024. Clamping force required is about 300 tons, and forming oil pressure about 1000 psi. Vents are provided in the form block to allow the escape of air from each bead cavity. The oil film left on the form block after each operation provides sufficient lubrication to draw the next part.

The technique is limited to short runs because production rate is slow. (Although 20 beads could be drawn in three seconds, total handling time for a panel was 3 to 4 min.)

Forming by Shot Peening

The major application of shot peening is to increase the fatigue life of metal parts by producing a uniform compressive stress in the surface layers. Shot peening is sometimes used as a metal-forming process, and is especially useful in the forming of large, irregularly shaped parts from aluminum alloy sheet stock.

General information on the process, equipment, and applications is given in the article "Shot Peening", pages 398 to 405 in Volume 2 of this Handbook.

Shot. When steel shot is used to peen-form aluminum alloy parts, the parts are usually treated chemically after forming to remove particles of iron or iron oxides that may be embedded in the surface.

Slugs cut from stainless steel or aluminum alloy wire are sometimes used. When peening with aluminum alloy slugs, no subsequent chemical treatment is needed, and the danger of over-peening and high localized residual stress (which sometimes occurs with steel or iron shot) is also eliminated.

Automatic or semiautomatic devices are available for the separation and removal of fines and undersize shot, and for the addition of new shot. Manual handling of shot and batch replacement may be more feasible for small-scale operations. The proportion of full-size shot in the system is usually maintained at a minimum of 85%.

Control. The effectiveness of shot peening depends on the size, shape,

material and velocity of the shot, and on the quantity of shot striking a unit area per unit time. The combined effect of these variables is known as peening intensity, which is measured on standard steel test strips according to SAE J442, and is expressed as an Almen-gage reading.

The angle at which the shot strikes the work also affects the peening intensity, which is proportional to the sine of the angle of impingement. The amount of breakdown of the shot will, of course, also affect peening intensity.

The extent of surface coverage as measured by visual or instrumental techniques is often used, together with Almen test strips, to control peening operations.

Applications. One of the earliest forming applications of shot peening was the contour forming of integrally stiffened aircraft-wing panels. Because of their extreme length and variable thickness, these parts are ill-suited for forming by mechanical processes. The shot peening of an aircraft-wing panel is described in the following example.

Example 543. Forming Integrally Stiffened Wing Panels by Shot Peening (Fig. 39)

Shot peening was used for contour forming integrally stiffened aircraft-wing panels (Fig. 39) ranging up to 24 in. in width and up to 50 ft in length. The panels were machined from alloy 7075-T6 after having been stretcher leveled. Basic thickness of the panel between the ribs ranged from 0.09 to 0.18 in. for tapered skins, and up to 0.312 in. thick for straight (no taper) skins. One surface of the panels had stiffening ribs spaced a few inches apart, and also a number of ¾-in.-thick "pads" for attaching the panels to the frame or for attaching inboard equipment to the panels. This structure made it almost impossible to press form the panels to the required smoothly curved contours.

Before being peen formed, the panels were first shot peened with SAE 230 cast steel shot, to improve fatigue resistance by cold working to a depth of 0.006 to 0.008 in. The panels were then peen formed on the same worktable, without being removed from the machine. Larger cast steel shot (SAE 550 or 930) was used to form the thicker sections of a panel and to obtain a greater depth of cold work (up to 0.016 in. on pad areas). Irregular curves were produced by peening selected local areas as needed, sometimes on the reverse side of the panel as well as on the outer surface. Gradual blending of areas was necessary to obtain smooth contours.

Oscillating air nozzles were used with air pressure up to 90 psi. Peening intensity was determined by means of Almen A test strips. Forming time per panel was 2 to 3 hr. After peening, the panels were chemically treated to remove ferrous residues and to improve corrosion resistance.

Other parts formed by shot peening include honeycomb panels and large tubular shapes. Large, irregularly shaped parts are conveniently formed by this method.

The process is usually carried out as a free-forming technique, without dies

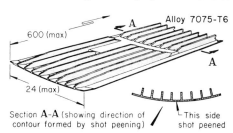

Fig. 39. Integrally stiffened wing panel that was formed by shot peening (Example 543)

or form blocks. Contour is checked against a template.

If a part is deformed beyond the specified amount, the contour can be corrected by peening the reverse side. Also, peening can be used as a salvage procedure to correct the contours of bent or distorted parts.

The peening intensity and the number of passes are varied depending on the material and the severity of forming required. Local areas can be subjected to the required treatment.

Drop Hammer Forming

Drop hammer forming is of value for limited production runs that do not warrant expensive tooling, and is often used in experimental work to make trial parts and parts that are expected to undergo frequent design changes.

Tooling costs are low, and finished parts can be produced quickly. However, only relatively shallow parts with liberal radii can be drawn, and material thickness must be in the range of about 0.024 to 0.064 in. Also, wrinkling occurs frequently, and a high degree of operator skill is required.

Equipment and Tools. Air-operated hammers with sensitive and accurate control are usually preferred to hammers operated by gravity or by steam.

The material is formed in a sequence of small steps. In a typical setup (Fig. 40) several plywood or rubber spacers are stacked on the die face, and one or more are removed after each stroke to form the workpiece progressively.

In a variation of this procedure, a series of dies can be used to accomplish the progressive forming. Only the last of these dies requires close tolerances. A rubber pad several inches thick is sometimes used between workpiece and punch in all except the final step.

Dies are simple and inexpensive. Bottom dies are cast from zinc alloy, and punches can also be made from zinc alloy. If requirements on sharpness of radii and accuracy of contour are not stringent, punches cast from lead are used for short runs. These need not be cast accurately, because they deform to the shape of the bottom die in a few strokes. For longer runs, tools can be made of cast iron or cast steel.

Lubrication requirements are similar to those for drawing operations.

Alloys used most frequently are 1100, 3003, 2024, 5052, 6061 and 7075. Annealed tempers permit the greatest severity of forming. Intermediate tempers of the non-heat-treatable alloys are often used for channel shapes and shallow, embossed panels. Heat treatable alloys can be partly formed in the annealed condition and given a restrike operation after heat treatment, or they can be formed in the fresh W temper.

With all processing conditions the same, aluminum alloy stock wrinkles more readily than the same thickness of steel sheet. For comparable results in forming, aluminum alloys must be about 40% thicker than steel.

Supplemental Forming Methods

A number of additional conventional forming processes are applied to aluminum alloy sheet, strip or wire in

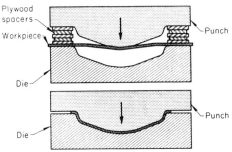

Fig. 40. Tooling and setup for drop hammer forming

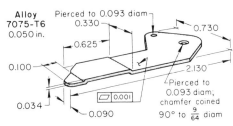

Fig. 41. Lever that was produced from solution heat treated and aged alloy 7075 strip by embossing, piercing, coining and blanking in a progressive die (Example 544)

conjunction with the processes already described in this article. Among the supplemental processes are embossing, coining, stamping, curling, expanding or bulging, contracting or necking, hole flanging, and beading or ribbing.

Embossing, Coining and Stamping. These three closely related methods for making shallow impressions and patterns by compression between a punch and a die are frequently combined with drawing. In these operations, the material must yield under impact and compression, and it must be ductile to avoid fracture in tension.

Uniform thickness in all areas of the workpiece generally is maintained in embossing; however, some stretching occurs. Simple designs are produced with light pressure, using a punch of the desired shape and an open female die. Complex patterns require high pressure and a closed matching female die or a rubber female die.

Coining differs from embossing in that metal is made to flow, thus producing local differences in metal thickness. The design on top and bottom surfaces may be different. Very high pressure is required.

Stamping produces cut lines of lettering or patterns in one side of the workpiece, to 0.020 to 0.040-in. depth. The depth of penetration must be carefully controlled to minimize distortion and to prevent the design from appearing on the opposite side. Outline or open-face stamps are preferred.

Alloy and temper are usually selected to have high elongation, the required tensile strength, and as low a yield strength as possible. The annealed temper yields the most accurate impressions, but a harder temper may be required for other reasons, as in the example that follows.

Example 544. Embossing and Coining of Alloy 7075 in the T6 Temper (Fig. 41)

The lever shown in Fig. 41 was produced from 0.050-in.-thick alloy 7075-T6 strip 2¾ in. wide, in the following sequence of operations in a progressive die of hardened tool steel:

1 Emboss the 0.034-in. offset.
2 Pierce two 0.093-in.-diam holes.
3 Coin one hole to a 90° chamfer and ⁹⁄₆₄-in. diameter (Fig. 41).
4 Shave chamfered hole.
5 Blank and flatten.

These operations were done in a 45-ton mechanical press operating at 125 strokes per minute. The punch for coin-chamfering the hole was designed to push the metal into the hole, because stock thickening around the hole was not permitted. The hole was shaved after coining to maintain size. After blanking and flattening, the part was tumbled in an abrasive medium for removal of burrs.

Although alloy 7075 is not recommended for cold working after being solution heat treated and aged (T6 temper), the flatness tolerance of 0.001 in. over the full length of the lever could not be maintained when the part was produced from alloy 7075 strip in the annealed condition and then heat treated.

Tools must be hard and tough. (For a detailed discussion and recommendations on the selection of die materials, the reader is referred to the article "The Selection of Material for Coining Dies", pages 717 to 719 in Volume 1 of this Handbook.) With stamping tools, only the punch is hardened, and the die or anvil is usually made of a low-carbon steel.

Tool surfaces must be highly polished and free from local imperfections. Lubrication is avoided if possible; when lubrication is necessary, alcohol or a similar volatile liquid should be used as the lubricant. Tools and blank must be kept free from any foreign particles.

Knuckle-joint presses with a precisely controlled short stroke, and designed to exert extremely high pressure at the bottom of the stroke, are most suitable for this application. Special precautions are taken to prevent the feeding of oversize blanks or of two blanks at once, and dies are sometimes mounted on hydropneumatic pressure-equalizing cushions to avoid breakage of the die or press frame.

Embossing, coining and stamping frequently impose special demands on tool design, particularly when done in combination with other forming operations. The following example describes an unusual tooling arrangement developed for embossing a zipper component.

Example 545. Use of Spring-Actuated Embossing Punches in Four-Operation Production of a Zipper Component (Fig. 42)

Figure 42 shows the progression of shapes that resulted from notching, piercing, forming and embossing of alloy 5056-O roll-formed wire in the production of a small zipper component. Forming, which was of the simple pressure-pad type, was done before embossing, to avoid distortion or cracking of the embossed area. Kerosine was the lubricant.

The tooling setup for embossing is also shown in Fig. 42. The upper punch and the separate auxiliary punches on each side of it were separately spring actuated. The lower, or embossing, punch was highly polished and, because of part design, had only a very small radius on the top corners. A 0.005-in. ledge was provided on each side of the lower punch to help supply additional metal in this location, and thus to prevent the development of cracks along the radius on each side of the embossing. The lower embossing punch also had a wider shoulder to prevent the workpiece from becoming distorted and undersize below the embossed area.

Curling or false wiring can be done in a variety of machines, such as press brakes, single-action punch presses, lathes, roll-forming machines, or special beading machines. The selection of machine depends on the shape and the number of parts required. Circular parts are usually curled on spinning lathes, and rectangular parts in presses. Long, relatively narrow parts can be curled in press brakes or roll-forming machines. Various types of machines have been built specifically for curling in high production quantities.

The edge to be curled should be of uniform height and free from roughness on the outside of the curl, and preferably should be rounded slightly before beginning the operation. The minimum radius for curling should be 1½ to 4 times the metal thickness, depending on alloy and temper.

Expanding or bulging of aluminum alloy parts can be carried out by several different methods, including segmented mechanical dies, rubber punches, or hydraulic pressure.

Segmented mechanical expanding dies are relatively inexpensive and are capable of high production rates, but are limited to certain shapes and may produce marks on thin stock and low-strength alloys.

Rubber punches are widely used and are applicable to extremely difficult operations or those impossible to do by other means. (Additional information on the use of rubber punches for bulging is given on page 216 in the article "Rubber-Pad Forming", in this volume.) Rubber is selected at hardness, tensile strength, and deflection most suitable for the workpiece shape. The rubber punch or pad must be correctly shaped and located to apply pressure to the shell wall at the required points; it must be kept free from oil; and it should be lubricated with talc, pumice, or other powder-type lubricant.

Water and oil can also be used to exert pressure directly against the workpiece, but this technique requires expensive tooling and controls, and is often messy.

Annealed alloys can be expanded more readily than tempered alloys. With alloys 1100-O, 3003-O and 5050-O, the diameter of a shell can be increased about 25%. Large increases in diameter can be made in two or more operations with intermediate annealing.

Different types of expanding or bulging operations are shown in Fig. 13 and 14. Bead-rolling machines are available for forming beads such as on the part in Fig. 13.

Contracting or necking operations reduce the diameter of a shell, usually at the open end. This entails reductions ranging in severity from the forming of a shallow circumferential groove to the forming of a bottle-neck shape.

The reduction in diameter, in a single operation, should not exceed 8 to 15%, depending on alloy, temper, and extent of prior work hardening. The angle from the body to the necked diameter should be less than 45°, to prevent collapse of the shell. It may be necessary to anneal the workpiece locally.

Rotary swaging is often used to reduce the diameter of thick-wall shells. This process is described in the article that begins on page 333 in this volume.

Hole flanging, the forming of a flange or collar around a hole in sheet stock, can be a critical operation. The hole should be punched from the side opposite the intended flange. This avoids splitting the severely stretched outer edge of the flange, which could be initiated by the burred edge of the hole.

Shallow-flanged holes can be produced in a single pierce-and-flange operation with a stepped punch. The edges of the pierced hole should also be as smooth as possible.

Low-strength, ductile alloys in the annealed temper will permit forming the deepest flanges and the sharpest bend radii. For more information on hole flanging, see the article on Bending of Low-Carbon Steel, page 89.

Beading or ribbing is usually the most economical way to provide stiffness and avoid oil-can or buckling effects in large panels. Beads that extend from edge to edge of the workpiece are conveniently formed by bending in a press brake or with corrugating rolls. Table 4 gives minimum bend radii for 90° cold bends, and thus provides an approximate guide to shape and dimension of beads formed by bending.

Beads that do not extend all the way across the part require a stretching or forming operation with a rubber-pad die or in a punch press with a rigid punch and a rigid die. A double-acting die and a blankholder can be used to prevent wrinkling at the ends of the beads, and deep parallel beads are often made one at a time.

Rubber-pad forming can also be used. Example 542 describes a situation in which a female die was preferred to a male die because it restricted metal movement to the immediate vicinity of the beads and thus helped to maintain critical dimensions.

Figure 38 illustrates the use of hydraulic forming to produce multiple beads or ribs on large flat parts made of thin material.

Drop hammer forming can be used for beading small quantities of parts.

Explosive Forming

Explosive forming is one of the high-energy-rate forming (HERF) methods that are employed in the production of aluminum alloy parts, mainly in the aerospace industries. It is often used to produce parts whose size exceeds the limits of conventional equipment or whose thickness requires pressures not obtainable with conventional equipment. It is also used to form small quantities of complex parts that would be more costly to produce by conventional techniques.

Deformation velocities are several hundred feet per second, as compared with 0.5 to about 20 ft per sec for conventional forming processes. The time required for the workpiece to deform to its final shape is a few milliseconds, with working pressures of several thousand to several hundred thousand pounds per square inch. Water usually serves as the pressure medium.

For details of equipment, tools and procedures, the reader is referred to the article that begins on page 250 in this volume, and to "Explosive Working of Metals", by Rinehart and Pearson (Macmillan, 1963).

Capabilities. Types of operations include panel forming (bending), piercing, flanging, shallow dishing, deep drawing, and cylindrical bulging. Part dimensions range from 1 in. to about 50 ft; work-metal thickness, from several thousandths of an inch to about 6 in.

Alloys. The process can be used with any aluminum alloy. Formability is a direct function of the ordinary tensile elongation values, but the function is different for each alloy, because of different strain-rate behavior. Alloy 1100-O is rated the most formable of all common metals by explosive forming.

Effect on Mechanical Properties. Changes in mechanical properties as a result of explosive free-forming operations are essentially the same as those observed with conventional forming techniques to produce the same part. Explosive forming in a die, however, often causes the metal to strike the die at extremely high velocity. The resulting high interface pressures can increase the yield and tensile strengths substantially. Forming capability is increased when critical forming velocities are exceeded.

Dies. Only a forming die or cavity is needed for explosive forming, because the shock wave acts as a punch. Some direction and concentration of the shock wave is obtained with suitably shaped and positioned "reflectors".

Cast iron and cast steel are the most frequently used die materials. A variety of other materials and combinations of materials are used, depending on the impact of the shock wave and of the workpiece against the die, the size of the die, dimensional tolerances on the part, and quantity of parts. These materials include low-melting cast alloys and plastics, reinforced concrete, concrete faced with plastic-glass composites, and high-impact steel.

The air between the workpiece and die cavity must be evacuated before forming, because the forming speed is so great that the air will be trapped between the workpiece and die rather than displaced as in conventional press forming. Trapped air and excessive lubrication cause malformed areas. The vent holes for evacuating the air must be placed in noncritical areas; otherwise, marks will appear on the formed parts. In thinner parts, the forming force will pierce holes in the parts, using the vent hole as a piercing die.

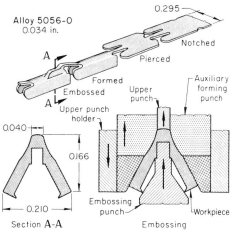

Fig. 42. Production of a zipper component from flat wire in four operations, using spring-loaded punches for embossing
(Example 545)

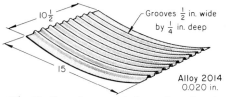

Fig. 43. Curved corrugated panel produced by explosive forming

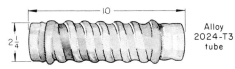

Fig. 44. Tubular part on which spirals were produced by explosive forming

Surface finish of the die cavity is important, because it is reproduced in mirror image on the workpiece.

Lubricants, if used, are usually extreme-pressure (EP) types such as No. 7, 9 or 10 in Table 1, or a mixture of paraffin and mineral oil. Because of the high velocity of forming and the extreme pressures, excessive lubrication must be avoided. Dies of low-melting alloys or dies with smooth surfaces require little or no lubrication.

Springback is of importance in die design. Increasing the explosive charge or reducing the standoff distance reduces springback. However, this increases die wear and may also fracture the more brittle die materials, and a compromise is often required.

Compensation is sometimes made for die wear by reducing charge size or increasing standoff distance to produce a controlled amount of springback and maintain dimensional tolerances.

Studies on alloy 2219 have shown springback to increase with decreasing sheet thickness between 0.250 in. and 0.032 in., and also to increase substantially with the application of a lubricant. Incremental forming has been observed to reduce the extent of springback. Draw radius, draw depth, and die material have shown no significant effects on springback behavior.

Examples of Applications. The forming of flat and moderately curved shapes has been one of the most useful applications of explosive forming. These have included parts ranging from small, detailed items a few square inches in area to large panels with areas in excess of 30 sq ft.

The curved corrugated panel shown in Fig. 43 was formed from alloy 2014 in the O, T4 and T6 tempers in a laminated epoxy-fiberglass die. The panel was formed in a single shot, using a detonating fuse as a source of energy.

Tubular parts are readily shaped by explosive forming, using a length of detonating cord suspended along the axis of the tube. For example, spirals were formed on the alloy 2024-T3 tube shown in Fig. 44. These spirals were ¼ in. high by ½ in. wide, with a 1-in. pitch. A tolerance of ±0.001 in. was maintained in forming.

The following two examples of parts produced by explosive forming give an indication of the versatility of the process. As in most explosive forming, water was used as the medium for transmittal of energy.

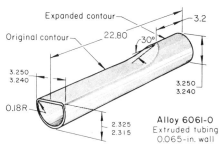

Fig. 45. Tubular part (upper left) in which 48 nozzles were produced by simultaneous explosive forming and piercing in a reinforced steel die (right) (Example 547)

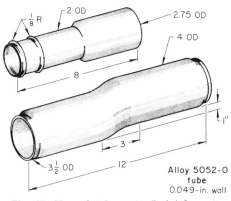

An alternative method would be to draw the expanded shape and weld it to the tubing.

Fig. 46. Adapter tube on which transitional shape was produced by electrohydraulic forming (Example 548)

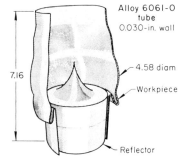

Fig. 47. Stepped tube and offset tube, originally produced as welded assemblies, that were produced as one-piece units by electrohydraulic forming (Example 549)

Energy-releasing spark gap was positioned at the free end of the tube. Shock waves reflected by the cone made the wall fold.

Fig. 48. Use of a shock-wave reflector for electrohydraulic free-forming of a fold in a rolled and welded tube (Example 550)

Example 546. Precision Explosive Forming of a Large Radar Lens

An approximately spherical radar lens, 78 in. in diameter by 22 in. deep, was explosive formed from an 0.087-in.-thick oversize sheet of alloy 6061-O.

A ring-shaped charge of plastic sheet explosive was located parallel with and directly above the blank, which was held against an evacuated die by a hold-down ring. The entire assembly was submerged in a tank of water.

The lens was formed approximately to required contour in two operations, and a final sizing operation was done immediately after solution heat treatment and quenching. The contour on the finished lens was held to a tolerance of ±0.007 in. at all points.

Example 547. Simultaneous Explosive Forming and Piercing (Fig. 45)

Figure 45 shows a tubular part in which 48 nozzle holes, on 0.30-in. centers, were produced in one operation by simultaneous explosive forming and piercing in a reinforced steel die. Previously, this part had been produced by attaching 48 nozzles to a tube, but air flow through the nozzles was unsatisfactory.

A water tank was not used in this operation. Instead, the tube was plugged at one end, placed in the upright die (Fig. 45) and filled with water. A partial vacuum was maintained between the tube and die during forming.

The explosive charge consisted of a 15-in. length of 50-grains-per-foot detonating cord enclosed in heavy-wall rubber hose. The tube and die were covered with a rubber mat 48 in. square by ½ in. thick. Tooling cost was $800. Production time was 6 min per piece.

Electrohydraulic Forming (EHF)

Another high-energy-rate forming (HERF) method used in the fabrication of aluminum alloy parts is electrohydraulic forming (EHF). In this process, either a spark-gap or an exploding bridgewire is employed to discharge electrical energy in water or another liquid. This generates an extremely high pressure and a shock wave similar to those produced in explosive forming. Once the energy is released in the transfer medium, the remainder of the operation is essentially the same as for explosive forming.

Capabilities of electrohydraulic forming differ somewhat from those of explosive forming. The spark-gap method can apply programmed repetitive shock waves of varying magnitude without removal of the workpiece from the die. The exploding-bridgewire method is less readily automated, but the shock wave can be localized and directed by the shape and placement of the wire.

Dimensional tolerances can be held to lower limits than with explosive forming, because the discharge of energy is more closely controlled. For this reason, electrohydraulic forming is sometimes used for a restrike or sizing operation after preliminary explosive forming to an approximate contour.

Commercial equipment is available that can produce about 3000 small or medium-size pieces per week.

Examples of Applications. The two examples that follow describe the application of electrohydraulic forming to aluminum alloy parts. Details of the operation are given in the first example.

Example 548. Use of EHF for Producing a Transitional Shape in Extruded Tubing (Fig. 46)

The adapter tube shown in Fig. 46 was produced by expanding a D-section of alloy 6061-O extruded tubing by the bridgewire method of electrohydraulic forming. The tube was formed in a two-piece split die that had a steel outer shell and a cast epoxy liner. A longitudinal seal and an O-ring seal at each end enabled evacuation of the space between the workpiece and the die. The entire assembly was immersed in water.

Two shots at 4000 joules each were needed, using a 6-in. length of alloy 6061 wire 0.030 in. in diameter. The part was lubricated with a proprietary compound based on a medium-weight mineral oil. Production rate was three pieces per hour; each piece required 15 min for setup and 5 min for fabrication. Total quantity produced was 300 pieces. Tooling cost was approximately $3000.

An alternative method considered for the production of this tube was hydraulic forming, but this was ruled out, because of high die costs and the localized forming required. Another alternative method was to form the expanded portion by drawing and then to weld it to the tube, but the weld area could not be consistently finished to quality requirements.

Each of the two parts discussed in the following example would normally be produced as a welded assembly of two drawn pieces, but each was made in one piece by EHF.

Example 549. Use of EHF That Eliminated Welding in the Production of Tubular Parts (Fig. 47)

Originally, the offset tube shown in Fig. 47 was made by drawing two longitudinal sections with an outside diameter of 3½ in. and welding the sections together, and the in-line stepped tube also shown in Fig. 47 was made by welding sections of 2-in. and 2.75-in. diameter to a preformed transition ring.

The two tubes were produced more economically as one-piece units by electrohydraulic forming. Production costs were reduced by eliminating trimming, welding, and grinding of welds. Dimensional variation was reduced and surface finish was improved.

Certain types of parts can be made by free-forming techniques, without the use of a die. These may involve the use of a reflector, in addition to the placement of the spark gap or bridge-wire, to direct and concentrate the effect of the shock wave:

Example 550. Free-Forming an Annular Fold in Rolled and Welded Tube (Fig. 48)

The part shown in Fig. 48 was formed without a die from an 8½-in. length of rolled and welded tube 3 in. in diameter. The workpiece was plugged at one end with a pointed low-carbon steel reflector, as shown in Fig. 48, and at the other end with the energy-releasing spark gap. The part was filled with water.

The contour and dimensions of the reflector were developed to expand and fold the tube wall as shown in Fig. 48. Dimensions were reproducible to 0.06 in.

Electromagnetic Forming (EMF)

Operations generally similar to those described for the preceding two HERF methods can be carried out by electromagnetic forming (also called magnetic-pulse forming). In this process, the discharge of a capacitor through a coil generates an intense magnetic field. This field interacts with the electric currents induced in a conductive workpiece to produce a force perpendicular to the workpiece surface.

Details of the process and of equipment, tools and procedures are described in the article "Electromagnetic Forming", which begins on page 256. The method is suitable for aluminum alloys because of their formability and high electrical conductivity.

Examples of Applications. The following two examples give an indication of the range of application of electromagnetic forming to aluminum alloys.

Example 551. Reverse Forming of a Tube Around a Steel Reinforcing Ring (Fig. 49)

By the use of electromagnetic forming, a 2-in.-OD, 0.050-in.-wall tube of alloy 3003-O was wrapped around a steel reinforcing ring and was simultaneously bulged to lock the ring tightly in place in a permanent assembly (see Fig. 49). An expansion coil was located just inside the end of the tube. The end section of the tube accelerated to a high radial velocity in the first few thousandths of an inch of movement during the magnetic impulse. The major portion of the forming resulted from the kinetic energy of the metal,

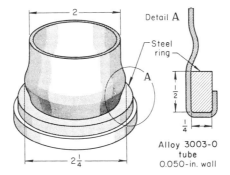

Fig. 49. Assembly produced in one step by electromagnetic reverse forming (Example 551)

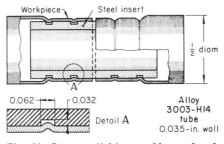

Fig. 50. Pressure-tight assembly produced by electromagnetically swaging an aluminum alloy tube onto a grooved steel insert (Example 552)

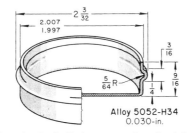

Fig. 51. Part that was produced at less cost in a punch press than by spinning (Example 553)

which caused the tube to wrap itself around the ring in a whiplike motion to produce the final form.

This assembly could not be produced economically by any method other than electromagnetic forming.

Pressure-tight joints, electrically or thermally conductive joints, torque joints, and structural joints between metals can be produced by EMF techniques in a variety of shapes. Joints between tubular members are the most common type. An example of such a joint is given below:

Example 552. Electromagnetic Swaging of a Tube Onto a Grooved Steel Insert (Fig. 50)

A metal-to-metal seal was produced by magnetic swaging of an alloy 3003-H14 tube onto a grooved tubular steel insert, as shown in Fig. 50, using a work coil and field-shaping insert that encircled the joint area. This seal remained intact at a pressure of 4000 psi, which was sufficient to burst the tube.

Selection of Method on the Basis of Quantity and Cost

The shape and size of the part to be formed usually limit the choice of a forming method to two or three techniques. Production cost for the given quantity then determines the method. **Punch-press operations** are best suited for long runs, because of high production rates, whereas spinning, press-brake forming, circle shearing, routing, and other operations with low tooling costs are preferred for short runs.

The following five examples illustrate specific production situations.

Example 553. Spinning Replaced by Lower-Cost Forming in a Punch Press for Quantity Production (Fig. 51)

The part shown in Fig. 51 was initially purchased in quantities of about 500 per year from an outside source, which produced it by spinning. When demand for this part increased to 5000 per year, tooling was obtained for its in-plant production in a punch press. The use of a blank-and-draw die costing $425 and a bulging die costing $325 made it possible to produce the part for 25% of the former purchase price of 30¢ per piece. Blank size was developed to control the depth at 9⁄16 ± 1⁄64 in. and thereby avoid a final trimming operation.

Example 554. Production of a Barrel-Shape Bowl by Drawing, Trimming and Nosing in a Punch Press (Fig. 52)

A barrel-shape bowl was produced in annual quantities of 20,000 by drawing, trimming and nosing in separate operations in a punch press. The tooling setup for nosing is illus-

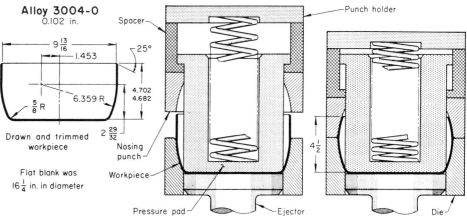

Fig. 52. Nosing a drawn and trimmed shell in a punch press to form a barrel-shape bowl (Example 554)

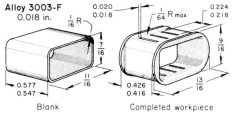

Alloy 3003-F
0.018 in.

Blank   Completed workpiece

Fig. 53. Blade holder that was flanged and pierced in a punch press from a blank cut from rectangular tubing (Example 555)

trated in Fig. 52. The bowl was produced at the rate of 300 pieces per hour.

To accomplish a 40% reduction of diameter in the drawing operation, while maintaining the surface contour and smoothness required, several aspects of tool design and procedure were critical. To avoid excessive work hardening, draw-die radius was about five times, and punch-nose radius about six times, the work-metal thickness. Also, precise trimming was necessary to make top and bottom surfaces parallel for the nosing operation, and a pressure pad held the shell rigidly in place for nosing (Fig. 52), because any variation in height around the bowl could have produced local concentrations of stress and caused the sidewall to buckle.

Example 555. Production of a Blade Holder From Rectangular Tubing by Flanging and Piercing in a Punch Press (Fig. 53)

The blade holder shown in Fig. 53 could have been made from a flat blank in a press brake and then welded. This method, however, would have been too slow for the economical production of 700,000 pieces per year.

A procedure was developed for producing the part in a punch press from a blank cut from rectangular tubing (Fig. 53). Blanks were cut at the rate of 3400 per hour. Both flanges were formed in a single operation in a double-flanging die, and the six slots were pierced, three per side, in two operations. Flanging and piercing were both done in a 10-ton mechanical punch press. Flanging was done at 1400 pieces per hour; piercing, at 600 pieces (1200 sides) per hour.

Because extruded rectangular tubing with 0.018-in. wall thickness could not be obtained, it was necessary to special-order alloy 3003 tubing cold drawn in nine mill operations. Material cost was $2.23 per pound. Alloys of lower ductility would have cold worked excessively and split during the severe flanging.

Example 556. Effect of Quantity on Method of Producing a Semicircular Flanged Cup (Table 12)

Table 12 compares the sequence of operations, the tooling and equipment, and the production rates for low-quantity and high-quantity production of a flanged semicircular shield from alloy 6061-O sheet 0.190 in. thick. The use of a draw die was required even for the lowest quantity (100 pieces), because there was no simpler means by which the shield could be drawn.

As shown in Table 12, the high-quantity method substituted individual press operations for circle shearing, for trimming with a router and drilling holes, and for band-saw cutting. The restrike operation, needed for control of dimensions in the low-quantity method, was eliminated by the use of a hydraulic press instead of a mechanical press for drawing in the high-quantity method.

Sometimes the use of press equipment for high-volume production offers other advantages in addition to the ex-

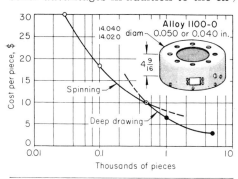

Item	Spinning(a)	Deep drawing(b)
Stock form	Sheet	Strip
Stock thickness, in. ...	0.050	0.040
Stock size, in.	96 by 48	22¼ wide
Diameter of blank, in. .	23	21¹⁵⁄₁₆
Tool cost	$560	$3300
Setup time, hr	4	5½
Lubricant	Grease(c)	Mineral oil(d)

(a) Sequence of operations: shear; cut circle; spin, in a 3-hp manual spinning lathe with 26-in. swing; trim; mill slot, in a milling machine; drill holes, in a drill press; pierce holes, in a 5½-ton open-back inclinable press. (b) Sequence of operations: blank, in a 125-ton punch press; draw, in a 300-ton toggle press or a 400-ton hydraulic press; trim; pierce and slot, in a 125-ton punch press. (c) Aluminum-spinning type. (d) With proprietary additive.

Fig. 54. Cost of a dust-cover housing in various quantities when formed by manual spinning vs deep drawing (Example 557)

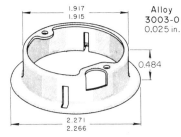

Fig. 55. Retainer ring produced by two different methods, depending on annual quantity required (Example 558)

pected higher production rates and lower unit labor costs. Ability to produce to closer dimensional tolerances is one. The following example describes three other advantages obtained in the production of a specific part.

Example 557. Effect of Quantity on Cost of a Housing Formed by Manual Spinning vs Deep Drawing (Fig. 54)

The unit costs for a dust-cover housing produced in various quantities by manual spinning and by deep drawing in a press are compared in Fig. 54. As shown, the quantity above which the more expensive press tooling was economically justified was about 500 pieces.

Three additional benefits besides lower unit labor costs and higher production rates were realized by the use of deep drawing for large quantities: (a) stock of 0.040-in. thickness could be used, instead of the 0.050-in. stock required for spinning (to compensate for thinout); (b) blank diameter was 21¹⁵⁄₁₆ in., compared with 23 in. for spinning; and (c) blanking from strip of a suitable width also permitted a layout with less waste of material than with the sheet stock used for spinning. The net result was that deep drawing required 31% less metal per piece than was used in spinning.

Additional production details and the sequence of operations for each method are given in the table that accompanies Fig. 54.

Compound dies and automated handling devices are commonly used in high-volume production. Compound dies replace utility tools and simple dies; automatic load and unload devices replace manual handling; coil stock with roll feed replaces individual blanks. Production procedures can be tailored for maximum economy at several different levels of production, as shown in the following two examples.

Example 558. Comparison of Methods for Producing a Retainer Ring in Annual Quantities of 5000 and 50,000 Pieces (Fig. 55)

When the retainer ring shown in Fig. 55 was produced in annual quantities of 5000 pieces, strips sheared from sheet material were used as the stock, and presses were hand fed. The sequence of operations was as follows: shear sheet into strips; blank and draw; redraw and pinch trim; and pierce holes and slots. The cost per piece was comparatively high, but additional investment in tooling to reduce labor costs could not be justified for the relatively low annual production.

When annual demand for the ring increased to 50,000 pieces, a new manufacturing procedure was developed, in which coil stock replaced sheared strips, but with the sequence of operations otherwise unchanged. A roll feed was substituted for hand feeding the blank-and-draw operation, and production rate for that operation was thereby increased tenfold. Equipment was added to speed loading and

Table 12. Comparison of Procedures Used for Producing a Flanged Half Cup in Low and High Quantities (Example 556)

Sequence of operations	Equipment and tooling	Production, pcs/hr(a)	Completed workpiece
Quantities of 100 to 2000 Pieces			Alloy 6061-O 0.190 in.
1 Shear sheet stock to 25 by 25 in.	Square shear	(180)	
2 Shear square sheet to 24½-in. circle(b)	Circle shear	(90)	
3 Draw flanged circular cup(c)	Draw die in 600-ton mechanical press	(220)	
4 Restrike drawn cup	Draw die in 600-ton mechanical press	(250)	
5 Trim outside contour	Swing-arm router with template	(120)	
6 Saw in half, to make two pieces	Band saw with template	90	
7 Drill five holes in flange	Swing-arm drill with template	60	
Quantities of 2000 Pieces or More			
1 Shear sheet stock to 25 by 25 in.	Square shear	(180)	
2 Blank square sheet to 24½-in. circle	Blanking die in punch press	(300)	
3 Draw flanged circular cup(c)	Draw die in 650-ton hydraulic press	(200)	
4 Trim contour; pierce ten holes in flange	Trim-and-pierce die in 600-ton mechanical press	(240)	
5 Part into two pieces	Parting die in 600-ton mechanical press	220	

(a) Production rates in parentheses represent operations done on workpieces that were subsequently cut in half to make two finished parts, and therefore rates in terms of finished parts are twice these values. (b) For quantities of 500 to 2000 pieces, this operation was replaced by blanking the 24½-in. circle in a punch press, using a blanking die. (c) A wax drawing compound was applied to both sides of the workpiece.

unloading for the piercing operation, and the output of pierced parts was increased by 300%. As a result of these changes in manufacturing procedure, the cost of each piece was reduced to about one-third of the cost per piece produced by the original method.

Example 559. Tooling and Procedure for Four Methods of Producing a Panel in Increasing Annual Quantities (Fig. 56)

Four different methods were developed for the economical production of the panel shown in Fig. 56. Total quantity considered was between 500 and one million pieces to be produced annually in four equal runs. Each method was designed for production of the panel at minimum unit cost in a specific quantity. The effect of quantity on cost per piece by the four methods is plotted in Fig. 56.

In method A, intended for annual production of 500 pieces, eight operations were needed: two shearing operations; three piercing operations; trimming corners before drawing; drawing; and trimming corners after drawing. Available general-purpose tooling, including a draw die, was used for all operations. All of the holes were pierced in a multiple-station turret punch press, except the large-diameter hole, the six holes on the bolt circle, and the large rectangular hole. A new stylus template cost $40. Production time per piece was 7.5 min.

Method B, developed for annual production of 2500 pieces, used ten operations, seven of which were the same as in method A. The turret punch-press operation became three operations. One pierced all the small holes in the top of the panel using a die that cost $985. Two operations, using available tools, pierced ten holes in the flanges after forming and trimming. Total production time for each piece was 2.4 min.

Method C, which further reduced production time per piece to 0.96 min, was intended for annual production of 10,000 to 100,000 pieces. In this four-operation method (shear to width; blank, trim and pierce; draw; and trim corners), a compound die that cost $1600 was used for blanking and trimming, and for piercing all holes and openings. The panels were drawn and corners were trimmed with tools that were available.

For very long runs (about one million pieces), the purchase of highly automated equipment at an estimated cost of $22,500 was proposed (method D). This method would produce the panel from coil stock instead of sheet and would require only three operations (blank and pierce; draw; and shimmy trim), for a total production time of 0.48 min per piece. The proposed equipment would include a coil-stock reel, a combination roll feed and straightener, a compound blank-and-pierce die with an unloader, and a shimmy trim die. Using coil stock reduced the material cost to 99¢ per piece.

Progressive dies are often used to reduce costs in high-speed production of large quantities of formed parts. The smaller number of operations can reduce labor costs for handling and result in a net savings, in spite of high tooling costs.

The following three examples describe specific applications of progressive-die tooling.

Example 560. Use of a Progressive Die That Eliminated the Need for Expensive Perforated Stock (Fig. 57)

For minimum tooling cost at an initial annual production quantity of 100,000 pieces, a top plate for a gas-mask cartridge (Fig. 57) was produced from perforated coil stock. The part was blanked, drawn and formed in a compound die. When production requirements reached 750,000 pieces per year, a progressive die was purchased at a cost of $1000, and was used to pierce, form and blank the part from unperforated coil stock. The change in method not only lowered costs appreciably but, by piercing only the needed 135 holes in the plate (Fig. 57), also eliminated the jagged edges that had been obtained with perforated stock, and thereby improved the handling characteristics of the plate.

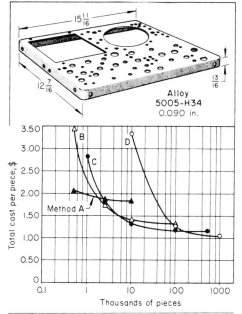

Alloy 5005-H34 0.090 in.

Method A — 500 Pieces per Year

Number of operations 8
Setup time ....3.1 hr
Production time per piece ....0.125 hr
Tooling cost $40
Setup cost, total(a) $74.40
Material cost per piece $1.07
Production cost per piece(b) $0.75

Method B — 2500 Pieces per Year

Number of operations 10
Setup time ....3.1 hr
Production time per piece ....0.040 hr
Tooling cost $985
Setup cost, total(a) $74.40
Material cost per piece $1.07
Production cost per piece(b) $0.24

Method C — 10,000 to 100,000 Pieces per Year

Number of operations 4
Setup time ....1.5 hr
Production time per piece ....0.016 hr
Tooling cost $1600
Setup cost, total(a) $36
Material cost per piece $1.07
Production cost per piece(b) $0.096

Method D — 1 Million Pieces per Year (Est)

Number of operations 3
Setup time ....9.5 hr
Production time per piece ....0.008 hr
Tooling cost $22,500
Setup cost, total(a) $228
Material cost per piece $0.99
Production cost per piece(b) $0.048

(a) Four setups per run of any quantity, at $6 per hour. (b) At $6 per hour.

Fig. 56. Effect of quantity on cost of a drawn and pierced panel produced by four different methods (Example 559)

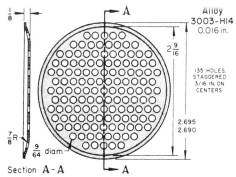

Alloy 3003-H14 0.016 in.

135 HOLES, STAGGERED 3/16 IN. ON CENTERS

Section A-A

When production was low, perforated stock saved on tooling costs, but extra holes caused rough edges on the blank, making handling difficult.

Fig. 57. Plate for a gas-mask cartridge that was produced from unperforated coil stock in a progressive die (Example 560)

Example 561. Change to the Use of a Fully Progressive Die for High-Volume Production (Fig. 58)

When the mine-lamp part shown in Fig. 58 was produced in annual quantities of about 5000 pieces, only the initial forming operations were done in a progressive die. Because it was difficult to form the short leg to the 0.068-in. and the 0.132-in. dimensions within tolerances, that leg was initially blanked oversize. Additional dies were used for trimming the leg, forming the hook, and sizing the hook, in three separate operations after initial forming in the progressive die.

When production requirements increased to 50,000 pieces per year, the three separate die operations resulted in high labor costs, tied up presses needed for other work, and led to safety problems. For production in this annual quantity, a progressive die was developed to produce a completely formed part. The 0.068-in. leg was blanked to size, the first forming die was modified, and a second forming operation was developed to produce the 0.132-in. dimension directly. With the use of the progressive die for all operations, the over-all cost per piece was reduced, and the production and safety problems were eliminated.

Example 562. Cost of a Zipper Component Produced in Various Quantities in Hand-Fed Dies vs a Progressive Die (Fig. 59)

Figure 59 shows a zipper component and plots the cost per thousand pieces for producing it in various quantities in simple hand-fed dies and in a progressive die. The hand-fed dies were used for temporary production, until a progressive die could be designed, constructed and put into service for an annual production of 20 to 25 million of these components. As shown by the curves for the two methods in Fig. 59, the permanent tooling was economically justified for a quantity of about 260,000 pieces, which was only two to three days' output for the progressive die.

The temporary tooling consisted of three separate dies (for blanking and cutoff; forming; and embossing) and a ½-ton press. Total cost was $1000, and maximum capacity was 200 pieces per hour. The permanent tooling — the progressive die (for blanking; forming and embossing; and cutoff) and a 1½-ton roll-feed press — was developed and constructed at a total cost of $12,000, and was rated at 13,200 pieces per hour. Labor cost per thousand pieces was reduced from $42 to 13¢ when the progressive die was used.

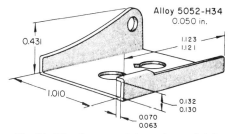

Alloy 5052-H34 0.050 in.

Fig. 58. Mine-lamp part formed completely in a progressive die (Example 561)

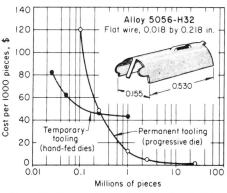

Alloy 5056-H32 Flat wire, 0.018 by 0.218 in.

Temporary tooling (hand-fed dies)

Permanent tooling (progressive die)

Fig. 59. Comparison of costs for mass-producing a zipper component with temporary and permanent tooling (Example 562)

Bending of Bars and Tubing

Aluminum alloy bars and tubing are bent with tools similar to those used for low-carbon steel bars and tubing (see the articles on Bending of Bars, page 305, and Bending of Tubing, page 308, in this volume). Most aluminum bars and tubing are bent in the annealed temper. Heat treated alloys can be bent, by using more bending force.

Tools should be polished to prevent marring the surface of the workpiece.

Lubrication is more critical in bending aluminum than for similar bends in steel. Aluminum is more likely to gall, especially when annealed. Mineral oil, with additives (see Table 1) to improve lubricity, is used.

Examples. Techniques and results in bending of aluminum alloy tubing are described in the next four examples.

Example 563. Application of Lubricants in Bending Alloy 6061-O Tubing (Fig. 60)

Fractures in the outer wall caused a 50% scrap rate when bending aluminum alloy 6061-O tubing with a 2-in. OD and 0.035-in. wall thickness. The tube was bent 90° on a 2½-in. centerline radius (Fig. 60). No wrinkles were allowed along the inner radius, and flattening could not exceed 10% in the bend area.

The piece had been bent in a rotary bender using a three-ball mandrel. Attempts to eliminate fracturing by reducing the force on the pressure die caused wrinkles.

The number of balls in the mandrel was reduced from three to two, and the mandrel and inside of the tube were thickly coated with a drawing compound. A very thin film of light mineral oil with a proprietary additive to improve lubricity was applied to the wiper die. With these precautions, the pieces could be bent without tearing, provided that (a) tooling was accurate and free of wear, (b) the form block was carefully centered to turn concentric with the machine, and (c) pressure actuating the pressure die was kept within 25 psi of that specified. (A reduction of 25 psi was sufficient to cause wrinkles; an excess of 25 psi caused fracture.)

Example 564. Bends of 90° in Alloy 6061-O and 6061-T6 Tubing

Bends of 90° were made in tubing of alloys 6061-O and 6061-T6 using a rotary bender and a ball mandrel. The tubing had a ½-in. OD and a 0.065-in. wall thickness. The bends were

made to a 1.25-in. centerline radius, which was the smallest radius practical for the 6061-T6 tubing. The 6061-O tubing could have been bent to a radius as small as ½ in.

The 6061-O tubing took 25 lb-ft of torque to bend, and thinned 25%. The 6061-T6 tubing needed 40 lb-ft of torque, but the outer wall thinned only 20%.

Example 565. Bends of 90° in Three Different Aluminum Alloys

Tubing made of aluminum alloys 6061-O, 3003-O and 5052-O was bent 90° to a 1-in. centerline radius using a rotary bender with a ball mandrel. The tubing had a ½-in. OD and a wall thickness of 0.065 in. In the bend area, the tubing was slightly flattened to an oval with a 5% difference in diameters.

The important differences in bending of the three alloys were the bending torque and the amount of wall thinning. The 6061-O tube bent with 30 lb-ft of torque, and the outer

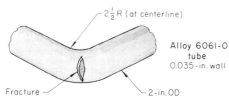

Fig. 60. Bend in aluminum tubing that required the use of a lubricant on both inside and outside surfaces to prevent fracture (Example 563)

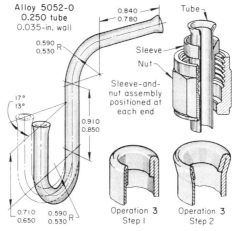

Fig. 61. Tubing bent to close dimensional and angular tolerances (Example 566)

wall thinned 30%. The two other alloys bent with 20 lb-ft of torque, but the outer walls thinned 55%.

Dimensions can be held to ±0.030 in., and angles to ±2°, as in this example:

Example 566. Bending Aluminum Tubing to Close Tolerances (Fig. 61)

The tube for an aerospace assembly shown in Fig. 61 was made of alloy 5052-O and had a 0.250-in. OD and 0.035-in. wall thickness. Fifty tubes were bent to a dimensional tolerance of ±0.030 in. and angular tolerances of ±2°. The length of tubing was determined by trial. Operations were as follows:

1 Cut tubing to length with a saw.
2 Deburr ends in a deburring machine.
3 Double flare one end.
4 Anodize.
5 Slide nut and sleeve on tube, to flared end.
6 Set up indexing bender; make trial bends.
7 Make all bends.
8 Slide second nut and sleeve onto tube, and double flare other end.

Production time for the 50 pieces was 4 hr 50 min for all operations except anodizing.

Straightening of Bars

Aluminum bars are straightened by the methods described in the article "Straightening of Bars, Shapes and Long Parts", which begins on page 322.

Stretching is used extensively as a mechanical method for stress relieving and to correct major contour deviations in rolled and extruded parts. The residual stress in a quenched part is reduced when it is stretched beyond the yield strength of the metal. The maximum rate of stress relief is obtained in the first 0.5% of permanent set. No net stress relief occurs after approximately 2% permanent set.

Aluminum alloys are normally stretched after solution heat treatment and before aging. For maximum effectiveness, the part should have a uniform cross section throughout the length and uniform mechanical properties throughout the cross section and along the length, to prevent excessive yielding in localized regions. Cold working subsequent to stretching, such as localized straightening operations, should be avoided, because it reintroduces residual stress.

Forming Aluminum

All methods, both hand and mechanical, commonly used to form other metals are used to form aluminum. The relative formability of each alloy in its various principal tempers is indicated in the "Workability" column of Table 2-1, which starts on page 9.

Lubrication of aluminum during forming depends upon several factors. Important among them are the type of equipment or tooling used and the severity of the forming. A short discussion of lubrication is therefore included with the description of each type of forming.

The verb "form" means to shape or mold into a different shape or in a particular pattern, and thus would include even casting. However, in most metalworking terminology, "forming" is generally understood to mean changing the shape by bending and deforming solid metal.

In the case of aluminum this is usually done at room temperature. In metalworking, "forming" includes Bending, Brake Forming, Stretch Forming, Roll Forming, Drawing, Spinning, Shear Forming, Flexible Die Forming and High Velocity Forming.

Other "forming" methods, such as machining, extruding, forging and casting do change the shape of the metal, by metal removal or at elevated temperatures. However, these processes employ different tooling and/or equipment and are discussed in separate chapters.

Aluminum is formed by the producers by rolling, drawing, extruding and forging to create the basic aluminum shapes from which the metalworker in turn makes all types of end products. As a group, the aluminum products fabricated from ingot by the producers are called "mill products."

The principal mill products utilized by the metalworker in forming are sheet, plate, rod, bar, wire and tube. *Sheet* thicknesses range from 0.006 through 0.249 inch; *plate* is 0.250 inch or more. *Rod* is ⅜ inch diameter or greater; *bar* is rectangular, hexagonal or octagonal in cross section, having at least one perpendicular distance between faces of ⅜ inch or greater. Wire is 0.374 inch or less.

Blanking

Blanking is a cutting operation which produces a blank of the proper size and shape for forming the desired product. Blanks for small parts are most often produced by punch-shearing. Sawing, milling, routing, or torch-cutting are generally used to produce large or heavy-gauge blanks.

A clean-cut blank edge is essential for efficient forming and is dependent upon properly sharpened and tempered punch and die and correct punch/die clearance. Incorrect clearance results in secondary or multiple shearing, producing poor edges and undesirably high loads on blanking equipment. Aluminum generally has greater optimum clearances than those recommended for brass and steel. Suggested punch clearances are as follows:

Aluminum Alloy	Amount of Clearance (% of Blank Thickness)
Soft	10
Medium-Strength	12
High-Strength	13

Light-gauge blanks may also be produced economically using steel-rule dies, which mate with an aluminum or steel die plate.

Proper shearing force is determined by multiplying the sectional area to be cut (thickness × perimeter of cut) by the ultimate shear strength of the alloy. Shear strengths for aluminum alloys in various tempers are given in Table 1-3. Standard mechanical punch presses, either roll or sheet-fed, are employed.

Router cutters having high-speed steel or carbide-tipped cutting edges are operated at 20,000 rpm or faster.

When blank quantities are small, guillotine shears are often used to produce straight-edged blanks, and circular shears for large, circular blanks.

Lubrication—Reduction of tool wear and easy stripping of blanks and scrap are achieved by applying machine oil to the work, using the heavier grades for thicker sections. Mixtures of machine oil with mineral spirits, as well as proprietary lubricants also are used successfully.

Bending Sheet and Plate

Light-gauge aluminum is being used increasingly for duct and other sheet metal and is easily bent into simple shapes on the versatile hand-operated *bending brake* found in practically every metalworking shop. This machine also is commonly known by several other names, including *apron* or *leaf brake, bar folder,* or *folding brake.* More complex shapes are formed by bending on press brakes fitted with proper dies and tooling. Cylindrical shells and large-diameter, seamed pipe are bent on 3-roll benders. Heavier, plate gauges are bent on greater-capacity bending and press brakes, and roll benders.

Approximate bend radii for 90-degree cold bends in various thickness of different aluminum alloy sheet and plate at several tempers are given in Table 3-1. These radii are generally greater than those for structural carbon steel; most aluminum products are used in either a strain-hardened or heat-treated condition.

Greater allowances must be made for springback in bending age-hardened or work-hardened aluminum, as compared with carbon steel. Soft alloys of aluminum have comparatively little springback. Where springback is a factor, it is compensated by "overforming" or bending the material beyond the limits actually desired in the final shape. Thick material springs back less than thinner stock in a given alloy and temper.

The proper amount of overforming is generally determined by trial, then controlled by the metal-worker in hand or bending brake operations. In press brake bending, springback is compensated for by die and other tool design, use of adjustable dies or adjustment of brake action.

Press-Brake Forming

Hydraulic and mechanical presses are used to form aluminum and other metals into complex shapes. Precisely shaped mating dies of hardened tool steel, Figure 3-1, are made in suitable lengths to produce shapes in one or more steps or passes through the press, the dies being changed as required.

Practices for brake forming aluminum generally are more like those for forming higher-strength alloy steels than for carbon steels. Yield strengths of cold-worked and heat-treated aluminum alloys approach their ultimate tensile strengths. For example 6061-T6, an aluminum alloy of good strength and suitable for many structural applications, has typical tensile and yield strengths of 45,000 and 40,000 psi, respectively, while structural carbon steel has a yield strength only about one half its tensile strength.

Bends made on press brakes usually are done either by the air-bending or by the bottoming method. In air bending, the punch has an acute angle between 30 and 60°, thus providing enough leeway so that for many bends springback compensation may be made by press adjustments alone.

TABLE 3-1

Approximate Bend Radii[1] for 90-degree Cold Bend in Various Aluminum Alloys of Different Thicknesses and Tempers

Alloy	Temper	RADII FOR VARIOUS THICKNESSES EXPRESSED IN TERMS OF THICKNESS "t"							
		1/64 in.	1/32 in.	1/16 in.	1/8 in.	3/16 in.	1/4 in.	3/8 in.	1/2 in.
1100	0	0	0	0	0	½t	1t	1t	1½t
	H12	0	0	0	½t	1t	1t	1½t	2t
	H14	0	0	0	1t	1t	1½t	2t	2½t
	H16	0	½t	1t	1½t	1½t	2½t	3t	4t
	H18	1t	1t	1½t	2½t	3t	3½t	4t	4½t
2014	0	0	0	0	½t	1t	1t	2½t	4t
	T3	1½t	2½t	3t	4t	5t	5t	6t	7t
	T4	1½t	2½t	3t	4t	5t	5t	6t	7t
	T6	3t	4t	4t	5t	6t	8t	8½t	9½t
2024	0	0	0	0	½t	1t	1t	2½t	4t
	T3	2½t	3t	4t	5t	5t	6t	7t	7½t
	T361	3t	4t	5t	6t	6t	8t	8½t	9½t
	T4	2½t	3t	4t	5t	5t	6t	7t	7½t
	T81	4½t	5½t	6t	7½t	8t	9t	10t	10½t
	T861	5t	6t	7t	8½t	9½t	10t	11½t	11½t
3003	0	0	0	0	0	½t	1t	1t	1½t
	H12	0	0	0	½t	1t	1t	1½t	2t
	H14	0	0	0	1t	1t	1½t	2t	2½t
	H16	½t	1t	1t	1½t	2½t	3t	3½t	4t
	H18	1t	1½t	2t	2½t	3½t	4½t	5½t	6½t
3004	0	0	0	0	½t	1t	1t	1t	1½t
	H32	0	0	½t	1t	1t	1½t	1½t	2t
	H34	0	1t	1t	1½t	1½t	2½t	2½t	3t
	H36	1t	1t	1½t	2½t	3t	3½t	4t	4½t
	H38	1t	1½t	2½t	3t	4t	5t	5½t	6½t
3105	H25	..	½t	½t	..	..	..	..	..
5005	0	0	0	0	0	½t	1t	1t	1½t
	H12	0	0	0	½t	1t	1t	1½t	2t
	H14	0	0	0	1t	1½t	1½t	2t	2½t
	H16	½t	1t	1t	1½t	2½t	3t	3½t	4t
	H18	1t	1½t	2t	2½t	3½t	4½t	5½t	6½t
	H32	0	0	0	½t	1t	1t	1½t	2t
	H34	0	0	0	1t	1½t	1½t	2t	2½t
	H36	½t	1t	1t	1½t	2½t	3t	3½t	4t
	H38	1t	1½t	2t	2½t	3½t	4½t	5½t	6½t

TABLE 3-1 (Concluded)

Approximate Bend Radii[1] for 90-degree Cold Bend in Various Aluminum Alloys of Different Thicknesses and Tempers

Alloy	Temper	RADII FOR VARIOUS THICKNESSES EXPRESSED IN TERMS OF THICKNESS "t"							
		1/64 in.	1/32 in.	1/16 in.	1/8 in.	3/16 in.	1/4 in.	3/8 in.	1/2 in.
5050	0	0	0	0	½t	1t	1t	...	...
	H32	0	0	0	1t	1t	1½t	...	...
	H34	0	0	1t	1½t	1½t	2t	...	...
	H36	1t	1t	1½t	2t	2½t	3t	...	...
	H38	1t	1½t	2½t	3t	4t	5t	...	...
5052	0	0	0	0	½t	1t	1t	1½t	1½t
	H32	0	0	1t	1½t	1½t	1½t	1½t	2t
	H34	0	1t	1½t	2t	2t	2½t	2½t	3t
	H36	1t	1t	1½t	2½t	3t	3½t	4t	4½t
	H38	1t	1½t	2½t	3t	4t	5t	5½t	6½t
5083	0	...	...	½t	1t	1t	1t	1½t	1½t
	H321	...	...	1t	1½t	1½t	1½t	2t	2½t
	H323	...	...	1½t	2t	2½t	3t	...	...
	H343	...	...	1½t	2½t	3t	3½t	...	...
5086	0	0	0	½t	1t	1t	1t	1½t	1½t
	H32	0	½t	1t	1½t	1½t	2t	2½t	3t
	H34	½t	1t	1½t	2t	2½t	3t	3½t	4t
	H36				3t	3½t	4t	4½t	5t
5154	0	0	0	½t	1t	1t	1t	1½t	1½t
	H32	0	½t	1t	1½t	1½t	2t	2½t	3½t
	H34	½t	1t	1½t	2t	2½t	3t	3½t	4t
	H36	1t	1½t	2t	3t	3½t	4t	4½t	5t
	H38	1½t	2½t	3t	4t	5t	5t	6½t	6½t
5252	H25	0	0	1t	2t	...	...	...	...
	H28	1t	1½t	2½t	3t	...	...	...	...
5254	0	0	0	½t	1t	1t	1t	1½t	1½t
	H32	0	½t	1t	1½t	1½t	2t	2½t	3½t
	H34	½t	1t	1½t	2t	2½t	3t	3½t	4t
	H36	1t	1½t	2t	3t	3½t	4t	4½t	5t
	H38	1½t	2½t	3t	4t	5t	5t	6½t	6½t
5454	0	0	½t	1t	1t	1t	1½t	1½t	2t
	H32	½t	½t	1t	2t	2t	2½t	3t	4t
	H34	½t	1t	1½t	2t	2½t	3t	3½t	4t
5456	0	...	...	...	1t	1½t	1½t	2t	2t
	H321	...	...	...	2t	2t	2½t	3t	3½t
	H323	...	...	1½t	2t	2½t	3t	...	...
	H343	...	...	1½t	2½t	3t	3½t	...	...
5457	0	0	0	0	0	½t	1t	1t	1½t
5652	0	0	0	0	½t	1t	1t	1½t	1½t
	H32	0	0	1t	1½t	1½t	1½t	1½t	2t
	H34	0	1t	1½t	2t	2t	2½t	2½t	3t
	H36	1t	1t	1½t	2½t	3t	3½t	4t	4½t
	H38	1t	1½t	2½t	3t	4t	5t	5½t	6½t
5657	H25	0	0	0	1t	...	...	...	...
	H28	1t	1½t	2½t	3t	...	...	...	...
6061	0	0	0	0	1t	1t	1t	1½t	2t
	T4	0	0	1t	1½t	2½t	3t	3½t	4t
	T6	1t	1t	1½t	2½t	3t	3½t	4½t	5t
7072	0	0	0	0	...	...	...	...	...
	H12	0	0	...	...	...	...	...	...
	H14	0	0	...	...	...	...	...	...
	H16	0	½t	...	...	...	...	...	...
	H18	1t	1t	...	...	...	...	...	...
7075	0	0	0	0	1t	1½t	2½t	3½t	4t
	T6	3t	4t	5t	6t	6t	8t	9t	9½t
7079	0	...	...	...	...	...	2½t	3½t	4t
	T6	...	...	...	...	...	8t	9t	9½t
7178	0	0	0	0	1½t	1½t	2½t	3½t	4t
	T6	3t	4t	5t	6t	6t	8t	9t	9½t

[1] The radii listed are the minimum recommended for bending sheets and plates without fracturing in a standard press brake with air bend dies. Other types of bending operations may require larger radii or permit smaller radii. The minimum permissible radii will also vary with the design and condition of the tooling.

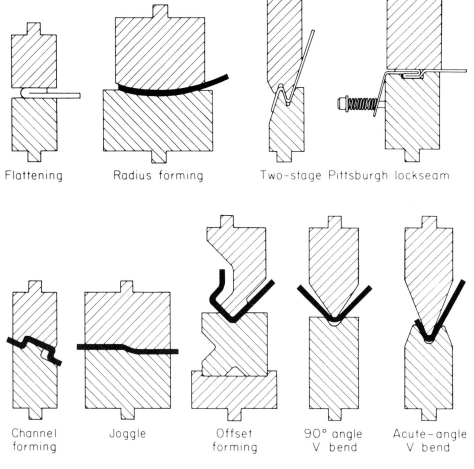

Flattening | Radius forming | Two-stage Pittsburgh lockseam

Channel forming | Joggle | Offset forming | 90° angle V bend | Acute-angle V bend

Fig. 3-1.   Typical mating punches and dies for press-brake work; cross-section of the formed shape is indicated for each operation. Punch and die are as long as required for workpiece and press capacity.

The term "air bending" is derived from the fact that the workpiece spans the gap between the nose of the punch and the edges of the ground die, Figure 3-2. In bottoming, the workpiece is in contact with the complete working surfaces of both punch and die, and accurate angular tolerances can thus be obtained. Bottoming requires three to five times greater pressure than air bending.

Surfaces of dies should be kept smooth and clean when forming aluminum to avoid undesirable marking of the work. For forming highly finished aluminum stock, rubber dies or pads, Figure 3-3, may be used, without lubrication, or with a light dusting of dry lubricant (such as Zn stearate) if desired.

For flattening edges, or producing lockseams, an aluminum sheet alloy of suitable thickness and temper and which is specifically rated as capable of 180° bend over zero radius, should be employed. Appropriate alloys are listed in Table 3-2. The smaller values of bend radius shown in Table 3-1 for the alloys and tempers in Table 3-2 are appropriate for 180° *bends made at right angles to the direction in which the sheet was rolled.*

Trials to determine the smallest practical radius for a given situation are recommended prior to making a production run, due to variations in tools, setup and materials. Periodic inspection of bends during production also is recommended for the same reasons.

Localized heating permits smaller-than-normal minimum bend radii and facilitates bending plate gauges, but temperatures be kept below 400°F to avoid serious loss in mechanical properties. Such practices are not generally recommended for heat-treated aluminum materials.

Roll Forming

A series of cylindrical dies in sets of two—male and female—called "roll sets" are arranged in the roll-bending machine so that sheet or plate is progressively formed to the final shape in a continuous operation. By changing roll sets, a wide variety of aluminum products including angles and channels, house siding, furniture tubing and picture frames, to name a few, may be produced at high production rates of 100 feet per minute and faster. Aluminum as thin as 0.005 inch may be roll-formed. Formed stages and roll-sets for producing a typical section are depicted in Figure 3-4.

Seamed aluminum tubing for a variety of applications is also produced on similar equipment called *tube mills,* which have appropriate roll-sets and welding heads, the latter to close the seam.

TABLE 3-2

Aluminum Alloys, Tempers and Gages Capable of Being Bent 180° Over a Zero Radius

Alloy and temper	$\frac{1}{64}$ in.	$\frac{1}{32}$ in.	$\frac{1}{16}$ in.	$\frac{1}{8}$ in.
1100-O	X	X	X	X
1100-H12	X	X	X	....
1100-H14	X	X	X	....
1100-H16	X	....	....	....
Alclad 2014-O	X	X	X	....
2024-O	X	X	X	....
3003-O	X	X	X	X
3003-H12	X	X	X	....
3003-H14	X	X	X	....
3004-O	X	X	X	X
3004-H32	X	X	....	....
3004 H34	X	....	....	....
5005-O	X	X	X	X
5005-H12	X	X	X	....
5005-H14	X	X	X	....
5005-H32	X	X	X	X
5005-H34	X	X	....	....
5050-O	X	X	X	X
5050-H32	X	X	X	....
5050-H34	X	X	....	....
5052-O	X	X	X	X
5052-H32	X	X	....	....
5052-H34	X	....	....	....
5086-O	X	X	X	X
5154-O	X	X	X	....
5154-H32	X	X	....	....
5657-H25	X	X	X	....
6061-O	X	X	X	....
6061-T4	X	X	....	....
7075-O	X	X	....	....

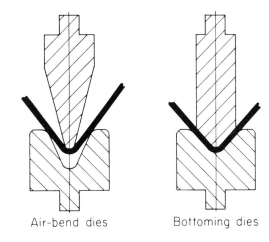

Air-bend dies   Bottoming dies

Fig. 3-2.   Air-bend dies and bottoming dies.

in a single stretch beyond its yield point. Hull panels for boats and for airplane skins are typical stretch-formed products in aluminum. Initial cost of equipment is high, but parts are produced economically because of low die costs and high production.

Depending upon the size of the part, the thickness of the aluminum sheet or plate and other factors, equipment of varying design and capacity is employed. There are three basic types of equipment and/or procedures, as follows:

Stretch-Forming—The sheet is held at each end by the jaws of a hydraulic stretcher, and is wrapped around the appropriate stationary die or form block, then stretched beyond its yield point, either by moving the blocks into the work, Figure 3-5, or by pulling around a stationary block.

Stretch-Wrap Forming—The workpiece is first stressed beyond its yield point, then wrapped around the form block, Figure 3-6.

Stretch-Draw Forming—With the sheet held in tension between two halves of mating dies of shallow configuration, mounted on a single-action press, the shape is a stretch-formed by closing the press, bringing the dies together, Figure 3-7.

Lubrication—Roll pressures are light and for some shapes no lubrication is employed. Where highly finished stock is being run, or where finish is otherwise a factor, non-staining, water-soluble oil is typically employed.

Stretch Forming

Compound curves, accurate dimensions, minimum reduction in material thickness, closely-controlled properties, wrinkle-free shapes and sometimes cost-savings over built-up components, may be achieved

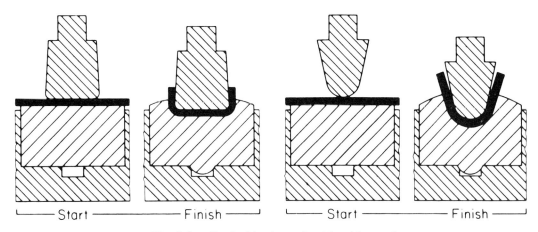

├─ Start ─────── Finish ─┤   ├─ Start ─────── Finish ─┤

Fig. 3-3.   Typical brake tools with rubber pad.

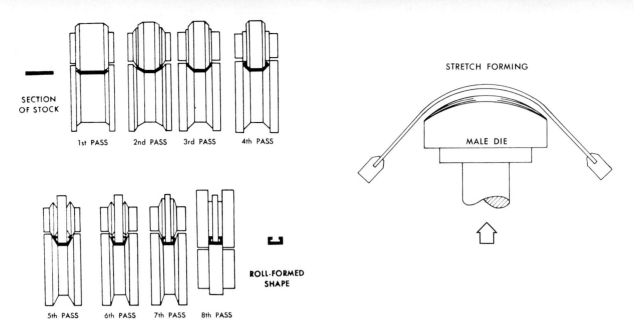

SECTION
OF STOCK

1st PASS   2nd PASS   3rd PASS   4th PASS

5th PASS   6th PASS   7th PASS   8th PASS

ROLL-FORMED
SHAPE

Fig. 3-4.   Evolution of a rolled shape.

STRETCH FORMING

MALE DIE

Fig. 3-5.   One type of stretch forming, in which the work is held stationary and the form-block moves.

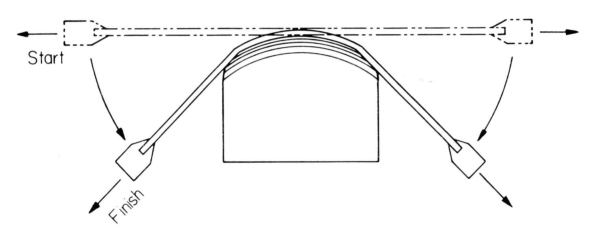

Start

Finish

Fig. 3-6.   Stretch-wrap forming.

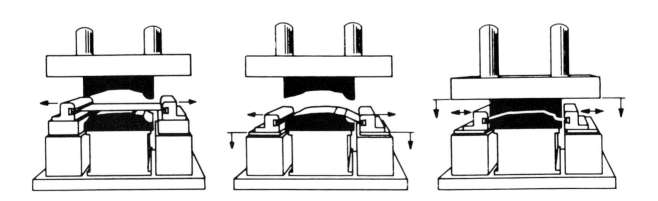

Fig. 3-7.   Stretch-draw forming. Left, gripper jaws grasp ends of blank and apply tensile load; center, blank is given partial form by drawing it down over punch; right, top die closes to complete forming.

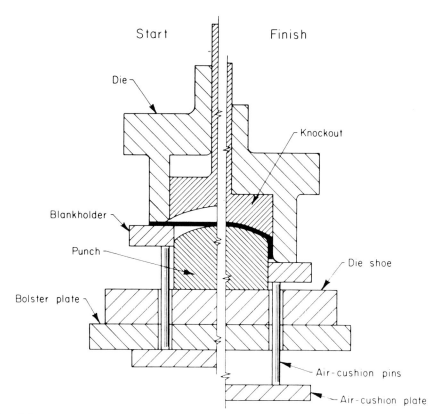

Start   Finish

Die

Knockout

Blankholder

Punch

Die shoe

Bolster plate

Air-cushion pins

Air-cushion plate

Fig. 3-8. Draw tool for single-action press with air cushion mounted under press bed.

Dies are made from cast aluminum, cast zinc, wood, reinforced concrete or plastics and are as light as possible, to make handling practicable. Steel dies are sometimes used for long runs. Forming of non-heat-treatable alloys usually is done in the soft O temper; heat-treatables in the W, O, or T4 tempers.

Lubrication—Light application of mineral oil, water-soluble oil or wax; sheets of Teflon, glass-cloth or rubber also may be used.

Drawing

Seamless, cup-like aluminum shapes are formed without wrinkles or drastically altering original metal thickness, on standard single-action presses for most shallow shells, and on double-action presses for deeper and more difficult draws. Both mechanical or hydraulic power is employed, the latter offering more control, which is particularly advantageous for deep and some complex shapes.

Dies and other tooling suitable for aluminum, Figures 3-8 and 3-9, should be designed for the alloy temper and gauge. Tools, for drawing stainless steel often may be adapted for drawing aluminum, but those for brass or mild steel are generally unsuitable. Power requirements usually are lower for aluminum, particularly in the softer alloys.

Blank size is somewhat critical and should be only enough larger than the finished developed area to permit proper workpiece holding during drawing and final trimming. Increased drawing pressures, possible

metal fracture, and unnecessary material waste, both from over-size blank and part spoilage, are common when blanks are too large. Typical sequence is shown in Figure 3-10.

Blankholder pressure is also critical in drawing aluminum. Insufficient pressure causes the blank to buckle; too high pressure restricts metal flow and shell walls fail as blank is formed. Some parts (if the draw reduction is very small) produced on a single-action press do not require a blankholder, but stock thickness should be increased somewhat if no blankholder is used, or an air, hydraulic, rubber, or spring cushion attachment to the press employed to prevent wrinkling.

Blankholders are essential on double-action presses or any presses where deeper draws are made; pressure must be controlled during drawing to insure smooth shells. Generally, the thinner the stock the narrower the allowable blankholder pressure range.

Optimum drawing speed is always important and should be determined by trial prior to each different run.

Clearances between punch and die vary according to alloy and thickness. Alloys of high strength and foil in the intermediate and hard tempers require the largest clearances, which are 15-20% greater than the blank thickness per side. Softer aluminum alloys need 10-15% clearance. Die sizes for single- and multiple-draw cylindrical aluminum shells are calculated as shown in Table 3-3.

The completed cylindrical shell has a smaller diameter than the blank from which it was made.

TABLE 3-3
Formulas for Calculating Draw-Die Openings

Operation	Size of Die Opening
1st Draw	Punch Diameter + 2.4 × blank thickness
2nd Draw	Punch Diameter + 2.3 × blank thickness
Subsequent Draws	Punch Diameter + 2.3 × blank thickness
Sizing Draw	Punch Diameter + 2.0 × blank thickness

Optimum diameter-reduction per draw must be determined by trial. A starting-point guide for determining proper initial reduction in diameter when drawing cylindrical shells in a widely used alloy is provided by Table 3-4, which gives suggestions for first-draw reductions in alloy 3003-0.

Reductions for first-draws in harder alloys often are 10-15% less than those shown. When the shape cannot be completed in a single draw, reductions in diameter in subsequent draws are made on a decreasing scale to compensate for the increased hardening of the metal.

Table 3-5 shows the effects of hardening (increasing the tensile properties) and optimum reductions in diameters, for deep shells in alloys 3003 and 5052, as successive draws are made. Where draws are particularly deep or complex, annealing may be required after the second or third draw.

Approximate ranges of drawing speeds for typical aluminum products are given in Table 3-6. The lower speeds indicated are for hard alloys and difficult draws.

Lubrication—Oils and compounds used for drawing aluminum must be evenly applied to the blanks to

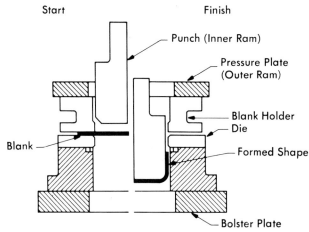

Fig. 3-9. Typical first-operation draw in a double-action press at the start (left) and finish (right) of the stroke.

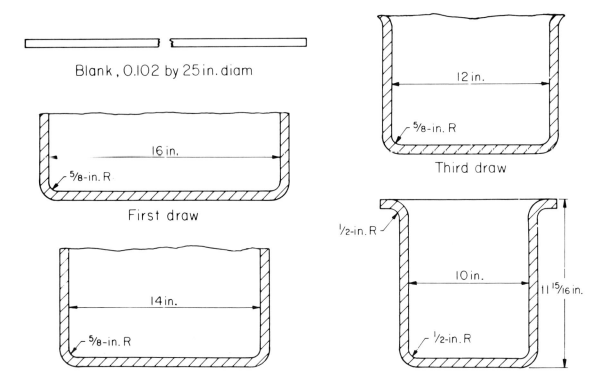

Fig. 3-10. Sequence of drawing operations for cylindrical shells.

TABLE 3-4
First-Reductions in Alloy 3003-0

For Blanks Having a Percent Thickness Ratio: t/D x 100		The Expected Percent Reduction in Diameter is:
Double-action with blankholder	Single-action with blankholder	$\dfrac{D - d\,(1)}{D} \times 100$
0.15	0.25	35
0.25	0.30	40
0.40	0.45	45
0.50	0.55	48

(1) D = diameter of blank before the draw
   d = diameter of shell after the draw

TABLE 3-6
Approximate Ranges of Drawing Speeds for Forming Typical Aluminum Products

Press (Mechanical)	Type of Work	Ram Velocity (feet per minute)
Single-action 5 to 20-ton	Shallow draws	160 to 190
Single-action 35 to 50-ton	Light draws	115 to 125
Single-action 60-ton	Shallow draws	150 to 160
Double-action 100 to 150-ton, single crank	Light draws	25 to 40
Double-action 125-ton, double crank	Large shallow draws	50 to 65
Double-action 160 to 250-ton, single crank	Medium and heavy draws	60 to 80

insure correct blankholder pressure preset by the press operator or setup man. Lubricants generally used are as follows:

Class of Draw	Typical Lubricant
Light up to 15% Reduction	Machine oil, SAE 30 to 40 or proprietary drawing compound.
Medium 15-30%	Graphite suspended in water-soluble or lard oil or proprietary drawing compound.
Severe 30% and up	Gear oil or proprietary drawing compound.

Flexible-Die Forming

Under high pressure, rubber and similar materials act as a hydraulic medium, exerting equal pressure in all directions. In drawing, rubber serves as an effective female die to form an aluminum blank around a punch or form block which has been contoured to the desired pattern. The rubber exerts (transmits) the pressure because it resists deformation; this serves to control local elongation in the aluminum sheet being formed.

Use of rubber pads for the female die greatly reduces die costs, simplifies machine setup, reduces tool wear and eliminates die marks on the finished product. Identical parts, but in different gauges of material,

TABLE 3-5
Effects of Drawing on Tensile Properties and Optimum Reductions in Diameter

Number of draws	Alloy 3003 — 0			
	Tensile strength, psi	Yield strength, psi	Elongation, % in 2 in.	Optimum diameter reduction, %*
0	16,000	6,000	30	
1	19,000	17,000	11	0.40D
2	22,000	21,000	9	0.20D
3	23,500	22,000	8	0.15D
4	24,500	22,500	8	0.15D
	Alloy 5052 — 0			
0	28,000	13,000	25	
1	34,500	32,000	6	0.40D
2	39,500	36,000	6	0.20D
3	43,000	37,000	6	0.15D
4	44,000	38,000	6	0.15D

* Example: Blank has 10 in. diameter; reduction on first draw is 40%, producing a part with 6 in. diameter, second-draw reduction is 20%, leaving a part with 4.8 in. diameter; third-draw reduction is 15%, leaving a 4.1 in. diameter; and fourth-draw reduction is another 15%, leaving a 3.29 in. diameter, as-drawn. Total reduction is approximately 67%.

Source: Metalworking With Aluminum, 2nd Ed., Aluminum Assn., Inc.

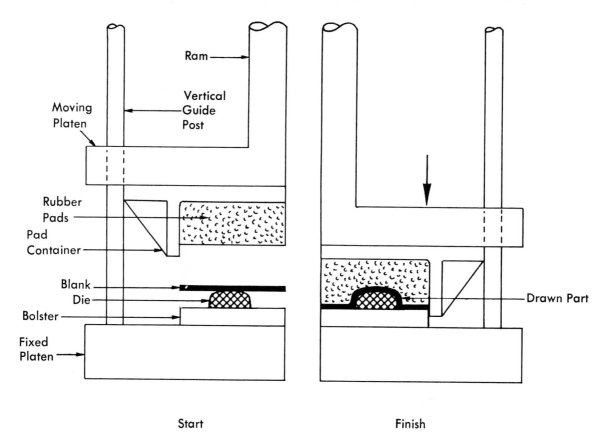

Moving Platen

Ram

Vertical Guide Post

Rubber Pads

Pad Container

Blank

Die

Bolster

Fixed Platen

Drawn Part

Start

Finish

Fig. 3-11. Guerin process forms parts using rubber pad "punch" in large hydraulic presses ranging from 1000 to 10,000 tons capacity. Note: Rubber pad is really the "die" and depth to which any part may be formed is a function of the thickness of the pad and many other variables.

may be made without making tool changes.

Several flexible-die processes are used for forming aluminum. Though operating details vary, these processes can be classified under two broad categories: (1) shallow-draw methods, which rely on the pressure exerted against the rubber pad to hold the blank as well as form the part; e.g., the Guerin and Verson-Wheelon processes; and (2) deeper-draw methods, which have independent blank-holding mechanisms, e.g., the Marform and Hydroform processes.

Guerin—The rubber-pad female die, contained in a steel box open on one face, is mounted on the ram or "punch-head" of a hydraulic press in the Guerin process, Figure 3-11. The male die, or punch, affixed to an appropriate bolster and with suitable blank-centering tooling, is fitted to the moving press platen. When blank is inserted and the press is activated, the ram forces the metal onto the die to complete the drawn part.

Verson-Wheelon—Hydraulic supply and controls and the press-feed table are the only moving parts of this press, which has no hydraulic-piston ram. The feed table holds the mounted male die, upon which the blank is centered, and this whole assembly is "fed" to the press, Figure 3-12.

The table travels on ways and is slid under the rubber working pad in the press head. Above this pad is a neoprene fluid cell which is inflated when the operator opens a valve, forcing pad and blank around

the male die to produce the aluminum shape. Higher side-forming pressures are obtained than those developed in the Guerin process.

Marform—For some draws, depths of three times the shell diameter may be obtained with this flexible die-forming process, Figure 3-13, which employs a distinctive die-holding mechanism that automatically controls the pressure applied. A steel container filled with laminated rubber padding, thicker than the shell to be drawn, is attached, open-face down, to the ram of a hydraulic press.

The fixed punch (male die) is mounted on the press bed, which encloses a second hydraulic cylinder. The blank-holder plate has a mating hole in its center to fit around the punch. This plate is attached to the work-end of a hydraulic piston, with its connecting rods extending through the press bed to the piston below.

The blank is placed in the holder; as the press is closed, the upper ram forces the rubber pad and the blank around the punch while the lower ram compresses the hydraulic fluid in its cylinder to apply the blank-holding pressure, controlled by a suitable valve in the lower cylinder.

Hydroform—The flexible "female die" of this process is a hydraulic forming chamber consisting of a steel dome or inverted funnel, closed at the larger, lower end by a flexible diaphragm, Figure 3-14.

Pressure in this chamber is varied as required to hold the blank when the press is closed, by means of

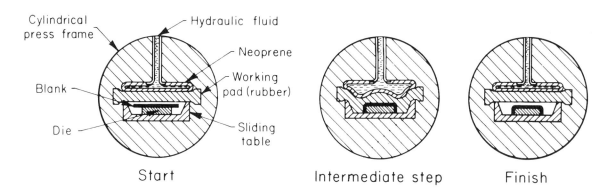

Fig. 3-12. Verson-Wheelon forming process employs hydraulic cell to apply even distribution of forming force from die mounted on sliding table to all blank surfaces.

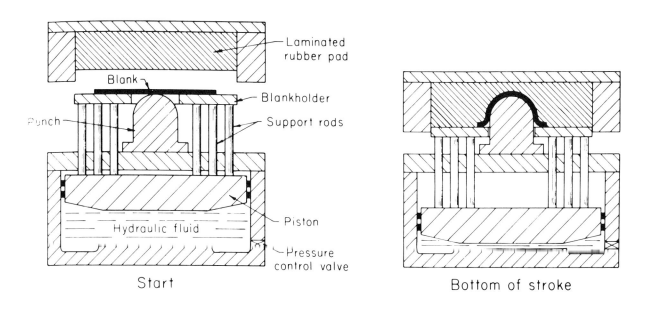

Fig. 3-13. Marform press operating sequence.

Source: Metalworking With Aluminum, 2nd Ed., Aluminum Assn., Inc.

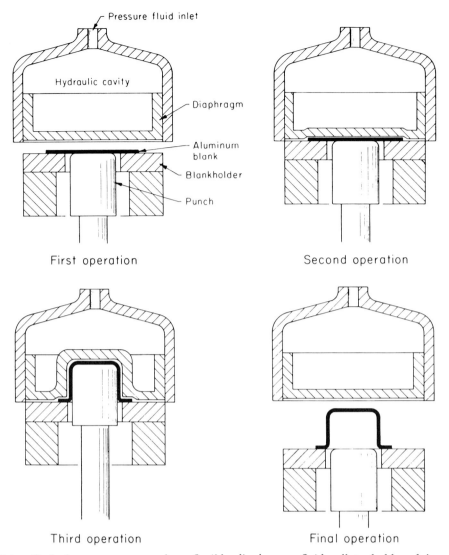

First operation

Second operation

Third operation

Final operation

Fig. 3-14. Hydroform process employs flexible diaphragm, fluid cell to hold and form blank.

fluid inlet and valve. The forming chamber is in turn mounted on the ram of a hydraulic press. The male-die punch is mounted on second hydraulic cylinder below the press bed.

Forming cycle consists of placing the blank on the blankholder, lowering the forming chamber to close the press; applying blankholder pressure in the upper cylinder; applying pressure in the lower cylinder to raise the punch, thus forcing the blank and flexible diaphragm upward into the forming chamber and drawing the part. The press is opened by reversing the process, and the part is removed.

Lubrication—Light lubrication, compatible with rubber, such as talc or graphite, to minimize friction and prolong tool life is usually adequate for either the Guerin or the Verson-Wheelon process. Frequently runs are made with no "drawing" lubrication whatever. Both the Marform and the Hydroform processes generally employ a compounded mineral oil drawing lubricant on underside of blank in areas contacting the steel blankholder. A satisfactory finish inside drawn products is obtained without lubricant, or with only light punch lubrication, by maintaining smooth, highly polished punch and draw ring surfaces.

Coining, Stamping and Embossing

Aluminum sheet the lighter gages of plate are coined, stamped and embossed with standard equipment. Knuckle-joint presses are employed for coining and press-embossing, and single-action mechanical presses for stamping sheet and plate. Light-gauge sheet and foil are frequently roll-embossed between an engraved steel roll which bears the pattern in relief and a smooth, rubber-faced roll. Mating male and female steel rolls also are used for sheet.

Coining and stamping *compress* the aluminum, and embossing *stretches* the metal. Frequently, one of these operations is combined with drawing, through suitable provisions in die design and press cycle.

Embossing of blanks cut from sheet usually is done in a press, using either open or closed dies, Figure 3-15. High pressures and correct tool radii and proper alloys are required. Urethene is often used as a "universal" punch when embossing aluminum sheet in soft tempers.

Coining forms images simultaneously on both sides of a flat blank, Figure 3-16. Usually, top and bottom dies carry different images and enclose the entire blank. Pressures are high to produce sharp images.

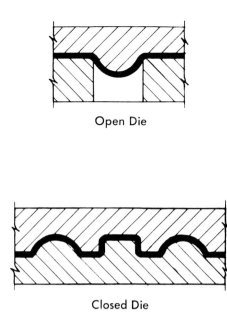

Open Die

Closed Die

Fig. 3-15. The two basic types of embossing dies.

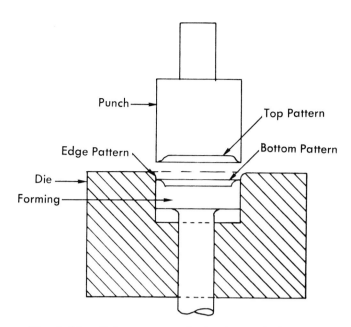

Fig. 3-16. Coining patterns both sides of blank; edge pattern may also be produced at same time.

Semicoining employs a closed die to effect metal flow from one part of the die to another, by combining embossing and coining, Figure 3-17.

Stamping is confined to only one side of the blank or other workpiece and employs a male die or stamp which has the raised pattern cut on its fact in sharp, projecting elements and characters. Similar roller dies also are used for stamping flat surfaces by rolling the die under pressure across the surface, or on cylindrical surfaces using a lathe, rotary swager, or similar equipment. Punch out and piercing often are combined with stamping in a single operation.

Lubricants—Very little and often no lubricant is used in coining and embossing. Where some lubrication is necessary, alcohol or similar volatile liquid is recommended.

Drop-Hammer Forming

Where only a few parts are required, tolerances of $\frac{1}{32}$ to $\frac{1}{16}$ inch are acceptable, and skilled operators are available, drop-hammer forming often makes possible quickest delivery of parts and relatively simple production of double-curvature shapes. Hammers are air operated and simple shapes frequently can be completed in a single blow. The process is confined to relatively shallow shapes. Metal wrinkling is somewhat more difficult to control in aluminum than in steel; aluminum sheet should be approximately 40% heavier than steel stock for a given part.

Supplementary Forming Processes

Supplementary operations used to finish hollow and complex parts initially formed by drawing or other means include expanding, contracting, beading, hole flanging, and ribbing.

Expanding—Either mechanical or hydraulic pressure, or a combination of the two, applied internally to expand or "bulge" shells such as door knobs or pitchers, Figure 3-18. Location and pattern of the expansion is determined by the pattern in an external split die. Pressure is applied to the workpiece by a flexible plug attached to the end of the workpiece or to an inner die. Either is inserted in the shell opening, accessible through the open top of the split die.

Contracting—More often called necking, contracting reduces shell diameter in localized areas, usually at the open end. Shallow grooves are usually produced on a simple groove-rolling machine, while bottle-like necks are made by spinning on a suitable mandrel, the reductions being made in several operations, Figure 3-19. Maximum reduction is about 15% per stage for soft aluminum alloys and about 8% for harder alloys. Angle between original and reduced diameters should not exceed 45° to prevent collapse of shell. Rotary swaging is used to contract heavy walled shells.

Beading—Edge curling or beading is used on sheet and on shells to stiffen openings and to provide smooth edges on finished part. Shell or sheet edges should be free of burrs or uneven cuts. Inside radius of bead varies with alloy, from approximately 1.5 times sheet thickness for soft material to 5 times for harder material. Circular parts are beaded on a lathe or a rotary-head die press, and rectangular parts in presses with suitable dies, Figure 3-20.

Hole Flanging—A flange or small collar may be produced in the wall or end of an aluminum shell, or in a sheet of aluminum, by blanking and edging a hole of desired size with a suitable punch or piercing tool. In a single stroke of the press, a collar height up to

Source: Metalworking With Aluminum, 2nd Ed., Aluminum Assn., Inc.

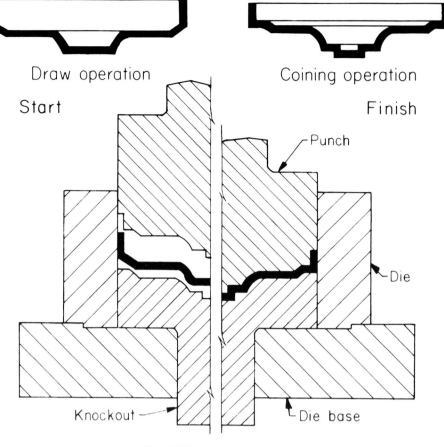

Draw operation   Coining operation

Start   Finish

Punch

Die

Knockout   Die base

Fig. 3-17. Semicoining tool.

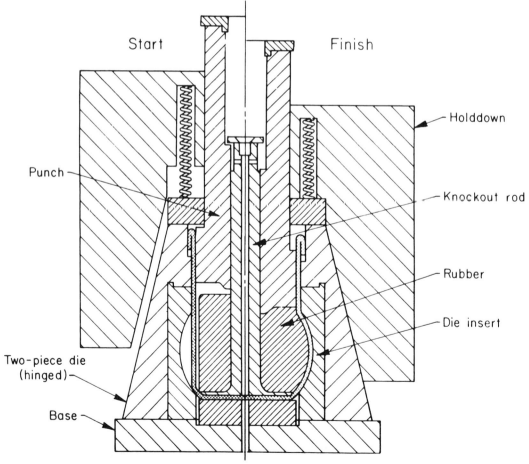

Start   Finish

Holddown

Punch

Knockout rod

Rubber

Die insert

Two-piece die
(hinged)

Base

Fig. 3-18. Bulging a percolator shell with a rubber punch.

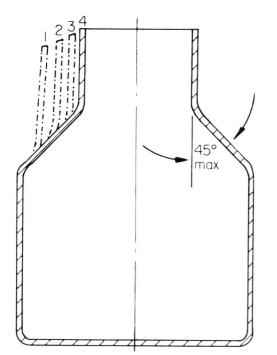

Fig. 3-19. *Typical necked part showing stage of reduction.*

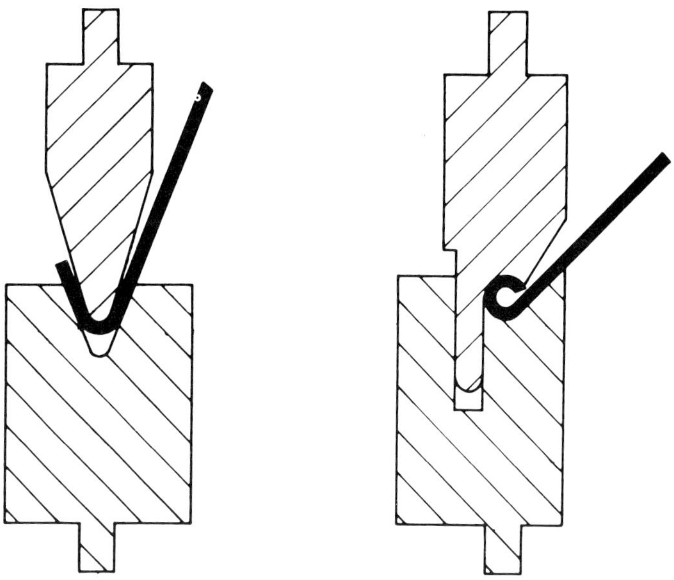

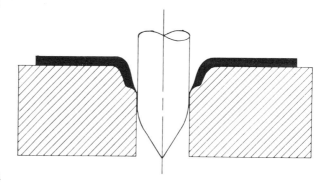

First operation   Second operation

Fig. 3-20. *Press-brake forming of bead in two operations using two sets of dies.*

one-fourth the hole diameter is possible with annealed material, Figure 3-21.

Flanging is done in a series of operations in sheet of intermediate temper, Figure 3-22. Clearance between punch and die should be 3 to 5% of metal thickness. Sheet should be lubricated with suitable aluminum drawing compound for smooth cutting and flanging.

Internal Ribbing—Ribs are formed in sheet material to add stiffness or minimize buckling or "oilcanning." When ribs extend from edge to edge of a sheet, rib forming is done on a press brake, or on corrugated rolls; maximum rib depths depend upon maximum bend radius for sheet alloy and temper.

When the sheet is pressed into the die cavity by a rubber pad under pressure, the resulting rib is termed "internal"; a rib similarly formed over a raised die element is called "external," Figure 3-23. Edge-to-edge external ribs may be formed to greater maximum depth than internal ribs of the same curvature, as external deformation is spread progressively over a larger area.

In contrast, all internal ribs and external ribs which do not extend to the edge of a sheet do not require extra material because they stretch the sheet locally, somewhat reducing the gage in the stretched areas; these "contained" ribs require special design and forming techniques.

Internal ribs are formed on hydraulic presses fitted with a low-cost wood or plastic forming block and rubber pad, or in a punch-and-die mechanical press, or by drop-hammer forming. Use of a pressure pad and a double-acting die helps prevent wrinkling near end of internal ribs formed on a mechanical press. A protective rubber blanket is often used to protect

Fig. 3-21. *Method of producing flange in annealed aluminum in one operation.*

the surface of the metal blank on the first blow, but is removed for final blows to produce the required impression.

Ribs generally are made as deep as possible without tearing the metal, for maximum structural advantage. Ends of contained ribs are blended into sheet surfaces with generous radii to prevent distortion. Material is in annealed (0) temper for deep ribs; for shallow ribs, intermediate tempers of non-heat-treatable alloys and freshly-quenched (W) temper of heat-treatable alloys may be used.

High-Energy-Rate Forming

Processes in this category form aluminum parts at unusually high forming velocities, Figure 3-24. Metal is moved into the die at the rate of several hundred feet per second. Conventional metal forming

Source: Metalworking With Aluminum, 2nd Ed., Aluminum Assn., Inc.

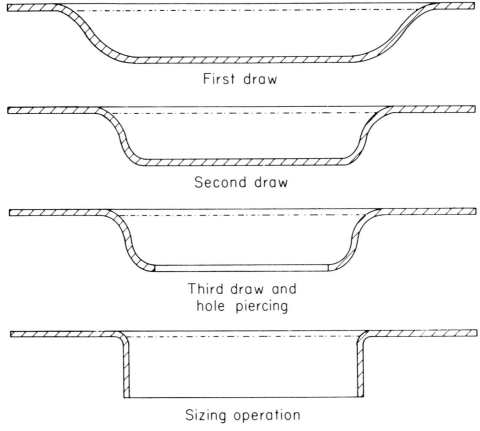

First draw

Second draw

Third draw and
hole piercing

Sizing operation

Fig. 3-22. Sequence of operations for producing fin collars. Material is usually in intermediate temper.

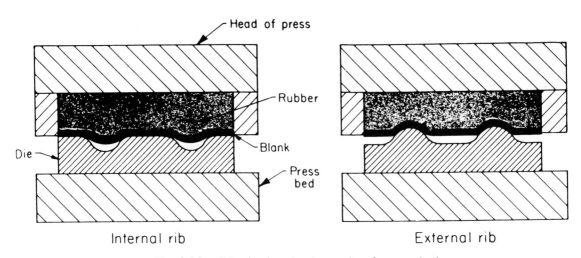

Internal rib

External rib

Fig. 3-23. Dies for forming internal and external ribs.

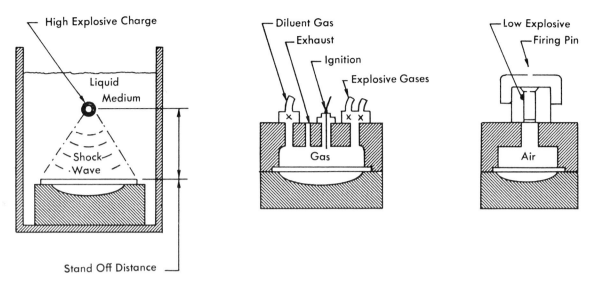

Fig. 3-24. *High-explosive charge, explosive gas, and low-explosive charge forming processes.*

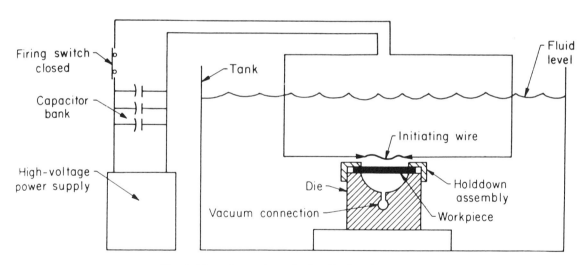

Fig. 3-25. *Open electrohydraulic forming system.*

takes place in the range of less than one foot to about forty feet per second. Large parts may be formed with accuracy and low cost.

The systems using the simplest equipment are those which employ high explosives; variations requiring somewhat more complicated equipment are the explosive gas and low-explosive charge methods. (See Figure 3-24.) Mating dies are not required and parts which are too large for existing press equipment can be produced. Explosive forming is the most-used high-energy-rate process.

High-voltage stored electrical energy supplied by a bank of large capacitors is employed in the *electro-*

hydraulic high-energy-rate forming process. This is somewhat related to explosive forming in that the electrical discharge is contained in a liquid, setting up shock waves which form the blank against the die surfaces. In a typical setup, the blank is clamped over the opening of a concave die. A vacuum is drawn in this closed cavity and the energy discharged into an "initiating wire," Figure 3-25, or into a transducer, Figure 3-26, to produce the shock wave.

In *electrospark* forming, another high-energy process, the stored electrical energy is released from a bank of capacitors into a spark gap to produce a high-intensity shock wave.

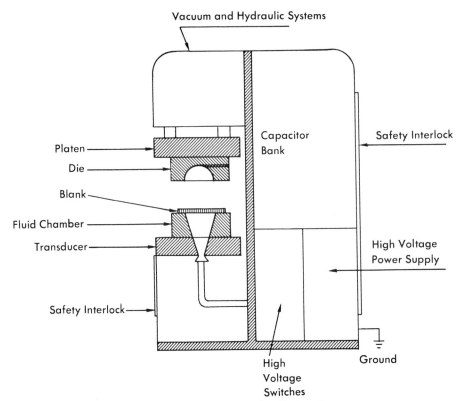

Fig. 3-26.   *Closed electrohydraulic forming system.*

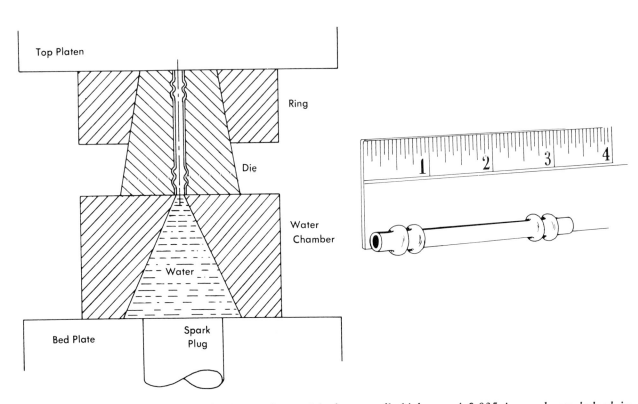

Fig. 3-27.   *The ¼ in.-diameter, aluminum tube on right has a wall thickness of 0.035 in., and was bulged in one operation by utilizing the liquid-punch aspect of the electrohydraulic process. Tooling is shown at left.*

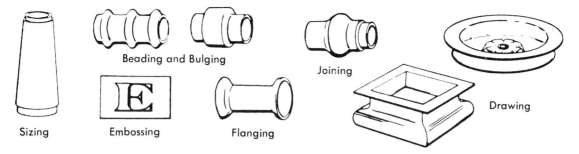

Beading and Bulging

Joining

Sizing

Embossing

Flanging

Drawing

Fig. 3-28. Typical configurations practical for forming by the electrohydraulic process.

The characteristic "liquid punch" feature of the electrohydraulic process makes it possible to form some shapes and materials that are impractical or impossible to form on conventional equipment, Figures 3-27 and 3-28. Most forming is done in a single operation, and only female dies are used. The process is limited in that it cannot form long straight sided shells.

Another process, called pneumatic-mechanical forming, Figure 3-29, employs high-pressure gas to drive a piston-ram at velocities of 200 to 800 inches per second (ips). Mechanical presses have tool velocities from 5 to 20 ips.

The *electromagnetic* process employs capacitor banks to build up a large potential of electrical energy, which is passed through coils, Figure 3-30, producing a high-intensity, pulsed magnetic field. This, in turn, induces a current in the conductive metal workpiece, which is held in a die. The coil is centered on the die and the interaction of the two electrical fields provides the force which deforms the metal into the die cavities.

Other Sheet-Forming Processes

Progressive forming of heat-treated alloys by differential elongation can be accomplished in the *Androform* process, which controls the stretch so that the exact amount required to form a desired contour

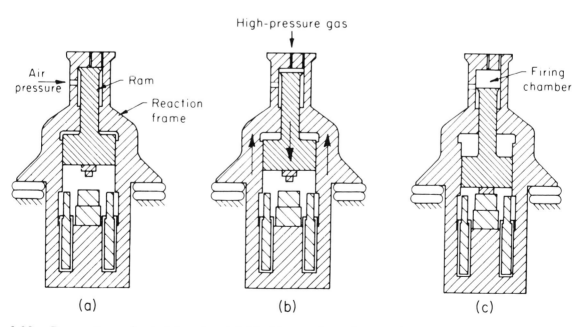

High-pressure gas

Air pressure

Ram

Reaction frame

Firing chamber

(a)

(b)

(c)

Fig. 3-29. Pneumatic-mechanical forming: (a) Machine ready to fire: mechanism in static balance. (b) High-pressure gas applied by sudden opening of top port drives the ram toward the workpiece at high speed. (c) Gas in firing chamber exerts equal and opposite thrust on ram head and reaction frame, so that each body has equal momentum upon impact.

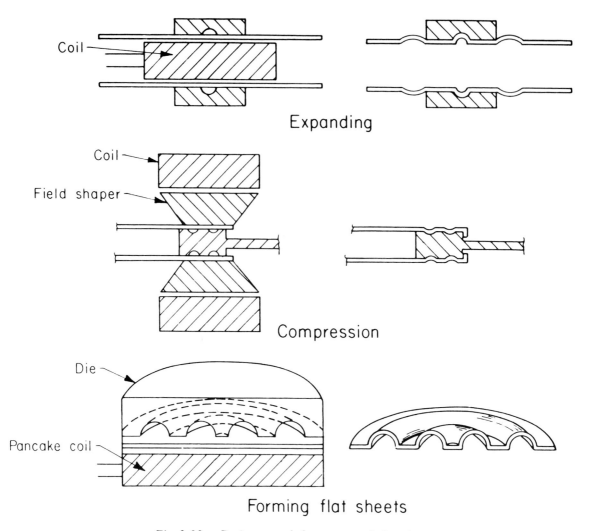

Coil

Expanding

Coil

Field shaper

Compression

Die

Pancake coil

Forming flat sheets

Fig. 3-30. Basic types of electromagnetic forming.

in a specific area is applied. Elongation in this process ranges from 1 to 1.5%. Machine control is accomplished by a hydraulic tracer arrangement; the work is pulled through the machine as shown in Figure 3-31.

Contour forming of heat-treated sheet or plate also is accomplished by *peen forming,* which employs peening guns and sometimes hand hammers. Heavy plate is usually milled in the flat to complex designs which may include integral bosses, ribs, openings, etc., then peen-formed to compound curvature, according to template pattern.

A high degree of operator skill insures excellent quality in relatively large components. The preferential compressive stress produced in the surface metal yields increased fatigue strength of the part and decreases the possibility of stress corrosion in susceptible alloys.

Large pieces of strong aluminum alloys in sheet and plate gauges can be formed on *hydraulic* equipment operating above 2000 psi, generally considered too high a pressure for safe forming with air. The blank is held against the opening of a convex die by the ram of a hydraulic cylinder, to which is attached an appropriate hydraulic head. As oil under pressure is introduced into the head, the blank is deformed into the

die, which is equipped with an air-relief or vacuum-pump port.

Light-gage sheet and foil can be formed on pneumatic equipment, Figure 3-32, similar to that described above for hydraulic forming. Hold-down cylinder and forming head are both operated by air pressure.

Spinning Aluminum

One of the oldest metalworking processes, spinning, continues to be used to produce hundreds of products in various metals. In its simplest form, a hardwood mandrel, having the desired contours of the bowl-shaped product to be made, is fixed in the chuck of a spinning lathe. Frequently, the mandrel and the chuck together are merely called the "chuck."

A flat, circular aluminum blank is held firmly against the end of the mandrel with an appropriate hold-down device. The lathe rotates and the operator exerts pressure on a long, blunt-ended tool made of hardwood or steel, which is in contact with the rotating blank, Figure 3-33. The blank is thus gradually drawn in and forced to take the shape of the mandrel. Reductions in wall thickness range from 20 to 30%. Spinning lathes also are used for trimming, beading, necking and surfacing operations.

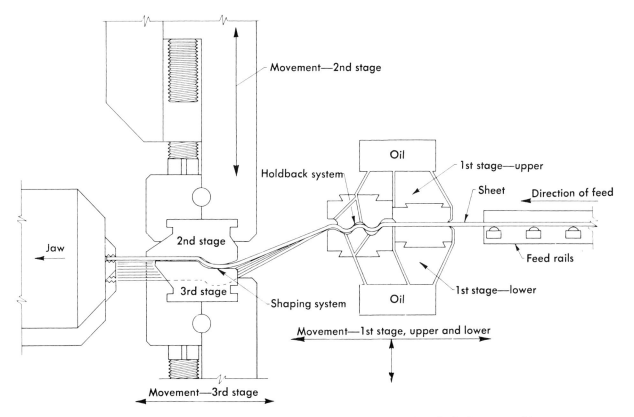

Fig. 3-31. Movement of sheet, and forming element stages in Androform machine.

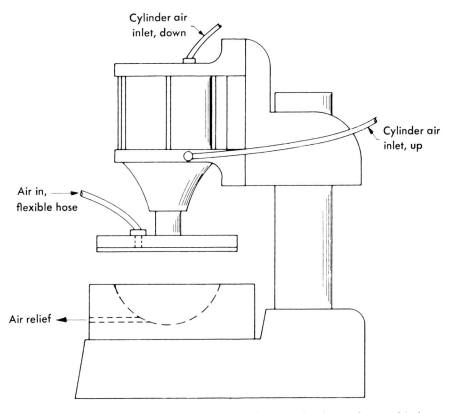

Fig. 3-32. Typical press for air forming light-gage aluminum sheet and foil.

Source: Metalworking With Aluminum, 2nd Ed., Aluminum Assn., Inc.

Equipment costs for spinning are relatively low, but labor costs usually are higher than are those for drawing, due to the essentially manual nature of the spinning process. However, the use of automatic lathes makes long runs economical. Many short runs, in either manual or power spinning, also are economical because of low die costs and short delivery times. Also, very large parts, which cannot be made by other processes, are produced on "spinning" machines which dwarf a man (see Shear Forming).

Spinning characteristics of aluminum are superior to those of most metals. Annealed commercially pure aluminum, alloy 1100, is most easily spun. Where higher yield strength is required, alloy 3003 is frequently used. For even higher strengths, a non-heat-treatable alloy, such as 5052, 5086, or 5456, is employed; these work-harden rapidly and must be annealed at intermittent points in the process, as required, or spun hot (400-500°F).

Aluminum tubes up to 40 ft long and 10 inches diameter may be tapered by spinning with the Dewey process. One end of a tubular blank is held in a rotating chuck which is contracted by forming rolls, mounted on a carriage that moves along the tube, and is controlled by template tracers. The Dewey process is also classified as shear forming.

Shear Forming Aluminum

Shear forming is a type of spinning, and some authorities treat the subjects as a single process. However, several distinctions between the two processes can be made. Blanks for spinning are relatively thin; reduction in thickness during spinning is relatively small. Forming therefore depends largely on the metal's ability to withstand bending and compressive stresses.

In shear forming, on the other hand, more metal is forced to flow over the mandrel. Here usually is a large reduction in wall thickness, as compared with that of the base of the part produced, which generally is little changed from the original blank thickness.

Proprietary shear-forming processes and machines include those trademarked Floturn and Hydrospin. Shear forming is also known as rotary extruding, spin forging and flow forming.

Depending upon alloy, blank thickness, part configuration and other factors, shear forming requires approximately ten times the power needed to make a similar shape, but with less difference between base and wall thickness, than that needed for spinning. Reductions in blank thickness as great as 75% are not uncommon in shear forming.

Basically, shear forming is accomplished by one or two small-diameter rollers which exert force on a workpiece affixed to a rotating mandrel. Two general types of machines are used, one to produce convex or conical bowls from flat, circular blanks, and the other to produce long, straight or tapered tubes from shorter cylindrical blanks by reducing wall thickness.

Variations include producing bowl-shaped parts from pre-drawn cups; cylindrical blanks may be made by extruding, drawing, bending-and-welding in a tube mill, and similar processes.

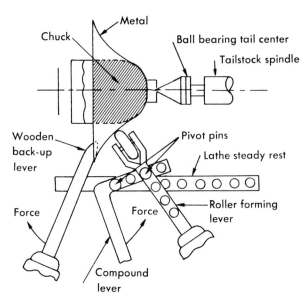

Fig. 3-33. *Manual power-lathe spinning setup, with compound lever arrangement to increase tool pressure operator can exert on workpiece.*

Lubrication—Proprietary spinning compounds, or tallow, beeswax, or petroleum jelly are used as lubricants for spinning light gauges and small aluminum shapes. Heavy-duty spinning compounds or "yellow laundry soap," a hard dense soap, are used for spinning heavier gauges, and for most shear forming.

Drawing Aluminum Wire, Rod and Tube

Drawn aluminum wire, rod and tubular products are produced by pulling rolled or extruded starter stock through a die that both forms and reduces the cross section. Most products are circular but some have angular sections. Rod, tube and a small percentage of some wire products are also produced by extrusion.

To produce wire, lengths of rolled or extruded rod are drawn cold through a series of dies until the desired wire size and shape are obtained. Annealing between draws is necessary when the material becomes too work hardened for further reduction. The as-drawn strength of the finished product in a given alloy is largely determined by extent of reduction after the last anneal. This final product may also be annealed or otherwise heat treated to develop specific properties required for the intended end use.

Aluminum tubing is drawn from lengths of extruded hollow bloom, a comparatively thick-walled tube. The bloom is swaged at one end to form starter stock that will pass easily through the die, and which is secured in the draw-clamp. As with wire, the tubing is drawn through progressively smaller dies until the desired reduction has been achieved. An internal mandrel is used to control inside diameter. Similar interannealing and final heat treating practices as used in wire production are employed.

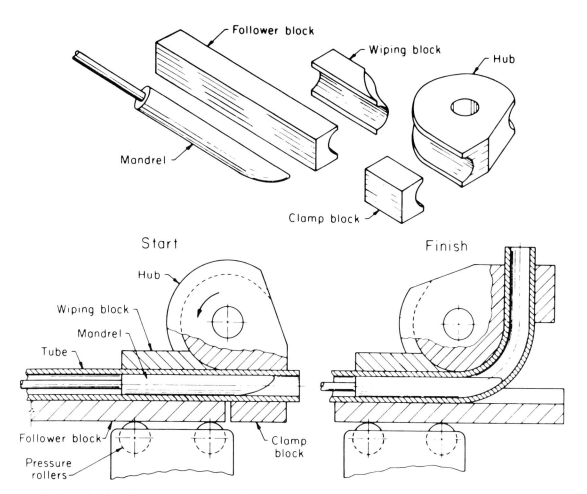

Fig. 3-34. *Tooling components and equipment diagram for draw-bending of aluminum tube.*

Forming Aluminum Tube, Shapes, Wire, Rod and Bar

Pressures for bending aluminum tube, shapes, and bar, as well as rod and wire, generally are lower than for bending similar steel products, and standard bending equipment is used for aluminum. The processes employed are almost always one or a combination of the following: *rotary draw bending; hand or machine compression bending; ram* and *press bending; roll bending;* and *stretch or tension bending.* In addition to these are the supplementary or special forming processes; *rotary swaging; expanding and flaring hollow shapes, cold heading* and *four slide forming*

Nearly any configuration can be produced by "tube"-bending processes, including multi-plane, multi-angle designs, circles, rectangular shapes, return bends, serpentine or other coils, and a wide variety of other designs combining basic bends.

Parts and stock are easy to handle because bending is usually done at room temperature and the aluminum itself is light-weight. Because the aluminum is bent "cold," no allowances in tool design for expansion or contraction are necessary. However, elevated bending can be done where required; heating to 400°F for non-heat-treatable alloys and to 350°F for heat-treatable alloys (providing the latter are not kept at temperature for more than 10 minutes to an hour, depending upon alloy) is sufficient for most forming, and little loss of properties is experienced.

Formability and minimum bend radii depend upon size of tube, alloy, temper and type of equipment. Variations in machine operation and adjustment of technique also can produce different results. Overforming is employed to compensate for springback in room-temperature bending; elevated-temperature bending minimizes springback, as yield strengths are low when aluminum is in the annealed condition.

Rotary Draw Bending

A general-purpose bending method for producing tubular products, draw bending, Figure 3-34, employs a rotary hub against which one end of the tube is clamped. As the hub is rotated, the tube is drawn around it to complete the bend. The free end of the tube is held securely between a wiper block and a follower block, the latter moving forward on a set of pressure rollers.

A suitably-shaped mandrel fastened to a long rod may be inserted in the free end of thin tubing and positioned in the bending area so that the hollow shape is supported in the follower- and clamp-block zones. Segmented mandrels may extend the full length of the bend, but plug and sheep-nose mandrels must be carefully positioned, extending just into the start of the bend, to avoid fracture.

Solid sections and unsymmetrical hollow shapes, either rolled or extruded, can also be formed. Small-

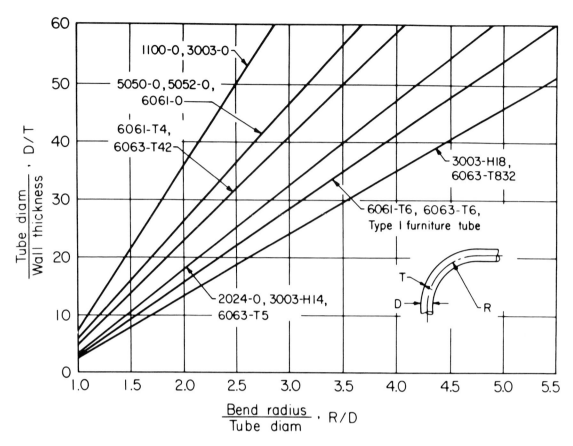

Fig. 3-35. Centerline bend radii relationships for various aluminum alloys, assuming fully-tooled draw-bending machine, under ideal conditions. (Round tube; 90° bends).

radius bends in thin-wall shapes can be made successfully. Various sizes of draw-bending equipment will handle tubular shapes of approximately ⅜ to 16 inches diameter; bends of 0 to 180° can be made in one operation, depending upon the specific combination of factors. Automatic draw-bending machines can produce parts of relatively small cross-section at rates ranging from 400 to 600 bends per hour.

Compound curves and overlapping bends cannot generally be made with this process; bends can be made only in one plane in each separate operation. While compound dies can be made to shorten the distance between bends in a given section, the general rule for minimum distance between bends is 2.5 times the section diameter.

Size and shape of section and ductility of the material determines the minimum centerline bend radius for a specific alloy and temper. Figure 3-35 presents minimum bend radii divided by tube diameter (R/D) plotted against tube diameter divided by its wall thickness (D/T), for several alloys and tempers. Table 3-7 gives similar data and lists specific minimum bend radii in inches. Table 3-8 shows typical radii for 180° cold bends in aluminum alloy wire.

Lubrication—Friction between surfaces of steel forming tools and the natural protective oxide on aluminum

stock creates the need to lubricate both work and tools, to reduce tool wear and help insure retention of original aluminum finished on formed part. Depending upon tool shape, and size and alloy of stock, lubricants commonly used include mineral oil, lard oil, proprietary water-soluble compounds and waxes.

Compression Bending

In this process, the bending form is stationary and the work is bent around it. When compression bending is done by hand, it is called merely *hand bending;* some flattening in tubes results unless a segmented mandrel or a filler material is employed.

Small-diameter tubing can be bent by hand successfully without internal or external support; however, a "hicky," which is a close-fitting flexible sleeve used by plumbers and electricians for bending small pipe and conduit generally is employed for such bending. For hand-bending larger tubes, the work is formed between two smooth wooden blocks fixed in proper position to a horizontal surface, the bend being completed in small increments.

Alternately, a hand-held bearing block or "shoe" is employed to force the work around a fixed, grooved bending block, made of wood or metal.

TABLE 3-7

Bend Radii for Round Seamless Tube, Assuming Fully Tooled Draw-Bending Machine and Ideal Bending Conditions[a]

Tube size, in.	Wall thickness, in.	Approximate minimum centerline bend radii, in. Alloy					
		1100-O 3003-O	5050-O 5052-O 6061-O	6061-T4 6063-T42	2024-O 3003-H14 6063-T5	6061-T6 6063-T6	3003-H18 6063-T832
3/8 OD	0.028	1/2	9/16	9/16	5/8	11/16	3/4
	0.035	7/16	1/2	1/2	9/16	5/8	11/16
	0.049	3/8	7/16	7/16	1/2	9/16	5/8
1/2 OD	0.035	5/8	3/4	13/16	7/8	1	1-1/8
	0.049	9/16	5/8	11/16	3/4	13/16	7/8
	0.065	1/2	9/16	5/8	11/16	3/4	13/16
3/4 OD	0.049	1	1-1/8	1-3/16	1-3/8	1-1/2	1-5/8
	0.065	7/8	1	1-1/8	1-1/4	1-3/8	1-1/2
	0.083	13/16	7/8	15/16	1-1/16	1-1/8	1-1/4
1 OD	0.049	1-1/2	1-3/4	1-7/8	2-3/16	2-3/8	2-3/4
	0.065	1-5/16	1-1/2	1-5/8	1-7/8	2	2-1/2
	0.083	1-3/16	1-3/8	1-1/2	1-5/8	1-3/4	2-1/4
	0.109	1-1/8	1-3/16	1-1/4	1-3/8	1-1/2	2
1-1/8 OD	0.049	1-3/4	2-1/8	2-3/8	2-5/8	2-7/8	3-3/8
	0.065	1-5/8	1-7/8	2	2-1/4	2-3/8	2-7/8
	0.083	1-3/8	1-5/8	1-3/4	2	2-1/8	2-1/2
	0.109	1-1/4	1-7/16	1-1/2	1-3/4	1-7/8	2-1/4
1-1/4 OD	0.049	2-1/8	2-1/2	2-3/4	3-1/8	3-1/2	4
	0.065	1-7/8	2-1/8	2-1/4	2-1/2	2-7/8	3-1/4
	0.083	1-5/8	1-7/8	2	2-1/4	2-1/2	2-3/4
	0.109	1-1/2	1-5/8	1-3/4	2	2-1/4	2-1/2
1-1/2 OD	0.065	2-3/8	2-7/8	3-1/8	3-1/2	3-7/8	4-3/8
	0.083	2-1/8	2-1/2	2-3/4	3	3-3/8	3-3/4
	0.109	1-7/8	2-1/8	2-3/8	2-5/8	2-7/8	3-1/4
	0.120	1-7/8	2-1/8	2-1/4	2-1/2	2-3/4	3
1-3/4 OD	0.065	3	3-1/2	4	4-1/2	5	5-3/4
	0.083	2-5/8	3	3-1/2	3-7/8	4-1/4	4-3/4
	0.109	2-3/8	2-3/4	3	3-3/8	3-3/4	4-1/4
	0.120	2-1/4	2-5/8	2-7/8	3-1/8	3-1/2	4
2 OD	0.065	3-3/4	4-1/2	5	5-3/4	6-1/2	7-1/4
	0.083	3-1/4	3-7/8	4-1/4	4-7/8	5-3/8	6
	0.109	2-7/8	3-3/8	3-5/8	4-1/8	4-1/2	5
	0.120	2-3/4	3-1/8	3-3/8	3-7/8	4-1/4	4-3/4
2-1/2 OD	0.083	4-1/2	5-1/2	6-1/4	7-1/4	8	8-7/8
	0.109	4	4-3/4	5-1/4	6	6-1/2	7-3/8
	0.120	3-3/4	4-1/2	4-3/4	5-1/2	6	6-3/4
3 OD	0.083	6	7-1/2	8-3/4	9-3/4	11	12-1/2
	0.109	5-1/4	6-1/2	7-1/4	8-1/4	9	10-1/4
	0.120	5	6	6-1/2	7-1/2	8-1/4	9-1/4

(a) "Fully tooled" means having all the tool components shown in Fig. 3-34. "Ideal bending conditions" involves proper design and alignment of tools, smooth machine operation, and proper lubrication.

TABLE 3-8

Typical Inside Radii for 180° Cold Bends in Aluminum Alloy Wire

Alloy and temper	Approximate diameter, in.			
	0.062 (1/16)	0.125 (1/8)	0.250 (1/4)	0.500 (1/2)
1100-O	....	....	1/4 to 1/2D	1/4 to 1/2D
1350-H19(1)	0 to 1D	0 to 1D	0 to 1D	0 to 1D
2011-T3	....	....	1/2D	1/2D
2011-T8	....	....	1/2 to 1D	1 to 1-1/2D
2017-T4, T451	....	....	1/2 to 1D	1 to 1-1/2D
2024-T4	....	....	1D	....
2024-T351	....	....	....	2 to 2-½D
5050-H38	0 to 1D	0 to 1D	1 to 2D	2 to 4D
5052-H38	0 to 1D	1 to 2D	2 to 4D	3 to 5D
5056-H34	0 to 1D	1 to 2D	2 to 4D	3 to 5D
5056-H38	0 to 1D	1 to 2D	2 to 4D	4 to 6 D
6061-T6, T651	0 to 1D	0 to 1D	1/2 to 1-1/2D	1/2 to 1-1/2D
6061-T81	0 to 1D	0 to 1D	1 to 2D	2 to 4D
6061-T91	0 to 1D	1 to 2D	2 to 4D	4 to 6 D
6061-T913	0 to 1D	1 to 2D	2 to 4D	4 to 6 D
6262-T9	....	....	1 to 1 1/2D	1 to 1-1/2D
7075-T6, T651	1/2 to 1-1/2D	1 to 2D	1-1/2 to 2-1/2D	2 to 3D

(1) Formerly designated EC

Source: Metalworking With Aluminum, 2nd Ed., Aluminum Assn., Inc.

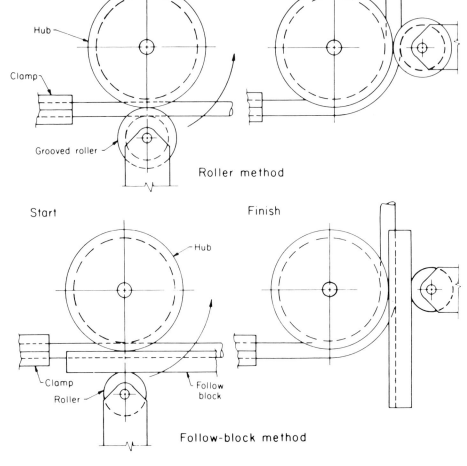

Start   Finish

Hub

Clamp

Grooved roller

Roller method

Start   Finish

Hub

Clamp

Roller   Follow
                          block

Follow-block method

Fig. 3-36.   Roller and follow-block method setups for machine compression bending.

In machine compression bending, the workpiece is forced around the stationary bending form by a grooved roller, or by a follow block which is pushed against the work by a smooth roller, Figure 3-36. The straight end of the workpiece is held by a clamp. Internal support for tubing is sometimes used where single bends are involved, but generally is impractical for multiple bends. This process is used for medium- to heavy-wall tubing and both hollow and solid shapes. Both smooth and "furniture-tubing" crushed bends can be made, the latter employing an added tool to make the inside wall collapse in a controlled manner.

All aluminum alloys can be bent by this process. If material is not soft or annealed, overforming is required to compensate for springback. Rule-of-thumb practical bend radius (R) for tubing with diameter-to-wall thickness ratios of 16 or less is $R = 4 \times$ tube diameter. Light lubrication is advisable.

Ram and Press Bending

Heavy-wall aluminum tubing, and rod and bar can be bent on the job site with portable hydraulic ram benders, Figure 3-37. Both portable models and larger stationary units are also used in the shop. The ram forces a curved, grooved "punch" against the

workpiece, which is supported at two fixed points by grooved dies.

The process is generally used for small quantities of large-radius bends. Portable tools are made in various sizes, the largest of which can bend 5-in. dia. pipe. Heavier shop equipment handles pipe up up to 15-in. dia. Minimum radius for ram bending is about four times diameter.

Press bending is a high-production modification of ram bending. Superior control is achieved through the use of wing dies, Figure 3-38, permitting several bends to be made in different planes of the same length of stock. Bend angle in press bending, as in raw bending, is controlled by the length of the stroke. Conventional mechanical or hydraulic presses are sometimes used, but presses specifically designed for bending are more versatile.

Most applications for press bending employ alloys 3003, 6061 and 6063 tube in various tempers, but all aluminum alloys may be bent by this process. As no internal support normally is employed, tube wall thickness and/or alloy temper must be suitable to avoid excessive flattening or buckling. Ratio of tube diameter to wall thickness should not be greater than 15 for most minimum-radius bending. Light lubricants are recommended.

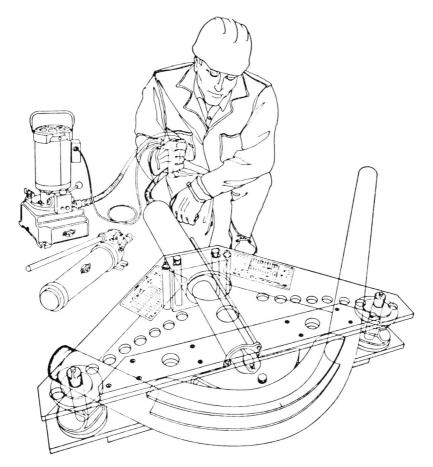

Fig. 3-37. Ram bender that can be operated either with portable or shop hydraulic pumps or by hand.

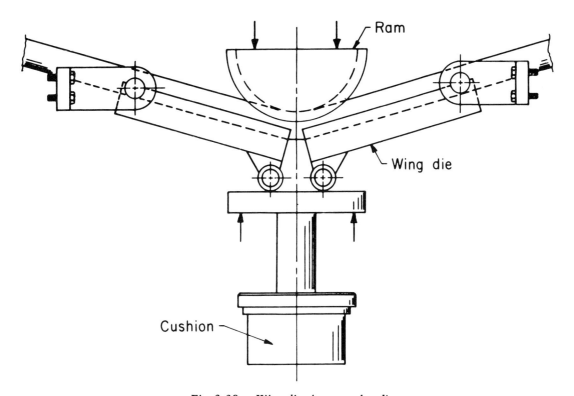

Fig. 3-38. Wing dies for press bending.

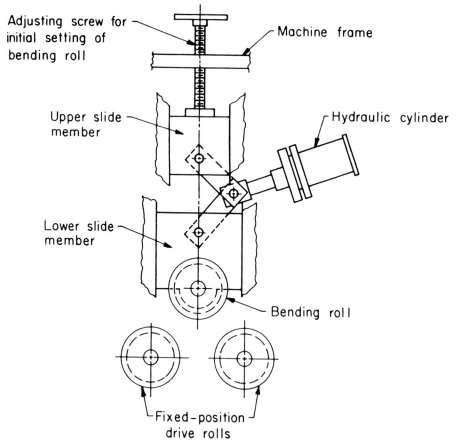

Fig. 3-39. Typical vertical-pyramid roll bending machine with hydraulic toggle control.

Roll Bending

Opposing compressive forces applied to the workpiece as it passes through a set of grooved forming rolls produce circular or spiral configurations in tube, rod, bar, and shapes. The stock is fed into drive rolls, which carry it to the forming rolls. The latter can be adjusted for various bend radii, and controlled so that bend are produced intermittently along a specified length, as in producing such items as round-cornered rectangular frames. Different sets of rolls are required for different cross sections of stock.

Two types of roll benders are in general use: (1) The *vertical-pyramid* machine, Figure 3-39, has a single moveable forming roll at the top and two fixed-position drive rolls at the bottom; all three rolls are generally driven. (2) The *pinch roll bender,* Figure 3-40, has two drive rolls, one of which is moveable, and one fixed. The moveable roll is adjusted to pinch the stock sufficiently to permit the applied power to carry it through the forming rolls, which are adjusted to produce a bend of the desired radius. These forming rolls are not driven.

Thin-wall tubing requires internal support to be roll-bent successfully. Annealed and intermediate

Fig. 3-40.   Finch-type roll bender.

tempers of non-heat-treatable alloys, and as-fabricated or as-quenched tempers of heat-treatable alloys are readily formed by roll bending.

Full-hard and fully heat-treated tempers are not recommended, except for large radii, due largely to excessive springback. Close tolerances are difficult to maintain. Lubricants generally are not employed, due to the positive friction at the drive rolls required in this process.

Stretch or Tension Bending

Compound and relatively small-radii bends can generally be produced in shapes that are difficult or impossible to bend by other methods, by stretch bending, Figure 3-41. As in stretch forming aluminum sheet or plate, the extruded section or similar workpiece to be stretch-bent is gripped at either end by hydraulic jaws.

One or both jaws is moved to wrap the workpiece around the bending form, which may be either stationary or moved into or against the workpiece, rotating through the required arc as the work progresses. In some cases, compressive force, applied through a shoe or roll at the tangent point outside the bend, is employed in conjunction with the tension.

This is one of the most versatile bending processes and both simple and complex bends can be made in one or more planes in a single workpiece. All tooling is designed to fit the contour of the part to be formed.

Lubrication—All forming tool surfaces should be lubricated for successful stretch bending; this includes compression shoe or roller, as well as the bending form. Water-soluble oils are easiest to remove, but medium-viscosity oils, waxes or paraffin are also suitable.

Rotary Swaging

Hollow or solid stock having a symmetrical cross section can be reduced to a predetermined round section by rotary swaging. The work is fed through a hollow spindle, which is slotted at one end to hold the dies and the die backers, Figure 3-42.

The backers contact successive pairs of opposing rolls, which exert the necessary force to cause the dies to strike opposing blows on the work at rates ranging from 1800 per minute for large machines to 4000 per minute for small machines. The work is fed through the swager at rates up to 8 in. per second. Typical products are pen and pencil bodies, ski poles, golf club shafts, umbrella poles, furniture components and refrigerator parts.

All aluminum wrought alloys can be swaged; annealed temper is preferred, except for light-wall tubing, which should be in an intermediate temper to prevent buckling. The freshly-quenched temper is best for swaging heat-treatable alloys. Swaging also can be used for internal threading, or producing multiple shoulders inside tubes; also preforming forging slugs, supplementary forming of deep-drawn shells, and fastening tubular components to a core, as in cable terminals.

Fig. 3-41. Stretch-bending a large extrusion.

Lubrication—Sparing lubrication with kerosene or light waxes is used for hand-fed swaging; machine-fed swaging usually employs more generous lubrication.

Expanding and Flaring Tubes and Hollow Shapes

Hollow shapes of symmetrical cross-section can be expanded or flared with adjustable work rolls in a cylindrical holder, or with cone-shaped punches. Using the correct tool, a portion or the entire length of a part may be *expanded* with uniform increase in internal and external peripheral dimensions, Figures 3-43 and 3-44. A varying increase in the diameter at the end of a tube can be produced by *flaring*, with maximum increase resulting at the open end, Figure 3-45. Expansion is accomplished by elongation of the metal around the circumference, in both processes. In flaring, some of the increase of circumference results in a reduction in length of the part.

Expanding—The two basic processes used to expand hollow sections are *tube rolling* and *tube punch-expanding*, as illustrated. Both of these can be used to expand round tubing, but only the punch method is suitable for non-cylindrical applications. Punches usually are segmented and can expand only their own length in each operation. No external support is used for the enlarged portion of the tube.

Extensive use of tube rolling is made in the fabrication of boilers, condensers and heat exchangers and in the production of bi-metallic tubes. Two different methods of tube rolling are used. The first method employs work rolls which can expand tube walls to only the length of the rolls in each operation; rolls must be contracted, moved forward and re-engaged to expand longer lengths.

When more than one roller length is thus expanded, the process is called "step rolling." The second type of roller head is designed to expand circular tubing continuously and can operate up to lengths of 20 feet.

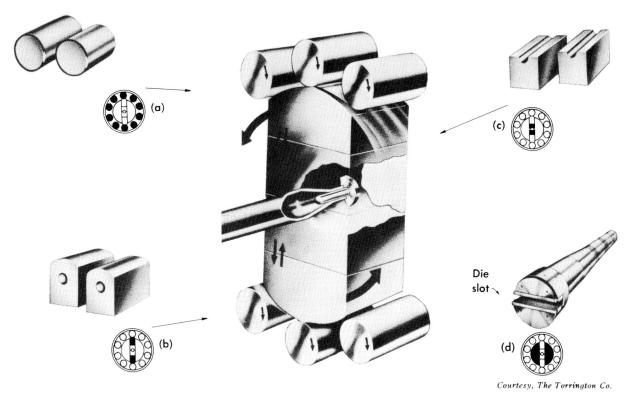

Fig. 3-42. Principal parts of a swaging machine: (a) hardened steel rolls; (b) backers; (c) die; (d) hollow spindle.

Flaring—The flaring punch is used with a split-ring clamping die to expand the tube end to the desired dimensions. Principal application is to provide support and sealing surfaces for tube fittings and other connections.

Alloy, temper, wall-thickness-to-tube diameter ratio and circumferential metallurgical properties are essential factors in the maximum percentage of successful expansion for a given tube. Drawn tubes generally have more desirable properties for expanding than do extruded tubes. Satisfactory expansion of welded tubing depends upon weld quality, bead smoothness, temper and alloy. For *punch-expanding* or *flaring* aluminum tubing, annealed material is recommended; an intermediate temper is best for most *tube-rolling* operations.

Lubrication—Work surfaces of tool and part should be lubricated at all times. Lard/mineral oil or water-soluble extreme-pressure drawing oils should be used where forming is severe; waxes or water-soluble lighter-duty oils are used for moderate forming.

Cold Heading

This process is named for the original and still the primary type of forming accomplished, namely upsetting the end of a wire to form a nail-head or other shape. Today cold heading also produces such complicated items as bolts, screws, rivets, and more complex fasteners, as well as multi-diameter pins and shafts.

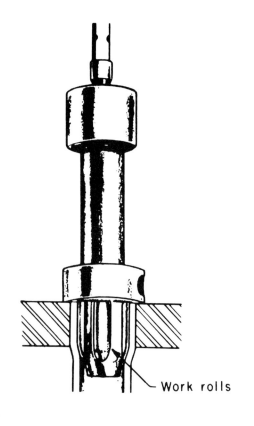

Fig. 3-43. Tube rolling.

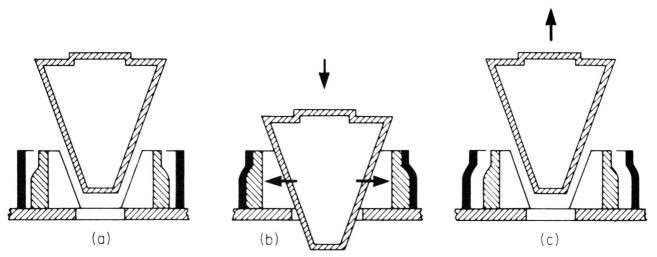

Fig. 3-44. Tube expanding with segmented tools and tapered punch. Tube wall is shown by heavy black line. (a) Part to be expanded is set into position over the outer periphery of the expanding dies. (b) Cone moves downward and exerts radial force on expander jaws; part is expanded. (c) Cone is retracted, collapsing jaws and dies.

Dies are often complex, Figure 3-46, and used singly or in combination, permit a series of upsets on the blank, extrusion of the blank to a smaller size, extrusion of a hole, and bending and trimming of the blank. The three basic operations of the cold heading machine which accomplish the foregoing work are: (1) shearing to cut off the desired length of stock; (2) holding one end of the blank in a die and upsetting the free end to form a head or other shape; and (3) extruding to form a diameter smaller than the original wire size.

Cold-heading machines can form wire as small as 0.020 in. and rod as large as 1.0 in. dia. Both open-die and solid-die cold-heading machines are used to produce aluminum parts. Depending upon size and complexity, production rates range from 50 to 450 pieces per minute.

Some cold-headed products require additional fabricating operations, such as threading or knurling. These often are carried out on hopper-fed rolling machines, rather than removing the metal by machining, to continue the controlled grain flow established during heading, provide additional strength through the additional cold work, and to take advantage of the high production rates attainable.

Aluminum wire alloys generally are well adapted to cold heading. Some, such as 2024-H13, require only 2/3 the pressure necessary for cold-heading annealed low-carbon steel wire. Aluminum wire and rod intended for cold heading should be specified for the purpose when ordered from the supplier to insure proper grain size and orientation, and unblemished surface.

Lubrication—A thin film of light machine oil is adequate for cold-heading many products; proprietary

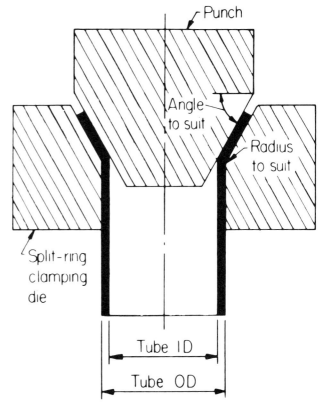

Fig. 3-45. Tube flaring tools.

Source: Metalworking With Aluminum, 2nd Ed., Aluminum Assn., Inc.

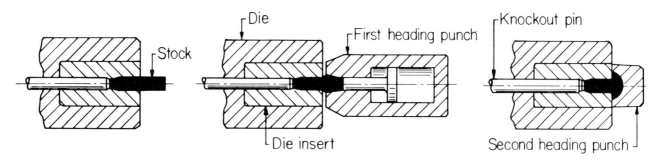

Fig. 3-46. *Dies and tooling for cold heading by double blow, with extrusion.*

waxes or tallow are used for severe forming, such as extrusion. Parts may not be completely formed if lubrication is excessive.

Four-Slide Press Forming

Aluminum wire and strip are formed by compression into noise suppressor rings for automotive alternators, paper clips, wire staples and zipper components on four-slide presses. In either vertical, Figure 3-47, or horizontal presses, four different tools are mounted on slides positioned 90° apart in the same plane.

The correct length of stock is fed to a fixed arbor or center post, against which it is held by the clamp element. Operating singly or in pairs, the tools cut off the stock, bend it around the arbor to form the part. Banking operations may be combined with bending, and on a four-slide machine it is possible to perform as many as ten separate operations in one cycle of the machine.

Tool design can provide for overforming when stock springback requires such compensation. While all wire or sheet alloys are suitable, typical examples of those commonly employed are 5052-H38 and 5056-H38, full-hard non-heat-treatable alloys, and

Courtesy, Torin Corporation

Fig. 3-47. *Vertical four-slide machine.*

6061-T6 and 7075-T6 heat-treatable alloys. Machines are available with capacities for wire as large as ½ in. dia. and sheet gages up to 4 in. wide. For alloy 7075-T6, wire diameters in excess of 3/16 in. are not recommended unless stock is suitably pre-cut to length and hopper fed, due to a tendency of this alloy to shear unevenly in the thicker sections.

Lubrication—Light mineral oil, straight or mixed with kerosene, is used for average four-slide forming. An aluminum drawing oil is employed for severe forming.

Section IV: Cold Extrusion

Cold (Impact) Extrusion of Aluminum Alloy Parts

By N. L. WARD

ALUMINUM ALLOYS are well adapted to cold extrusion (often called impact extrusion). The lower-strength, more ductile alloys such as 1100 and 3003 are easiest to extrude. When higher mechanical properties are required in the final product, heat treatable grades are used, but extrusions from these metals are more susceptible to defects, such as laps or cracks, than are those from the lower-strength alloys.

Although nearly all aluminum alloys can be cold extruded, the five alloys listed in Table 1 are most commonly used. The alloys in Table 1 are listed in the order of decreasing extrudability based on pressure requirements. The easiest-to-extrude alloy (1100) has been assigned an arbitrary value of 1.0 in this comparison.

Temper of Work Metal. The softer an alloy is, the more easily it extrudes. Many extrusions are produced directly from slugs purchased in the O (annealed, recrystallized) temper. In other applications, especially when slugs are machined from bars, the slugs are annealed after machining and before surface preparation, even though the bars were purchased in the O temper. Sometimes the raw material is purchased in the F (as-fabricated) temper, and then the cut or punched slugs are annealed before being extruded.

Table 1. Relative Pressure Requirements for Cold Extruding Annealed Slugs of Five Aluminum Alloys (Alloy 1100 = 1.0)

Alloy	Relative extrusion pressure
1100	1.0
3003	1.2
6061	1.6
2014	1.8
7075	2.3

When extruding alloys that will be heat treated, such as 6061, common practice is to extrude the slug in the O temper, solution treat the preform to the T4 temper, and then size or finish extrude. This procedure has two advantages: (a) after solution treatment, the metal is reasonably soft, and will permit sizing or additional working; and (b) distortion caused by solution treatment can be corrected in final sizing. After sizing, the part can be aged to the T6 temper, if required.

Size of Extrusions. Equipment is readily available that can produce backward and forward extrusions up to 16 in. in diameter. Backward extrusions can be up to 60 in. long. The length of forward extrusions is limited only by the cross section of the part and the capacity of the press — unless a flange necessitates backing the extrusion out of the die, in which case the maximum length is about 60 in.

Hydraulic extrusion and forging presses, suitably modified, are used for making very large extrusions. Parts up to 33 in. in diameter have been produced by backward extrusion from high-strength aluminum alloys in a 14,000-ton extrusion press. Similar extrusions up to 40 in. in diameter have been produced in large forging presses.

Presses

Both mechanical and hydraulic presses are used in extruding aluminum. For detailed information on presses, see the article on Presses and Auxiliary Equipment, which begins on page 1 in this volume.

Presses for extruding aluminum alloys are not necessarily different from those used for extruding steel. There are, however, two considerations that enter into the selection of a press for aluminum: (a) because aluminum extrudes easily, the process is often applied to the forming of deep cuplike or tubular parts, and for this the press should have a long stroke; and (b) also because aluminum extrudes easily, the process is often used for mass production, which requires that the press be capable of high speeds.

The press must have a stroke long enough to permit removal of the longest part to be produced. Except for single-purpose equipment for relatively short extrusions, a stroke of at least 24 in. is required in large mechanical presses. A stroke of 36 in. or more is de-

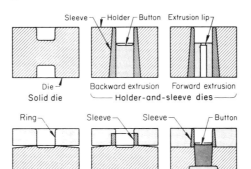

Fig. 1. Three types of dies used in the cold extrusion of aluminum alloy parts

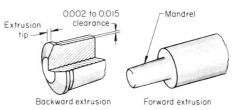

Fig. 2. Typical punches for backward and forward extrusion of aluminum alloy parts

sirable in intermediate and large hydraulic presses. Long shells are sometimes cold extruded in short-stroke, knuckle-type presses, in which the punch is tilted forward or backward for removal of the workpiece.

Because of their high speeds, mechanical crank presses generally are preferred for producing parts requiring up to about 1200 tons of force. Production of as many as 70 extrusions per minute (4200 per hour) is not unusual, and higher production rates are often obtained. For this reason, auxiliary press equipment is usually designed for a high degree of automation when aluminum is to be extruded.

Cold heading machines also are used for cold extruding aluminum parts. Hollow aluminum rivets are formed and extruded in cold headers in mass-production quantities. In general, the extruded parts are small and usually require an upsetting operation that can be done economically in a cold header.

Tooling

Tools designed especially for extruding aluminum may be different from those used for steel, because aluminum extrudes more easily. For instance, a punch used for backward extrusion of steel should not have a length-to-diameter ratio greater than about 3 to 1, whereas this ratio, under favorable conditions, can be as high as 17 to 1 for aluminum (although a 10-to-1 ratio is usually the practical maximum).

Dies. Three basic types of dies for extruding aluminum are shown in Fig. 1. Solid dies are usually the most economical to make. Generally, a cavity is provided in each end, so that the die can

Table 2. Typical Steels for Tools Used in Extruding Aluminum (a)

Tool	AISI steel	Rockwell C hardness
Die, solid	W1	65 to 67
Die sleeve(b)	D2	60 to 62
	L6	56 to 62
	H13	48 to 52
Die button(c)	H11	48 to 50
	H13	48 to 50
	L6	50 to 52
	H21	47 to 50
	T1	58 to 60
Ejector	D2	55 to 57
	S1	52 to 54
Punch	S1	54 to 56
	D2	58 to 60
	H13	50 to 52
Stripper	L6	56 to 58
Mandrel, forward	S1	52 to 54
	H13	50 to 52
Holder	H11	42 to 48
	H13	42 to 48
	4130	36 to 44
	4140	36 to 44

(a) See also the article "Cold Extrusion", page 475 in this volume. (b) Sintered carbide is sometimes used for die sleeves. (c) Maraging steel is sometimes used for die buttons.

be reversed when one end becomes cracked or worn.

Holder-and-sleeve dies are used when extrusion pressures are extremely high. This type of die consists of a shrink ring or rings (the holder), a sleeve, and an insert (button). The die sleeve is prestressed in compression in the shrink ring to match the tension stress expected during extrusion.

Horizontal split dies are composed of as many as four parts: a shrink ring; a sleeve, or insert; and a one-piece or two-piece base. (Figure 1 identifies the one-piece base as a die bottom, and the components of the two-piece base as a holder and a backer.)

Compared to the die cavities used in the backward extrusion of steel (see the article "Cold Extrusion", page 475 in this volume), the die cavities for aluminum shown in Fig. 1 are notably shallow, reflecting a major difference in the extrusion characteristics of the two metals. Steel is more difficult to extrude, requiring higher pressures and continuous die support of the workpiece throughout the extrusion cycle. In contrast, aluminum extrudes readily, and when the punch strikes the slug in backward extrusion, the metal squirts up the sides of the punch, following the punch contours without the external restraint or support afforded by a surrounding die cavity.

Punches. Typical punches for forward and backward extrusion are shown in Fig. 2. In backward extruding of deep cuplike parts, specially designed punches may be used to facilitate stripping, as described in Example 693.

Tool Materials. Typical steels and their working hardnesses for extrusion of aluminum are given in Table 2. For further details on tool materials, see the article "Cold Extrusion", page 475.

Stock for Slugs

Slugs for extrusions are obtained by blanking from plate; sawing, shearing or machining from bars; or by casting. In general, the methods for preparing aluminum slugs are similar to those for preparing slugs from other metals and are thus subject to the same advantages and limitations (see Table 8 in "Cold Extrusion", page 482).

Rolled aluminum alloy plate is widely employed as a source of cold extrusion stock. The high speed at which slugs can be prepared is the major advantage of blanking from rolled plate. Hot rolled plate is suitable for high-quantity production of slugs when tolerance on the volume of the slug is not close (up to ±10%, for example). When closer tolerances are required, the plate must be cold rolled after hot rolling. When slug thickness is greater than about 2 in., or the thickness-to-diameter ratio is greater than about one-to-one, blanking from plate is uneconomical, if not impossible. Blanking is also excessively wasteful of metal, which negates a principal advantage of the cold extrusion process.

Sawing from bars is widely used as a method of obtaining slugs. Aluminum alloys are easily sawed by several methods, but the fastest uses a circular saw with inserted carbide tips. More accurate slugs are produced by sawing than

by blanking; however, as in blanking, a considerable amount of metal is lost.

The properties of aluminum and its alloys that provide high extrudability likewise cause low shearability; thus, shearing generally results in severely distorted slugs. Consequently, shearing is used less in producing aluminum slugs than steel slugs.

When "doughnut" slugs are required, they can be sawed from tubing, or they can be punched, drilled or extruded. Machined slugs (such as those produced in an automatic bar machine) are generally more accurate but cost more than those produced by other methods.

Cast slugs can also be used; the choice of cast slugs is made on a basis of adequate quality at lower fabricating cost. Sometimes compositions that are not readily available in plate or bar stock can be successfully cast and extruded. Often there is a saving in metal when a preform can be cast to shape.

Tolerance on volume of the slug may vary from ±2% to ±10%, depending on design and economic considerations. When extrusions are trimmed, as most are, slug tolerance in the upper part of the above range can be tolerated. When extrusions are not trimmed and dimensions are critical, volume tolerance of the slugs must be held close to the bottom of the range. In high-quantity production of parts such as thin-wall containers, the degree to which slug volume must be controlled is often dictated by metal cost.

Surface Preparation

Slugs of the more extrudable aluminum alloys, such as 1100 and 3003, are often given no surface preparation before a lubricant is applied prior to extrusion. For slugs of the less extrudable aluminum alloys or for maximum extrusion severity, or both, preparation of the surface for retention of lubricant may be required. One method is to etch the slugs in a heated caustic solution, followed by water rinsing, nitric acid desmutting, and a final rinse in water. For the most severe extrusion, slug surfaces are given a phosphate coating before the lubricant is applied.

For details of alkaline etching, acid desmutting, and phosphate coating, see pages 619, 020 and 627 in the article "Cleaning and Finishing of Aluminum and Aluminum Alloys", in Volume 2 of this Handbook.

Lubricants. Aluminum and aluminum alloys can be successfully extruded with lubricants such as high-viscosity oil, grease, wax, tallow, and sodium-tallow soap. Zinc stearate, applied by dry tumbling, is an excellent lubricant for extruding aluminum.

The lubricant should be applied to clean metal surfaces, free from foreign oil, grease and dirt. Preliminary etching of the surfaces (see above) increases the effectiveness of the lubricant.

For the most difficult aluminum extrusions (less extrudable alloys or greater severity, or both), the slugs should be given a phosphate treatment followed by application of a soap that reacts with the surface to form a lubricating layer similar to that formed when extruding steel.

Shallow Cuplike Parts

Simple, shallow cuplike parts can be extruded from most of the wrought aluminum alloys without difficulty. If the wall thickness is uniform and the bottom is nearly flat, shallow cups can be produced in one hit (blow) at high production rates; but if the shape is more complex, at least two hits are often needed. In the three examples that follow, two hits were required. In the first example, an internal boss prevented completion of the extrusion in one hit; in Examples 690 and 691, the extrusions had stepped walls.

Example 689. Use of a Preform for Producing a Complex Bottom (Fig. 3)

The housing shown in Fig. 3 required two extrusion operations because of the internal boss, which was formed by backward extru-

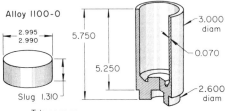

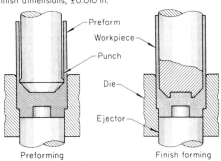

Press .... Hydraulic, 350-ton
Die .... Two-station
Type of slug ... Sawed from bar, and annealed
Lubricant .... Zinc stearate
Production rate:
First operation .... 350 pieces per hour
Second operation .... 250 pieces per hour
Tool life, minimum .... 100,000 pieces

Fig. 3. Housing that was extruded in two operations because of an internal boss (Example 689)

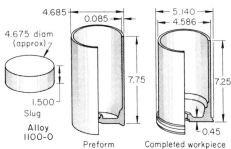

Press .... Hydraulic, 2500-ton(a)
Die .... Two-station
Type of slug ... Sawed from bar, and annealed
Lubricant .... Zinc stearate
Production rate .... 60 to 75 pieces per hour
Tool life, minimum .... 50,000 pieces

(a) 900 tons required for extruding and 1350 tons for sizing.

Fig. 4. Cartridge case that was completed in two press operations because of a stepped wall (Example 690)

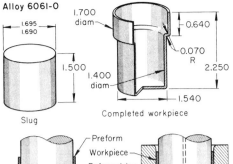

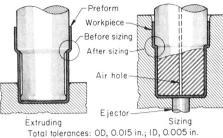

Total tolerances: OD, 0.015 in.; ID, 0.005 in.

Press .... Mechanical, crank-type, 90-ton
Die .... Two-station
Type of slug .... Sawed and annealed
Lubricant .... Zinc stearate (first operation);
              liquid wax, dip (second operation)
Production rate .... 700 to 750 pieces per hour
Tool life, minimum .... 500,000 pieces

Fig. 5. Stepped-wall cup that was extruded and then sized to set 0.070-in. radii (Example 691)

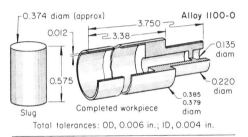

Total tolerances: OD, 0.006 in.; ID, 0.004 in.

Press .... Mechanical, horizontal, 150-ton
Die .... Single-station
Type of slug .. Sawed or machined from bar,
            and annealed
Lubricant .... Zinc stearate
Production rate .. 4200 pcs/hr (100% efficiency)
Tool life, minimum .... 1 million pieces

Fig. 6. Long part that was extruded in one hit. Ratio of length to diameter (10 to 1) is about maximum for one-hit extrusion of alloy 1100-O. (Example 692)

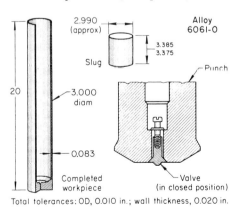

Total tolerances: OD, 0.010 in.; wall thickness, 0.020 in.

Press .... Hydraulic, 800-ton(a)
Die .... Single-station
Type of slug .... Sawed from bar, and annealed
Lubricant .... Zinc stearate
Production rate .... 300 pieces per hour
Tool life, minimum .... 50,000 pieces

(a) Workpiece was sized in a 30-ton hydraulic press after solution treatment and before aging.

Fig. 7. Long part that was extruded in one hit, and valved punch used for ease in stripping (Example 693)

sion in a second operation, as shown in Fig. 3. The blended angle in the preform functioned as a support for the finishing punch during extrusion of the internal boss. This counteracted the side pressure that was created as the metal flowed into the cavity of the finishing punch.

Additional processing details are given in the table that accompanies Fig. 3.

Example 690. Double Backward Extruding, Piercing and Finish Forming in Two Hits (Fig. 4)

The cartridge case shown in Fig. 4 was completed in two press operations. The preform, also shown in Fig. 4, was extruded in one operation. A stepped punch permitted the metal to fill the thicker wall portion first, after which wall thickness was reduced to 0.085 in. After being trimmed to length and pierced, the preform was upset (stepped flange) and finish formed in a second operation. Stamping of identification numbers on the bottom, tapering of the tubular section 0.0165 in. per inch, and forming of the primer seat were also

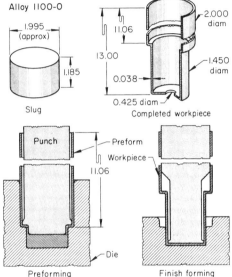

Total tolerances: 2.000 OD, 0.010 in.; 1.450 OD, 0.005 in.; wall thickness, 0.005 in.

Press .... Mechanical, 190-ton
Die .... Two-station
Type of slug .... Sawed from bar, and annealed
Lubricant .... Zinc stearate
Production rate .... 1500 pieces per hour
Tool life, minimum .... 250,000 pieces

Fig. 8. Flare case that was extruded in two operations (Example 694)

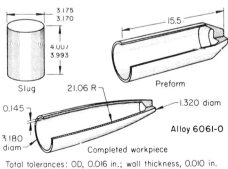

Total tolerances: OD, 0.016 in.; wall thickness, 0.010 in.

Press .... Hydraulic, 800-ton(a)
Die .... Two-station
Type of slug .... Sawed from bar, and annealed
Lubricant ....Zinc stearate(b)
Production rate .... 300 pieces per hour
Tool life, minimum .... 75,000 pieces

(a) Pressure set at 450 tons. (b) For extrusion of preform. Preform was lubricated with a solution of lanolin, zinc stearate, and trichlorethylene before finish forming.

Fig. 9. Motor housing that was extruded in two operations (Example 695)

done in the second operation. Additional manufacturing details are given in the table that accompanies Fig. 4.

Example 691. Extrusion and Sizing of Stepped-Wall Cups (Fig. 5)

A stepped-wall cup was made in two operations as shown in Fig. 5. The preform was extruded from a slug of solution-annealed 6061 alloy using a stepped punch with back relief on the smaller diameter, as shown in Fig. 5. The preform was then solution treated at 970 F, relubricated and finish formed as shown. A steady stream of air through the punch helped to keep the extrusion in the die during finish forming and also facilitated stripping it from the punch. Additional processing details are given in the table with Fig. 5.

Deep Cuplike Parts

Although cups having a length as great as 17 times the diameter have been produced, this extreme condition is seldom found in practice because a punch this slender is likely to deflect and cause nonuniform wall thickness in the backward extruded product.

In the four examples that follow, the lengths of the cuplike parts range from nearly ten diameters (Example 692) to about five (Example 695). This is a typical range of length-to-diameter ratios used in backward extruding deep cups.

Length of cup and number of operations (use of preform) are not necessarily related. Whether or not a preform is required depends mainly on the shape, particularly of the closed end. This is evident in Examples 692 and 693, in which two long parts were produced with only one hit each.

When forming deep cups from heat treatable alloys such as 6061, if the amount of reduction is 25% or more in the preform, the workpiece should be reannealed and relubricated between preforming and finish extruding (see Example 695).

Example 692. One-Hit Extrusion of a Part Ten Diameters Long (Fig. 6)

The hypodermic syringe shown in Fig. 6 was produced in one hit in a high-speed horizontal press. The 10-to-1 length-to-diameter ratio of this part was close to the practical maximum for extrusion in one hit, because of the high probability of lateral deflection of a long, slender punch. Processing details are given in the table with Fig. 6.

Example 693. Use of a Valved Punch for Ease in Stripping a Part Seven Diameters Long Extruded in One Hit (Fig. 7)

The part shown in Fig. 7 was extruded in one hit from an annealed 6061 alloy slug. It was then solution heat treated, relubricated, sized (ironed) in another press, and aged to the T6 temper.

In extruding straight-wall parts like the one in Fig. 7, stripping can be a problem because the punch creates a vacuum. In this application, the problem was solved by the use of a punch that incorporated a valve (shown in Fig. 7). The valve was closed when the punch moved down, and opened as the punch withdrew. Additional processing details are given with Fig. 7.

Example 694. Extruding a Deep, Two-Diameter Cup in Two Operations (Fig. 8)

The flare case shown in Fig. 8 was produced in two extrusion operations. The first hit formed the 11.06-in. tubular section shown as the preform in Fig. 8. In the second hit, the small-diameter bottom section was formed from the heavy section of the preform. Slugs were annealed before the first extrusion operation, but intermediate annealing and relubrication were not required. After extrusion, the

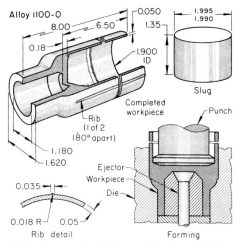

Rib detail

0.035
0.018 R 0.05

Total tolerances: OD, 0.004 in.; wall thickness, 0.005 in.

Press .... Mechanical, crank-type, 190-ton
Die .... Single-station
Type of slug .... Sawed from bar, and annealed
Lubricant .... Zinc stearate
Production rate .... 1500 pieces per hour
Tool life, minimum .... 75,000 pieces

Fig. 10. Flare casing with two outside ribs that was produced in one hit by backward-forward extrusion (Example 696)

workpiece was trimmed to length and the bottom hole was pierced. Processing details are given in the table with Fig. 8.

Example 695. Extrusion of a Tapered-Wall Motor Housing in Two Operations (Fig. 9)

Two extrusion operations were needed to form the motor housing shown in Fig. 9. This part was made of annealed 6061 alloy and required reannealing and relubricating between the two extrusion operations. After finish forming, the housing was solution heat treated and aged to the T6 temper. Additional processing details are given with Fig. 9.

Parts With Complex Shapes

Producing extrusions from aluminum and aluminum alloys in a single hit is not necessarily confined to simple shapes. The extrusions described in Examples 696 to 700, which follow, were all produced in a single hit despite their relatively complex shapes. For extrusions with longitudinal flutes, stems or grooves, the use of one of the most extrudable alloys, such as 1100, is helpful in minimizing difficulties. Sometimes, however, a less extrudable alloy can be used to form a complex shape in one hit, as in Example 700.

Successful extrusion of complex shapes, especially in a single hit, depends greatly on tool design and slug design. Ordinarily, some development work is required for each new job before it can be put into production.

Example 696. One-Hit Extrusion of a Casing With Outside Ribs (Fig. 10)

Figure 10 shows a flare casing with two longitudinal locating ribs on its outside diameter that was produced in one hit by backward-forward extrusion. The tool setup is also shown in Fig. 10, and processing details are given in the accompanying table.

Example 697. Use of a Tubular Slug and Punch for Double Backward Extrusion (Fig. 11)

The container shown in Fig. 11 was extruded by the double backward technique in one hit by using the tubular slug and hollow punch also shown in Fig. 11. Considerable develop-

ment in tooling and slug dimensions was required before uniform wall thickness could be obtained for both the large and small diameters. Processing details are given in the table that accompanies Fig. 11.

Example 698. Maximum Extrudability for a Complex Shape (Fig. 12)

The hydraulic cylinder body shown in Fig. 12 was extruded from a solid slug in one hit. Alloy 1100, which has maximum extrudability, was required for this part because of the abrupt changes in section of the cylinder body. Surface cracks and laps resulted when more difficult-to-extrude alloys were used. The different wall thicknesses and steps in this design represent near-maximum severity for extruding in one hit, even with the most extrudable alloy. During development of this part, it was necessary to change the face angles, shorten the steps, and blend the outside ribs more gradually to insure complete fillout. Additional processing details are given in the table with Fig. 12.

Example 699. Use of a Doughnut Slug in Backward-Forward Extrusion in One Hit (Fig. 13)

The housing shown in Fig. 13 was extruded by the backward-forward technique in a single hit from a drilled (or pierced) slug. The tooling setup used in this operation is also shown in Fig. 13. The eight splines were formed in the small diameter by forward extrusion, using the serrated portion of the punch. At the same time, the ribbed cup portion of the workpiece was formed by backward extrusion with the

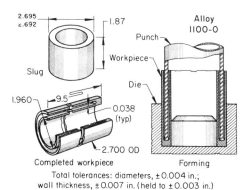

Total tolerances: diameters, ±0.004 in.; wall thickness, ±0.007 in. (held to ±0.003 in.)

Press .... Hydraulic, 350-ton
Die .... Single-station
Type of slug .... Sawed from tubing(a)
Lubricant .... Liquid wax (dip)
Production rate .... 300 pieces per hour
Tool life, minimum .... 50,000 pieces

(a) An alternate method was to extrude a cup-shaped slug to the same dimensions in a header, then machine square the open end and remove the closed end by machining. Slugs were annealed after sawing or heading.

Fig. 11. Double-wall container produced by extruding a tubular slug with a hollow punch (Example 697)

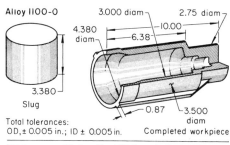

Total tolerances:
OD, ±0.005 in.; ID ±0.005 in.

Press ...... Hydraulic, 800-ton (set at 500 tons)
Die .... Single-station
Type of slug .... Sawed from bar, and annealed
Lubricant .... Zinc stearate
Production rate .... 300 pieces per hour
Tool life, minimum .... 70,000 pieces

Fig. 12. Hydraulic cylinder body extruded in one hit. Complexity of configuration is about the maximum producible by one-hit extrusion of alloy 1100-O. (Example 698)

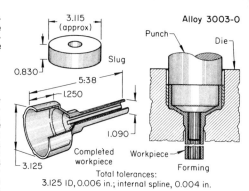

Total tolerances:
3.125 ID, 0.006 in.; internal spline, 0.004 in.

Press ...... Mechanical, horizontal, 1000-ton(a)
Die .... Single-station
Type of slug .... Sawed from bar(b)
Lubricant .... Liquid wax (dip)
Production rate .... 1500 pieces per hour
Tool life, minimum .... 200,000 pieces

(a) 375 tons required. (b) Hole was drilled or pierced; slugs were then annealed.

Fig. 13. Splined housing extruded in one hit from a doughnut slug (Example 699)

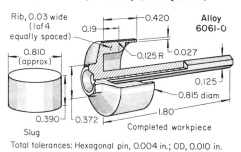

Total tolerances: Hexagonal pin, 0.004 in.; OD, 0.010 in.

Press .... Mechanical, horizontal, 150-ton
Die .... Single-station
Type of slug .... Stamped wafer
Lubricant .... Zinc stearate
Production rate .. 3900 pcs/hr (100% efficiency)
Tool life, minimum .... 300,000 pieces

Fig. 14. Striker with ribs and a center column that was extruded from a wafer slug in one hit (Example 700)

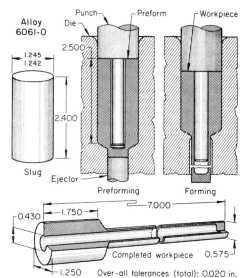

Over-all tolerances (total): 0.020 in.

Press .... Mechanical, crank-type, 190-ton
Dies .... Two
Type of slug .... Sawed from bar, and annealed
Lubricant .... Zinc stearate(a)
Production, first hit ...... 1200 pieces per hour
Production, second hit ...... 700 pieces per hour
Tool life, minimum .... 150,000 pieces

(a) For extruding the preform; dipped in a solution of lanolin, zinc stearate, and trichlorethylene before finish forming.

Fig. 15. Burster tube that was extruded in two operations (Example 701)

intermediate diameter of the punch. Length of the cup section was controlled by a step in the punch that confined the metal in the die.

For additional processing details, see the table that accompanies Fig. 13.

Example 700. Production of Ribs and Center Column by Double Backward Extrusion in One Hit (Fig. 14)

The striker shown in Fig. 14 was extruded from a wafer slug in one hit by the double backward technique. This part, which incorporated a hexagonal boss on the outside, a four-rib tubular section, and an inside hexagonal stem, represents near-maximum complexity of shape for one hit, especially when made from an alloy (6061) that has less than maximum extrudability (see Table 1). Despite its complexity, this part was produced at a rate of 65 per minute in a horizontal press. Other processing details are given with Fig. 14.

Example 701. Two-Operation Extrusion of a Complex Shape From Alloy 6061 (Fig. 15)

A burster tube was produced by forward extrusion in two operations, as shown in Fig. 15. The preform was extruded from an annealed slug, after which the preform was reannealed, relubricated and finish formed in a second extrusion operation. After the second extrusion, the part was solution treated and aged to the T6 temper. Additional processing details are given in the table that accompanies Fig. 15.

Dimensional Accuracy

In general, aluminum extrusions are manufactured to close tolerances. The closeness depends on size, shape, alloy, wall thickness, type of tooling, and press equipment. Lubrication and slug fit in the die are also important.

Wall-thickness tolerances range from ± 0.001 to ± 0.005 in. for relatively thin-wall cylindrical shapes of moderate size extruded from low-strength alloys, but may be as great as ± 0.010 to ± 0.015 in. for large parts of high-strength alloys. Wall-thickness tolerances for rectangular shells range from ± 0.005 to ± 0.015 in., depending on size, alloy and nominal wall thickness. Diameter tolerances typically range from ± 0.001 in. for small parts to ± 0.010 to ± 0.015 in. for large, high-strength alloy parts. Closer control of diameter can be achieved on small, heavy-wall parts by centerless grinding the extrusions (provided the alloy is one that can be ground satisfactorily). Dimensional tolerances in the forged portion of the impact are influenced by the same variables as those listed above, but a range of ± 0.005 to ± 0.015 in. is typical. Variations in extruded length usually necessitate a separate trimming operation.

Surface finish typically ranges from 20 to 70 micro-in. Smoother surfaces can sometimes be obtained by using extreme care in surface preparation and lubrication of the work metal, and by paying close attention to the surface condition of the tools.

Extruding Aluminum

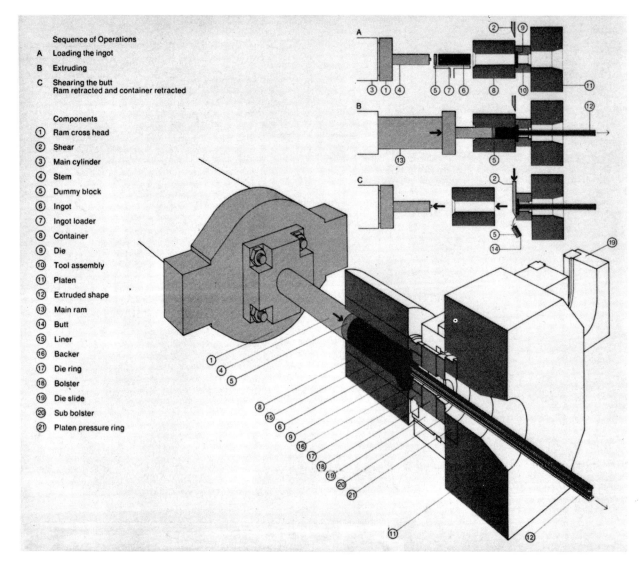

Fig. 5-1. Schematic showing principal features of extrusion press tooling.

Both solid and hollow shapes are produced in long lengths by forcing metal from a container through an opening in a steel die, Figure 5-1. Virtually any parallel-surface configuration can be produced.

Commercially, the process has been in use since the late 19th century. Its first large growth occurred during the Second World War when extruded aluminum components for aircraft were produced in large quantity. A markedly rapid expansion of the industry developed after the war with the introduction of intermediate-strength alloys, which are heat treatable at the press and have good extrudability.

Today, curtain wall systems for high-rise buildings, truck and trailer components, door and window frames, aircraft structurals, and hundreds of other

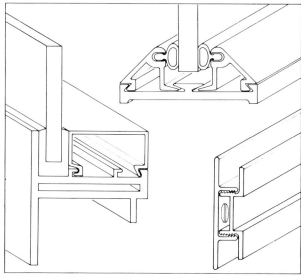

Fig. 5-2. Typical aluminum extrusions.

TABLE 5-1

Aluminum Alloys Commonly Used for Various Extruded Products

Tube and pipe	1060, 1100, 2014, 2024, 3003, 5083, 5086, 5154, 5454, 6061, 6063, 6351, 7075
Architectural shapes	6063, 6061
Aircraft shapes	2014, 2024, 7075, 7178
Structural shapes	5083, 5086, 6061, 6063, 6351, 7004
Electrical bus conductor	6101, 1350

items are made as a single section of an extruded aluminum alloy, Figure 5-2.

Many of these would otherwise have to be produced by fabricating, assembling and joining several separate component parts. In some cases, multiple identical parts of superior quality are produced at low cost from a single extrusion, sectioned at appropriate intervals. Examples of such products are drawer pulls, integral body-and-base for electric motors, heat sinks for electronic components, latches and cleats, and many others.

Horizontal, hydraulic extrusion presses exerting 1200 to 2500 tons pressure are used to produce the largest number and variety of aluminum extrusions, but presses up to 15,000 tons capacity are employed to "push" large and/or complex shapes, and those made of the harder alloys.

Auxiliary equipment includes various types of furnaces for pre-heating aluminum billets, ingot containers and other press tooling; and larger furnaces for heat-treating extrusions made of certain alloys. Also included in the extrusion plant is equipment, for straightening extruded lengths when required, as well as conveyors and saws for cutting the shapes into shorter lengths as specified.

Extrusions are classified according to their general cross-sectional configuration as rod, bar, solid shapes, semihollow shapes, hollow shapes, structural and stepped shapes, and tube.

An extrusion may be either symmetrical or asymmetrical in cross section, which in turn may be constant or stepped along its length.

A stepped extrusion is produced by running its smallest section first, stopping the press to change special dies, and repeating this process until the largest and final section is run. Its two or more cross sections increase in size consecutively, but may be either identical or different in sectional contour; the principal limitation in this regard is that each section must be smaller and completely contained at all points by solid metal of the adjacent, larger section.

The largest section of a stepped extrusion is called the *major* and the smallest the *minor*; in-between sections, if any, are called *intermediate*. "Steps," as they are termed, can be made in any extrudable alloy and have proven particularly useful in producing high-strength alloy wing spars and other tapered, cantilevered structurals for jet aircraft. Tapering is done by machining, which is less costly for steps than for heavy plate, since much less metal must be removed from a step.

Extrusion press tooling consists of a container to hold the ingot, a tool carrier for housing the die and its support tooling, and a ram that is actuated to deliver the hydraulic extrusion pressure. A mandrel is used behind the die to produce hollow shapes and tube.

Mandrels are either separate tools used when extruding hollow ingots, or are components of specially constructed dies enabling tube or hollow shapes to be produced from solid ingot. Although aluminum can be extruded cold, most extruding is done at elevated temperatures because aluminum is more easily worked at higher temperatures and therefore smaller, less expensive presses may be used.

The alloys generally used for the principal types of extruded aluminum products are listed in Table 5-1.

Section V:
Forging and Forging Design

Forging of Aluminum Alloys

ALUMINUM ALLOYS can be forged into essentially the same shapes as are forgeable from low-carbon steel. However, for a given forging shape, the pressure requirements vary over a wide range, depending primarily on chemical composition of the alloy and forging temperature. Thus, although some of the low-strength aluminum alloys, such as 1100, require considerably less forging pressure than 1020 steel, a high-strength aluminum alloy, such as 7075, requires considerably more pressure to produce the same forged shape. Several aluminum alloys require approximately the same forging pressures as required by low-carbon steels. Forging-pressure requirements, as they are related to forging temperature and upset reduction, are compared for two aluminum alloys and for 1020 steel in Fig. 1.

Forging Methods

Methods used for forging aluminum alloys include open-die, closed-die, upset and roll forging, and ring rolling. Two of these are sometimes used in sequence to obtain a desired shape.

Open-die forging (hand forging) is often used to produce small quantities, for which the construction of expensive closed dies is not justified. The quantity that warrants the use of closed dies varies considerably, depending largely on the size and shape of the forging; it can be fewer than ten pieces (see Example 40, in the article on Open-Die Forging). However, open-die forging is by no means confined to small quantities. For example, as many as 2000 "biscuit" forgings have been produced in open dies when it was desired to obtain the properties of a forging but closed dies were not economical.

Open-die forging is also used to make preforms, which are later completed in closed dies. As is true for other metals, the complexity of shapes that can be consistently reproduced from aluminum in open dies depends greatly on operator skill.

Closed-Die Forging. By far the greatest tonnage of aluminum forgings is produced in closed dies. Three types of

aluminum forgings are shaped in closed dies: blocker-type, conventional, and close-tolerance.

Blocker-type forgings are produced in relatively inexpensive dies, and in dimensions and forged details they are less refined and require more machining than conventional closed-die forgings. A blocker-type forging costs less than a comparable conventional forging, but it requires more machining.

Conventional closed-die forgings are the most common type. They are produced to commercial tolerances.

Close-tolerance forgings cost more than their conventional counterparts, but the increased cost is sometimes justified because machining costs are less.

Upset forging is sometimes the sole process used in forging a specific shape from aluminum. Large bolts are an example. For other products, upset forging is used as a preliminary operation to reduce the number of impressions, to reduce die wear, or to save metal, when the products are finish forged in closed dies. Wheel and gear forgings are typical products for which upsetting is advantageously used in conjunction with closed-die forging, mainly to save metal.

In upset forging of aluminum alloys, the unsupported length of round sections to be upset must not exceed three diameters. For upsetting a square or rectangular shape, the unsupported length must not exceed three times the diagonal of the cross section.

Roll forging can be used as a preliminary operation to save metal or to reduce the number of closed-die operations, the same as in the forging of steel (see the articles "Closed-Die Forging", page 49, and "Roll Forging", page 95 in this volume). The decision as to whether or not roll forging is to be used as a preliminary operation in a particular application is based primarily on cost.

Ring rolling is being used successfully to produce ringlike parts from aluminum. The technique used for ring rolling of aluminum is essentially the same as that used for steel (see the article "Ring Rolling", page 105). The temperatures used for ring rolling aluminum are basically the same as those used for forging by other methods. Care must be exercised to avoid overheating the metal during ring rolling or to permit cooling to a temperature that will result in cold working.

The economy of ring rolling is dependent primarily on the size and contours of the forging. For some parts, it is more economical to cut rings from extruded hollow cylinders.

Forging Alloys and Temperatures

Fifteen aluminum alloys most commonly used for forgings are listed in Table 1. Generally, all of these alloys can be forged to the same severity, although more power or more blows are required for some than for others.

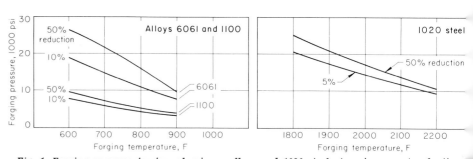

Fig. 1. Forging pressure for two aluminum alloys and 1020 steel at various upset reductions and forging temperatures (SOURCE: "Forging Materials and Practices", by A. M. Sabroff, F. W. Boulger and H. J. Henning, Reinhold Book Corp., New York, 1968)

Temperature ranges for forging these alloys are included in Table 1. The recommended forging temperature range for most of the alloys is relatively narrow (less than 100 F for several alloys; for no alloy is the range greater than 160 F). Maintaining temperature is not usually a problem, because the temperature of the metal being forged increases from hot working; in addition, dies are heated for forging aluminum, and this minimizes temperature loss.

Forgeability

Figure 2 illustrates the relative forgeability of the ten alloys that comprise the major tonnage of aluminum alloy forgings. The arbitrary units shown on the vertical axis of Fig. 2 are based principally on deformation per unit of energy absorbed at the various temperatures ordinarily used for forging these alloys. The difficulty of forging the alloys to specific degrees of severity was also considered in establishing these arbitrary units.

Alloys 1100 and 3003 are the most easily forged and would be rated higher than 5 units in Fig. 2 (forgeability increases as the arbitrary unit increases), but both of these alloys have limited use as forgings, because they cannot be strengthened by heat treatment.

Effect of Temperature. As shown in Fig. 2, the forgeability of all alloys shown on the chart is affected by forging temperature. There is considerable variation in the effect of temperature on forgeability; alloy 4032 shows the most marked response. The effect of temperature on forging load and pressure for alloy 6061 is shown in Fig. 3. The nearly twofold increase in load between 900 F (the top of the forging range for 6061) and 750 F (60 F below the recommended range) indicates why the recommended forging temperature ranges for aluminum alloys, especially the high-strength alloys, are narrow.

In practice, forging is usually begun with the forging stock at the high side of the temperature range for the alloy being forged. Forging continues until the part is finished or until the work metal is too cold.

Reheating and Intermediate Operations. Aluminum alloys are rarely reheated for further forging unless intermediate operations, especially those requiring separate die sets, are required. Hydraulic press forgings are usually completed in two sets of dies (blocking and finishing) or two pairs of impressions in a single die set. Dies used in hammer forging commonly contain auxiliary impressions for fullering, edging, bending, or flattening, in addition to those used for blocking and finishing.

Blocking works the metal for desired grain direction, and imparts the general shape and contour to the forging. Also, by forming progressively and by gradually reducing the section, mechanical properties of the forging are benefited. Finishing refines the forging into its final shape, squeezing excess metal into the flash space that surrounds the finishing die impression.

Sometimes, minor increases in corner and fillet radii or draft permit producing in one heating a forging that otherwise would require reheating. On the other hand, intermediate punchout or trimming, although reducing the amount of power required for forging, may necessitate a reheat.

Table 1. Forging Temperatures for Aluminum Alloys

Alloy	Forging temperature, F	Alloy	Forging temperature, F
1100	600-760	4032	780-860
2014	785-860	5083	760-860
2025	785-840	6061, 6151	810-900
2218	760-840	7039	720-820
2219	800-880	7075	720-820
2618	770-850	7079	760-850
3003	600-760	X7080	700-825

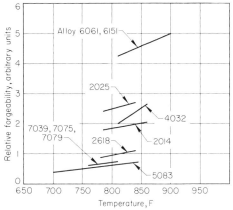

Fig. 2. Forgeability and forging temperatures of ten aluminum alloys. Forgeability increases as the arbitrary unit increases.

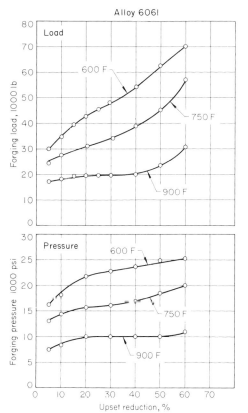

Fig. 3. Forging load and pressure curves for upset reduction of alloy 6061 at a strain rate of 0.6 per second (SOURCE: "A Study of Forging Variables", U. S. Air Force Report ML-TDR-64-95, 1964)

Hammers and Presses

Types of hammers and presses used for forging aluminum alloys are the same as are used for forging steel. However, more power may be required for forging a shape from a high-strength aluminum alloy than from steel. (For more detailed information on hammers and presses used for forging, see the article "Hammers and Presses for Forging", pages 1 to 11, and the one on pages 12 to 18, dealing with selection.)

Hammers. Gravity drop hammers or, more often, power drop hammers are used for open-die forging of aluminum alloys. The control of length of stroke and force and speed of the blows provided by power drop hammers is particularly useful in forging aluminum alloys because of their sensitivity to strain rate. Power drop hammers are also used in closed-die forging, provided an applied draft of not less than about 7° can be tolerated.

Presses. Mechanical presses are used extensively for closed-die forging. They are best adapted to forgings of moderate size and to relatively simple shapes that do not require complex preforming operations. They combine impact with a squeezing action, which is more compatible than hammer impact with the flow characteristics of aluminum alloys. Also the minimum applied draft requirement is decreased to about 3°. For many applications, mechanical presses are preferred over hydraulic presses because they are less expensive and production rates are higher.

Although the fastest hydraulic presses are slower acting than mechanical presses, hydraulic presses are sometimes favored for producing large or intricate forgings. The squeezing action of a hydraulic press is gentler than that of a mechanical press. Thus, a hydraulic press may be better suited to the flow characteristics of aluminum alloys when large and intricate sections are forged. Example 130, which follows, describes the forging of an intricate aircraft wheel, with a plan area of about 214 sq in., in a hydraulic press. In contrast, Example 131 describes the forging, extruding, and hot forming of an automobile wheel, with a finished plan area of about 189 sq in., in a series of mechanical presses.

Example 130. Use of a Hydraulic Press for Forging an Intricate Wheel (Fig. 4)

The wheel shown in Fig. 4 was forged in an 8000-ton hydraulic press. Because of the intricate design, small draft angles, and abrupt changes of section, the slower movement of metal obtained by hydraulic action was necessary for acceptable results.

The wheel was forged from a 2014 alloy billet weighing 48 lb, heated to 860 F and then forged in four press strokes, using three die impressions. Average production rate was 32 wheels per hour. Dies were lubricated with a graphite-water mixture with soap, and the forgings were cleaned by the standard methods described in the section in this article on Cleaning (page 132).

Example 131. Forging, Extruding and Hot Forming an Automobile Wheel in Mechanical Presses (Fig. 5)

Figure 5 shows the progression of shapes in the production of an automobile wheel from alloy 6061 bar stock by forging, extruding and hot forming. The extruded preform had to be heated for forming because elongation of about 25% was required in the rim area

Table 2. Recommended Steels and Hardnesses for Dies and Die Inserts for Hammer and Press Forging of Aluminum Alloys

Maximum severity	Total quantity to be forged			
	100 to 10,000		10,000 and over	
	Tool steel	Brinell hardness	Tool steel	Brinell hardness
Hammer Forging				
Part 1 ..	6G, 6F2	341-375	6G, 6F2	341-375
Part 2 ..	6G, 6F2	302-331	6G, 6F2	341-375
			H12(a)	405-448
Part 3 ..	6G, 6F2	269-293	6G, 6F2	302-331
Part 4 ..	6G, 6F2	341-375	6G, 6F2(b)	341-375
	H11	405-433	H11	405-433
Part 5 ..	6G, 6F2	269-293	6G, 6F2(c)	269-293
Press Forging				
Part 1 ..	6G, 6F2	341-375	6F3	375-405
			H12(a)	448-477
Part 2 ..	6G, 6F2	341-375	6G, 6F2(d)	341-375
			H12(a)	448-477
Part 3 ..	6G, 6F2	302-331	6G, 6F2(e)	302-331
Part 4 ..	6G, 6F2	341-375	6G, 6F2(f)	341-375
	H11	405-433		
Part 5 ..	6G, 6F2	341-375	6G, 6F2(g)	341-375

Nominal Compositions of Tool Steels

Steel 6F2 .... 0.55 C, 0.75 Mn, 0.25 Si, 1.00 Ni, 1.00 Cr, 0.10 V (optional), 0.30 Mo

Steel 6G .... 0.55 C, 0.80 Mn, 0.25 Si, 1.00 Cr, 0.10 V, 0.45 Mo

Steel H11 .... 0.35 C, 5.00 Cr, 0.40 V, 1.50 Mo

Steel H12 .... 0.35 C, 5.00 Cr, 0.40 V, 1.50 W, 1.50 Mo

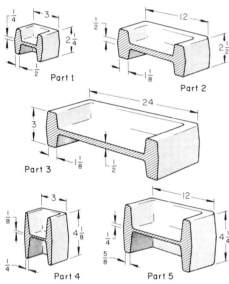

Part 1

Part 2

Part 3

Part 4

Part 5

(a) Recommended for long runs — for example, 50,000 forgings. (b) With either steel, use inserts of H11 at 405 to 433 Bhn. (c) With either steel, use inserts of 6G or 6F2 at 302 to 331 Bhn. (d) With either steel, use inserts of 6F3 at 405 to 448 Bhn. (e) With either steel, use inserts of 6G or 6F2 at 341 to 375 Bhn. (f) With either steel, use inserts of H12 at 429 to 448 Bhn. (g) With either steel, use inserts of H12 at 429 to 448 Bhn. For long runs (50,000 forgings), a solid block made of H12 at 477 to 514 Bhn is recommended.

The sequence and details of the operations in the production of the wheel were:

1 — Preparation of Slug (Fig. 5a). The slug was sawed to length from 8-in.-diam round bar 10 to 12 ft long, in a high-speed band saw at 3500 sfm to obtain smooth parallel surfaces. The slug was cleaned and deburred by airless abrasive blasting with aluminum oxide pellets or steel shot of 0.030-in. maximum particle size.

2 — Forging of Slug Into Blank for Extrusion (Fig. 5b). The slug was spray lubricated with a compound consisting of powdered graphite and water mixed with isopropyl alcohol; when dry, the spray lubricant left a thin film of powdered graphite on the surface of the slug. The slug was induction heated to 850 ± 10 F; transfer time was 25 sec, to allow

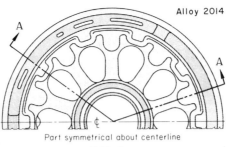

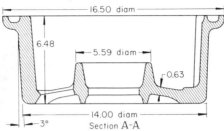

Alloy 2014

Part symmetrical about centerline

16.50 diam

6.48

5.59 diam

0.63

14.00 diam

3°

Section A-A

Fig. 4. Intricate aircraft wheel forged in a hydraulic press (Example 130)

for temperature equalization. The blank was forged from the slug at 825 to 850 F in a 2000-ton mechanical forging press; die faces were sprayed with lubricant before each hit. Outside diameter of the hot blank was trimmed smooth in a 250/400-ton trim press; trim dies were lubricated with a mixture of kerosene and light machine oil.

3 — Extruding of Forged Blank Into Preform (Fig. 5c). The blank was spray lubricated with a mixture of powdered graphite and water diluted with isopropyl alcohol and, when dry, was induction heated to 825 to 850 F; transfer time was 20 sec, to allow for temperature equalization. The preform was extruded from the forged blank at 825 ± 15 F in a 6000-ton mechanical forging press. After the extrusion was water quenched to room temperature, the ends were trimmed to length in a high-speed lathe, and inside edges were deburred with a facing or cutoff tool.

4 — First Hot Forming of Wheel (Fig. 5d). The extrusion was spray lubricated with powdered graphite and water mixed with isopropyl alcohol and, when dry, was induction heated to 875 ± 10 F. The heated extrusion was then formed to a preliminary shape of the wheel rim, in a 400-ton mechanical press with a 20-in. stroke. The workpiece was then solution heat treated at 980 to 1000 F in a conveyorized gas-fired forced-jet furnace.

5 — Restrike Hot Forming and Piercing of Wheel (Fig. 5e). The workpiece, at 830 to 870 F, was restruck, to form the rim and the crown of the wheel in a 2000-ton mechanical press. The formed wheel was quenched for 2 min in water at 212 F, and then was air

cooled while resting on a flat surface. With the wheel at room temperature, bolt holes, valve hole, and slots were pierced, in two hits in a 400-ton mechanical press; then the rim was restruck and holes were countersunk, in a 1000-ton mechanical press. The completed wheel was artificially aged for 3 to 4 hr at 360 to 375 F in a conveyorized furnace.

Dies

Forging of aluminum requires the use of dies specially designed for aluminum, for at least three reasons:

1. Aluminum is seldom fullered or bent in the forging sequence; two forging stages, preforming and finishing, are most commonly used for aluminum.
2. Allowances for shrinkage are greater than for steel.
3. Temperature control of dies for forging aluminum is critical; therefore, facilities for heating dies and controlling die temperature during forging must be considered in die design.

Finish on dies used for forging of aluminum is more critical than that on dies used for steel. Cavities must be highly polished to obtain acceptable surface finish on the forgings.

Die Materials. Table 2 lists materials for dies and die inserts for forging aluminum. Recommendations are based on the quantity to be forged, type of equipment used (press or hammer), and severity and size of the forging to be produced.

The hardness of prehardened die blocks for forging a given shape is often one range lower for aluminum than for steel. For example, if a die block with a hardness of 388 to 429 Bhn is used for forging a specific size and shape from steel, a block with a hardness of 341 to 375 Bhn is used for aluminum. Dies of lower hardness can be used for forging aluminum because die wear is seldom a problem.

Die breakage, however, *is* a problem in forging aluminum, because of the forces applied. Breakage is minimized by the use of softer dies.

For hot upset forging, both the gripper dies and the heading tools are usually made of die steels such as 6G and 6F2 at a hardness of Rockwell C 42 to 46. If quantities are large (50,000 or more), tools for hot upsetting are usually made of H11, H12 or H13 hot work steels at Rockwell C 46 to 50.

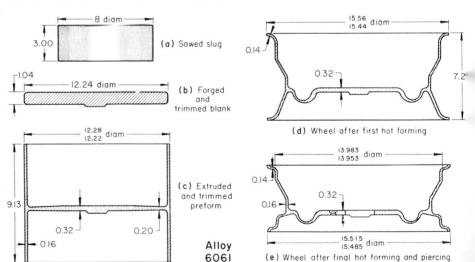

(a) Sawed slug

8 diam

3.00

(b) Forged and trimmed blank

1.04

12.24 diam

(c) Extruded and trimmed preform

12.28 / 12.22 diam

9.13

0.32   0.20

0.16

Alloy 6061

(d) Wheel after first hot forming

15.56 / 15.44 diam

0.14

0.32

7.2

(e) Wheel after final hot forming and piercing

13.983 / 13.953 diam

0.14

0.32

0.16

15.515 / 15.485 diam

Fig. 5. Stages in the production of an automobile wheel by forging, extruding and hot forming (Example 131)

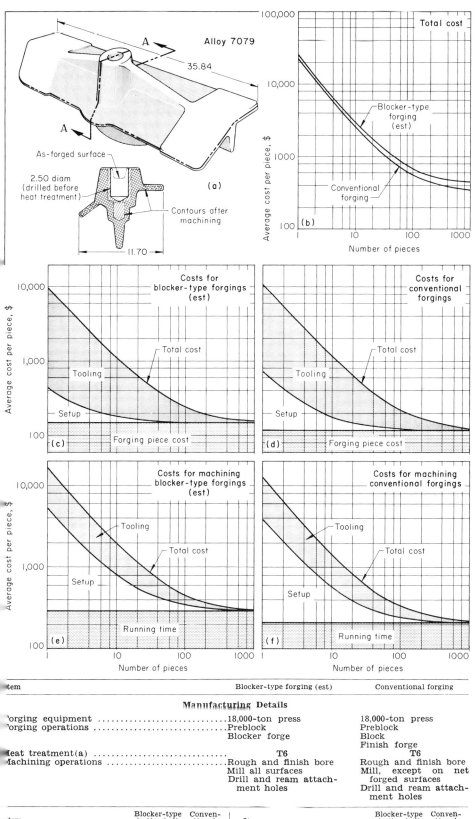

Item	Blocker-type forging (est)	Conventional forging
Manufacturing Details		
Forging equipment	18,000-ton press	18,000-ton press
Forging operations	Preblock Blocker forge	Preblock Block Finish forge
Heat treatment(a)	T6	T6
Machining operations	Rough and finish bore Mill all surfaces Drill and ream attachment holes	Rough and finish bore Mill, except on net forged surfaces Drill and ream attachment holes

Item	Blocker-type (estimated)	Conventional	Item	Blocker-type (estimated)	Conventional
Forging Costs — Unit One			**Machining Costs — Unit One**		
Die	$ 9,000	$10,025	Tooling	$11,423	$ 8,423
Setup	300	600	Setup	4,950	3,600
Forging piece cost	150	118	Running cost	291	211
Total forging cost, unit one	$ 9,450	$10,743	Total machining cost, unit one	$16,664	$12,234
Total forging plus machining cost, unit one				$26,114	$22,977

(a) Heat treating was done after the hole had been machined in the boss, because the hole reduced the mass enough so that the required tensile properties could be developed.

Fig. 6. Unit cost and effect of quantity on cost of producing terminal fittings from blocker-type and conventional closed-die forgings (Example 132)

For roll forging and ring rolling, tool materials used for aluminum are the same as those used for steel (see the articles "Roll Forging" and "Ring Rolling", pages 95 and 105 in this volume).

Preparation of Stock

The two methods most used for cutting stock into lengths for forging are sawing and shearing. Abrasive cut-off may be used, but it is slower than sawing for cutting aluminum, and, like sawing, produces burrs.

Sawing with a circular saw having carbide-tipped blades is the fastest and generally the most satisfactory method. Sawing, however, produces burrs that may nucleate defects when the stock is forged in closed dies. Burrs are best removed in a radiusing machine, but if one is not available, any other method of deburring can be used.

Shearing is used less for aluminum than for steel. Because the aluminum billets are softer, they are more likely to be mutilated in shearing, and generally have more ragged sheared ends than do sheared steel billets. Ragged ends may result in cold shuts in closed-die forgings. If shearing is the only method available, the ends of the billets should be "conditioned" to remove rough edges and torn areas. A radiusing machine is ordinarily used.

Heating for Forging

Gas-fired semimuffle furnaces are the most widely used for heating aluminum for forging, mainly because gas is widely available and is usually the least expensive source of heat. Furnace design and construction necessarily vary with the requirements of the operation.

Oil-fired furnaces may be used if gas is not available. The oil must be low in sulfur content to avoid high-temperature oxidation, especially if used in a semimuffle furnace rather than a full-muffle furnace.

Electric furnaces are entirely satisfactory for heating aluminum, but in most areas they cost more to operate than fuel-fired types, and hence they are seldom used.

Temperature Control. Because of the relatively narrow temperature ranges for forging aluminum alloys (see Fig. 2 and Table 1), good control of temperature is important.

The furnace should be equipped with pyrometric controls that can maintain temperature within ±10 F. Furnaces used for heating aluminum forging stock usually have three zones: preheat, high heat, and discharge. Recording temperature-control instruments should be used for both the preheat and high-heat zones.

Heated billets are usually temperature-checked with a prod-type pyrometer just before being placed in the forging machine. It is generally desirable to have the billets near the high side of the forging-temperature range when forging begins and to finish as quickly as possible before the temperature drops excessively.

Heating time required varies, depending on the section thickness of the stock and on furnace capabilities. A major reason for using a recording controller is that it allows the operator to observe furnace behavior. From the time-temperature chart, it is possible to judge when the billet has reached furnace temperature.

Time at temperature is not critical for aluminum alloys. Long soaking times provide no advantage but, except for the high-magnesium alloys such as 5083, are seldom harmful. Long soaking times are sometimes difficult to avoid, as when a press breaks down. When forging a high-magnesium alloy, if the operation is delayed so that soaking time will be more than 4 hr, the billets should be removed from the furnace or the furnace should be shut down. Before forging is resumed, the billets should be reheated.

Heating of Dies

Dies are always heated for closed-die forging of aluminum. The temperature to which they are heated depends mainly on the type of forging equipment used. When used in hammers or mechanical presses, where forging is extremely rapid, dies are usually heated to and maintained at 375 F. When used in hydraulic presses, where action is slower, dies usually are heated to 800 F, to maintain forging temperature.

In general practice, dies are heated slowly to the established temperature in ovens, and are placed in the press when forging is scheduled to start. Die heaters are immediately started so that die temperature will be maintained throughout the production run. Dies are also kept at the required temperature by means of embedded heating elements, strip heaters, or various types of gas burners. Sometimes combinations of these methods are used, depending largely on die size.

Lubricants

Dies are always lubricated for forging aluminum. Lubrication practice is generally the same as for forging other metals: spraying with colloidal graphite mixed with water. If metal flow is a problem, as in forging metal into narrow rib sections, soap is added to the graphite mixture.

Excess lubricant may become a problem in forging aluminum, especially in dies that have intricate cavities. The preferred practice is to blow off excess lubricant with an air hose.

Trimming

Aluminum alloy forgings are usually cold trimmed. The method used depends largely on the size, quantity and shape of the forging. Large forgings, especially in small quantities, are usually trimmed by sawing off the flash. Web sections are removed by punchout or machining.

Trimming tools are ordinarily used for trimming large quantities, especially of small forgings that are relatively intricate and require several punchouts.

For normal trimming, both the punch and the die are often made of 6G or 6F2 die block steel (Table 2) at a hardness of about 444 to 477 Bhn. Tools of these steels are cheaper because they are often made from pieces of worn-out or broken forging dies. Blades for normal trimming are sometimes made by

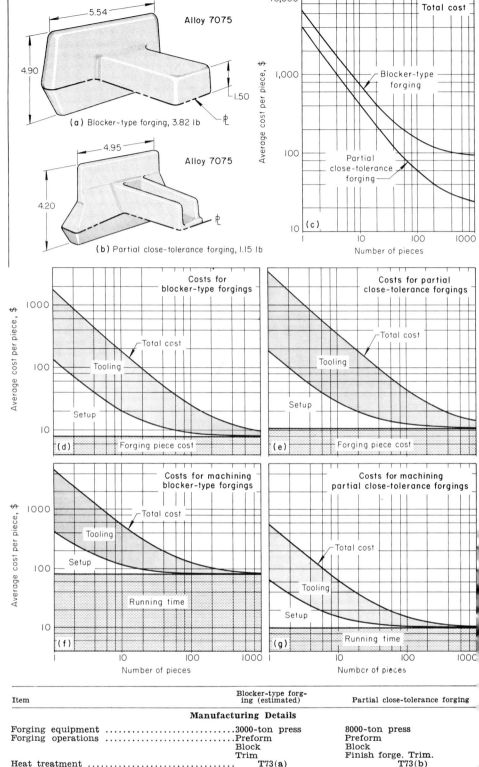

Item	Blocker-type forging (estimated)	Partial close-tolerance forging
Manufacturing Details		
Forging equipment	3000-ton press	8000-ton press
Forging operations	Preform Block Trim	Preform Block Finish forge. Trim.
Heat treatment	T73(a)	T73(b)
Machining operations	Mill all over Drill and ream	Mill outside of channel and adjacent flat surfaces Drill and ream

Item	Blocker-type	Partial close-tol.	Item	Blocker-type	Partial close-tol.
Forging Costs — Unit One			**Machining Costs — Unit One**		
Die	$1675	$3250	Tooling	$4312	$ 500
Setup	125	180	Setup	356	54
Forging piece cost	8	11	Running cost	80	10
Total forging cost, unit one	$1808	$3441	Total machining cost, unit one	$4748	$ 564
Total forging plus machining cost, unit one				$6556	$4005

(a) Forgings were heat treated after being rough machined to within 0.10 in. of finished dimensions. (b) Forgings were heat treated before any machining was done.

Fig. 7. Unit cost and effect of quantity on cost of producing machined fittings from blocker-type and partial close-tolerance forgings (Example 133)

hard facing a low-carbon steel such as 1020. O1 tool steel hardened to Rockwell C 58 to 60 has also been used successfully for normal trimming of aluminum forgings.

When close trimming is required, a high-alloy tool steel (such as D2) hardened to Rockwell C 58 to 60, for both the die and the punch, offers better results and longer life than the tool steels used for normal trimming.

Cleaning

Forgings should be cleaned as soon as possible after being forged. The following treatment removes lubricant residue and oxide, leaving a smooth surface and a natural aluminum color:

1. Etch in a 4 to 8% (by weight) aqueous solution of caustic soda at 160 F, for ½ to 5 min.
2. Immediately rinse in hot water (170 F or higher) for ½ to 5 min.
3. Desmut by immersion in a 10% (by volume) aqueous solution of nitric acid at 190 F minimum.
4. Rinse in hot water.

The immersion time in steps 1 and 2 varies depending on the amount of oxide and soil that have accumulated during heating and forging.

(For additional information on the cleaning of aluminum alloys, see the article that begins on page 611 in Volume 2 of this Handbook.)

Surface Finish

Surface finish after forging and etching in caustic is generally good, although it is likely to vary considerably from one portion of a forging to another, especially on forgings of maximum severity.

Surface finish of 125 micro-in. or better is considered normal for forged and etched aluminum alloys. Under closely controlled production conditions, surfaces smoother than 125 micro-in. often can be obtained.

As noted earlier, the finish of die cavities for forging of aluminum should be better than the cavity finish for forging of steel, because surface marks in the die cavity are more easily transferred to the surfaces of aluminum. A finish of 6 micro-in. or better is usually specified on dies for forging aluminum.

Selection of Method on the Basis of Quantity and Cost

Except when mechanical properties and required grain flow dictate the use of a specific forging procedure, the five following methods of producing a part are competitive:

1. Machine it entirely from wrought plate or bar stock.
2. Use an open-die forging, which usually involves considerable machining.
3. Use a blocker-type forging, which avoids the cost of finishing dies and normally needs less machining than would be required by an open-die forging.
4. Use a conventional closed-die forging, which needs less machining than a blocker-type forging.
5. Use a close-tolerance (minimum-draft) forging, which requires minimal machining or, for some parts, no machining.

As the amount of machining decreases from methods 1 through 5, machining cost also decreases, but this is accompanied by a gradual increase in the cost of forging, principally die and setup costs.

The cost of a forged part can be determined only by considering both forging cost and machining cost. Quantity of parts to be produced affects choice of method and costs. Both of the examples that follow show the cost breakdown for producing the first finish-machined part (against which all tool costs are charged) and, in addition, the effect of quantity on forging, machining, and total costs.

Example 132. Blocker-Type vs Conventional Forgings for Terminal Fittings (Fig. 6)

An important consideration in the manufacture of terminal fittings (see Fig. 6a) was that of minimizing their susceptibility to stress corrosion in service. One way to do this was to limit the amount of cut grain, particularly in critical locations, that resulted from machining. Thus, regardless of cost, a conventional rather than a blocker-type forging was preferred. Fortunately, as shown in Fig. 6, the cost of machined conventional forgings was less than that estimated for machined blocker-type forgings.

Unit-one costs for forging and for machining of the blocker-type and the conventional forgings are summarized in the table with Fig. 6. The charts in Fig. 6(c) to (f) show the effect of quantity on forging and machining costs per piece for the two types of forgings. Total costs per piece are compared in Fig. 6(b), which shows that the fitting produced from the conventional forging was more economical in all quantities from 1 to 1000 pieces. Manufacturing details for the two types of forging are presented in the top part of the table with Fig. 6.

Example 133. Blocker-Type vs Partial Close-Tolerance Forgings for Sponson Attachment Fittings (Fig. 7)

Initially, sponson attachment fittings having a finished weight of 0.37 lb each were machined from blocker-type forgings weighing 3.82 lb (Fig. 7a). As shown by the comparison of unit-one costs in the table that accompanies Fig. 7, a change to the use of partial close-tolerance forgings weighing 1.15 lb (Fig. 7b) decreased machining cost for unit one from $4748 to $564, so that despite the $1633 increase in forging cost, unit one cost less when machined from the partial close-tolerance forging. The charts in Fig. 7(c) to (g) show the effect of quantity on forging, machining and total costs per piece for fittings produced from both types of forgings. Manufacturing details for the two production methods are given in the table with Fig. 7.

Die Forging Design

Types of Forgings

All forgings fall into two general classes—hand forgings and die forgings. Hand forgings are sometimes called open die forgings—as the name suggests, the metal is not confined laterally when being forged to the desired shape. The forger manipulates the stock between repeated squeezes of the hydraulic press, or ring roller or blows of the hammer in progressively shaping the forging to the desired form.

Die Forgings

This book concentrates on the more common forging type, die forgings—sometimes also called closed die forgings. These forgings receive their accurate and uniform shapes from a hammering or pressing of the forging stock in counterpart cavities or impressions cut into a set of dies.

The primary equipment used to make die forgings includes hammers, mechanical presses, hydraulic presses and mechanical upsetters, each type possessing its own particular advantages. Forging design, forging tolerances, quantities required, and alloy selected must all be considered in determining the best and most economical equipment to use in making a specific part.

Die Forging Types

Die forgings may be broadly classed as blocker-type, conventional, or precision. Other, more special, die forgings are those of can- or tube-type, impacts, and no-drafts.

Blocker-Type Forgings

A blocker-type forging is generously designed, with large fillet and corner radii and with thick webs and ribs, so that it can be produced in a set of finishing dies only. Producing such a forging may typically require a unit pressure of 10 to 15 tons per square inch of projected plan area, depending on the alloy and the complexity of the design. This is less pressure than is necessary to

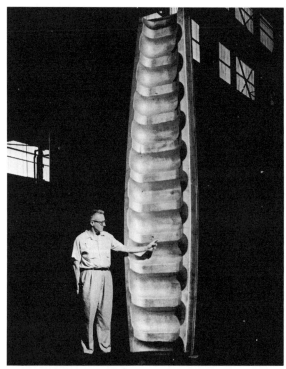

Fig. 1—*Only a finishing set of dies was used to make this blocker-type forging of an aircraft wing rib in 7079-F alloy. The rib is 168 inches long, weighs 3,100 lbs., and has a plan area of 5,700 sq. inches.*

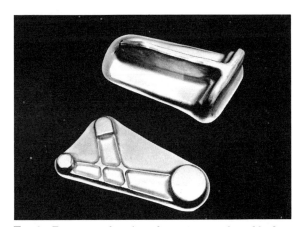

Fig. 2—*Two examples of configurations made as blocker-type forgings.*

make a more intricate forging. The projected plan area of the forging is used to arrive at the estimated total tonnage required.

A blocker-type forging generally requires machining on all surfaces. Economics may dictate such a design if quantity requirements are limited or if the finished part tolerances necessitate complete machining. A blocker-type forging is an end product and should not be confused with a blocker forging, which is a preliminary shape requiring a subsequent finishing die operation to attain its final shape. Figs. 1, 2 and 3 illustrate typical blocker-type forgings varying from small to very large.

Conventional Forgings

Most common of all die forging types, a conventional forging is more intricate in configuration than a blocker-type forging, having proportionately lighter sections, sharper details and closer tolerances, and thus is more difficult to forge. The design differences between these two types of forging are illustrated graphically in Figs. 4 and 5. A conventional forging normally requires only partial final machining. A typical unit pressure of 15 to 25 tons per square inch of plan area is required and usually a blocking operation is required prior to the finishing operation. Typical forgings of the conventional type are shown in Figs. 6, 7 and 8.

The designer must evaluate the cost difference—a blocker-type forging has a lower die cost but will be heavier, requiring more extensive machining; a conventional forging has a higher die cost but will be lighter, requiring much less machining. Only a cost comparison by the customer can determine which type of forging will give lowest total cost.

Precision Forgings

A precision forging denotes closer-than-normal tolerances. It may also involve a more intricate forging design than a conventional type and may include smaller fillet radii, corner radii, draft angles and thinner webs and ribs. See Figs. 9, 10 and 11 for typical precision forgings. The higher cost of a precision forging, including increased cost of dies, must be justified in the reduced machining required for its end use. This type of forging may typically require pressures of 25 to 50 tons per square inch of plan area.

Can and Tube Forgings

Can- and tube-type forgings are shapes which are

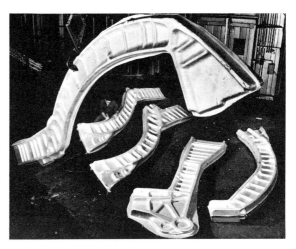

Fig. 3—*These five blocker-type forgings of aircraft main frames in 7075-F alloy vary in weight from 2,400 to 3,200 lbs., and from 14 to 23 feet in length.*

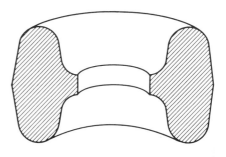

BLOCKER-TYPE FORGING – REQUIRES ONLY ONE DIE OPERATION AND A TRIMMING AND PIERCING OPERATION TO REMOVE SURPLUS METAL.

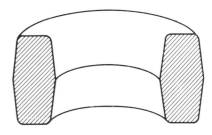

CONVENTIONAL FORGING – REQUIRES TWO DIE OPERATIONS AND A TRIMMING AND PIERCING OPERATION TO REMOVE SURPLUS METAL.

Fig. 4—*Blocker-type forgings save on die and production costs though machining may be increased somewhat.*

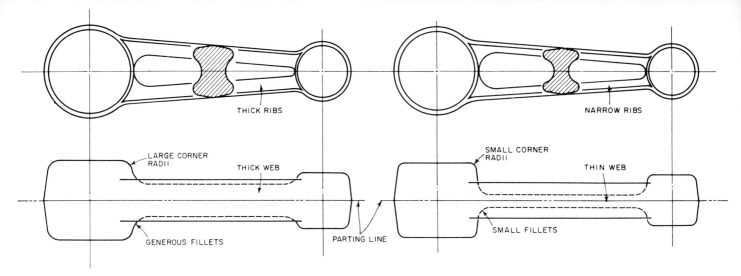

THICK RIBS

LARGE CORNER RADII

THICK WEB

GENEROUS FILLETS

PARTING LINE

NARROW RIBS

SMALL CORNER RADII

THIN WEB

SMALL FILLETS

BLOCKER-TYPE FORGING

CONVENTIONAL-TYPE FORGING

FIG. 5—*These two connecting rods illustrate the usual differences between blocker-type and conventional forging designs.*

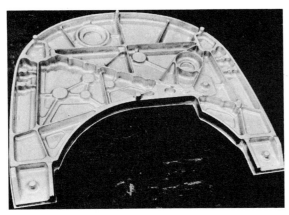

FIG. 6—*Note the sharper and greater amount of detail in this conventional-type forging of an aircraft engine firewall, as compared with blocker-type forgings in Figs. 1-3. A set of blocking or preliminary shaping dies and a set of finishing dies are necessary. This forging in 2014-T6 alloy weighs 87 lbs. and is 39 inches in over-all length.*

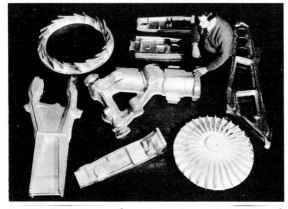

FIG. 7—*Intricate configuration, close tolerances and sharp detail are characteristic of the conventional forging process used to make these eight varied aircraft structural and engine parts.*

open at one or both ends. They are sometimes called extruded forgings; the term is appropriate, as the dies may be designed to extrude the tubular walls of the forgings. They are usually produced on forging press equipment. The side walls may include longitudinal ribs and may be flanged at one open end. The interior or exterior surfaces of the bottom wall may be configured with details normally possible in conventional forgings. Figs. 12 and 13 show forgings of this type.

No-Draft Forgings

As suggested by the name, these are draftless forgings (Fig. 14). Normally, a no-draft forging is the most difficult of all forgings to make because of the typically close design proportions and tolerances. They differ from precision or conventional types of forgings in the draftless feature and the relatively high vertical wall height-to-width ratio, which require specialized die-making and forging facilities. No-draft forgings require the least amount of machining of any forging type, which may offset generally higher forging and die costs.

Basic Design Features

A discussion of forging design cannot practically cover in detail all the considerations that arise from the infinite variations in size, shape and function of different specific parts. However, certain fundamentals apply in all cases and it is essential, for good forging design, that they be known and adhered to.

These fundamentals are graphically presented in the following pages as they relate to the usual problems that confront the designer. The exam-

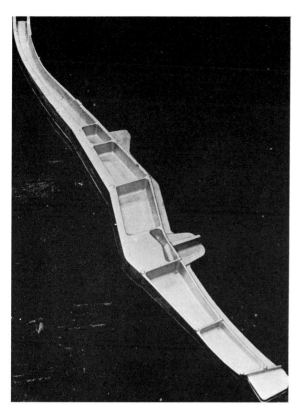

FIG. 8—*Conventional-type forging in 7075-T6 alloy produced this aircraft spar bulkhead that is 107 inches long and weighs 144 lbs.*

FIG. 10—*Numerous and large-sized punchouts made it possible to precision-forge thin walls in this aircraft nose-wheel truss. The unit is made of 2014-T6 alloy, it has an over-all length of 104 inches and weighs 133 lbs.*

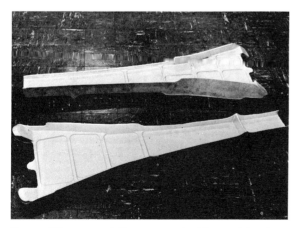

FIG. 9—*Three sets of dies are required in precision forging to provide close tolerances, and sharper, thinner configuration than possible in conventional forging. This aircraft spar forging, made of 7075-T6 alloy, is 64 inches long and weighs only 45 lbs.*

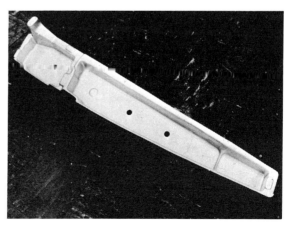

FIG. 11—*Precision forging produced this aircraft bulkhead in 7075-T6 alloy. Length is 41 inches, weight is 41 lbs.*

FIG. 13—*Rough machining on both ends of this tube-type forging minimizes the final machining operation. The part is made of 2014-T61 alloy, weighs 23.6 lbs., and has an over-all length of 24 inches.*

FIG. 12—*On this can-type forging, the head end (at top) was rough-machined prior to heat-treating to obtain optimum mechanical properties. The slots were machined to facilitate the final machining operations. This part is made of 2014-T6 alloy, weighs 199 lbs., and is 30.5 inches long.*

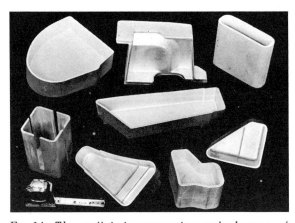

FIG. 14—*The small design proportions and tolerances of precision no-draft forgings, as illustrated, require special die-making and forging facilities.*

ples cited will, for the most part, refer to relatively simple shapes. The principles involved become all the more significant with increasing complexity of design.

Parting Line

The planes of separation between the upper and lower parts of a closed die set are called the parting line. It is established usually, but not always, through the maximum periphery of the forged part. It may be straight or irregular. It must be designated on all forging drawings. Its position can measurably affect the initial cost and ultimate wear of dies, the ease of forging, the grain flow,

related mechanical properties, and the machining requirements for the finished part. The diagrams in Figs. 15 through 23 show various methods of positioning the parting line.

Maximum Periphery—It is preferable to place the parting line around the largest periphery of the forging. It is easier to force metal laterally in a spreading action than it is to fill deep, narrow die impressions, as indicated in Fig. 15.

Flat-Sided Forgings—These present an opportunity to reduce die costs, since the only machining is in the lower block, the upper being a completely flat surface (Fig. 16). This simplifies production by eliminating the possibility of mismatch between the upper and lower impressions.

While a top die is always essential, in flat-sided designs the forge shop can use a stock or "standard" flat-top die to mate with the impression die. Obviously, there can be no integrally forged characters appearing on the flat surface when a standard flat-top die is used.

Inclination of the Parting Line—Forgings in which the parting line is inclined to the forging plane may present difficulties in trimming if the inclination is too great. As pointed out in Fig. 17, it is generally good practice to limit the inclination to no more than 75° out of parallel with the forging plane, thereby avoiding raggedly trimmed edges.

Parting Line Effect on Grain Flow

Location of the parting line has a critical bearing on grain flow and the directional properties of the forged piece. In the forging process, excess metal flows out of the cavity into the gutter as the dies are forced together. In this flow toward the parting line, objectionable flow patterns may be created if the flow path is not smooth, as illustrated in Fig. 18. A parting line on the outer side of a rib should be placed either adjacent to the web section or at the end of the rib opposite the adjoining web section. The placement of the line at an intermediate step can result in irregularities.

Webs at Different Levels

On forgings with a web of varying planes enclosed by ribs, the parting line should follow the centerlines of the enclosed webs (Fig. 19).

The same forging could also have a satisfactory parting line at either the top or bottom surface. Since both are plane surfaces, a flat parting line would result. A die plug protruding above the parting line to form the forging recess is required, but it would not be objectionable.

Parting Line Can Modify Forging Design

Fig. 20 shows a part with various placements of the parting line. The top illustration shows a simple solution—putting the large flat surface on the parting line, with all of the impression in one die. This is an economical way to produce the part.

The second illustration shows an approach that is undesirable because of the unbalanced lateral forces exerted on the die. A counterlock (See Fig.

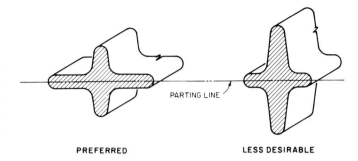

PREFERRED   **LESS DESIRABLE**

FIG. 15—*Place the parting line through the largest cross section of the forging in order to avoid narrow, deep, die impressions.*

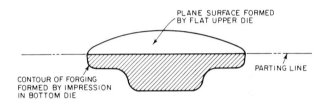

FIG. 16—*A flat surface at the parting line reduces die costs, simplifies the trimming operation and eliminates any die mismatching.*

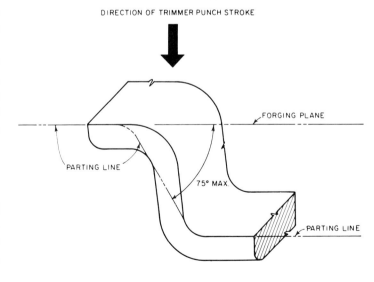

FIG. 17—*A raggedly trimmed edge on the forging may result if the flash on the parting line is inclined more than 75°.*

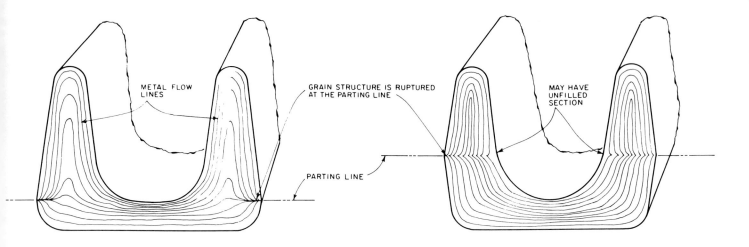

UNDESIRABLE — THESE PARTING LINES RESULT IN METAL FLOW PATTERNS THAT CAUSE FORGING DEFECTS

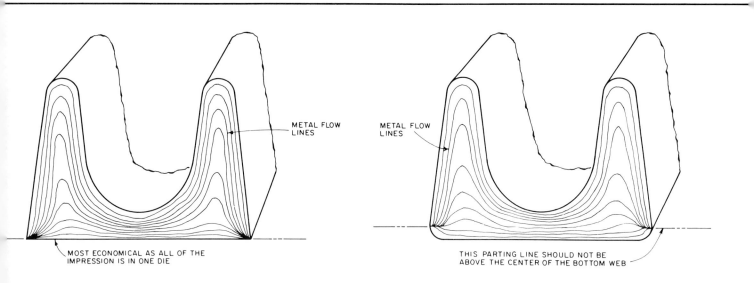

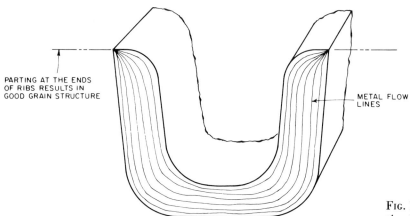

PARTING AT THE ENDS OF RIBS RESULTS IN GOOD GRAIN STRUCTURE

METAL FLOW LINES

FIG. 18—*Various parting line locations on a channel section have differing effects.*

RECOMMENDED — THE FLOW LINES ARE SMOOTH AT STRESSED SECTIONS WITH THESE PARTING LINES

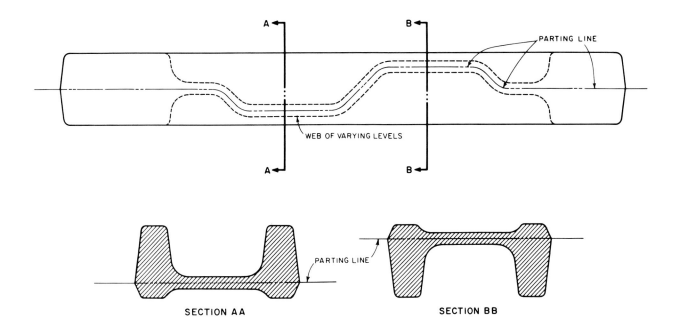

WEB OF VARYING LEVELS

PARTING LINE

SECTION AA

SECTION BB

PARTING LINE

FIG. 19—*A parting line outside a rib or wall should follow the web inside the forging.*

21) would have to be machined in the dies to resist the side thrust. This means more expensive dies.

The third illustration demonstrates an irregular parting line, but with the forging inclined to minimize side thrust. This is good practice. The part is relatively light in weight, will have good grain flow, and provides a natural draft that permits forging of the end flange at a true right angle.

The bottom sketch indicates a method that is highly desirable from the standpoint of unit cost per forging. By producing the part as a double forging, which is sawed apart into two units, considerable economy is achieved—particularly if the end surfaces will have to be machined anyway.

Die Side Thrust

While working clearance at the press or hammer guides is necessary for proper functioning, it can be a cause of match errors, especially when die-side thrust is induced by an irregular parting line. Side thrust increases as the parting line inclines from parallel to the forging plane.

In Fig. 21, the upper illustration shows the problem created by inclination of the parting line, although it agrees with the recommended practice

in following the web center. As shown in the middle illustration, a solution of the side thrust problem can be achieved by sinking counterlocks into the dies—but this is expensive and potentially troublesome.

The preferred solution is shown at the bottom. The part has been inclined with respect to the forging plane, thus balancing the side thrust and eliminating the need for counterlocks.

Normal to Forging Plane

When the parting line is inclined with respect to the forging plane, or the principal dimensions of the piece are laid out in another set of axes, draft is nonetheless referenced to the direction of the stroke of the hammer or the press (Fig. 22).

Intersection of Parting Line and Forging Plane

As indicated in Fig. 22, draft angles cannot be laid out until the forging plane is first established. A simple method of positioning the forging plane with respect to an irregular parting line is indicated in Fig. 23. By selecting points approximately .50 inch or less beyond the ends of the forging as shown, the intersection of the parting line and forging plane can be located easily with

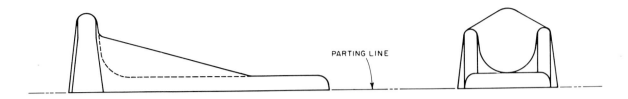

ECONOMICAL – FORGING IMPRESSION IS ONLY IN ONE DIE BUT FORGING SECTIONS ARE SLIGHTLY HEAVIER

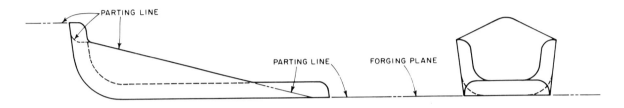

UNDESIRABLE – DESIGN REQUIRES EXPENSIVE COUNTERLOCK TO TAKE SIDE THRUST FORCES

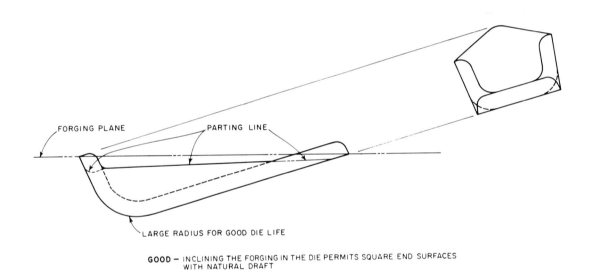

GOOD – INCLINING THE FORGING IN THE DIE PERMITS SQUARE END SURFACES WITH NATURAL DRAFT

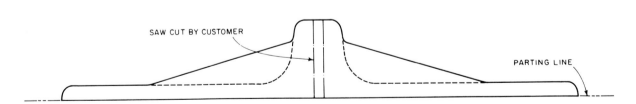

PREFERRED – A DOUBLE FORGING OFFERS THE MOST ADVANTAGES IN PRODUCTION

FIG. 20—*These examples illustrate how parting line choices can modify a forging design.*

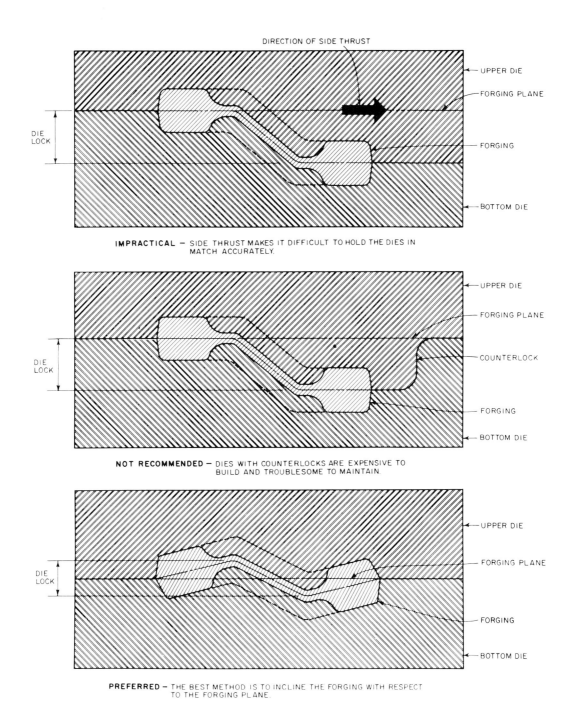

DIRECTION OF SIDE THRUST

UPPER DIE

FORGING PLANE

DIE LOCK

FORGING

BOTTOM DIE

IMPRACTICAL — SIDE THRUST MAKES IT DIFFICULT TO HOLD THE DIES IN MATCH ACCURATELY.

UPPER DIE

FORGING PLANE

DIE LOCK

COUNTERLOCK

FORGING

BOTTOM DIE

NOT RECOMMENDED — DIES WITH COUNTERLOCKS ARE EXPENSIVE TO BUILD AND TROUBLESOME TO MAINTAIN.

UPPER DIE

FORGING PLANE

DIE LOCK

FORGING

BOTTOM DIE

PREFERRED — THE BEST METHOD IS TO INCLINE THE FORGING WITH RESPECT TO THE FORGING PLANE.

FIG. 21—*The forging plane should be positioned in such a way as to eliminate side thrust when locked dies are required.*

definitely established even dimensions outside of the forging proper.

Draft Angles

Draft refers to the taper given to internal and external sides of a closed-die forging to facilitate its removal from the die cavity. Draft is normally expressed as an angle from the direction of the ram travel. Draft not only ensures good forgings with a minimum of production difficulty, but also reduces diesinking expense by adding rigidity to the die cutter. For reasons of clarity, the given draft

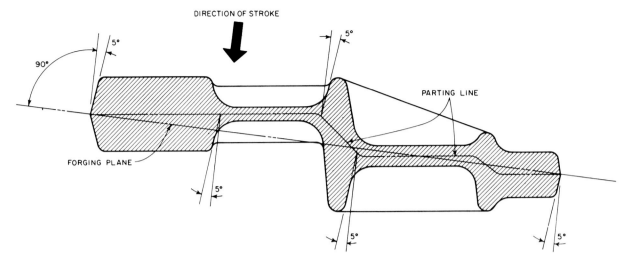

FIG. 22—*Minimum draft is measured from a perpendicular to the forging plane.*

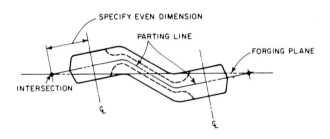

FIG. 23—*This method of establishing the forging plane is recommended.*

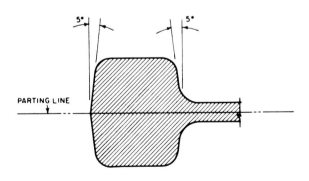

FIG. 24—*The usual standard draft angle for hammer or press forgings is 5°.*

angles are called out repeatedly within the following illustrations. Normally, draft angle callouts are specified singly under the general notes, but are omitted from the field of the drawing if they are uniform throughout the part.

Standard Draft Angles

Standard draft angles refer to those most commonly used. A fully equipped die shop must have die cutters not only in all standard draft angles but in a variety of diameters as well. The standard draft angles are $7°$, $5°$, $3°$, $1°$ and $0°$. If other draft angles are specified, special die cutters have to be made. Fig. 24 depicts a commonly used $5°$ draft angle.

In most cases, draft angles less than $5°$ preclude the use of hammer equipment because additional mechanical aids are required to eject the forging from the die cavity.

Table 1 shows standard draft angle dimensional information useful for die making and drawing purposes.

Draft on Cylindrical Ends

Cylindrical sections are assumed to have standard draft at the parting line. The customary diesinking practice is to leave the narrow tangential flats in these areas. As illustrated in Fig. 25, it is not necessary to specify draft on drawings at such detail; only cylindrical contours need to be indicated.

Matching Parting Line Contours

Matching parting line contours at the parting line

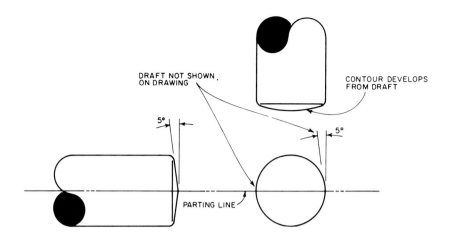

Fig. 25—*Cylindrical sections have standard draft at the parting line.*

on the outer periphery is recommended where the top and bottom die contours do not coincide from normal diesinking. This can be achieved by the following three methods.

When the matching portion is small, the method in Fig. 26 is recommended. Weight increase is insignificant and diesinking is the simplest possible. Adding the 5° (Ref.) as shown removes any doubt as to the intended construction.

The method in Fig. 27 is recommended when the matching portion is substantial and weight saving is important. Diesinking is routine in this case. The pad thickness may vary from .06 inch on small forgings to .50 inch on very large forgings. The method in Fig. 28 adds less material than in Fig. 26, but more than in Fig. 27. It also adds to the diesinking. The original 5° draft cut leaves a jog or step at the parting line. An additional cut removes this step by a matching straight line tangent to the bottom radius.

Blending of draft angles can be troublesome and should be avoided where possible. As shown in Fig. 29, this can be done around the entire periphery of a boss by applying the method shown in Fig. 26 or the method in Fig. 27. However, if the lower portion had matching draft around the entire boss, there would still unavoidably remain a portion of the web that must be blended from the normal to the matching draft. The drawing should include a specific note defining the distance in which this transition is to be made.

DEPTH	DRAFT ANGLES					DEPTH
	1°	3°	5°	7°	10°	
1/32	.0005	.0016	.0027	.0038	.0055	1/32
1/16	.0011	.0033	.0055	.0077	.011	1/16
3/32	.0016	.0049	.008	.0115	.0165	3/32
1/8	.0022	.0066	.0109	.015	.022	1/8
3/16	.0033	.0098	.016	.023	.033	3/16
1/4	.0044	.013	.022	.031	.044	1/4
5/16	.0055	.016	.027	.038	.055	5/16
3/8	.0065	.020	.033	.046	.066	3/8
7/16	.0076	.023	.038	.054	.077	7/16
1/2	.0087	.026	.044	.061	.088	1/2
5/8	.011	.033	.055	.077	.110	5/8
3/4	.013	.039	.066	.092	.132	3/4
7/8	.015	.046	.077	.107	.154	7/8
1	.017	.052	.087	.123	.176	1
	1°	3°	5°	7°	10°	

TABLE 1—*Draft Dimensions for Standard Draft Angles.*

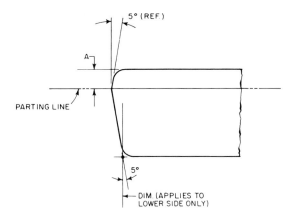

FIG. 26—*This is recommended when "A" is small.*

Constant Draft Angles for Best Die Economy

The blending of varying draft angles results in additional diesinking expense. There are important economies to be achieved by designing forgings with *constant* draft angles since surfaces with draft are generally formed by conical cutters (Fig. 30).

A radius at the tip of a tool blends the drafted surface with the rest of the forging or forms a full radius at the edge of a rib. The size of the tool body determines the minimum fillet radius in a die between adjoining surfaces that have the same draft.

Ribs, sidewalls and bosses, with constant draft but changing in depth, will vary in width at the base as a result of the draft. If the diesinking cutter is traversed in a straight line, the top of the rib on a forging will be straight (in plan view) and of constant width. However, the base of the rib will vary in width and will be curved or irregular, as shown in Fig. 31.

To make a rib of varying height with top and base widths parallel to each other requires blending of draft angles and increases die costs. This should be done only in cases where it is imperative and not as a random choice. Fig. 32 shows various choices and their effects.

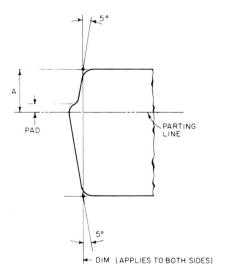

FIG. 27—*This is recommended when "A" is substantial and weight-saving is important.*

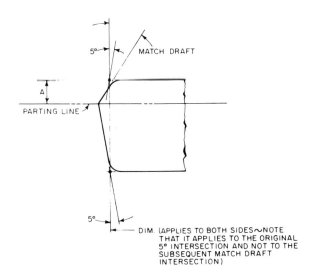

FIG. 28—*When "A" is substantial, this method adds less material than in Fig. 26, but more than in Fig. 27.*

Some Undercuts—Or Back Drafts—Are Possible

Undercuts on forgings are possible but require careful consideration in their applications. Undercuts may increase costs slightly as the forging removal from the dies may be retarded. A forging with undercuts on both sides of the parting line, as shown in Fig. 33, cannot be made. Since the die halves must separate in order to remove the forging, the die separation would mutilate the forging in overcoming the back draft resistance on both sides.

Undercuts in the bottom die only can be forged within the limits as shown in Fig. 34. The forging must be removed from the bottom die at an angle because of the back draft. The draft angle opposite the back draft must be larger by a recommended 6° to allow the forging to be removed. This applies to all similar surfaces.

An undercut can also be produced by inclining the forging plane to eliminate the back draft (Fig. 35).

Some types of forgings can be fabricated with back draft. However, these parts require a secondary operation with the use of additional tooling. The extent of the back draft of these parts should, at the time of original design, be thoroughly discussed with a competent forging vendor. The in-

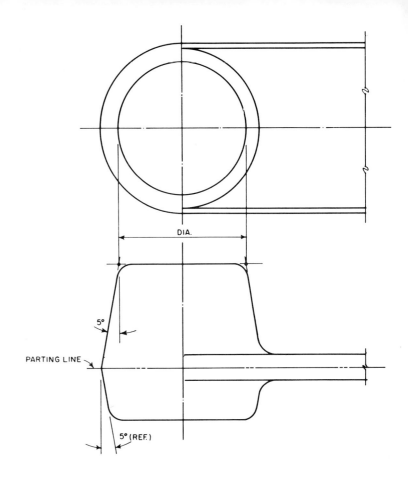

Fig. 29—*Blending of draft is avoided as illustrated.*

Fig. 30—*Die surfaces with draft are machined with conical diesinking cutters.*

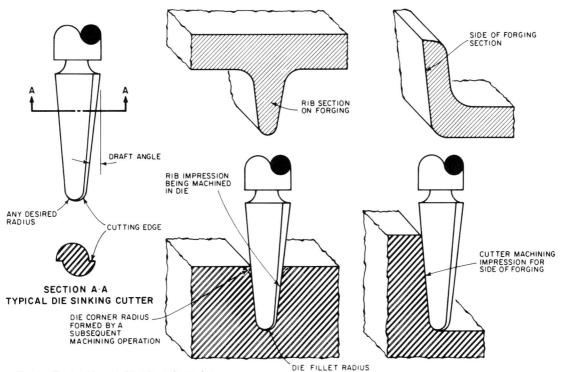

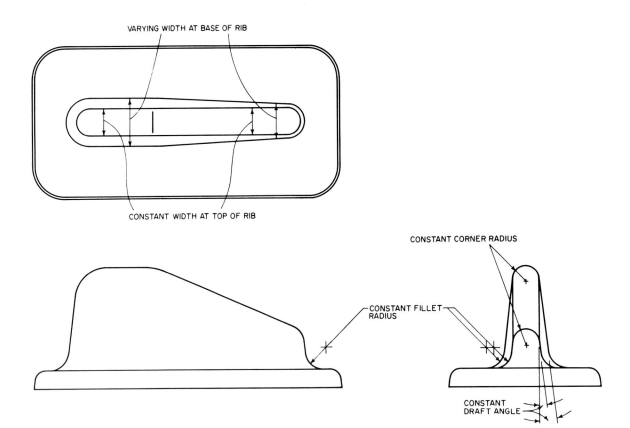

FIG. 31—*Keeping the draft angle, fillet radius, corner radius, and top width all constant along a rib with tapered or varying height simplifies diesinking.*

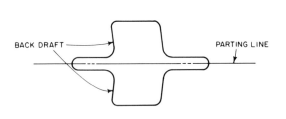

FIG. 33—*Back draft in both top and bottom dies does not permit the dies to be separated.*

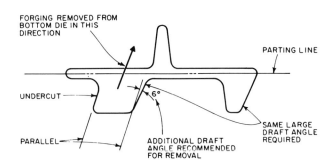

FIG. 34—*Undercut requires opposite surfaces to have a larger draft angle to compensate in removal.*

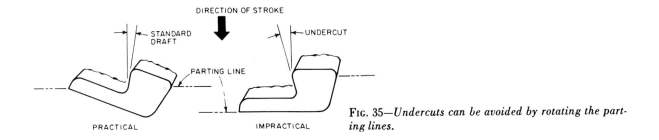

FIG. 35—*Undercuts can be avoided by rotating the parting lines.*

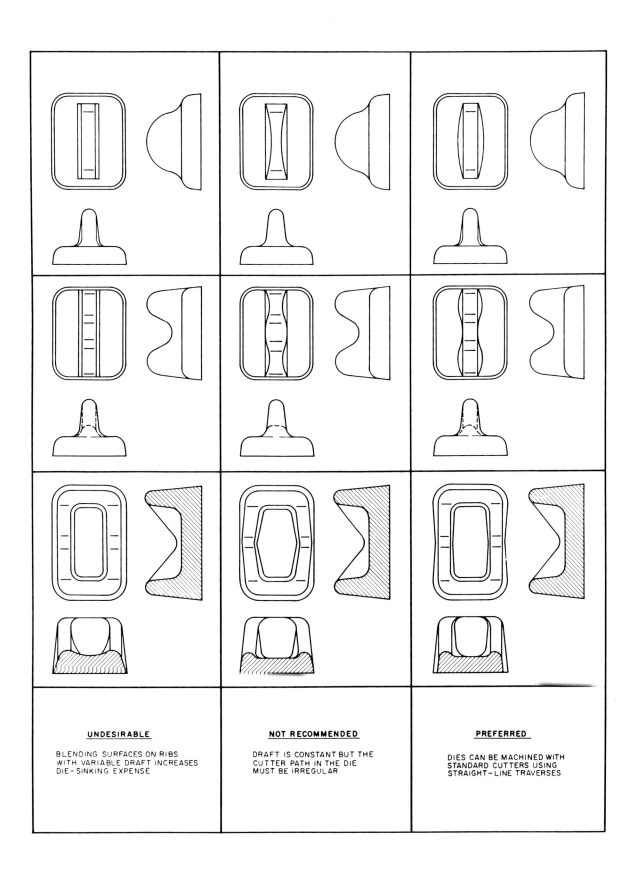

UNDESIRABLE	NOT RECOMMENDED	PREFERRED
BLENDING SURFACES ON RIBS WITH VARIABLE DRAFT INCREASES DIE-SINKING EXPENSE	DRAFT IS CONSTANT BUT THE CUTTER PATH IN THE DIE MUST BE IRREGULAR	DIES CAN BE MACHINED WITH STANDARD CUTTERS USING STRAIGHT-LINE TRAVERSES

Fig. 32—*How draft contours are shown on varying heights can affect costs.*

Source: Aluminum Forging Design Manual, Aluminum Assn., Inc.

creased costs of secondary tooling and increased piece price may outweigh the costs of conventional forging and machining costs. It should be pointed out that the parts shown in Fig. 36 have the advantage of greater strength due to an uninterrupted grain flow.

Corner Radii

A corner radius is formed by the intersection of two surfaces with an included angle (within the forging) less than 180°, or excluded angle (outside the forging) greater than 180°. When minimum dimensions for corner radii are established, two points are considered: 1) the radius as a stress concentrator in the die, and 2) pressure necessary to fill the die cavity.

A sharp edge or corner on a forged piece requires a corresponding sharp recess in the die since the forging is a positive shape and the die cavity a direct opposite or negative shape. Thus, a forging corner radius is formed by a corresponding die fillet radius.

When die fillet radii are excessively sharp, the force of metal under pressure and the stress-raising corner effect can cause checking or the development of small cracks in the die after only a few pieces have been forged. This adverse effect on die life is compounded, since greater forging pressure is required to fill sharp die fillets than large die fillets. Die life becomes short, hence uneconomical.

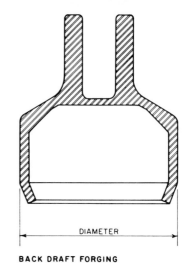

BACK DRAFT FORGING

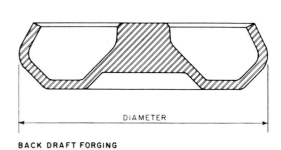

BACK DRAFT FORGING

FIG. 36—*Two back draft forgings showing lip sections preformed by a secondary operation.*

FIG. 37—*The corner radius is determined by the height from the parting line. See Table 2 for value of R_R.*

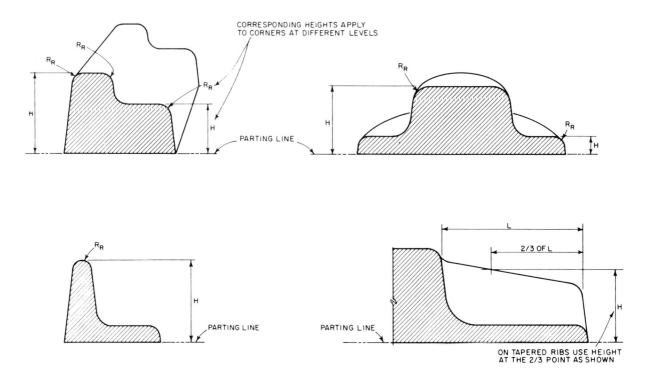

106

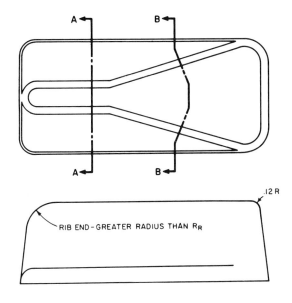

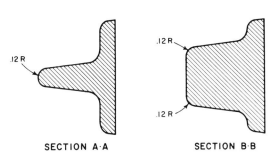

SECTION A·A   SECTION B·B

FIG. 38—*Diesinking costs are minimized when a constant corner radius is used as illustrated.*

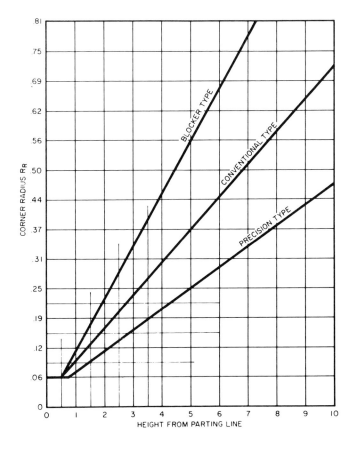

TABLE 2—*Recommended Size of Corner Radius.*

Minimum Corner Radii

Minimum corner radii limit the use of very high, thin ribs. With a full radius at its edge and standard draft on the sides, a rib should not be any thinner than twice "R_R". A thicker rib or flange may have a flat edge with two corner radii, each equal to "R_R". However, it is more desirable to use a full radius equal to one-half the rib thickness. See Table 2 for the recommended corner radii sizes. Here the height from the parting line determines the size of the corner radius, as shown in Fig. 37.

Suggested Corner Radii

The above chart shows recommended corner radii for the three classes of die forgings; the smallest radii are indicated ·for precision-type forgings, larger for the conventional-type, and the largest for the blocker-type. When designing any of the three types, every effort should be made to specify the maximum radii permissible, in order to keep forging costs down to a minimum.

Constant Corner Radii Reduce Die Costs

The blending of corner radii on forgings should be carefully avoided to an even greater degree than blending fillets. Forging corner radii, as expressed physically in the die cavity, constitute fillets sunk by milling cutters of similar sized radii and, accordingly, are much more difficult to blend. Constant corner radii as shown in Fig. 38 will achieve economies in die cost.

Larger Radii at Rib Ends

At rib or flange ends, a radius larger than the corner radius is recommended to permit forging fill

Source: Aluminum Forging Design Manual, Aluminum Assn., Inc.

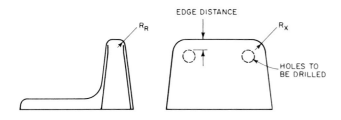

FIG. 39—*The R_X radius should be as large as possible to improve forging fillability.*

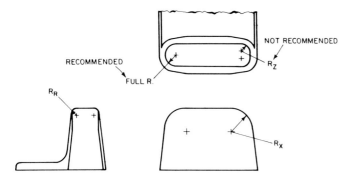

FIG. 40—*At rib ends, a full radius as shown is recommended.*

FIG. 41—*A rib or flange edge that is rounded with a full radius gives the most durably shaped die impression.*

without excessive difficulty. The die cavity is sunk by moving the die milling cutter in the same arc as the large radius at such an end. (This is not the same as the blending of radii, which requires difficult diesinking).

The suggested R_X radius indicated in Fig. 39 may be as follows:

1) Equal to edge distance plus hole radius
2) Three times R_R
3) As large as possible

While it is recommended that R_X be as large as possible, the size of the radius in the plan view is also important. A full radius as shown at the left of the plan view in Fig. 40 is recommended. Such a die cavity is sunk by moving a full-width diameter cutter in the same arc as R_X, a simple diesinking operation. If the arc is not a full radius (R_Z shown at the right which is not the same as R_R), it requires added diesinking cuts in blending these radii through the distance of R_X.

Sharp Corner Radii Cause Premature Die Failure

As shown in Fig. 41, a rib or flange edge that is rounded with a full radius will reduce die problems. The top or edge of a rib should be rounded with a minimum radius of R_R, the value depending upon height from the parting line. Die life is reduced when deep, thin ribs are forged. The force required to fill a deep rib cavity, particularly when it is adjacent to a very thin web, develops severe die stresses. Therefore, ribs that are next to very thin webs should be made as low as the design will permit.

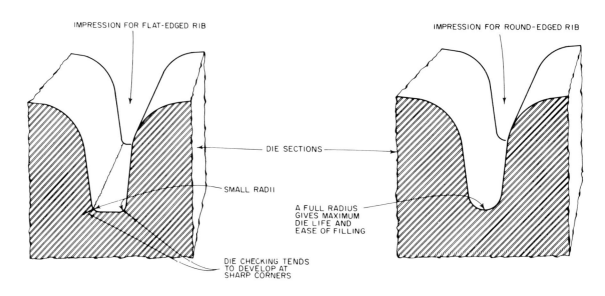

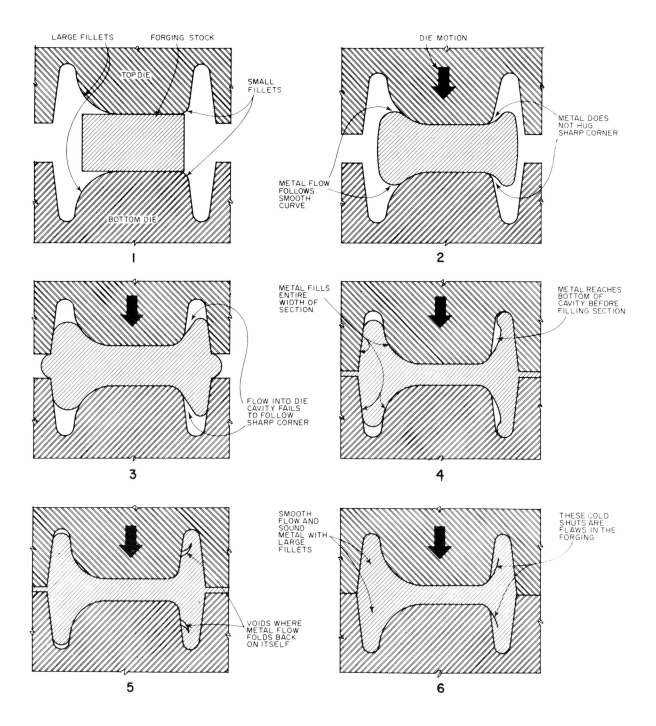

FIG. 42—*Progressive forging steps demonstrate how small fillets may cause unfilled sections, laps, and cold shuts. The fillet radii referred to pertain to the forging as these are formed by corresponding die corner radii.*

Fillet Radii

A fillet radius is at the intersection of two surfaces with an included angle (within the forging) greater than 180°, or an excluded angle (outside the forging) less than 180°.

Minimum Fillet Radii

One of the most important contributions a designer can make to the most economical forging of a blocker-, conventional- or precision-type is in

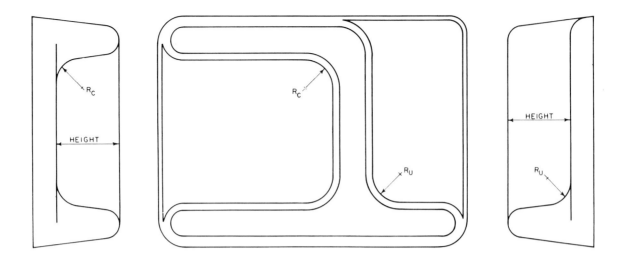

FIG. 43—*The fillet radius is determined by the height between the adjoining surface levels.*

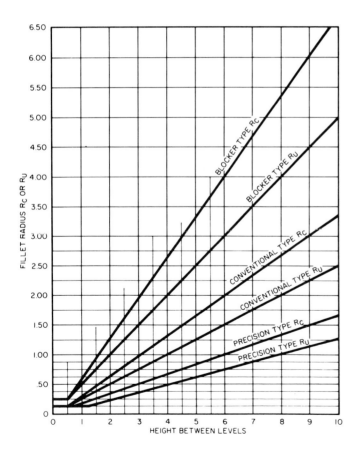

TABLE 3—*Recommended Size of Fillet Radius.*

the allowance of generous radii for fillets and corners. This assures sound quality of the part as well as economy.

Liberal fillets on forgings permit the forging stock to follow the die contours more easily during the forging process. Small fillets may cause momentary voids beyond the bend in the flow path of the metal. These voids are subsequently filled, but the interrupted flow results in a flaw in the forging (See Fig. 42).

Suggested Fillet Radii

As shown in Fig. 43, use a fillet radius equal to R_C (Minimum) where the flow of metal into the die gutter at the parting line is confined. If the forging stock must fill ribs on the outside periphery, web fillets at least as large as R_C are indicated. Where the web is very broad, larger fillets may be advisable.

When opposing ribs do not confine the metal flow to the gutter, values of R_U should be used for sound forgings. An area may be considered non-confined if its outside periphery is confined less than 50 per cent of the total periphery.

The sizes of fillet radii required are governed by the step height from the surface where the fillet occurs to the adjoining surface level.

Table 3 gives recommended fillet radii for the three different classes of die forgings—precision, conventional and blocker types. Adherence to the standards indicated here is generally essential in good forging design. Significant decreases from these standards could result in an increase in forging costs.

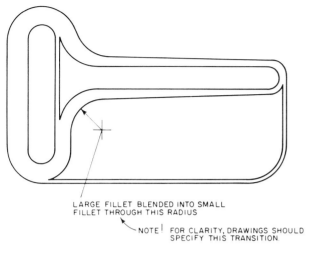

LARGE FILLET BLENDED INTO SMALL
FILLET THROUGH THIS RADIUS

NOTE! FOR CLARITY, DRAWINGS SHOULD
SPECIFY THIS TRANSITION.

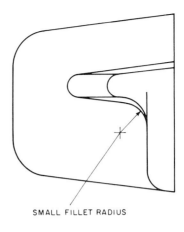

SMALL FILLET RADIUS

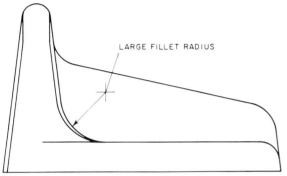

LARGE FILLET RADIUS

Fig. 44—*Differing fillet radii are blended through the plan view intersection radius.*

Where to Blend Fillet Radii

Extra diesinking cost results from designs requiring the blending of different fillet radii. However, when it is necessary to blend different radii, the change is made at the plan view intersections as shown in Fig. 44.

Larger Fillets at Intersections Less Than 90°

At intersections of less than 90°, and with rib heights of one inch or more, larger fillet radii are suggested (Fig. 45) in order to avoid forging flaws. These larger radii are taken normal to the angle bisector.

Large Fillets Prevent Flow-Throughs

Larger than normal fillets may be necessary to prevent "flow-throughs" when the web is enclosed by ribs and either web or ribs are excessively thin, and also when the width between ribs is over ten times the rib height. An inadequate fillet at the base of the rib causes the metal to flow through into the die gutter rather than into the rib cavity. The result is a shear of the grain structure.

No Inside Intersection Radius in Plan View Smaller Than Fillet Radius

An inside radius in the plan view at the base of the web equal to or larger than the fillet radius is recommended from the forging standpoint, as it results in a uniform condition at this base. A smaller inside radius results in a nonuniform condition—an actual valley or trough that may be detrimental in forging. It also requires a blending of radii. The fillet radius is continued into the die cavity from both directions. There remains a sharp die edge where these radii intersect. The inside radius where the sharp edge begins is used to break the edge constantly along the intersection into the web (See Fig. 46).

Webs:
Minimum Web Thicknesses

The minimum dimensions of webs depend for the

Source: Aluminum Forging Design Manual, Aluminum Assn., Inc.

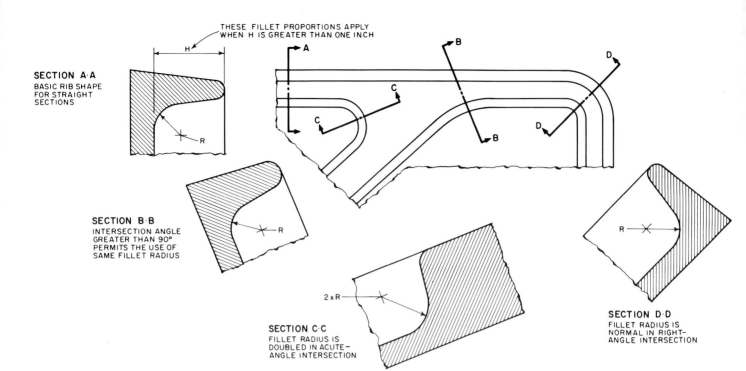

SECTION A·A
BASIC RIB SHAPE
FOR STRAIGHT
SECTIONS

THESE FILLET PROPORTIONS APPLY
WHEN H IS GREATER THAN ONE INCH

SECTION B·B
INTERSECTION ANGLE
GREATER THAN 90°
PERMITS THE USE OF
SAME FILLET RADIUS

SECTION C·C
FILLET RADIUS IS
DOUBLED IN ACUTE-
ANGLE INTERSECTION

SECTION D·D
FILLET RADIUS IS
NORMAL IN RIGHT-
ANGLE INTERSECTION

Fig. 45—*At acute angle intersections of high ribs, the fillet radius should be increased.*

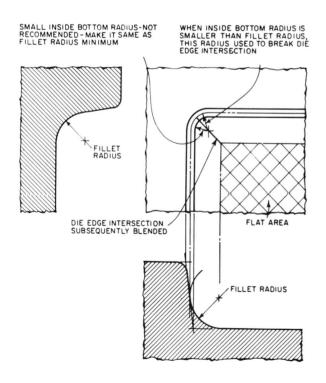

SMALL INSIDE BOTTOM RADIUS-NOT
RECOMMENDED-MAKE IT SAME AS
FILLET RADIUS MINIMUM

WHEN INSIDE BOTTOM RADIUS IS
SMALLER THAN FILLET RADIUS,
THIS RADIUS USED TO BREAK DIE
EDGE INTERSECTION

FILLET
RADIUS

DIE EDGE INTERSECTION
SUBSEQUENTLY BLENDED

FLAT AREA

FILLET RADIUS

Fig. 46—*To improve forgeability, the bottom radius at inside intersections should be equal to or greater than the fillet radius.*

Precision- or conventional-type forgings		
Within Average Width—Inches	Within Total Area—Sq. In.	Thickness —Inches
3	10	.09
4	30	.12
6	60	.16
8	100	.19
11	200	.25
14	350	.31
18	550	.37
22	850	.44
26	1200	.50
34	2000	.62
41	3000	.75
47	4000	1.25
52	5000	2.00

NOTE Use the larger web thickness when width and area are not on same line.

TABLE 4—*Recommended Size of Minimum Web Thickness.*

most part on the size of the forging (expressed as area at the parting line) and on the average width (Fig. 47). Punchout holes are not included in the plan area when determining the minimum web thickness. However, these punchout holes should be of sufficient size to facilitate the forging operation.

Table 4 shows web thickness values applicable to either precision- or conventional-type forgings. On blocker-type forgings, the web thicknesses

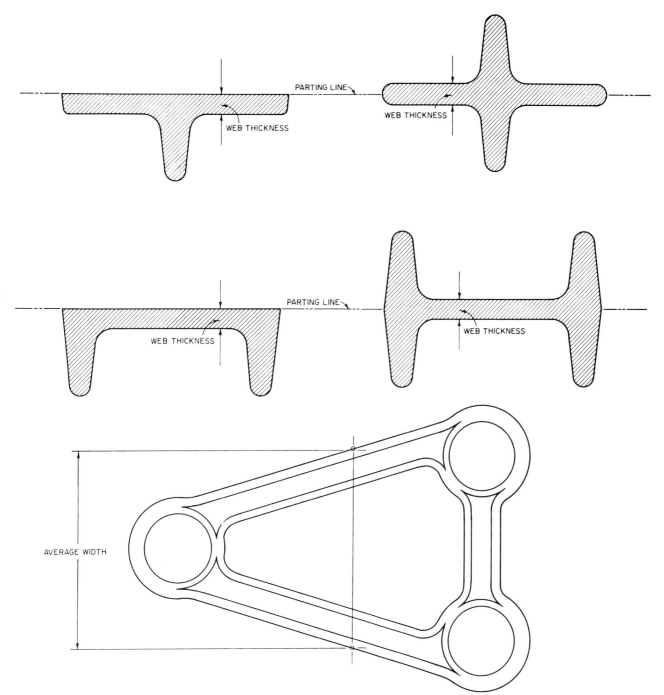

F<small>IG</small>. 47—*The minimum web thickness is determined by the total projected plan area (excluding punchout areas if any), or the average width at the parting line.*

usually are considerably greater than these table values. This is due to the natural summation of a finish allowance per surface, an amount to take care of the adverse effect of the forging tolerances, and the base web thickness. In any event, the minimum web thickness on a blocker-type forging should not be less than 1½ times the table value.

Effect of Thin Webs

It is difficult to maintain the dimensional tolerance on a thin web because, being thin, it cools and shrinks faster than other parts of the forging. Abnormal dimensional relationships may develop in such cases. Because of the tendency of thin sections to warp in heat treatment, additional straightening operations may be necessary and costs will increase. Thin webs and ribs tend to cause die checking, unfilled sections and flow-through.

Forging thin webs may also cause a temporary deflection in the dies, resulting in a web thicker at

Source: Aluminum Forging Design Manual, Aluminum Assn., Inc.

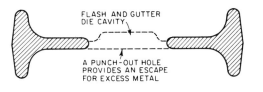
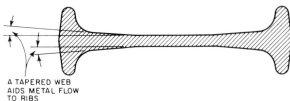

FLASH AND GUTTER
DIE CAVITY

A PUNCH-OUT HOLE
PROVIDES AN ESCAPE
FOR EXCESS METAL

A TAPERED WEB
AIDS METAL FLOW
TO RIBS

FIG. 48—*Punchouts and web tapers minimize the difficulty in forging thin webs.*

the middle than at the outer periphery. When forging excessively thin webs, this die deflection can become permanent.

Web Tapers or Punchouts Beneficial

The difficulty in forging thin webs may be lessened by web tapers or punchout holes—aids that are especially recommended for confined webs of wide expanse, and enclosed by high ribs as shown in Fig. 48.

Punchout holes are the more desirable alternative, since they reduce the total projected plan area and the pressure required to make the forging. Even greater benefit is derived if punchouts are located in central areas where the metal flow resistance is at its greatest. Incorporating a flash and gutter cavity in the dies at these interior points provides a very useful means of escape for surplus metal. A few large punchouts are more economical and helpful in forging than many smaller holes with the same total area. Small holes may even add to the cost without improving the forgeability. Round punchout holes are preferred for ease of trimming.

If the web must be designed without punchouts, the best alternative is to incorporate web tapers by increasing the web thickness at the outer periphery. This design procedure also reduces the forging pressure required, although less than with the use of punchouts. Tapers improve the metal flow and permit easier filling of the rib cavities.

Die Deflection

Die deflection occurs on all forgings, regardless of the equipment used, but on most forgings it is so minute that it is not apparent. However, it is noticeable on large-area forgings that are exceptionally long and narrow and have very thin webs. The result of this die deflection is a thickening at the center of the forging as indicated in Fig. 49.

Die deflection can be anticipated but cannot be predicted precisely. In sinking the die cavity, it is

FIG. 49—*Forging thin and wide webs causes die deflection which results in a thickening at the center.*

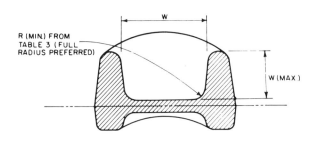

W

R (MIN) FROM
TABLE 3 (FULL
RADIUS PREFERRED)

W (MAX)

FIG. 50—*Recesses should be as shallow and as rounded as possible.*

possible to compensate for the estimated deflection, but the special sinking involves more cost and time. To avoid compensation by diesinking, larger die closure tolerance is recommended. It may also be advisable to increase the straightness tolerance. Incorporating large punchouts in the central areas of these forgings also helps reduce or avoid die deflection.

Pockets and Recesses

Recesses are utilized in order to obtain desirable grain direction and, more frequently, to obtain better mechanical properties by reducing section thickness.

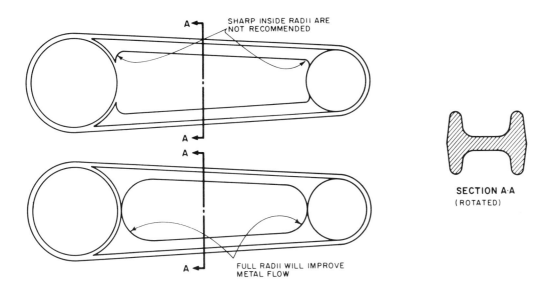

SHARP INSIDE RADII ARE NOT RECOMMENDED

FULL RADII WILL IMPROVE METAL FLOW

SECTION A·A
(ROTATED)

FIG. 51—*Rounded recesses improve forgeability.*

Recesses in forgings are formed by corresponding raised sections or "plugs" in the dies. It is good practice, in the interest of die life and forging reliability, to hold the depth of pockets and recesses to a minimum (Fig. 50).

Simple contours and generous fillets are recommended wherever possible, as illustrated in Fig. 51. They permit the use of smooth and durable die shapes that induce better metal flow.

"Bathtub" Sections

Dished or "bathtub"-type forgings become impractical when the wall thickness exceeds the web thickness. The walls should be no thicker than the web as shown in Fig. 52. If the final part requires a thinner web, it can be forged heavy and subsequently machined to size.

Punchouts

Besides aiding in the production of forgings with thin webs as previously stated, punchout holes are used for functional reasons, such as lightening or providing clearance, or minimizing subsequent machining. As in web centers, punchouts may be beneficial in bosses or hubs, with the greater advantages resulting from large-hole areas.

The proportions of forged recesses in Fig. 50 govern the depth of the forged pockets left for piercing. Punchout holes are incorporated by various

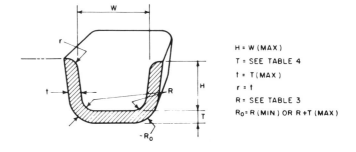

$$H = W \ (MAX)$$
$$T = SEE \ TABLE \ 4$$
$$t = T \ (MAX)$$
$$r = t$$
$$R = SEE \ TABLE \ 3$$
$$R_0 = R \ (MIN) \ OR \ R + T \ (MAX)$$

FIG. 52—*"Bathtub"-type forgings should follow the above design recommendations.*

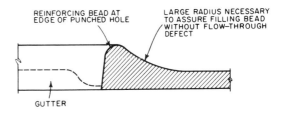

REINFORCING BEAD AT EDGE OF PUNCHED HOLE

LARGE RADIUS NECESSARY TO ASSURE FILLING BEAD WITHOUT FLOW–THROUGH DEFECT

GUTTER

FIG. 53—*A large fillet radius as shown or a suitable taper is mandatory to prevent flow-through defects at reinforced punchouts.*

means, such as die punching, machining, routing or sawing.

Where high strength is required, punchout holes may be reinforced with a bead as indicated in Fig. 53. A reinforcing bead is not beneficial to the forging operation and should be generously blended with a very large fillet or suitable taper into the web. This is necessary to prevent the forging flaw called "flow-through," since the metal tends to flow more readily into the gutter basin than into the bead cavity.

Recessing Bosses to Aid Coining Operation

When bosses are to be subsequently coin-pressed to obtain close tolerances, a recess cavity (Fig. 54) is recommended, where possible, to facilitate the coining operation. The recess reduces the projected area and the pressure required, because only the flat boss faces are then sized.

Double Forgings

Double or siamese forgings (Fig. 55) may be desirable in terms of the forging process as well as from an economical standpoint. When a forged shape imposes a severe side thrust on the dies and raises consequent manufacturing problems, the side thrust can be balanced and the problems reduced by making the part as a double forging.

Depending on the design, it may be more economical to make the double forging consist of two symmetrical or neuter parts, of two left-hand parts, or of two right-hand parts. A right- and a left-hand part could also be combined and made as one double forging—but this must be carefully considered from the cost standpoint if the quantity of both is not equal. The method may then be feasible only when total requirements are small. A

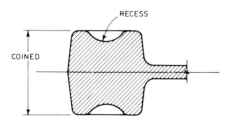

FIG. 54—*Recesses reduce the pressure required to coin press.*

double forging could be supplied either as-forged or separated into the two parts.

Symmetrical Forgings

Another economic possibility is to design a part symmetrically as one forging, from which either a right- or a left-hand part could be machined (Fig. 56). This method eliminates the need for a second set of dies. However, the cost would be slightly more, because of the material added to make the part symmetrical. If much material must be added to make a part symmetrical, it will likewise cost more to machine off the surplus. This design possibility can only be justified if the total estimated cost of dies, forgings, and machining provides a saving over the cost of individual left- and right-hand forgings. The total piece requirements greatly influence this evaluation.

Can- and Tube-Type Forgings

It is impractical to set up design proportions to indicate limitations on can- and tube-type forgings. A study must be made by the forging vendor on each individual part to determine the forging design. In determining what the size dimensions should be on a given part, the vendor must also resolve such details as die sizes and over-all die stackup, press clearance necessary to remove the forging, metal-extrusion ratio, forging pressure required, handling means, extracting method, initial billet size, die sizing and straightening needs, forging machining requirements and other considerations.

It is possible to make forged tubes as large as 100-inch diameter by 100-inch over-all length and with a tubular wall as thin as 1 inch. While round parts are relatively easy to make, a departure from the round shape increases forging difficulty, and this difficulty increases even more when the tubular wall thickness is not uniform.

The illustrations in Figs. 57, 58, 59 and 60 show some of the wide variety of can- and tube-type forgings that have actually been made.

No-Draft Forgings

It is much more difficult to design a producible forging of the no-draft type than of the conventional type. Although no-draft forgings require the least amount of subsequent machining (offsetting higher initial costs), this type of design cannot be applied to every conceivable forging. It should be used only if the part configuration is completely suitable.

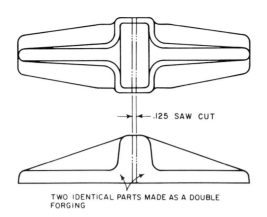

.125 SAW CUT

TWO IDENTICAL PARTS MADE AS A DOUBLE
FORGING

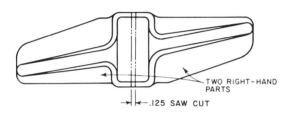

TWO RIGHT-HAND
PARTS

.125 SAW CUT

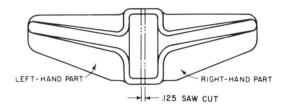

LEFT-HAND PART

RIGHT-HAND PART

.125 SAW CUT

Fig. 55—*Double forgings may be economical as pairs of symmetrical parts or as pairs of right- or left-hand parts, but a pair of opposite-hand parts may not be economical.*

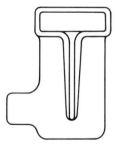

LEFT-HAND FORGING

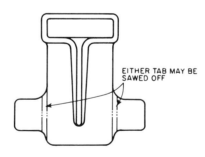

EITHER TAB MAY BE
SAWED OFF

SYMMETRICAL FORGING

RIGHT-HAND FORGING

Fig. 56—*A symmetrical forging may be economical, especially if the opposite-hand parts after machining are nearly symmetrical.*

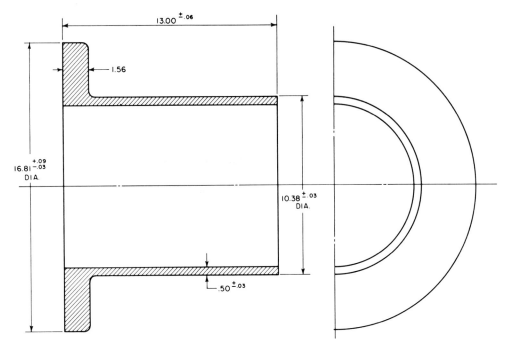

Fig. 57—*Flanged tube.*

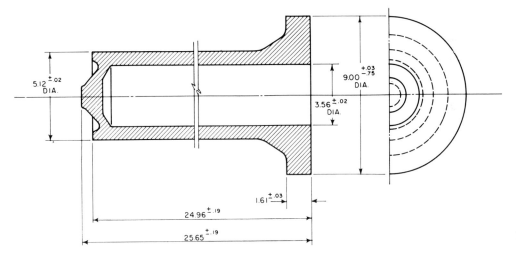

Fig. 58—*Piston.*

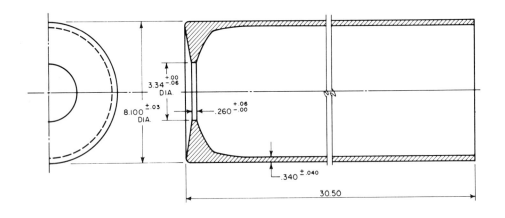

Fig. 59—*Shell.*

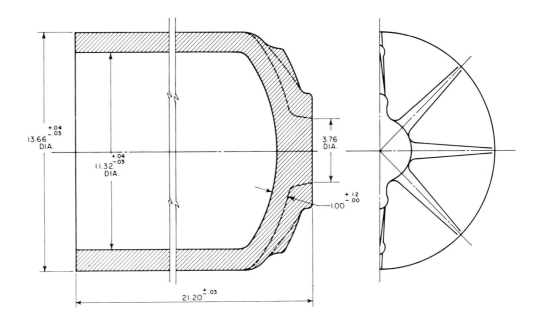

F<small>IG</small>. 60—*Tank.*

Since many factors are involved in determining an adaptable shape, no design proportions can be established that would apply, regardless of the part configuration, and still always be attractive to the customer. The design proportions and tolerances indicated for the precision-type forging can be reduced somewhat for the no-draft, but the final design can only be resolved mutually between the vendor and the customer on an individual part basis.

Many no-drafts require the use of electrical discharge equipment to sink the die cavity, which may be too narrow and deep to be sunk with conventional milling cutters; or require the use of inserts or segments which, when assembled into the die, produce the narrow cavities. Besides the die construction, the vendor must also be concerned with the die life and strength, the die tolerance limitation, and the means of extracting the part upon completion of forging.

Making the forging is very exacting. Many of the no-drafts are made in so-called "sealed" dies where the material completely fills the die cavity with extremely small or no provision made for the escape of surplus material. This demands that the starting slug be of an exact volume and shape precisely contoured to produce a sound forging. Despite optimum design, the means for removing a no-draft forging from the dies can also be a constant problem.

Some no-draft designs can be produced only by resorting to in-process machining of the slug or even (after the final operation) of the forging itself. This may occur with webs too thin to forge or with side walls that cannot be properly contoured by forging. The forging of a no-draft can be simple and routine (as in the case of a round can or even a rectangular shape), or it may be extremely difficult (as in the example of an irregularly shaped and thin-walled frame). Since each part must be designed on an individual basis because of varying configurations, adequate communication is required between the vendor and the customer to establish a mutually acceptable no-draft design.

Tolerances for Die Forgings

Aluminum alloy forgings can be produced to close tolerances and machined to precise, stable dimensions. An experienced and capable producer can offer valuable assistance in handling dimensional control problems.

How Dimensional Accuracy is Influenced by Design

A forging's proportions have a great deal to do with its dimensional accuracy. Shrinkage, warpage and other deviations usually can be anticipated and their effects minimized by appropriate design precautions.

Shrinkage is the dimensional contraction that occurs when a forging cools to room temperature after it is removed from the die. The extent of shrinkage depends on the temperature of the part as it comes from the die and on the forging alloy's coefficient of thermal expansion.

By providing a simple, well-proportioned shape and ample fillets, the designer can be assured that the average forged part will be within its straightness tolerance. When it is necessary to employ odd shapes, radical section changes, or extremely long, thin members, the likelihood of warpage is increased. Fig. 61 is an example of a potentially troublesome part.

Suggested Die Forging Tolerances

The tolerances tabulated in the following pages are for general application. Most die forgings, when produced to meet these limits, will combine reasonable tooling costs and piece-cost with adequate dimensional accuracy. In individual cases, however, tolerances smaller than standard values may be justified. Certain dimensions often require close limits—to suit fixtures used in subsequent processing, to assure clearance for mating parts, or to satisfy other conditions stemming from a forging's application. The vendor's engineering department should be consulted when changes are desired in tolerance values. Their estimate of the cost increase will help decide whether very close tolerance limits, or such other measures as additional machining, will result in the most economical forging.

In most cases, tolerances vary for the different types of forgings (precision, conventional and blocker). Tighter-than-necessary tolerances should be avoided as these invariably result in higher forging costs.

A properly dimensioned drawing will result in the minimum possible tolerances, whereas poor dimensioning can result in a buildup of tolerances. *Unless a drawing explicitly specifies otherwise, each class of tolerance is separate and independent of every other class of tolerance.* All applicable tolerances should be specified on the drawing.

Die-Closure Tolerances

Die-closure tolerance pertains to thicknesses across and perpendicular to the fundamental parting line and is affected by the closing of the dies. This tolerance normally includes the initial die-sinking limits, the subsequent die polishing necessary to maintain smooth die cavity surfaces in production (correcting for "die wear") and an

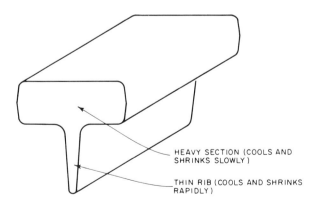

HEAVY SECTION (COOLS AND SHRINKS SLOWLY)

THIN RIB (COOLS AND SHRINKS RAPIDLY)

FIG. 61—*Combinations of heavy and light sections are the principal cause of warping during heat treatment.*

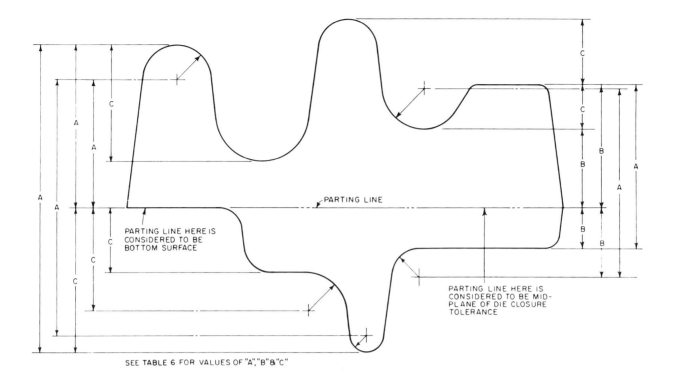

FIG. 62—*The dimensioning as shown is intended only to illustrate the* application *of tolerances—the* method *of dimensioning is unfavorable and* not recommended.

allowance for die deflection (which creates a thickening at the middle, especially with thin webs).

In addition to thicknesses, there are dimensions perpendicular to the fundamental parting line that are covered by varying tolerances. They fall into categories with tolerances applicable as follows:

A. Full-die closure tolerance
   1. All thicknesses, whether the forging impression is all in one die half or in two die halves
   2. Center dimensions across parting line or from center to parting line when the impression is all in one die

B. One-half die closure tolerance plus a symmetry tolerance of ±.015
   1. Dimensions from surface to parting line when impression is in both dies
   2. All center dimensions to parting line when impression is in both dies

C. All other dimensions are covered by dimensional tolerances

The dimensioning in Fig. 62 is intended only to illustrate the *application* of tolerances—the *method* of dimensioning is unfavorable and *not recommended* in drafting practice.

Table 5 shows the recommended die closure tolerances. It should be noted that the applicable tolerance is determined by the weight or the plan area of the forging—whichever is greater. **Note:** Use the larger tolerance when weight and plan area are not on same line.

Coining Tolerances

Coining tolerance is ±.005 minimum. It is similar to die closure tolerance as it is applied to surfaces across and parallel to the parting line. It is limited to small areas only and usually to portions of forgings such as boss faces. The coining operation is performed on cold forgings after heat treating and prior to aging.

When two or more sets of bosses (Fig. 63) are coined simultaneously, each set of bosses will have the faces parallel to one another and within the coining tolerance. However, the coining operation may not straighten the forging and it may spring back to its original distorted shape if any warpage existed before the coining.

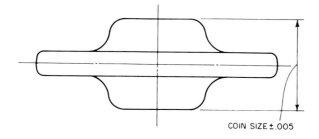

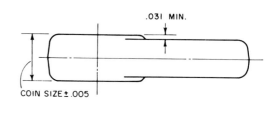

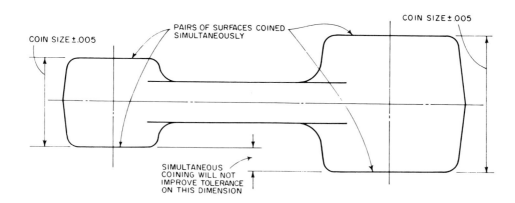

FIG. 63—*Coin sizing refines dimensional relationships between opposing flat surfaces.*

Dimensional Tolerances

Dimensional tolerances (sometimes called length and width tolerances) usually apply to dimensions essentially parallel to the fundamental parting line. They also actually apply to all dimensions not otherwise covered by the die closure tolerances. Dimensional tolerances consist of two factors—a shrinkage tolerance and an allowance per surface. The shrinkage tolerance is solely for the oversize or undersize variations that may occur because of shrinkage differences. The per-surface allowance is a "plus material" amount on the forging, which is frequently called "die wear allowance."

This allowance includes the diesinking limits, die wear, and die dress-outs; it results in larger outside dimensions and smaller inside dimensions.

Dimensional tolerances shown in Table 6 depend both on the size and type of dimension. The individual dimension may be affected by shrinkage only or by both shrinkage and die wear. Center dimensions are affected only by shrinkage. Dimensions from a center line to a surface are affected by both shrinkage and die wear allowance. Dimensions to two surfaces are affected by shrinkage and two die wear allowances. Fig. 64 illustrates how these tolerances are applied.

Die wear is principally the result of die cavity polishing, used whenever necessary to maintain the smoothness of die surfaces required for proper metal flow.

On cold-worked die forgings, greater-than-normal dimensional tolerances may be necessary and are determined on an individual part basis.

Match Tolerances

Match tolerance is the maximum shift or misalignment variation allowed between the two die halves at and parallel to the parting line, as shown in Fig. 65. The features on one side of the forging are slightly out of line with those on the other side because of this shift. Mismatching is caused when

122

Weight in Pounds (Within)	Plan Area in Sq. Inches (Within)	Precision Type	Conventional Type	Blocker Type
0-½	10	+.020 —.010	+.020 —.010	+.031 —.016
½-1	30	+.020 —.010	+.031 —.016	+.047 —.031
1-5	100	+.031 —.010	+.047 —.016	+.062 —.031
5-20	400	+.047 —.016	+.062 —.031	+.093 —.062
20-50	750	+.062 —.016	+.093 —.031	+.125 —.062
50-100	1000	+.093 —.016	+.125 —.031	+.187 —.062
100-200	2000	+.125 —.016	+.187 —.031	+.250 —.062
200-500	3500		+.250 —.031	+.375 —.062
500 Up	5000			+.500 —.062

NOTE Use the larger tolerance when weight and plan area are not on same line.

TABLE 5—*Suggested Die Closure Tolerances.*

Forging Type	"A" Shrinkage Variation Per Inch	"B" and "C"	
		Per Each Surface On Forgings Max. Dim. to 60 Inches	Per Each Surface On Forgings Max. Dim. Over 60 Inches
Blocker	+.002 —.002	+.047 —.015	+.078 —.015
Conventional	+.002 —.002	+.020 —.010	+.047 —.015
Precision	+.0015 —.0015	+.010 —.010	+.020 —.010

NOTE (a) Dimensional tolerances apply to any dimensions other than those covered by die closure tolerances, even to dimensions perpendicular to the parting line. These are dimensions:
(1) Between opposite outside surfaces
(2) Between opposite inside surfaces
(3) Between centerlines
(4) Between center and outside surface
(5) Between center and inside surface
(6) Between steps
(b) See Fig. 64 for tolerance application.

TABLE 6—*Suggested Dimensional Tolerances.*

Weight in Pounds (Within)	Overall Length in Inches (Within)	Precision Type	Conventional & Blocker Types
0-1	10	.010	.015
1-5	17	.015	.020
5-20	25	.020	.030
20-50	50	.030	.045
50-100	75	.045	.060
100-200	100	.060	.080
200-500	150		.100
500 Up	250		.120

NOTE Use the larger tolerance when weight and overall length are not on same line.

TABLE 7—*Suggested Match Tolerances.*

the forging forces are exerted parallel to the forging plane. To counteract these forces and maintain match on the forging, guide holders, guide pins and counterlocks are employed.

Match tolerances are applied separately from and independently of all other tolerances.

Match tolerances depend on the weight or over-all length of the forging, whichever is greater, as indicated in Table 7.

Straightness Tolerances

Straightness tolerance is a deviation applicable generally to flat surfaces and is a total indicator reading (T.I.R.) limit.

On a continuous flat surface, it is the total maximum deviation from a plane surface. On noncontinuous surfaces, the deviation is a total flatness relationship of all parallel surfaces; but it does not include the step tolerance that may exist between any two surfaces, nor is it applicable to any surfaces that are inclined to the major surfaces being measured.

Contoured or tapered surfaces are not covered by the specified straightness tolerance, but must be within the specified dimensional tolerances, which should also be large enough to allow for any warpage existing at these areas. The contour envelope tolerance method is sometimes used.

On cylindrical forgings, the straightness tolerance is applicable to the axis of the part.

Straightness tolerances are measured separately from and independently of all other tolerances.

Warpage in a forging, caused by differential cooling of varying sections, occurs both after the hot forging operation and (especially) during the quenching after solution heat treating. Straightening is done when the forgings are cold—as soon as possible after solution heat treating, but prior to aging treatment.

Sometimes an additional set of dies is used for straightening, but the total production requirements must be high enough to warrant the cost. In most cases, however, forgings are straightened in hydraulic arbor presses, utilizing V-blocks or other simple supports. This process is not as positive as die straightening and must sometimes be repeated to bring the part within allowable straightness tolerance. However, it may be the most economical method.

The use of stress-relief dies on cold forgings is effective not only in straightening the forging but also in substantially reducing residual stresses.

The over-all length of the forging determines the amount of straightness tolerance, as shown in Table 8.

Although the straightness tolerance is independent of, and in addition to, all other tolerances, it may be difficult or even impossible to measure it separately from other tolerance deviations, because of part configuration. This applies particularly to ring, tubular and contoured shaped forgings. However, the straightness tolerance must be considered and an allowance made for it. On such shapes, a .0015 inch total tolerance per inch of dimension should be added to the dimension tolerance as an allowance for the straightness deviation.

On ring-type and tubular-type forgings, this larger tolerance would be applicable only to the diameters, with the additional straightness allowance allowed for a possible ovality condition. The general straightness tolerance would otherwise apply to the flat surfaces. An ovality is permissible even though the drawing omits any mention of ovality, but it must not exceed the diametral tolerance limits.

If the ovality is specified and is restricted to only a portion of the total diametral tolerance, both tolerances can easily be checked by conventional methods. On extremely thin sectioned ring forgings, which may present severe ovality problems, it may be necessary to specify an ovality tolerance even greater than the diametral tolerance. This would require that the diameters be measured with "PI" tapes to determine if they are within the diametral tolerances.

On a contoured shape, there is no practical method

Overall Length in Inches (Within)	Tolerance (T.I.R.)
10	.015
20	.030
30	.045
40	.060
50	.075
60	.090
90	.120
150	.180
Over 150	.250

TABLE 8—*Suggested Straightness Tolerances.*

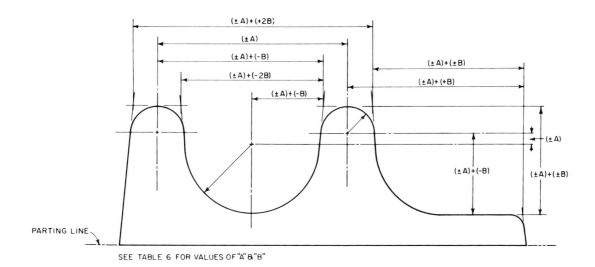

FIG. 64—*This sketch shows only how dimensional tolerances apply with various types of dimensions, but the method of dimensioning is unfavorable and not recommended.*

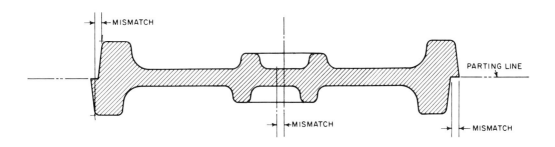

FIG. 65—*A misalignment between the dies results in mismatch discrepancies on the forging.*

of checking the straightness deviation separately; it must therefore be included in the dimensional tolerance check.

Methods and Procedures for Checking Straightness

The method prescribed for measuring straightness should verify that the surface or surfaces do not deviate by more than the tolerance from the required plane surface. On cylindrical parts, it must assure that the actual axis does not exceed the straightness limit with respect to the true axis.

If a forging is flat on one side, or nearly so, a straightedge can be used to check for straightness.

However, it requires experience and careful inspection to detect twist conditions that may exist, or to make certain that a whole area is within the T.I.R. reading, since only a line contact can be checked in sliding the straightedge over the entire surface.

Another method is to place the forging, if one side is entirely flat, against a surface plate and use feeler gages to check the straightness deviation (Fig. 66). Extremely narrow parts could be checked in this manner. Forgings of any appreciable width cannot be checked at the middle portions, since feeler gages can only verify that the outside periphery is within tolerance.

Source: Aluminum Forging Design Manual, Aluminum Assn., Inc.

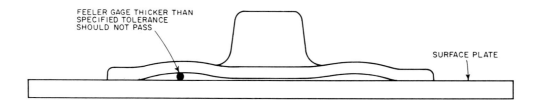

FEELER GAGE THICKER THAN SPECIFIED TOLERANCE SHOULD NOT PASS

SURFACE PLATE

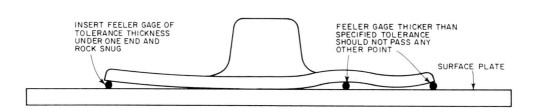

INSERT FEELER GAGE OF TOLERANCE THICKNESS UNDER ONE END AND ROCK SNUG

FEELER GAGE THICKER THAN SPECIFIED TOLERANCE SHOULD NOT PASS ANY OTHER POINT

SURFACE PLATE

FIG. 66—*These methods of checking straightness may be used only on very narrow parts.*

The recommended method is to position the forging on a surface plate on three supports, at least two being adjustable, and adjust them so that the top surfaces of the forging are parallel with the surface plate. Checking the top rather than the bottom surfaces is suggested because these are more accessible.

Since the straightness tolerance is separate from, and independent of, all other tolerances, and the forging is supported on the bottom side while the top side is checked, all other forging tolerances must be excluded from the straightness check. In this case, for example, the forging may have a die closure variation, even an allowable taper. Such variations are avoided by using the adjustable supports and working to a plane established by the top surfaces.

Getting the best straightness reading on the top surfaces may require a few adjustments of the supports before a satisfactory checking plane, from which all the top surfaces can be checked, is established. This plane may vary from forging to forging of the same lot. Most forgings do not have large and adequately continuous areas to establish the checking plane. Any offsets, from one level to another, needed to determine the plane must not be set up to the drawing dimensions, but must be to the actual forging step measurements. The dimensional variations in such steps are covered by dimensional tolerances and should not be absorbed into the straightness allowance.

Once the horizontal plane is established, the dial

FIG. 67—*A surface gage is used to ensure that this large airframe forging is within straightness tolerance while the forging is being straightened following the solution heat treatment. Later, a dial indicator is used for accurate inspection after mounting the forging on a surface place.*

indicator used for checking straightness should be run over the top surface area as much as is practical. Whenever the dial indicator is at the end of one level, it should be started at the same dial reading on the adjacent level in order to continue the straightness relationship. Narrow or small areas such as ribs or pockets can be disregarded. The total dial reading variation should not exceed the straightness tolerance.

In all methods described, the straightness check is typical for the common drawing callout stating that the forging must be straight within a specified amount.

If a drawing calls out a plus and minus straightness tolerance, the drawing must establish the plane from which the tolerance can be measured by giving specific locating dimensions that define the plane. If such dimensions are omitted, the applicable straightness tolerance is considered to be the total of the plus and minus amounts.

When a drawing callout specifies that the straightness (or flatness) must be within "X" amount in "Y" inches, an entirely different check is required. This callout defines a rate of change and requires that a straightedge of "Y" length be used—it is slid over the flat areas, and lack of contact with the straightedge must nowhere exceed "X" inches. This type of checking is relatively simple in comparison to that required by the more common straightness callout.

Contour Checking

Contoured shapes may vary from the theoretically perfect contours, in part because of distortion and also because the accuracy of contours is affected by diesinking limits, die wear and shrinkage variations.

The method of checking contoured shapes would depend on the tolerances specified. A contour with a constant and uniform tolerance could be checked with a template and feeler gage; a contour with a variable tolerance might require a special fixture with appropriate features incorporated to check out the tolerance requirements.

Flash Extension Tolerances

Flash extension tolerances govern the accuracy with which flash must be trimmed from the forging. The length of projection (measured from the body of the forging) left after trimming may vary from zero (theoretical intersection of the draft angle at the parting line) to the dimension specified. Standard flash extension tolerances, Table 9 are based on net weight or over-all length of the forging, whichever is greater.

Negative Trim

While most forgings are supplied with a slight flash extension remaining, there are some requirements for flush trimming that prohibit any flash protrusions. In such cases, a negative trim tolerance is essential; this allows the trimming to cut into the body and removes part of the draft material. The tolerances for this negative trim should be specified on the drawing and should be at least one half of the tolerances for a protruding trim. As flush trimming adds to costs, this requirement is usually applied only to specific portions and not to the entire periphery of the parting line.

Trimmed Surfaces

Unless the requirement is specified otherwise, the trimmed surfaces will vary, depending on the method of trimming, which may be either shearing, sawing, machining or grinding.

Weight in Pounds (Within)	Overall Length in Inches (Within)	Conventional & Precision Types	Blocker Type
½	5	.015 (a)	—
5	15	.030 (a)	.120
25	30	.060 (a)	.180
50	60	.120	.250
100	120	.120	.500
Over 100	Over 120	.250	.500

NOTE Use the larger tolerance when weight and overall length are not on same line.

(a) These tolerances apply for die trimming and should be doubled for saw trimming. All other tolerances shown apply for saw trimming.

TABLE 9—*Suggested Flash Extension Tolerances.*

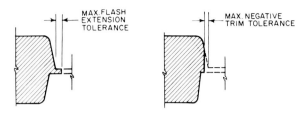

FIG. 68—*The flash extension or negative trim tolerance is taken from the protruding mismatched draft intersection at the parting line.*

DIE FORGINGS		
No. Pieces	Plus	Minus
1-2	1 pc.	0 pcs.
3-5	2 "	1 "
6-19	3 "	1 "
20-29	4 "	2 "
30-39	5 "	2 "
40-49	6 "	3 "
50-59	7 "	3 "
60-69	8 "	4 "
70-79	9 "	4 "
80-99	10 "	5 "
100-199	10%	5.0%
200-299	9%	4.5%
300-599	8%	4.0%
600-1249	7%	3.5%
1250-2999	6%	3.0%
3000-9999	5%	2.5%
10,000-39,999	4%	2.0%
40,000-299,999	3%	1.5%
300,000 and up	2%	1.0%

TABLE 11—*Standard Quantity Tolerances.*

Fig. 68 indicates how the flash trim tolerance applies, but is not recommended drafting practice.

It shows that the flash extension or negative trim tolerance is taken at the parting line from the portion that protrudes because of the mismatch condition.

The flash extension or negative trim tolerance applies in all cases, even if the drawing dimensions are specified at the parting line.

Draft Angle Tolerances

Draft angle tolerances shown in Table 10 are the permissible variations from the specified draft angles.

Draft Angle	Tolerance
Up to 3°	±½°
3° and over	±1°

TABLE 10—*Standard Draft Angle Tolerances.*

Angular Tolerance

Standard angular tolerance applies to angle dimensions other than draft angles. This tolerance is ±½° for general application and is also applicable to unspecified but implied 90° angles.

Radii Tolerances

Standard tolerances for both corner and fillet radii are ±.03 on dimensions up to .30 and ±10 per cent on dimensions over .30.

Quantity Tolerances

Quantity tolerances are the shipping limits within which an order is considered to be complete. Table 11 indicates standard tolerances.

Knockout and Vent Mark Tolerances

Knockout pins or ejectors (Fig. 69) are necessary to extract forgings of small draft angles (3° or less) from the die cavity. Sometimes knockouts are used to facilitate removal of heavy forgings or simply to speed up production.

Raised or Depressed Areas

The area enclosed by the knockout is likely to be raised on the forging but it may occasionally be depressed. The height or depth of such knockout marks is normally held to within .03 inch maximum.

Knockout Fins

Metal may flow between the die and the knockout pin, creating a thin circumferential fin. This also is normally trimmed off to within .06 inch maximum.

Die Venting May Be Required

Vent holes are incorporated into the die cavity (Fig. 70) to facilitate and assure forging fill in troublesome pockets. The vent holes allow trapped gas to escape and allow metal to fill the cavity.

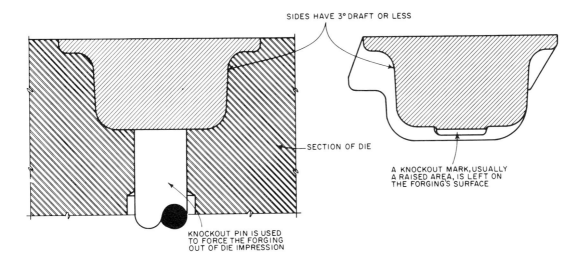

SIDES HAVE 3° DRAFT OR LESS

SECTION OF DIE

A KNOCKOUT MARK, USUALLY A RAISED AREA, IS LEFT ON THE FORGING'S SURFACE

KNOCKOUT PIN IS USED TO FORCE THE FORGING OUT OF DIE IMPRESSION

Fig. 69—*Die knockout pins or ejectors are required on deep forgings and when draft angles are 3° or less.*

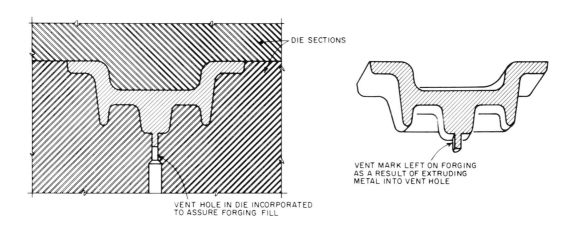

DIE SECTIONS

VENT MARK LEFT ON FORGING AS A RESULT OF EXTRUDING METAL INTO VENT HOLE

VENT HOLE IN DIE INCORPORATED TO ASSURE FORGING FILL

Fig. 70—*Die vent holes are incorporated which allow trapped air or lubricant to escape and thus assure die fillability when making forgings in a single press stroke.*

Vent Marks

Protrusions formed in die vents are normally removed to within .06-inch maximum height.

Tightening the normal maximum for knockout marks, knockout fins and vent marks will increase costs. Specifying no restrictions regarding these marks may present advantages if the part is subsequently to be machined at these areas and if no handling problems arise.

The location and size of knockouts and the number and location of vent holes are determined by the forging vendor at the time of quotation.

Surface Roughness

Die forgings are normally supplied with clean etched surfaces and are smooth within 250 RMS. Smoother surfaces are possible but must be considered on an individual basis. Forgings supplied in the rough-machined state have such surfaces usually within a roughness rating of 500 RMS.

Tooling Points Shown on Drawings

Every effort should be made to have the drawing dimensioned so explicitly that the customer and the vendor can agree precisely in their dimensional findings when making a layout inspection of a forging. One method by which this can be accomplished is to indicate tooling points on the drawing that represent actual points of fixture contact when machining or when inspecting layouts. These tooling points can also be used to establish datum planes from which all possible dimensions originate.

By having a common starting set-up when checking a forging dimensionally, it is possible to avoid inspection differences which otherwise occur all too frequently. A tooling point or similar dimensioning system reduces layout time as it eliminates many preliminary setups. It also gives more positive verification that adequate finish allowance has been provided before machining begins.

A tooling point system or a similar system of dimensioning is strongly recommended. More and more companies are adopting such methods of dimensioning.

Fig. 72 illustrates the use of tooling points and the datum planes these establish.

Finish Allowances for Machining

A designer must be familiar with both the magnitude and the application of the tolerances required on a forging to determine the necessary amount of finish allowance on the machined surfaces (Fig. 73). Surfaces parallel to the parting line are affected by the die closure and straightness tolerances.

Surfaces perpendicular to the parting line are affected by dimensional, straightness and match tolerances. Only the adverse effect of these tolerances need be considered, and this amount should be added to a minimum clean-up allowance on each surface, to assure satisfactory machining. The minimum machining allowance is arbitrary and varies from .02 inch on very small forgings to as much as .25 inch on large forgings.

Initial Machining Setup

To lessen any possible adverse effect of forging tolerances, the designer must know how the forging will be positioned in the initial machining setup. For example, a forging fixtured on one side of the parting line is not affected by either the match tolerance or the minus die closure tolerance on that side, but these same tolerances do affect the opposite side of the parting line and must be considered. Not knowing how a forging is to be fixtured makes it necessary to allow the full machining allowance for the adverse forging tolerances on both sides of the parting line.

The foregoing example is a further recommendation for the growing practice of showing tooling points on drawings or using other such means of indicating the machining fixturing points.

Small Forgings

To make it possible to machine a forging to sharp corners, sufficient material must be provided; nor-

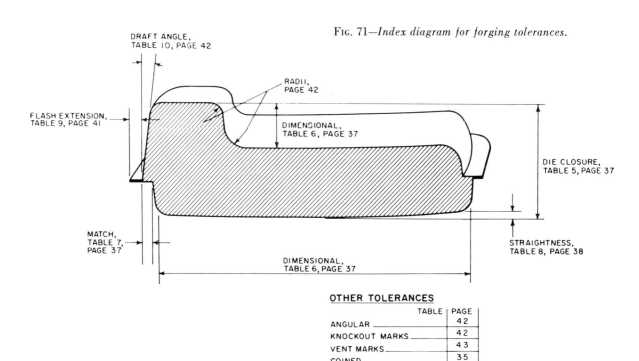

Fig. 71—*Index diagram for forging tolerances.*

DRAFT ANGLE, TABLE 10, PAGE 42

RADII, PAGE 42

FLASH EXTENSION, TABLE 9, PAGE 41

DIMENSIONAL, TABLE 6, PAGE 37

DIE CLOSURE, TABLE 5, PAGE 37

MATCH, TABLE 7, PAGE 37

STRAIGHTNESS, TABLE 8, PAGE 38

DIMENSIONAL, TABLE 6, PAGE 37

OTHER TOLERANCES

	TABLE	PAGE
ANGULAR		42
KNOCKOUT MARKS		42
VENT MARKS		43
COINED		35
QUANTITIES	II	42

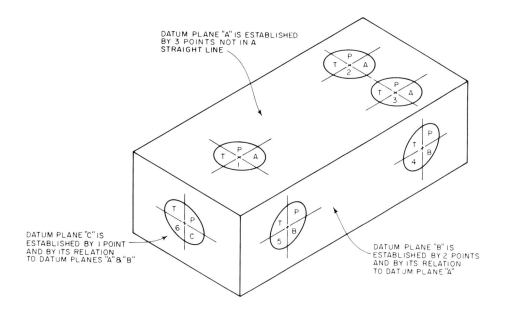

DATUM PLANE "A" IS ESTABLISHED
BY 3 POINTS NOT IN A
STRAIGHT LINE

DATUM PLANE "C" IS
ESTABLISHED BY 1 POINT
AND BY ITS RELATION
TO DATUM PLANES "A" & "B"

DATUM PLANE "B" IS
ESTABLISHED BY 2 POINTS
AND BY ITS RELATION
TO DATUM PLANE "A"

FIG. 72—*Establishing the three basic datum planes.*

mally these corners are rounded on the forging. In many cases, by adding a machining allowance equal to the required corner radius, adequate material is provided to compensate for forging tolerances as well as to machine to sharp corners. This practice will usually work out well on small forgings (maximum length of 8 inches). However, to be certain, the necessary finish allowance should be calculated from the applicable forging tolerances.

Large Forgings

On large forgings, it is imperative that the finish allowance on all surfaces be calculated on an individual basis to assure completely satisfactory machining. The finish allowance per surface varies considerably on the same forging, because of the relation of different surfaces to the parting line and to the datum planes. Fig. 74 illustrates what factors are involved and totaled to give complete machining assurance.

Additional Tolerances

The following tolerances are being specified more and more often:

Out-of-Round Tolerances

The out-of-round tolerance is the allowable roundness or ovality deviation from a perfect circle. Generally, it is expressed as T.I.R. tolerance, which requires that the actual diameter must fall within two concentric circles with a total differ-

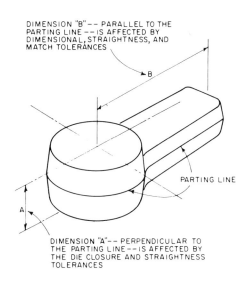

DIMENSION "B" -- PARALLEL TO THE
PARTING LINE -- IS AFFECTED BY
DIMENSIONAL, STRAIGHTNESS, AND
MATCH TOLERANCES

B

PARTING LINE

A

DIMENSION "A" -- PERPENDICULAR TO
THE PARTING LINE -- IS AFFECTED BY
THE DIE CLOSURE AND STRAIGHTNESS
TOLERANCES

FIG. 73—*The relationship of a dimension to the parting line determines which tolerances affect its accuracy.*

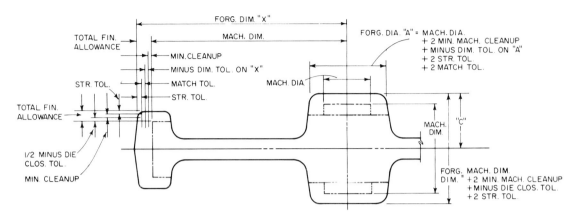

MACHINING SETUP UNKNOWN—
BOTH SIDES OF PARTING LINE IDENTICAL

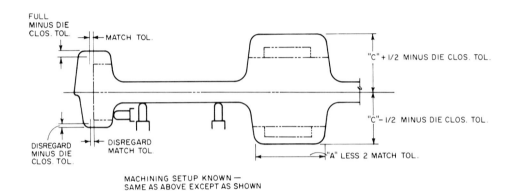

MACHINING SETUP KNOWN —
SAME AS ABOVE EXCEPT AS SHOWN

FIG. 74—*Examples illustrate how finish allowances are determined (tolerances exaggerated for clarity).*

ence equal to the tolerance. When specified as a radial tolerance, it defines the space allowable radially between two concentric circles. In the absence of any drawing comment pertaining to out-of-roundness, it is assumed that any such deviations must fall within the diametral tolerances.

Flexible parts such as thin-walled rings or tubes may require greater out-of-round tolerances than diametral tolerances. In such cases, the part is measured across the major and minor axes to determine the out-of-roundness variation, and measured circumferentially with so-called "pi tapes" to verify if it is within the diametral tolerance.

Concentricity Tolerances

Concentricity tolerance is the maximum eccentricity from the true axis between two or more diameters or features. It expresses the allowable diametral zone about the true axis or the T.I.R. limit. The drawing should specify the diameter or feature to which the concentricity tolerance applies and the diameter or feature establishing the datum axis. If the drawing specifies no concentricity tolerance, it is assumed that any such deviation must fall within the dimensional tolerances for the diameters or features.

Squareness Tolerances

The squareness tolerance, also called perpendicularity tolerance, is the allowable deviation from true squareness and represents a zone between two parallel planes.

When specified, the drawing note should indicate the feature or features to which the tolerance applies and the feature establishing the datum plane.

Flatness Tolerances

The flatness tolerance applies to plane surfaces and has been covered under straightness tolerances.

Break All Sharp Edges

A drawing callout such as "break all sharp edges" is normally interpreted to be applicable to all surfaces except at the flash trim. Thus, all marks caused by die checking, die venting, die knockouts, or handling are to be removed.

A similar drawing callout with an addition that specifies the amount of radius or chamfer required (either maximum or minimum) can increase costs unnecessarily, especially if the tolerances are restrictive. Unrestrictive tolerances such as .12 inch maximum or .005 inch minimum would be fairly easy to control.

Actually, radius or chamfer requirements would apply only to knockout marks, as other marks would normally be removed flush with the forging contour. Removing the sharp edges on the knockout marks, which would require such operations as very careful grinding, machining, or controlled tumbling to comply with the dimensional requirement, would be difficult.

If the callout "break all sharp edges" is intended to apply also to the flash trim, the drawing should specify such as additional requirement. Removing sharp edges from the flash extension presents a greater problem because of the much larger periphery involved.

Forging Drafting Conventions

A forging drawing should be prepared so that the designed forging can be produced economically and machined satisfactorily; it should show the forging so explicitly and completely that nothing is left to be misinterpreted. This chapter explains how to make such drawings. In addition to general good drafting practice, a few special conventions generally used in the forging industry are covered.

Full Scale

A full-scale drawing minimizes possible confusion and errors, since it depicts the part in true proportions. Drawings that are not made to full scale cause mistakes so frequently that they should be avoided if possible. A small-scale drawing may be handy to use, but this convenience may even be costly if errors result. Enlarged views may be necessary when details are so minute that full-scale views would be too difficult to read.

Simplified Drawing Practice

Simplified drawing practice should be used, showing neither more nor less than is essential. However, this does not imply any short-cutting that creates a questionable drawing. A simplified drawing should have no artistic frills—which contribute nothing—but should have completely and clearly detailed information. General notes preferably near the title block should be used to avoid cluttering the field of drawing.

The following note can be used to avoid duplicating dimensions, especially if these apply repeatedly throughout the drawing.

NOTE Unless otherwise indicated
Draft angles_____
Corner radii_____
Fillet radii_____

A similar note will save work and prevent littering dimensions with tolerances.

NOTE Forging tolerances unless otherwise indicated: Die closure_____
Dimensional_____
Match_____
Straight within_____
Flash extension_____

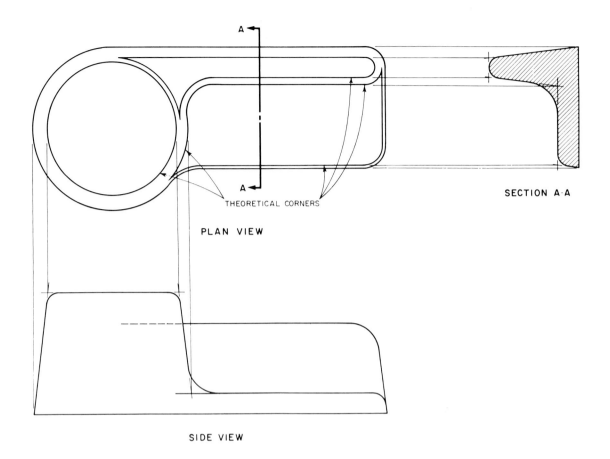

A

A

SECTION A·A

THEORETICAL CORNERS

PLAN VIEW

SIDE VIEW

FIG. 75—*Depicting the plan view lines as the theoretical intersection points of the corner and fillet radii of the side views brings out the shape of the part more vividly.*

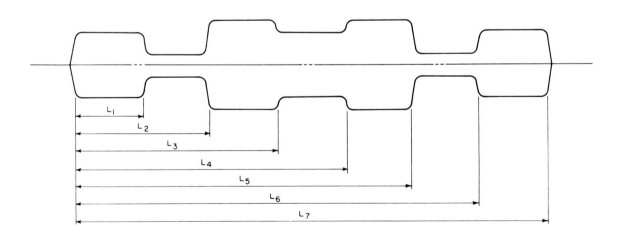

L_1

L_2

L_3

L_4

L_5

L_6

L_7

FIG. 77—*Use a common reference to avoid chain dimensions.*

Plan View Lines Shown as Intersecting Planes

Perhaps the principal difference from conventional drafting technique is the delineation of lines in the plan view. The method of showing all plan view lines (Fig. 75) as if the corner and fillet radii were all theoretically sharp-corners, is common on forging drawings. Thus, these radii are ignored, and the lines shown result from continuing the draft angles and terminating them at the top and bottom surface planes. This method depicts the draft more vividly in the plan view and simplifies the work of the draftsman. All other plane intersections are depicted by lines indicating a change of direction.

Dimensions to Points of Intersection

The dimensions are likewise taken to the theoretical points of intersection or sharp corners. In most cases they are taken to the tops of the forging with the draft material added on. A note and sketch similar to Fig. 76 will ensure that the point is understood by everyone.

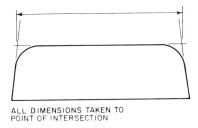

ALL DIMENSIONS TAKEN TO
POINT OF INTERSECTION

FIG. 76—*The above sketch with note is conventional on forging drawings.*

Decimal Dimensions

Most drawings are now specified in decimal dimensions and the trend is increasing; all data in this manual are, therefore, given in decimals.

Good Dimensioning Practice

It is most important to use a proper method of dimensioning. Dimensions should be related to the subsequent machining operations and should even follow the sequence of these operations, if possible.

In making his own drawing, the forging vendor must follow the customer's drawing exactly, to avoid inspection controversies. The responsibility rests with the customer to dimension properly. If the vendor finds any dimensional irregularities, the customer is advised and must resolve them before the die impressions are begun.

Target Points on Drawings

Target points on customer drawings are a valuable aid in preventing inspection controversies between the vendor and the customer. These represent fixed contact points in fixturing the forging to assure identical setups, either in layout dimensional inspection or in machining. With identical setups, the dimensional findings should, likewise, be the same. Without such information, inspection differences are unavoidable since identical setups would occur only by chance. This subject has been previously discussed in Chapter 2 on tolerances.

Avoid Chain Dimensioning

Chain dimensioning (Fig. 77) should be avoided to prevent an accumulation of tolerances.

Reference Dimensions

Reference dimensions (normally labelled "Ref." adjacent to the dimension) are used for reference

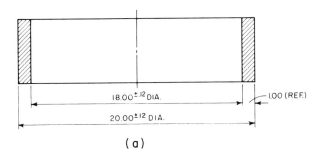

(a)

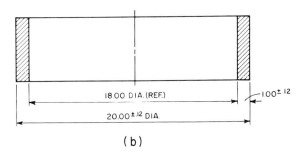

(b)

FIG. 78—*Selecting the basic dimensions properly can reduce the limits on the referenced dimensions.*

purposes only, not for manufacturing or inspection. They may result from other dimensions, or be duplicated elsewhere on the drawing, or they may be references to other drawings. Reference dimensions should be used discriminately and only if required for clarification.

Variables with Differing Dimensional Methods

The following illustrates two different methods of dimensioning and the variable effect on the resultant dimensions.

In Fig. 78(a) if the outside and inside diameters are at the extreme tolerances, the resultant wall thickness may vary plus or minus .12 inch. In Fig. 78(b), if the outside diameter and the wall thickness are at the extreme tolerances, the resultant inside diameter may vary plus or minus .36 inch. In both Fig. 78(a) and (b), the referenced dimensions should not be verified for size or tolerance, as these are only resultants from the given dimensions and tolerances.

This example is given only to show how the results may vary on referenced dimensions when different base dimensions are used. The customer should select the *method* of dimensioning which produces the best results.

Combine Tolerances on Side Walls

A side wall with normal draft angle formed by a bottom die cavity and a protruding top die is affected by both dimensional and match tolerances. Checking these tolerances separately is difficult and causes inspection controversies. To avoid this difficulty, it is recommended to combine both tolerances and add their sum to the side wall dimension with an explanatory note, as illustrated in Fig. 79.

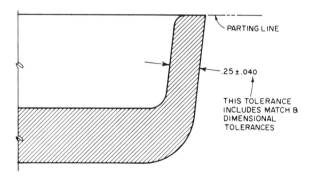

FIG. 79—*Tolerancing on side walls as shown simplifies inspection.*

Designate Forging Plane When Parting Line is Irregular

The parting line should always be specified on the drawing but the flash extension at the parting line periphery should not be pictured. When the parting line is irregular, the forging plane must also be designated (Fig. 80) for die-making purposes and for drawing completeness, since draft angles are usually taken normal to the forging plane. There is no need to indicate the forging plane when it coincides with the parting line.

Uniform Draft Indicated by Concentric Radii

At plan view intersections of plane surfaces—at different levels but parallel to each other—concentric radii indicate uniform draft, as shown in Fig. 81. These are incorporated easily and naturally in sinking the die cavity with conical cutters. When not shown as concentric radii, these areas require difficult and more costly hand-worked die blending.

Dimensioning Bosses Inclined to Forging Plane

Bosses inclined to the forging plane should be dimensioned at the points of tangency to simplify diesinking and to obtain round bosses, as illustrated in Fig. 82. When so dimensioned, the die may be initially inclined to the required angle and the boss cavity sunk with a straight-sided cutter. After the die is returned to its normal position, a conical cutter cuts the normal draft tangent to the already incorporated bottom radius but only around that part of the periphery where it is necessary.

If this same boss cavity were sunk to the usual point of intersection dimensioning, the bottom radius would actually take on an oval contour instead of the intended round contour, and the forged boss would appear to be discrepant.

Dimensioning Acute Angle Intersections

When ribs intersect at an acute angle, the method of dimensioning in Fig. 83 is recommended. By not specifying the radius, the variations within standard tolerances remain at a minimum.

Matching Parting Line Contours
(See Chapter 1)

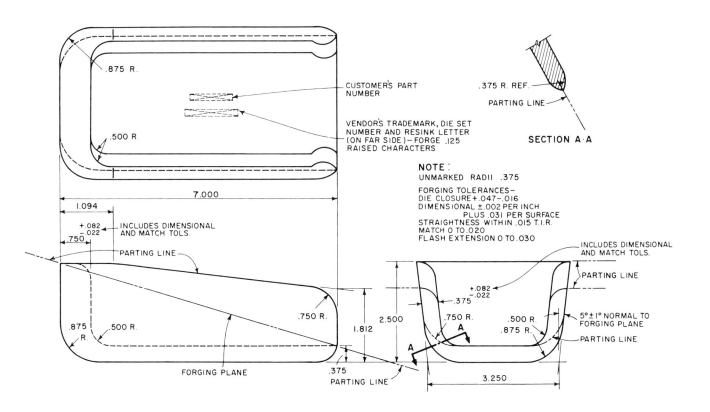

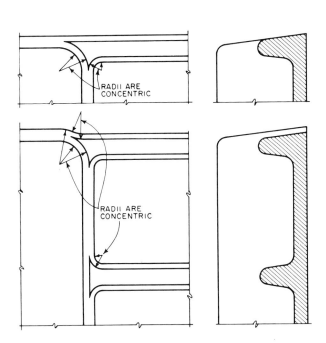

FIG. 80—*When the parting line is irregular, the forging plane should be designated as indicated.*

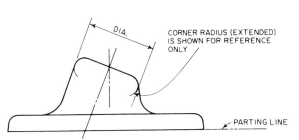

FIG. 82—*The normal rule of dimensioning to points of intersection should not be applied to bosses inclined to the forging plane. In such cases, the illustrated dimensioning to the tangency of the corner radius will result in a round rather than an oval boss and will also simplify diesinking.*

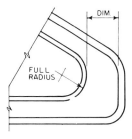

FIG. 81—*Concentric radii indicate uniform draft at the intersections.*

FIG. 83—*Specifying the thickness dimension at acute angle intersections minimizes the effect of forging tolerances as compared to specifying the radius dimension.*

Source: Aluminum Forging Design Manual, Aluminum Assn., Inc.

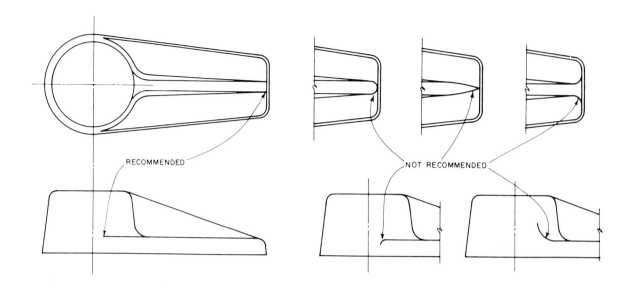

FIG. 84—*Proper and improper methods of showing intersections of webs and tapered ribs.*

How to Show Intersections of Webs and Tapered Ribs

The recommended delineation to show intersections of webs and tapered ribs is illustrated in Fig. 84 at the left. This method follows the concept of disregarding radii and showing the forging as though it has sharp corners. The views at the right are examples of improper drawings.

Dimension Plan View Radii at Inside Intersections

The radii in the plan view at inside intersections are not considered fillet radii and must be specified separately (Fig. 85). These are incorporated in the die by moving the cutter in a radial path, which results in the previously described concentric radii indicating uniform draft. It is preferred practice to dimension these radii at the bottom of the draft, making them at least as large as the general fillet radii, to assure adequacy where fillets are most important.

Various Methods of Incorporating Fillet Radii at Rib Intersections

There are various ways of depicting blends or transitions of differing fillet radii at rib intersections. The drawing should indicate exactly what is required. The four methods in Fig. 86 are used commonly, and each produces a different physical effect.

Dimensioning an Offset in Plan View

A recommended method of dimensioning a plan view offset is to the tangency of the outside radius

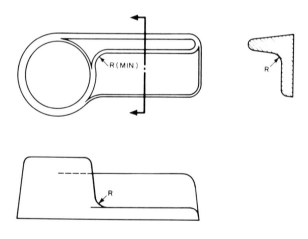

FIG. 85—*Radii at inside intersections in plan views should be individually dimensioned, preferably to the draft bottom and at least as large as the fillet radius as indicated to improve forgeability.*

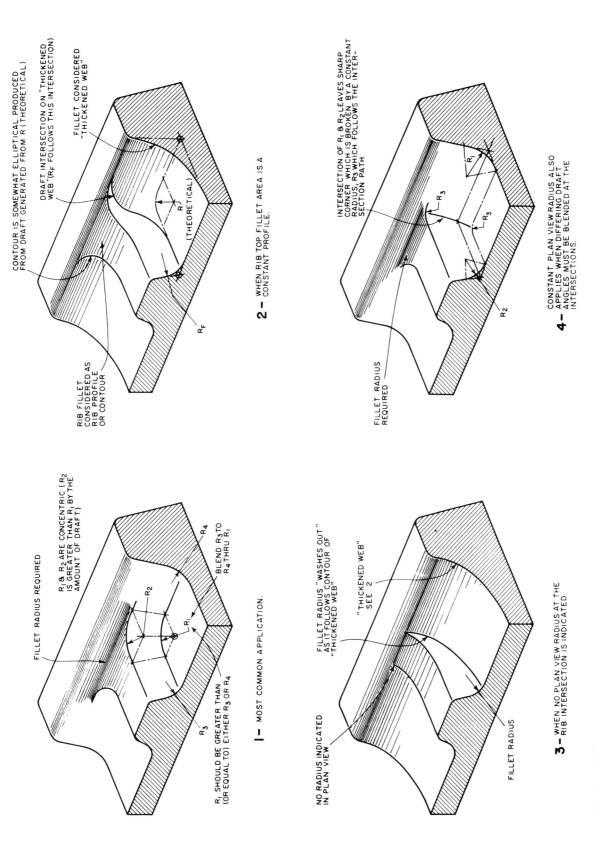

CONTOUR IS SOMEWHAT ELLIPTICAL PRODUCED
FROM DRAFT GENERATED FROM R (THEORETICAL)

DRAFT INTERSECTION ON "THICKENED
WEB" (Rᶠ FOLLOWS THIS INTERSECTION)

FILLET CONSIDERED
"THICKENED WEB"

RIB FILLET
CONSIDERED AS
RIB PROFILE
OR CONTOUR

R
(THEORETICAL)

Rᶠ

2 – WHEN RIB TOP FILLET AREA IS A
CONSTANT PROFILE.

INTERSECTION OF R₁ & R₂ LEAVES SHARP
CORNER WHICH IS BROKEN BY A CONSTANT
RADIUS, R₃ WHICH FOLLOWS THE INTER-
SECTION PATH

FILLET RADIUS
REQUIRED

R₁

R₃

R₃

R₂

4 – CONSTANT PLAN VIEW RADIUS ALSO
APPLIES WHEN DIFFERING DRAFT
ANGLES MUST BE BLENDED AT THE
INTERSECTIONS.

FILLET RADIUS REQUIRED

R₁ & R₂ ARE CONCENTRIC (R₂
IS GREATER THAN R₁ BY THE
AMOUNT OF DRAFT)

R₄

R₂

R₁

BLEND R₃ TO
R₄ THRU R₁

R₃

R₁ SHOULD BE GREATER THAN
(OR EQUAL TO) EITHER R₃ OR R₄

1 – MOST COMMON APPLICATION.

NO RADIUS INDICATED
IN PLAN VIEW

FILLET RADIUS "WASHES OUT"
AS IT FOLLOWS CONTOUR OF
"THICKENED WEB"

"THICKENED WEB"
SEE 2

FILLET RADIUS

3 – WHEN NO PLAN VIEW RADIUS AT THE
RIB INTERSECTION IS INDICATED.

Fɪɢ. 86—*Different methods of illustrating fillet radii at
rib intersections.*

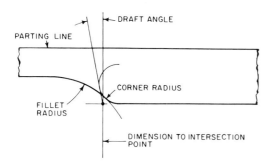

DRAWING LAYOUT SEQUENCE

1. INTERSECTION POINT
2. DRAFT ANGLE
3. CORNER RADIUS
4. FILLET RADIUS

DIE CONSTRUCTION SEQUENCE FOLLOWS

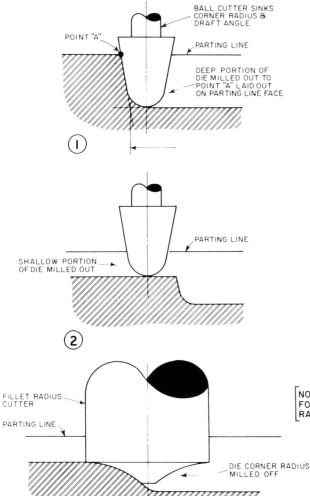

as shown in Fig. 87. It is also satisfactory to locate the center of the same radius. Dimensioning to the intersection of the outside and inside radii should be avoided—this approach is ambiguous, especially if the two radii are unequal.

Dimensioning Shallow Steps Between Two Surfaces

The general point of intersection rule applies on a shallow step between two surfaces and locates the corner radius; this is constructed first, followed by the fillet radius. Any exception to this must be specifically shown on the drawing as, for example, when the fillet radius is to be positioned first. The views in Fig. 88 illustrate both the drawing and the step-by-step die construction.

Deviation from Normal Dimensioning

There are cases where it is preferable to deviate from the normal practice of dimensioning to the point of intersection of the corner radius. Thus, where the corner radius is much larger than the thickness of web, as illustrated in Fig. 89, the drawing should clearly indicate that the dimension

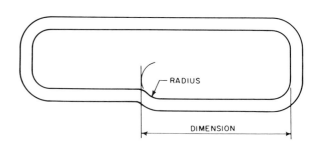

Fig. 87 *Dimensioning offsets to the tangent (or to the center) of the radius is recommended. Avoid dimensioning to the intersection of the outside and inside radius because it is too vague.*

NOTE! DIE CORNER RADIUS FORMS FORGING FILLET RADIUS & VICE-VERSA

Fig. 88—*Step-by-step drawing and diesinking sequence in incorporating a shallow step.*

is taken to the parting line. This is more measurable and helps to avoid layout controversies.

Draft Projections at Rib Ends with Large Radii

The draft contour is a function of the depth of the impression from the parting line. At a rib end with an end radius larger than the corner radius, the draft develops naturally when the ball die cutter follows the path of the large radius (Fig. 90). Note that the top lines are projected from the theoretically sharp corners of the die cutter, the large end radius being taken into consideration. On cylindrical parts with the parting line through the diameter, the draft configuration is developed similarly.

Draft Projections on Tapered Webs

The draft in the plan view should indicate the change in web thickness as shown in Fig. 91. The projections reflect the web thickening with the taper or developed curve lines.

Pads Added at Parting Line

When the top and bottom die impressions do not match at the parting line periphery, pads are recommended to match the protruding die impression. This permits the flash to be split equally about the parting line and simplifies diesinking. If both dies need matching, jogging the die flash

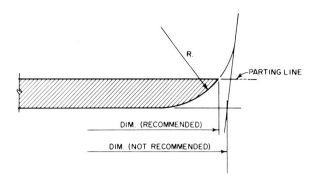

Fig. 89—*Illustrated is an example where the usual point of intersection dimension rule should be avoided.*

would require more work. If only one die requires matching, incorporating all of the flash in the other die would make the forging appear to be out of match at the parting line. Adding small pads solves the problem easily. Such pads vary from .06 inch thickness on small forgings to .50 inch on very large forgings.

The illustrations under the subject "Matching Parting Line Contours" also cover these pads.

Fig. 90—*With a large radius at rib end, draft decreases naturally at extremity as shown.*

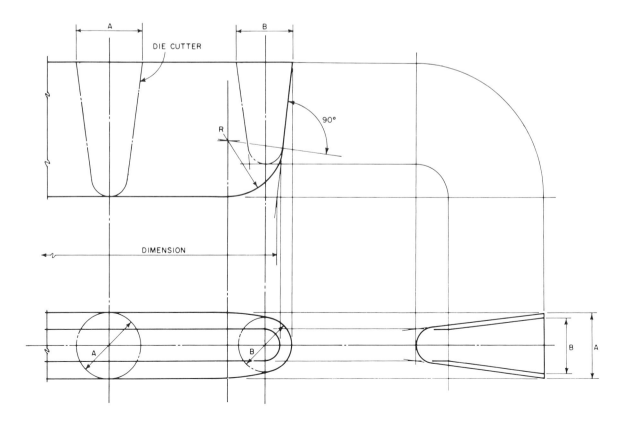

Source: Aluminum Forging Design Manual, Aluminum Assn., Inc.

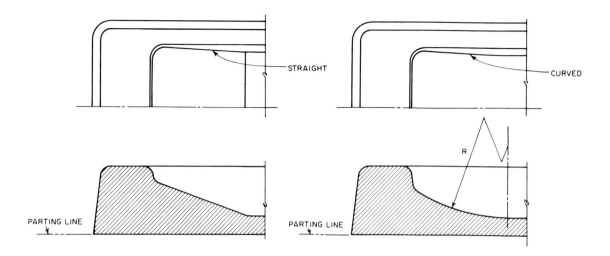

F<small>IG</small>. 91—*The web thickening pattern determines the draft line projections.*

Match Marks

Match marks are useful to the inspector at the primary equipment to determine quickly whether the forging is being made within the match tolerance. If not, production is stopped and the dies are adjusted to meet the tolerance. These match marks are very slight ridges placed in line across the parting line, generally on the drafted surfaces; they are approximately .015 inch high by .375 inch long on each side of the parting line. The forging vendor determines the match marks, which need not be shown on the customer drawings.

Vent and Knockout Marks

The vendor decides whether a specific forging requires that vents or knockouts (ejectors) be incorporated in the dies. Marks resulting from die vents and knockouts were previously explained in Chapter 2 on tolerances. The customer's drawings need not indicate these marks.

Types of Identification Characters on Forgings

The types of identification characters appearing on forgings may be either permanent or temporary. The permanent types include integral, impression-stamped, vibra-stamped and electro-etched characters. The temporary characters are ink stamped.

The integral characters are either raised or depressed and are formed by opposite or negative characters in the forging die. The most common are raised characters obtained from depressed lettering stamped into the die impression. These are also the most economical, since the die stamping is routine and performed only once. If distinctive and superior characters are preferred, these can be provided by a more expensive die engraving and may be either raised or depressed.

Integral characters are forged, and therefore must be located on a surface parallel or nearly parallel to the forging plane and in an area where the metal flow is relatively retarded, such as near the center. The area must also be flat and large enough for the necessary lettering.

The standard sizes of lettering stamped into the dies are: .06 inch, .09 inch, .13 inch, .16 inch, .19 inch, .25 inch, .31 inch and .38 inch. The lettering size should be proportional to the forging size. The height of integral characters above the adjoining surface is from approximately .015 inch on small forgings to .031 inch on large forgings. Exceeding these heights may invite difficulty in obtaining uniform lettering or may cause lettering washouts, especially in areas of excessive metal movement.

Impression-stamped, vibra-stamped, or electro-etched characters must be added on each individual forging. This increases costs, since it demands more handling and more careful attention. Of the three methods, impression stamping is strongly preferred.

The desirable location for lettering is a flat, adequately large and accessible surface. The normal depth of these characters is a maximum of .015

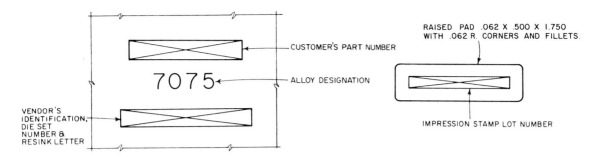

RAISED PAD .062 X .500 X 1.750
WITH .062 R. CORNERS AND FILLETS.

CUSTOMER'S PART NUMBER

ALLOY DESIGNATION

VENDOR'S IDENTIFICATION, DIE SET NUMBER & RESINK LETTER

IMPRESSION STAMP LOT NUMBER

ALL LETTERING TO BE .250 CHARACTERS, RAISED.

Fig. 92—*Typical drawing identification callouts.*

inch. If a specific depth is designated, special equipment becomes necessary to control the operation.

Impression stamping is frequently located on raised pads deliberately used where the stress raising effect of such stamping is feared. These pads should be large enough to accommodate all the stamping easily.

Ink-stamped characters are temporary and may be easily obliterated. Because of its impermanent nature, ink-stamping can only be done at the completion of all forging operations. This procedure is not routine and demands special handling. If the forging configuration is such that it is not possible to obtain integral characters, or if integral characters are illegible, rubber ink-stamping may be used.

Kinds of Identification

The essential identification (Fig. 92) that must appear on a forging is determined by the customer. Part of the identification is also helpful to the vendor in processing forgings through his shop. If overlooked on the original customer drawing, the vendor may propose identification but it must be approved before being applied. The identification may include the customer's part number, the vendor's trademark and die set number, the alloy designation, the lot number, an inspection symbol, and a serial number.

The part number, vendor's identification, and alloy designation should preferably be in integral characters, since they do not change.

The lot number (sometimes called melt, heat or heat-treat number), the inspection symbol, and the serial number change and must be applied individually on each forging.

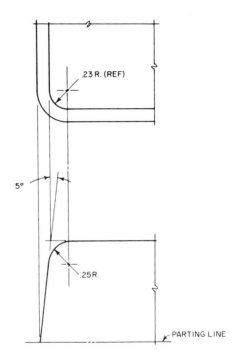

.23 R. (REF)

5°

.25 R.

PARTING LINE

Fig. 93—*The referenced plan view radius is smaller than the corner radius by the amount of the draft.*

Contours Defined by Ordinates

The layout of a contour defined by ordinate dimensions is done with a flexible spline or numerical control to obtain the truest possible curvature, unless otherwise specified. If the contour takes a decided change, this portion should have sufficient ordinate points to define the desired curve adequately.

Outside Corner Radii in Plan View

When the general corner radius applies to an outside corner radius in the plan view, it is drawn

Source: Aluminum Forging Design Manual, Aluminum Assn., Inc.

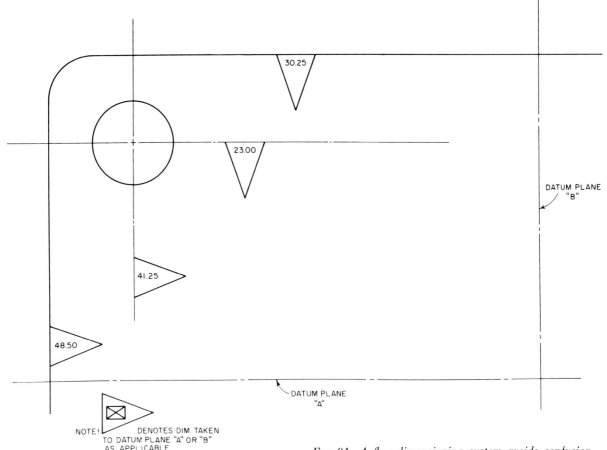

NOTE! DENOTES DIM. TAKEN TO DATUM PLANE "A" OR "B" AS APPLICABLE

FIG. 94—*A flag dimensioning system avoids confusion and cluttering of dimension lines where space is limited.*

smaller because of the draft angle and in keeping with the practice of showing plan view lines as intersections of the draft and the top surfaces as shown in Fig. 93.

Dimensioning in Crowded Areas

To avoid crossing the solid drawing lines with extension and dimension lines (this muddles up a drawing and makes it difficult to read, especially where details are compacted), a flag system of dimensioning is suggested as shown in Fig. 94. The dimension is placed inside the flag, which has one side coinciding with the extension line and the opposite point directed toward the datum line from which the dimension is taken. The extension line is kept as short as possible. A general drawing note should be added to explain this method of dimensioning. The drawing will be relatively clear and easy to interpret.

Another system would be to do the same as above, but omit the flag; however, such a drawing would not give assurance of proper interpretation.

Engineering Terms

Basic Dimension: A basic dimension defines the theoretically perfect size or location of a feature and is without tolerance. It establishes a base from which allowable deviations are to be measured.

Datum: A datum establishes the exact feature from which other features are located or measured. It may be a center, line, plane, or diameter from which dimensions originate.

True Position (T.P.): The true position signifies the theoretically perfect position of a feature.

MMC: This abbreviation stands for "maximum material condition" of a feature and would define a maximum outside diameter and a minimum inside diameter. This expression is used with form tolerance, which is minimum when the feature is at maximum size, but increases the form tolerance when the feature is smaller by the difference from MMC.

RFS: This abbreviation stands for "regardless of feature size." It is used with form tolerances and

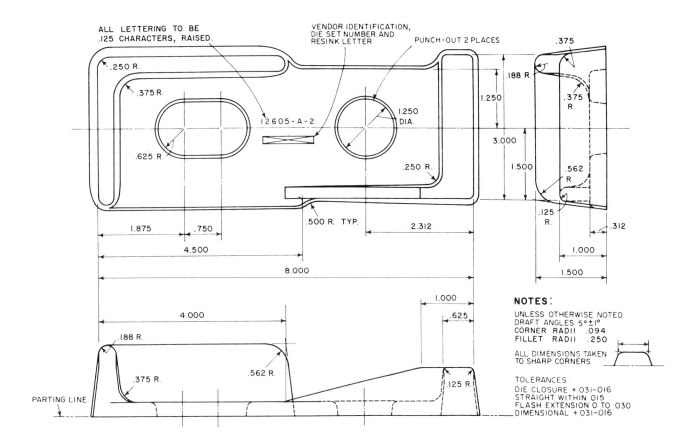

ALL LETTERING TO BE .125 CHARACTERS, RAISED.

VENDOR IDENTIFICATION, DIE SET NUMBER AND RESINK LETTER

PUNCH-OUT 2 PLACES

.250 R.

.375 R.

.625 R.

12605-A-2

1.250 DIA.

.250 R.

.500 R. TYP.

.188 R.

.375 R.

.562 R.

.125 R.

.312

.375

1.250

3.000

1.500

1.000

1.500

1.875   .750

4.500

2.312

8.000

4.000

1.000

.625

.188 R.

.375 R.

.562 R.

.125 R.

PARTING LINE

NOTES:
UNLESS OTHERWISE NOTED DRAFT ANGLES 5°±1°
CORNER RADII .094
FILLET RADII .250

ALL DIMENSIONS TAKEN TO SHARP CORNERS

TOLERANCES
DIE CLOSURE +.031-.016
STRAIGHT WITHIN .015
FLASH EXTENSION 0 TO .030
DIMENSIONAL +.031-.016

FIG. 95—*Locate integral identification near center of forging to assure legible characters.*

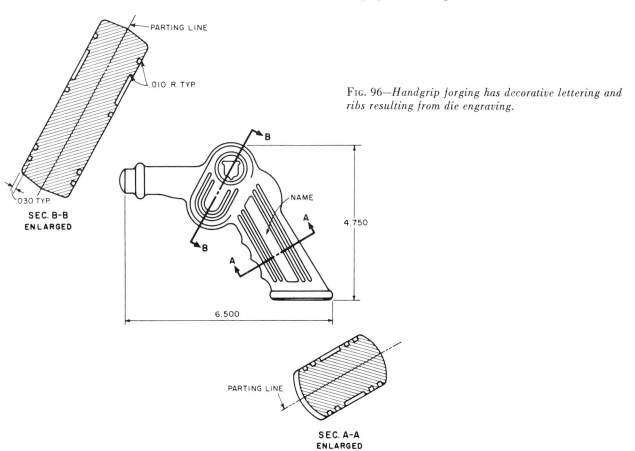

PARTING LINE

.010 R. TYP.

.030 TYP.

SEC. B-B ENLARGED

FIG. 96—*Handgrip forging has decorative lettering and ribs resulting from die engraving.*

B

NAME

A

A

B

4.750

6.500

PARTING LINE

SEC. A-A ENLARGED

Source: Aluminum Forging Design Manual, Aluminum Assn., Inc.

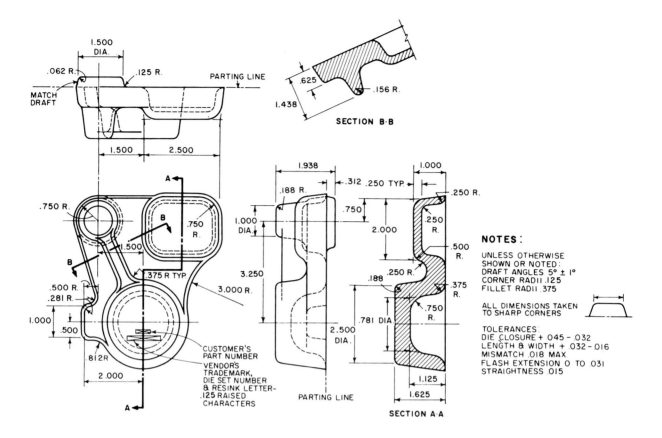

FIG. 97—*Recesses forged by die plugs protruding across flat parting line.*

with MMC callouts. It signifies that the form tolerance must not be exceeded, regardless of the actual size of the feature.

T.I.R.: This abbreviation stands for "total indicator reading" and signifies the maximum tolerance. It may represent a diametral tolerance zone or a tolerance zone between two parallel planes. The callout "F.I.R." means the same and stands for "full indicator reading."

Dimension "Max.": The word "Max." defines the high limit of the dimension, with zero being the low limit.

Dimension "Min.": The word "Min." defines the low limit of the dimension, with infinity (or whatever is practical) as the high limit.

Dimension "Typ.": The word "Typ." implies that the dimension is applicable to all similar sized features.

Typical Forging Drawings: The following illustrations are typical forging drawings: Figs. 95, 96, 97, 98 and 99.

FIG. 98—*When parting lines are irregular, forging plane should be indicated.*

FIG. 99—*Typical forging drawing for forged part to be produced on a mechanical upsetter shows location and size of part numbers and lettering.*

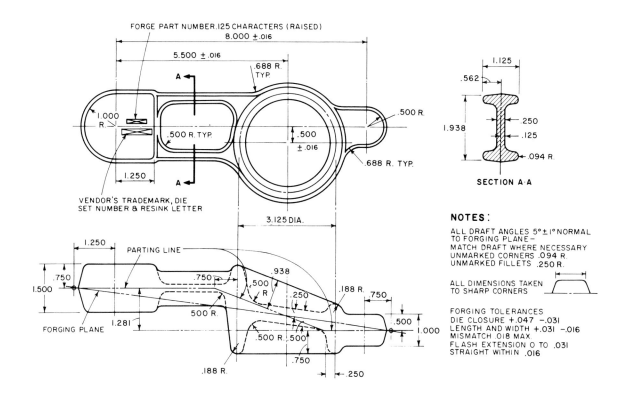

FORGE PART NUMBER.125 CHARACTERS (RAISED)

8.000 ±.016

5.500 ±.016

.688 R. TYP.

1.000 R.

.500 R. TYP.

A

.500 ±.016

.500 R.

.688 R. TYP.

1.250

VENDOR'S TRADEMARK, DIE SET NUMBER & RESINK LETTER

3.125 DIA.

1.125

.562

1.938

.250

.125

.094 R.

SECTION A·A

NOTES:

ALL DRAFT ANGLES 5°±1° NORMAL TO FORGING PLANE—
MATCH DRAFT WHERE NECESSARY
UNMARKED CORNERS .094 R.
UNMARKED FILLETS .250 R.

ALL DIMENSIONS TAKEN TO SHARP CORNERS

FORGING TOLERANCES
DIE CLOSURE +.047 −.031
LENGTH AND WIDTH +.031 −.016
MISMATCH .018 MAX.
FLASH EXTENSION O TO .031
STRAIGHT WITHIN .016

1.250

PARTING LINE

.750

1.500

.750

.938

.500 R

.250

.188 R.

.750

.750

1.281

500 R.

FORGING PLANE

.500 R. .500

.500

1.000

.188 R.

.750

.250

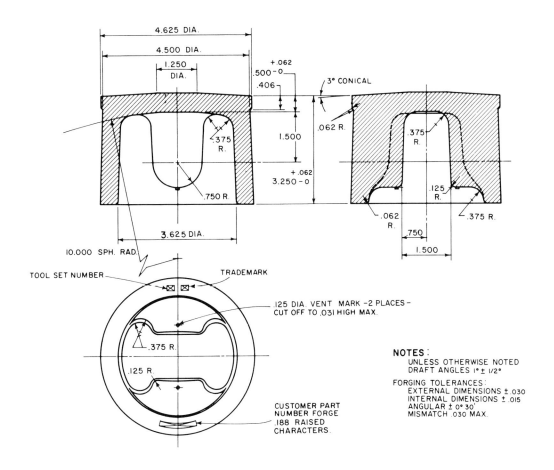

4.625 DIA.

4.500 DIA.

1.250 DIA.

+.062
.500 −0

.406

3° CONICAL

.062 R.

.375 R.

1.500

.375 R.

+.062
3.250 −0

.125 R.

.062 R.

.750 R.

.062 R.

.375 R.

.750

1.500

3.625 DIA.

10.000 SPH. RAD.

TOOL SET NUMBER

TRADEMARK

.125 DIA. VENT MARK −2 PLACES −
CUT OFF TO .031 HIGH MAX.

.375 R.

.125 R.

CUSTOMER PART NUMBER FORGE .188 RAISED CHARACTERS.

NOTES:
UNLESS OTHERWISE NOTED
DRAFT ANGLES 1° ± 1/2°

FORGING TOLERANCES:
EXTERNAL DIMENSIONS ±.030
INTERNAL DIMENSIONS ±.015
ANGULAR ± 0° 30'
MISMATCH .030 MAX.

Section VI:
Melting and Casting

Foundry Melting of Aluminum Alloys

By the ASM Committee on Production of Aluminum Alloy Castings

FURNACES for melting of aluminum alloys in the foundry may be broadly classified into three types:

1 Direct fuel-fired furnaces
2 Indirect fuel-fired furnaces
3 Electrically heated furnaces.

Direct Fuel-Fired Furnaces

The direct fuel-fired type is exemplified by the reverberatory furnace, which can be of either of two fundamental designs — wet-hearth and dry-hearth. In a wet-hearth furnace, the products of combustion are in direct contact with the top of the molten bath, and heat transfer is by a combination of convection and radiation. In a dry-hearth furnace, the charge of solid aluminum is placed on a sloping hearth above the level of the molten metal so that the charge is completely enveloped in hot gases. Heat is absorbed rapidly by the solid charge, which melts and drains from the sloping hearth into the wet holding basin or chamber.

Dry-hearth furnaces can melt faster than wet-hearth furnaces, but metal losses from oxidation are greater in dry-hearth than in wet-hearth melting. Another disadvantage of dry-hearth melting is that keeping the hearth clean, which is mandatory, is a laborious task. A dry-hearth furnace is useful, however, for melting scrap that contains ferrous metal inserts, because the inserts stay on the hearth.

Of the two types of reverberatory furnaces, wet-hearth furnaces are the more widely used. Figures 1 and 2 show details of construction of wet-hearth furnaces of two different designs. The furnace shown in Fig. 1 is charged through two adjoining wells; the one in Fig. 2 is charged by means of a charging ramp.

Reverberatory furnaces generally are used to melt large amounts of aluminum to supply holding furnaces, or used to remelt scrap metal, and may be large enough to hold up to 90 tons of molten aluminum alloy. The larger furnaces are disproportionately wider and longer than smaller furnaces, because bath depth is held to a maximum of about 30 in. regardless of the size of the furnace. Roof height above the molten metal depends on the height of the charging door, and that height depends on the kind of charge used. Roof height also depends on the heat-release factor relating the furnace volume to the Btu input. In general, furnace builders prefer not to exceed 30,000 Btu per cubic foot of space above the bath of molten metal.

Heating. Reverberatory furnaces can be heated by gas or oil. Some burners can use either gas or oil, to take advantage of changes in availability and cost of fuel. The size and number of burners for a furnace are selected to give the desired rate of melting. Fuel efficiency of 30% in melting aluminum is considered good.

Burners can be of either the nozzle-mix or the premix type. Both have performed satisfactorily in specific installations, although nozzle-mix burners are the more commonly used. Regardless of the type of burner used the flames should not impinge on the metal — which would cause turbulence, excessive oxidation, and pickup of hydrogen.

Most reverberatory furnaces utilize a nozzle-mix burner that will throw a long flame, making use of "double-pass firing". This begins with a luminous or semiluminous flame, relatively high in the combustion chamber, that radiates heat to the refractory walls and roof. As the walls and roof become incandescent, they reradiate the heat to the bath. On the return path to the flue, which is in the same wall as the burners, convective heat is transferred from the gases. This provides a double transfer of heat: radiation on the outgoing path and convection on the return path.

The exhaust port of a reverberatory furnace should have a cross-sectional area that will provide a slight positive pressure in the furnace during melting.

Charging. A wet-hearth furnace is charged by placing the charge material

*R. W. DIVELY, *Chairman,* Metallurgist, Technical Service, Goodyear Aerospace Corp.; A. B. BRADLEY, Executive Vice President, Warwick Industrial Furnace and Engineering Co.; JOHN W. CLARKE (deceased), formerly Consultant – Foundry Dept., Erie Foundries, General Electric Co.; DONALD A. JOHNSON, Senior Process Engineer, Metallurgical Operations, Energy Controls Div., Bendix Corp.

T. E. KRAMER, Vice President – Operations, Ross Pattern & Foundry, Inc.; WILLIAM A. MADER, Vice President, Technical Services, Oberdorfer Foundries, Inc.; LAWSON E. MARSH, Manager, Casting Engineering and Development, Morris Bean & Co.; A. M. MONTGOMERY, Section Head, Castings and Forgings Div., Alcoa Research Laboratories, Aluminum Co. of America; CARL H. MUTH, Vice President and Plant Manager, Uni-

versal Castings Corp.; WILLIAM OBERNDORFER, Plant Metallurgist, Kokomo Casting Plant, Chrysler Corp.; CHARLES PELLEGRINI, Assistant Plant Manager, Tilton Plant, Arwood Corp.; JACK H. THOMPSON, Vice President – Manufacturing, Bodine Foundry Co.; R. A. TITLOW, Production Manager, Bedford (Indiana) Plant, Central Foundry Div., General Motors Corp.

ANTHONY V. VECCHIOTTI, Monroe Forgings, Inc. (formerly Manager, Permanent Mold Div., Rochester Bronze & Aluminum Foundry Co., Inc.); F. R. WIEHL, Staff Materials Engineer, Central Research Laboratory, Singer Co.; GEORGE R. WLODYGA, Engineer, Cast Metals Process Development, Manufacturing Development Office, Ford Motor Co.; JOHN A. WYMAN, Metallurgist, Permold Inc.

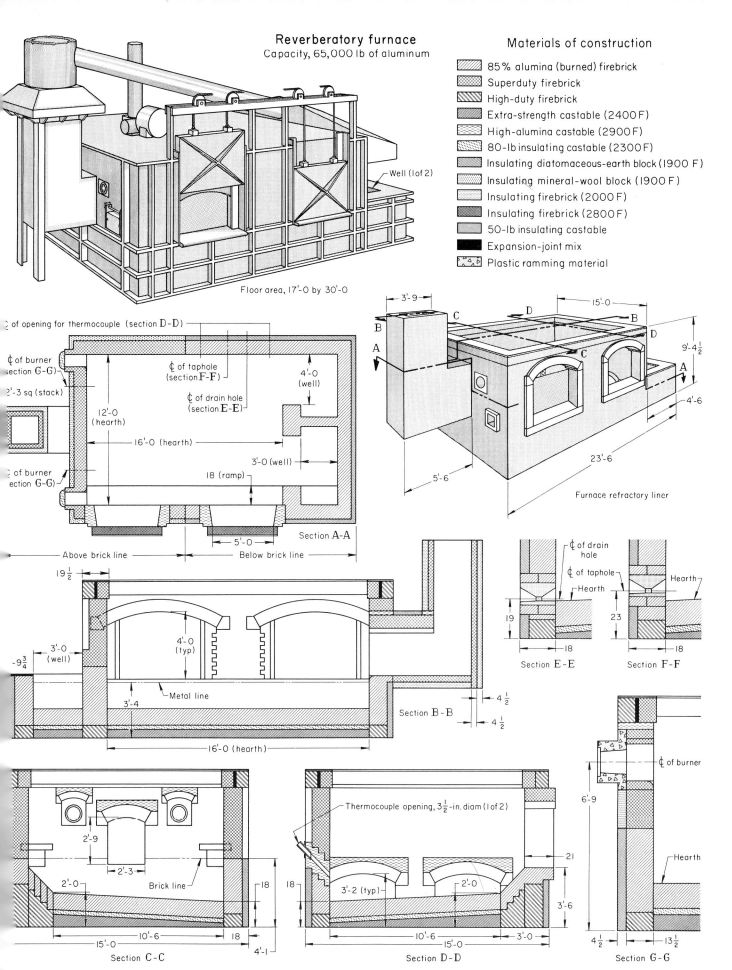

Reverberatory furnace
Capacity, 65,000 lb of aluminum

Materials of construction

- 85% alumina (burned) firebrick
- Superduty firebrick
- High-duty firebrick
- Extra-strength castable (2400 F)
- High-alumina castable (2900 F)
- 80-lb insulating castable (2300 F)
- Insulating diatomaceous-earth block (1900 F)
- Insulating mineral-wool block (1900 F)
- Insulating firebrick (2000 F)
- Insulating firebrick (2800 F)
- 50-lb insulating castable
- Expansion-joint mix
- Plastic ramming material

Floor area, 17'-0 by 30'-0

Well (1 of 2)

Furnace refractory liner

₵ of opening for thermocouple (section D-D)
₵ of burner (section G-G)
2'-3 sq (stack)
₵ of taphole (section F-F)
₵ of drain hole (section E-E)
₵ of burner (section G-G)
12'-0 (hearth)
16'-0 (hearth)
4'-0 (well)
3'-0 (well)
18 (ramp)
5'-0
Above brick line
Below brick line
Section A-A

3'-9
15'-0
9'-4½
4'-6
5'-6
23'-6

19½
3'-0 (well)
9¾
4'-0 (typ)
Metal line
3'-4
16'-0 (hearth)
4½
4½
Section B-B

₵ of drain hole
₵ of taphole
Hearth
19
18
Section E-E

Hearth
23
18
Section F-F

2'-9
2'-3
Brick line
2'-0
18
15'-0
10'-6
18
4'-1
Section C-C

Thermocouple opening, 3½-in. diam (1 of 2)
18
18
3'-2 (typ)
2'-0
21
3'-6
10'-6
3'-0
15'-0
Section D-D

₵ of burner
6'-9
Hearth
4½
13½
Section G-G

Fig. 1. Details of a reverberatory furnace with a capacity of 65,000 lb of aluminum. Furnace is charged through two open wells at right end.

Source: Metals Handbook, 8th Ed., Vol. 5, ASM

(solid or liquid) directly into the chamber or into a well. This procedure minimizes oxidation of the charge material. Molten metal may be charged through a launder (a refractory trough).

The melting efficiency of a wet-hearth furnace may be increased by preheating ingots and heavy scrap. Charge materials can be preheated by placing them at the base of the stack before they are charged into the furnace. This practice not only increases furnace efficiency at no extra cost for fuel, but also ensures that the charge material is moisture-free — which is an essential condition.

Dry-hearth furnaces are charged by placing solid material on the hearth, which slopes at an angle of 10° to 15°, on which the metal melts. Oxides, tramp iron, and other nonmelting materials stay on the hearth as the molten aluminum runs into the bath.

Tapping. Molten metal may be removed from a reverberatory furnace through tapholes or by tilt pouring. Siphons, pumps and hand ladles may also be used.

Tapholes are plugged with fiber refractory cones, clay, or mixtures of sand and clay. Some furnaces have a taphole in a sump for removal of sludge. In addition, an upper taphole is used for pouring. Some furnaces use air-displacement pumps to deliver molten metal in measured quantities.

Indirect Fuel-Fired Furnaces

In an indirect fuel-fired furnace, a barrier of some sort prevents contact of the hot combustion gases with the metal to be melted. Thus, there can be no pickup of the products of combustion by the metal charge, such as occurs in a direct fuel-fired furnace. Crucible, or pot, furnaces are the most typical of the indirect fuel-fired furnaces. In a crucible furnace, there is a wall of silicon carbide or metal between the combustion gases and the metal charge.

Crucible (pot) furnaces are much used in aluminum foundries for melting or holding, or both, because of their versatility for alloy change. The major components of crucible furnaces for melting aluminum alloys are essentially the same as those of crucible furnaces used for melting of other metals.

In the simplest form of crucible furnace, the pot is stationary, and the molten metal is ladled from it for casting. In a lift-out crucible furnace (Fig. 3), the pot has a pouring spout, and it is removed from the furnace by means of tongs and used as a pouring ladle. Tilting crucible furnaces (Fig. 4) are also widely used. In the method used for heating, a tilting furnace does not differ fundamentally from a stationary-pot or a lift-out furnace. As indicated in Fig. 4, the entire furnace can be tilted to permit pouring directly into a transfer ladle.

Crucible furnaces are made in capacities of 30 to 2000 lb. The crucible (or pot) may be made of a refractory material or of refractory-coated cast iron. Refractory-coated iron crucibles must be recoated frequently (preferably, every day).

Table 1. Effect of Preheating Aluminum Ingots to 750 F With Flue Gas Before Charging Int[o] 275-Lb Crucible for Melting at 1200 F

Condition during melting	Ingots at room temperature	Ingots preheated to 75[0]
Melting rate, lb per hr	190	30[ ]
Increase in melting rate, %	...	60.[ ]
Temperature drop of melt by charging 10% of crucible capacity, F	63	
Fuel-oil consumption per 100 lb of melt, lb	6.7	4.[ ]
Reduction in fuel-oil consumption, %	...	32.[ ]
Flue temperature, F	1925	102[ ]

SOURCE: R. J. Kissling and J. F. Wallace, *Foundry*, Dec 1964, 64-70, Table VI

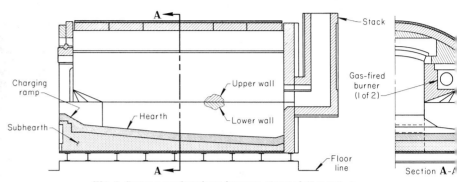

Fig. 2. Large reverberatory furnace charged through a ramp

Refractory crucibles have a thick wall (1³⁄₁₆ to 2½ in., depending on size) to provide strength, which makes them costly and results in poor heat transfer. However, a refractory crucible is preferred to an iron crucible when no contamination by iron is permissible. In addition, because of their long life, refractory crucibles usually cost less than iron crucibles per ton of aluminum melted.

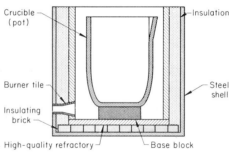

Fig. 3. Lift-out crucible (pot) furnace

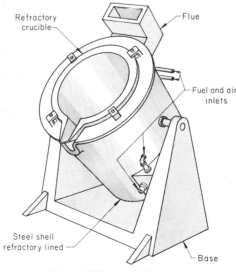

Fig. 4. Tilting crucible furnace

Most refractory crucibles are ma[de] of carbon-bonded silicon carbide or a mixture of clay and graphite, [de]pending on the conditions of melti[ng] and on the alloys being melted. Silic[on] carbide is preferred for accelerat[ed] melting by flame heating, because [it] conducts heat better than the mixt[ure] of clay and graphite.

Cast iron crucibles are cast to s[ize] and shape, normally with a flange [for] support. Walls are usually 1 to 2 [in.] thick. Molten aluminum attacks c[ast] iron, but less rapidly than it atta[cks] steel; steel crucibles are never used [for] melting of aluminum. An uncoa[ted] cast iron pot (usually, gray iron) [is] sometimes used for melting of so[me] aluminum die-casting alloys, for wh[ich] contamination by iron is of less imp[or]tance. Contamination increases wh[en] the alloy is held in the pot for extend[ed] periods or at high temperatures.

Burners are located so that [the] flame is tangential to the crucible, [in] order to avoid a direct blast of fla[me] against the wall of the crucible. Fla[me] impingement shortens crucible life a[nd] makes it more difficult to control [the] temperature of the molten metal.

The shell of a crucible furnace [is] usually lined with brick that is back[ed] with several inches of insulation, [al]though it may be lined only with 4 t[o 6] in. of insulating brick. Castable [re]fractory linings are also used.

The thermal efficiency of cruci[ble] melting is low (15 to 30%) — prim[ar]ily because of the loss of heat to [the] flue gases. Thermal efficiency can [be] increased by utilizing the heat in [the] flue gases to preheat the charge. T[his] can be done by the use of a preheat[ing] chamber (see Fig. 6 on page 419 [in] the article on Foundry Melting of C[op]per). As shown in Table 1, preheat[ing] of aluminum ingots has increas[ed] melting rate by 60.5% while reduc[ing] fuel consumption by 32.8%. (For ad[di]tional discussion of the use and be[ne]fits of preheating, see the section "P[re]heating the Charge", page 419 in [the] article on Melting of Copper Alloy[s].)

Electric Furnaces

Most electric-furnace melting of aluminum alloys for casting is done in low-frequency induction furnaces, of the channel (core) and the coreless types, although high-frequency induction furnaces and electric-resistance crucible furnaces are used also and sometimes prove to be more suitable for specific applications.

Channel (core-type) low-frequency induction furnaces are used to supply molten aluminum for all methods of casting. Most channel induction furnaces for melting aluminum are 60-cycle furnaces, and range from 20 to 200 kw for capacities of 700 to 3000 lb of aluminum, with melting rates of 100 to 1000 lb per hour. These furnaces are controlled by voltage-regulated transformers and contactors. For a more detailed description of 60-cycle channel induction furnaces, see page 349 in the article "Melting of Gray Iron", in this volume.

The powerful electromagnetic field present in the channels causes the molten metal to flow from the sides to the center of each channel, from which it is forced in opposite directions out the ends of the channels. This flowing action stirs and mixes the molten metal enough so that mechanical stirring rarely is needed; it also helps to maintain uniform temperature throughout the molten metal.

Most nonmetallics (oxides, nitrides, carbides, borides and fluxes) rise to the surface of the molten metal, from which they can be skimmed, when the power is off. Some oxides may not rise to the surface, but will deposit on the channel walls while the power is on. Gaseous fluxing through the channels and across the bottom of the furnace can prevent the deposition of oxides. The fluxing will lift residues to the top for skimming. Solid salts used as surface fluxes should be applied only when the power is turned off. All cleaning, skimming and degassing should then be done before the power is turned on. Otherwise, solid salts will be stirred into the metal and will collect in the channels. Surface fluxing may not be effective if the metal is held at a temperature below 1200 F. For temperatures below 1200 F, the metal should be skimmed without fluxing, and then fluxed in another, hotter furnace.

Core-type low-frequency induction furnaces will melt about 5 lb of aluminum per kilowatt-hour; thus, they are more efficient than any burner-type furnace. Thermal efficiency per pound of aluminum melted and heated to pouring temperature can be 50% for 8-hr operation, and as high as 70% for 24-hr operation. The loss by oxidation is low, because the heat is generated within the metal. Also, the metal is cleaner than when melted in burner-type furnaces.

For greater capacity or for continuous operation, a holding hearth may be connected to the melting hearth, with separate controls for each hearth. In these combination units, metal melted in one side, goes by gravity to the holding side. When such units are used only as holding furnaces for purposes such

as large die-casting operations, they are charged with hot metal.

Another style of channel furnace is horizontal, and has a single power unit for two chambers. Both chambers are open, and the channels are sloped for easier cleaning. Cold or hot metal generally is charged in the shallow end, so that the deep end becomes the holding chamber. Electromagnetic forces circulate the metal through both chambers.

Generally, the furnace hearth and channels are lined with 4 to 6 in. of high-alumina castable refractory, with 2 to 4 in. of insulation backup for the hearth. Only the outside walls of the channels are insulated. Because failures are more common in the inductors than in the hearth, the furnace is constructed to allow separate relining of the inductors and the hearth.

In start-up of a new or relined channel furnace, the refractory of the channel and the hearth is first brought to a red heat — by the use of torch or electric heat in the channels, and of torch heat for the hearth. Sufficient molten metal is then added to fill the channels. Core-type furnaces require that a heel of molten metal be kept in the furnace.

Coreless low-frequency induction furnaces are used mostly to melt turnings, foil, and other fines. Coreless furnaces have the same melting and stirring action as channel (core-type) furnaces, and so there is little loss of metal by oxidation. (Coreless induction furnaces are discussed in detail and illustrated in the article "Melting of Gray Iron", page 349 in this volume.)

Electromagnetic forces in a coreless furnace produce intense stirring, which lifts the center of the surface of the molten metal to a higher level than the level at the crucible wall. Nonmetallics gather as a ring around the furnace walls in the plane of the center of the power coil. The circulation washes a fresh charge quickly into the molten bath, resulting in high recovery of metal. The bath remains at lower temperature than would be practical for melting in the well of a reverberatory furnace.

A coreless furnace has no channels to clean, and it is not necessary to keep a molten heel in the furnace. It is thus adaptable to batch-type operation. The initial charge should consist of large shapes, to at least 15% of furnace capacity. Following meltdown of the large shapes, subsequent charges may consist of any convenient forms, and can be comprised entirely of fines.

Coreless low-frequency induction furnaces are made in sizes ranging from 75 to 750 kw, with capacities of 350 to 7000 lb, and can melt 270 to 3500 lb of aluminum per hour. Coreless furnaces are costly (typically, about $200 per kilowatt), because of the expensive electrical apparatus needed. Power consumption is about 1 kwhr for each 4 lb of aluminum melted. This is about 80% of the efficiency for a channel (core-type) induction furnace. However, coreless furnaces can melt more metal per unit of floor area than any other type of furnace.

Coreless low-frequency induction furnaces have walls made of high-alumina castable refractory or ramming mix, in a thick-

ness of 1 to 3 in., and require heavy insulation only in the hearth floor. Because of the insulation provided by the water-cooled induction coils that surround the refractory walls, no further insulation in the walls is required.

High-frequency induction furnaces, because of their high initial cost and relatively small capacity, are limited almost entirely to use in specialty foundries. An advantage of high-frequency furnaces is that they can be used to melt metal fines, such as chips, without initially being charged with thicker material, whereas for melting by low frequency, the initial charge must consist of at least 15% of much thicker material.

There are two types of high-frequency induction furnaces: a lift-coil type, with capacities of 5 to 100 lb of aluminum; and a tilting type, with capacities of 20 to 1000 lb. The hearth of both types is a crucible. In tilting furnaces, the crucible is cemented into the coil; in lift-coil furnaces, the crucible is removable, when the coil is raised, for transfer to the pouring area.

The entire melt can be poured from a high-frequency furnace; thus, it is convenient for intermittent use. As in other induction furnaces, the electromagnetic stirring action permits a relatively low temperature in the molten bath, thus minimizing oxidation and promoting better uniformity in the composition of the bath.

In efficiency, high-frequency induction furnaces are intermediate between core-type and coreless low-frequency furnaces.

Except for the crucible, high-frequency furnaces are made like coreless low-frequency furnaces. The heat should be generated only in the aluminum, because the generation of heat in the refractory will reduce melting efficiency and cause hot spots that will shorten the life of the crucible. For this reason, crucibles are made of clay and graphite (generally with a minimum of graphite). The entire charge or any part of it may be placed in the crucible at the start.

Electric-resistance crucible furnaces are low-capacity furnaces. Although slow in melting, they are easy to keep clean and, unlike similar gas-fired or oil-fired units, generate no combustion products.

Heat input is limited by the wall area, but slower melting may be satisfactory for some operations, as in batch casting. Melting costs are higher with electric-resistance crucible furnaces than with crucible furnaces fired by natural gas. In the application described in the example that follows, however, electric-resistance furnaces yielded lower melting costs than furnaces fired with a propane-air mixture.

Example 454. Saving in Melting Cost by Change From Propane-Fired to Resistance Furnaces

In an investment casting foundry, an average of 850 lb of aluminum alloys was melted and poured during an 8-hr shift (the maximum amount was 1500 lb in 8 hr). The alloys cast in this foundry were mainly C355, A356 and D612 (40E).

This output was melted in four ribbon-element electric-resistance furnaces with combined capacity of 1050 lb fully charged, using power at 220 volts, 3-phase and 60 cps. The two sizes of furnace were as follows:

Capacity, lb	300	150
Rated power, kw	40	20
Secondary volts	57	90
Time for cold start, hr ..	2 to 3	1½ to 2

Either size of furnace could melt 50% of capacity as a reload per hour. Energy cost was $0.0096 per pound of aluminum melted, based on consumption of 0.6 kwhr per pound and a cost of $0.016 per kwhr. These furnaces replaced gas-fired furnaces of equal total capacity, for which energy cost for the propane-air mixture, rated at 690 Btu per cu ft, was $0.184 per therm (100,000 Btu) — equal to $0.0176 per pound of aluminum melted. The electric furnaces, fully instrumented, cost approximately $5000 each for the larger size and $3000 each for the smaller size.

It is important to note that in the preceding example the gas used was propane, which is costly. In most localities, natural gas is available, and in those localities where natural gas costs 5¢ per therm, the use of natural gas for melting would result in a saving of one-half the cost of resistance melting. One advantage of resistance melting is the lower ambient temperature near the furnace, which provides greater operator comfort.

Central Melting. For large-quantity production of castings, it is often preferred to supply holding furnaces from one central melting area. Central melting offers the following advantages:

1 Larger melting furnaces can be used, resulting in a smaller capital investment per ton of metal melted, and in more efficient operation.
2 Dirt, heat, fumes and smoke can be confined more easily in one area.
3 Melting and supervision of melting can be more efficient.
4 The hazards of melting can be isolated from other areas.
5 More room can be available in the casting area, for cooler, safer working conditions.
6 Molten metal can be supplied to each casting station at the required rate.
7 The grade of casting metal can be quickly changed in a holding furnace.
8 Usually, less metal is lost from oxidation.

Central melting furnaces commonly have capacities of 5 to 90 tons. Total melting capacity should be adequate for peak production.

Materials of Construction for Furnaces and Accessories

Silicon carbide bonded with carbon is the most commonly used crucible material for melting and holding aluminum alloys. Bonding the silicon carbide with silicon nitride provides a better crucible than is obtained with carbon bonding, but nitride-bonded crucibles cost more and are less commonly used. Silicon carbide crucibles bonded with carbon can, with good cleaning and maintenance practice, last for long periods of operation (up to 18 months, in some foundries).

Crucibles of cast iron are not used for melting or holding aluminum that must not pick up iron, because there are no protective washes or coatings to make cast iron pots acceptable without excessive maintenance.

Ladles with capacities of up to 20 lb of molten aluminum generally are made of clay and graphite and are held with hand tongs. With care to avoid abrasion, such ladles have good life, but they will not last as long as ladles made of silicon carbide.

Lances and diffusion heads that are used in gas fluxing are generally made of clay and graphite, cast iron, or porcelain enameled steel. Cast iron tools are attacked at the surface of the molten metal and require frequent replacement, unless they are kept thoroughly coated with a protective material such as a mixture of iron oxide and sodium silicate. Clay and graphite tools are subject to damage from shock and erosion, and must be replaced after about one month of use.

Thermocouple shields are normally made of silicon carbide bonded with carbon or with silicon nitride, or made of cast iron coated with a mixture of iron oxide and sodium silicate or with another protective material. Under normal conditions, such shields give long life. If molten aluminum enters the shield or protection tube, a burnout will result, which gives erroneous temperature readings. The end result may be overheated metal and serious damage to the refractories and the furnace.

Stirring rods, skimmers, hoes and other tools used in working with molten aluminum usually are made of low-carbon steel. If such tools are not coated, they will be attacked — which will result in some contamination of the molten aluminum. However, because contact with the molten aluminum is short, the amount of contamination is not usually significant.

Charging Practice

The furnace charge may be made up of any one or a combination of: returned gates and risers, returns from machining operations, prealloyed ingot, primary metal together with alloying elements or hardeners, and molten metal. The selection of metal for the charge depends on melting equipment and capacity, composition and quality of the alloy needed, cost, and available analytical equipment.

Direct charging into a holding furnace is never as desirable as separate melting, because there is less opportunity to clean the metal in direct charging. Direct charging of scrap is a source of oxide. The presence of water, oil or dirt on direct-charged metal will result in defective castings besides being a hazard to personnel. If solid metal is charged directly into a holding furnace, the chilling effect will promote the formation of sludge.

Purchased scrap may be in the form of briquetted chips, castings, clippings or other solid scrap that has been analyzed and classified.

Clean scrap is scrap that has been subjected to abrasive blasting to remove dirt, heavy oxide, and embedded sand, and heated above 500 F for at least 4 hr to remove contaminants such as water, oil and wax.

Machining scrap, such as borings and turnings, should be subjected to treatment in centrifuges, drum dryers, magnetic separators, and screens. Generated scrap of this type is sometimes briquetted, although it is usually fed into reverberatory melting furnaces without briquetting. All scrap must be clean and dry to prevent excessive metal loss and to prevent explosions.

Foundry Scrap. Floor sweepings and dross can constitute a costly loss of metal if not recovered. However, to prevent contamination of other charging materials, or an explosion, such material should be melted in a separate furnace and treated to remove dirt and oxide. The recovered metal is cast into ingots for remelting in small quantities with the normal charge for regular production.

Scrap-to-Ingot Ratio. The proportionate amounts of scrap (such as gates and risers) to new ingot in the charge depends to some extent on the requirements of the castings to be poured, but usually to a much greater extent on the control facilities in a particular foundry. For instance, in some foundries where requirements are extremely high (such as for the highest-quality aircraft castings) and facilities for reprocessing are minimal, only virgin ingot is used; gates, risers and sprues are sold. In most aluminum foundries, however, the yield is less than 50% (per cent by weight of salable castings compared to the amount of metal melted); thus, the practical approach is to reprocess the accumulated scrap.

Common practice is to melt all gates, risers, sprues, and scrap castings in a reverberatory furnace. Chemical analysis is made on each batch melted. The metal is cast into pigs, each of which is identified as to composition. Pigs having approved composition are melted for casting in a ratio as high as nine parts remelt to one part virgin ingot. Aircraft-quality castings can be successfully produced by this practice.

Molten metal, purchased from smelters that may be as much as several hundred miles distant, is used as charge material in some plants. Special aluminum alloys, partly alloyed metal, and pure aluminum are all available for shipment in the molten condition to the plant where they are to be cast. The molten metal is transported in special crucibles carried on trailer trucks that provide a payload capacity of 20,000 to 30,000 lb. The molten metal is transferred from the truck to a holding furnace by troughs or ladles.

Effect of Size of Charge Material on Melting Procedure. Melting of aluminum demands minimum disturbance of the bath. However, thin metal scrap and fines, which are likely to float, must be submerged in the molten bath by being washed down with pumped molten metal, or by the use of bars to break the surface so as to wet the fine scrap and permit it to begin melting.

Intermediate-size pieces (gates and risers, for example) usually can be charged directly into the molten bath without chilling the bath to any significant extent.

Large pieces should not be charged cold directly into a molten bath, because this chills the bath and causes alloying elements to precipitate as sludge. Large pieces melt slowly on exposure to flame heating, because of the low surface-to-volume ratio and high thermal conductivity of the solid metal. Large pieces melt best when exposed on a raised hearth to a direct flame that may be as much as 1000 F hotter than the molten metal. When a

Table 2. Designations and Compositions of Selected Aluminum Alloys in Casting and Ingot Forms, as Registered With The Aluminum Association

Alloy designation — Aluminum Assn	Commercial	Product form(a)	Si	Fe	Cu	Mn	Mg	Cr or Ni	Zn	Sn or Ti	Others Each	Others Total
295.0	195	S	0.7-1.5	1.0	4.0-5.0	0.35	0.03	...	0.35	0.25Ti	0.05	0.15
295.1	195	Ingot	0.7-1.5	0.8	4.0-5.0	0.35	0.03	...	0.35	0.25Ti	0.05	0.15
295.2	195	Ingot	0.7-1.2	0.8	4.0-5.0	0.30	0.03	...	0.30	0.20Ti	0.05	0.15
B295.0	B195	P	2.0-3.0	1.2	4.0-5.0	0.35	0.05	0.35Ni	0.50	0.25Ti	...	0.35
B295.1	B195	Ingot	2.0-3.0	0.9	4.0-5.0	0.35	0.05	0.35Ni	0.50	0.25Ti	...	0.35
B295.2	B195	Ingot	2.0-3.0	0.8	4.0-5.0	0.30	0.03	...	0.30	0.20Ti	0.05	0.15
319.0	319	S&P	5.5-6.5	1.0	3.0-4.0	0.50	0.10	0.35Ni	1.0	0.25Ti	...	0.50
319.1	319	Ingot	5.5-6.5	0.8	3.0-4.0	0.50	0.10	0.35Ni	1.0	0.25Ti	...	0.50
319.2	319	Ingot	5.5-6.5	0.6	3.0-4.0	0.10	0.10	0.10Ni	0.10	0.20Ti	...	0.20
A332.0	A132	P	11.0-13.0	1.2	0.50-1.5	0.35	0.7-1.3	2.0-3.0Ni	0.35	0.25Ti	0.05	...
A332.1	A132	Ingot	11.0-13.0	0.9	0.50-1.5	0.35	0.8-1.3	2.0-3.0Ni	0.35	0.25Ti	0.05	...
A332.2	A132	Ingot	11.0-13.0	0.9	0.50-1.5	0.10	0.9-1.3	2.0-3.0Ni	0.10	0.20Ti	0.05	0.15
F332.0	F132	P	8.5-10.5	1.2	2.0-4.0	0.50	0.50-1.5	0.50Ni	1.0	0.25Ti	...	0.50
F332.1	F132	Ingot	8.5-10.5	0.9	2.0-4.0	0.50	0.6-1.5	0.50Ni	1.0	0.25Ti	...	0.50
F332.2	F132	Ingot	8.5-10.0	0.6	2.0-4.0	0.10	0.9-1.3	0.10Ni	0.10	0.20Ti	...	0.30
333.0	333	P	8.0-10.0	1.0	3.0-4.0	0.50	0.05-0.50	0.50Ni	1.0	0.25Ti	...	0.50
333.1	333	Ingot	8.0-10.0	0.8	3.0-4.0	0.50	0.10-0.50	0.50Ni	1.0	0.25Ti	...	0.50
355.0	355	S&P	4.5-5.5	0.6(c)	1.0-1.5	0.50(c)	0.40-0.6	0.25Cr	0.30	0.25Ti	0.05	0.15
355.1	355	Ingot	4.5-5.5	0.50(c)	1.0-1.5	0.50(c)	0.45-0.6	0.25Cr	0.30	0.25Ti	0.05	0.15
355.2	355	Ingot	4.5-5.5	0.14-0.25	1.0-1.5	0.05	0.50-0.6	...	0.05	0.20Ti	0.05	0.15
C355.0	C355	S&P	4.5-5.5	0.20	1.0-1.5	0.10	0.40-0.6	...	0.10	0.20Ti	0.05	0.15
C355.2	C355	Ingot	4.5-5.5	0.13	1.0-1.5	0.05	0.45-0.6	...	0.05	0.20Ti	0.05	0.15
356.0	356	S&P	6.5-7.5	0.6	0.25	0.35	0.20-0.40	...	0.35	0.25Ti	0.05	0.15
356.1	356	Ingot	6.5-7.5	0.50	0.25	0.35	0.25-0.40	...	0.35	0.25Ti	0.05	0.15
356.2	356	Ingot	6.5-7.5	0.12-0.25	0.10	0.05	0.30-0.40	...	0.05	0.20Ti	0.05	0.15
A356.0	A356	S&P	6.5-7.5	0.20	0.20	0.10	0.20-0.40	...	0.10	0.20Ti	0.05	0.15
A356.2	A356	Ingot	6.5-7.5	0.11	0.10	0.05	0.30-0.40	...	0.05	0.20Ti	0.05	0.15
360.0(d)	360	D	9.0-10.0	2.0	0.6	0.35	0.40-0.6	0.50Ni	0.50	0.15Sn	...	0.25
360.2	360	Ingot	9.0-10.0	0.7-1.1	0.10	0.10	0.45-0.6	0.10Ni	0.10	0.10Sn	...	0.20
A360.0(d)	A360	D	9.0-10.0	1.3	0.6	0.35	0.40-0.6	0.50Ni	0.50	...	...	0.25
A360.1(d)	A360	Ingot	9.0-10.0	1.0	0.6	0.35	0.45-0.6	0.50Ni	0.40	...	...	0.25
A360.2	A360	Ingot	9.0-10.0	0.6	0.10	0.05	0.45-0.6	...	0.05	...	0.05	0.15
364.0	364	D	7.5-9.5	1.5	0.20	0.10	0.20-0.40	(e)	0.15	0.15Sn	0.05(f)	0.15
364.2	364	Ingot	7.5-9.5	0.7-1.1	0.20	0.10	0.25-0.40	(e)	0.15	0.15Sn	0.05(f)	0.15
380.0(d)	380	D	7.5-9.5	2.0	3.0-4.0	0.50	0.10	0.50Ni	3.0	0.35Sn	...	0.50
380.2	380	Ingot	7.5-9.5	0.7-1.1	3.0-4.0	0.10	0.10	0.10Ni	0.10	0.10Sn	...	0.20
A380.0(d)	A380	D	7.5-9.5	1.3	3.0-4.0	0.50	0.10	0.50Ni	3.0	0.35Sn	...	0.50
A380.1(d)	A380	Ingot	7.5-9.5	1.0	3.0-4.0	0.50	0.10	0.50Ni	2.9	0.35Sn	...	0.50
A380.2	A380	Ingot	7.5-9.5	0.6	3.0-4.0	0.10	0.10	0.10Ni	0.10	...	0.05	0.15
B380.0	A380	D	7.5-9.5	2.0	3.0-4.0	0.50	0.10	0.50Ni	1.0	0.35Sn	...	0.50
B380.1	A380	Ingot	7.5-9.5	1.0	3.0-4.0	0.50	0.10	0.50Ni	0.9	0.35Sn	...	0.50
384.0	384	D	10.5-12.0	1.3	3.0-4.5	0.50	0.10	0.50Ni	3.0	0.35Sn	...	0.50
384.1	384	Ingot	10.5-12.0	1.0	3.0-4.5	0.50	0.10	0.50Ni	2.9	0.35Sn	...	0.50
384.2	384	Ingot	10.5-12.0	0.6-1.0	3.0-4.5	0.10	0.10	0.10Ni	0.10	0.10Sn	...	0.20
A384.0	384	D	10.5-12.0	1.3	3.0-4.5	0.50	0.10	0.50Ni	1.0	0.35Sn	...	0.50
A384.1	384	Ingot	10.5-12.0	1.0	3.0-4.5	0.50	0.10	0.50Ni	0.9	0.35Sn	...	0.50
413.0(d)	13	D	11.0-13.0	2.0	0.6	0.35	0.10	0.50Ni	0.50	0.15Sn	...	0.25
413.2	13	Ingot	11.0-13.0	0.7-1.1	0.10	0.10	0.07	0.10Ni	0.10	0.10Sn	...	0.20
A413.0(d)	A13	D	11.0-13.0	1.3	0.6	0.35	0.10	0.50Ni	0.50	0.15Sn	...	0.25
A413.1(d)	A13	Ingot	11.0-13.0	1.0	0.6	0.35	0.10	0.50Ni	0.40	0.15Sn	...	0.25
A413.2	A13	Ingot	11.0-13.0	0.6	0.10	0.05	0.03	0.05Ni	0.05	0.05Sn	...	0.10
443.0	43	S	4.5-6.0	0.8	0.6	0.50	0.05	0.25Cr	0.50	0.25Ti	...	0.35
443.1	43	Ingot	4.5-6.0	0.6	0.6	0.50	0.05	0.25Cr	0.50	0.25Ti	...	0.35
443.2	43	Ingot	4.5-6.0	0.6	0.10	0.10	0.05	...	0.10	0.20Ti	0.05	0.15
A443.0	43	S	4.5-6.0	0.8	0.30	0.50	0.05	0.25Cr	0.50	0.25Ti	...	0.35
A443.1	43	Ingot	4.5-6.0	0.6	0.30	0.50	0.05	0.25Cr	0.50	0.25Ti	...	0.35
B443.0	43	S&P	4.5-6.0	0.8	0.15	0.35	0.05	...	0.35	0.25Ti	0.05	0.15
B443.1	43	Ingot	4.5-6.0	0.6	0.15	0.35	0.05	...	0.35	0.25Ti	0.05	0.15
C443.0	A43	D	4.5-6.0	2.0	0.6	0.35	0.10	0.50Ni	0.50	0.15Sn	...	0.25
C443.1	A43	Ingot	4.5-6.0	1.0	0.6	0.35	0.10	0.50Ni	0.40	0.15Sn	...	0.25
C443.2	A43	Ingot	4.5-6.0	0.7-1.1	0.10	0.10	0.05	...	0.10	...	0.05	0.15
A444.0	A344	P	6.5-7.5	0.20	0.10	0.10	0.05	...	0.10	0.20Ti	0.05	0.15
A444.2	A344	Ingot	6.5-7.5	0.12	0.05	0.05	0.05	...	0.05	0.20Ti	0.05	0.15
514.0	214	S	0.35	0.50	0.15	0.35	3.5-4.5	...	0.15	0.25Ti	0.05	0.15
514.1	214	Ingot	0.35	0.40	0.15	0.35	3.6-4.5	...	0.15	0.25Ti	0.05	0.15
514.2	214	Ingot	0.30	0.30	0.10	0.10	3.6-4.5	...	0.10	0.20Ti	0.05	0.15
A514.0	A214	P	0.30	0.40	0.10	0.30	3.5-4.5	...	1.4-2.2	0.20Ti	0.05	0.15
A514.2	A214	Ingot	0.30	0.30	0.10	0.10	3.6-4.5	...	1.4-2.2	0.20Ti	0.05	0.15
B514.0	B214	S	1.4-2.2	0.6	0.35	0.8	3.5-4.5	0.25Cr	0.35	0.25Ti	0.05	0.15
B514.2	B214	Ingot	1.4-2.2	0.30	0.10	0.10	3.6-4.5	...	0.10	0.20Ti	0.05	0.15
F514.0	F214	S	0.30-0.7	0.50	0.15	0.35	3.5-4.5	...	0.15	0.25Ti	0.05	0.15
F514.1	F214	Ingot	0.30-0.7	0.40	0.15	0.35	3.6-4.5	...	0.15	0.25Ti	0.05	0.15
F514.2	F214	Ingot	0.30-0.7	0.30	0.10	0.10	3.6-4.5	...	0.10	0.20Ti	0.05	0.15
518.0	218	D	0.35	1.8	0.25	0.35	7.5-8.5	0.15Ni	0.15	0.15Sn	...	0.25
518.1	218	Ingot	0.35	1.0	0.25	0.35	7.6-8.5	0.15Ni	0.15	0.15Sn	...	0.25
518.2	218	Ingot	0.25	0.7	0.10	0.10	7.6-8.5	0.05Ni	...	0.05Sn	...	0.10
520.0	220	S	0.25	0.30	0.25	0.15	9.5-10.6	...	0.15	0.25Ti	0.05	0.15
520.2	220	Ingot	0.15	0.20	0.20	0.10	9.6-10.6	...	0.10	0.20Ti	0.05	0.15
535.0	Almag 35	S	0.15	0.15	0.05	0.10-0.25	6.2-7.5	...	...	0.10-0.25Ti	0.05(g)	0.15
535.2	Almag 35	Ingot	0.10	0.10	0.05	0.10-0.25	6.6-7.5	...	...	0.10-0.25Ti	0.05(g)	0.15
B535.0	B218	S	0.15	0.15	0.10	0.05	6.5-7.5	...	...	0.10-0.25Ti	0.05	0.15
B535.2	B218	Ingot	0.10	0.12	0.05	0.05	6.6-7.5	...	...	0.10-0.25Ti	0.05	0.15
A712.0	A612	S	0.15	0.50	0.35-0.65	0.05	0.6-0.8	...	6.0-7.0	0.25Ti	0.05	0.15
A712.1	A612	Ingot	0.15	0.40	0.35-0.65	0.05	0.65-0.8	...	6.0-7.0	0.25Ti	0.05	0.15
C712.0	C612	S	0.30	0.7-1.4	0.35-0.65	0.05	0.25-0.45	...	6.0-7.0	0.20Ti	0.05	0.15
C712.1	C612	Ingot	0.30	0.7-1.1	0.35-0.65	0.05	0.30-0.45	...	6.0-7.0	0.20Ti	0.05	0.15
D712.0	D612, 40E	S	0.30	0.50	0.25	0.10	0.50-0.65	0.40-0.6Cr	5.0-6.5	0.15-0.25Ti	0.05	0.20
D712.1	D612, 40E	Ingot	0.15	0.40	0.25	0.10	0.50-0.65	0.40-0.6Cr	5.0-6.5	0.15-0.25Ti	0.05	**0.20**

(a) S = sand casting; P = permanent mold casting; D = die casting. (b) Percentages are maximums, unless given as a range; for all alloys and forms, remainder is aluminum. (c) If iron content exceeds 0.45%, manganese content shall not be less than one-half the iron content.

(d) A360.1 ingot is used to produce 360.0 and A360.0 castings; A380.1 ingot, to produce 380.0 and A380.0 castings; A413.1 ingot, to produce 413.0 and A413.0 castings. (e) 0.25 to 0.50 Cr; 0.15 max Ni. (f) Beryllium, 0.02 to 0.04%. (g) Beryllium, 0.003 to 0.007%; boron, 0.002% max.

piece reaches the melting temperature, the liquid metal bursts through the skin of oxide and runs into the bath, leaving the oxide on the hearth. By this technique, large ingots or scrap are added to the bath with a minimum of agitation and temperature disturbance. However, melting in this manner greatly increases the metal loss due to oxidation.

Characteristics of Molten Aluminum

Molten aluminum alloys are extremely reactive and combine readily with other metals, with gases, and sometimes with refractories.

Molten aluminum dissolves iron from crucibles. Therefore, aluminum is usually melted and handled in refractory (most often, silicon carbide) containers. High-alumina brick bonded with phosphoric acid is ordinarily used for furnace linings.

The surface tension of molten aluminum is high, and when augmented by the formation of a film of oxide, surface tension is so great that it causes difficulty in casting thin sections. Alloy additions reduce surface tension, but broaden the solidification range — which is likely to cause shrinkage problems. The surface tension of molten aluminum is great enough to keep a charge of fines floating on top of the molten bath.

Compositions that are high in alloy content, such as the high-silicon diecasting alloys, are susceptible to precipitation of the alloying elements, thus forming sludge. The rate of sludge formation increases as the temperature of the molten bath decreases.

Aluminum alloys solidify with a maximum of nearly 10% volume contraction, which must be considered in the design of the gating system for a casting. Molten aluminum weighs only 145 to 150 lb per cubic foot, whereas solid aluminum weighs 160 to 165 lb per cubic foot.

Composition Control

For convenience in making up the charge, and to minimize the chance of error, most foundries use standard prealloyed ingot for melting, rather than doing their own alloying. Prealloyed ingot is available in all standard compositions. Table 2 lists designations and composition limits of a number of widely used aluminum alloys, in casting and ingot forms, as registered with The Aluminum Association.

Most alloying elements found in aluminum castings (such as copper, iron, silicon, manganese, zinc, nickel, chromium and titanium) are not readily lost by oxidation, evaporation or precipitation. Alloying elements that melt at temperatures higher than the melting temperature of aluminum, such as chromium, iron, silicon, manganese and nickel, are added to the molten metal in the form of rich alloy ingot (generally known as hardener ingot or master alloy). The addition of these metals in pure form is impractical, because of their high melting temperatures. Copper (usually in the form of

scrap cathodes or wire), magnesium, zinc and tin are added as pure metals. Silicon may be added as metallic silicon that contains 99% Si.

Some elements, such as magnesium, sodium and calcium, are removed from the molten bath by oxidation, chlorination and evaporation. Loss of these elements is accelerated by prolonged holding at temperature, by high temperature, and by fluxing and stirring. These ingredients are added to the molten bath in elemental form as required, to compensate for loss.

Some aluminum alloys, such as A380, A13 and 43, do not change significantly in composition when remelted, unless they have become contaminated, because they contain only copper and silicon (or silicon alone) as specified alloying elements. Conversely, alloys such as 355, 356, A360, 214 and 218 do change significantly in remelting, because of losses in magnesium. The usual practice is to add magnesium in stick form to compensate for the loss. If the magnesium is allowed to go below the specified amount in these alloys, their mechanical properties are reduced.

When melting the dip-brazable alloys, such as C612 and D612 (40E), precise control of composition is mandatory if silicon content exceeds 0.30%, castings are susceptible to aluminum-silicon eutectic melting, which is likely to occur during dip brazing.

Prevention of Segregation. For melting of some alloys, frequent stirring of the molten bath is needed to prevent segregation (especially if the temperature is near the lower end of the range), because of the weight of some alloying components. For instance, aluminum-zinc-magnesium alloys that contain chromium need frequent stirring to keep the chromium properly distributed. Excessive stirring must be avoided, to minimize oxidation.

Foundry returns, such as gates and risers, may be accumulated, melted, and cast as remelt ingots. This practice, however, is unnecessary when the foundry returns are carefully separated according to composition, or when facilities exist for quick analysis of molten aluminum before it is poured.

Control of Purchased Scrap. Foundries that produce a large volume of castings usually try to reduce their metal costs by the use of scrap metal purchased from other plants. Common practice is to blend this scrap with their own return scrap (castings, gates, risers and trimmings).

The purchased scrap may be in the form of chips, borings, clippings, and rejected castings. The scrap, baled or loose, may contain copper or magnesium, but the most common contaminant in purchased scrap is iron (in the form of dowels, screws and other fasteners in the castings, or as dust or chips that are mingled with the finer scrap). All chips and fines should be processed to remove water, oil, dust, and free iron.

Chemical analysis must be made of every lot of scrap metal. Samples for testing should be representative of the entire lot. Each lot of scrap should be segregated and numbered, so that scrap from different lots can be blend-

ed to obtain a casting alloy that conforms with specifications.

Formulated Alloys. An alloy composition can be formulated by adding alloying elements to unalloyed aluminum, provided the elements are sufficiently pure and are added to high-purity ingot. This method for making a casting alloy requires precise control of weights in making the charge, and requires a means for making frequent chemical analyses.

Control of Impurities

Because of its reactivity, molten aluminum is easily contaminated. The principal contaminants are iron, oxides and hydrogen.

Iron. When iron content of the ingot exceeds 0.9% in piston alloys such as F132, an undesirable acicular grain structure develops in the thicker sections. When iron content exceeds 1.2% in the higher-silicon alloys, sludging is likely to occur, particularly if the temperature of the molten metal drops below 1200 F. However, the amount of iron that can be tolerated depends to some extent on the amount of manganese and chromium present.

To prevent sludging, % Fe + 2(% Mn) + 3(% Cr) ordinarily should not exceed 1.9%. For example, if iron content is 1.2%, and manganese is 0.2%, the chromium must not exceed 0.1%. This is calculated as: $1.2 + (2 \times 0.2) + (3 \times 0.1) = 1.9$. When this total exceeds 1.9%, the castings are likely to contain hard spots that impair machining and that may start stress cracks in service.

The above formula is useful for predicting susceptibility to sludge formation. However, metal temperature and, to some extent, agitation of the molten metal also influence susceptibility to sludge formation. At higher holding temperatures, or with an agitated bath (as in induction furnaces), a sludge factor higher than the 1.9% given above can be tolerated. Conversely, when holding temperature is lowered, or the bath is not agitated, a sludge factor lower than 1.9% should be maintained.

Iron may combine with silicon during solidification, to precipitate coarse alpha or beta (Al-Fe-Si) constituents. Excess iron also causes shrinkage in castings; the shrinkage becomes worse as the iron increases beyond 1%. An application in which severe shrinkage was caused by excess iron is described in the example that follows.

Example 455. Prevention of Excess Iron That Caused Shrinkage Voids in a Sand Casting (Fig. 5)

The sand cast alloy 319 base shown in Fig. 5 was required to be leakproof in the cup section, because it was used as an oil reservoir in service. Standard practice produced acceptable castings until some were cast that had shrinkage where the ribs joined the cup (see Fig. 5). Shrinkage voids as large as ½ in. in diameter by ½ in. deep were found in these castings, and the castings would have leaked in service. Some voids were revealed by a frosty surface appearance over the void area.

Chemical analysis of the defective castings showed the iron content to be 1.86% — considerably above the 1.0% maximum allowable for alloy 319, as well as above the 0.78% iron content of the ingot (see table with Fig. 5). The excess iron was the cause of the shrinkage, and the iron pickup was found to come from the cast iron shields on the thermocouple used in the melting furnace. Protective recoating of the shields after cleaning had not been adequate. Acceptable castings were again produced after the thermocouple shields were properly coated.

Manufacturing details for the castings are given in the table that accompanies Fig. 5.

To prevent occurrences such as the one described in the preceding example, the molten aluminum should be sampled from opposite sides or corners of the furnace, and the metal should be analyzed before it is cast. These analyses indicate whether or not adjustment is required. If the iron content is too high, best practice is to dilute the bath with pure aluminum. Additions of alloying elements such as copper and silicon (depending on the desired composition) may also be required to bring the molten bath into specified limits. After the composition has been adjusted, new samples should be analyzed before the metal is cast.

Oxides. Oxidized metal must be removed from the melt. If it remains in the molten metal, the castings will contain harmful inclusions. Magnesium is a strong oxide former. Thus, the oxide content is most difficult to control when melting and casting alloys that contain magnesium.

Extra care must be taken in melting and casting alloys such as 218 (8% Mg), 214 (4% Mg), A360 (0.5% Mg), and 364 and 356 (each with 0.3% Mg), to prevent oxidation. Other alloys, such as A380, 384 and A13, are specified to contain not more than 0.1% Mg, but even this small amount reduces the fluidity of the molten alloy by promoting the formation of oxides. When magnesium is specified only as a maximum, best practice is to keep it as low as possible.

Oxides of aluminum and magnesium form quickly on the surface of the molten bath, making a thin, tenacious skin that prevents further oxidation as long as the surface is not disturbed. Molten aluminum also reacts with moisture to form aluminum oxide, releasing hydrogen. Moisture on charge materials, tools, fluxes and refractories causes rapid oxidation of the metal, and in extreme cases an explosion can result. All tools should be heated to at least 250 F before they are immersed in molten aluminum, to ensure that they are free from moisture.

Oxidation also is caused by excessive stirring, overheating of the molten metal, pouring from too great a height, splashing of the metal, or brushing the metal surface with the ladle before dipping.

Data that show the effect of holding temperature on oxidation rate are given in Fig. 6.

After prolonged storage in outdoor or otherwise damp areas, aluminum ingots or castings have oxidized surfaces that have combined with water to produce hydrated oxides. It is dangerous to immerse these powdery white or gray oxides in molten aluminum before preheating to drive off the water.

Agitation of the molten bath results in suspension of the surface oxide skin in the molten metal. The density of the oxides is nearly the same as that of the molten metal, and thus the oxides are likely to be carried into the castings. Large particles of oxide are

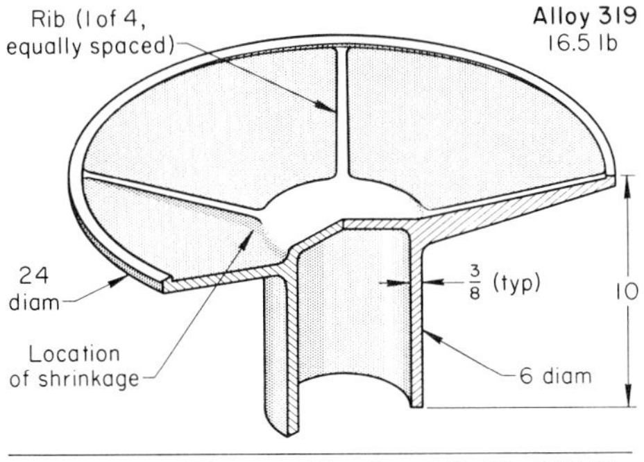

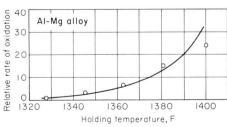

Rib (1 of 4, equally spaced)   Alloy 319 16.5 lb

24 diam

Location of shrinkage

3/8 (typ)   10

6 diam

Ingot composition ...3.95 Cu, 6.60 Si, 0.78 Fe, 0.35 Mn, 0.07 Mg, 0.90 Zn, 0.03 Ni, 0.11 Ti, 0.08 Cr, 0.07 total other unspecified elements
Molding method ....Green sand(a)
Weight of trimmed casting ....16.5 lb
Number of castings per mold ....One
Weight of metal poured per mold ....21 lb
Pouring temperature ....1550 F
Production rate ....11 castings per hour
Annual production requirement ...200 castings
Cost per casting $10

(a) Flask size, 27 by 30 by 6-over-10 in. Molds were made in a stripper and rollover machine.

Fig. 5. Sand cast base in which excess iron, picked up from inadequately coated thermocouple shields, caused shrinkage voids (Example 455)

gray to black and may be spongy. Oxides affect fluidity of aluminum, and also impair thermal conductivity and mechanical properties of the casting.

The origin of oxides is sometimes difficult to establish. In one foundry, for example, melting procedure was blamed for defective castings, because the castings contained excessive amounts of oxide. Careful observation of the entire operation, however, revealed that an operator was repeatedly ladling metal from the molten bath and pouring it back, which caused excessive oxidation.

Oxides that form on the surface of the molten bath can be removed by surface-cleaning fluxes. These fluxes usually contain low-melting-point ingredients that react exothermically on the surface of the bath. The oxides separate from the metal to form a dry, powdery, floating dross that can be skimmed. In this fluxing process, some dense oxides may sink to the bottom. These can be removed by gaseous fluxing or, if the furnace has one, through the drain hole. Usually, the taphole of a furnace is above the bottom drain hole, so that oxides that have settled to the bottom will not flow out the taphole.

Hydrogen is the only gas that dissolves to any significant extent in mol-

ten aluminum alloys, and if not removed it will cause porosity in the castings.

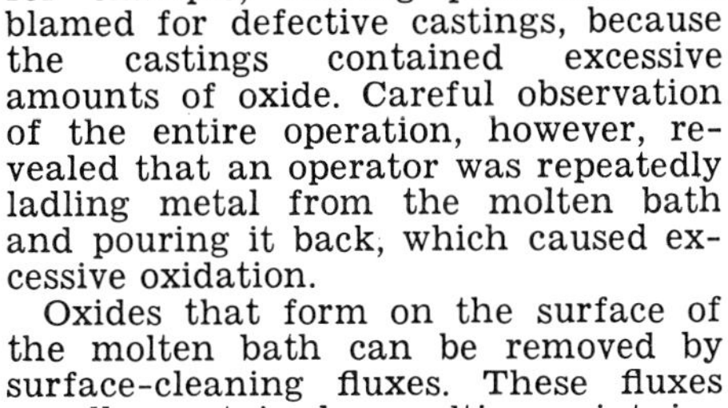

As shown in Fig. 7, the amount of hydrogen that dissolves in molten aluminum alloys at temperatures under 1250 F is usually insignificant, but the amount dissolved increases sharply as metal temperature increases. The rate of increase is proportional to the square root of the hydrogen partial pressure; however, this rate of increase is theoretical, because it assumes a condition of equilibrium — which requires time to attain in a large furnace of molten metal.

Hydrogen is introduced into molten aluminum by moisture and dirt in the charge, and by the products of combustion in heating the metal. If the fuel-to-air ratio is rich, the excess hydrocarbons supply hydrogen to dissolve in the aluminum. Flux can be a source of hydrogen, and even tools can contribute unless they are kept dry and are preheated before use.

Degassing. When molten metal is cooled from a higher temperature to a lower temperature for pouring (for instance, from 1500 to 1300 F), dissolved hydrogen is given up in conformance with the equilibrium conditions. However, the dissolved hydrogen is given up slowly. Thus, in foundry practice, additional degassing may be required. For instance, in one foundry casting various aluminum alloys, the number of castings rejected for over-all porosity increased to alarming proportions during normal operation. Tests showed that the porosity resulted from hydrogen gas that was introduced into the molten metal by melting and holding the metal at 1500 F for ½ to 3 hr. Three corrective steps were taken: (a) metal temperature was reduced to 1300 F before castings were poured; (b) the ratio of air to oil in the melting furnace was changed to provide oxidizing flames, thus reducing the possibility of hydrogen pickup from this source; and (c) the metal was degassed with a mixture of nitrogen and chlorine. These steps were effective in eliminating porosity.

Degassing fluxes to remove hydrogen are recommended for use after the surface of the bath has been fluxed for the removal of oxides. The degassing fluxes also help to lift fine oxides and particles to the top of the bath. Removal of hydrogen by degassing is a mechanical action; hydrogen does not combine with the degassing agents.

Degassing agents include chlorine gas, nitrogen-chlorine mixtures, and hexachloroethane.

Chlorine, the least expensive degassing agent, is used in small amounts. Chlorine is stored in cylinders or in tanks as a liquid under pressure. It can be drawn off as a gas in small quantities without causing tank freeze-up. When large quantities are needed, an evaporator that converts the liquid into gas is required to avoid tank freeze-up.

Chlorine reacts with aluminum and forms aluminum chloride gas ("white smoke"), which bubbles up through the surface of the bath. As the bubbles rise, they raise oxide particles to the surface, thus imparting a mechanical as well as a chemical action.

Time required for degassing an aluminum bath with chlorine can be as little as 5 min for a very small bath or as long as 1½ hr for a 100,000-lb bath. Degassing time usually is judged by experience, although gas tests

Relative rates of oxidation are based on total weight of oxide generated (insoluble in NaOH), with amount at 1328 F being assigned an arbitrary value of one.

Fig. 6. Effect of holding temperature on oxidation rate of a molten Al-Mg alloy (A. H. Hinton, *Foundry,* July 1964, p 49)

(discussed later in this section) may be used for control. Generally, a flow of gas for less than five minutes is not adequate for degassing. The rate of flow is usually based on experience, but the rate must not be so rapid as to cause excessive turbulence in the molten metal. A gentle rolling action of the molten metal is preferred.

Chlorine removes magnesium, sodium and calcium from the bath. To meet specifications, these elements may have to be replenished after degassing with chlorine.

A disadvantage of chlorine is its toxicity. Where chlorine is used, good ventilation is mandatory.

Nitrogen-Chlorine Mixtures. Mixtures of nitrogen and chlorine, ranging from 90% N and 10% Cl to 70% N and 30% Cl, are commonly used. These are effective fluxes, and they cause less aluminum chloride gas ("white smoke") than does chlorine alone and are less toxic.

In one foundry, a mixture of 90% nitrogen and 10% chlorine was used to degas 2000-lb batches of alloy F132 (SAE 332) in a ladle. Degassing for 10 to 12 min produced metal suitable for the production of automotive pistons that were required to be free from porosity. Degassing produced metal having a specific gravity of 2.74 at 39 F, which compares favorably with the ideal specific gravity of 2.76 at 39 F that is characteristic for SAE 332 alloy. This degassing procedure has been used to process 300 million pounds of metal that yielded porosity-free castings.

Hexachloroethane is a solid compound containing carbon and chlorine, and is added in pellet form or as granules packaged in aluminum foil. The pellet or packet is plunged to the bottom of the molten metal so that aluminum chloride gas bubbles up through the bath to provide cleaning action. Generally, this method is restricted to small heats.

Regardless of which gas is used, it is admitted to the bath through fluxing tubes. The tubes, usually made of graphite or of porcelain enameled steel, are inserted in the bath so that they nearly reach the bottom. Apparatus for degassing is available in both stationary and portable units. A typical setup for degassing in a ladle is illustrated in Fig. 8.

Tests for Gas. A simple test for the presence of gas in an aluminum casting alloy can be made by pouring a small, open-face casting in sand, under closely controlled conditions. The surface condition of the casting indicates the gas content of the metal. Gas in metal causes popping in the surface during solidification, resulting in a frosty appearance. A machined cross section of the casting will show gas porosity as uniform pinholes if the machined surface is properly prepared (machined with sharp tools); otherwise, because the metal is soft, the holes may be obliterated. More accurate indication of porosity can be obtained by polishing the surface and then subjecting it to abrasive blasting to open up the holes. The degree of accuracy obtainable by this test depends greatly on close control of all pouring conditions.

The reduced-pressure test for gas is made by pouring a sample casting in a crucible so that it cools and solidifies at a pressure of 25 to 27 in. of mercury. Gas in the molten metal will cause it to bubble, and will result in holes in the sample casting. Gas-free metal will lie quietly, resulting in a sound casting.

Hydrogen content can be measured more accurately by the use of equipment that bubbles dry nitrogen through the molten metal. The evolved gas (a mixture of nitrogen and hydrogen) is collected, and hydrogen con-

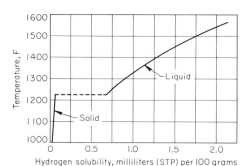

Fig. 7. Solubility of hydrogen in aluminum, as a function of temperature at one atmosphere hydrogen pressure (A. H. Hinton, Foundry, July 1964)

tent is determined from the thermal conductivity of the gas mixture. However, this method is better suited for research than for use in production.

Cleaning of the furnace and handling equipment is important for keeping impurities at an acceptable level. Iron crucibles should be coated regularly — at least once a week. Crucibles made of silicon carbide should be scraped each day, preferably at the end of each shift. The oxide can be scraped off while the crucible is hot. A wooden scraper is less likely to harm the crucible than is a metal scraper.

The walls of reverberatory furnaces should be scraped at least once during each 8-hr shift. If heavy scrap is being charged, more frequent cleaning is required. It is common practice, especially in melting alloys that have high silicon content, to remove sludge from the furnace at least once a week. Usually, this is done in nonproductive periods, by heating the molten metal to 1450 F, scraping the walls of the furnace, and stirring the sludge back into solution. Sludge that does not dissolve during this treatment must be scraped out. (See the section "Control of Sludge", which follows.)

For overnight or over weekends, it is common practice to save fuel by keeping the furnace temperature just slightly above the freezing point of the metal. This practice may cause sludge to form, but the sludge can be dis-

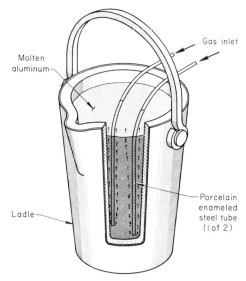

Fig. 8. Typical setup for degassing of molten aluminum alloy in a ladle

solved by heating to 1450 F for 2 hr before normal operation is resumed. Many foundries keep furnace temperature at 1200 to 1250 F over weekends, which eliminates sludge formation.

Control of Sludge

Sludge, also called "sand", "sugar", and "silicon dropout", forms and settles out of aluminum alloy baths that contain about 5% or more of silicon. However, the sludge itself does not contain silicon, but is a compound of iron, manganese and chromium.

Sludge formation is more common in die casting than when casting in sand or permanent molds, because: (a) lower temperatures are used in die casting, and (b) the higher silicon and higher iron content of aluminum die-casting alloys makes them more susceptible to sludge formation.

Sludge in castings generally is first revealed by a reduction in the life of tools used in machining the castings. The reduced tool life is caused by hard spots in the castings, which appear as small shiny spots in the machined surface. Metallographic examination reveals the sludge particles.

Chemical analysis can also be used to establish the presence of excessive amounts of sludging elements in the metal. In one foundry, for example, the analysis of a casting that contained sludge was: 3.36 Cu, 1.24 Fe, 9.23 Si, 0.41 Mn, 0.02 Mg, 2.59 Zn, 0.09 Ni, 0.14 Cr, rem Al. In this composition, the total of % Fe + 2(% Mn) + 3(% Cr) was 2.48% — which is well above the normally allowable 1.90% (see the discussion under "Iron" in the section or Control of Impurities, page 395).

In addition to causing difficulty in the castings, sludge formation can deplete the molten bath of specified alloying elements.

Sometimes sludge originates in the central melting furnace and is then transferred to the holding furnace, although the temperature of a melting furnace is usually high enough that little or no sludge is formed. The source of sludge is usually the holding furnace. This furnace can contain as much as 6 in. of sludge segregated at the bottom. If this sludge is stirred to ladling depth, it will be poured into the castings. A holding furnace that forms excessive amounts of sludge may be operating at 20 to 50 F below the recommended minimum holding temperature of 1200 F. If solid metal is being charged into the furnace, the chilling effect will encourage sludge formation. Sludge formation can be minimized by:

1 Keeping the iron content as low as possible
2 Maintaining a minimum temperature of 1350 F in the melting furnace
3 Maintaining a minimum temperature of 1200 F in the holding furnace.

When excessive amounts of sludge have formed in a holding furnace (or a combination melting and holding furnace), the best procedure is to scoop the sludge out and dump it. An alternative procedure is to hold the molten bath at 1450 F and stir it frequently until the sludge has dissolved. The latter procedure is less desirable, however, because the high temperature promotes oxidation and hydrogen pickup, the stirring also increases oxide formation, and the stirred-in sludge reduces the fluidity of the metal and causes hard spots in the castings.

Temperature Control

Furnaces should be equipped with automatic controls that can maintain an established temperature within ±10 F. Instruments should be checked and calibrated regularly.

Bath Temperature. Poor control of bath temperature is a common cause of difficulty in the production of aluminum alloy castings. The most common difficulty is the formation of sludge (see the preceding section, "Control of Sludge").

Pouring temperature is chosen by experience, depending on alloy composition, molding process used, section thicknesses, and gating systems. If the metal is poured too cold, defects such as misruns, cold shuts, and shrinkage are likely to result. If the metal is poured too hot, coarse grain, porosity, excessive shrinkage, and hot tearing are likely. Best practice is to pour a casting at the lowest temperature that will provide soundness.

Control During Pouring. Pouring into many molds from a single ladle of molten metal is not good practice, because of the wide range of metal temperature. Preferred practice is to ladle out metal for no more than one, two or three molds, depending on the poured weight and on the temperature sensitivity of the castings. The temperature of the metal in the ladle should be measured before pouring, to ascertain that the pre-established pouring temperature is maintained.

Control of Grain Size

The grain size of aluminum alloy castings can range from approximately 0.005-in. diam to as large as ½-in. diam. The grain size of the metal in a casting can be observed visually after polishing and etching.

Fine grain is generally desired in aluminum castings. (Generally, a fine grain structure is considered to be one with grains no larger than 0.040-in. average diameter.) Although *any* porosity, caused by gas or by shrinkage, is undesirable, coarse porosity is the most undesirable. The coarseness of porosity is proportional to grain size. Consequently, porosity is finer and less harmful in fine-grain castings. Also, the mechanical properties, such as tensile strength and elongation, of fine-grain castings are usually better than those of coarse-grain castings.

Shrinkage and hot cracking are generally associated with coarse grain structure. Fine grain minimizes shrinkage, causing castings to be sounder. The grain size of aluminum alloy castings is influenced by pouring temperature, solidification rate, and presence or absence of grain-refining elements.

Pouring Temperature. For all aluminum alloys, the grain size increases as pouring temperature is increased. This is a major reason why castings should be poured at the lowest temperature that will result in sound metal.

Solidification Rate. Rapid solidification results in a finer grain size than when solidification takes place slowly, all other factors being equal. Thus, aluminum cast in steel dies or gray iron permanent molds is likely to have a finer grain than the same metal cast in sand, investment or plaster molds.

Grain size may vary from one location to another in sand castings because of differences in thickness, and because of the way different portions of the casting are affected by gates, risers and chills. Thin or chilled sections will have the finest grain, and the coarsest grain will develop at gates and risers.

Grain-refining elements, such as titanium, boron and zirconium, are helpful in maintaining fine grain size. Additions of these elements in the ingot are usually adequate for producing fine-grain castings. However, when the charge consists partly of scrap, additional grain-refining elements usually must be added to the molten metal.

Transferring of Molten Aluminum

Equipment for transferring molten aluminum can range from a small hand ladle to a large truck having an insulated container capable of holding 10 to 15 tons of molten metal. Distance of transfer can range from a few feet to several hundred miles.

Some furnaces are designed so that molten metal can be removed only by ladling, either manual or mechanized. Other types of furnaces are constructed to permit tilting for pouring into ladles. Still other furnaces have a taphole that can be unplugged to allow the metal to flow into ladles.

Siphons and pumps may be used to transfer molten metal. The pumps are made of refractory materials and can pump to a molten-metal head of several feet. All pipes, troughs and ladles must be well insulated with refractory material to minimize loss of heat.

Minimizing Heat Loss and Turbulence. Because of its extremely high heat conductivity and its sensitivity to oxidation, molten aluminum must be transferred with as little turbulence as possible. It is preferable to have furnaces near the molds, and to pour by hand, rather than to transfer metal from a central furnace if several transfers are needed before the casting can be poured.

Where central melting is used, it is advisable to have several intermediate holding furnaces that can be hot charged directly from the central unit. Each holding furnace can be fluxed and degassed, and left for 15 to 20 min before pouring. Often, holding furnaces are used in pairs. When this is done, metal is ladled from one furnace while the other is being hot charged, fluxed, and allowed to remain undisturbed for a short time to permit oxides produced by pouring to come to the surface, and permit sludge to settle.

Pouring should be controlled so that the elapsed time between taking the metal from the furnace and pouring the castings is as short as possible. Segregation of components from the molten metal (sludge formation) increases as elapsed time between removal from the furnace and pouring increases. This interval should also be uniform from one ladle to another.

Safety

Furnaces used for melting aluminum should be provided with safeguards against the following four hazards:

1 Failure of air supply for combustion
2 Failure of fuel supply
3 Excess fuel pressure
4 Failure of pilot flames.

Pressure-sensing switches can be used to detect pressure drops in combustion air and fuel supply, and also a rise in pressure of fuel supply. Such switches can operate safety shutoff valves and actuate an alarm signal. This type of equipment is the minimum practical safety system to be used where a furnace is not tended constantly. Additional controls are needed to prevent attempted start-up of a furnace that has an excess of fuel.

Melting furnaces generally have back pressures in the heating chamber that cause hot gases to leak out. These hot gases can heat the controls and cause malfunction. Controls need more attention and maintenance under these conditions.

Ventilation is important in melting aluminum, because chlorine gas, the most commonly used agent for degassing and fluxing, is toxic and corrosive.

Fans to remove fumes are generally less effective than an exhaust stack, and they need more maintenance. If a fan or blower is needed to help exhaust the gases and fumes, it is good practice to mount it outdoors on the roof. The blower should discharge the exhausted gases through a venturi tube in the middle of the stack. In large installations, the waste gases may need to be washed before they can be discharged into the atmosphere.

Water is an extreme hazard in contact with molten aluminum, and should never be allowed to get below the surface of a bath. The expansive force of water being rapidly converted to steam in a bath of molten aluminum can cause a violent, destructive explosion. Because of this threat to life and equipment, all incoming charges of metal must be dry. Where internal moisture may be present (particularly likely for large charge pieces), the charge should be preheated to ensure dryness. Also, all tools must be dried before they go into the furnace, and the area surrounding the furnace must be dry.

Splashing of molten aluminum is very dangerous, and operating personnel should wear protective, flame-resisting clothing, safety glasses or face shields, spats, and safety shoes. Ladles and other handling equipment must be controlled to prevent spilling or splashing. Gray iron should not be used where there is danger of its breaking, which can cause splashing or spilling of molten metal.

Aluminum can react violently with many oxides of metals, causing an exothermic reaction. Certain salts react violently with aluminum. Only tested fluxes should be added to aluminum.

Production of Aluminum Alloy Castings

*By the ASM Committee on Production of Aluminum Alloy Castings**

ALUMINUM ALLOYS can be cast by any of the commercial casting processes. Sand casting, permanent mold casting, and die casting are the processes most often used.

Nominal compositions of the casting alloys mentioned in this article are given in Table 1, along with their commercial designations and corresponding ASTM designations (where they exist).

Designations for commercial aluminum alloys often carry a letter prefix to denote an impurity level or the presence of a secondary alloying element. For example, alloy 356 is a 7% silicon, 0.3% magnesium alloy; alloy A356 has the same basic composition, but a limit of 0.2% iron is imposed. Also, alloy 214 can be purchased in three modifications — A214, B214 and F214. Although each of these alloys has about 4% magnesium as the major alloying element, A214 is alloyed with 1.8% zinc, B214 with 1.8% silicon, and F214 with 0.5% silicon.

Melting. Aluminum alloys are melted in direct or indirect fuel-fired furnaces or in electrically heated furnaces, as described in the preceding article, which begins on page 389.

Castability of aluminum alloys varies with composition. The aluminum-silicon alloys, such as alloys 13, 43, 355 and 356, are the easiest to cast — providing the greatest fluidity for casting of deep, thin sections. Generally, the higher the silicon content up to the eutectic composition (about 12.5% silicon), the easier an alloy is to cast. Hypereutectic alloys are more difficult to cast. Alloys that contain substantial amounts of magnesium, such as alloys 214, 218 and 220, are the most difficult to cast.

For all practical purposes, the suitability of aluminum alloys for casting in shell or carbon dioxide molds is the same as for casting in sand molds. Because various techniques are available for plaster mold and investment mold casting, it is possible to cast almost any of the aluminum alloys by these processes. Aluminum alloys for casting in plaster molds or investment molds are usually selected because of properties other than castability.

Sand Casting

Sand casting is the most versatile method for casting aluminum alloys, providing the greatest latitude for size, shape, and alloys cast. It is preferred for making large castings, because the limits on maximum size and maximum section thickness are higher; section thicknesses up to 6 in. are feasible. Also, sand casting is usually selected for the production of small quantities

of castings of almost any size, because of the relatively low tooling cost.

Disadvantages of sand casting, compared with other casting methods, are: greater cost per casting (omitting cost of tooling), rougher surfaces, and greater dimensional variation.

Molding sands, molding procedures, pattern practice, core practice, and equipment used for making molds and cores are essentially the same as are used for sand casting of other metals. These are discussed in the articles on Sand Molding (page 155), Patterns for Sand Molding (page 149), and Sand Cores and Coremaking (page 209), in this volume.

Aluminum alloys are generally easier to cast in sand molds than are iron or steel, for the following reasons: (a) because casting temperatures are lower, there is usually no mold burn-in; (b) no mold or core coatings or washes are required; (c) because of lower casting temperatures, less gas forms from mold and core components; and (d) because aluminum alloys weigh less, fewer castings are defective because of mold failure.

Sand. The principal differences between sand mixtures for casting aluminum alloys and those for casting ferrous or copper-base alloys are: (a) sands of finer grain are used for alu-

minum alloys; (b) sand mixtures can have lower green compressive strength, thereby permitting easier shakeout; and (c) only a minimum of additives is needed.

The selection of molding sand depends on: (a) the surface finish specified for the casting, (b) the size of the casting, (c) the alloy to be cast, and (d) the method used and the equipment available for the preparation of the sand mixture.

Molding sands used for casting aluminum alloys are:

1 Natural molding sands, containing natural clay, which serves as the binder
2 Compounded mixtures commonly referred to as synthetic sands, which are prepared from clay-free silica sands to which bentonite clays are added to obtain specific sand properties.

Molding-sand mixtures are predominantly silica sand grains, clay and water; olivine, zircon and chromite sands are also used. For most applications, additives are used sparingly, or not at all. Cellulose materials or wood flour are sometimes added to mixtures for molds that have large surface areas and are susceptible to sand buckles. Also, in casting heavy sections of alloys 218 and 220, inhibiting agents are often added to the molding-sand mixture to prevent mold-metal reactions.

Table 1. Nominal Compositions of Aluminum Casting Alloys Mentioned in This Article

(For composition ranges of most of these alloys, in casting and ingot forms, and for Aluminum Assn designations, see Table 2, page 394, in the article "Foundry Melting of Aluminum Alloys".)

Alloy designation Commercial	ASTM B26, B85 and B108	Casting process(a)	Cu	Si	Mg	Zn	Other(b)
13	S12B	D	...	12.0	...	...	...
A13	S12A	D	...	12.0	...	...	1.3 Fe max
43	S5A, B, C	S, P, D	...	5.3	...	...	...
D132	...	P	3.5	9.0	0.8	...	0.8 Ni
F132	SC103A	P	3.0	9.5	1.0	...	...
195	C4A	S	4.5	0.8	...	...	...
B195	...	P	4.5	2.5	...	...	...
214	G4A	S	...	...	4.0	...	...
A214	GZ42A	P, D	...	...	4.0	1.8	...
B214	GS42A	S, P	...	1.8	4.0	...	...
F214	...	S	...	0.5	4.0	...	...
218	G8A	D	...	...	8.0	...	...
B218	...	S	...	...	7.0	...	...
Almag 35	GM70B	S, P, D	...	...	7.0	...	0.2 Mn
220	G10A	S	...	...	10.0	...	...
319	SC64D	S, P	3.5	6.0	...	...	...
333	SC94A	P	3.5	9.0	...	...	...
A344	...	P	...	7.0	...	...	0.2 Fe max
355	SC51A	S, P	1.3	5.0	0.5	...	...
C355	SC51B	P	1.3	5.0	0.5	...	0.2 Fe max
356	SG70A	S, P	...	7.0	0.3	...	...
A356	SG70B	P	...	7.0	0.3	...	0.2 Fe max
360	SG100B	D	...	9.5	0.5	...	...
A360	SG100A	D	...	9.5	0.5	...	1.3 Fe max
364	...	D	...	8.5	0.3	...	0.4 Cr, 0.03 Be
380	SC84B	D	3.5	8.5	...	...	...
A380	SC84A	D	3.5	8.5	...	...	1.3 Fe max
384	SC114A	D	3.8	12.0	...	...	...
A612	ZG61B	S	0.5	...	0.7	6.5	...
C612	ZC60A	S, P	0.5	...	0.4	6.5	1.0 Fe
D612, 40E	ZG61A	S, P	...	...	0.6	5.8	0.5 Cr
RR350	...	S	5.0 Cu, 1.5 Ni, 0.25 Mn, 0.25 Co, 0.25 Zr, 0.25 Sb, 0.2 Ti				

(a) S = sand casting, P = permanent mold casting, D = die casting. (b) About 0.15% Ti is specified in some alloys, but 0.25% Ti max usually is noted.

*For committee list, see page 389.

The smoothness of the surface of a casting is governed by the fineness of the sand and the moisture content of the mixture: the finer the sand and the lower the moisture content, the smoother the casting surface.

In natural sands, various degrees of fineness are obtainable, up to AFS 270. Clay content may vary from 12% to 28%. A typical natural molding sand has a fineness of AFS 140; clay content, 15%; moisture content, 8%; permeability, AFS 15 to 20; and green compressive strength, 6 to 8 psi.

In compounded, or synthetic, sand mixtures, fine-grain silica sand (fineness of AFS 100 to 180) is blended with bentonite and water. Because sand for casting aluminum alloys does not require high hot strength, southern bentonite is commonly used. In the preparation of these mixtures, mechanical mulling equipment is required, to develop the desired sand properties. Compounded sand mixtures have greater permeability than natural sand mixtures. A typical compounded sand mixture contains silica sand having a fineness of AFS 130, 4 to 5% southern bentonite, and 3.5 to 4.5% water. Permeability is typically AFS 25 to 30, and green compressive strength is usually 8 to 10 psi.

A semisynthetic sand blending naturally bonded sand and sharp silica sand of compatible grain fineness has been used with good results, particularly for large castings and in automatic sand-preparation systems.

Green vs Dry Sand Molds. Green sand molds are ordinarily used for casting aluminum alloys. Dry sand molds may be used because they provide greater accuracy and smoother casting surfaces, but dry sand molding is most often selected when complexity of the casting is a factor. Lack of strength in a green sand mold that allows core shift is sometimes a reason for using dry sand molds, as in the example that follows.

Example 456. Use of a Dry Sand Mold to Prevent Core Shift (Fig. 1)

The housing casting shown in Fig. 1 was originally cast in a green sand mold. The casting required a pin core (see section A-A in Fig. 1). At first, this core extended through the casting and entered the riser; it was positioned by means of a core-setting fixture. However, the pin core frequently tilted during closing of the mold or pouring of the casting, which broke the core print and made the cored hole difficult to clean up by machining. Castings rejected during rough inspection amounted to 8%, and an additional 6% were rejected during or after machining.

In an effort to correct the problem, the pin core was shortened from 4⅜ to 2⅛ in., as shown at the lower right in Fig. 1, so that it cored the 13/16-in.-diam hole only partway through the casting (the remainder of the hole was developed subsequently by end milling). The top of the core was then just below the parting line and could not be positioned by a core-setting fixture. The core-shift problem persisted and rejections because the hole failed to clean up during machining remained at 6%.

Finally, pattern equipment was constructed for dry sand molding, with production of two castings per mold. The dry sand mold held the pin cores more firmly, and rejection at rough casting inspection and in the machine shop decreased to less than 1% each. As a result of the heat transferred from the molten metal, the dry sand core projections ultimately collapsed and could be poured like beach sand from the solidified castings.

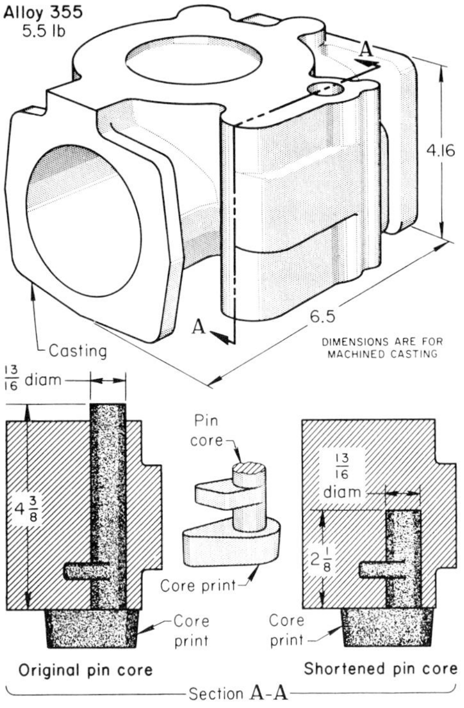

Alloy 355
5.5 lb

DIMENSIONS ARE FOR MACHINED CASTING

Casting

Original pin core — Section A-A — Shortened pin core

Item	Green sand mold	Dry sand mold
Castings per mold	One	Two
Metal poured per mold, lb	15	25
Shakeout method	Manual	Jolting table
Production, castings per hr	2	2.7
Total castings produced	500	5000

Fig. 1. Housing that was cast in a dry sand mold to prevent core shift that occurred when a green sand mold was used (Example 456)

Although the cost of the pattern equipment was 75% greater, cost per casting decreased 30% (including cleanup and heat treating) as a result of increased production and the sharp decrease in rejections. In both types of molds, pouring temperature of the metal was 1300 F. Additional casting details are given in the table with Fig. 1.

Example 480 in this article describes an application in which centrifugal casting in a dry sand mold enabled the successful production of castings with thin sections that had been impossible to cast without misruns and cold shuts when investment casting had been used.

For aluminum alloy castings of certain shapes, the greater strength of dry sand molds may be a disadvantage, restricting contraction of the castings and resulting in hot tears or cracks.

Cores of all conventional types (oil-bonded sand, carbon dioxide process, phenolic-resin-bonded, urea-formaldehyde-resin-bonded, shell, and hot-box) are adaptable to sand casting of aluminum alloys.

For information on the production of cores, see the articles on Sand Cores and Coremaking (page 209), Shell Molding (page 181), and Carbon Dioxide Molding (page 203). Each type of core has advantages and disadvantages, and selection of a particular type should be made only after a study of casting requirements and foundry facilities.

Although the basic formulating principles of each coremaking process apply to the production of cores for aluminum alloy castings, the low density of aluminum alloys permits the use of lower-strength cores than are required for casting the heavier metals. The recommendations given below should be followed whenever possible.

1. Sands of fine grain size should be used.
2. Thorough baking or curing of cores is required, regardless of the process used.
3. Sand mixtures should be those that generate a minimum of gas.
4. Cores should have a permeable structure, to permit rapid escape of gas.
5. Cores should be strong enough to withstand handling, placement and pouring.
6. Cores should be capable of collapsing quickly, to prevent undue restriction on the solidifying metal. (Because aluminum alloys are hot short — that is, their strength just below the solidification temperature is quite low — any resistance to contraction during cooling through this range may result in a cracked casting.)
7. The core binder should burn out sufficiently during the pouring of the mold to permit easy core knockout.

Typical oil-bonded core-sand mixtures and applications for which they are best suited are given in Table 2.

Because it is more difficult for a low-density metal to drive off core gases than for a heavier metal, cores used for casting aluminum alloys must have high permeability and must generate only a minimum of gas. In the example that follows, it was necessary to change the core-sand mixture to prevent gas blows that caused defective castings.

Example 457. Change in Core Composition to Prevent Gas Blows (Fig. 2)

The cover casting shown in Fig. 2 had a long flat core that was held at each end by a core print. The shape of the core prevented core gas from escaping through the core prints. The core gas was blown through the wall of the casting, causing the formation of an oxide skin as the wall resealed itself (see section A-A in Fig. 2), or the migration of a large gas bubble into the adjacent boss, producing gas holes (see section B-B in Fig. 2). In pressure tests, the seal over the oxide skin broke.

Although both kinds of defects should have been revealed by radiography, the angle of some of the oxide skins made it impossible to obtain 100% accuracy in radiographic inspection. Scrap rate from these defects was 25%.

An attempt to vent the gas through a passage in the core was unsuccessful, so the core composition was changed to one that would generate less gas. The original cores contained 0.5% oil binder and 0.55% corn flour, which resulted in the evolution of 3.44 cu cm of gas per gram of mixture. The revised core mixture, containing a maximum of 1.75% synthetic resin binder and 0.87% water, caused a reduction in gas evolved to 1.7 cu cm per gram. After being baked, these cores were still strong enough to withstand handling and setting; during baking, the cores were supported in green molding sand. Casting rejection rate decreased to approximately 10%.

By using core driers for support during baking, it was possible to use a mixture that contained 1% proprietary core binder and 2% water. With this sand mixture, evolved gas was reduced to 0.2 cu cm per gram, and casting scrap rate to less than 2%.

All three types of cores were baked in a continuous oven at 425 F for 1½ hr. Additional casting details are given in the table that accompanies Fig. 2.

Patterns and core boxes used for making molds and cores for aluminum alloy castings are essentially the same as those for castings from other metals, except for shrinkage allowances. (Shrinkage allowances for aluminum alloys, and various other casting metals, are given in Table 12 on page 164 in the article on Sand Molding.)

As in sand casting of other metals, the choice of pattern equipment depends largely on the quantity of castings to be produced. For small-quantity production, loose wood patterns are ordinarily used; for progressively larger quantities, wood patterns on boards, and then metal match-plate patterns, are used. Relations of quantity and cost per casting for the three common types of patterns are given in Example 153 in the article on Patterns for Sand Molding, in this volume.

Pattern shift, or improper alignment of the cope and drag sections of a pattern, can result in nonuniform thickness of casting walls. Pattern shift is not easily detected when the parting line is on a flat surface. Example 461 in the present article describes an application in which shift of one pattern on a three-pattern match plate resulted in wall thinning and consequent cold shuts. Although the occurrence of cold shuts was reduced by a redesign of the gating system, the problem was not solved until the pattern shift had been corrected.

Gates and Risers. Because molten aluminum alloys are extremely susceptible to formation of dross during pouring, gating systems must be designed to reduce turbulence and to prevent any dross that does form from entering the mold cavity.

One method of minimizing turbulence is the use of a tapered rectangular sprue, with the runner in the drag section of the mold and the gates in the cope section. The top of the sprue should be two to three times as large as the bottom of the sprue. The runner where it joins the sprue should be about four times as large as the sprue exit. Total cross-sectional area of all of the gates should equal the maximum cross-sectional area of the runner, or exceed it by a small amount. Beyond each gate, the cross-sectional area of the runner should be reduced by an amount equal to the gate area. The runner should extend beyond the last gate.

Another method of reducing turbulence is the addition of a strainer core, fiber-glass screen, or perforated steel at the bottom of the sprue. This restricts the flow of metal.

Proper placement of runners and gates prevents dross from entering the mold cavity. A common arrangement is to have the runners in the drag and the gates in the cope.

A well, or receiving basin, should be provided below the sprue, in the drag. This smooths the flow of the molten metal into the runners. Molten metal should not be forced to flow around sharp corners.

Gates should be limited to the fewest that will feed the casting (to minimize molding, casting and cleaning costs), but should not be so few that cold shuts or hot spots result. When feeding must be improved, it is better to use more gates than to increase the pouring temperature.

Thin castings of uniform thickness usually need no risers, but they do need vents opposite the gates to permit air and gases to escape as the metal

enters the mold. Castings of nonuniform thickness, or with heavy sections, need risers to prevent shrinkage defects. The best way of gating such castings is through a riser into a heavy section. The incoming metal heats the riser and gate, and then flows to the thinner sections. Solidification progresses toward the heavier sections, and as shrinkage takes place, metal is fed by the riser. The gate into the riser should be narrow, so that it will solidify quickly, preventing metal from backfeeding into the runner. The gate from the riser into the casting should be wider. The riser should be large enough to stay molten longer than the section that it feeds.

Top risers are often used for heavy sections, such as wheel hubs, that cannot be gated from runners. Top risers receive metal through the mold cavity and feed it back as solidification takes place. Top risers must be larger than the risers connected with the gating system, so that the metal will remain molten long enough. Refractory sleeves or fiber-glass liners are sometimes used around top risers to insulate them and increase their efficiency, by keeping the metal molten for a longer time. Exothermic materials may also be used to keep the riser molten.

Chills, which are metal forms molded into the sand, improve directional solidification and help risers to feed the casting. Chills permit control of the solidification of small bosses and pads on aluminum alloy castings and assure their soundness.

Some experimentation may be needed to find the best arrangement of risers and chills to prevent shrinkage defects. The three examples that follow describe applications in which shrinkage defects were prevented by addition, enlargement, or relocation of risers and chills.

Examples 458, 459 and 460. Changes in Risering and Gating to Prevent Shrinkage Defects

Example 458 — Boxlike Casting (Fig. 3). The casting shown in Fig. 3 was originally made with a riser on the flat face A to feed the heavy sections on the side of the casting. Attempts to chill the solid boss B were not successful, and shrinkage caused the formation of spongy metal in this area (see bottom view of casting in Fig. 3). Shrinkage cavities also formed on an inside wall (at point C in Fig 3), and a series of small linear shrinks extended along the side of boss D.

Sound castings were produced after the following changes were made: a riser was added at the side of boss B, and the original large riser on face A was extended out over the casting; the cast iron chills on the bottom of boss B were retained, but a zircon sand core was used between boss B and the small casting section directly above it. Castings produced by the revised practice passed x-ray inspection for MIL-C-6021, class 1A, and a pressure test at 50 psi. Castings were poured in green sand molds, one casting per mold

Table 2. Compositions, Properties and Suitability of Typical Core-Sand Mixtures for Aluminum Alloy Castings

Sands (and fineness)	Binders	Properties(a)	Suitability
700 lb washed silica sand (AFS 65); 300 lb bank sand (AFS 120)	14 lb cereal flour; 2 lb western bentonite; 4 qt core oil; 3 qt kerosene; 18 qt water	CS: 1.0-1.1 TS: 180-200 H: 80-90 P: 60-70	General-purpose mix for large or small cores; good surface finish, sag resistance
700 lb washed silica sand (AFS 65); 300 lb bank sand (AFS 120)	10 lb cereal flour; 7.5 lb powdered urea-formaldehyde; 3 qt kerosene; 12 qt water; 1 pt liquid parting	CS: 0.8-0.9 TS: 180-200 H: 80-85 P: 60-70	General-purpose mix giving better ejectability; curable in dielectric oven
600 lb washed silica sand (AFS 65); 400 lb sand-blast sand (AFS 38)	2 lb cereal flour; 4 qt core oil; 3 qt kerosene; 20 qt water	CS: 0.5-0.6 TS: 225-250 H: 90-95 P: 150-200	Special-purpose mix for intricate cores requiring excellent venting characteristics
1000 lb washed silica sand (AFS 75); 28 lb inert fines (silica flour or fly ash)	7 qt core oil; no water	CS: 0.2-0.25 TS: 150-200 H: 70-80 P: 70-90	Special-purpose facing for intricate, difficult-draw cores; may need wire reinforcement
1000 lb washed silica sand (AFS 65)	40 lb sodium silicate; 10 lb wood flour; 2 pt kerosene	TS: 275 H: 90-95 P: 90-110	General-purpose mix for large or small cores; CO_2-gas cured

(a) CS = compressive strength (green), in psi; TS = tensile strength (baked), in psi; H = hardness (baked), in AFS units; P = permeability, in AFS units.

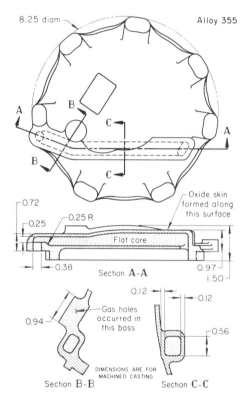

8.25 diam   Alloy 355

A   B   C   A

B   C

0.72
0.25   0.25 R
Flat core
Oxide skin formed along this surface
0.38   0.97
Section A-A   1.50

0.12   0.12
0.94   Gas holes occurred in this boss   0.56

DIMENSIONS ARE FOR MACHINED CASTING

Section B-B   Section C-C

Molding method ....Green sand
Number of castings per mold ....One
Weight of trimmed casting ....1.8 lb
Weight of metal poured per mold ......5.75 lb
Pouring temperature ....1320 F
Mold temperature ....Room
Shakeout method ....Manual
Production rate ....5 castings per hour(a)
Total production ....5000 castings

(a) Through heat treatment, to T6 temper

Fig. 2. Sand cast cover for which core composition was revised to prevent defects caused by core gas (Example 457)

Weight of metal poured per mold was 24 lb; trimmed castings weighed 5 lb apiece. Pouring temperature of the metal was 1330 F.

Example 459 — Manifold-body castings (Fig. 4) had severe shrinkage defects in the areas indicated when they were cast with only three risers as shown at the left in Fig. 4. The three risers, which were connected to a main, header-type riser, solidified without properly feeding the casting.

Feeding and solidification were improved by the addition of four risers as shown in the middle view in Fig. 4. In addition, the three cavities for the original risers were coated with soot by torching them with a city-gas flame, in order to insulate them and thus improve feed from the main riser. A third improvement was to add chills to the areas indicated in the lower middle view and the right-hand view in Fig. 4.

X-ray inspection of castings produced with this improved risering showed no shrinkage defects, but pressure testing revealed shrinkage over a solid boss (see view at left in Fig. 4), which extended all the way through the casting. The riser that had been added to this boss, and that also was connected to the main riser, was only ⅞ in. in diameter. By increasing the diameter of the riser to 1¼ in., castings were produced that were pressure-tight to 30 psi in the rough stage, and that withstood 1800-psi pressure after machining.

Castings were poured one to a mold, with 22.4 lb of metal being required for each 8.6-lb casting. Pouring temperature was 1300 F; shakeout was manual.

Example 460 -- Fan Casting (Fig. 5). The casting shown in Fig. 5 was originally poured from alloy 319, using the simple gating system shown at the upper right in Fig. 5. Castings produced with this gating system were entirely satisfactory. Because the customer wanted higher strength in the castings, alloy specification was changed to B218 (7% Mg). With the gating, risering, and pouring techniques used for alloy 319, castings produced from alloy B218 were unsound; radiography revealed internal shrinkage.

Then gates were relocated as shown in the lower right-hand portion of Fig. 5. Risers were attached to the leading edges (heavy side) of the blades in the areas where shrinkage had occurred. Shrinkage was eliminated, but because of the lack of fluidity of alloy B218, misruns occurred at the tips of the trailing edges (thin side) of the blades. Venting and increasing the pouring temperature failed to prevent misruns.

Sound castings were produced when the gating system was revised as shown at the left in Fig. 5. Risers on the leading edges were allowed to remain, and thin gates were added at the ends of the blades, to prevent misruns.

Misruns and cold shuts often can be eliminated by revision of gating systems. In the preceding example, misruns were prevented by the addition of thin gates. The two examples that follow describe other applications in which gating systems were redesigned to improve metal flow and directional solidification, and thereby to avoid cold shuts or misruns. In the first of these examples, however, cold shuts were not eliminated until pattern shift that caused thinning of the casting wall had been corrected.

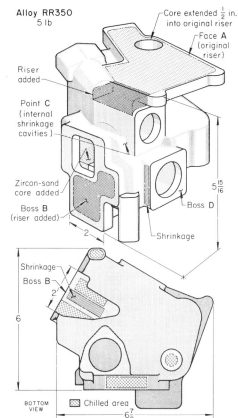

Fig. 3. *Casting for which risering was revised to prevent shrinkage defects* (Example 458)

Example 461. Redesign of Runner That Helped to Prevent Cold Shuts (Fig. 6)

Cover plates for gearbox housings were cast from alloy 319, three at a time in a green sand mold made from a three-pattern match plate. As originally gated (left-hand view in Fig. 6), many of these castings had cold shuts in the area indicated in Fig. 6, and rejection rate was excessive.

At first, metal temperature was investigated as the cause of the cold shuts. When heavy-section castings were poured along with the cover plates, low-temperature metal was required to ensure soundness in the heavy castings, and this increased the occurrence of cold shuts in the cover plates. Normal pouring temperature for the plates was 1350 F. When the metal temperature was raised to 1425 F, fewer cold shuts occurred, but rejections were still excessive. At 1500 F, few or no cold shuts occurred, but the rejection rate for dross and

centerline shrinkage exceeded the highest rate for cold shuts.

In a study of the gating system, it was found that most of the metal flowed into the casting through the gate farthest from the sprue. Thus, considerable heat was lost to the mold before the metal reached the end of the casting near the sprue, and the first metal to reach this end solidified before supplemental metal could flow into the portion of the cavity where the cold shuts occurred. This was corrected by starting with a thicker runner and decreasing its size after each of the first two gates (see "Improved gating" in Fig. 6), which provided a uniform flow of metal at the same temperature through all three gates. With the improved gating, cold shuts were encountered in fewer castings but still exceeded an acceptable level.

Randomly selected castings with cold shuts were sectioned for further study, and some were found to have only 60% of specified wall thickness in the cold-shut area (upper right view in Fig. 6). Investigation showed that one pattern on the three-pattern match plate had undergone a transverse shift when the match plate was made. The pattern shift was corrected, and production was resumed, using the improved gating system. Castings were poured at 1375 F, and rejection rate from cold shuts dropped to less than 0.2%. Also, it was found that the castings could be poured at 1275 to 1425 F at a satisfactory level of acceptability.

Example 462. Redesign of Gating System That Prevented Dross and Misruns (Fig. 7)

Circular plates originally were cast four at a time in a 14-by-14-in. sand mold by means of a centrally located 1-in.-diam sprue, as shown in Fig. 7(a). Because a lip-pour ladle was used, the stream of metal started about 7 in. above the top of the mold during pouring. Pouring temperature was about 1575 F. Under these conditions, the surface finish of castings produced was unacceptably rough because of

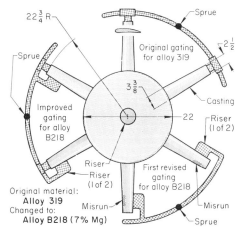

This fan casting was successfully poured in a sand mold from alloy 319 with the gating shown at upper right, but required two revisions of gating system as shown when alloy was changed to B218 for increased strength. The casting was poured through three sprues.

Fig. 5. *Revisions of gating necessitated by change in casting alloy* (Example 460)

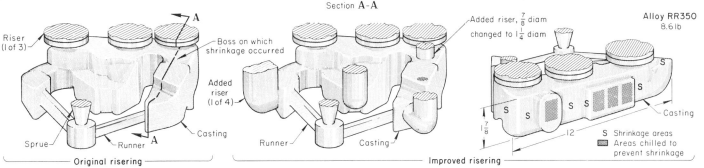

Fig. 4. *Revision of risering system that, with addition of chills, prevented shrinkage in a sand cast manifold body* (Example 459)

dross, numerous castings also had areas of burned-on sand, and misruns caused rejection of about 15% of the castings.

Sand burn-on was minimized by reducing the pouring temperature to 1450 F. To correct the causes of the other defects, the gating system was revised as shown in Fig. 7(b). The sprue was moved to one side of the mold to permit lowering of the pouring height, and sprue diameter was reduced to ⅝ in. These modifications reduced the metal turbulence that had caused air entrapment and dross formation. Also, the mold was vented to eliminate back pressure, which had caused misruns; as a result, the rejection rate because of misruns dropped to less than 5%.

Hot Tears. Aluminum alloy castings have very low hot strength and are thus more susceptible to hot tearing than are ferrous metal castings. Sometimes hot tearing can be prevented by careful selection of core materials, but more often minor redesign of the casting is the more practical approach. A redesign of casting struts that elimi-

nated a problem with hot tearing is described in the example that follows.

Example 463. Redesign of a Casting to Prevent Hot Tears (Fig. 8)

Originally, hot tearing occurred at the junction of cross ribs and outside walls in the upper and lower struts of a turbine air intake casting, as indicated in Fig. 8(a) and (c). About 30% of the castings were rejected because of this defect.

The castings were produced in a sand mold from aluminum alloy 356.

The unequal thickness of the outer wall and of the two ribs of the struts caused an uneven freezing pattern, and hot spots that developed at the junction of the cross ribs and outside walls caused tearing. The design was revised to alter the thicknesses of the sections forming the junctions to those shown in Fig. 8(b) and (d). The more uniform sections brought about a more uniform freezing pattern. After this design revision, no castings were rejected for hot tears.

Tolerances assigned to sand castings are relatively generous, because sand casting is not a precision process. Variations in dimensions result from the way sand is rammed onto the pattern, the techniques for drawing the pattern and setting the cores, and the expansion of the sand when the metal is poured. The size of the casting and the location of the parting plane are major factors in the accuracy that can be achieved. Table 3 gives suggested tolerances for aluminum alloy castings produced in green sand molds. Somewhat closer tolerances are possible when the castings are made in dry sand molds.

Although Table 3 shows 0.150 in. as the minimum wall thickness, thinner sections can be cast if the area is small, if metal flow is optimum, and if provision is made for feeding the thin-

Table 3. Suggested Dimensional Tolerances for Aluminum Alloy Sand Castings

Type A Dimension: Between Two Points in Same Part of Mold, Not Affected by Parting Plane or Core

Specified dimension, in.	Tolerance, in. Critical	Tolerance, in. Noncritical
Up through 6 ..	±0.030	±0.040
Over 6 to 12 ...	±0.030, +0.003 in. per in. over 6 in.	±0.040, +0.004 in. per in. over 6 in.
Over 12	±0.048, +0.002 in. per in. over 12 in.	±0.064, +0.002 in. per in. over 12 in.

Type B Dimension: Across Parting Plane. Type A Dimension Plus the Following:

Projected area of casting, $A_1 \times A_3$, sq in.	Added tolerance for parting plane, in.
Up through 10	0.020
Over 10 to 50	0.035
Over 50 to 100	0.045
Over 100 to 250	0.060
Over 250 to 500	0.090

Type C Dimension: Affected by Core. Type A Dimension Plus the Following:

Projected area of casting affected by core, $A_3 \times G$, sq in.	Added tolerance for core, in.
Up through 10	0.020
Over 10 to 50	0.035
Over 50 to 100	0.045
Over 100 to 500	0.060
Over 500 to 1000	0.090

D Dimension: Draft

Location	Draft Critical	Draft Noncritical
Outside wall	2°	3°
Recesses	3°	5°
Cores	2°	3°

E Dimension: Minimum Wall Thickness:
0.150 in.

F Dimension: Allowance for Finish

Maximum dimension, in.	Nominal allowance, in.
Up through 6	0.060
Over 6 to 12	0.090
Over 12 to 18	0.120
Over 18 to 24	0.150

Minimum Diameter of Cored Holes: 0.250 in.

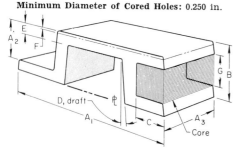

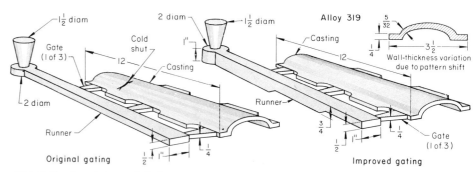

Fig. 6. Sand cast cover plate in which occurrence of cold shuts was prevented by redesigning the runner so that it was thicker at the sprue end and decreased in steps (as shown), and by correcting pattern shift responsible for wall thinning in cold-shut area (Example 461)

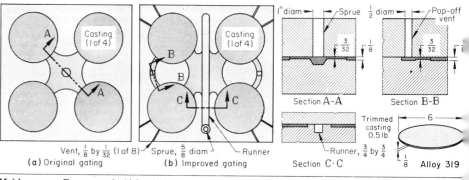

Mold ....Green sand, 14-by-14-in. slip flask	Pouring temperature:
Castings per mold ....Four	Original gating 1575
Weight of trimmed casting ....½ lb	Improved gating 1450
Weight of metal poured per mold ....4 lb	Production rate ....72 castings per hou
Surface inspection ....Visual	Cost per casting, 1000-piece lots $0.4

Fig. 7. Original and improved gating for casting of circular plates in a sand mold. Improved gating minimized formation of dross, and reduced rejection rate for misruns from 15% to less than 5%. (Example 462)

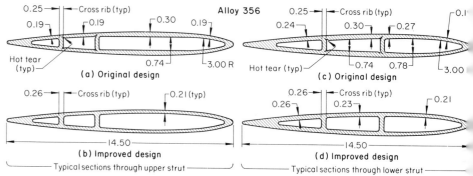

Fig. 8. Original design of cross sections of struts of a turbine air intake casting, and redesign that eliminated hot tears (Example 463)

ner section. For instance, the example that follows describes how an aircraft casting with thinner walls was made.

Example 464. Design to Permit Pouring of Thin Walls (Fig. 9)

The casting shown in Fig. 9 was an access door for a fuselage for an airplane. To make it as light in weight as possible, the walls had to be kept thin (0.08 ± 0.01 in.). Because such thin walls were likely to present feeding problems, ribs 0.12 ± 0.01 in. thick were used to conduct molten metal to all parts of the casting. Major dimensions are shown in Fig. 9. Rejections from misruns or cold shuts were within acceptable limits.

Shakeout and Cleaning. Mechanized shakeout can be used for most aluminum alloy castings, but some require special handling. At shakeout, aluminum alloy castings will bend under relatively low stress. Dropping of molds may be enough to cause bending. Castings with thin sections are more likely to bend than thick, chunky ones. Proper handling at shakeout will reduce or eliminate subsequent straightening operations. Castings that are subject to warpage should be allowed to remain in the mold for a longer time before shakeout.

The removal of internal cores is often a problem, especially when only a thin shell of metal surrounds a heavy core. On large castings and cores, pneumatic chipping hammers are used to break up the cores. For castings produced in squeezer-type molds, a core knockout machine is recommended. These machines have a pneumatic chipping hammer mounted on a frame directly above an anvil. The gate or riser on the casting is placed between the hammer and the anvil, and the hammer is started. Vibration is transmitted through the gates and casting, to break up the cores and thus facilitate their removal. For castings that are to be heat treated, if cores cannot be removed easily, they may be left in the casting. The heat treating temperature will completely burn out the binder, and the core sand can be poured out. However, this technique may contaminate both the heat treating furnace and the quench tank.

Gates and risers are removed from aluminum castings by band sawing, friction sawing, shearing or breaking. Band sawing is most widely used. The saws operate at 900 to 4000 ft per minute. Small gates can often be removed by shearing in a mechanical press.

Snag grinding for casting cleanup is done on both coated abrasive belts and grinding wheels. Under many conditions, coated abrasive belts offer improved production, better surface finish, and better working conditions. Grit sizes used range from 24 to 150 mesh. Longer belt life and faster cutting will result if a wax-type lubricant is used.

Fins and lumps that, because of their location, cannot be ground off may be removed by carbide-tipped rotary files in high-speed air-powered rotary hand tools. Speeds for the rotary files can vary from 2500 to 18,000 rpm. Small chipping hammers and hand files are also used for removing fins and lumps.

Sand remaining on the surfaces of the castings can be removed by abrasive blasting (grit or sand), water

tumbling, or wire brushing. Many clean castings are subjected to one of these operations to give them a uniform surface finish. Abrasive blasting with iron or steel shot or grit is likely to leave a fine residue of iron embedded in the casting surface, which will discolor when exposed to moisture.

Warpage and distortion, which frequently occur as a result of solidification stresses, handling or heat treatment, can be corrected by straightening in presses or manually, with mallets. The use of straightening and

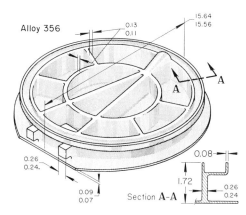

Fig. 9. Fuselage access door that was sand cast in aluminum alloy 356 to minimum wall thickness for its shape (Example 464)

Table 4. Costs for Producing an Aluminum Casting by Sand Molding, Using a Shell Core (Example 465) (a)

Production Details

Type of pattern	Metal cope and drag
Flask size	15 by 22 by 7 over 6 in. (pop-off)
Number of cores per mold	One
Weight of core	4.7 lb
Weight of trimmed casting	10.2 lb
Weight of metal poured per mold	18.9 lb
Actual yield	53.97%

Costs per Casting

Metal(b)	$3.570
Core material	0.235
Molding	0.203
Coremaking	0.190
Pouring and shakeout	0.833
Sawing, deburring and grinding	0.283
Heat treating (to T6 temper)	1.020
Abrasive cleaning	0.054
Inspection	0.063
Shipping	0.036
Total direct cost per casting	$6.487
Direct cost per pound	$0.636
Sales expenses per pound	0.091
Total cost per pound	$0.727

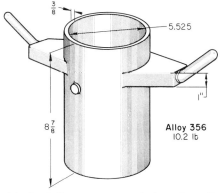

(a) A shell core was used to reduce the amount of machining on the bore. (b) Cost of molten metal; based on ingot cost of $0.265 per pound and melting cost of $0.085 per pound.

checking fixtures is recommended. Castings can be straightened more easily if they are heated. Heat treated castings should be straightened before they age (as soon after quenching as possible).

Straightening problems can be reduced by using care in shakeout and subsequent handling of the castings, including proper packing and placement of castings for heat treatment.

Surface Finish. Sand castings have rougher surfaces than do castings made by other methods. The surface finish of castings made in green sand molds is commonly 300 to 650 micro-in. Finishes of 500 micro-in. are normal. The use of fine sands and low metal pouring temperatures will result in castings with surface finishes near the low end of the above range. Surface finish can be further improved by use of dry sand molds.

Cost of producing an aluminum alloy sand casting in a given quantity is influenced primarily by the cost of the casting metal (determined by the weight of metal poured per mold, and the net weight of the casting), melting cost, molding method and number of castings per mold, type of pattern used, core costs, and type and amount of finishing required. A typical cost analysis for producing an aluminum alloy sand casting is given in the example that follows.

Example 465. Cost of Producing a 10.2-Lb Aluminum Alloy Sand Casting (Table 4)

The casting shown in Table 4 was produced in a green sand mold with a shell core. Cost and processing details are given in Table 4. Metal cost per casting was approximately half of the total cost, which is typical.

The use of a shell core reduced the amount of machining on the bore. An oil-sand core would have given a poorer surface, and more machining would have been required.

The number of castings to be produced has a major effect on cost per casting, mainly because different pattern equipment is used as quantity increases (see the discussion and Fig. 5 on page 152 in the article on Patterns for Sand Molding).

The two examples that follow compare molding practice, pattern equipment, and man-hours for producing 100 and 1000 castings.

Examples 466 and 467. Effect of Quantity on Molding Practice and Labor Time for Two Aluminum Alloy Sand Castings

Example 466 — 1-Lb Casting (Table 5). The casting shown at the left in Table 5 was produced one to a mold with a wood pattern on a follow board when 100 castings were ordered, and two to a mold with an aluminum match-plate pattern when 1000 castings were ordered. Costs of the two types of patterns, and labor times for producing the casting in 100-casting lots by both methods, are compared in Table 5. Total labor time per 100 castings was more than twice as much for the 100-piece order as for the 1000-piece order, but pattern cost was 2½ times as much for the aluminum match-plate pattern as for the wood pattern on a follow board.

Example 467 — 0.2-Lb Casting (Table 5). Eight 0.2-lb castings (illustration at right in Table 5) could be produced per mold when an aluminum match-plate pattern was used, in contrast to one casting per mold when a wood pattern on a follow board was used. As shown in the comparison in Table 5, total labor time was only about one-fifth as much per 100 castings for the high-production method as for the low-production method, but pattern cost was about 2¼ times as much.

Shell Molding

The shell molding process is used in aluminum foundries to obtain greater dimensional accuracy and better surface finish on castings than can be obtained by sand casting, and, occasionally, to decrease cost. Equipment, materials and procedures for making shell molds and cores for aluminum alloy castings are generally the same as those for gray iron and other metals (see the article on Shell Molding, page 181). However, because of the characteristics of aluminum alloys, special considerations (as discussed subsequently) are required for molds and cores.

Precision metal patterns and a considerable amount of special equipment are required for shell molding. Because of the cost of patterns and equipment, shell molding is most applicable to high-volume production, but shell molds and cores are also used for low-volume production when green sand molding fails to produce good castings. For instance, in Example 465, a shell core was used along with a green sand mold to obtain a smoother surface (and, consequently, less machining) on the bore of the casting. Shell molding is often used because less machining is required on the castings.

The aluminum alloys that can be cast in sand molds can be cast in shell molds.

Molds. Because aluminum alloys solidify over a range of temperature and go through a mushy stage instead of forming a skin, heat-transfer requirements of the shell are quite different for aluminum alloys than for iron. Aluminum gives up its heat three times as fast as iron, which causes greater thermal shock to the mold. Before the metal solidifies, stresses are set up in the mold that can result in cracking or buckling of the mold, and damage to the casting.

Consequently, careful selection of sand, resin and processing procedure is important. Only subangular sands should be used, particularly for molds that have large flat surfaces (up to 20 by 30 in.). A four-screen sand with about 5% pan fines of less than 325-mesh is recommended. The sand must be dry and free from clay.

A dry mixture of sand and resin is preferable to coated sand, because the sand fines act as a buffer to thermal shock. In some foundries, iron oxide or wood flour is added as a filler. Fillers serve several purposes: (a) they prevent buckling of the shell; (b) they promote collapsibility of the shell at the proper time; and (c) they prevent reaction of the resin with molten aluminum. Fillers also can be used to reduce shell strength, for applications in which a weaker shell may be desirable. Fillers often reduce shell strength so much that more resin must be used. When fillers are added, resin content should be 5 to 10%, rather than the 3 to 6% that is generally adequate.

Cores. Aluminum alloys have very low strength at temperatures just below the solidification range; therefore, it is mandatory that cores have low hot strength so that they will not cause hot tears in the castings by re-stricting metal contraction. Cores must be strong enough to resist breaking in handling and assembling, and yet be weak enough to collapse readily as the casting cools. This combination of properties can be obtained by: (a) use of additives, such as iron oxide or wood flour; (b) reduction of binder (resin) to the lowest possible level; and (c) use of round-grain sands. The most common practice is to make cores from round-grain sands (mixtures made with round grains have lower strength than those made with subangular grains). The sands are cold or hot coated with 2 to 4% resin. These cores are satisfactory for most applications.

Gating and Pouring. As with sand castings, an important objective in the design of the gating system for shell mold castings of aluminum alloys is to minimize turbulence and prevent dross from entering the mold cavity. The principles of gating systems discussed in the preceding section on Sand Casting (see "Gates and Risers", page 401) apply equally to shell molding.

The cope and drag halves of shell molds are held together by bonding with resin, by stapling the edges, or by bolting; these methods also can be used in combination.

Pouring practice is essentially the same as for pouring sand castings. Because aluminum alloys weigh only about one-third as much as the same volume of gray iron or steel, mold backup is seldom required. Most molds are poured in the horizontal position.

Dimensional Accuracy. The close tolerances that can be held when casting in shell molds is a major reason for their use. Dimensional tolerances for shell mold casting are closer than for casting in permanent molds and are approximately equal to those for plaster mold casting (see Table 7).

Surface finish of shell mold castings can vary considerably, depending largely on the grade of sand used in the sand-resin mixture. A fine subangular sand will produce the best surface finish. Surface finish is commonly 250 to 450 micro-in. With rigid control, smoother finishes can be obtained (in Example 468, shell mold castings were produced with a finish estimated at 125 micro-in.).

Cost. The production variables that affect cost of castings produced by sand molding (see Table 4) also affect cost of shell mold castings. Production quantity and yield (net weight of the casting compared with the weight of metal poured per casting) have a significant effect on total cost per casting. Rigorous inspection requirements, small-quantity production, and low yield are reflected in high cost per casting in the example that follows.

Example 468. Cost of Producing an Electronics Housing by Shell Molding (Table 6)

Table 6 shows a cast housing for electronics equipment and gives production details and an analysis of costs for this high-quality casting.

The housing was cast in a shell mold (cope, drag and core). Both mold halves and the core were made by core blowing; the cope and the drag were solid, and the core was hollow. The housing was produced in conformance with material specification QQ-A-601, heat treated to the T6 temper, and inspected in accordance with MIL-C-6021.

Inspection required chemical analysis of each heat of metal and radiographic inspection of each casting. Test bars were poured along with the castings, and were heat treated

Table 5. Molding Practice and Labor Time for Producing Two Different Aluminum Alloy Castings in Quantities of 100 and 1000 (Examples 466 and 467)

Item	Example 466 100-piece order	Example 466 1000-piece order	Example 467 100-piece order	Example 467 1000-piece order
Molding Practice				
Castings per mold	One	Two	One	Eight
Weight of trimmed castings per mold, lb	1	2	0.2	1.6
Weight of metal poured per mold, lb	6	8	3.5	8
Actual yield, %	16.6	25	5.7	20
Pattern equipment	Wood on follow board(a)	Aluminum match plate(b)	Wood on follow board	Aluminum match plate
Cost of pattern equipment	$1000	$2500	$175	$400
Labor, Man-Hours per 100 Castings				
Molding	33.33	10.00	25.00	2.50
Coremaking	20.00	8.33	...	...
Metal melting and pouring	1.66	1.00	1.47	0.44
Shakeout	2.00	1.11	2.00	0.25
Removing risers and gates	2.17	1.66	1.67	1.18
Sand blasting	1.25	1.25	0.57	0.57
Grinding	6.66	6.66	1.04	1.04
Heat treating (to T6 temper)	2.77	2.77	0.83	0.83
Total man-hr per 100 pieces	69.84	32.78	32.58	6.81

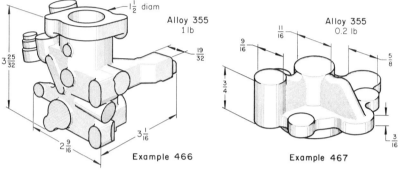

(a) Two wood core boxes were used. (b) Two aluminum core boxes were used.

Table 6. Production Details and Costs for a Shell Mold Cast Electronics Housing (Example 468)

Production Details

Castings per mold	One
Weight of trimmed casting	3 lb
Weight of metal poured per mold	15 lb
Actual yield	20%
Scrap, startup	36.4% (a)
Scrap, production	2.7% (b)
Pouring temperature	1360 F
Mold temperature	Room
Shakeout method	Vibrating screen
Surface finish (estimated)	125 micro-in.

Costs per Casting

	Good	Scrap	Total
Materials:			
Metal(c)	$0.972	$0.005	$0.977
Mold(d)	0.459	0.020	0.479
Core(e)	0.210	0.009	0.219
X-ray material			1.566
Packing material			0.030
Total			$3.271
Labor:			
Molding(f)	$0.882	$0.037	$ 0.919
Mold assembly and pouring	1.603	0.067	1.670
Removing mold, gates, risers	0.326	0.014	0.340
Finishing			1.663
Inspection			2.611
Heat treating (to T6 temper)			0.200
Total			$ 7.403
Manufacturing overhead			11.075
Selling and administration			5.438
Total cost per casting			$27.187(g)

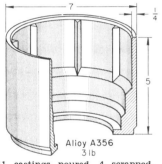

Alloy A356
3 lb

(a) 11 castings poured, 4 scrapped. (b) 74 castings poured, 2 scrapped. (c) 3 lb at $0.324 per pound. (d) Cope and drag; 25.5 lb at $0.018 per pound. (e) Zircon sand; 5 lb at $0.042 per pound. (f) Of cope, drag and core. (g) Casting with only visual inspection would cost $18.

with them. The castings were further inspected by fluorescent penetrant methods.

As noted in Table 6, the total cost per casting could have been reduced by 33% with only visual inspection.

Plaster Mold Casting

Plaster mold casting will produce aluminum alloy castings that have greater dimensional accuracy and smoother surfaces than can be obtained by sand casting or permanent mold casting.

Details of mold materials, patterns and procedures for the various recognized plaster mold processes are presented in the article on Plaster Mold Casting, which begins on page 222.

Applicability. Plaster mold casting is used extensively for casting of aluminum alloy impellers such as those for air-conditioning equipment; it is the most economical method for obtaining the required accuracy and surface finish of the blades. Other applications of plaster mold casting include match-plate patterns, molds for rubber and plastics, and precision electronics components such as wave guides.

Alloys Cast. The aluminum alloys that can be cast successfully in sand molds are suitable also for casting in plaster molds. However, alloys 43, A344, 355 and 356 are preferred, because they have high fluidity and resist hot cracking. Alloy 43 is satisfactory when high mechanical properties are not required, whereas the heat treatable alloys such as A344, 355 and 356 are used when high mechanical properties are required. The alloy cast can also have a significant effect on distortion, as demonstrated in the following example.

Example 469. Effect of Alloy Selection on Casting Distortion (Fig. 10)

Figure 10 shows a plaster mold casting for which an aluminum alloy containing 4.8% zinc and 2.3% magnesium was specified. This alloy was chosen because the foundry had found from previous experience that distortion was usually less when it was used, because it age hardens in 20 days at room temperature, and does not require heat treatment. However, the casting as originally designed was not producible with this alloy.

The design was revised for casting the center bar solid instead of recessed. This revision introduced considerable distortion. The thin sections froze and started contracting before the heavier bar section froze, and the casting distorted 0.020 in. out of position at each end. To correct this problem, chills were located along the bar section as shown in Fig. 10, and distortion was reduced, so that the castings were within acceptable dimensional limits.

It was next decided to pour castings to the original design from alloy 356, a more castable alloy, but one that requires heat treatment. All of the castings were sound and passed the pressure-tightness test, and distortion was sufficiently low that the parts stayed within tolerances, as cast. To minimize distortion in heat treatment, the castings were quenched in an air blast, rather than in a liquid.

The Al-Zn-Mg alloy used in the preceding example has a higher pouring temperature than alloy 356 and does not feed isolated areas of the casting from risers as well as 356. However, when a casting is designed so as to encourage distortion in heat treatment, the Al-Zn-Mg alloy, because of its ability to age harden at room temperature, may offer an advantage over alloy 356.

Dimensional tolerances for plaster mold castings of aluminum alloys are given in Table 7. Noncritical linear tolerances not affected by parting planes are like those used for die casting.

Wall Thickness. Because cooling rate is slow in plaster molds, walls as thin as 0.024 in. have been successfully cast. It is seldom practical, however, to cast walls that are thinner than 0.040 in. and a minimum wall thickness greater than 0.040 in. is preferred.

Because the percentage of rejected castings is normally reflected in the selling price of acceptable castings, thinner-wall castings (with higher rejection rates) predictably cost more. Also, production schedules become more difficult to meet as wall thickness decreases.

The minimum practical wall thickness for a specific casting is often determined by producing sample castings from loose wood patterns, as in the example that follows.

Example 470. Effect of Wall Thickness on Rejection Rate (Fig. 11)

For the flanged elbow casting shown in Fig. 11, it was necessary to determine the minimum practical wall thickness, using alloy

Table 7. Suggested Dimensional Tolerances for Aluminum Alloy Plaster Mold Castings

Type A Dimension: Between Two Points in Same Part of Mold, Not Affected by Parting Plane or Core

Specified dimension, in.	Tolerance, in. Critical	Noncritical
Up through 1	±0.005	±0.010
Over 1	±0.005, +0.001 in. per in. over 1 in.	±0.010, +0.002 in. per in. over 1 in.

Type B Dimension: Across Parting Plane. Type A Dimension Plus the Following:

Projected area of casting, $A_1 \times A_3$, sq in.	Added tolerance for parting plane, in.
Up through 10	0.005
Over 10 to 50	0.010
Over 50 to 100	0.020
Over 100	0.030

Type C Dimension: Affected by Core. Type A Dimension Plus the Following:

Projected area of casting affected by core, $A_3 \times G$, sq in.	Added tolerance for core, in.
Up through 10	0.005
Over 10 to 50	0.020
Over 50 to 100	0.030
Over 100	0.045

D Dimension: Draft

Critical locations	0°
Noncritical locations	2°

E Dimension: Minimum Wall Thickness: 0.060 in.

F Dimension: Allowance for Finish

Maximum dimension, in.	Nominal allowance, in.
Up through 5	0.020
Over 5 to 12	0.030
Over 12 to 18	0.040

Minimum Diameter of Cored Holes: 0.250 in.

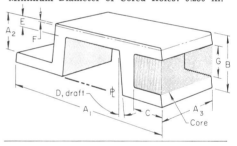

356 and the plaster mold process. Wall thickness was reduced progressively by modifying the pattern equipment, and castings were produced with three different wall thicknesses — 0.040, 0.060 and 0.080 in. Significant variables were carefully controlled, to eliminate any extraneous influence on the tests. The results of the tests were evaluated in terms of the percentage of rejected castings, as follows: 0.040-in. wall, 80% rejections; 0.060-in., 35%; and 0.080-in., 10%.

Surface Finish. An important advantage of plaster mold casting is the smooth as-cast finish that can be obtained. Surface finish is generally 125 micro-in. or better, and finishes as smooth as 32 micro-in. have been cast.

Production Practice. Several examples that describe the casting of aluminum alloys in plaster molds are presented in the article on Plaster Mold Casting, which begins on page 222 in this volume. The principal subjects of these examples, together with the alloys that were cast in the applications described, are listed in Table 8.

Investment Casting

Aluminum alloys may be cast in either ceramic-shell or solid investment molds. Molds can be poured by gravity, by gas or metal pressure, by centrifugal force, or by the vacuum-assist method. Procedures for investment casting of aluminum alloys are generally the same as those employed for other metals (see the article on Investment Casting, which begins on page 237 in this volume).

Applicability. Castings produced by investment molding are costly compared with those produced by the sand molding, permanent molding, or die-casting processes. The investment process should not be considered for castings that can be produced to acceptable standards by one of these other processes. The investment process is used when required shape, reproduction of surface detail, or dimensional accuracy is beyond the capabilities of the more conventional casting processes, and when machining to meet such requirements is impossible or prohibitively expensive. Components of electronics equipment, aerospace parts, and intricate parts for various instruments are the major applications of aluminum alloy investment castings. Sometimes, however, investment castings are produced in large quantities (see Examples 286 to 289, page 244, in the article "Investment Casting" in this volume).

Size Limitations. Although there are no theoretical limitations on size of an investment casting, there are practical limitations; a dimension of 20 in. is considered maximum for most castings. Section thicknesses are usually no greater than ½ in., although sections 4 in. thick have been successfully cast in aluminum alloys.

Alloys C355 and A356 are most commonly used for investment castings, because they have good fluidity and also because their properties are generally acceptable for a wide range of applications. Alloys 40E, A612 and D612 are frequently specified, even though their foundry characteristics are near the opposite extreme from C355 and A356. For alloys 40E, A612 and D612, it is necessary to use more elaborate gating systems for late-stage feeding, which results in a lower yield per unit of metal poured; also, higher preheat temperatures for the molds are usually required for producing sound castings of these alloys.

Mechanical properties of investment castings, when properly engineered, are similar to those of sand and permanent mold castings of the same alloy. The investment process permits considerable versatility in control of solidification pattern and rate.

Patterns used for investment casting of aluminum alloys are usually made of wax, although they may be made of plastic. Patternmaking practice is the same as that used for investment casting of other metals (see pages 239 to 241 in the article on Investment Casting, in this volume).

Core practice is the same as that used for other metals; see page 241 in the article on Investment Casting.

Mold Materials. In all commercially important investment materials for investment casting of aluminum alloys, various grades of silica comprise the refractory portion, and calcium sulfate hemihydrate is the bonding agent. The

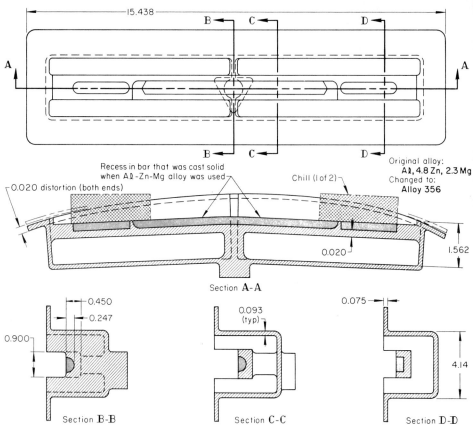

Fig. 10. Plaster mold casting for which change of alloy minimized distortion (Example 469)

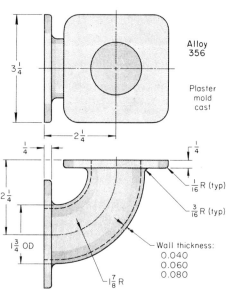

Fig. 11. Elbow that was plaster mold cast to three wall thicknesses to determine effect of thickness on rejection rate. Rate was 80% with 0.040-in. wall, 35% with 0.060, 10% with 0.080. (Example 470)

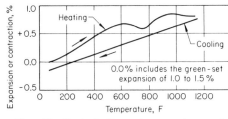

Fig. 12. Typical thermal expansion and contraction of an investment mold material bonded with calcium sulfate

Table 8. Examples in the Article "Plaster Mold Casting" (Page 222) That Deal With Aluminum Alloys

Alloy	Subject of example	Example No.
355 ..	Prevention of dross, gas holes	273
C355 ..	Prevention of porosity	274
356 ..	Cost analysis	272
	Prevention of cold shuts	276
	Prevention of shrinks, distortion and misruns	277
A356 ..	Prevention of misruns	275
... ..	Surface-finish limits	271

materials are available as dry blends formulated to individual specifications. A typical composition of a dry blend is as follows:

Silica:
Cristobalite 35.5%
Silica flour 29.0%
Calcium sulfate 33.5%
Diatomaceous earth 2.0%
Potassium sulfate .... 0.15 to 0.30%

Proportions of the refractory and the bond are designed to control the amount of expansion during green setting (initial drying) and firing. Typical thermal expansion and contraction characteristics are shown in Fig. 12.

A highly absorbent diatomaceous earth is used to provide adequate permeability. Potassium sulfate is used to nucleate the calcium sulfate and shorten the setting time. Sulfates of magnesium or aluminum can be used instead of potassium sulfate. The amounts used are influenced by the properties of the raw calcium sulfate.

If blended in the foundry, the dry refractory materials are usually ground to specified fineness in a rock mill. A typical screen analysis is given at the top of the next page.

Material	—% thru screen with mesh size of:					
	−325	+325	270	230	200	100
Cristobalite .	90	5	2	2	3	1
Silica flour ..	60-70	8-14	2-6	2-6	10-20	3
Blend	80-90	9	5	5	6	1

Preparation of Mold Materials.
The dry blend is mixed with 25 to 30% water (by volume), using a mixing speed of 1200 to 1800 rpm. The temperature of the water should be maintained within ±2 F. The amount of water is based on the required consistency of the mixture. Optimum consistency is that at which there is a minimum of solid separation during the preset period. When it is necessary to prolong the setting time, a retardant, such as sodium citrate, may be added as an aqueous solution. The addition of a foam-suppressing agent is sometimes required, especially if mixing is done in an evacuated chamber. For greater mechanical strength, 1 to 2% of milled fibrous materials can be added. Best dispersion of the fibers is obtained by wetting them and adding them to the water before mixing with the dry materials.

Wet blending is preferably done in a vacuum, to minimize air entrapment and to shorten setting time. Longer setting time results in more separation of solids from the blended slurry, which creates water-streak effects in the castings.

Viscosity control of the slurry is discussed on page 246 in the article on Investment Casting. Abnormally high viscosity, usually caused by too little water, is likely to result in an incompletely invested mold, and to cause defective castings (usually from globules of metal adhering to the casting surface). When viscosity is too low, the cause is usually too much water in the slurry. Low-viscosity slurries are likely to cause water streaks and loss of fine detail on castings.

Preparation of Molds.
Ceramic-shell molds for investment casting are prepared by dipping the pattern assembly in the slurry several times. Procedures are described on page 245 and illustrated on page 238 in the article on Investment Casting, in this volume.

Procedures for solid mold investing for casting aluminum alloys are similar to those used for casting other metals. Precoating of the pattern assembly is not required, however, because the mold material can withstand metal temperatures of 2000 F (or sometimes higher) — which is far above the pouring temperatures for aluminum alloys.

A solid mold investment is made by inverting the pattern assembly and sealing it to a metal plate. An open-end flask (preferably made from a stabilized 300 series stainless steel) is placed over the pattern assembly, and the flask is filled with the slurry, usually by means of a nozzle connected to the mixing chamber and operated by a butterfly valve. The plate that supports the pattern assembly and flask is usually vibrated and oscillated to eliminate air bubbles that might cling to the surface of the pattern. When the invested mold has set, it is unsealed from the metal plate. If the mold is to be cast with vacuum, a recess is formed in the end of the mold opposite the pouring cup, while the investment material is still soft. This recess helps to ensure a good seal for the vacuum during pouring.

Drying. Molds are usually held at room temperature for 1 to 2 hr before dewaxing (or removal of other pattern material) and firing. They should not be held at room temperature for more than 48 hr before dewaxing unless provision is made to retard the rate of evaporation of moisture from the mold. The minimum time of 1 hr at room temperature is to permit complete expansion. Too much time at room temperature permits excessive drying, which is likely to result in cracking of the mold during dewaxing and firing.

Dewaxing and Firing. The wax patterns can be removed by any one of several methods, which are described on pages 248 and 249 in the article on Investment Casting. Because mold failure from wax expansion is not a problem with solid investment molds (which are more commonly used for aluminum than are ceramic-shell molds), the wax is usually removed by exposure to steam or solvent, or by heating for 2 to 3 hr in an oven at 300 to 400 F.

It is essential that nearly all of the wax be removed while the mold still retains most of its moisture. If an appreciable amount of wax remains, it will penetrate the mold during firing. This is likely to result in porous castings, as described in the next example.

Example 471. Change in Mold-Dewaxing Practice That Prevented Porosity in Castings

A 3-in.-diam flowmeter, investment cast from alloy C355, contained 21 closely spaced vanes 0.050 in. thick. Development of the vanes required extensive use of blind vacuum-assist chambers and a gating system that was largely closed, which prevented good wax drainage from the mold. When a large load of molds was placed in the oven, the upper regions of the molds were dehydrated before the wax was completely removed. This resulted in severe wax penetration, even after the molds had been fired, and consequently in porosity in the castings. Rejection rate reached 35%.

Complete removal of the wax was accomplished by increasing the dewaxing time from 1½ to 2½ hr and decreasing oven temperature from 400 to 300 F. The number of molds per load was reduced from 32 to 25. These changes in practice eliminated the problem of casting porosity.

Molds are usually fired at 1200 F. Rate of heating should be 200 to 400 F per hour and rate of cooling should be 50 to 150 F per hour, depending mainly on mold thickness and complexity of the coring.

Length of time at 1200 F is usually 20 to 40 hr, depending on mold thickness. The usual practice is to cool the molds from 1200 F to 400 or 650 F (a mold-temperature range commonly used for casting) and then to hold for 3 to 6 hr to ensure uniformity of temperature. If casting is to be done with the molds at room temperature, they are cooled from 1200 F at a controlled rate down to room temperature.

Melting practice as discussed in the article on Foundry Melting of Aluminum Alloys, which begins on page 389, applies to melting and to control of composition for investment casting.

Because the volume of metal handled at any one time in investment casting

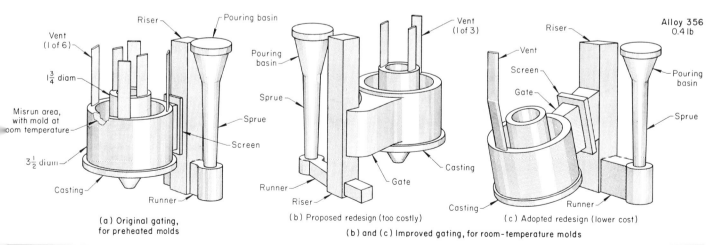

(a) Original gating, for preheated molds

(b) Proposed redesign (too costly)

(c) Adopted redesign (lower cost)

(b) and (c) Improved gating, for room-temperature molds

Pattern-die material ....Aluminum	Casting practice ....Gravity, hand ladle	Shakeout method ....Vibratory
Pattern material ....Wax	Pouring temperature ....1400 F	Number of castings per mold ....Three
Type of investment ....Ceramic shell	Original mold temperature ....650 F	Weight of trimmed casting ....0.4 lb
Pattern-removal method ....Heating	Revised mold temperature ....Room	Weight of metal poured per mold ....2.5 lb

Fig. 13. Redesigns of gating system for an investment cast flowmeter support that permitted pouring in room-temperature molds without misruns in outer casting wall (Example 472)

is generally smaller than in sand or permanent mold casting, precautions must be taken to prevent excessive variation of metal temperature. Ordinarily, it is not good practice to cast many molds in a single transfer of hot metal, because variation in temperature from start to end of pouring is too great to provide good mold-to-mold uniformity of castings. It is usually preferable to ladle out just enough metal for one, two or three molds, depending on poured weight and on temperature sensitivity of the particular alloy or casting.

Mold temperature for pouring is ordinarily in the range of 400 to 1000 F. The lower end of the range is generally used for castings that have thick, easily filled sections and that require a high degree of soundness. The higher end is used for castings that have thin, difficult-to-fill sections and that require only visual inspection.

In some applications, molds are poured at temperatures below 400 F. For instance, Example 291 in the article on Investment Casting describes the use of a mold at 200 F to prevent porosity in the bore of a valve body cast from alloy 356. Occasionally, solid molds (and frequently, ceramic-shell molds) are poured at room temperature. However, the incidence of mold failure is high for solid molds cooled below 400 F, unless the cooling rate from 400 F to room temperature has been very slow. The shell molds are less susceptible to failure.

Gating and Feeding. The practices for avoiding air entrapment and metal turbulence, and for placement of gates, risers, chills and vents, that apply to other casting processes apply also to investment casting.

Investment molds are usually preheated, which facilitates solidification control and casting of thin sections. In many applications, less elaborate gating systems are needed for investment casting than for sand or shell mold casting. However, because investment molds have relatively low permeability and molten aluminum alloys have low static pressure, thin sections may be difficult to cast. Usually, however, the

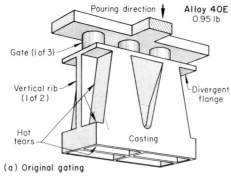

(a) Original gating

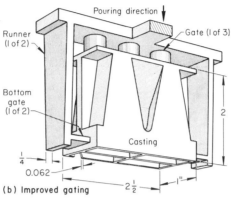

(b) Improved gating

Master-pattern material	Steel
Pattern-die material	Low-melting alloy
Pattern material	Wax
Type of investment	Silica-plaster, solid
Pattern-removal method	Heating
Casting practice	Vacuum-assist, hand ladle
Pouring temperature	1275 F
Mold temperature	400 F
Shakeout method	Vibratory, water blast
Number of castings per mold	Two
Weight of trimmed casting	0.95 lb
Weight of metal poured per mold	3.2 lb
Surface finish	125 micro-in.(a)

(a) Measured by tracer stylus

Fig. 14. *Change in gating that prevented hot tears in an investment cast component for an antenna array horn* (Example 473)

above factors do not impose severe limitations on design of gating systems for the casting of thin sections.

Example 480 in this article describes an application in which it was necessary to change from investment casting to centrifuged dry sand casting to prevent misruns and cold shuts. However, by use of vacuum assist and hot molds, it is possible to cast extremely thin sections in investment molds without difficulty.

Although vacuum assist in pouring will overcome some mold-filling problems (see Example 476), the gating system must provide arrangements for adequate venting, and sufficient static pressure. Gating changes are often required to eliminate casting defects, as in the four examples that follow.

Examples 472 to 475. Changes in Gating That Prevented Casting Defects

Example 472 — Misruns (Fig. 13). The flow-meter-support casting shown in Fig. 13 was required to be pressure-tight at 1500 psi after machining. Originally, the castings were poured horizontally in molds preheated to 650 F, using the gating system shown in Fig. 13(a). Sound castings were produced by this procedure, but preheating of molds caused a scheduling problem. To improve production flow, the preheating cycle was eliminated. When molds were poured at room temperature with the original gating system, misruns consistently occurred in the outer shroud of the castings (Fig. 13a).

To prevent misruns in castings poured in room-temperature molds, it was proposed to redesign the gating system as shown in Fig. 13(b). This would provide a tangential, rather than a direct, gate, and a runner long enough to furnish adequate metal velocity at the gate entry and thus to ensure filling of the shroud. This system, however, would have increased costs unacceptably, and so was not used.

By modifying the original gating system as shown in Fig. 13(c), sound castings were produced in room-temperature molds. In this modification, the casting was tilted about 20° so that the metal entered the shroud with sufficient velocity to fill it, but also without turbulence.

Bottom-fill systems were required for this casting, to suppress the formation of aluminum oxide films caused by turbulence in the area of the gate screen. Ceramic-shell investment molds were used in preference to solid molds, because of the greater stability of the ceramic shell and consequent lower cost for cleaning. Additional production details are given in the table that accompanies Fig. 13.

Example 473 — Hot Tears (Fig. 14). An investment cast component for an antenna array horn was required to be visually sound after being etched in 10% NaOH. With the gating system originally used for this casting (Fig. 14a), small hot tears resulted from solidification shrinkage between flanges, walls and vertical ribs. Scrap rate was about 50%.

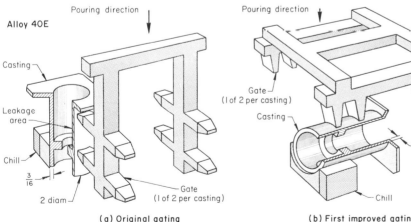

(a) Original gating

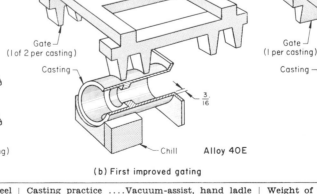

(b) First improved gating

(c) Final improved gating

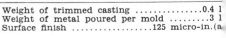

Master-pattern material	Steel	
Pattern-die material	Low-melting alloy	
Pattern material	Wax	
Type of investment	Silica-plaster, solid	
Pattern-removal method	Heating	
Casting practice	Vacuum-assist, hand ladle	
Pouring temperature	1375 F	
Mold temperature	650 F	
Shakeout method	Vibratory	
Number of castings per mold	Four	
Weight of trimmed casting	0.4 l	
Weight of metal poured per mold	3 l	
Surface finish	125 micro-in.(a	

(a) Measured by tracer stylus

Fig. 15. *Changes in gating system that minimized leakage due to porosity in an investment casting for radar plumbing* (Example 474)

To prevent the hot tears, the gating system was redesigned as shown in Fig. 14(b). The redesign incorporated two vertical runners, which extended to the bottom of the mold, and two additional gates. The added runners and gates provided a second supply of hot metal to feed the lower portion of the casting. Although the new gating system was more costly than the original, the additional cost was estimated as only one-third the cost of the castings that were rejected when the original method was used. Additional production details are given with Fig. 14.

Example 474 — Porosity (Fig. 15). A flanged cylindrical component for radar plumbing, investment cast from alloy 40E, had to withstand air pressure of 45 psi in an underwater test. This casting had 3/16-in. wall sections, which are relatively heavy for production from 40E by investment casting—particularly to a cylindrical shape requiring such soundness.

Preproduction samples were poured with the gating system shown in Fig. 15(a), with the casting in the vertical position. A chill was placed at the end of the isolated heavy boss, to initiate directional freezing there. The metal was fed to the casting through two gates — one near the flange and one near the internal shelf of the casting. Ten castings were poured. Although verified to grade A-B by radiographic and penetrant inspection, all ten castings leaked in the underwater air-pressure test — in an area roughly 1 in. in diameter between the two gates (Fig. 15a).

It was suspected that the porosity responsible for the leakage was caused by a hot spot between the two gates, resulting from passage of most of the metal into the casting through the bottom gate. Also, in some castings, the bottom gate was mislocated above or below the shelf, which contributed to the problem.

The gating system was redesigned as shown in Fig. 15(b). The chill at the boss was re-

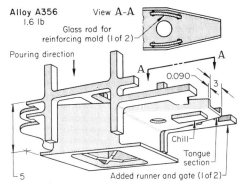

Alloy A356
1.6 lb

View A-A

Glass rod for reinforcing mold (1 of 2)

Pouring direction

0.090

3

Chill

Tongue section

Added runner and gate (1 of 2)

Pattern-die material ....Aluminum (machined)
Pattern material ....Wax
Type of investment ....Silica-plaster, solid
Pattern-removal method ....Heating
Casting practice ....Vacuum assist, hand ladle
Pouring temperature ....1225 F
Mold temperature ....650 F
Shakeout method ....Vibratory
Number of castings per mold ....One
Weight of trimmed casting ....1.6 lb
Weight of metal poured per mold ....3.8 lb

Fig. 16. Investment cast support fitting for which gates, runners and a chill were added to prevent microshrinkage, and mold was reinforced to avoid inclusions (Example 475)

tained, but the casting position was changed to horizontal so that metal flowed through both gates at an equal (and faster) rate. About 80% of the castings produced with this gating were sound; in those castings that were defective, the gate near the internal shelf was mislocated.

The gating system was further improved by the use of one large gate per casting, with the longer dimension of the gate parallel to the length of the casting (Fig. 15c). This change further decreased rejects.

Subsequently, alloy 356 replaced alloy 40E, and the single-gate design was satisfactory for the new alloy as well. Additional processing details are given in the table with Fig. 15.

Example 475 — Microshrinkage (Fig. 16). Gating for an investment cast fitting for a helicopter bellcrank support was redesigned as shown in Fig. 16. As originally gated, this casting had microshrinkage in the floor of the tongue section; rejections ranged from 30 to 70%, and the remainder of the castings were only marginally acceptable.

In the improved gating (Fig. 16), two runners were extended, and connected with two feed gates, to supply metal to the tongue, and an aluminum chill was placed at the underside of the tongue to promote directional freezing. These modifications eliminated rejection of castings for microshrinkage.

Failure of the mold during pouring was another problem. Along the large radii blending the tongue section into the main body, fragments of the mold became dislodged, and were dispersed at random throughout the casting as inclusions. To strengthen the mold, glass reinforcing rods were added, as shown in view A-A in Fig. 16. As a result, inclusions were eliminated from the castings, and scab formation was reduced along the tongue radius, thus removing the need for special cleaning.

Production details for this casting are given in the table with Fig. 16.

Vacuum assist is widely used in investment casting of aluminum alloys. Often only a small amount of vacuum assist provides the difference between defective and sound castings. The most common method of evacuating a solid investment mold is to set the bottom of the flask over the connection to the vacuum system. When this method is ineffective, a complex arrangement of channels such as that described in the following example can be used.

Example 476. Use of Special Vacuum-Assist Channels to Prevent Misruns (Fig. 17)

Figure 17 shows the pattern for an investment cast alloy A356 electronics housing with thin (0.060-in.) partitioning walls extending up from a horizontal platform. Conventional vacuum assist was initially intended as an aid in filling the mold, but on trial pouring of the casting, misruns caused by air entrapment occurred in the upper part of the thin walls. Because direct vents and gates to these walls would have been prohibitively expensive, the mold was provided with a separate vacuum-assist system (Fig. 17) that was molded in wax integrally with the gates, sprues and runners, and was connected to a vacuum pump. A solid glass rod (Fig. 17) provided mechanical support to the vacuum and runner systems. This arrangement provided full vacuum assist to the upper areas of the casting, and the 0.060-in. walls were produced without misruns. Production details are given in the table with Fig. 17.

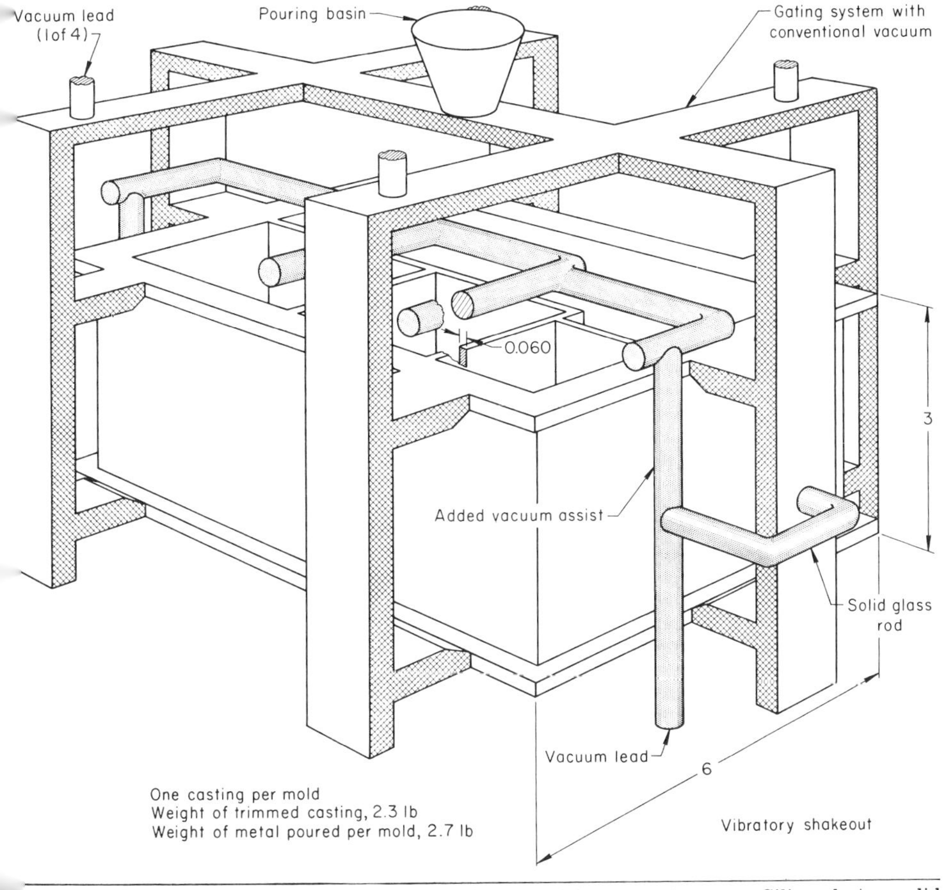

Centrifuging the Mold. Although vacuum assist is the most widely used method of preventing misruns, centrifuging of the mold is also effective and is sometimes used. One such application is described in the next example.

Example 477. Casting Thin Sections by Centrifuging the Mold (Fig. 18)

A casting (which is shown in Fig. 18) for the leading-edge assembly of an aileron was made of aluminum alloy 356 by the investment process. All casting walls were required to be 0.090 in. thick. By centrifuging the mold, pressure was exerted on the molten metal, forcing it rapidly into all parts of the mold, and good castings were produced.

Dimensional Accuracy. The accuracy that can be maintained on aluminum

Vacuum lead (1 of 4)

Pouring basin

Gating system with conventional vacuum

0.060

Added vacuum assist

3

Solid glass rod

Vacuum lead

6

Vibratory shakeout

One casting per mold
Weight of trimmed casting, 2.3 lb
Weight of metal poured per mold, 2.7 lb

Master-pattern material ....Steel
Pattern-die material ....Low-melting alloy
Pattern material ....Wax

Type of investment ....Silica-plaster, solid
Pouring temperature ....1275 F
Mold temperature ....400 F

Fig. 17. Pattern for an alloy A356 electronics housing that was poured in an investment mold with special vacuum-assist channels, to prevent misruns (Example 476)

alloy investment castings depends on the accuracy of the pattern. Fine detail, back draft, and undercuts can be reproduced. Many patterns are accurate within ±0.0015 in. per inch. Small castings can be produced in multiple-cavity molds (sometimes, hundreds of castings per mold) to a high degree of accuracy. Because pattern shrinkage can cause problems with large castings (large masses of wax are likely to form shrink hollows), section thickness is most often limited to a maximum of ½ in. A high degree of dimensional accuracy can be maintained in walls as thin as 0.030 in., and in ribs as thin as 0.015 in.

Machining allowance usually is 0.010 to 0.040 in. Dimensional tolerances for aluminum alloy investment castings

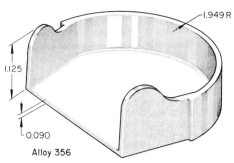

Fig. 18. Casting with thin walls that was produced in an investment mold by centrifuging (Example 477)

are commonly ±0.004 in. per inch up to 3 in., ±0.002 in. per inch additional from 3 to 10 in., and ±0.001 in. per inch additional over 10 in.

Avoidance of Casting Defects. Careful planning of pattern orientation, gating system, correct mold temperature, and method of removing air from molds will prevent misruns, hot tears, porosity, microshrinkage, inclusions and other defects in aluminum alloy investment castings.

Pattern orientation must be such as to avoid entrapment of air during both investing and casting operations. It is essential that patterns with large flat areas be oriented so that these areas are not in a horizontal position, because the flowing metal is likely to erode particles of the investment and entrap them as inclusions. Placing the pattern so that the metal will have to flow upward causes less erosion. Also, the pattern must be oriented so that the risering system will be able to perform most effectively.

Change in mold temperature often eliminates porosity (see Example 291 in the article on Investment Casting), and vacuum assist is frequently employed to prevent misruns and entrapment of air (Example 476).

Often a change in the gating system will eliminate misruns, hot tears, porosity and microshrinkage in castings, as described in Examples 472 to 475.

Cost of investment castings is high compared with the cost of castings produced by other methods. For example, in sand or permanent mold casting, cost of the metal is ordinarily about half the casting cost. In contrast, cost of the metal for an investment casting is usually an insignificant part of the total cost.

The number of operations involved in producing investment castings, the complexity of the castings, the metallurgical and quality control procedures required, and the use of mold materials that cannot be recovered contribute to the high cost of these castings. Any cost savings that can be anticipated are mainly the result of eliminating or minimizing subsequent operations, such as cleanup and machining.

Cost details in the example that follows suggest some of the reasons why the cost of investment castings is high. For instance, in this example the cost of the aluminum is only $0.25 per casting, or approximately 1.7% of the total cost of $14.90. The cost of the other materials and the cost of operations are both higher than for other casting processes.

Example 478. Cost Analysis for Investment Casting of Fuel-Control Housings (Table 9)

Fuel-control housings required 100% fluorescent penetrant and x-ray inspection to MIL-C-6021F, class 1A, grades A and B. These housings were cast in a two-cavity solid investment mold (see Table 9), using soluble-wax cores.

An analysis of the costs per piece for producing these castings is presented in Table 9. The price per casting was reduced 2 to 3% each time the size of the production lot was doubled, up to 500-casting lots. For lot sizes of 500 to 2500 castings, the price per casting was reduced 3 to 5% each time the lot size was doubled. Price reductions based on volume ceased at 2500 to 5000 castings.

Permanent Mold Casting

More aluminum alloy castings are made by the permanent mold process than by any other process except die casting. Semipermanent mold casting wherein molds are made of metal but cores are expendable, is also used for aluminum alloys.

Aluminum alloy castings weighing as much as 780 lb each have been produced in permanent molds, but the majority weigh less than 30 lb each.

Alloys identified with the letter P in Table 1 are those most commonly used for casting in permanent molds. The castability of these alloys is by no means equal. The alloys with a high silicon content have best castability, and those with a high magnesium content have poorest castability.

Tolerances. Suggested dimensional tolerances for permanent and semipermanent mold castings are given in Table 10. Closer tolerances can be maintained in permanent mold casting than in sand casting; sometimes, this is the reason for selecting the permanent mold process.

Surface finish of permanent mold castings is smoother than that of sand castings. Surfaces of 275 to 300 micro-in. are normal. Type and thickness of mold coating, condition of the mold surface, and metal pouring temperature are the major variables that influence surface finish. With close control of these variables, finishes smoother than 275 micro-in. can be produced.

Mechanical properties are often better for permanent mold castings than for similar sand castings produced from the same alloy, because of the more rapid cooling in metal molds.

Applicability. Because tooling cost for permanent mold casting is higher than for sand casting, the permanent mold process is most often restricted to use for intermediate to high production. Where the permanent mold process is used to make small quantities, it is most often to obtain greater dimensional accuracy, which will minimize or eliminate machining operations.

A common practice is to cast in green sand in the prototype or limited-production stage and, as production requirements increase, to determine whether permanent mold or semipermanent mold casting will be the more practical. This sequence was followed in the application described in Example 481.

Procedure and Control. Casting procedures for making permanent mold castings of aluminum alloys, together

Table 9. Cost Analysis for an Investment Cast Fuel-Control Housing (Example 478)

Item	Cost per casting
Labor and Burden	
Cores (soluble-wax)	$0.64
Core repair	0.67
Pattern (wax)	0.76
Chills (wax)	0.17
Pattern repair	0.44
Total pattern cost	$ 2.68
Sprue and riser (wax) ...	$0.18
Gate-and-chill assembly ..	0.34
Mechanical core supports .	0.20
Total gating cost	0.72
Molding(a)	1.30
Mold baking; wax removal	$0.70
Melt and pour metal	1.85
Total foundry cost	2.55
Pushout and vibrate	$0.30
Waterblast (core removal)	0.12
Cutoff	0.25
Total cleaning cost	0.67
Grind	$0.30
File	0.70
Sand blast	0.25
Total finishing cost	1.25
Visual inspection	$0.18
Dimensional inspection ...	1.25
Total, foundry inspection	1.43
Total cost, labor & burden	$10.60
Materials	
Soluble wax	$0.15
Pattern wax	0.14
Investment	0.75
Metal	0.25
Total materials cost ...	$ 1.29
Other Expenses	
Rejects (15% scrap)	$ 1.90
Heat treating (T6 temper)	0.20
Penetrant inspection	0.04
X-ray inspection (5 views)	0.87
Total cost per casting(b)	$14.90

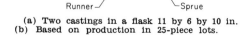

(a) Two castings in a flask 11 by 6 by 10 in.
(b) Based on production in 25-piece lots.

with the control of casting defects, dimensional accuracy, surface finish and cost, are discussed in the article on Permanent Mold Casting, which begins on page 265 in this volume. The subjects dealt with in that article are machines, mold design, cores, mold materials, mold life, mold coatings, mold temperature and control, removal from molds, casting design, dimensional accuracy, surface finish, casting defects, and cost.

Production Examples. Thirty-six examples of production, design and cost factors involving permanent mold casting of aluminum alloys are included in the article on Permanent Mold Casting. The principal subjects of these examples, as well as the alloys that were cast in the applications described, are listed in Table 11.

Table 10. Suggested Dimensional Tolerances for Permanent and Semipermanent Mold Aluminum Alloy Castings

Type A Dimension: Between Two Points in Same Part of Mold, Not Affected by Parting Plane or Moving Parts

Specified dimension, in.	Tolerance, in.	
	Critical	Noncritical
Up through 1 ..	±0.010	±0.015
Over 1	±0.010, +0.0015 in. per in. over 1 in.	±0.015, +0.002 in. per in. over 1 in.

Type B Dimension: Across Parting Plane. Type A Dimension Plus the Following:

Projected area of casting, $A_1 \times A_3$, sq in.	Added tolerance for parting plane, in.
Up through 10	0.010
Over 10 to 50	0.015
Over 50 to 100	0.020
Over 100 to 250	0.025
Over 250 to 500	0.030

Type C Dimension: Affected by Moving Parts. Type A Dimension Plus the Following:

Projected area of casting affected by moving part, $A_3 \times G$, sq in.	Added tolerance, in.	
	Metal core or mold	Sand core
Up through 10	0.010	0.015
Over 10 to 50	0.015	0.025
Over 50 to 100	0.015	0.030
Over 100 to 500	0.022	0.040
Over 500 to 1000	0.032	0.060

D Dimension: Draft

	Draft	
Location	Critical	Noncritical
Outside surface	2°	3°
Recesses	2°	5°
Cores	1°	2°

E Dimension: Minimum Wall Thickness

Maximum dimension, in.	Minimum wall thickness, in.
Up through 3	0.140
Over 3 to 6	0.160
Over 6	0.188

F Dimension: Allowance for Finish

Maximum dimension, in.	Nominal allowance, in.	
	Metal core or mold	Sand core
Up through 6	0.030	0.060
Over 6 to 12	0.045	0.090
Over 12 to 18	0.060	0.120
Over 18 to 24	0.090	0.180

Minimum Diameter of Cored Holes: 0.375 in.

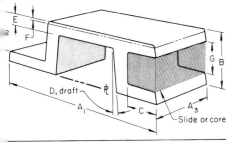

Die Casting

Die casting is used for mass production of small to intermediate-size aluminum alloy castings. Ordinarily, when a casting can be made by any of the major methods, sand mold casting is used for prototype or limited production (because tooling cost is lowest and design changes can be made at minimum cost), permanent mold casting is used when the design is fixed and production is medium to high, and die casting is used for mass production.

Alloys Cast. The alloys in Table 1 that are designated as D are those most commonly used for die casting. Castability of alloys follows the general rule — namely, the high-silicon alloys have the best castability and the high-magnesium alloys have the poorest. Alloys 13 and A13 are extensively used for die casting.

Size and Weight Limitations. Casting size and weight limit the application of die casting. Although equipment is available that can produce aluminum alloy die castings that weigh as much as 50 lb each, most weigh considerably less. Components that have a relatively large plan area are routinely produced by die casting (see Fig. 28 in the article on Die Casting), but as plan area increases, especially for thin work, difficulty in producing sound castings becomes greater.

Machines. Cold-chamber machines are almost universally used for die casting of aluminum alloys. Hot-chamber machines are generally unsatisfactory, mainly because the molten metal is constantly in contact with some metal component in a hot-chamber machine, and severe contamination of the aluminum by iron is likely to take place.

Horizontal machines are more widely used than vertical machines, although vertical machines are sometimes preferred, as when center gating is used (see Example 361). For information on the various types of die-casting machines, see the article on Die Casting, beginning on page 285 in this volume.

Dies for die casting aluminum alloys may be single-cavity, multiple-cavity, combination, or unit-type, depending mainly on the size and shape of the casting and on production requirements. These types of dies are described in the article on Die Casting, pages 290 to 294.

Dies used for casting aluminum alloys are subjected to more rigorous service than are those used for casting lower-melting metals, such as zinc alloys. They must be made of a material that will resist softening at the casting temperature (1150 to 1300 F). Hot work tool steels (such as H13) hardened to Rockwell C 44 to 48 are most commonly used. Large dies are commonly constructed as unit dies — that is, as a master holding block with various dies inserted. The master holding block is made of an alloy steel such as 4140, frequently in the form of a casting, and the inserted dies are made of a hot work tool steel. Moving parts, such as slides and cores, are made of nitrided 7140 steel or of a hot work tool steel, which can also be nitrided to prolong service life.

Heat checking, from repeated stressing at elevated temperature, is the most common cause of failure of die-casting dies used for casting aluminum alloys. Heat checks in the dies result in poor surfaces on the castings.

The example that follows describes an application in which material for a die insert was reselected in an effort to eliminate a problem resulting from heat checking.

Example 479. Use of Maraging Steel to Increase Life of a Die Insert

An H13 tool steel runner-block insert, located just before the gate of the die for a 26-lb aluminum alloy die casting, formed one side of the main runner channel leading from the biscuit to the gate of the die cavity, as well as one side of the gate and a portion of the casting surface adjacent to it. The runner channel averaged ¾ in. deep and 2 in. wide before spreading out into a 7½-in. modified fan gate. Because of its location in the die, the insert was subjected to severe erosion, pressure and heat. Heat checking developed rapidly, and the insert had a service life of only 35,000 shots before it cracked to the extent that it was no longer usable. Other inserts in the same die lasted for 100,000 to 175,000 shots before failure. Because 12 similar dies were operating in the plant, the poor service life of the runner-block inserts became a costly and troublesome problem.

In an attempt to solve the problem, a runner-block insert made of 18% nickel maraging steel was tried in an experimental runner block, and all performance details were recorded. This insert lasted for nearly 100,000 shots — almost three times the life of the H13 insert.

Three more runner-block inserts were made of the maraging steel. One failed by cracking at 20,000 shots; the failure was attributed to insufficient aging of the steel. The two others were re-aged and ran for 60,000 and 96,000 shots. Because the second aging treatment was beneficial, a longer aging cycle was specified. Subsequent inserts lasted for 70,000 to 100,000 shots, and so maraging steel was adopted as the standard material for the runner-block inserts. The increased service life obtained with the maraging steel justified its higher cost.

A maraging steel was used experimentally for two different components in other dies, without success. Early failure by cracking occurred in both instances. In these applications, it was found that placement of the cooling channel was much more critical with the maraging steel than with H13. Cooling channels placed less than 1 in. from the die surface almost certainly led to early failure of the tooling component.

Table 11. Examples in the Article "Permanent Mold Casting" (Page 265) That Deal With Aluminum Alloys

Alloy or subject	Example No
Alloys Cast	
Almag 35	314
43	320
F132	316, 319, 326, 341
B195	318
319	315, 323, 343, 345, 346, 350
333	327, 339
355	317, 329
356 ....321, 322, 324, 333, 338, 342, 344, 347, 348, 349, 352, 353
Subjects of Examples	
Molding practice 312, 313, 314, 316
Core practice 322, 328, 336
Gating system .... 315 through 320
Mold cooling .... 321 through 324
Degassing the melt 326
Pouring temperature 327
Removal of casting from mold 328, 329
Casting design 312, 333, 334
Dimensional accuracy 335, 336
Surface finish 338
Casting defects ... 313, 314, 316, 318, 319, 320, 321, 323, 324, 327, 328, 329
Costs .... 341 through 353

Because the use of maraging steels for die-casting dies is relatively new, there is much to be learned about their suitability. However, the experience described in the preceding example indicates that they have some merit for this application.

Gating, one of the most critical aspects of die design, is discussed in detail in the Appendices on pages 315 to 333. Of the 20 examples included there, 16 relate to aluminum alloys (see Table 12 for example numbers).

Melting practice, including furnaces and control of metal composition, is discussed in detail in the article on Foundry Melting of Aluminum Alloys, page 389, and is also treated on pages 301 and 303 in the article on Die Casting. Often, the metal is purchased in the molten condition to established specifications, and is transported in insulated vessels by truck from the melting facility to the die-casting plant. Plants that purchase molten metal are equipped with holding furnaces, and often have some standby melting equipment that can be placed in service if the molten metal is not delivered on schedule.

Tolerances. Greater dimensional accuracy is possible with die casting than with other commonly used casting methods. The tolerance that can be maintained on a particular dimension depends largely on whether the dimension is within one die half or is across the die parting line. Allowance must be made for movable die components.

Total tolerance is comprised of a basic tolerance (within one die half and not affected by movable die components) plus an allowance for movable components (if they exist) plus an allowance for parting-line influence. To avoid the calculation of total tolerance, especially for complicated designs, tolerances for aluminum alloy die castings can be determined graphically from the charts shown in Fig. 19.

Sample Calculation Illustrating Use of Fig. 19. Consider an aluminum alloy die casting with a dimension of 25.59 in. for which the tolerance is to be determined. This dimension specifies the distance between an external and a shrink surface, both of which are formed by movable parts of the die that have a slide width of 11.81 in. One of the slides is pulled perpendicular to, the other parallel to, the size-limiting surfaces. The surfaces involve both die halves, with the dimension measured parallel to the die parting plane. The area of the casting is computed as 372 sq in.

The sketches in the upper left-hand corner of Fig. 19 indicate that group II meets the basic conditions of the casting surfaces with which the specified dimension is concerned. As shown, the middle curve of the left-hand chart will define the basic tolerance.

Because the size-limiting surfaces (the surfaces that limit the dimension) are formed by movable parts of the die, with one moving perpendicular and one parallel to the size-limiting surfaces, from the sketches at the bottom of Fig. 19 it is determined that condition 4 of group II is applicable. Therefore, line 4 of the center chart will define the additional allowance to basic tolerance for movable die sections. However, where the movable-die-component dimension under consideration is greater than 4 in. (it is 11.81 in. in this example), further allowance, in the form of a percentage, is made for movable die sections, mainly because of the greater clearance required between the rigid die block and the movable slide. The additional allowance for movable die sections and the percentage increase because of large size are combined and shown in the top chart.

Where both die halves are involved in forming the size-limiting surface, a further allowance is required to compensate for mismatch because of clearance between the die guide pins and the mating bushings, die movement from the pressure of the injected metal, incomplete closing of the die as a result of flash on the surface, and other variables. This allowance is determined from the chart at the extreme right. Dimensions parallel and perpendicular to the die parting plane are treated separately, and appropriate curves are plotted.

The sample calculation here is plotted on the charts in Fig. 19 to assist the reader in understanding this graphical method for determining tolerance. The dimension, 25.59 in., is used as the starting point on the scale at the left of the basic-tolerance chart. By drawing a line horizontally until the curve for group II is intersected, and by dropping vertically to the scale, a basic tolerance for this dimension is determined as 0.0319 in. Continuing the horizontal line and moving to the center chart, line 4 (pertinent to this example) will be intersected. If the movable-die-component dimension under study were less than 4 in., a vertical line downward from this point of intersection would give the additional allowance. However, because the dimension is greater than 4 in. (11.81 in.), the values on the center chart are not used. Instead, a line is drawn upward from the point of intersection with line 4, to intersect in the topmost chart with the line representing the width of the slide (11.81 in.). From the point of intersection, a line is drawn horizontally to the left, to the scale. As shown, the additional allowance for movable die components is 0.0105 in. (allowance for a movable slide plus a percentage for its being over 4 in. wide).

Because both die halves are involved in producing the pertinent size-limiting surfaces, a further allowance is necessary, based on the total surface area of the die casting that would tend to separate the die halves when the molten metal is injected. For the casting under consideration, the area is 372 sq in., and the dimension being considered is measured parallel to the parting line.

Using the chart at the extreme right, from a point on the vertical scale corresponding to the computed area of the casting (372 sq in.), a horizontal line is drawn to the right until it intersects the curve representing dimensions parallel to the parting line. From the point of intersection, a line is dropped vertically to the scale. The amount indicated (0.0058 in.) is added to the cumulative tolerance for the 25.59-in. dimension.

These individual tolerances are summarized below. The accumulation, 0.0482 in., is the minimum tolerance practical for a dimension of 25.59 in. on a production casting.

1 Basic tolerance ....0.0319 in.
2 Allowance for movable parts.....0.0105
3 Allowance for parting-line
    influence 0.0058
    Total tolerance ....0.0482 in.

Mechanical Properties. The as-cast strength of an aluminum alloy die casting may be higher than for its sand cast counterpart, because cooling is more rapid in metal dies than in a sand mold. But strength also depends greatly on porosity, which is likely to be present in a die casting. If there is an appreciable amount of porosity, the strength may be lower than for a similar casting made in a sand mold.

Procedure and Control. The article "Die Casting", which begins on page

285 in this volume, describes the equipment, dies and procedures for making aluminum alloy die castings. It also discusses die temperature; die lubricants; casting design; and control of composition, dimensions, surface finish, and casting defects.

Production Examples. Twenty-three examples involving die casting of aluminum alloys are presented in the article on Die Casting (and Appendices). The subjects of these examples, together with the alloys cast in the applications described, are listed in Table 12.

Composite Molds

Composite mold assemblies are molds constructed of several components, at least one of which differs from the others in regard to the process by which it was made and in molding material. Although the use of composite mold assemblies for casting aluminum alloys is not new, stringent requirements by the aerospace, electronics and air conditioning industries have greatly expanded applications. For details (including six typical examples of practice), see the article on Composite Mold Casting, page 232 in this volume.

Selection of Casting Process

The appropriate casting process is selected on the basis of the size, weight and shape of the casting, the quantity to be produced, the mechanical properties and dimensional accuracy required and the cost of making the casting to these requirements by the various processes.

Stringent requirements as to properties or accuracy may limit the choice to two processes. Castings of extremely intricate design, for example, can be produced by either the plaster mold or the investment method; the choice between the two processes depends on the size and shape of the casting, and the cost. If the casting is small, the investment method probably will be chosen; for a large casting, the plaster mold method will be more suitable.

When a casting can be made successfully by three or more processes, the quantity required is usually the deciding factor. A 10-lb casting of average complexity and with no unusual requirements as to properties or dimensional accuracy can (and probably will) be cast by four different methods between prototype and high-production stages. In the development (prototype) stage, sand casting is used; in the low-production stage, the semipermanent mold process (metal mold, expendable cores); for medium production, the permanent mold process (metal mold, metal cores); and for high production, the die-casting process. Cost per casting decreases, and tooling costs increase, as quantity increases and an appropriate molding method is selected.

Cost is usually related closely to quantity and the weight of the casting. Charts that serve as guides to the selection of a casting process are widely used. One plant uses the chart shown in Fig. 20. This chart relates casting weight and casting cost for six different processes. (The two curves fo

Table 12. Examples in the Article "Die Casting" and Appendices (Pages 285 to 333) That Deal With Aluminum Alloys

Alloy	Subject of example	Example No.
13	Gating practice	395
A13	Gating practice	361, 364
	Machine selection	361
43, 360	Costs, permanent mold	
	vs die casting	387
380	Costs	374, 375, 376, 386
	Gating practice	390-394; 396-405

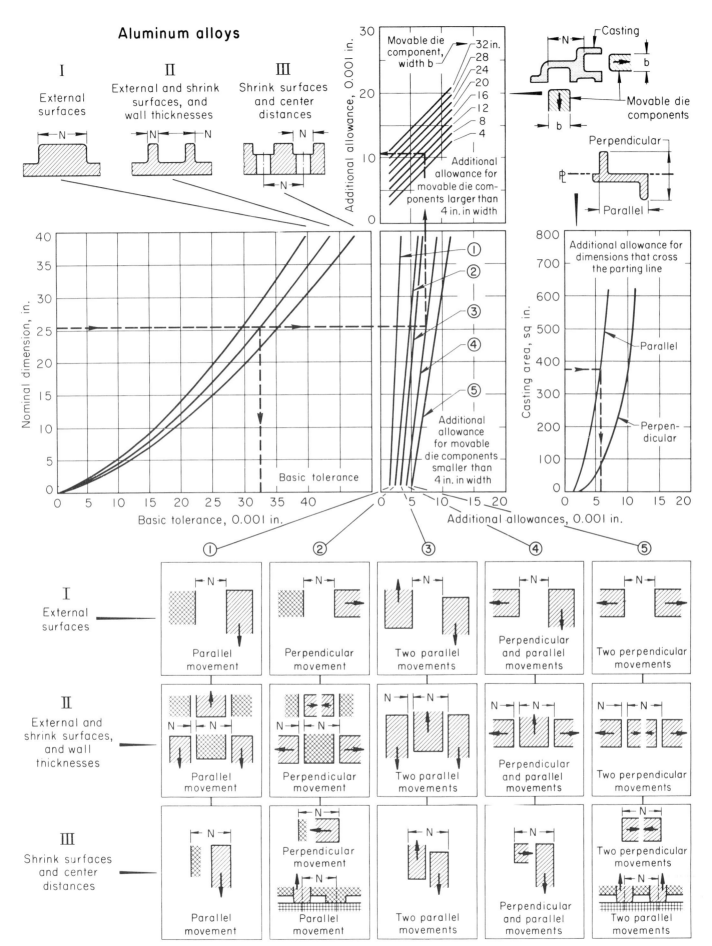

Aluminum alloys

I — External surfaces

II — External and shrink surfaces, and wall thicknesses

III — Shrink surfaces and center distances

Movable die component, width b — 32 in. / 28 / 24 / 20 / 16 / 12 / 8 / 4

Additional allowance, 0.001 in.

Additional allowance for movable die components larger than 4 in. in width

Casting

Movable die components

Perpendicular

Parallel

Additional allowance for dimensions that cross the parting line

Parallel

Perpendicular

Casting area, sq in.

Nominal dimension, in.

Basic tolerance

Additional allowance for movable die components smaller than 4 in. in width

Basic tolerance, 0.001 in.

Additional allowances, 0.001 in.

I — External surfaces

① Parallel movement ② Perpendicular movement ③ Two parallel movements ④ Perpendicular and parallel movements ⑤ Two perpendicular movements

II — External and shrink surfaces, and wall thicknesses

Parallel movement / Perpendicular movement / Two parallel movements / Perpendicular and parallel movements / Two perpendicular movements

III — Shrink surfaces and center distances

Parallel movement / Perpendicular movement / Parallel movement / Two parallel movements / Perpendicular and parallel movements / Two perpendicular movements / Two parallel movements

Fig. 19. Charts for determining total tolerance on dimensions of aluminum alloy die castings. See text for sample calculation illustrating use of these charts. (From Gustav Lieby, "Design of Die Castings", in German, 1949; in English, American Foundrymen's Society, 1957)

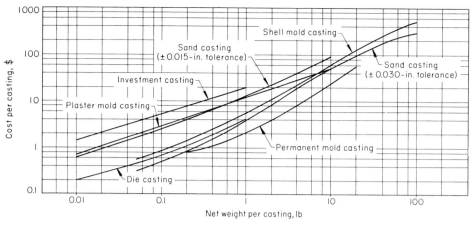

Fig. 20. Guide to selection of the lowest-cost process for casting aluminum alloys, based on net weight of the casting

sand casting assume casting to two different tolerances.) Each curve spans the weight range that this plant regards as practical for the casting method. This chart does not consider property requirements.

In thin-wall castings of some designs, the light weight of aluminum fails to provide sufficient pressure of molten metal to force the metal into the thin sections. For such castings, it may be necessary to change the casting process to provide for the application of additional pressure to the metal — as described in the following example.

Example 480. Change From Investment Casting to Centrifuged Dry Sand Casting to Produce Sound Thin-Wall Sections (Fig. 21)

The design for the fin-shoe slide casting shown in Fig. 21 called for maintenance of thin-wall sections (0.100 in., tapering to 0.040 in.), a surface roughness not exceeding 250 micro-in., and the use of an aluminum alloy capable of providing a minimum tensile strength of 32,000 psi, a minimum yield strength of 20,000 psi, and a minimum elongation of 5%. The mechanical properties were to be checked on separately cast test bars taken from the same heat from which the casting was poured.

To obtain the minimum wall thickness desired (0.040 in.), the investment process with gravity pouring was selected. Although its mold-filling ability is inferior to that of aluminum alloy 356, alloy 195 was chosen, primarily because it would provide the specified mechanical properties. This combination of alloy and process proved unsuccessful; all castings were rejected because of cold shuts and misruns.

Next, a close-tolerance dry sand mold containing three equally spaced cavities around a sprue was tried. By spinning the mold at approximately 800 rpm, enough pressure was exerted on the molten aluminum to produce sound castings. The resulting mechanical properties and surface conditions were satisfactory also. From an analysis of the production record of this part, it was concluded that even a 0.095-in. section tapering to 0.035 in. could have been poured of alloy 195 without incurring an excessive number of rejections.

Selection Based on Quantity and Cost. When the quantity of castings to be produced is high, the use of more expensive tooling is justified. Example 387 in the article on Die Casting and Example 350 in the article on Permanent Mold Casting show how cost per casting is affected by quantity, and Example 350 shows how selection of molding process is determined by the quantity to be cast.

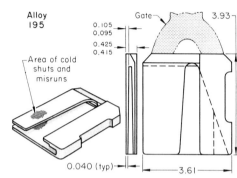

Fig. 21. Thin-wall fin-shoe slide for which the process was changed from gravity-pour investment casting to centrifuged dry sand casting, to prevent cold shuts and misruns (Example 480)

For many castings, such as the gearbox discussed in the following example, sand casting with simple pattern equipment is used during development, and then the process is changed to one better suited to volume production — to the quality required.

Example 481. Change From Sand Casting for Prototypes to Semipermanent Mold Casting for Quantity Production

During the development stage, a 12-lb gearbox casting for a business machine was cast from alloy 356 in green sand, using a simple split wood pattern and wood core boxes. The casting required five cores, which were made from an oil-sand mixture. Production rate was one casting per hour. With the completion of design changes, the casting was studied to determine the most suitable method for production in larger quantities.

Although the casting could have been produced at the required rate in sand molds by the use of two sets of patterns, three other important considerations (tolerances, reproducibility and cost) indicated the use of the semipermanent mold process (metal mold with shell cores). The metal mold would hold close tolerances on the outside of the casting, and the shell cores (five assembled into one core) would hold close tolerances on the inside of the casting.

A high degree of reproducibility was required because the castings were to be machined in two different plants, where inspection and setup sequences also would be somewhat different. The machined products were checked by identical gages at the customer's incoming inspection. Also, one of the cored surfaces was to be a starting point for some of the machining operations. The metal mold with shell cores provided better reproducibility than sand molds, and the cast surfaces were smoother. It was estimated that production costs would be lower for the semipermanent mold process.

In producing castings by the semipermanent mold process, a self-pouring, 18-by-24-in. casting machine was used. Molds were made of low-carbon steel and were coated with a proprietary graphite suspension. Molds were still usable after producing 30,000 castings, although they had been repaired several times by changing inserts in high-wear areas.

Pouring temperature was 1300 F when metal was poured in green sand molds. For the semipermanent mold process, pouring temperature was 1450 F and mold temperature was 700 to 800 F. Thirteen castings per hour were produced in semipermanent molds.

Where forging is competitive with casting, quantity is usually the deciding factor in selection of process. The ex-

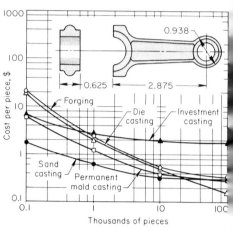

Quantity	Tooling cost(a)	Cost per piece(b)	Cost per piece, tools amortized
Die Casting(c)			
100	$1800	$0.75	$18.75
1,000	1800	0.15	1.95
10,000	3800	0.12	0.50
100,000	3800	0.12	0.16
Permanent Mold Casting(d)			
100	$ 550	$0.52	$ 6.02
1,000	900	0.33	1.23
10,000	900	0.28	0.37
100,000	900	0.28	0.29
Investment Casting(e)			
100	$ 375	$2.50	$ 6.25
1,000	375	2.30	2.67
10,000	375	1.90	1.93
100,000	375	1.80	1.80
Sand Casting(f)			
100	$ 130	$0.45	$ 1.75
1,000	260	0.36	0.62
10,000	390	0.30	0.33
100,000	390	0.30	0.30
Forging(g)			
100	$2000	$0.52	$21.00
1,000	2000	0.33	2.38
10,000	2000	0.28	0.50
100,000	2000	0.28	0.32

(a) Design and quality of tools based on pilot-run requirements for 100 and 1000 pieces and production-run requirements for 10,000 and 100,000 pieces. The 100,000 quantity would be produced at the rate of 10,000 pieces per month. (b) Not including amortization of tools. (c) A single-cavity die would be adequate for production of up to 1000 pieces. A multiple cavity die would be more efficient for the larger quantities. (d) A single-cavity mold would be adequate for 100 pieces. For 1000 pieces or more, a multiple-cavity mold would be used. (e) One set of tools would be capable of producing all quantities. (f) One pattern on a match plate would be sufficient to produce 100 pieces. For 1000 pieces, two patterns on a match plate, and for 10,000 and 100,000 pieces, three patterns on a match plate, would be used. (g) Assumes that one forging die would be adequate to produce all quantities.

Fig. 22. Cost of producing an aluminum connecting rod by four casting processes and as a forging, in various quantities (Example 482)

ample that follows presents costs for making a part in various quantities by four casting processes and by forging.

Example 482. Cost of Producing a Connecting Rod by Four Casting Processes and Forging (Fig. 22)

Figure 22 compares die casting, permanent mold casting, investment casting, sand casting and forging for producing the connecting rod shown. In making this comparison, the most favorable aluminum alloy for each process was assumed. Cost for various quantities is given in the table with Fig. 22, and type of cooling required for each quantity is summarized in the footnotes to the table. The effect of quantity on cost for each process is evident from the chart.

Straightening and Weld Repair

Warped or bent castings can be straightened in a press or by the use of hand tools. Special fixtures for straightening and checking castings are useful. If aluminum alloy castings require hot straightening, they must not be heated above their aging temperature, nor beyond a critical time limit. Heat treated castings should be straightened as soon after quenching as possible, before aging occurs. The need for straightening can be reduced by care in shakeout, handling, and stacking techniques.

Weld Repair. Welding is used to repair aluminum alloy castings, even those used in some high-stress applications. Welding will repair misruns, shrinkage, and surface defects. For some castings, weld repairing is less expensive than prevention of defects by redesign of the casting or by modification of the molding practice. Generally, however, welding cannot be used when the casting must be polished or anodized, because the welded zone will show.

For weld repair of castings for general applications, all defective areas should be cleaned of dirt and unsound metal; the welding rod should have the same composition as the casting; and welding should be done before heat treatment.

For high-stress applications, typical procedures for repair welding are:

1 Clean to remove dirt and to expose the entire defect. (The casting may be inspected by the fluorescent penetrant method.)
2 Weld to repair the defect, using the tungsten inert-gas process (preferably) and filler rod of the same alloy as the casting. Welders must be certified.
3 Inspect the weld radiographically.
4 Heat treat the casting.
5 Identify the casting with the standard weld symbol.
6 Finish the welded area to proper contour and smoothness.
7 Inspect the welded area by appropriate methods.

Sealing Procedures

Some porosity is to be expected in aluminum alloy castings. For many applications, porosity is not detrimental to the application, but when castings are to be subjected to internal or external liquid or gas pressure, the pores must be sealed.

Porosity often can be minimized or eliminated by changing the design of the casting, by revising the gating and feeding system, or by using proper techniques in melting and handling of the metal. Degassing the molten metal will reduce gas absorption and thereby decrease the number and the size of the pores.

There are two types of impregnants used for sealing castings — polyester resins and sodium silicate. Because of their low viscosity and surface tension, polyester-resin sealants have excellent penetration, filling minute porous areas readily during the impregnation cycle. Also, they are recommended for corrosion-resistance applications, because they have excellent resistance to aqueous atmospheres, petroleum products, glycols, alcohols, mild acids, and certain salts.

Sodium silicate sealant has less corrosion resistance than the polyester resins (partly because sodium silicate is water soluble), and therefore it is unsatisfactory for some applications. The curing and service temperature should be kept below 212 F to prevent the water from evaporating, which could break up the silicate deposited in the pores.

The steps for applying a sealant are similar for both the polyester resin and sodium silicate types:

1 Castings are cleaned of all foreign material.
2 Sealant is applied under vacuum in an autoclave.
3 Excess sealant is removed. Some sealants require a vapor degreasing operation, and others are removed by solvent cleaning.
4 Sealant is cured by placing the castings in an oven at the temperature specified for each type of sealant.

Casting Aluminum

Casting characteristics of aluminum foundry alloys enable the designer and metalworker to use aluminum castings for end-products ranging in size from an ounce or so to those weighing 18,000 pounds or more.

There are two general categories of aluminum casting processes. One group utilizes *metal molds,* and includes die and permanent mold casting; both in number of units produced, and in tonnage, these are are the major processes currently in use.

Also of vital importance to modern industry are the principal processes in the other chief casting category for aluminum, in which *refractory mold* materials are used instead of metals. These "refractories" include a variety of foundry sands and plasters, employed chiefly in the two types of casting names for these materials: *sand* and *plaster* casting.

Materials are often borrowed from one process and combined with those of another to produce castings having improved soundness, mechanical properties and/or dimensional control. Overall economy achieved by these techniques is measured against costs of producing the part by machining or other methods; savings frequently are considerable.

Many other materials and nearly all of the known special casting techniques also are used for aluminum in reproducing intricate designs, or meeting particularly exacting specifications. Investment casting (lost wax technique) and centrifugal casting (spinning a mold fixed to a long arm, to exert pressure on the molten metal) are examples of these techniques.

Average pouring temperature ranges used for casting aluminum, depending upon the alloy and the casting conditions, are:

Die casting	1150 to 1250°F
Permanent mold casting	1300 to 1400°F
Sand and plaster casting	1250 to 1400°F

Over 80% of all aluminum castings shipped each year in the United States are produced by either the die or the permanent mold processes.

Die Casting

Aluminum can be die cast in a single machine at the rate of 400 to 1,000 pieces per hour, when producing small parts in a multiple-cavity die. Die castings of aluminum range in size from a few ounces to more than 80 pounds. Large, single-cavity dies are used to cast a 25-pound component, for example, at rates averaging about 30 pieces per hour. Dies are initially relatively high in cost, but are economical for long runs; 200,000 to 1,000,000 pieces per die may be produced.

Cold-chamber machines are most suitable for long-run die casting aluminum because the shot cylinder, used to inject the molten metal into the closed die cavity, is outside the furnace on this type equipment. This avoids prolonged contact of the molten aluminum with the steel cylinder and plunger parts, which rapidly deteriorates the steel.

Press capacity is rated in tons of injection/locking pressure, which in turn is the chief factor in determining the maximum size of a die casting. In the mid 1950's, the largest die casting machines were 1,000 tons. Currently machines of 2,500 tons and more are available.

Aluminum die castings are used by every industry in a wide range of components. The principal alloys employed in the largest-volume applications are given in Table 8-1.

TABLE 8-1

Aluminum Alloys Generally Used in Typical Die Cast Products

Aluminum Alloy	Typical Die-Cast Products
Lawnmower housings, gear cases, air-cooled cylinder heads	380.0
Cooking utensils, cover plates, instrument cases	360.0
Pistons, connecting rods, engine housings	A413.0
Business machine frames, dental equipment, street lamp housings	413.0
Conveyor and escalator components, aircraft and marine fittings and hardware items	518.0

One complete die casting cycle consists of the following steps: (1) lubricating the open die and sleeve; (2) closing and locking the die; (3) ladling or pumping the molten aluminum into the water-cooled injection sleeve on the press; (4) actuating the hydraulic plunger to force the aluminum from sleeve chamber into die cavity; (5) maintaining correct pressure the required time to allow casting to solidify or "freeze" and (6) opening the die and ejecting the casting.

Permanent Mold Casting

A versatile foundry process, permanent mold casting is used to produce medium to long runs of aluminum castings, most of them weighing less than 20 pounds, and some as much as 200 pounds. Finish and detail are both generally excellent and metallurgical properties are superior to all other types of castings, except those made with special procedures and termed "premium quality" castings.

High-strength or high-temperature cast iron, containing small amounts of chromium, nickel and molybdenum are used for the metal molds and cores. Coring also is machined from die steel and may be a single piece, or segmented. When sand, plaster, carbon-dioxide-cured or shell cores are used alone or in combination with each other and/or with steel cores in permanent metal molds, the process is called *semi-permanent* mold casting.

Pressure-tightness is excellent in the fine-grained metal structure obtained in aluminum permanent mold castings. Aluminum foundry alloys typically used to make various types of products are listed in Table 8-2.

Variations of the permanent mold process range from filling the metal mold by gravity flow from a hand ladle to machine-fed fully automatic high-speed permanent molding setups.

In the former, mold and core movement and ejection of the solidified casting are accomplished manually. In the latter process, mold operation is fully automatic and is accomplished by electric eye and similar sensing devices, which actuate hydraulic or pneumatic pistons.

Automatic pouring is accomplished by suitable tilting furnaces or basins attached to mold as pouring crucibles. For *pressure permanent mold casting,* the mold cavity is filled with aluminum by a low-level vacuum applied to the cavity, or by enclosing the molds in a pouring furnace in which the atmosphere is under pressure. Both feeding and surface detail are improved.

Permanent mold casting quality is affected by the fluidity, feeding and resistance to hot cracking of the alloy, and by adequate solidification control, which is accomplished by satisfactory risering, proper gating, mold design, pouring technique, temperature control and mold coating. Similar procedures, but with their own design characteristics and separate values, are essential factors in producing quality sand castings.

Sand Casting

As in casting other metals with this time-honored foundry process, proper selection, control and processing of mold and cores sands have important effects on both production quality and cost. Both

TABLE 8-2
Typical Permanent Mold Aluminum Alloys

Carburetor bodies, waffle irons	443.0
Aircraft and missile components requiring high strength, impellers, timing gears, compressors	355.0, C355.0, 357.0
Machine-tool parts, aircraft wheels, pump parts, marine hardware, valve bodies	356.0, A356.0
Automotive and diesel pistons, pulleys and sheaves	F332.0
Ornamental hardware and architectural fittings	A514.0

TABLE 8-3
Representative Products Sand Cast in Various Aluminum Alloys

Pipe fittings, cooking utensils, ornamental parts. marine fittings	443.0
Air compressor fittings, crankcases, gear housings	319.0, 335.0 C355.0
Automotive transmission cases, oil pans, rear axle housings, water cooled cylinder blocks, pump bodies	356.0, A356.0, 357.0
Architectural and ornamental components, marine fittings, dairy and food handling equipment	F514.0
Aircraft fittings, truck and bus frame components, levers, brackets	520.0
General purpose sand castings that require strength without heat treatment or that need to be brazed	A712.0

natural and synthetic sands are used, the latter producing sound castings with only slightly rough surfaces and with high reliability, often at lowest cost.

Aluminum sand casting equipment and procedures are similar to those used for other metals, as is the versatility of the process. Almost any shape for which a pattern and coring can be made can be sand cast in aluminum. and there is no known maximum limit to size or weight.

While the process is most used for small quantities, production costs on long runs may be as low as those for permanent mold and, in some cases, as for die casting. This is made possible by the use of high-speed molding machines, conveyors, automatic pouring, and automatic knockout equipment.

Typical sand-casting aluminum-alloy combinations are given in Table 8-3.

TABLE 8-4
Mechanical Properties of Some
High Strength Aluminum Casting Alloys

Alloy	Tensile strength, psi		Yield strength, psi		Elongation, % in 2 in.	
	(a)	(b)	(a)	(b)	(a)	(b)
Sand Castings						
520.0—T4	42,000	32,000	22,000	17,000	12.0	3.0
Permanent Mold Castings						
356.0—T6	33,000	25,000	22,000	17,000	3.0	0.8

Alloy	Tensile strength, psi	Yield strength, psi	Elongation, % in 2 in.
Premium-Quality (Composite Mold) Castings(c)			
354.0—T62	50,000	42,000	2.0
C355.0—T62	44,000	33,000	3.0
A356.0—T62	40,000	30,000	3.0
A357.0—T62	50,000	40,000	3.0
359.0—T62	47,000	38,000	3.0

(a) Minimum guaranteed values for separately cast sand and permanent mold test bars. (b) Specimens cut from castings; values equal to 75% of minimum tensile and yield strength and 25% of elongation required of separately cast test bars (a). (c) Minimum properties of specimens cut from designated high-stress areas of castings; from Volume III, Aluminum.

TABLE 8-5
Comparison of Aluminum
Casting Methods(a)

	Die	Perma-nent mold	Sand	Plaster or invest-ment	Com-posite(b)
Strength	B	A	B	B	A
Structural density	C	A	B	B	A
Reproducibility	A	B	C	B	A
Pressure tightness	C	A	B	B	A
Cost per piece (c)	A	B	C	D	D
Production rate(c)	A	B	C	D	C
Flexibility as to alloys	C	B	A	B	B
Tolerances	A	B	C	A	A
Design flexibility	C	B	A	A	A
Size limitation	B	B	A	C	B
Surface finish	A	B	C	A	A
Time to obtain tooling	B	B	A	B	C
Pattern or mold cost(d)	C	B	A	B	D

(a) Ratings A, B, C and D indicate relative advantage, A being best. (b) Applicable to specific or critical areas of premium-quality castings in the permanent mold and plaster portions of the molds. (c) Although this rating covers the majority of castings, in the case of multiple patterns or mold cavities, sand or permanent mold may take first place. (d) The cost of die casting dies plus the cost of tooling for machining is frequently less than the same over-all cost for sand or permanent mold castings.

Other Casting Processes Used for Aluminum

Plaster Casting—Plaster molds of various types give fine reproduction of detail and surface finish and have excellent insulating value. This keeps the aluminum molten for longer periods so that it can completely fill narrow cavities, thus permitting thinner sections and adjacent thick and thin sections to be cast.

Tolerances are held sufficiently well to eliminate machining of many cast parts; however, close machining tolerances cannot be met and some allowance for metal removal by subsequent machinery must be made, if such is required. Mold and core patterns may be made of plastic or rubber, reproducing detail with high fidelity.

The plaster process combines the advantages of a liquid-mold-material method with those of based sand molding. Alloys used for sand casting generally are suitable for plaster casting. Bladed impellers of all types are typical of plaster-cast aluminum products.

Premium-Quality Casting—A number of conventional foundry processes are used in a selective manner to produce premium-quality castings in aluminum. Close dimensional, metallurgical and finish control is essential. Premium-quality techniques are employed at every step. The principal cost advantage over a fabricated assembly of high-strength wrought elements often lies in the elimination of machining. Comparative aluminum casting tensile values are given in Table 8-4.

Investment Casting—This is one of man's oldest known foundry processes. Investment casting employs a mold cavity made by dipping or pouring liquid mold material (such as a plaster slurry) around an expendable wax or plastic pattern and letting it dry. The mold is then heated to melt or burn the pattern away, leaving a cavity and a pouring sprue.

Surface detail is excellent and dimensional tolerances, which generally can be held to ± 0.0015 in. per in. on the pattern, are correspondingly close. Alloys 443.0 and 356.0 are the most popular for aluminum investment casting. Typical of the intricate parts produced by this method are instrument components, jewelry, art objects, dental fittings and equipment, sporting goods, and aerospace devices.

Centrifugal Casting—True centrifugal casting employs no central core because the cylindrical mold is spun while the metal is molten, forcing it against the walls farthest from the center of rotation, thus producing a hollow cylindrical casting. In *semi-centrifugal* casting, irregular contours inside the cylindrical casting are produced through the use of central cores of appropriate design. *Centrifuge casting* also uses centrifugal force to drive the molten metal against mold walls and into narrow cavities. It is employed for non-symmetrical shapes which cannot be rotated about their own axis. In this process, a central sprue connects to multiple molds mounted on the periphery of a wheel, which is rotated as the metal is poured. A variation employs a rotating arm, with a single mold mounted at its outer end. Properly designed mold, made of any suitable material may be used. Typical aluminum products made by this process include wheels, some fan blades and intricate rotor parts.

Application and product factors important in selecting principal aluminum casting process are summarized in Table 8-5.

Source: Metalworking With Aluminum, 2nd Ed., Aluminum Assn., Inc.

Section VII:
Machining

Machining of Aluminum Alloys

*By the ASM Committee on Machining of Aluminum Alloys**

ALUMINUM alloys can be machined rapidly and economically; because of their complex metallurgical structure, their machining characteristics are superior to those of pure aluminum.

Effect of Microstructure. The microconstituents present in aluminum alloys have important effects on machining characteristics: Nonabrasive constituents have a beneficial effect, and insoluble, abrasive constituents exert a detrimental effect on tool life and surface quality. Constituents that are insoluble but soft and nonabrasive are beneficial, because they assist in chip breakage; such constituents are purposely added in formulating high-strength free-cutting alloys for processing in high-speed automatic bar and chucking machines.

In general, the softer alloys — and, to a lesser extent, some of the harder alloys — are likely to form a built-up edge on the cutting lip of the tool; this edge consists of aluminum particles that have become welded to the tool edge because they were melted by the heat generated in cutting. Edge build-up can be minimized by using effective cutting fluids and by employing tools with surfaces that are free of grinding marks and scratches.

Alloys containing more than 10% silicon are the most difficult to machine, because hard particles of free silicon cause rapid tool wear. Alloys containing more than 5% silicon will not finish to the bright machined surfaces of other high-strength aluminum alloys, but will have slightly gray surfaces with little luster. Chips are torn rather than sheared from the work,

and special precautions (such as the use of lubricant-containing cutting fluids) must be taken to avoid buildup of burrs on cutting edges.

Cast Alloys. Cast alloys containing copper, magnesium or zinc as the principal alloying elements impose few machining problems. Tools with small rake angles normally can be used with little danger of burring the part or of developing buildup on the cutting edges of tools. Alloys having silicon as the major alloying element require tools with larger rake angles, and they are more economically machined at lower speeds and feeds.

Wrought Alloys. Most wrought aluminum alloys have excellent machining characteristics; several are well suited to multiple-operation machining. To utilize fully the free-machining qualities of aluminum alloys, thorough familiarity with recommended tool designs and machining practices is an essential requirement.

Strain-Hardenable Alloys. Alloys in this group (including commercially pure aluminum) contain no alloying elements that would render them hardenable by solution heat treatment and precipitation; however, they can be strengthened to some extent by cold work. In machining, a continuous chip is formed that must be directed away from the workpiece by tools with generous side and back rake angles, thus preventing scratching of the finished surface with the work-hardened chips. These alloys machine easily, although tool pressures are high as a result of high friction. To obtain good surface finish, sharp tools are mandatory, be-

cause the alloys are gummy. Machinability is improved by cold working; alloys in the full-hard temper are easier to machine to a good finish than those in the annealed condition.

Heat Treatable Alloys. Most of the alloys of this group contain fairly high percentages of alloying elements such as copper, silicon, magnesium and zinc. They can be machined to a good finish with or without cutting fluid, but a cutting fluid is recommended for most operations. Turnings usually occur as long, continuous curls, except for the free-machining alloys, which contain chip-breaking constituents.

Heat treatable alloys are more machinable in the heat treated tempers than in the softer as-fabricated or annealed condition.

Machinability groupings for aluminum alloys are useful in specifying tool forms. For this purpose, alloys are classified into five groups: A, B, C, D and E, in increasing order of chip length and in decreasing order of finish quality, as defined in the footnotes of Table 1. Ratings for most commercial aluminum alloys are given in Table 1, and typical chips for each rating are illustrated in Fig. 1.

Cutting Force and Power

The cutting force, and hence the power, required to machine aluminum is less than might be expected on the basis of its mechanical properties. Although the cutting force required to machine similar metals is often in direct proportion to tensile strength, this proportion is not necessarily valid with

*JOHN LONGABAUGH, *Chairman,* Chief Metallurgist, Outboard Marine Corp.; ALFRED A. BOULD, Assistant Section Chief, Facilities Dept., Grumman Aircraft Engineering Corp.; R. COUCHMAN, Assistant Chief, Fabricating Metallurgy Div., Alcoa Research Laboratories, Aluminum Co. of America.

JOHN H. DEN BOER, Metallurgical Supervisor, Alloys Plant, Reynolds Metals Co.; A. J. KAISER, Chief Tool Engineer – Metals, Pinsetter Plant, Bowling Div., Brunswick Corp.; VIRGIL J. KNIERIM, Staff Metallurgist,

Elbeeco Plant, Aircraft Div., Aeroquip Corp.; JOSEPH KOCHANEK, Manager of Production Engineering, Chandler Evans Corp.; WILL LADD, Assistant Head, Production Engineering, Globe Industries, Inc.; E. R. LOEBACH, formerly with Automotive Div., Studebaker Corp.

CARL REXER, Department Head, Apparatus and Optical Div., Eastman Kodak Co.; EARL J. ROBERTS, Senior Manufacturing Research Engineer, Lockheed-Georgia Co. Div., Lockheed Aircraft Corp.; ALFRED SPOLIDORO, Senior Engineer, Merrimack Valley Works, Western Electric Co., Inc.

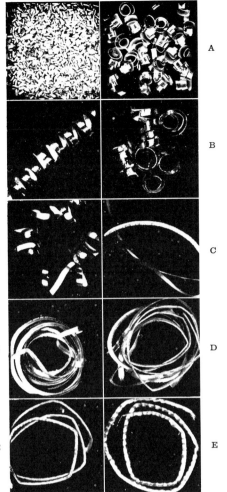

Table 1. Machinability Ratings of Aluminum Alloys

Alloy(a)	Tempers(a)	Rating(b)	Alloy(a)	Tempers(a)	Rating(b)
Casting Alloys			1100	O, H112, H12	E
13, 43	F	E	1100	H14 to H18	D
108, A108	F	B	2011	T3, T4, T6, T8	A
113, C113	F	B	2014(c)	O	C
A132	T551, T65	C	2014(c)	T3, T4, T6	B
F132	T5	C	2017	O	C
138	F	B	2017	T4	B
A140	F	A	2018	T61	B
142	T21, T571, T61, T77	B	2024(c)	T3, T4, T6, T8	B
195	T4, T6, T7, T62	B	2219	T3, T6, T8	B
214, A214	F	B	2618	T6	B
F214	F	B	3003(c)	O, H112, H12	E
218, B218	F	B	3003(c)	H14 to H18	D
220	T4	B	3004(c)	O, H112, H32	D
319, 333	F	C	3004(c)	H34 to H38	C
319, 333	T5, T6, T7	B	5005	O, H112, H12, H32	E
344	F	D	5005	H14 to H18	D
354	T61, T62	B	5005	H34 to H38	D
355	T51, T6, T61, T62, T7, T71	B	5050	O, H112, H32	D
C355	T61	B	5050	H34 to H38	C
356	T51, T6, T7, T71	C	5052	O, H112, H32	D
A356, A357	T61	B	5052	H34 to H38	C
357	T6	B	5056	O	D
359	T61, T62	B	5056	H18, H38	C
360	F	C	5083	O, H112, H321, H323	D
A360	F	C	5083	H131, H343	C
364	F, T5	C	5086, 5154	O, H112, H32	D
380, A380	F, T5	B	5086, 5154	H34 to H38	C
603, 607 (Ternalloy 5 & 7)	F	B	5257, 5357	O	D
A612, C612	F	B	5257, 5357	H25, H28, H38	C
D612 (40E)	F	B	5454, 5456	O, H112, H311	D
613 (Tenzaloy)	F	B	5454, 5456	H343	C
750, A750, B750	T5	A	5457	O	D
Red X8	T4, T51	B	5457	H25, H28, H38	C
Red X11 & X20	T5	E	5557, 5657	O	E
Tens 50	T6	B	5557, 5657	H25, H28, H38	D
Wrought Alloys			6061(c)	O	D
EC	O, H111, H112, H12	E	6061(c)	T4, T6	C
EC	H14 to H19	D	6063	O, T2, T4	D
			6063	T5, T6, T8	C
			6262	T4, T9	B
			6463	O, T1	D
			6463	T4, T5, T6	C
			7075(c)	T6, T73	B
			7079	T6	B
			7178(c)	T6	B

(a) Alloys and tempers are those commonly used. Alloy modifications designated by other second digits and temper variations designated by added numerals will have the same ratings.

(b) A, B, C, D and E are relative ratings in increasing order of chip length (see Fig. 1) and decreasing order of quality of finish and are defined as:

  A – Free cutting, very small broken chips and excellent finish
  B – Curled or easily broken chips and good-to-excellent finish
  C – Continuous chips and good finish
  D – Continuous chips and satisfactory finish
  E – Optimum tool design and machine settings required to obtain satisfactory control of chip and finish.

(c) Includes clad alloys and tempers.

Machin-ability rating	Alloy	Speed, sfm	Feed, ipr Left photo	Feed, ipr Right photo
A	....	2011-T3	400	0.0026	0.0060
B	....	2024-T4	100	0.0060	0.0104
C	....	6061-T6	400	0.0060	0.0104
D	....	3004-H32	400	0.0060	0.0104
E	....	1100-H12	400	0.0060	0.0104

Fig. 1. Typical chips for machinability ratings A to E (Table 1) for aluminum alloys. All chips were made with 20°-rake tool and 0.100-in. depth of cut.

dissimilar metals. For example, the common mechanical properties of 2017-T4 aluminum alloy and of hot rolled low-carbon steel are quite similar (Table 2) but, as Fig. 2 shows, the cutting force required in turning aluminum is only about 35% that required in turning low-carbon steel. Consequently, as shown in Fig. 3, the number of cubic inches of metal that can be removed

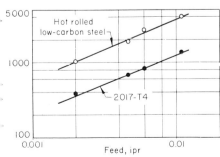

Fig. 2. Effect of feed on cutting force for low-carbon steel and aluminum alloy 2017-T4 with comparable mechanical properties

per minute per unit horsepower expended is approximately three times as great for aluminum alloy 2017-T4 as for hot rolled low-carbon steel of closely similar tensile strength.

Selection of Alloy and Temper

An application often dictates the use of a specific alloy or temper, or both. Under these conditions, composition cannot be changed for the sake of im-

Table 2. Comparison of Common Mechanical Properties of 2017-T4 Aluminum Alloy and Hot Rolled Low-Carbon Steel

Mechanical property	Aluminum alloy 2017-T4	Hot rolled low-carbon steel
Tensile strength, psi	63,800	65,200
0.2% yield strength, psi	40,300	40,200(a)
Elongation in 4 diam, %	26.0	32.7
Shear strength, psi	40,500	47,000
Brinell hardness number:		
500-kg, 10-mm ball	113	110
3000-kg, 10-mm ball	132	128

(a) Yield point is 44,800 psi.

proving machinability. However, there is often a marked difference in machinability among different tempers of the same alloy. Thus, it may be feasible to do some or all of the machining operations with the alloy in the most favorable condition for machining and then to convert the alloy to the temper specified for the end use.

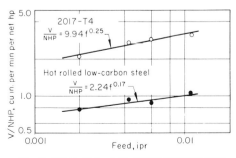

$$\frac{V}{NHP} = 9.94 f^{0.25}$$ 2017-T4

$$\frac{V}{NHP} = 2.24 f^{0.17}$$ Hot rolled low-carbon steel

Fig. 3. Effect of feed on metal removal rate per net horsepower for low-carbon steel and aluminum alloy 2017-T4 with comparable mechanical properties

Source: Metals Handbook, 8th Ed., Vol. 3, ASM

For some applications, two or more alloys are equally acceptable. Under these conditions, machinability can be a major consideration in making the final selection. For example, high-strength, free-cutting alloy 2011 can be machined to an excellent surface finish at high speed and feed, with a low rate of tool wear. The chips formed are finely broken. Alloy 2011 is therefore recommended for all general and high-production machining where a free-cutting alloy is desired. Alloy 2011 is especially desirable for multiple-operation machining, mainly because it machines with a broken chip.

Stock for multiple-operation machining is also available in alloys 2017, 2024, 6061 and 6262, in several heat treated tempers.

Alloys 2024-T4, 2017-T4 and 7075-T6 produce continuous chips that must be broken by a chip breaker in the tool. Alloys 6061-T6 and 5056-H38 are a little

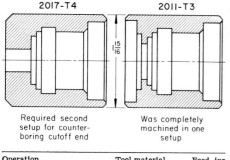

Operation	Tool material	Feed, ipr
Operations for Part Made of Alloy 2011-T3		
1 Subland drill ...	High speed steel	0.0035
Turn	High speed steel	0.0035
2 Step drill	Carbide	0.001
Form	Carbide	0.0007
3 Step drill	Carbide	0.001
4 Recess	Carbide	0.0006
5 Cutoff	High speed steel	0.0013

Speed was 915 rpm (460 sfm). Production rate was 103 pieces per hour (35 sec per piece).

Fig. 4. Substitution of alloy 2011-T3 for 2017-T4 to eliminate a second machining setup (Example 867)

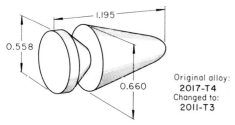

Fig. 5. Part for which a change from alloy 2017-T4 to 2011-T3 solved chip problem and increased production (Example 868)

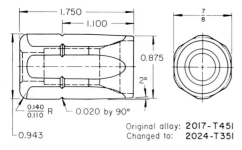

Fig. 6. Part for which change from alloy 2017-T451 to 2024-T351 increased production rate (Example 869)

more difficult to machine, and they produce chips that are difficult to control. The softer alloys 5052, 3003 and 1100 are likely to produce gummy chips. Wrought alloy 4032 and cast alloys 220, 13 and A132 are quite abrasive, and high rates of tool wear result.

Examples 867 through 871, which follow, describe applications in which a change to an alloy and temper having better machinability improved results. In Examples 872 and 873, only temper was changed (see also Example 910).

Examples 867 to 873. Alloy and Temper Selection for Better Machinability

Example 867 — 2017-T4 to 2011-T3 (Fig. 4). When the part shown in Fig. 4 was made of alloy 2017-T4, it had to go through a second processing step (which involved realigning the part) for counterboring the cutoff end, because stringy chips were formed. With alloy 2011-T3, all machining could be completed in the first sequence of operations by use of a recessing tool. This change in alloy resulted in a 38% increase in production rate and a decrease of 23% in manufacturing costs.

Example 868 — 2017-T4 to 2011-T3 (Fig. 5). The part shown in Fig. 5 was originally specified in 2017-T4 rod. During rough forming and skiving, chips packed in the tool area and in the bed of the machine, requiring frequent stopping to remove them. Under these conditions, one man could operate two

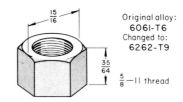

Fig. 7. Hexagonal nut for which a change from alloy 6061-T6 to 6262-T9 resulted in saving of material and less burring of the tapped thread (Example 870)

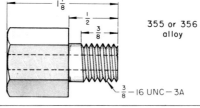

Operating conditions	Alloy 355	Alloy 356
Speed, sfm	150	130
Cutting fluid	Soluble oil	
Chaser life per set, pieces	800	750
Production, pieces per hr	300	275

Fig. 8. Threaded fitting produced from two different cast aluminum alloys (Example 871)

machines, and maximum production rate was 650 pieces per hour.

The alloy was changed to 2011-T3 to obtain smaller chips. It was then possible to reduce the cycle time from 3.2 to 2.8 sec by increasing speed from 2500 to 3000 rpm and changing feed. One man could then operate three machines, and production rate was increased to 1000 pieces per hour.

The weight of the blank, before it was machined, was 0.0472 lb; the weight of the part, after it was machined, was 0.0220 lb.

Example 869 — 2017-T451 to 2024-T351 (Fig. 6). In drilling and turning the part shown in Fig. 6 from ⅞-in. hexagonal bar stock, a change in material from 2017-T451 to 2024-T351 resulted in a large increase in production rate, because of increased speeds and feeds. Drilling feed was increased from 0.0035 ipr to 0.0068 ipr, and turning speed from 1062 rpm (280 sfm) to 1215 rpm (321 sfm). In addition, tool wear and size variation were reduced, and surface finish was improved.

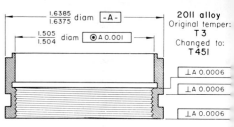

Operation	Tool material	Feed, ipr
1 Turn	High speed steel	0.0045
Drill	High speed steel	0.0045
2 Bore	Carbide	0.0045
Form	Carbide	0.001
3 Shave	Carbide	0.001
4 Internal form ..	Carbide	0.0009
5 Bore	Carbide	0.0015
Cutoff	High speed steel	0.001

Speed was 1277 rpm (550 sfm). Production was 300 pieces per hour (12 sec per piece).

Fig. 9. Part made of alloy 2011 for which change from T3 to T451 temper decreased cost 25% by eliminating bar-cutoff operation and 15-hr stress-relieving treatment for preventing out-of-roundness (Example 872)

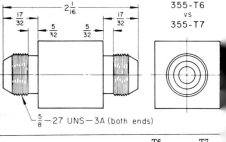

Item	T6 temper(a)	T7 temper(b)
Chasers used, sets(c)	1	2
Grinds, total number(d)	2	3
Total tool cost for run(e) ..	$5.60	$10.85
Tool life, pieces(f)	800	500
Production, pieces per hour	300	300

(a) Tensile strength, approximately 32,000 psi. (b) Tensile strength, approximately 35,000 psi. (c) Chasers cost $4.90 per set. (d) Cost for grinding $0.35 per grind per set. (e) 600 pieces per run. (f) Per set of chasers. Chasers not completely used during run.

Fig. 10. Part made of alloy 355 for which tool life in threading was improved by change from T7 to T6 temper (Example 873)

The blank weighed 0.117 lb, and 0.067 lb of stock was removed in machining in an automatic bar machine. When alloy 2017-T451 was used, 170 parts were produced per hour at a machining cost of 14¢ each. When alloy 2024-T351 was used production rate increased to 245 pieces per hour, and cost per piece decreased to 13¢.

Example 870 — 6061-T6 to 6262-T9 (Fig. 7). When alloy 6061-T6 was used for a hexagonal nut (Fig. 7), a lead of three threads chamfered on the tap form was required to produce a thread without tearing. A length of ³⁄₁₆ in. had to be cut off after tapping. After changing to the freer-cutting 6262-T9, lead was reduced to 1½ threads, so that only ⅛ in. had to be cut off. Material saving was 8.5%. Because 6262-T9 produced fewer burrs on the tapped threads, frequency of tool grinding was reduced.

With 6061-T6, the workpiece before tapping weighed 0.0560 lb, and with 6262-T9, weighed 0.0512 lb. The finished nut in both alloys weighed 0.0279 lb. Production rate was 890 pieces per hour with both alloys.

Example 871 — 356 vs 355 (Fig. 8). A turret lathe with a self-opening die was used for thread fittings made of two different cast aluminum alloys (355 and 356). As indicated in the table accompanying Fig. 8, tool life was greater in threading alloy 355, probably because of the lower content of silicon in 355. The increase in production rate was because of the greater speed used in threading.

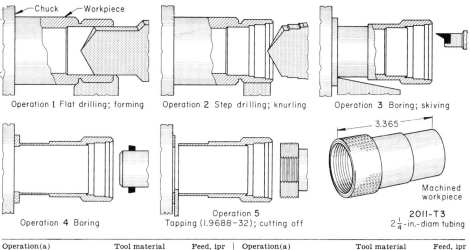

Operation 1 Flat drilling; forming Operation 2 Step drilling; knurling Operation 3 Boring; skiving

Operation 4 Boring Operation 5 Tapping (1.9688-32); cutting off 2011-T3 2¼-in.-diam tubing

Machined workpiece

3.365

Operation(a)		Tool material	Feed, ipr
1	Flat drill	Carbide	0.004
	Form	Carbide	0.001
2	Step drill	Carbide	0.004
	Knurl	High speed steel	0.012
3	Bore	Carbide	0.0007
	Skive	Carbide	0.002
4	Bore	Carbide	0.006
5	Tap	High speed steel	0.0015
	Cutoff	High speed steel	0.001

(a) For all operations, speed was 1044 rpm (618 sfm max), and cutting fluid was a low-viscosity mineral oil with 5% fatty additive. Cycle time was 30 sec per piece.

Fig. 11. Machining a part from tubing, which resulted in greater production rate and lower metal cost than when part was machined from bar stock (Example 874)

ing the 355 alloy. To obtain acceptable thread finish, a slower speed was required for the 356 alloy. Chasers cost $4.90 per set and each sharpening cost $0.35 per set.

Example 872 — 2011-T3 to 2011-T451 (Fig. 9). The part shown in Fig. 9 was originally machined from 2011-T3 bar stock. Because of the relatively large diameter and thin wall, an out-of-round condition ranging from 0.004 to 0.010 in. TIR resulted. It was necessary to cut the bars and to stress relieve them at 325 F for 15 hr before machining, to reduce runout to within 0.001 in. However, by changing to alloy 2011-T451, the long and costly heat treating operation was eliminated and the runout condition was adequately controlled. This change in temper specification resulted in cost savings of about 25%.

The details of procedure used in machining this part in an automatic bar machine are given with Fig. 9.

Example 873 — 355-T6 vs 355-T7 (Fig. 10). In die threading of the workpiece shown in Fig. 10, the T6 temper machined with greater tool life than the T7 temper of cast alloy 355. However, the T7 temper was chosen, because thread finish requirements could be met more easily on the harder temper.

Bar vs Tubing

Many parts can be machined equally well from either bar stock or tubing. When either of these product forms can be used, cost per piece machined is the determining factor. To determine cost, initial cost of bar versus tube, cost of additional machining to make the part from bar stock, and value of the additional scrap that results from machining bar stock must be considered. Because of the high cost of producing small tubing, total cost per piece machined may be greater when tubing of small sizes (less than about 1¼-in.-diam) is used. For parts requiring a diameter greater than 1¼ in., tubing is usually cheaper.

The following example describes an application where an appreciable saving was effected by changing from bar to tubing.

Example 874. Tubing vs Bar Stock (Fig. 11)

The part shown in Fig. 11 was originally machined from 2011-T3 bar stock. Changing to tubing (2¼-in.-diam, ⅜-in. wall) of the same alloy and temper resulted in a 38.4% increase in production rate and a 16% reduction in metal cost.

A speed of 1044 rpm (618 sfm) was used for machining both bar and tube. Cycle time was 30 sec per part when the tubing was used. The sequence of operations, tool material, and rates of feed for machining the part from tubing are given with Fig. 11.

General Machining Conditions

Power requirements for machining are proportional to speed and cutting force, and the power lost in bearings and gears of the machine increases with speed. Power requirements for machining aluminum decrease somewhat as the rake angle of the cutting tool is increased. Typical power requirements for several wrought and cast alloys, as measured at the cutter, using single-point tools with 0° and 20° rake angles are given in Table 3.

Cutting force for aluminum alloys can vary widely at low speeds, such as 100 to 200 sfm, rising momentarily to peak values several times higher than normal. At higher speeds, cutting force for machining 2011-T3 alloy rises slightly with increasing speed, but for most alloys it decreases. The over-all effect of speed on cutting force is small: As speed increases up to about 1000 sfm, cutting force changes slightly; above 1000 sfm, the effect of speed is negligible. Increasing the speed does not produce much more heat, but it does shorten the time available for removing the heat from the tool. The effect of speed on cutting force for several aluminum alloys is plotted in Fig. 12. Heating of tool surfaces is not

Table 3. Power Requirements for Machining Aluminum Alloys

| Alloy | Power, hp/cu in./min, for: | |
	0° rake	20° rake
F132-T5	0.20 to 0.50	0.20 to 0.40
356-T51	0.30 to 1.00	0.25 to 0.45
2011-T3	0.20 to 0.30	0.15 to 0.25
2024-T351	0.30 to 0.50	0.20 to 0.40
6061-T651	0.30 to 0.50	0.25 to 0.35

sufficient to have a harmful effect on a high speed steel tool until the speed exceeds about 700 sfm. High speed steel may be used for speeds well beyond this limit, but carbide tools are recommended for long tool life.

Cutting speed for aluminum alloys is determined by the limits of the machine tool and by the workpiece. Speeds as high as 15,000 sfm have been used in rare instances; even higher speeds have been achieved with experimental equipment. However, in most practice, mainly because of limitations imposed by available spindle speed, available horsepower, and dynamic balance of the part, machining speeds are seldom higher than 2000 sfm, and they are more commonly less than 1000 sfm, as indicated by the examples in this article.

Cutting speed should be as high as is practical, to save time and to minimize temperature rise in the part, as described later in connection with thermal expansion. As cutting speed is increased above 100 to 200 sfm, the probability of forming a built-up edge on the cutter is reduced, chips break more readily, and finish is improved.

Depth of cut should be as great as possible within the limits of part strength, chucking equipment, power of the machine tool, and amount of stock to be removed, to minimize the number of cuts required. As depth of cut is increased, cutting force increases. Depth of cut must be limited to a value that will not distort the workpiece or cause it to slip, nor overload the machine. Depth of cut in roughing may be as high as 0.250 in. for small work or up to 1.500 in. for medium or large work. At the opposite extreme, depth of cut in finishing is often less than 0.025 in.

Feed will depend on the finish desired, and the strength and rigidity of the workpiece and of the machine. Finishing cuts require a light feed of 0.002 to 0.006 ipr; rough cuts may use a feed of 0.006 to 0.080 ipr. Alloys with machinability ratings of D and E are best machined with a feed in the lower end of the range.

Tool Design

Tools intended for machining aluminum and its softer alloys should be ground to allow considerably more side rake and back rake than are customary when machining steel. Thus, they approach the contours of tools designed for cutting hardwood. The larger rake angles are recommended for finishing tools and for the machining of alloys that are not free-cutting, especially the softer alloys, which require exceptionally acute and keen cutting edges. Smaller rake angles can be used for the free-cutting alloys and for roughing cuts, where a sturdy tool is required for the heavier cuts and feeds employed. Suggested rake angles, as related to alloy machinability rating (see Table 1), are as follows:

Rating	Rake angle
A	0° to 20°
B	20°
C	20° to 30°
D	40°
E	40°

Tool forms for machining aluminum alloys with machinability ratings of A and B with single-point tools are given in Table 4. Variations of these may be desirable, depending on machining conditions or shape of the workpiece.

Clearance angle is important to proper functioning of the tool. Too small a clearance will permit the side or heel of the tool to rub the work and generate heat, whereas too large an angle will cause the tool to dig into the work and chatter. This angle must be carried around the side of the tool that advances into the work. For most applications, clearance angles of 6° to 10° are suitable. The side rake angle imparts to the tool a slicing action that assists materially in shearing the chip from the stock. This angle is important and should be held within the ranges recommended in subsequent sections of this article.

Cutting-Edge Finish. For maximum performance, it is essential that tool cutting edges be keen, smooth, and free from grinding-wheel scratches, burrs, or wire edges. Keen edges may be obtained by finish grinding on a fine abrasive wheel, and then lapping, or hand stoning with a fine oilstone. Neither the angles nor the contour of the cutting edge should be appreciably modified during tool finishing.

Tool Material

Water-hardening tool steel, such as W1, heat treated to Rockwell C 65 to 68, is an adequate cutting tool material when production runs are short and speeds are low. However, tool steels of this type soften rapidly if the temperature of the cutting edge exceeds 300 F. In addition, tools made from water-hardening tool steel have low resistance to edge wear.

High speed steel tools are generally satisfactory for machining all but the high-silicon alloys, which are quite abrasive and should be machined with carbide tools, unless runs are short; for short runs, high speed steel is usually satisfactory.

Carbide Tools. Because of the brittleness of the tool tip, the lip angle for carbide tools is usually greater than those recommended for high speed steel tools, in order to provide maximum support to the edge. This is shown in Table 4, where smaller relief angles are indicated for carbide tools. The rake angles can also be decreased to zero or negative to increase the lip angle, but negative rake angles are generally not recommended. When very light finishing cuts are made, it is sometimes feasible to reverse this practice and use higher rake angles and smaller lip angles.

Carbide tools retain sharp edges over a longer period between regrinds than carbon or high speed steel tools, provided they are not used for heavy intermittent cuts. A better finish is obtained, because of the great hardness of the tool tip compared to that of the stock. Carbide tools are particularly useful for machining alloys of high silicon content, many of which cannot otherwise be machined satisfactorily under production conditions.

Diamond tools are used only in operations where an exceptionally high finish is required, particularly on high-

silicon alloys, in which particles of free silicon will, in time, slightly dull the cutting edge of even carbide tools. Finishing cuts with diamond tools seldom exceed a few thousandths of an inch.

Diamond tools are usually made with either circular or faceted cutting edges, the latter being the more common. With the faceted cutter, there may be as many as five facets on one cutting edge, each varying in size from 0.02 to 0.06 in. Cutting angles of 74° to 90° and top rake angles of 6° to 10° are used. Rake should not be less than −6°. The tool should be set on, or slightly above, the centerline of the work.

Cutting Fluid

Cutting fluid for aluminum can be a soluble-oil emulsion, a mineral oil, or an aqueous chemical solution. Cutting oils that contain compounds of sulfur or chlorine or both are seldom used, and are not usually required for ma-

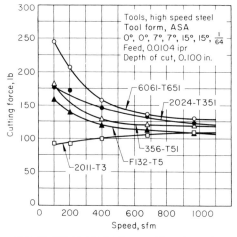

Fig. 12. Effect of speed on cutting force for five aluminum alloys

chining aluminum. Also, many of them will leave stains on the work. There are exceptions, however, as indicated in Example 894.

Soluble oil mixed with water in ratios of one part oil to 20 to 30 parts water is the cutting fluid most widely used for machining aluminum alloys. Soluble-oil emulsions are cheap, highly efficient for cooling and removing chips, and usually are adequate for preventing built-up edges. A soluble oil was used in most of the examples described in this article.

Mineral oil used as a cutting fluid may contain a fatty additive, such as lard oil, neat's-foot oil, oleic acid, or butyl stearate. However, mineral oil that contains no additive and that has a viscosity from 40 to 300 SUS at 100 F is most often used. As cutting speed is increased, viscosity of the oil should be decreased to provide easier flow, and therefore greater cooling. Straight mineral seal oil (viscosity of approximately 40 SUS at 100 F) has been effective in many applications (see Examples 885, 886 and 925). Kerosine, which is slightly less viscous than mineral seal oil, is also used (see Example 882).

Chemical solutions are effective as cutting fluids for machining aluminum, and are especially desirable when a

Table 4. Design of Single-Point Tools for Machining Aluminum Alloys of A and B Machinability Ratings

Tool details	High speed steel Rough-ing	Finish-ing	Carbide Rough-ing	Finish-ing
Back rake	20°	20°	20°	20°
Side rake	20°	20°	20°	20°
End relief	10°	10°	7°	7°
Side relief	10°	10°	7°	7°
End cutting edge ..	5°	5°	5°	5°
Side cutting edge ..	10°	10°	10°	10°
Nose radius, in. ...	0.063	0.20	0.063	0.20

transparent fluid is needed to permit viewing the work during machining. These solutions vary in composition, but most of them contain amines, nitrites, phosphates, borates, soaps, wetting agents, glycols and germicides. Some of these solutions stain aluminum alloys.

Continuous filtering of cutting fluids for removal of chips, slivers, grindings and other foreign material is especially desirable, because aluminum alloys are relatively soft and are easily damaged by a contaminated cutting fluid.

Stick grease is sometimes used in band sawing, circular sawing, and abrasive-belt, abrasive-disk or abrasive-wheel polishing and grinding, when requirements are not too severe and a flood of lubricant is not required.

Distortion and Dimensional Variation

Because aluminum alloys have a low modulus of elasticity (about 10 million psi), they will distort more than most metals for a given clamping or chucking force. Moderate clamping forces should be used, to avoid dimensional variations due to distortion. High clamping pressures are not required because cutting forces are low.

Thermal Expansion. The coefficient of thermal expansion of aluminum alloys (10 to 14 micro-in. per in. per °F is higher than that of most metals commonly machined. Therefore, dimensional accuracy of finished parts requires that the part be kept cool during machining. When turning between centers, it is important to avoid expansion, which will put excessive pressure on the centers. High cutting speed helps keep the part cool, because most of the heat introduced into the part during a given rotation is removed with the chip during the next rotation and the time for diffusion of heat is short. A cutting fluid is effective in removing heat that is not removed with the chips. Live centers are recommended to minimize frictional heating at the center. Dull tools cause a heat rise in the workpiece; therefore, cutting tools should be kept sharp.

Residual stress can be induced by dull or improperly designed cutter that cold works the surface; by excessive chucking or clamping force; or by faulty clamping. Distortion from residual stress is most noticeable in slender parts.

Distortion resulting from machining stresses can be minimized or eliminated either by employing a series of light cuts as the part approaches finished size, or by stress relieving the part be-

Table 5. Design of Single-Point Tools for Turning Aluminum Alloys
(See text for discussion of applications for high and low ends of the ranges.)

Back rake angle	10° to 30°
Side rake angle	10° to 40°
End relief angle	7° to 10°
Side relief angle	7° to 10°
End cutting-edge angle	5° to 20°
Side cutting-edge angle	10° to 30°
Nose radius	0 to 0.20 in.

Table 6. Nominal Speeds for Turning Aluminum Alloys

	Speed, sfm	
Operation	Non-heat-treated cast alloys	All other alloys and tempers
High Speed Steel Tools (M2 or T5)		
Single-point roughing ..	750	600
Single-point finishing ..	1000	800
Forming and cutoff	550	450
Carbide Tools (C-2)		
Single-point roughing(a):		
Brazed tips	1600	1100
Disposable tips	2000	1400
Forming and cutoff ...	1200	825

NOTE: Speeds for single-point turning are based on 0.150-in. depth of cut and feed of 0.015 ipr for roughing, and 0.025-in. depth of cut and feed of 0.007 ipr for finishing. Speeds for form turning are based on feeds of 0.0035, 0.003 and 0.002 ipr for tool widths of ½, 1 and 2 in., respectively. Speeds for cutoff are based on a feed rate of 0.002 ipr.

(a) For finish turning, use maximum speed of the machine and C-3 carbide.

tween rough and finish machining. For heat treatable alloys, it is preferable to do all rough machining on material in the solution-treated-and-aged condition, rather than in the less ductile annealed condition, because the less ductile structure is more machinable.

Distortion resulting from machining stress often can be minimized by purchasing the alloy in a stress-relieved condition, normally designated as T451, T651 or T851 if the metal has been stress relieved by stretching. Tx52 denotes stress relief by compression, and Tx53, stress relief by heat treating.

A major source of dimensional variation arises from the presence of movement or "play" in the feed mechanism of the machine. When the machining conditions or the tool cause forces that take up the play completely, no variations in dimensions are encountered. However, when low cutting forces (typical of those required for machining aluminum) are combined with a small feed and light cut, the total force may be insufficient to overcome tool-slide friction. Then, some movement may still occur, and the tool may float.

Turning

As indicated in Fig. 2 and 3, the cutting force, and hence the power, required to turn aluminum is considerably less than that for turning low-carbon steel of approximately the same hardness and tensile properties.

Tool Design. The recommended angles for a single-point lathe tool are given in Table 5. Cutting angles should be on the high end of the ranges for alloys that are not heat treatable or that are more ductile than the free-cutting alloys. (See Fig. 2 in the article "Turning" for definitions of the standard angles of a single-point tool.)

Because carbide tools are more brittle than high speed steel tools, they will chip or break when the cutting angles are too large. As a result, the lower half of each range given in Table 5 should be used for carbide tools. In turning free-cutting alloys, increasing the side relief or side rake angle, or both, will reduce the power required. Because the power needed for turning aluminum alloys is small (about one-third that needed for machining soft low-carbon steel), a turning tool ground with angles that are too large is likely to hog the work metal. The tool floats in operation, so that any backlash or play in the spindle or machine ways causes difficulty in holding tolerances. Tool life and surface finish also suffer. Surface finish can be improved by grinding a large nose radius on the turning tool. However, maximum nose radius depends partly on the allowable fillet on the workpiece when turning to a shoulder. As the nose radius is made larger, cutting force and horsepower requirement increase (see Fig. 3 in the article "Turning"). On small-diameter stock, increased cutting force may cause the work metal to

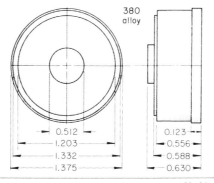

380 alloy

0.512
1.203
1.332
1.375

0.123
0.556
0.588
0.630

Item	Standard machine	Machine with tracer
Production, pieces per hour ..	19	67
Setup time, hr	2	1½
Tooling cost	$10	$2
Total pieces per setup	1000	1000

Fig. 13. Die casting that was faced and turned in an eight-station chucking machine with and without a tracer attachment (Example 875)

bend away from the tool, so that stock supports or rests are required. A nose radius that is too large also causes chatter, which results in poor surface finish and, possibly, tool breakage.

Another way to improve surface finish is to grind the end cutting edge of the tool parallel to the work for a width equal to 1½ to 2 times the feed rate in inches per revolution. This flat edge will cut behind the nose of the tool to smooth out ridges caused by the feed. Too wide a flat will cause chatter, and a negative angle will leave a taper equal in length to the width of the flat, on the work at the end of the turn.

Tool Honing. Honing of a carbide tool with a diamond-impregnated stone will improve the surface finish on the workpiece and will extend the life of the tool. Disposable carbide inserts have a honed edge when purchased, and no additional honing is necessary.

Tool Material. Carbide tools, either brazed-insert or disposable-insert, last far longer than high speed steel tools

for turning any aluminum alloy; for turning the high-silicon alloys, the use of carbide tools is mandatory for optimum results.

Speed used in turning aluminum alloys depends to some extent on the alloy and condition, but far more on tool material and type of tool — single-point, form or cutoff.

The effect of alloy composition and condition is small in selecting a turning speed, except for the non-heat-treated cast alloys. Nominal speeds for turning aluminum with high speed steel and carbide tools are given in Table 6. These speeds are based on feeds and depths of cut that are typical for turning aluminum alloys (footnote to Table 6), and on the assumptions that the setup is rigid, that a cutting fluid is used, and that the workpiece can be rotated to attain these surface speeds without causing excessive vibration. When conditions are below normal, speeds must be scaled down from those given in Table 6. Likewise, under nearly ideal conditions, higher speeds are often used successfully.

Feed. For rough turning with single-point tools, regardless of tool material, a feed of 0.015 ipr is common for all aluminum alloys. For finish turning, a feed of 0.007 ipr is recommended; this feed will usually result in a surface finish of 63 to 125 micro-in. Sometimes lighter feeds are used, to provide a better finish.

In form turning, width of the form tool is the major variable that affects the rate of feed. For all alloys and tool materials, a feed rate of 0.0035 ipr is generally satisfactory for form tools no wider than 0.500 in. Rate of feed should be decreased as width of the form tool increases. Feed rates of 0.003 and 0.002 ipr are recommended for form tool widths of 1 and 2 in., respectively.

For cutoff tools, a feed rate of 0.002 ipr is usually satisfactory, regardless of the alloy being turned, tool material, or width of the cutoff tool.

Depth of cut in turning aluminum often depends on the power available. The speeds given in Table 6 are based on 0.150-in. depth of cut for roughing and 0.025 in. for finishing. When power is available, roughing cuts of 0.250 in. are common. Finishing cuts of less than 0.025 often result in better surface finish.

Cutting fluid is recommended for turning all aluminum alloys (see section "Cutting Fluids" on the preceding page).

Procedures and equipment for turning that are the same for all metals are discussed in the article "Turning", which begins on page 1 of this volume. Because aluminum alloys are far less sensitive to abrupt changes in speed,

Table 7. Nominal Speeds and Feeds for Boring Aluminum Alloys

	Speed, sfm	
Boring operation	Non-heat-treated cast alloys	All other alloys and tempers
High Speed Steel Tools (M2 or T5)		
Roughing (feed, 0.015 ipr)	675	550
Finishing (feed, 0.008 ipr)	750	600
Carbide Tools (C-3)		
Roughing (feed, 0.020 ipr)	1450	1000
Finishing (feed, 0.010 ipr)	1600	1100
Depth of cut: rough, 0.10 in.; finish, 0.010 in.		

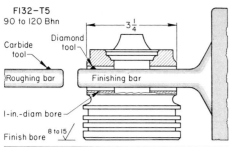

Carbide tool
Diamond tool
Roughing bar
Finishing bar
1-in.-diam bore
Finish bore 8 to 15
3 1/4

Speed, rough and finish .....3340 rpm (870 sfm)
Feed, rough and finish ....4.5 ipm
Metal removed:
  Rough boring ....0.050 in.
  Finish boring ....0.010 in.
Length of cut ....3¼ in.
Number of passes ....1 rough, 1 finish
Cutting fluid ....Soluble-oil:water (1:25)
Production rate ....212 pieces per hour

Tolerance, rough bore ....±0.001 in.
Tolerance, finish bore ....±0.0004 in.

Fig. 14. Rough and finish boring of two in-line holes in a permanent mold casting (Example 876)

feed and depth of cut than many other metals, they are especially well adapted to turning in automatic equipment. The following example compares productivity, setup time, and tooling cost for turning and facing aluminum die castings in a standard chucking machine, compared with a chucking machine equipped with a tracer attachment. Various form turning and cutoff operations are described in the examples in the section on Multiple-Operation Machining, page 454 in this article.

Example 875. Turning With an Automatic Tracing Attachment (Fig. 13)

Use of an automatic tracing attachment on an eight-station chucking machine resulted in lower tooling costs and a higher production rate in machining the alloy 380 die casting shown in Fig. 13. Machining consisted of facing and turning the 0.512, 1.203, 1.332 and 1.375-in. diameters. A 1-to-20 mixture of soluble oil and water was used as the cutting fluid. Comparative data obtained in a standard chucking machine and in a similar machine with tracer are shown in the table accompanying Fig. 13.

Boring

Boring of aluminum alloys, particularly the alloys with high silicon content, requires the use of tools with acute rake and clearance angles. In general, rake angles are increased as silicon content is decreased. Recommended radial or side rake angles range from 5° to 15°; axial or back rake angles, from 0° to 30°. Clearance angles are held to 10°.

Tool Material. Although high speed steel tools are used to some extent for boring aluminum, carbide tools permit higher surface speeds (up to 1000 sfm or more), with markedly longer tool life. Carbide cutters readily yield surface finishes of 10 to 20 micro-in.

When used in conjunction with precision boring machines, diamond tools can produce surface finishes of 1 micro-in. They are also capable of holding size over a long production run. If the cut is continuous and the work metal contains no hard spots, diamond tools are most effective in boring the abrasive high-silicon alloys.

Tool Sharpening. For optimum tool life, cutting edges and adjacent surfaces must be free of burrs and

scratches. Hand stoning of cutting edges with an oil stone is recommended. When a carbide boring tool is sharpened with a 400 or 500-grit diamond wheel, surface finishes of 3 to 4 micro-in. can be obtained.

Speed and Feed. The optimum speed for boring aluminum alloys depends somewhat on alloy and temper, but largely on tool material and whether the operation is roughing or finishing. Selection of feed depends largely on tool material and whether the operation is roughing or finishing.

Nominal speeds and feeds for rough and finish boring with high speed steel and carbide tools are given in Table 7. Speed is increased for a shallower depth of cut and lighter feed, regardless of alloy or tool material. Under some conditions, speeds much higher than those shown in Table 7 can be used successfully. For instance, in Example 880, speed of boring is 2930 sfm, which is nearly five times the average of the speeds given in Table 7 for boring with high speed steel tools; however, the boring tool used in Example 880 was engaged for only a fraction of each revolution.

Depth of Cut. Speeds and feeds given in Table 7 are based on a 0.10-in. depth of cut for roughing and 0.010 in. for finishing. Depth of cut is sometimes greater than 0.10 in. for rough boring if power is available and the setup can be made sufficiently rigid. Finishing cuts significantly less than 0.010 in. in depth are seldom used.

Cutting fluid is recommended but boring has been done dry. There is usually some sacrifice of productivity, dimensional accuracy or surface finish when aluminum is bored without a cutting fluid. A mixture of one part soluble oil to 20 to 30 parts water is most commonly used; also, mineral oil, or mineral oil mixed with up to 50% lard oil, is often used, especially when the best possible surface finish is desired. Sometimes mixtures of kerosine and lubricating oil are used, as in Example 880.

Procedures and equipment common to the boring of all metals are covered in detail in the article "Boring", in this volume. Types of machines that are used are listed on pages 20 and 21. Tools are discussed on page 22. Specific procedures for aluminum alloys are described in the five examples that follow.

Example 876. Boring of In-Line Holes in an Automotive Piston (Fig. 14)

Figure 14 shows the technique used for boring two in-line piston-pin holes. Rough boring was done with a carbide tool that entered from the left. As the rough boring tool retracted, a diamond finishing tool entered from the right and finish bored both holes. Boring was done in a six-spindle, double-end horizontal boring machine equipped with three fixtures for boring three pistons in one cycle. Details of the operation are given with Fig. 14.

Example 877. Multiple Boring of a Die Casting (Table 8)

Five different diameters were rough bored and three diameters were finish bored in an alloy 380 die-cast gear box. Boring tool details are shown in Table 8. Roughing and fin-

Table 8. Rough and Finish Boring of an Alloy 380 Die Casting (Example 877)

Conditions or Results for All Operations

Boring machine ...2-spindle, driven by 15-hp motor, hydraulically operated across table	Tool life per grind, roughing ......2000 pieces
Tools ....Carbide, double-end(a)	Tool life per grind, finishing ......1000 pieces
Tool angles, roughing:	Speed, roughing and finishing ......1000 rpm
Radial rake ....0°	Cutting fluid ....Soluble-oil:water (1:25)
Axial rake ....15°	Setup time (permanent setup) ....3 hr
Clearance ....10°	Downtime for changing tools ....1 hr
Tool angles, finishing:	Cycle time, roughing and finishing: 0.0730 hr
Radial rake ....15°	Production rate ....14 pieces per hour
Axial rake ....0°	Tolerance, significant dimensions ...0.0006 in.
Clearance ....10°	Surface finish ....40 micro-in.
	Weight of finished casting ....18 lb, 7 oz

Operation 1. Rough Bore 1.687-In.-Diam Clearance Hole

Speed ....450 sfm
Feed ....0.004 ipr
Depth of cut ....1/16 to 1/8 in.

Operation 2. Rough Bore 1.860-In.-Diam Hole to 1.875-In. Diam

Speed ....503 sfm
Feed ....0.004 ipr
Depth of cut ....1/16 in.

Operation 3. Rough Bore Clearance Hole to 2.125-In. Diam

Speed ....556 sfm
Feed ....0.004 ipr
Depth of cut ....Up to 1/8 in.

Operation 4. Rough Bore 2.430-In.-Diam Hole to 2.4408-In. Diam

Speed ....640 sfm
Feed ....0.004 ipr
Depth of cut ....1/16 to 1/8 in.

Operation 5. Rough Bore 3.610-In.-Diam Hole to 3.625-In. Diam

Speed ....960 sfm
Feed ....0.004 ipr
Depth of cut ....Up to 0.590 in.

Operation 6. Finish Bore 1.875-In.-Diam Hole to +0.001, −0.000 In.

Speed ....450 sfm
Feed ....0.004 ipr
Depth of cut ....0.007 in.

Operation 7. Finish Bore 2.4408-In.-Diam Hole to +0.0006, −0.0000 In.

Speed ....640 sfm
Feed ....0.004 ipr
Depth of cut ....0.005 in.

Operation 8. Finish Bore 3.625-In.-Diam Hole to +0.002, −0.000 In.

Speed ....960 sfm
Feed ....0.004 ipr
Depth of cut ....0.007 in.

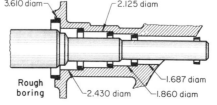

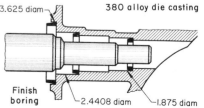

(a) Roughing tool, ½ by ⅝ in.; fixed. Finishing tool, mounted in bar with 0.003-in. float.

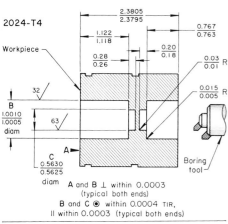

Workpiece

A and B ⊥ within 0.0003
(typical both ends)
B and C ⊙ within 0.0004 TIR,
ǁ within 0.0003 (typical both ends)

Speed ....1200 rpm (318 sfm)
Feed ....1.4 ipm
Cutting fluid ......Kerosine plus proprietary oil
Production rate ....9 pieces per hour
Tool life per grind ....800 lineal in.

Fig. 15. Rough and finish boring of a heat treated aluminum alloy forging (Example 878)

ishing operations were done in the same machine. The roughing cutters were held in fixed position; finishing cutters were permitted to float about 0.003 in. Additional details of the boring operations are given in Table 8.

Example 878. Boring of Concentric Holes (Fig. 15)

Two small and two large holes were rough and finish bored from opposite sides of a heat treated aluminum forging, as shown in Fig. 15. It was required that the large and small holes be concentric within 0.0004 in. TIR, parallel within 0.0003 in., and square with the surface within 0.0003 in. The operation was done in a double-end, precision boring mill, and carbide tools were used. Details are given with Fig. 15.

Example 879. Boring With Numerical Control (Fig. 16)

A connecting-rod forging (Fig. 16) was loaded into a multiple-station milling fixture with numerical control that permitted milling all boss faces to required thickness at one setting by rotating the machine table through 180°. Hole locations were established by center drilling on the same program, and holes were drilled, leaving 0.040 in. of stock to be removed by a single-point boring tool. Boring speed was held to 196 sfm to minimize whip of the tool holder assembly. Machining and tooling details of the boring operation accompany Fig. 16.

Example 880. Boring to Produce a Concave Surface (Fig. 17)

The concave surface of a plunger top (Fig. 17), which was used to provide the shape of the bottom of aluminum ingots as they were cast, was produced by boring 6-in. plate in a 10-hp horizontal boring mill. The T4 high speed steel tools were hand ground, using a back rake angle of 25° to 30° and side rake angle of 0° for roughing. The same back rake angle was used for the finishing tool, but the side rake angle was increased to 30°. Additional details are given in Fig. 17.

Planing and Shaping

Techniques and equipment used for planing and shaping of other metals are generally applicable to aluminum alloys. Description of planing methods is presented in the article "Planing", starting on page 45. Similar information for shaping appears in the article "Shaping", starting on page 52.

Planing. Either high speed steel or carbide tools for planing aluminum usually have a back rake angle of 30° or more (sometimes as much as 60°) and 0° side rake. A speed of 300 sfm is

generally recommended as maximum; however, this speed is higher than can be obtained with most planers.

Roughing feeds are about 0.090 in. per stroke when depth of cut is near the recommended maximum of ½ in. When shallow cuts are necessary (for lack of power or other reasons), a heavier feed can be used. For a 0.10-in. depth of cut, feed can be increased to about 0.125 in. per stroke.

Finish planing of aluminum alloys is usually done with a cut no deeper than 0.010 to 0.015 in. and a feed equal to three fourths the width of the broadnose finishing tool (see the section on planer tools, in the article "Planing", in this volume).

Aluminum alloys are often planed without a cutting fluid. A cutting fluid is helpful in producing a better surface finish, but flooding with cutting fluid is seldom feasible. When surface finish is a primary objective, application of a mixture of kerosine and lubricating oil, or of kerosine and lard oil, by means of

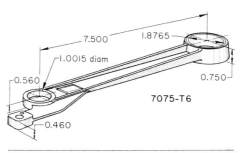

7075-T6

Tool material ....High speed steel
Radial and axial rake angles ....15°
Clearance angle ....8°

Operating Conditions

Speed ....400 rpm (196 sfm max)
Feed ....0.006 ipr
Cutting fluid ...Soluble-oil:water (1:25); flood

Tolerance and Finish

Tolerance ....±0.0005 in.
Surface finish of bore ....40 micro-in.

Fig. 16. Connecting-rod forging that was milled, drilled and bored (3 pieces per hour) with numerical control. Data in table are for boring. (Example 879)

a swab is common practice. Sprayed cutting fluid is effective. Soluble-oil mixtures are ordinarily used in cutting-fluid spray systems.

Typical techniques and operating conditions for planing of aluminum are described in the following example.

Example 881. Planing a Mold Assembly (Table 9)

A subassembly of alloy 3003 sheet was used in a mold for direct chill casting of aluminum. The bottom edge of the mold had to be beveled so that water flowing down the mold would be directed toward the ingot. The bevel was planed on the sheet before it was rolled into a cylinder. Lengths and widths of the sheets to be beveled varied according to the size of mold being constructed. The surface of the bevel had to be smooth enough so that water could flow without deflection; surface roughness was 16 micro-in. In planing this workpiece, attempts were made to use more than one tool at a time, but this proved difficult because chips could not be disposed of readily. Tool and processing details are given in Table 9.

Shaping. Tool forms, tool materials, and cutting fluids for shaping aluminum are the same as for planing.

Maximum speed in shaping is usually the maximum ram speed of the machine. Feed and depth of cut also depend to some extent on machine capabilities. A feed of 0.020 to 0.030 in. per stroke for roughing and about 0.010 in. per stroke for finishing are common. Depth of cut is often as much as 0.10 in. for roughing and 0.020 in. or less for finishing. Typical practice for shaping is given in the following example.

Example 882. Machining Ingot Slices in a Shaper (Table 10)

Cast ingot slices 10 in. square were shaped in a 12-in. crank shaper. The same shaping practice was used on all aluminum alloys, and production rate varied from 5 to 15 min per slice. Surface finish was 63 micro-in. Table 10 gives tool and processing details.

Broaching

All aluminum alloys can be broached successfully with standard broaching equipment, and by the same general procedures as for other metals. However, better surface finish and dimensional accuracy are obtained with heat treated alloys. Details of equipment and procedures that are common to broaching of all metals are dealt with in the article "Broaching", which begins on page 58 in this volume.

The principal limitation in broaching aluminum is the difficulty in maintaining an accurate relation between the broached hole and other surfaces of the workpiece, even when the starting hole is accurately located.

Tool Material. The general-purpose high speed steels, such as M2, are used for most tools for broaching aluminum. In some high-production operations, especially when broaching high-silicon alloys, broaches made of the more highly alloyed high speed steels or of carbide have proved economical. Surface treatments such as chromium plating or oxidizing help to prolong the life of high speed steel broaches.

A fine finish on the tool can be important. In one application, the life of a high speed steel broach was in-

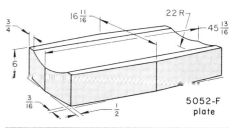

5052-F plate

Speed ....255 rpm (2930 sfm)
Feed, roughing ....0.025 ipr
Feed, finishing ....0.0125 ipr
Depth of cut, roughing ....0.250 in.
Depth of cut, finishing ....0.015 to 0.025 in.
Cutting fluid ....Kerosine:lubricating-oil (1:1);
150 sus at 100 F
Setup time ....45 min
Downtime for changing tools ....15 min
Production rate ....2 to 3 pieces per hour
Tool material ....T4 high speed steel
Tool life per grind ....20 to 30 pieces

Tolerance on significant dimensions .....¹⁄₆₄ in.
Surface finish ....64 micro-in.

Rough boring was done in two or three passes, depending on setup; finish boring, in one pass. Roughing and finishing tools were on the same boring bar, which was 4 in. in diameter and supported at one end.

Fig. 17. Plunger top on which concave surface was produced by boring (Example 880)

creased from 2000 to 7400 pieces when the cutting edges were wet blasted with a superfine abrasive.

Broach Design. In rough broaching, a coarse tooth pitch is desirable, with only two or three teeth in contact and cutting at any one time. For internal finish broaching, best results are obtained if only two teeth are cutting; in external finish broaching, it is often best to have only one tooth engaging at a time.

Broaches used for aluminum should have a face angle of 10° and a land and clearance angle of 3½° for external surface broaching, and of 2° for internal broaching. Although a large clearance angle provides better cutting action, it markedly reduces broach life. Thus, clearance angles should be kept to a minimum to reduce loss of size when the broach is sharpened.

Speed and Feed. A speed range of 30 to 50 sfm is generally recommended for broaching aluminum alloys. When rigidity, supply of cutting fluid, and hardness of the work metal are nearly ideal, the upper portion of the range can be used. When one or more of these conditions is less than ideal, the speed may be reduced.

Greater feed per tooth (chip load) is recommended for broaching aluminum alloys than for steel. A feed of 0.006 in. per tooth is usually optimum for spline broaching and about 0.003 in. per tooth for broaching round holes.

Cutting fluid is required for best results. A copious supply of soluble oil mixed with water is satisfactory for most applications, although mineral oil, or mineral oil mixed with lard oil, will usually improve surface finish. (See the section on Cutting Fluids, in this article.)

Production Practice. The four examples that follow give details of typical practice in broaching aluminum. For the four different workpieces described in these examples, broaching was the most feasible and least costly method of obtaining the required results. See also Example 128 in "Broaching".

Example 883. Broaching of Internal Splines (Fig. 18)

Internal splines were broached in a 2017-T4 aluminum clutch housing (Fig. 18). The splined hole contained eight teeth with 32 diametral pitch, 20° pressure angle, and partial dedendum; internal diameter was 0.2185 in. The length of the broaching cut was 0.295 in. The pull broach (details in Fig. 18) was made of high speed steel, and broaching was done in a 1-ton vertical machine. Processing data are given in the table accompanying Fig. 18.

Example 884. Broaching of External Splines (Fig. 19)

External splines were broached in the 2.027-in. diameter of a workpiece made from 2¹¹₁₆-in.-diam 2011-T3 bar stock (Fig. 19). Tolerance was ±0.001 in. and surface finish was 16 micro-in. The broach, made of M3 high speed steel, was pushed over the workpiece by a 1200-lb load. Processing details are given with Fig. 19.

Example 885. Broaching in a Single-Spindle Automatic Bar Machine (Fig. 20)

Internal splines were broached in a workpiece fabricated from 1-in.-diam 2011-T3 bar stock (Fig. 20). Broaching in a single-spindle automatic bar machine, in conjunction with other machining operations, proved the most economical procedure for making this workpiece, even though the machine spindle had

Table 9. Planing Alloy 3003 Mold Assembly (Example 881)

Machine	Horizontal planing mill, 30-hp motor, 33-ft bed
Tool material	High speed steel
Tool angles	60° back rake, 0° side rake

Operating Conditions

Speed	100 sfm
Feed	0.020 in. per stroke
Depth of cut	¼ in.
Cutting fluid	Kerosine:lubricating-oil (1:1); 150 sus at 100 F
Setup time	4 to 5 min
Downtime for tool change	15 min per shift
Production rate	4 to 5 pieces per hour
Tool life	Approx 40 pieces per grind

Table 10. Shaping Aluminum Alloys (Example 882)

Machine	Shaper with 12-in. crank, 2-hp motor
Tool material	High speed steel
Tool design	30° back rake, 0° side rake, ⅛-in. nose radius

Operating Conditions

Speed	120 strokes per min (220 sfm avg)
Feed:	
Roughing	0.025 in. per stroke
Finishing	0.010 in. per stroke
Depth of cut:	
Roughing	0.090 to 0.100 in.
Finishing	0.020 in.
Cutting fluid	Kerosine
Setup time	5 min
Downtime for changing tools	2 min
Production time	5 to 15 min per piece
Tool life	20 pieces per grind

to be completely stopped during broaching. The broach was made of M3 (class 1) high speed steel. Additional processing details are given in the table with Fig. 20.

Example 886. Broaching in a Multiple-Spindle Automatic Bar Machine (Fig. 21)

Both internal and external splines were broached in a workpiece made from ⅝-in.-diam 2011-T3 bar stock. Broaches were made of T2 tool steel, and broaching was done in a multiple-spindle automatic bar machine. During broaching, both workpiece and broach rotated at 3000 rpm. Details of the workpiece and the broaches are shown in Fig. 21; operating conditions and results are given in the table that accompanies Fig. 21.

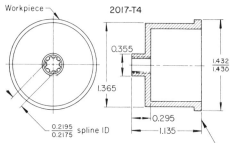

Speed	30 sfm
Feed per tooth	0.002 in.
Length of stroke	6 in.
Cutting fluid	Soluble-oil:water (1:25)
Setup time	30 min
Production rate	180 pieces per hour
Tool life per grind	2000 pieces
Total tool life	40,000 pieces

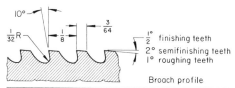

Fig. 18. Clutch housing and details of broach used for producing the internal splines (Example 883)

Drilling in Drill Presses

Although standard twist drills and drilling equipment used for steel may be employed in drilling aluminum alloys, optimum results require drills of special design, as well as higher rotational speeds and heavier feeds. Drills for aluminum normally are made with deep, well-polished flutes, narrow margins, and large helix angles. Proper drill design and drilling practice will frequently permit the removal of three to four times as much aluminum as steel per unit of power. The article

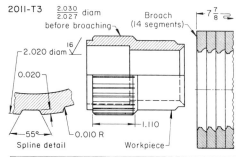

Speed	3½ strokes per min
Feed per tooth	0.020 in.
Cutting fluid	Soluble-oil:water (1:25)
Production rate	200 pieces per hour
Tool life per grind	1200 pieces

Fig. 19. Broaching external splines (Example 884)

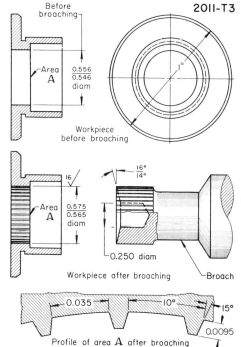

Feed (see note below)	0.015 ipr
Depth of cut	0.0095 in.
Cutting fluid	Mineral seal oil
Production rate	180 pieces per hour
Tool life per grind	25,000 pieces
Tolerance	±0.005 in.
Finish obtained	16 micro-in.

NOTE. Because of the short stroke, it was necessary to produce full tooth form with the front edge of the broach, as in push-pull broaching. Feed of 0.015 ipr refers to elapsed time based on normal spindle speed, although the spindle was stopped during broaching.

Fig. 20. Broaching internal splines in a single-spindle automatic bar machine (Example 885)

"Drilling", starting on page 75, discusses general equipment and practice.

For drilling in drill presses, the helix angle of the drill should be increased with the depth of the hole to be drilled, from a low-helix 24° angle for very shallow holes in thin stock, to a high-helix (40° to 48°) angle for deep holes — for which freer cutting is important (see Table 11).

The high-helix drill has a more acute cutting angle, resulting in more rapid penetration, and freer and cleaner cutting. Lands and margin are narrower than on the low-helix drill, resulting in reduced friction and increased chip space in the flutes. The slightly greater resistance to chip movement can be overcome by polishing the flutes and by supplying ample cutting fluid. This type of drill is recommended for deep holes, but is unsuitable for drilling thin stock because of its tendency to "hog in".

A twist drill with a 28° helix is suitable for holes of medium depth, up to about six drill diameters, whereas a drill with a 24° (or less) helix is recommended for thin stock, because it has less tendency to overfeed.

The point angle supplied on standard twist drills is 116° to 118°. The angle should be about 130° to 140° for drilling most aluminum alloys, to facilitate chip removal and minimize burring. However, drills for high-silicon alloys should have a less obtuse point, down to about 90°, for ease of penetration. For drilling thin sheet, the point angle should be very obtuse, to permit the drill to cut to its full diameter before the point breaks through. With this type of drill, a spur point may be necessary to assist in centering.

The standard lip clearance of 12° to 13° should be increased to about 17° for heavy feeds and for softer alloys. Insufficient lip clearance will cause excessive drill breakage. The drill cutting lips must be keen and smooth, and all surfaces over which the chip passes must be polished to minimize friction and chip buildup. Recommended point angles, helix angles, and lip clearances are summarized in Table 11.

Drill Material. Most drills for aluminum are made of high speed steel; M1, M7 and M10 are the most common grades. Only rarely can the extra cost for drills made of a more highly alloyed grade of high speed steel or of carbide be justified for conventional drilling in drill presses.

Speed and Feed. Because, with most drill presses, the peripheral speed of small-diameter drills is relatively low, they may be operated at the maximum efficient rotational speed of the machine. In general, high speed steel drills can be operated at a maximum of about 600 sfm. When variable speed is available, drill life can be increased in drilling deeper holes by bringing the drill up to speed gradually.

Because of the ease of penetrating most aluminum alloys, feeds up to twice those used for drilling steel can be employed. Feed varies with drill diameter, the larger-diameter drills permitting heavier feeds. A feed of 0.001 ipr is recommended for 1/16-in.-diam drills. The feed is increased to 0.003 ipr for 1/8-in.-diam drills, 0.007 for 1/4-in.-

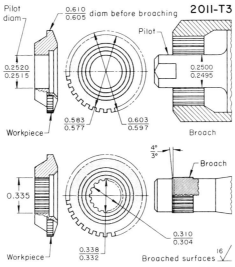

Feed(a):
External broaching .... 0.0055 ipr
Internal broaching .... 0.007 ipr
Depth of cut(b):
External broaching .... 0.010 in.
Internal broaching .... 0.014 in.
Cutting fluid .... Mineral seal oil
Production rate .... 923 pieces per hour
Tool life per grind:
External broaching .... 32,000 pieces
Internal broaching .... 47,500 pieces

Tolerance .... ±0.003 in.
Surface finish .... 16 micro-in.

(a) Broach feed per revolution of work spindle. (b) Depth of tooth form on part.

Fig. 21. Broaching internal and external splines in a multiple-spindle automatic bar machine (Example 886)

0.012 for 1/2-in., 0.016 for 3/4-in., 0.020 for 1 in., 0.025 for 1 1/2 in., and 0.030 for 2 in.

Cutting Fluid. Drilling of thin sections does not require a cutting fluid, but it is essential to drill life and hole quality that a copious supply of cutting fluid be provided for all deep-hole drilling. Soluble-oil emulsions or kerosine and lard-oil mixtures are satisfactory for general drilling. In drilling to a depth greater than six times the drill diameter, the workpiece should be kept cool by spraying. Also, the drill should be withdrawn several times during drilling to insure that the cutting fluid floods the hole completely.

Drilling in Automatic Bar and Chucking Machines

When drilling is done in multiple-operation machines, it is especially important that the tool be correctly ground and set. Standard twist drills

Table 11. Tool Angles for Drilling Aluminum Alloys With High Speed Steel Drills in Drill Presses

Point angle (θ):
  Thin stock: 118° to 150°; thinned point(a)
  General work .... 118° to 140°
  Al-Si alloys .... Down to 90°
Helix angle:
  Thin stock .... 24°
  Medium depth(b) .... 28°
  Deep holes(c) .... 40° to 48°
Lip clearance:
  Soft alloys .... 17°
  Strong alloys .... 15°
  Al-Si alloys .... 12°

(a) Diameter ÷ 1.8 stock thickness = tan θ/2. (b) Up to six times drill diameter. (c) Over six times drill diameter.

are generally used for drilling holes up to six diameters deep. For drilling deeper holes, drills that pass the chips up the flutes more readily are recommended. When machining 2017-T4, 2024-T4 and 2011-T3, straight-flute drills generally are used for drilling holes deeper than six diameters. Either high-helix or low-helix drills can be used for drilling deep holes. The web of the high-helix drill is uniform in thickness the entire length of the body, providing large flutes for the chips. Wide flutes also characterize the low-helix drill. Both types give good results, particularly in the drilling of soft or gummy alloys. For holes with a high ratio of depth to diameter, half-round or gun drills are sometimes used.

When standard twist drills are used for drilling deeper than three diameters, it may be necessary to enlarge the flutes. This may be done with a thin grinding wheel that has been dressed to a radius. The flute is held at an angle to the wheel to insure the proper curvature in the flute. All flutes on a drill should be ground alike.

Drill Margin. Margins along the edges of flutes support the drill in the hole and keep the drill cutting the correct diameter. When drilling aluminum alloys, standard drill margins often may be reduced in width without loss of necessary support. The narrower margin reduces friction between the drill and the hole, thus reducing the amount of heat generated. In many production jobs, a narrower margin has greatly increased drill life.

Web Thickness. For drilling aluminum alloys, web thickness at the point should be reduced as the drill is ground back. This will reduce the end pressure on the drill, because the chisel point does not cut but compresses the metal ahead of it. Generally, the web can be somewhat thinner at the point without making the drill susceptible to breakage when drilling aluminum alloys than when drilling steel.

For small-diameter drills, "notched-point" thinning is common. On larger drills, this type of point may produce a poor chip, and therefore the entire flute is ground at the point. The notched point is obtained by using the sharp corner of an abrasive wheel, the side of the wheel following the angle of the chisel point. The drill should be held at an angle to the wheel to form a slight rake for the new cutting edge, which is ground to the center of the point of the drill.

When the entire flute at the point is thinned by grinding, a thin wheel that has been dressed to a radius is used. The drill is held so that the flute is at an angle to the wheel, as when widening the flute. Most of the metal should be ground off the back of the land, and care must be taken not to grind the rake formed by the helix angle from the cutting edge or to destroy the shape of the cutting edge.

Thinning of the web must be done uniformly in each flute, to insure that the cut remains balanced on both sides of the centerline of the drill.

Cutting-Lip Angle. In general drilling practice, if holes are not too deep, a standard included cutting-lip angle of 118° will give satisfactory performance. However, if deeper holes are drilled with this cutting-lip angle, the chip produced does not come out easily. For drilling deeper holes, larger included cutting-lip angles are used, forming a narrower chip that readily passes up the flutes.

Occasionally, smaller cutting-lip angles may be employed, because the transverse forces at the cutting edges are greater and the tool can drill without runout. However, a broader chip is produced.

When several drills are used in the same hole, each succeeding tool should have a slightly more blunt cutting-lip angle than that of the preceding one, so that it can center at the outside of the cutting edges.

Clearance angle behind the cutting edges should be 12° to 20°. Larger clearances are used for straight-flute drills and for drills ground with large cutting-lip angles. Clearance should extend from periphery to center, so that the chisel point is at an angle of 130° to 145° with the cutting edges.

Rake angles are set by the helix angle of the drill. For standard twist drills, this is usually 20° to 25°; for high-helix drills, 40° to 43°; for low-helix drills, 7° to 15°; and for straight-flute and half-round drills, 0°.

Center Drills. When a drill starts against a flat surface, it may skid sideways before cutting, particularly if it is small or protrudes considerably from the holder. This may cause the drill to break or to cut off-center. Therefore, except with large, rigidly held drills, a center drill is recommended to provide an accurate start.

For maximum rigidity, center drills should be of relatively large diameter and short length. Unless a countersink of a special angle is to be left in the workpiece, an included cutting-lip angle of 90° should be used. In general, for proper centering, the outside of the cutting lips of the drill that follows the center drill should strike the stock first, insuring adequate support.

Depth of Hole. In multiple-operation machines, to prevent chips from jamming in the flutes and causing drill breakage when deep holes are being drilled, a limit must be set on the depth drilled with each entry of the tool. The maximum depths, in terms of drill diameter, that can be drilled per entry under normal production conditions are given in Table 12.

Before re-entry, the drill should be completely backed out of the hole, so that the chips can be washed away.

The type of workpiece, the number of positions on the machine available for drilling, and the type of machine determine practice for drilling deep holes. Sometimes it is economical to use several drills for drilling deep holes.

For holes more than eight diameters deep, half-round or gun drills are often used. To insure adequate support for the half-round drill when it starts cutting, another type of drill should be used to drill a starting hole, three diameters or more deep. The half-round drill can drill four diameters deeper in the first entry of the started hole.

Drill Speed. Generally, small-diameter, high speed steel drills can be operated at speeds up to 600 sfm. How-

Table 12. Maximum Depths Per Drill Entry for Drilling in Automatic Bar and Chucking Machines

	Depth, in drill diameters						
	First drill			Second drill			
Drill type	First entry	Second entry	Third entry	First entry	Second entry	Third entry	Subsequent entries
Standard twist drill	4	1½	¾	...	...	...	...
High or low helix, or straight flute ...	5	2	1	1½	¾	½	½

Table 13. Feeds for Drilling Aluminum Alloys in Automatic Bar and Chucking Machines

Drill diam, in.	Tolerance, in.	Feed, ipr	
		2011-T3	Other alloys
0.0625	±0.0015	0.0040	0.004
0.125	±0.002	0.0120	0.010
0.187	±0.002	0.0144	0.012
0.250	±0.002	0.0168	0.014
0.375	±0.0025	0.0204	0.017
0.500	±0.0025	0.0204	0.017
0.750	±0.003	0.0204	0.017

ever, when larger drills are used to remove large quantities of metal at a rapid rate, lower speeds will give more economical drill life. A guide in choosing proper speeds for most conditions is the following:

Drill diameter	Speed
Less than 1 in.	600 sfm
1 to 1½ in.	550
Over 1½ in.	450

Feed for drilling in multiple-operation machines depends on the size and strength of the drill; finish, tolerance and concentricity desired; and power available. As feed is increased, torque on the drill increases, until the breaking point may be reached. On the other hand, lower feed produces thinner chips, which are more likely to clog the flutes than thicker chips. Clogging is likely to break the drill or mar the finish of the workpiece.

Recommended drill feeds are given in Table 13 for drill sizes up to 0.750 in. in diameter. Feeds for larger drills usually depend on the power available in the machine.

For greater accuracy and better finish, lower feed may be necessary. For deep holes, machined with several entries, feed should be decreased 15% for each successive entry. Lower feed should be used to drill thin-wall parts.

Power Requirements. When large quantities of metal are removed, lower feed may be necessary, to keep the

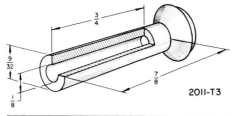

Drilling condition(a)	Original	Improved
Speed, rpm	6050	4365
Speed, sfm	198	143
Feed, ipr:		
First drilling(b)	0.0064	0.0088
Second drilling(c)	0.0057	0.0079
Cycle time, sec	10½	10½

(a) In both original and improved methods, ⅛-in.-diam tapered-shank high speed steel drills were used, and cutting fluid was a 1-to-25 mixture of soluble oil and water. (b) To depth of ½ in. (c) Remaining ¼-in. depth.

Fig. 22. Stud for which reduction of spindle speed eliminated drill breakage without reducing cycle time, because of increase in feed (Example 887)

power within the limits available in the machine. When drilling with standard drills (ground to 118° included cutting-lip angle and 15° clearance) to four diameters deep in 2017-T4 and 2024-T4, 1.5 to 2 cu in. of metal can be removed per minute per horsepower. For 2011-T3, the rate is 2.5 to 3 cu in. per minute per horsepower. These figures are based on a feed of 0.017 ipr. With lower feed, the rate of metal removal decreases.

Drill Size vs Hole Size. Drills, when properly ground and set, will cut aluminum alloys to size or not more than 0.002 in. oversize. However, any condition that causes overheating is likely to decrease the size of the hole when it is measured after the workpiece has cooled. This is especially noticeable when drilling large holes. Drilling of deep holes at high feed rate will decrease hole size in relation to drill size. Sometimes other tools working simultaneously will generate enough heat to cause the production of holes close to or even smaller than drill size, as measured after the workpiece has cooled to room temperature.

Drilling Practice (Production Examples)

Because aluminum alloys are easily machined, rates of drill penetration are rapid and chip disposal can be a problem; for this reason, some sacrifice in speed may be necessary to permit disposal of the chips, as described in the following example.

Example 887. Decrease in Speed to Eliminate Drill Breakage (Fig. 22)

Repeated drill breakage occurred in the ⅛-in.-diam blind hole of the 2011-T3 stud shown in Fig. 22. Excessive spindle speed was the cause of drill failure. By reducing speed from 6050 to 4365 rpm and increasing the feed rate, the problem was eliminated without decreasing the cycle time. Drilling conditions at both speeds are given with Fig. 22.

Drill Design. The point angle of a drill can be a source of difficulty in drilling. When steel and other hard metals are drilled, a large included angle is used. With aluminum alloys such as 7075 and 2024, there is little difficulty in using the same point angle as for steel, but the softer, more gummy aluminum alloys require a smaller point angle. When a small angle is employed, abrasive wear is distributed more evenly over the cutting edge, thereby improving drill performance. A change in drill design that improved both drill life and the quality of drilled holes is described in the following example.

Example 888. Step Drill for Hand Drilling (Fig. 23)

In drilling holes in 7079 alloy, using portable hand tools with conventional twist drills having the standard recommended drill point, hole size could not be maintained and drill-point life was very short (one hole per grind).

As a result, operators used excessive pressure, which caused a heavy burr to appear on breakthrough of the drill point. Many holes had to be reamed after drilling, but frequently tolerances had already been exceeded in the drilling operation, and therefore the work had to be scrapped.

Drill design was modified. As shown in Fig. 23, the drill point was ground to a ⅜-in.-diam step with a 3° lip-relief clearance. High pressures were no longer needed. Tolerances could be maintained with the split-point step drill shown in Fig. 23.

Manufacturers' vs User's Standards. Drill life can sometimes be greatly improved by establishing standards of drill design more exacting than those of the manufacturer, as described in the example that follows.

Example 889. Effect of Drill-Design Standards on Tool Consumption (Table 14)

A user observed that when drills were purchased to manufacturers' standards, several details of design varied from lot to lot and from manufacturer to manufacturer. Because of these variations, drills could not be resharpened in an automatic drill grinder with precision, and many drills had to be discarded when they became dull.

When the user established his own standards for drill design and dimensions, the number of drills required for a given amount of work over a nine-month period decreased from 44,000 to 36,000. Furthermore, 50% of the drills made to the user's standard could be resharpened in an automatic drill grinder and reclaimed for further use. Details of this comparison are given in Table 14.

Workpiece Size and Shape. In the fabrication of airframe structures, part size and shape markedly affect the selection of drilling conditions and

equipment. Although few problems are encountered when drilling holes in aluminum in standard bench or floor-type drilling machines, important benefits have accrued from the use of portable or other special tools. The two examples that follow describe techniques used in drilling large numbers of holes in aircraft components.

Examples 890 and 891. Techniques for Drilling Holes in Wing Panels and Skins

Example 890 — Color-Coded Templates. More than 11,000 fasteners — 22,000 holes — were required in an aircraft wing-panel assembly. Because these panels acted as fuel tanks, preparation of the holes was especially critical, to assure a leakproof assembly.

The original method of hole preparation on upper and lower wing panels involved three steps: (a) pilot holes were drilled, using a hand drill and drill block; (b) holes were drilled to size; and (c) holes were countersunk or counterbored, or both.

A revised method of hole preparation involved color-coded drill templates and an automatic tool that would drill, countersink and counterbore in one operation. The first hole in a panel was drilled by conventional means. The automatic tool was then locked into the drill template, using the first hole as the locating point. Because the tool provided a controlled feed and location for the next hole, the entire operation was semiautomatic.

Use of the color-coded templates was not complicated. For example, a yellow template might indicate drill and countersink only, and a blue ring around a hole in the yellow template might indicate drill, countersink and counterbore.

Two drill sizes were used: 0.187 in. +0.001, −0.000 in., and 0.187 in. +0.003, −0.000 in. Drill speed was varied, depending on the depth of the hole. Holes ¼ in. deep or less

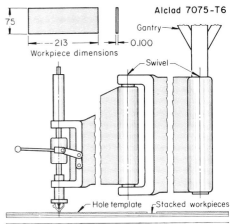

Drill Details

Material ....High speed steel
Diameter ....No. 40 (0.0980 in.)
Helix, land, web, and flute .....Same as user's standard in Table 14

Operating Conditions

Speed ....3700 rpm (96 sfm)
Feed ....Manual plunge
Depth of drilling ..0.200 in. (including pockets)
Cutting fluid ....Soluble-oil:water (1:30)
Setup time ....½ hr each for two operators
Drilling time ....2 hr for 12,000 holes

Fig. 24. Stack drilling aircraft wing skins (Example 891)

were drilled at 6000 rpm (295 sfm); those ⁵⁄₁₆ in. deep or more were drilled at 3000 rpm (147 sfm). Time saved in drilling each panel assembly by the improved method amounted to 4000 hr.

Example 891 — Stack Drilling (Fig. 24). To drill 5000 holes in an alclad 7075-T6 aircraft wing skin (213 in. long by 75 in. wide by 0.100 in. thick), two high-cycle, radial-arm drill units were employed. These units were equipped with double-swivel 6-ft arms (Fig. 24), independent overhead longitudinal-travel gantries, and a common overhead transverse-travel gantry. All motions were powered. The wing skins were stacked on an 8-by-24-ft table and were clamped with a hole template.

Holes were drilled in two stages. In the first stage, pilot holes and tooling holes for chemical milling were drilled in skins stacked five high. After chemical milling, the primary hole pattern was drilled through two-high stacks of skins. The chemically milled pockets limited the stack to two high in the second operation, because the drill was free to "walk" when passing through the pockets.

Because of the large number of holes to be drilled and the size of the parts, two operators and two drilling units were employed. The two operators drilled an average of 12,000 No. 40 holes in approximately 2 hr. This was equivalent to a hole every 1.2 sec, including the time for positioning of the drill units.

Handling the workpiece was facilitated by a vacuum lift suspended from one of the overhead traveling gantries. The vacuum lift also helped to protect the smooth surface of the parts.

Initially, a spray mist cutting fluid was applied near the top of the drill, through the open portion of the pilot bracket, but drill breakage was high. Therefore, a hole was drilled through the pilot bracket and pilot, and a small reservoir was counterbored in the pilot bracket, to feed cutting fluid by gravity to the drill, close to the work. Machining conditions and tool details are given with Fig. 24.

Combining Operations. For efficient production, drilling is often combined with one or more other machining operations, and some sacrifice in speed or feed may be required on one operation to accommodate another. This is offset by savings of tools and time. The next example describes a combination of drilling, reaming and spotfacing. For a combination drilling-and-counter-sinking application, see Example 161.

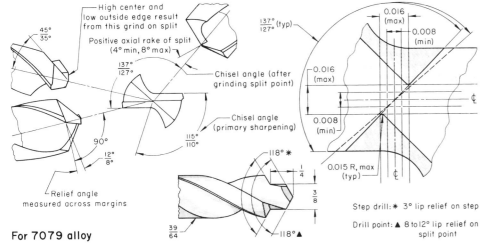

For 7079 alloy

Fig. 23. Modified drill design that improved dimensional accuracy in hand drilling airframe structures of 7079 alloy (Example 888)

Table 14. Comparison of Manufacturers' and User's Standards for Drills (Example 889) (a)

Tool details	Manufacturers' standard	User's standard
Number of drills used in 9 months ..	44,000	36,000(b)
Drill diameters	No. 50 to ¼ in.	No. 50 to ¼ in.
Drill lengths	3 to 7½ in.	3 to 7½ in.
Flute lengths	1 to 3½ in.	1 to 3½ in.
Helix angle	33°	33° ± 30'
Land width	Not specified	40 to 50% of diameter, ±0.003 in.
Web thickness:		
Sizes No. 40 to 50	Not specified	23% of diameter parallel for ⅜ in. and subsequent increase of 0.013 ± 0.003 in. per in.
Sizes No. 30 to ¼ in.	Not specified	15% of diameter parallel for ⅜ in. and subsequent increase of 0.013 ± 0.003 in. per in.
Flute	Not specified	Polished, conforming to land width and web thickness

(a) Drills were used in the same machines, at the same speeds and feeds. (b) Of the drills, 50% could be automatically resharpened and reclaimed for further use.

Example 892. Combining Drilling With Reaming and Spotfacing (Table 15)

Originally, the procedure for machining the casting shown in the sketch with Table 15 was as follows: (a) straddle mill the 2-in. dimension in a milling machine; (b) drill the five holes in a drill press equipped with a multiple-spindle drill head; and (c) ream the five holes in a drill press, moving the fixture from spindle to spindle.

In an improved procedure, the workpiece was machined completely in a radial drilling machine with a 36-in. table. The sequence of operations and processing details are given in Table 15. Except for spotfacing one side of the hub, all operations were performed in one setting.

Production rate and perishable-tool costs for the two methods were:

	Original	Improved
Production, pieces per hr	18	82
Tools, cost per set	$116	$90
Cost of fixtures	$950	$2805

Deep-Hole Drilling

Gun drills, tipped with either carbide or high speed steel have replaced twist drills for many deep-hole drilling applications, regardless of the metal being drilled (see discussion of gun drilling on pages 81 and 82 in the article "Drilling", in this volume). In gun drilling, the maximum depth of hole that can be drilled successfully is generally related to drill size (Table 16). Length-to-diameter relationships shown in Table 16 are generally standard, although gun drills having much greater length-to-diameter ratios are often used — as in Examples 165 and 893.

Gun drills, with a single-flute cutting head and grooved shank, must have a sufficient flow of cutting fluid under high pressure at the point where the cutting edge contacts the work, to keep the cutting edge cool and to insure that the chips will be forced out through the chip groove. Cutting fluid is normally applied at a pressure of 500 to 600 psi for drills ⅜ in. in diameter or smaller or at 300 to 400 psi for larger drills. A pump of 5-hp capacity is usually required for average applications. A paraffin-base oil with a viscosity of 100 to 125 sus at 100 F has been used satisfactorily in gun drilling aluminum with a ⅜-in.-diam drill at a speed of 300 sfm (for high speed steel) or 600 sfm (for carbide) and feeds of 0.001 to 0.003 ipr.

Although deep-drilling problems have been alleviated to some extent by the development of gun drills and special gun-drilling equipment, this equipment is expensive and cannot always be justified. Example 148, in the article "Drilling", describes an application in which holes seven diameters deep were drilled in alloy 6061-T6 in a turret lathe. The following example describes another deep-hole drilling application that utilized available equipment (in this instance, a boring mill).

Example 893. Deep-Hole Drilling in a Boring Mill (Fig. 25)

The 36-in.-diam, 36-in.-long explosive forming die illustrated in Fig. 25 was originally made up from nine 4-in.-thick aluminum alloy plates. Because no plate stock obtainable was wide enough to make a 36-in.-diam one-piece plate, each round plate was made by doweling together two 4-in.-thick half-sections. As each 4-in. plate section was completed by machining the die cavity hole through its center and drilling 12 tie-bolt holes, it was mated to the next 4-in.-thick plate until the die was completed. Each in-

Table 15. Seven-Operation Drilling, Reaming and Spotfacing of a Casting (Example 892) (a)

Operation 1
(Drilling hole A halfway)(b)

Speed .... 860 rpm (146 sfm)
Feed .... 0.006 ipr
Tool life per grind .... 500 pieces

Operation 2
(Through drilling hole A)(b)

Speed .... 860 rpm (146 sfm)
Feed .... 0.006 ipr
Tool life per grind .... 500 pieces

Operation 3
(Reaming hole A)(c)

Speed .... 500 rpm (90 sfm)
Feed .... 0.017 ipr
Tool life per grind .... 2500 pieces

Operation 4
(Spotfacing one side of hub)(d)

Speed .... 500 rpm (196 sfm)
Feed .... 0.017 ipr
Depth of cut .... ⅛ in.
Tool life per grind .... 5000 pieces

Operations 5 and 6
(Drilling and reaming holes B and C)(e)

Speed .... 1500 rpm (196 sfm)
Feed .... 0.010 ipr
Tool life per grind .... 500 pieces

Operation 7
(Spotfacing opposite side of hub)(d)

Speed .... 500 rpm (196 sfm)
Feed .... 0.017 ipr
Depth of cut .... ⅛ in.
Tool life per grind .... 5000 pieces

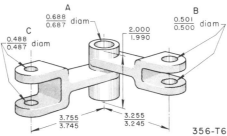

356-T6

(a) Operations were performed on casting shown above, a distributing lever. Total setup time for all operations was 2 hr; cycle time for each operation was 0.732 min. Downtime for changing tools was 1½ hr; cutting fluid was a 1-to-25 mixture of soluble oil and water; finish obtained in reamed holes was 100 micro-in. (b) a 21/32-in.-diam high speed steel drill with high-spiral polished flutes and 125° point angle was used. (c) The six-flute reamer was 11/16 in. in diameter, with a 45° lead angle and 0.015-in. land. (d) Four-flute spotfacing tool was 1½ in. in diameter, with sharp land and 10° rake angle. Tool was used with a 0.686-in.-diam pilot, ½ in. long. (e) Holes B and C were drilled and reamed with subland drills having two-flute drill portions, four-flute reamer portions and 125° point angle. Drill portion for holes B was 31/64 in. in diameter; reamer portion was 0.500 in. Drill portion for holes C was 27/64 in. in diameter; reamer portion was 0.488 in.

dividual plate was placed on the preceding plate so that the half-section cut lines were 90° from those in the preceding plate. Then each section was doweled with two pins to the next, completing the die.

By the improved method of producing these dies, four 36-in.-diam, 9-in.-thick forgings were obtained. These forgings were machined (as were the 4-in.-thick plates) individually and doweled to one another to maintain alignment. The assembly was then set up in a boring mill as shown in Fig. 25. Each of the 1⅝-in.-diam tie-bolt holes was drilled in one pass using a standard gun drill. Drilling time was reduced from 7 hr by the original method to ½ hr by the improved method.

The boring mill was modified by adding a hydraulic pump with a capacity of 40.6 gal per min to supply cutting fluid to the drill point at 300 psi. A baffle plate and filter system were installed to handle the flow of oil.

This modification of the boring mill provided satisfactory deep-hole drilling at a cost of $1000 for the modification. Estimated cost for a new deep-hole drilling machine for this job was $25,000.

Reaming

The machines, basic designs of reamers, and techniques discussed in the article "Reaming", which begins on page 93 of this volume, are generally applicable to aluminum alloys.

Reamer Design. Because it is less likely to cause chatter, a spiral-flute reamer — either solid, expandable or adjustable — is generally preferable to a straight-flute reamer for finishing holes in aluminum alloys. In most applications, it is advantageous to use a reamer with a negative spiral (that is, one spiraled in the direction opposite to rotation), to prevent the reamer from feeding itself into the hole. Flutes should be large enough to pass the chips readily, and there should be enough flutes to provide adequate support to the tool. The margins of straight-flute reamers should be as narrow as possible, to reduce friction between tool and work.

Straight-flute reamers are designed with an even number of blades arranged opposite each other in pairs, but with flute spacing varied slightly to prevent chatter and marking.

Spiral flutes (right-hand cut, left-hand spiral) are frequently more effective in reducing chatter. However, a spiral-flute reamer must have sufficient spiral so that two or more flutes overlap in the length of the reamed hole. The spiral angle must be held to a minimum, because the steeper the angle, the more end pressure is required to feed the reamer through the hole. Additional reamer design data are given in Table 17.

Table 16. Relation of Drill Diameter to Approximate Maximum Depth of Hole in Gun Drilling

Drill diameter, in.	Depth of hole, in drill diameters	Drill diameter, in.	Depth of hole, in drill diameters
Up to ½	12	1½ to 2	5
½ to 1	7	2 to 2½	4
1 to 1½	6	2½ to 3	3

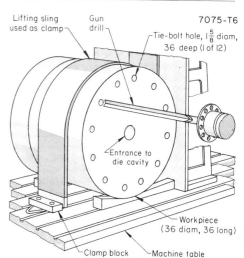

7075-T6

Fig. 25. Setup for deep-hole drilling an explosive forming die in a boring mill (Example 893)

Table 17. Reamer Design and Operating Conditions for Reaming Aluminum Alloys

Reamer Design

Reamer size:
Hand reaming . . . .1.01 times drill diameter
Machine reaming . .1.02 times drill diameter
Flute type . . . . .Straight to 10° spiral
Tooth spacing:
Straight flute . . . . .Uneven(a)
Spiral flute . . . . .Even
Tooth style:
Roughing . . . . .Solid or nicked
Finishing . . . . .Solid
Top rake .5° to 8°
Clearance angles:
Primary .4° to 7°
Secondary . . . . .15° to 20°
Cutting angle . . . . .85° to 91°
Land width . . . . .0.020 to 0.060 in.(b)

Operating Conditions

Speed, roughing:
Hard alloys . . . . .Up to 200 sfm
Soft alloys . . . . .60 to 100 sfm
Speed, finishing:
Straight reamers . . . . .Up to 400 sfm
Taper reamers . . . . .Up to 300 sfm
Feed:
Roughing . . . . .0.013 to 0.035 ipr
Finishing . . . . .0.003 to 0.010 ipr

(a) To avoid chatter. (b) Land width is approximately 1/25 of reamer diameter.

When the hole has close tolerances and rigid surface finish requirements, reaming procedure must sometimes be altered. If the design of the workpiece permits, spiral-flute reamers with 7° hook will produce fine finishes, especially on angular surfaces. When reaming diameters of 0.750 in. or larger, a carbide-tipped expandable reamer will produce good finish and provide extended tool life.

Speed and Feed. Nominal speed for reaming the non-heat-treated cast alloys with high speed steel (M1, M7 or M10) reamers is 400 sfm. For all other cast and wrought alloys, speed should be about 300 sfm.

When reaming the non-heat-treated cast alloys with carbide tools, nominal speed is 850 sfm. For other cast and wrought alloys, nominal reaming speed is 700 sfm.

Feed rate in reaming aluminum alloys is generally the same for all alloys and tool materials; hole size, however, does affect optimum feed. A feed of 0.005 ipr is a good starting point in reaming 1/8-in.-diam holes. Nominal rate of feed increases as hole diameter increases: 0.008 ipr for 1/4-in.-diam holes, 0.012 for 1/2-in., 0.016 for 1-in., 0.020 for 1 1/2-in., and 0.030 for 2-in.

Cutting Fluid. At high reaming speed, a cutting fluid is required, to reduce temperature in the workpiece, minimize distortion, and prevent undersize reaming. For reaming with high speed steel reamers, mixtures of lard oil and paraffin oil or kerosine, or of petroleum and turpentine, are especially recommended. Sulfurized and chlorinated oils are often used (see Example 894), but they are likely to stain the work. With carbide reamers, emulsions of soluble oil and water are the most widely used cutting fluids.

Reaming and Burnishing. When difficulty is encountered in obtaining the desired tolerance and surface finish, it may be necessary to employ two-stage finishing — for instance, to ream the hole 0.0005 in. under the specified dimension, and then to burnish it to size and finish requirements

(see the article "Roller Burnishing", which begins on page 105 of this volume). The following example describes two-stage ream-and-burnish finishing.

Example 894. Reaming and Burnishing to Close Tolerance (Fig. 26)

Two of the three inside diameters of the part shown in Fig. 26 were sized to tolerance (+0.005, −0.000 in.) by reaming. For the 1.122/1.121-in. diameter, however, a two-stage operation was required: reaming to 1.1210/1.1205 in. and then burnishing to final size and specified finish (63 micro-in.). All inside diameters were concentric within 0.002 in. TIR. A sulfurized and chlorinated mineral oil was used as cutting fluid in reaming.

Reaming in Automatic Machines. A finishing reamer for use in automatic bar and chucking machines is shown in Fig. 27. This reamer finishes three diameters and faces the part to length. A radial rake angle of approximately 7° helps improve surface finish, particularly in reaming angular surfaces. The varied angular spacing of the flutes is intended to minimize slip, deflection and chatter.

Burnishing

In the roller burnishing of aluminum, tools of hardened and polished steel are normally employed to finish a surface by compressing the surface while either the tool or the work is rotating. The burnishing of an in-line hole in a 356-T6 casting for accurate size control is described in Example 214, in the article "Roller Burnishing".

Holes in aluminum are also sometimes burnished in production by pressing a bearing-grade steel ball through the bore to improve the finish.

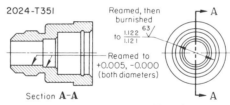

Fig. 26. Part in which two diameters were sized by reaming, and one by reaming and burnishing (Example 894)

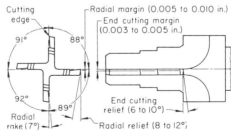

Fig. 27. Design of a finishing reamer used for reaming aluminum in automatic bar and chucking machines

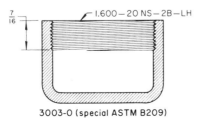

Fig. 28. Booster cup tapped by two different methods (Example 895)

Tapping

Taps for producing threads in aluminum are usually made of one of the general-purpose grades of high speed steel such as M1, M7 or M10. Taps should have polished flutes and ample backoff behind the land, to prevent pickup of work metal when the tap is withdrawn. Pitch diameters should be one thread class higher than those normally used for steel.

Taps with a diameter less than 3/8 in. should have no more than two flutes; larger taps should have the maximum number of flutes that will give the relationships of land width to circumference shown in the following table:

Tap circumference, in.	Optimum land, %
1/2 to 1	33
1 to 1 3/4	25
Over 1 3/4	20

Land width can also be expressed as 1 1/2 to 3 times the pitch.

Taps for through holes and the harder aluminum alloys should be provided with a hook angle of 10° to 20°, a spiral point, 3 to 4 threads chamfer, and a pitch diameter of GH2 (basic plus 0.0005 to 0.001 in.) or GH3 (basic plus 0.001 to 0.0015 in.). Taps for blind holes and soft alloys should have 10° to 15° hook and 40° right-hand spiral flutes.

For tapping blind holes less than 1/8 in. in diameter, spiral flutes should be avoided. For best size control, it is preferable not to bring the chip up the flute but to push it ahead of the tap, with a spiral point.

Efficiency of tapping may be greatly improved by a change in tooling or method — for instance, a change from a solid tap to a collapsible tap, as in the following example:

Example 895. Solid vs Collapsible Tap (Fig. 28)

An extruded booster cup for high explosive (Fig. 28) was tapped originally in a single-spindle chucking machine with a thread-lead cam, using a solid tap. The machine was loaded by hand, and cycle time was 11 1/2 sec. In backing out, the solid tap left chips attached to the part, so that a cleaning operation with a nylon brush was required. Also, chips wedged in the solid tap, and the tap had to be cleaned out after tapping only a few parts.

Replacement of the solid tap by a collapsible revolving tap (capacity, 1 3/4 in.) made it unnecessary to back out the tap. The job was changed to a six-spindle chucking machine, of 2 3/8-in. capacity, which had a thread-lead cam. Cycle time was reduced to 4 sec per part. Rotating the tap and collapsing it prevented the chips from sticking, eliminating the brushing operation and the cleaning of the tap. The cutting fluid, a light spindle oil, satisfactorily removed the chips during tapping. The chasers were ground with a lead like a solid gun tap (as was the original solid tap), to propel the chips forward.

Tapping speed recommended for aluminum is considerably higher than speeds used for steel. Alloy composition and condition, thread pitch, and method of tapping are major factors affecting tapping speed.

Assuming that the thread pitch is fine (18 to 24) and that the operation can be closely controlled (as in lead-screw tapping), the nominal speeds in the following table are generally suitable for use in tapping aluminum alloys:

Alloy	Speed, sfm
Non-heat-treated cast alloys	115
Heat treated cast alloys (solution treated and aged)	90
Cold drawn wrought alloys	125
Heat treated wrought alloys (solution treated and aged)	100

For coarser pitches, such as 8 to 12, any of the above speeds will be decreased, because of the difficulty in controlling the machine. For short thread lengths, speeds for tapping a coarse thread should be about one half the speeds given above. For long threads of the same pitch, the speed can be faster than for short threads, because of the longer time between starting and stopping. The use of lead-control devices permits higher tapping speeds than when no control is used. For instance, a speed of 115 sfm was used to tap 10–24 UNC threads in 2024-T4. The holes were blind and approximately ½ in. deep. However, lead-screw control was used. Under the same conditions but without lead-screw control, speed would have been 60 sfm max.

Cutting Fluid. Lard oil diluted with kerosine or other low-viscosity mineral oil is usually preferred for tapping aluminum. Low-viscosity commercial cutting oils are also used successfully. Soluble-oil emulsions are sometimes used, but they will not provide as good a finish as the other cutting fluids mentioned. However, the example that follows describes an application where a soluble oil was more effective than a mineral oil, probably because of the lower viscosity of the soluble-oil emulsion, which allowed it to penetrate more readily to the cutting edges of the tap and also allowed it to flow in greater volume for flushing away chips.

Example 896. Mineral Oil vs Soluble Oil for Tapping

An automatic tapping machine was used for cutting 6–32 UNC-2B threads in through holes (¼ in. deep) in alloy 2024-T4. Taps were straight-flute, spiral-point, with 15° chamfer angle and 18° hook, and were operated at 4150 rpm (122 sfm). Cutting fluid was mineral oil.

Chip congestion, together with buildup of work metal on the cutting edges of the tap, resulted in rough threads and tap breakage. Variations in tapping speed were tried, but did not alleviate these problems. However, by substituting soluble oil (in a 1-to-20 mixture with water) for mineral oil as the cutting fluid, thread finish became acceptable, and productivity and tap life were increased:

	Mineral oil	Soluble oil
Holes tapped per hour	1480	1520
Total tap life, holes	6250	8900

Best results are obtained when the cutting fluid is applied with pressure, especially when tapping blind holes.

Production Procedure. The three examples that follow describe the effect of thread size, close tolerances, and tapping blind versus through holes.

Example 897. Effect of Thread Size on Tap Life (Table 18)

Special tapping machines were used in a study to determine the effects of thread size on tap life in tapping two different aluminum alloys. Operating details and results are given in Table 18. As these data show, regardless of size, tap life was much less in tapping cast alloy 355-T6 than in tapping 6061-T6 bar stock. This agreed with experience in other machining operations in the plant.

Table 18. Effect of Thread Size on Tap Life in Alloys 355-T6 and 6061-T6 (Example 897)

Item	10–24 UNC-3B	3/8–24 UNF-3B	9/16–18 UNF-3B
Conditions Common to Both Materials(a)			
Diameter of tap-drilled hole, in.	0.155/0.151	0.334/0.328	0.508/0.502
Depth of thread, in.	7/16	Through	½
Speed of tap, rpm	250	200	150
Speed of tap, sfm	12.5	20	22
Taps for 355-T6 (AMS 4212) Aluminum Castings			
Number of flutes	3	3	4
Flute helix angle	55°	30°	0°
Hook angle	5°	7°	10°
Number of chamfered threads	1½	5	2
Tap life per grind, holes	*150*	*100*	*80*
Taps for 6061-T6 (AMS 4150) Aluminum Bar Stock			
Number of flutes (straight flutes)	2	3	4
Hook angle	10°	10°	10°
Number of chamfered threads	1½	5	2
Tap life per grind, holes	*200*	*300*	*200*

(a) Cutting fluid for all tapping operations consisted of lard oil and kerosine (1:1).

In tapping the cast alloy, tap life decreased as tap size increased — which is normal, because as size increases so does the amount of metal being removed. However, this relation did not hold true for tapping the bar stock; tap life was 300 holes per grind in tapping the 3/8–24 threads, whereas in tapping the 10–24 threads, tap life was only 200 holes per grind.

Example 898. Tapping Aluminum Castings to Close Tolerances

Turboprop-engine components made of alloy 355-T6 (AMS 4212) required stud fits in 20 blind holes (per casting) tapped to a depth of about ½ in. with ¼–20 UNC-5B threads. The completed assembly was required to withstand pressure of 4500 psi without leakage through the threads, and specifications permitted that only two holes per casting could be repaired by the use of inserts.

With the tapping procedure originally used, holes were undersize or bell-mouthed, and threads were torn. About 21% of the tapped castings required repair, and about 4% were beyond repair and were scrapped.

After experimentation, the following procedure was found to produce acceptable results, and was adopted:

1. Drill holes to 0.200/0.195-in. diameter.
2. Ream to 0.206/0.202-in. diameter.
3. Rough tap, leaving 0.005 to 0.008 in. of stock per side, for removal in finish tapping.
4. Finish tap to size.

Example 899. Tapping Blind vs Through Holes

Aircraft-engine components made of alloy 355-T6 (AMS 4212) had blind and through holes that required ¼–20 UNC-2B threads to a depth of ½ in. The blind holes (19/32 in. deep) were reamed after being drilled, to reduce the size and quantity of chips generated in tapping and thereby minimize the packing of chips in the 3/32-in. clearance space. The through holes (½ in. deep) were tapped without having been reamed. Tap life and cost, and production rate for the blind and through holes were as follows:

	Blind holes	Through holes
Tap life per grind, holes	275	400
Cost per tap	$2.14	$1.81
Holes tapped per hour	18	22

Example 900. Tapping a Thin-Wall Workpiece (Fig. 29)

A vertical tapping machine was used to tap the 3/64-in. wall portion of the workpiece shown in Fig. 29. The part was made of alloy 6063-T5, which has a yield strength of only 21,000 psi. Such relatively low strength, in combination with the thin wall, posed a size-retention problem in tapping: the outward pressure from tapping force caused the wall to expand, but the wall returned to normal size after the tap was removed, leaving the tapped holes undersize.

To avoid this problem, a tap ground oversize to GH7 pitch-diameter limit (see Table 4, page 110, in the article "Tapping") was used. As an additional precaution, an eight-flute tap was used, because the closer spacing of the lands provided extra support for the thin wall and distributed the cutting force more uniformly around the workpiece. Tap details and operating conditions are listed in the table that accompanies Fig. 29.

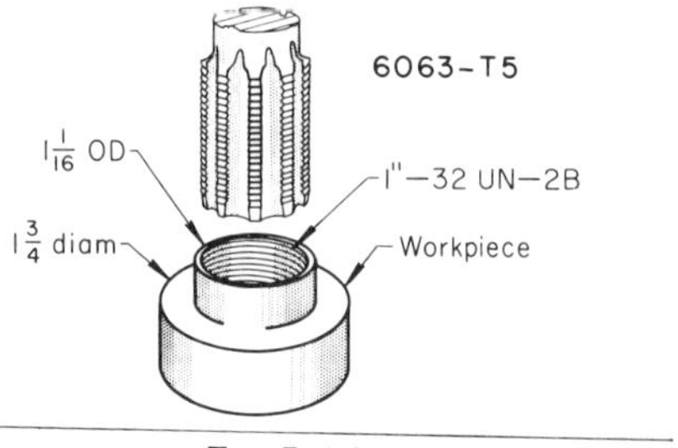

Tap Details

Material	M1 high speed steel
Number of flutes	8
Hook angle	12°
Chamfer angle	11° 15′ (approx 3½ threads)
Chamfer relief per land	0.006 to 0.008 in.
Pitch-diameter limit	GH7

Operating Conditions

Diameter of tap-drilled hole	31/32 in.
Wall thickness of threaded portion	3/64 in.
Length of threaded portion	3/8 in.
Per cent of full thread	76
Speed	344 rpm (90 sfm)
Cutting fluid	Mineral oil

Fig. 29. Tapping a thin-wall aluminum part (Example 900)

Form Tapping. If chips are a serious problem and if the hole wall is thick enough to support the pressure of the tool, a form (chipless) tap may be used (see page 118 in the article "Tapping", in this volume). Although a 75% thread is generally recommended for cut threads, tap drilling for 55 to 65% thread is practical for threads produced with a form tap. All aluminum alloys except the high-silicon (12%) die-casting alloys can be tapped with form taps.

In some applications, form taps have been successfully operated at speeds twice as fast as are used for their cutting-type counterparts. Limitations are the same for form tapping as for cutting tapping and the same cutting fluids are used. The following example compares performance of cutting taps and form taps.

Example 901. Tapping: Cutting vs Forming

Performance of No. 4-40 cutting taps was compared with that of form (chipless) taps in tapping a through hole in a ¼-in. section of alloy 380 die castings. Both taps were used in a lead-screw machine, at 3000 rpm. The cutting fluid was a high-grade cutting oil with low sulfur content. Although production rate for both taps was 400 pieces per hour, production rate per setup with the form tap (1200 pieces) was double the rate obtained when the cutting tap was used.

In tapping these die castings, a form tap was superior to a cutting tap in all sizes from No. 2 through No. 8, provided the hole wall was thick enough to support the pressure of the form tap.

Single-Point Threading

Single-point threading tools of conventional design are used to cut both internal and external threads on aluminum alloys. Speeds of 500 sfm are common, although higher speeds have been used. Typical practice is represented by the following example:

Example 902. Single-Point Threading of Die Castings (Fig. 30)

A fine-pitch thread (pitch diameter, 1.6580/1.6514 in.) was machined in an alloy 380 die casting (Fig. 30) with a single-point carbide tool. This alloy was susceptible to chipping and tearing if high cutting pressure was applied, particularly if the die casting was porous in the area being threaded.

Die Threading

Circular chasers for die threading aluminum alloys should have a hook angle of 20° and a face angle of 2°. When threading with tangential chasers, a combination of nominal back rake angle of 20° and 0° side rake angle is generally best.

To avoid damage to the first few threads, chasers should have a lead chamfer of 25° to 35° for 1½ threads. This chamfer will assure a smooth, even start.

Speeds up to 130 sfm for the non-heat-treated cast alloys and about 100 sfm for the other alloys can be used, if the length and pitch of the thread and the equipment used permit control at these speeds. Speeds no more than half of the above are more often used, because at the higher speeds control is more difficult, especially when threading short lengths or close to a shoulder.

Examples 871 and 873, in this article, compare two alloys and two tempers in die threading. In Example 871, alloys 355 and 356 were threaded in a turret lathe, and in Example 873, the threading characteristics of the T6 and T7 tempers of alloy 355 are compared.

Multiple-Operation Machining in Bar and Chucking Machines

The commercial aluminum alloys preferred for machining in automatic bar and chucking machines are 2011, 2017, 2024, 6061 and 6262. Alloy 2011 is the most widely used, because it produces chips that break easily without the aid of a chip breaker (see Fig. 1 and Table 1). Alloy 2011 is also heat treatable and usually is machined in the T3 temper, but if the part has thin walls or if distortion is probable, the stress-relieved T451 temper is recommended (Example 872). Although it is not always possible to change the alloy to improve machinability, when alloy 2011 will satisfy service requirements, substantial over-all savings are possible with its use (Examples 867 and 868).

Alloy 2017 machines well, but it produces chips that do not break readily unless a chip breaker is used. Alloy

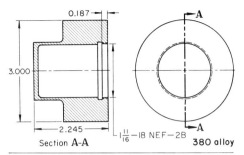

Details of Single-Point Threading Tool

Material	Carbide
Cutting-edge angle	60°
Top rake angle	20°
Clearance angle	7°

Operating Conditions

Speed	475 sfm
Diameter of bore	1¹¹⁄₁₆ in.
Length of threads	0.187 in.
Cutting fluid	Soluble-oil:water (1:25)
Setup time	1 hr
Cycle time	40 sec
Production rate	75 pieces per hour

Fig. 30. Die casting threaded in a single-spindle chucking machine with a threading attachment (Example 902)

2024 has similar machining characteristics. Example 869 describes an application where production rate increased and machining cost decreased when 2017 was replaced by 2024.

Alloy 6061 is the most ductile of the alloys recommended for multiple-operation machining, and consequently

Table 19. Speeds and Feeds for Machining 2011 Aluminum Alloy Round Bar Stock in Automatic Bar and Chucking Machines

Width or depth of cut, in.	Size of hole, in.	High speed steel Speed, sfm	Feed, ipr	Carbide Speed, sfm	Feed, ipr
Width:	**Form Tools, Circular or Dovetail**				
0.500	....	700	0.003	1000-1500	0.007-0.010
1.000	....	700	0.002	950-1450	0.006-0.009
1.500	....	650	0.001	950-1450	0.005-0.008
2.000	....	650	0.001	925-1425	0.004-0.005
	Twist Drills				
....	0.250	600	0.014	900-1400	0.012-0.016
....	0.500	600	0.017	850-1350	0.014-0.018
....	0.750	600	0.017	850-1350	0.016-0.019
....	1.000	550	0.019	800-1300	0.016-0.019
....	1.250	550	0.020	750-1250	0.018-0.022
Depth:	**Turning or Box Tools**				
0.125	....	700	0.008	1000-1500	0.017-0.024
0.250	....	700	0.006	950-1450	0.016-0.024
0.375	....	675	0.004	925-1425	0.013-0.019
0.500	....	650	0.002	900-1400	0.011-0.016
	Hollow Mills				
0.062	....	650	0.012	900-1400	0.036-0.048
0.125	....	625	0.010	850-1350	0.029-0.038
0.187	....	600	0.008	825-1325	0.025-0.034
0.250	....	600	0.007	800-1300	0.022-0.029
	Knurling Tools on Cross Slide				
....	....	700	0.010	1000-1500	0.060-0.080
....	....	700	0.020	1000-1500	0.120-0.160
....	....	700	0.010	1000-1500	0.060-0.080
	Chamfering and Facing				
....	....	700	0.002	1000-1500	0.024-0.030
	Reamers				
....	½ max	600	0.009	825-1350	0.026-0.034
....	½ min	600	0.015	825-1350	0.036-0.048
Width:	**Cutoff Tools**				
0.062	....	700	0.003	1000-1500	0.009-0.012
0.125	....	700	0.004	1000-1500	0.011-0.014
0.187	....	700	0.004	1000-1500	0.011-0.014
0.250	....	700	0.004	1000-1500	0.012-0.016

is the most difficult to machine. The chips produced are tough and stringy, and a chip breaker is essential. Alloy 6262 has slightly better machining characteristics than 6061, but still requires a chip breaker. When service requirements permit, 6262 can be substituted for 6061 (for instance, see Example 870, which involves tapping).

Speed and Feed. With carbide tools, speeds of 1000 to 1500 sfm are common; with high speed steel tools, speeds of 550 to 700 sfm are satisfactory. Table 19 gives speeds and feeds for machining 2011 aluminum alloy with high speed steel and carbide tools. The highest spindle speed possible is recommended for most automatic operations. Factors that determine maximum spindle speed include size and shape of the part, machining operations to be performed, and machine limitations.

Feeds employed vary with cutting conditions, dimensional tolerances, and the surface finish required. Overlapping operations, part size and shape, or machining conditions may require lower-than-normal feeds. The feeds shown in Table 19 are related to a specific tool and cut, and are applicable to most automatic machining operations. The lower feeds within the ranges are recommended for best surface finish and close dimensional tolerances, especially when machining the less free-cutting alloys, such as 6061 and 6262.

Cutting Fluid. A generous flow of cutting fluid is essential. A low-viscosity mineral oil is preferred for machining aluminum alloys in automatic machines; it dissipates heat quickly, washes away the chips, and — because of its low viscosity — allows fine chips to settle out in the sumps of larger equipment. This settling action prevents clogging of the sump drains.

When high temperatures or high pressures are encountered at the cutting point of the tool, special oils containing 5 to 10% of fatty additives in a light mineral oil are recommended. Among the fatty additives commonly used are oleic acid, neat's-foot oil, and lard oil. The flash point of cutting fluids should be above 270 F to reduce danger from fire.

Tool Design. The following suggestions for tools used on automatic machines provide initial guidance:

Cutoff Tools. A front angle of 23° and clearance angles of 8° to 12° are satisfactory. For deep cuts with heavy feeds, the front angle should be reduced to 10° to 15° and a chip breaker should be used for all alloys except 2011.

Form Tools. Rake angles of 5° to 10° are employed for all alloys recommended except 2011, which requires a rake angle of 0° to 3°. Where feasible, chip breakers are used for all alloys except 2011, or cams can be notched, provided the tool does not leave the work and make a plunge return.

Knee Tools. Clearance angles of 8° to 15° (usually provided on the holders) and rake angles of 15° to 20° are employed for all alloys except 2011.

Drills. See the section "Drilling in Automatic Bar and Chucking Machines", page 448 in this article.

Reamers. Standard twist drills can be used for reaming the smaller diameters. Straight reamers should employ rake angles of 5° to 10° and clearance angles of 10°. The lands on reamers should be made as narrow as possible, in order to reduce heating to a minimum in close-tolerance reaming.

Counterbores. Stepped counterbores with a rake angle of 7° are recommended for all alloys except 2011, which requires a 0° rake. Narrow lands are essential to reduce heat.

Taps and Chasers. Taps should be of the ground-thread type with polished flutes, narrow lands to reduce heat, ample chip room, and rake angles of 10° to 20°, depending on the alloy being machined. Threading ratios that are used for brass can also be used for aluminum, and thread rolling procedures are the same for both metals. Chaser dies and fluteless taps are suitable for use on aluminum.

Recessing tools, because of their fragility, should be made rigid and as large as possible; they should be provided with clearance angles of 5° to 10° and rake angles of 0° to 5°. Freer cutting can be obtained with larger rake angles, but chatter will develop unless the tool is extremely rigid. Chip breakers should be used for all alloys except 2011.

Box Tools. Tool holders for box tools commonly provide a front clearance angle of 8°; a cutting angle of 82° insures that the cutting face of the tool is parallel to the work axis. The top rake angle for machining 2011 alloy is 0°. Box tools for machining the other recommended alloys should be provided with a tapered V-groove ground on the face of the tool, parallel to the cutting edge; this groove will act as a chip breaker. If the groove is too wide, it will not break the chips.

Dimensional Control. Variations in the dimensions of consecutive pieces in one production lot machined in a single-spindle automatic bar machine are illustrated by the following example.

Example 903. Variation in Diameter of 29 Consecutive Pieces (Fig. 31)

Figure 31 shows the spread and distribution of variations in the form-turned 0.126/0.124-in. diameter on the 2011-T3 part shown in the inset sketch, as indicated by measurements made on 29 consecutively produced pieces. With a total variation range of 0.0009 in., the 29 parts were within less than half the allowable tolerance of ±0.001 in. on the 0.125-in. diameter. The reasonably even distribution of dimensions indicates that the ½-in. single-spindle automatic bar machine used was in good condition.

Where machining to close tolerances or to close relations between dimensions is imperative, careful selection of machine and the use of special procedures may be required, as shown in Example 904. In Example 905, the design of the part was changed so that close tolerances could be met, and in Example 906 close concentricity between turned and bored diameters was obtained by redesigning the part to be machined in a turret lathe.

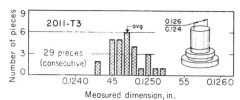

Fig. 31. Variation in diameter of parts produced in a single-spindle automatic bar machine (Example 903)

Example 904. Close Tolerances on 7075-T6 Gyro Cases (Fig. 32)

Figure 32 shows the close tolerances and dimensional relationships specified for gyro cases made from 2-in.-diam bar stock of alloy 7075-T6, and illustrates and gives details of the secondary machining operations by which these specifications were met. The cases were turned and bored in a prior operation, leaving about 0.040 in. on all diameters to be finish turned or bored.

The operations shown in Fig. 32 were performed in a 9-in. manually operated turret lathe that had spindle runout within 0.00005 in. and taper no more than 0.0001 in. in 6 in. An engine lathe of equivalent accuracy could have been used, but a turret lathe was preferred because all tools could be preset in the turret. Special equipment used on the turret lathe included a threading attachment and an air gage. (The use of either an air gage or an electronic gage insures greater speed and

accuracy in repositioning than usually are obtainable when dial indicators are used.)

To prevent overheating and consequent dimensional change of a locating surface, three cuts were made in the initial boring operation (on diameter A, in operation 1 in Fig. 32); 0.005 in. was left after the first cut, and 0.0005 in. after the second, for finishing. Operations 3 and 4 were done using a non-galling friction-drive mandrel made by pressing a nylon sleeve over an aluminum arbor, the sleeve being held by a screw and washer.

Additional procedures used to assure meeting dimensional requirements were:

1 Rough machined workpieces were cooled to room temperature before further operations were performed, because a temperature rise of 10 F would increase a 2-in. diameter about 0.0002 in.

2 Spindle rotation and power feeds were kept in the same direction for all operations, because tolerances that could be held were not always the same for both directions.

3 Because tool-point radii could not exceed 0.005 in., the points were honed to produce acceptable surface finishes.

Example 905. Design Change to Permit Use of Automatic Chucking Machine (Fig. 33)

The problem of holding size and concentricity in turning an alloy 380 die casting was solved by changing the design of the part, as shown in Fig. 33. The redesigned part could be machined in one setup, rather than two. Setup time and machining time were less, because turning was done in one chucking machine instead of two single-spindle turret lathes. By chucking at a location not over the bore, close control of size was possible. Also, close concentricity could be held in machining the revised part, because the pilot (0.5001-in. diameter) could be turned without unchucking the workpiece. The shank was cut off in a final operation. Cutting fluid was a 1-to-20 mixture of soluble oil and water.

Example 906. Close Concentricity Between Turned and Bored Diameters (Fig. 34)

Six machining operations were performed on the permanent mold casting for a gearbox cover shown in Fig. 34. Two boring operations (rough and finish) and chamfering were performed with tools set in the same holder. The 2.876/2.874-in. diameter had to be held concentric with the 7.5015/7.5005-in. diameter within 0.002 in. TIR. To accomplish this, both diameters were machined in the same setting. By machining on a turret lathe, it was possible to include the groove. Processing details are given in the table accompanying Fig. 34.

Production practices that have been followed in machining aluminum alloys in multiple-operation automatic machines under a variety of conditions are described in the three examples that follow. Other applications of multiple-operation machining are de-

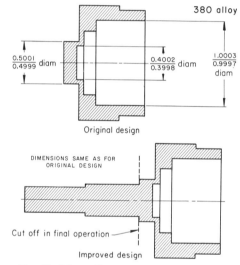

Fig. 33. Die casting redesigned to improve concentricity and dimensional accuracy in turning operations in an automatic chucking machine (Example 905)

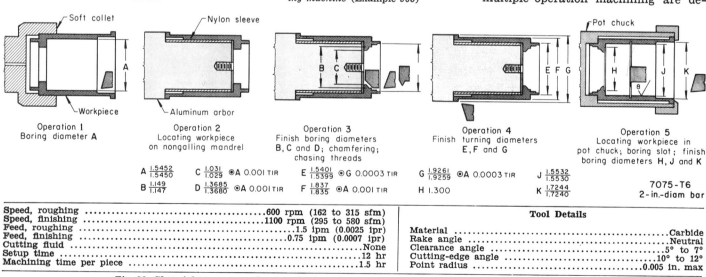

A $\frac{1.5452}{1.5450}$	C $\frac{1.031}{1.029}$ ⊚A 0.001 TIR	E $\frac{1.5401}{1.5399}$ ⊚G 0.0003 TIR	G $\frac{1.9261}{1.9259}$ ⊚A 0.0003 TIR	J $\frac{1.5532}{1.5530}$	
B $\frac{1.149}{1.147}$	D $\frac{1.3685}{1.3680}$ ⊚A 0.001 TIR	F $\frac{1.837}{1.835}$ ⊚A 0.001 TIR	H 1.300	K $\frac{1.7244}{1.7240}$	

7075-T6
2-in.-diam bar

Speed, roughing ....600 rpm (162 to 315 sfm)		
Speed, finishing ....1100 rpm (295 to 580 sfm)		**Tool Details**
Feed, roughing ....1.5 ipm (0.0025 ipr)		
Feed, finishing ....0.75 ipm (0.0007 ipr)		Material ....Carbide
Cutting fluid ....None		Rake angle ....Neutral
Setup time ....12 hr		Clearance angle ....5° to 7°
Machining time per piece ....1.5 hr		Cutting-edge angle ....10° to 12°
		Point radius ....0.005 in. max

Fig. 32. Close-tolerance secondary machining of gyro cases in a manual turret lathe (Example 904)

scribed in Examples 867, 868, 869, 872, 895, 904, 905 and 906, in this article.

Example 907. Machining of Thin-Wall Parts From Bar Stock (Fig. 35)

The multiple-operation machining of thin-wall parts from 2011-T3 bar stock is illustrated in Fig. 35. For all operations, spindle speed was 2053 rpm (maximum surface speed,

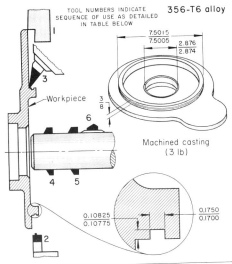

356-T6 alloy

TOOL NUMBERS INDICATE SEQUENCE OF USE AS DETAILED IN TABLE BELOW

Workpiece

Machined casting (3 lb)

Production rate	11.3 pieces per hour
Cycle time	5.27 min
Setup time	2 hr
Cutting fluid	Soluble-oil:water (1:25)

Operation 1. Face Mounting Surface
(Front of cross slide)

Tool:
Type ..Carbide insert (⅜-in. inscribed triangle)
Angles ....0° rake, 10° clearance
Life per grind ......1200 pieces (400 each index)
Operating conditions:
Speed ....550 rpm (2100 sfm)
Feed ....0.005 ipr
Depth of cut ....0.060 in.

Operation 2. Machine Groove
(Rear of cross slide)

Tool:
Type ....Carbide
Angles ....0° rake, 10° clearance
Life per grind ....2000 pieces
Operating conditions:
Speed ....550 rpm (1100 sfm)
Feed ....0.005 ipr
Depth of cut ....0.100 in.

Operation 3. Turn 7.5015/7.5005-In. Diameter
(Turret)

Tool:
Type ....Carbide in microbore cartridge
Angles ....10° rake, 10° clearance
Life per grind ....1500 pieces
Operating conditions:
Speed ....550 rpm (1100 sfm)
Feed ....0.005 ipr
Depth of cut ....0.010 in.

Operations 4, 5 and 6. Rough and Finish Bore 2.876/2.874-In. Diameter, and Chamfer
(Turret)

Rough boring tool:
Type ....Double-edged carbide cutter, fixed firm in boring bar
Angles .....10° axial, 0° radial rake; 10° clearance
Life per grind ....1500 pieces
Finish boring tool:
Type ....Double-edged carbide cutter, with 0.003-in. float in boring bar
Angles .....0° axial, 10° radial rake; 10° clearance
Life per grind ....2000 pieces
Chamfering tool:
Type ....Carbide
Angles ....0° rake, 10° clearance
Life per grind ....5000 pieces
Operating conditions:
Speed ....550 rpm (415 sfm)
Feed ....0.005 ipr
Depth of roughing cut ....0.060 in.
Depth of finishing cut ....0.010 in.

Fig. 34. Six-operation machining of a cast gear-box cover in a turret lathe (Example 906)

Source: Metals Handbook, 8th Ed., Vol. 3, ASM

676 sfm), and cutting fluid was a low-viscosity mineral oil with 5% fatty additive. Production rate was 240 pieces per hour. Tool materials and feeds are listed in the table with Fig. 35.

Example 908. Fourteen Operations to Produce a Thin-Wall Part From Bar Stock (Fig. 36)

The process used to machine the part shown in Fig. 36 resulted from about ten years of development. Except for straddle milling and anodizing, the part was completed when it left the automatic bar machine. The single-stage integrated machining operation produced concentric internal and external surfaces.

The first-station operations differed from conventional practice in that (a) an unusually wide forming cut was made, and (b) the use of a 45° spotting drill was eliminated, because the rigid bar to which the form drill was attached made spot drilling unnecessary.

Special features of the second-station operations included a form tool that closely controlled the width dimension and an adequate supply of cutting fluid to exterior surfaces and to the drill point, to insure dissipation of heat. Also, a slight angle was provided on the facing portion of the form tool to avoid a backoff tooling mark.

The operations at the third station were conventional form turning and form reaming; dimensional relations of diameters and lengths were fully controlled. The reamer left a maximum of 0.0012 in. of stock for the internal roller burnishing that followed.

The roller burnishing operation (at the fourth station) was selected in preference to ball burnishing because it required less end pressure (higher pressures could affect the drill slide adversely) and because minute shavings suspended in the cutting fluid were less likely to mar the surface finish. With roller burnishing, it was possible to obtain a 16-micro-in. surface finish and to meet a tolerance of 0.0003 in. without difficulty. The 0.707-in. diameter was shaved in preparation for thread rolling. An opposing roll on the shave tool holder served to maintain close dimensional tolerances, taking the place of the cross-slide cam-and-stop arrangement conventionally employed for this purpose in cross-forming operations.

The fifth-station operation consisted of thread rolling an outside surface and power recessing an inside surface. Because the part was made of one of the harder aluminum alloys (2024-T351), there was a probability that the two end (or outer) threads would shear or move outward during thread rolling. This was corrected by rolling an excess length of thread that was removed in the next operation. The power recessing operation was an improvement over stationary drawback recessing, because it provided an improved surface finish and eliminated chips that would normally hang in the O-ring groove.

The sixth-station operations removed the excess thread length and finish formed the sealing cone seat.

In the seventh station, the part number was marked on the workpiece; opposing support was provided to protect the thin-wall section.

Tapping of a 36-pitch internal thread and cutoff of the part were done in the eighth (final) station. The tapping operation was completed before the cutoff blade made contact with the work.

Example 909. Machining an Aircraft Forging (Fig. 37)

The forging shown in Fig. 37 was processed in two chucking operations in a six-spindle automatic chucking machine. Details of the machined part and of the operations are given in Fig. 37, and in the table with it.

In machining this part, major considerations were rigidity of holding chucks, and elimination of heavy side feeds and vibration. As noted in the machining sequence, the long end of the forging was machined first and the short end was chucked, because this arrangement was more able to resist the leverage of side-cutting forces, particularly at the outer extremity of the part. In both chucking operations, the use of side-cutting tools was held to a minimum.

The 45° metal-to-metal sealing surface, shown in the fourth position of the first chucking operation, was highly critical. To eliminate chatter and out-of-roundness, this surface was machined with roller support.

To prevent chucking marks in the second chucking operation, the chuck jaws did not grip finish-machined surfaces.

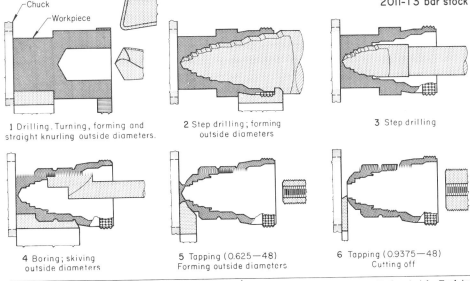

2011-T3 bar stock

1 Drilling. Turning, forming and straight knurling outside diameters.

2 Step drilling; forming outside diameters

3 Step drilling

4 Boring; skiving outside diameters

5 Tapping (0.625—48) Forming outside diameters

6 Tapping (0.9375—48) Cutting off

Operation	Tool material	Feed, ipr
Spindle Station 1		
Drill; turn	High speed steel	0.0045
Form; knurl	High speed steel	0.0016
Spindle Station 2		
Step drill	Carbide	0.0045
Form	Carbide	0.0015
Spindle Station 3		
Step drill	Carbide	0.0025

Operation	Tool material	Feed, ipr
Spindle Station 4		
Bore	Carbide	0.001
Skive	Carbide	0.002
Spindle Station 5		
Tap	High speed steel	0.0022
Form	Carbide	0.0011
Spindle Station 6		
Tap	High speed steel	0.0015
Cut off	High speed steel	0.001

Fig. 35. Operations for producing a complicated thin-wall part in an automatic bar machine (Example 907)

Milling

The characteristics of chip formation sometimes cause difficulty in milling of aluminum alloys. In some applications, chip ejection in the milling of deep slots or heavy cuts can be improved by changing from an alloy in the O or F temper to one in the T4 or T6 temper. In the T tempers, the chip is much less likely to clog the cutter. However, when aluminum is milled in the heat treated condition, production rate may be lower, because a lighter feed rate may be necessary, as demonstrated in the example that follows.

Example 910. Effect of Alloy Condition on Feed in End Milling (Fig. 38)

The alloy 7075 part shown in Fig. 38 was originally machined in the as-forged (F) condition. An engineering change required that the part have higher strength, and it was subsequently machined in the solution-treated-and-aged (T6) condition. As indicated by the data that accompany Fig. 38, the change in heat treatment necessitated a 50% reduction in feed; at the original feed, the higher strength of the T6 material produced excessive deflection in the end-milling cutters. When the part was machined in the F temper, the gummy nature of the chips had required close attention to cutter speed to utilize centrifugal force in ejecting chips from the path of the cutter.

If the operation described in Example 910 had been peripheral or face milling, it would probably have been unnecessary to reduce the feed rate, because the setup in peripheral or face milling usually has considerably greater rigidity than in end milling.

Power Requirements. Metal removal rates greater than 3.0 cu in. per horsepower per minute can be attained readily in production milling of aluminum alloys (see Example 915, where metal was removed at the rate of 6.75 cu in. per horsepower per minute). Some rules applicable to milling aluminum are:

1 If feed per tooth is doubled, the horsepower at the cutter must be increased in the ratio of 3 to 2, or 50%.
2 If the width of cut is doubled, the horsepower at the cutter must be doubled.
3 If the depth of cut is doubled, the horsepower at the cutter must be increased in the ratio of 1.9 to 1, or 90%.
4 If the depth of cut is halved and horsepower at the cutter remains the same, the feed may be increased by a factor of 2.5.
5 If the speed of the cutter is doubled and the feed per tooth is halved, the horsepower at the cutter must be increased by about 30%.

The example that follows illustrates the range of variables in slotting.

Example 911. Metal Removal Rates in Milling With Carbide Cutters (Table 20)

Tests were made with interlocking cutters of special design, using carbide inserts brazed to the cutter bodies. Each cutter half had two teeth, and its complement had two teeth of opposite helix. This gave each cutter unit four staggered teeth, with lapped faces and generous chip spaces for gang slotting. Cutters were 8 in. in diameter, with 25° positive axial rake, 15° radial rake, 0.06-in. corner radius, and 7° clearance on cutting edges. Spindle speed in all tests was 3600 rpm, using a 2.5-in.-diam arbor that was directly connected to a driving motor that provided a maximum of 100 hp to the milling cutter.

All tests were conducted on 7075-T6 aluminum plates (560 by 20 by 2 in.) that were mounted on vacuum chucks. A flood of soluble oil served as cutting fluid. Preliminary data are given in the upper portion of Table 20.

Based on the relationship between power requirement and optimum cutter life, the cutters employed in the tests were standardized in a production setup and additional data were obtained from production runs, as shown in the lower part of Table 20.

Cutter Design. For efficiency in milling aluminum, the cutter should have a radial rake angle of 10° to 20°, an axial rake angle of 15° to 45°, and end or peripheral clearance of 10° to 12°. Form-relieved cutters should have a relief of 10° on the profile.

Best results can be obtained with a cutter that has fewer teeth and larger positive rake angles than cutters for milling steel. Fewer teeth permit more chip space, which is especially important in milling aluminum, because speeds are usually much greater than those used in milling steel. To prevent chatter, however, the cutter should have enough teeth so that at least two teeth are engaged at all times.

Because of the high speeds used in milling aluminum, careful consideration must be given to the effect of centrifugal force on the cutter. This is more important with cutters of large diameter. Cutter bodies in which teeth are wedge locked and from which some of the teeth have been removed to provide greater chip space should not be operated at high speed. All cutters for high-speed milling that have inserted

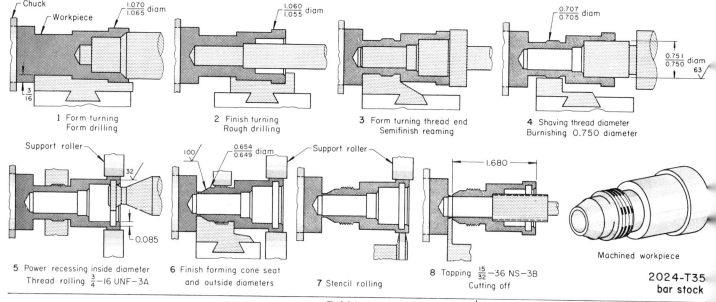

1 Form turning / Form drilling

2 Finish turning / Rough drilling

3 Form turning thread end / Semifinish reaming

4 Shaving thread diameter / Burnishing 0.750 diameter

5 Power recessing inside diameter / Thread rolling ¾–16 UNF–3A

6 Finish forming cone seat and outside diameters

7 Stencil rolling

8 Tapping 15/32–36 NS–3B / Cutting off

Machined workpiece

2024-T35 bar stock

Operation	Speed, sfm	Feed, ipr	Tool data		Pieces per grind
			Material	Type	
1 Form turn	324	0.0019	M2 high speed steel	0° rake, dovetail	800
Form drill	226	0.0052	High speed steel	Standard 118°	1600
2 Finish turn(a)	324	0.0019	M2 high speed steel	0° rake, dovetail	800
Rough drill	138	0.0052	High speed steel	Standard 118°	1600
3 Form turn	219	0.0019	M2 high speed steel	0° rake, dovetail	800
Ream(b)	226	0.0052	M3 high speed steel	.....	1600
4 Shave	219	0.0019	M2 high speed steel	0° rake	800
Burnish(c)	230	0.0052	M10 high speed steel	Standard	1600
5 Power recess(d)	282	0.001	M3 high speed steel	12° rake	1000
Thread roll	216	0.014	High speed steel	Standard	....
6 Finish form(e)	219	0.0019	M2 high speed steel	0° rake, dovetail	800
7 Stencil roll(f)	...	.....	M1 high speed steel	(g)	(h)
8 Tap	47	0.0052	High speed steel	16° to 18° hook angle	1600
Cutoff	130	0.0019	M2 high speed steel	Standard	1000

Stock ......1⅛-in. bar, weighing 0.166 lb before and 0.052 lb after, machining
Machine ....⅝-in. eight-spindle automatic bar machine
Spindle speed ....1169 rpm
Production rate ....211 pieces per hour

(a) Finish for both diameters to 0.005 in. TIR, with 0.005-in. depth of cut. (b) Ream all inside diameters to 0.002 in. TIR, leaving stock on 0.750-in. diameter for burnishing. (c) Burnish 0.750-in. diameter to 63-micro-in. finish. (d) Support rollers used with power recess tool to maintain 32-micro-in. finish and 0.002 in. TIR. Cut depth, 0.085 in. (e) Support rollers used to hold 0.005 in. TIR on all diameters on thread end and 100-micro-in. finish on 37° cone seat. Depth of cut, 0.068 in. (f) Support rolls used. (g) Sharp face, 3/32 in. high. (h) Minimum roll life of 15,000 pieces per grind.

Fig. 36. Setup, sequence of operations and machining details for producing a thin-wall coupling in an automatic bar machine (Example 908)

teeth (brazed or mechanically secured) should be dynamically balanced. Careful attention should be given to cutter adapters, cutter holders, arbors, spacers, and other components that rotate with the cutter.

End mills for aluminum should have sharp rake angles, with sufficient clearance to prevent "heeling". Neither rake nor clearance angles should be excessive, or "digging-in" will result. The cutter should contact the workpiece in such a manner that any torsional, or lateral, deflection will decrease the depth of cut.

Flute form and surface finish in the flute are important. Consequently, many of these cutters are made by grinding from the solid after heat treatment. The lips of an end mill (either plain two-flute or ball-nose) that is to be used for making plunge cuts directly into solid aluminum should have slightly greater clearances than is normal for these cutters, to prevent "heeling". Preferably, the faces of the cutting edges should have a surface finish of 1.5 micro-in., and should never be rougher than 3.5 micro-in.

In making plunge cuts directly into aluminum, the problem of chip ejection becomes acute. For this reason, it is best to feed the cutter into the material in such a way that, for each axial advance of the cutter (equal to about half the cutter diameter), the cutter is fed laterally about one diameter in an oscillating pattern, until the desired depth of cut is reached, rather than making a purely axial cut.

For milling slots, or pockets, where the end of the cutter is in contact with the workpiece, it is usually best to have the direction the same for the cut and the helix. However, when profiling with the periphery of the cutter, where the end of the cutter is not in contact with the workpiece, a combination of right-hand cut, left-hand helix gives the best results.

Router bits are a special type of end mill, modified to insure chip ejection at the speeds normally used for these cutters. Some cutters for general routing purposes may have two flutes with a helix angle of 25°. The best over-all performance in routing accurate slots or grooves is with a two-flute cutter having a 45° helix angle, with the direction of helix and of cut the same.

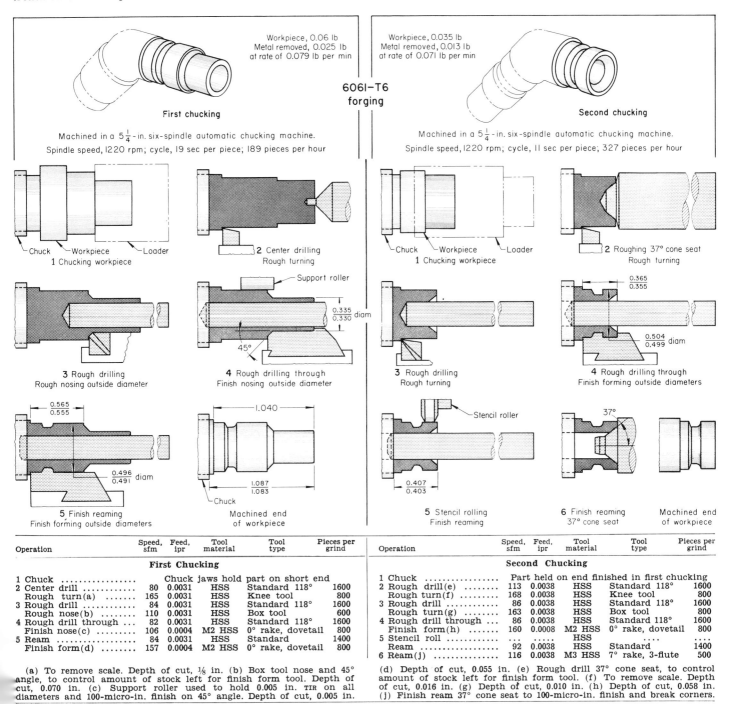

Operation	Speed, sfm	Feed, ipr	Tool material	Tool type	Pieces per grind
First Chucking					
1 Chuck	Chuck jaws hold part on short end				
2 Center drill	80	0.0031	HSS	Standard 118°	1600
Rough turn(a)	165	0.0031	HSS	Knee tool	800
3 Rough drill	84	0.0031	HSS	Standard 118°	1600
Rough nose(b)	110	0.0031	HSS	Box tool	600
4 Rough drill through ...	82	0.0031	HSS	Standard 118°	1600
Finish nose(c)	106	0.0004	M2 HSS	0° rake, dovetail	800
5 Ream	84	0.0031	HSS	Standard	1400
Finish form(d)	157	0.0004	M2 HSS	0° rake, dovetail	800

(a) To remove scale. Depth of cut, ⅛ in. (b) Box tool nose and 45° angle, to control amount of stock left for finish form tool. Depth of cut, 0.070 in. (c) Support roller used to hold 0.005 in. TIR on all diameters and 100-micro-in. finish on 45° angle. Depth of cut, 0.005 in.

Operation	Speed, sfm	Feed, ipr	Tool material	Tool type	Pieces per grind
Second Chucking					
1 Chuck	Part held on end finished in first chucking				
2 Rough drill(e)	113	0.0038	HSS	Standard 118°	1600
Rough turn(f)	168	0.0038	HSS	Knee tool	800
3 Rough drill	86	0.0038	HSS	Standard 118°	1600
Rough turn(g)	163	0.0038	HSS	Box tool	800
4 Rough drill through ...	86	0.0038	HSS	Standard 118°	1600
Finish form(h)	160	0.0008	M2 HSS	0° rake, dovetail	800
5 Stencil roll	...	...	HSS	....	...
Ream	92	0.0038	HSS	Standard	1400
6 Ream(j)	116	0.0038	M3 HSS	7° rake, 3-flute	500

(d) Depth of cut, 0.055 in. (e) Rough drill 37° cone seat, to control amount of stock left for finish form tool. (f) To remove scale. Depth of cut, 0.016 in. (g) Depth of cut, 0.010 in. (h) Depth of cut, 0.058 in. (j) Finish ream 37° cone seat to 100-micro-in. finish and break corners.

Fig. 37. Machining a 6061-T6 forging in two chuckings in a six-spindle automatic chucking machine (Example 909)

Cutters for routing stacked sheet stock should be designed with a single flute and a helix angle of 25° to 45°. An integral pilot running in an outboard bearing is used on some of these cutters to help control deflection.

All cutters should have a 15° hook angle on the cutting lip. The flute should be of 0.09-in. uniform depth, with a smooth gullet extending ⅛ in. inward from the lip. The lips should be radially relieved on the periphery to 0.003 to 0.007 in. per 1/16-in. width of land behind the cutting edge.

In the example that follows, an end mill assembly with an unsupported length of nine diameters was used.

Example 912. End Milling With a Long Unsupported Cutter (Fig. 39)

The angular aluminum alloy aircraft forging illustrated in Fig. 39 was end milled in a vertical, three-dimensional, numerically controlled profiler. Milling operations on surfaces other than indicated in Fig. 39 were also performed by end milling, but offered no problem because the spindle could be brought closer to the work. For end milling the portion shown, it was necessary to have an unsupported length of nine to one (cutter and adapter), to permit the spindle to clear the workpiece. Although greater unsupported length can be tolerated in milling aluminum than with harder metals, nine to one is unusual, and special techniques are needed. The special tapered adapter shown in Fig. 39 was helpful in maintaining rigidity. During all end milling of the area shown, and especially during roughing, the cutter was kept uniformly loaded, to minimize vibration and chatter. Acceptable surface finish was obtained by using an extremely light (0.007 in.) cut in the finishing operation. By using this technique, the finishing cutters had an indefinitely long life.

The heavy fixture to which the workpiece was clamped also added rigidity to the setup. The workpiece was clamped at various points on the edges. Cutter and operating details are given in the table with Fig. 39.

Speed. Nominal speeds for peripheral, face and end milling are given in Tables 21 and 22. Factors affecting speed are alloy being milled, tool material, and depth of cut (roughing or finishing). A major variable that is not reflected in the tables is chip disposal. Provided that chips can be adequately ejected from the cutting zone, speeds for carbide cutters are limited mainly by the capabilities of the machine. However, when the speed is too high for a particular setup, the cutter teeth may not have sufficient time to remove stock at the proper rate because of erratic feeding; the cutter teeth may "dig and ride" or "cut and skip". Optimum speed depends on the machine, work metal, depth of cut, and power.

Under certain conditions, milling speeds as high as 15,000 sfm have been used. However, speeds this high are rarely feasible. Speeds of 2000 to 4000 sfm are frequently used, as illustrated by the next two examples. In Example 913, metal was removed by face mills in a vertical position, and only a portion of the area presented to the cutter was milled. Thus, chip disposal was not a problem. In Example 914, two opposite sides of a casting were face milled simultaneously in a duplex machine.

Example 913. Face Milling a Die Casting at High Speed (Table 23)

The die-cast gear box shown in Table 23 required two surfaces to be milled parallel to each other within ±0.010 in. By using a milling machine with a large table, both sides

Table 20. Performance Data for Carbide Milling Cutters Used in Slotting (Example 911)

Number of cutters on arbor	Width of slots, in.	Depth per slot, in.	Total feed per min, in.	Feed per tooth, in.	Power consumed at cutter, hp	Metal removed per min, cu in.	Metal removed per hp per min, cu in.
			Preliminary Test Data				
5	1.370	0.640	72	0.010	80	315	3.94
5	1.370	0.640	60	0.0083	80	262	3.28
4	1.725	1.250	17	0.0023	53	150	2.83
4	1.725	0.880	120	0.0167	100	728	7.28
3	1.550	0.600	63	0.0087	65	177	2.72
			Production Data				
11	1.695	0.231(a)	86	0.012	100	377	3.77
11	1.445	0.275(a)	86	0.012	100	377	3.77

(a) Depth of cut per pass

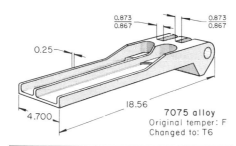

Operating condition	F temper	T6 temper
Speed, sfm	400	400
Feed, ipt	0.008	0.004
Depth of cut, in.	2.5	2.5
Width of cut, in.	0.870	0.870
Cutting fluid	Soluble-oil:water (1:25)	
Setup time, min	20	20
Time per piece, hr	2	4.2

Machining was done in horizontal and vertical 15-hp milling machines. Cutters were radial, wheel-type end mills of high speed steel, 2.5 in. in diameter and 0.870 in. wide, with 10° radial rake, 30° axial rake. One drill jig and two milling fixtures were used for holding work.

Fig. 38. Forging for which change from F to T6 temper required a 50% reduction of milling feed (Example 910)

of the gear box could be milled by placing two boxes on the machine table at one time, one side being milled in the first station and the opposite side in the second station. Because of the shape of the workpiece (relatively small surface to be milled in proportion to the total area presented to the cutters), chip disposal was not a problem, and speed could be higher than normal. Machine, cutter and operating details are given in Table 23.

Example 914. Face Milling Parallel Sides Simultaneously in a Duplex Machine (Fig. 40)

Face milling two opposite sides was the first machining operation performed on the casting shown in Fig. 40. Maintaining required dimensions in subsequent operations depended greatly on the accuracy obtained in milling the sides. Parallelism was easily maintained by milling the two sides simultaneously, because the workpiece did not have to be moved and reclamped.

A 10-hp duplex machine was used for this operation. This type of machine afforded two advantages in addition to good dimensional control. First, after the initial cut, the spindles were advanced slightly to take a "skim" (finish) cut as the table returned to the start position. Second, milling both sides at one time increased productivity compared with milling each side separately. Details of the milling cutters and operation are tabulated below Fig. 40.

Feed. Nominal feeds for peripheral, face and end milling are given in Tables 21 and 22. For wheel-type cutters (peripheral and face), the alloy being milled has little effect on feed. Depth of cut has some effect, although usually this is not large. Some reduction in feed is usually made when high speed steel cutters are replaced by carbide

cutters, mainly because the speeds are usually greater for carbide cutters. Depth of cut (roughing or finishing), particularly in face milling, has some effect on the rate of feed selected.

For end milling, the principal factor affecting rate of feed is cutter diameter (as shown in Table 22), because small end-milling cutters lack rigidity.

For additional information on feed, see pages 184 to 186, in "Milling".

Depth of cut is commonly about 0.250 in. for roughing and 0.025 in. or less for finishing. If power is available, depth of cut can be several times greater than the above when large amounts of metal are to be removed.

In machining aircraft components, skin milling, which involves deep cuts (sometimes 2 in. or more), is common practice. Machines used for skin milling are basically planer mills that have evolved into elaborate tracer-controlled machines. The milling is ordinarily done by means of large peripheral-type (slabbing) cutters.

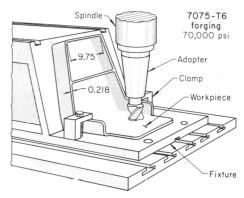

Cutter Details

Type	End mill
Size	2-in. diam with 0.187-in. corner radius, 4-in. cutter length, 1¼-in.-diam shank, 6½-in. over-all length
Number of teeth	2
Material	High speed steel

Operating Conditions

Speed	800 rpm (420 sfm)
Feed	0.008 ipt
Depth of cut:	
Roughing	¼ in. approx
Finishing, first pass	0.050 in.
Finishing, second pass	0.007 in.
Cutting fluid	Soluble-oil:water
Setup time(a)	2 hr, 10 min
Production rate	4 hr per piece
Tool life per grind, roughing	12 pieces
Tolerance	±0.010 in.
Finish obtained	63 micro-in.

(a) 2 hr for attaching project plate to table and 10 min for attaching workpiece to fixture

Fig. 39. Milling setup arranged so that the spindle cleared the workpiece (Example 912)

Table 21. Nominal Speeds and Feeds for Peripheral and Face Milling of Aluminum Alloys With High Speed Steel Cutters

Alloy	Speed(a), sfm Roughing	Finishing	Feed(a), ipt Roughing	Finishing	Speed(a), sfm Roughing	Finishing	Feed(a), ipt Roughing	Finishing
	Peripheral Milling(b)				Face Milling(c)			
Non-heat-treated, cast	900	1300	0.018	0.016	1000	1500	0.022	0.014
Heat treated, cast	900	1300	0.016	0.014	800	1200	0.022	0.014
Cold drawn, wrought	850	1200	0.016	0.014	800	1200	0.022	0.014
Heat treated, wrought	650	900	0.016	0.014	800	1200	0.022	0.014

(a) Roughing cuts, 0.250 in. deep; finishing cuts, 0.025 in. deep. (b) High speed steel cutters (M2 or M7). (c) High speed steel cutters (M2 or M7). If carbide cutters are used, maximum speed of the machine is allowed, but feed should be decreased 10 to 15%.

Table 22. Nominal Speeds and Feeds for End Milling of Aluminum Alloys With High Speed Steel and Carbide Cutters

Alloy	Speed(a), sfm Roughing	Finishing	Feed(a), ipt Roughing, cutter diam, in. 1/4	3/4	1 to 2	Finishing, cutter diam, in. 1/4	3/4	1 to 2
High Speed Steel Cutters (M2 or M7)								
Non-heat-treated, cast	800	1000	0.004	0.008	0.010	0.003	0.005	0.007
Heat treated, cast	600	800	0.004	0.008	0.010	0.003	0.005	0.007
Cold drawn, wrought	600	800	0.004	0.008	0.010	0.003	0.005	0.007
Heat treated, wrought	600	800	0.003	0.008	0.010	0.002	0.005	0.007
Carbide Cutters								
All castings	1000	1300	0.004	0.008	0.010	0.003	0.005	0.007
Cold drawn, wrought	1000	1300	0.004	0.008	0.010	0.003	0.005	0.007
Heat treated, wrought	1000	1300	0.003	0.008	0.010	0.002	0.005	0.007

(a) Roughing cuts, 0.050 in. deep; finishing cuts, 0.015 in. deep.

The example that follows gives details of a skin milling operation in which the depth of cut was far greater than that made in conventional milling.

Example 915. Skin Milling of an Aircraft Wing Skin (Table 24)

Climb milling with a peripheral cutter was used to skin mill a billet of 7075-T6 alloy 133 in. long by 66 in. wide by 3 in. thick. A cutter having only four teeth was used, which reduced the chip problem when milling at high speed with an unusually deep (2 in.) cut. Metal removal was at the rate of 6.75

Table 23. Processing Details for Face Milling a Die-Cast Gear Box (Example 913) (a)

Machine .... Three-spindle profile-milling machine; table size, 132 by 28 in.

Cutter:
Type: Face, insert-blade, 14-in.-diam body
Material .... C-2 carbide inserts, alloy steel body
Inserts .... Mechanically secured, four cutting edges
Angles .... 5° pos axial and radial rake

Operating Conditions

Speed .... 650 rpm (2330 sfm)
Feed .... 0.011 ipt
Depth of cut:
Roughing .... 1/8 to 3/16 in.
Finishing .... 0.015 in.
Cutting fluid .... None
Setup time .... 1.5 hr
Downtime for changing tools .... 10 min
Production rate .... 11.3 pieces per hour
Cutter life .. 300 pieces per edge (four edges)

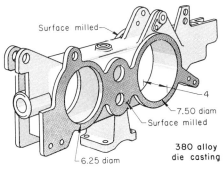

Surface milled
4
7.50 diam
Surface milled
380 alloy die casting
6.25 diam

(a) Data are for milling the two faces of the gear box, illustrated above, to parallelism within ±0.010 in., and to a 45-micro-in. finish.

cu in. per horsepower per minute (675 cu in. per min in the 100-hp machine used). Table 24 gives details of the machine, cutter and operation.

Cutting fluid should be supplied copiously and under pressure to the tool and workpiece. It is important, particularly with carbide cutters, that the cutting fluid be supplied uniformly and consistently to all parts of the cutter, to prevent overheating and sudden chilling of the carbide tips. Rapid heating and cooling is extremely detrimental to the life of carbide cutters.

For high-speed milling, emulsions of soluble oil and water at a 1-to-15 ratio are recommended; for low-speed milling, a ratio of 1 to 30 is recommended. Kerosine is effective with form cutters. When modified T-slot cutters were used to mill a blade-root slot in aluminum wheels for axial-flow compressors to a tolerance of less than 0.001 in., no cutting fluid except kerosine could produce the required accuracy and surface finish (see the sections on cutting fluids on page 443 in this article and on page 188 in the article "Milling").

Form milling is often an economical method for machining complicated shapes in aluminum. The complexity of form that can be built into the design of a cutter is limited, as, for example, when the tangent of the curvature approaches 90° to the horizontal plane. As a result, secondary operations are sometimes required to complete a complex form.

Basic types of form cutters have cam-relieved teeth or shaped teeth. Cam-relieved teeth are sharpened by grinding the tooth faces without changing the form. If surface finish is a secondary consideration, straight-tooth cutters are used, because they are easier to sharpen. However, if surface finish is important, helical cutters must be used. Although helical cutters may be operated at higher speeds and greater feeds than straight-tooth cutters, they require considerably greater care when being sharpened.

Shape form cutters are made either with integral teeth or blade inserts. These cutters are less expensive than integral-tooth, cam-relieved cutters, but they require more equipment and more skill in grinding.

Feasibility of form milling depends on several variables, including cutter cost, volume of production, design of workpiece, and type of milling machine available. Thus, for small production lots, the cost of a single form cutter must be compared with the cost of several cutters of less complex shape. For form milling, the workpiece must be fairly large, have no thin sections, and must be capable of being well secured. Finally, form milling requires high-powered equipment that is rugged and in good operating condition.

The example that follows describes an application of form milling and shows the production quantity required to justify a high-cost form cutter.

Example 916. Cost of Standard vs Form Milling (Fig. 41)

The contour of the workpiece shown in Fig. 41 could be milled equally well by using five standard cutters for five separate operations or by using one specially designed form cutter that could mill the contour in a single operation. The operations performed by both methods are listed in the table accompanying Fig. 41. Although cost of cutters was the same for form and standard milling, time for form milling was only about one-third that for standard milling.

Automatic Control. The generally good machining characteristics of aluminum alloys make them especially well adapted to automatic control, by which extremely complex shapes can be milled efficiently. The two examples that follow give details of two widely different applications where automatic control was used. The first of the two examples deals with rise-and-fall mill-

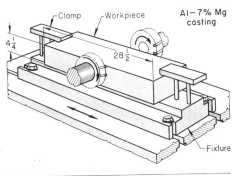

Al—7% Mg casting
Clamp
Workpiece
4 1/4
28 1/2
Fixture

Cutter Details

Type .... Face mill, inserted blade
Size .... 6-in. diam
Number of teeth 12
Material .... Carbide-tipped blades

Operating Conditions

Speed .... 2345 rpm (3680 sfm)
Feed .... 0.0055 ipt
Depth of cut .... 1/8 in. max
Cutting fluid .... None
Setup time .... 1.5 hr
Downtime for changing tools .... 15 min
Production rate .... 31 pieces per hour
Cutter life .... 100 pieces per grind (approx)
Tolerances:
Flatness .... Within 0.001 in.
Width .... ±0.003 in.
Parallelism error .... 0.005 in. max
Finish .... 63 micro-in. max

Fig. 40. Face milling parallel surfaces on opposite sides of a casting simultaneously (Example 914)

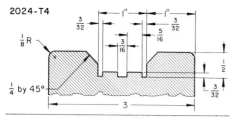

Operating Conditions(a)

Form milling (one pass)(b) ....3 ipm feed
Standard milling (five passes)(c)
 1 Side mill slot ....8 ipm feed
 2 Side mill center slot ....8 ipm feed
 3 Straddle mill reliefs ....5 ipm feed
 4 Straddle mill two ¼-in.-by-45°
   chamfers ....8 ipm feed
 5 Straddle mill two ⅛-in. radii ......8 ipm feed

Time and Cost Analysis

Time per piece:
 Form milling ....2.54 min
 Standard milling ....7.79 min
  Time saved using form milling ....5.25 min
Value of time saved per piece,
 using form cutter(d) $0.877

(a) For all operations, cutter speed was 75 sfm, and sulfurized oil was used as cutting fluid. (b) Cutter cost $100. (c) Each cutter cost $20 (total, $100). (d) At $10 per hr.

Fig. 41. Contour that could be milled in a single pass using a form cutter or in five operations using standard milling cutters (Example 916)

ing of a relatively small part; the second example describes the milling of a large forging to about one-fourth of its as-forged weight.

Example 917. Milling a Channel-Shaped Part With Tracer Control (Fig. 42)

The channel-shaped part shown in Fig. 42 was machined from a 3-by-5-in. segment of alloy 7075-T6 bar stock. The machining sequence was as follows:

1 The channel portion was rough and finish milled to final dimensions.
2 One flange of the channel was milled to 0.160 in. thick and the opposite flange was milled to 0.100 in. thick.
3 The flanges were profiled to final contour and the ends milled to desired shape.

Other details are given with Fig. 42.

Example 918. Milling a 1670-Lb Forging With Numerical Control (Fig. 43)

The part shown in Fig. 43 was made from a 7075 alloy blocker forging that weighed 1670 lb. Over-all measurements of the forging were 133 by 68 by 16 in., and those of the finished part were 131 by 66 by 14 in. The weight of the finished part was 393 lb, 1277 lb of metal having been removed in machining. With the part held in a special milling fixture, rough profile machining was performed in a tape-controlled three-axis profile milling machine. A special boring fixture was used for rough line boring the 5.50 and 8.75-in.-diam trunnion holes. After roughing cuts were completed, approximately 0.120 in. of metal remained to be removed by finish machining after the forging was heat treated to the T6 temper. Special fixtures prevented warpage during heat treating and in finish milling. Machining was completed using the same numerical-tape-controlled machine. Details of the process, machine and cutter are given with Fig. 43.

Dimensional accuracy is affected by residual stress in the workpiece, induced stress caused by milling, built-up edge on cutters, and dull cutters. Workpieces with complex shapes or variable section thickness, especially in the aged condition, are more difficult to mill to close tolerances. To achieve dimensional stability and maintain close tolerances, residual stress must be avoided. Some of the methods include straddle or opposed-cutter milling,

Table 24. Processing Details for Skin Milling an Aircraft Wing Skin (Example 915)

Machine ....Skin mill, 45 by 12 ft, gantry type; 100 hp; 3600 rpm; vacuum-chuck holding; original cost, $500,000
Cutter:
 Type ....Peripheral
 Material ....C-2 carbide inserts, brazed to 4340 steel body
 Number of teeth 4
 Size ....11-in.-diam, 6 in. wide
 Rake angles ....25° axial, 12° radial
 Clearance ....7° primary, 12° secondary
 Hook angle ....15°

Operating Conditions

Speed ....3600 rpm (10,400 sfm)
Feed ....0.006 ipt (75 ipm)
Depth of cut ....2 in.
Width of cut ....4½ in.
Cutting fluid ....Soluble-oil:water (1:30)
Setup time ....1 hr(a)
Production time ....40 hr per skin

Tolerance ....±0.005 in.

(a) Average time for moving billet to table, locating billet, installing and setting cutter.

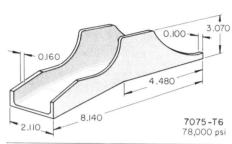

7075-T6
78,000 psi

Machine ......Horizontal-bed milling machine 22 by 96 in., with hydraulic tracer rise and fall
Cutter:
 Material ....Modified M2 high speed steel
 Size ....12-in. diam
 Rake angles ....15° radial, 30° axial
Accessories ....Contour templates and mill fixtures

Operating Conditions

Speed ....310 rpm (974 sfm)
Feed ....0.005 ipt
Depth of cut ....2.50 in.
Cutting fluid ....Soluble-oil:water (1:25)
Production rate ....1 piece per hour
Setup time ....5 min

Tolerance on significant dimensions ..±0.002 in.

Fig. 42. Channel-shaped part that was milled in a horizontal-bed machine equipped with hydraulic tracer (Example 917)

rough milling before heat treating, rough milling and straightening (hot or cold) before final milling, and milling and final straightening (hot or cold). The neutral axis of each increment of the workpiece should be the centerline for stock removal.

In the following example, distortion in a machined part was virtually eliminated by an improvement in the heat treating process — namely, by the use of a subzero quench in cooling the original forging from the solution-treating temperature.

Example 919. Eliminating Distortion in a Milled Part by Subzero Quenching (Fig. 44)

The fitting shown in Fig. 44 was forged of alloy 7075 and machined in the T6 condition. To overcome the distortion that resulted, the part had to be annealed, hot straightened, and heat treated a second time. In an attempt to avoid these corrective measures, premachining processing was changed to the following: Solution heat treat the as-received forging, quench in liquid nitrogen at −320 F, and age to the T6 condition. After machining, the finished part was again solution treated, water quenched, and aged to the T6 condition.

When the new method was employed, tooling holes were within ±0.002 in. of alignment, whereas the same holes in a part made by the old method had been out of alignment by as much as 0.020 in. Also, the new method saved about 9 hr per cycle. (Straightening time alone for the old method was 8 hr.)

Sawing

Contour cutting of aluminum alloys is usually done by band sawing; straight cutting is done on a circular saw, band saw, power hacksaw, or abrasive cutoff wheel. Circular saws or band saws are preferred for rapid cutoff of rod and bar stock; either can be readily adapted for high-speed, automatic work handling.

Linear feed rates as high as 30 to 80 in. per min are sometimes used in cutoff of stock 2 to 8 in. thick, for cutting rates of 50 to 250 sq in. per min.

Recommended tooth angles and contours for the three types of saws are given in Table 25.

Circular Sawing. Peripheral speeds are 2000 to 15,000 sfm for circular saws, depending on the saw material, the type of cut and the ability of the machine to withstand high speeds (Table 25). The limiting factor is usually the maximum *safe* operating speed of the machine and blade.

Feed rate for circular sawing ranges from 4 to 24 ipm, depending mainly on the alloy being sawed [see footnote (c) in Table 25]. Width of section being sawed and speed of the saw have some bearing on the rate of feed.

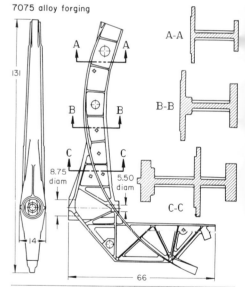

7075 alloy forging

Machine ....Three-axis profile milling machine, numerically controlled, 172 by 52 by 18 in.
Cutter:
 Material ....Modified M2 high speed steel
 Number of cutters 27
 Size of cutters ...0.75-in.-diam by 3¾ in. long to 3.00-in.-diam by 8 in. long
 Rake angles ....10° radial, 30° axial

Operating Conditions

Speed ....200 to 450 sfm
Feed ....0.006 to 0.013 ipt
Depth of cut, axial dimension ...0.12 to 7.00 in.
Width of cut,
 radial dimension ......0.37 in. to cutter diam
Machining time, each part ....91 hr(a)
Cutting fluid ....Soluble-oil:water (1:25)

Tolerance on critical dimensions .....±0.002 in.
Surface finish ....60 to 120 micro-in.

(a) Roughing, 29 hr; finishing, 62 hr

Fig. 43. Part that was machined from a large blocker forging by numerically controlled profile milling (Example 918)

Recommended operating conditions for circular saws having carbide teeth are given also in Table 26. For smoother cuts, blades may have about twice as many teeth as indicated in Table 26—especially blades of large diameter (24 to 84 in.).

In production sawing, carbide-tipped blades usually have much longer life than high speed steel blades, as shown in the example that follows. In this example, speed is less than half that recommended in Table 25 and feed is more than twice the rate shown in Table 25. The relative thinness of the plate (¼ in.) was probably the main reason for the marked deviation from the recommended speed and feed.

Example 920. High Speed Steel vs Carbide-Tipped Blades in Circular Sawing (Table 27)

Average blade life between grinds when sawing ¼-in. 7075-T6 plate with high speed steel blades was approximately 8 hr, because heat generated in sawing caused aluminum chips to weld to the blades. A carbide-tipped saw blade eliminated the chip-welding problem, and blade life between grinds was about 00 hr. Conditions of sawing with the carbide-tipped blades are shown in Table 27.

Selection of sawing machine and handling equipment can have a marked effect on efficiency, as demonstrated in the following example.

Example 921. Circular Sawing of Large Plates

Alloy 7075-T6 plates, 180 by 32 by 1½ in. and weighing about 800 lb, were cut on a diagonal with a table saw having a 14-in.-diam blade with carbide-tipped teeth. A stand equipped with rollers was used to support the plate, which was placed on the stand by a fork lift truck. Four men were required to guide, hold down, and push the plate through the sawing operation.

Production time was cut by one third (from 0 to 20 min per piece), and only one operator was required, when a special sawing machine with an over-arm clamping fixture with five pivot holddowns was installed. This special machine used a 28-in.-diam blade with carbide-tipped teeth. The automatic head feed, and swivel action of the fixture and holddowns, enabled the equipment to make longitudinal cuts of 16 ft in a single setup or 23 ft in two setups. The machine was capable of sawing plate up to 5 in. thick.

Band Sawing. Hard-tooth, flexible-back carbon steel bands are used at about 2500 sfm for heavy cuts, or 5000 sfm for medium cuts; spring temper bands, at speeds up to 7500 sfm, may be used in sawing thin sheet (Table 25). ("Friction" sawing may employ even higher speeds.) For data on speeds for contour band sawing various aluminum alloys in several ranges of thickness, see Table 8 on page 222.

Feed rates in band sawing usually range from 2 to 24 ipm, varying inversely with thickness of the section being cut. If the work-metal thickness is less than ¼ in., near-maximum feed can be used, whereas if the thickness is 2 in. or more, a feed near the low side of the above range should be used.

The two examples that follow compare milling and contour band sawing for producing a shape from an aluminum alloy plate and in fabricating a honeycomb core. In both applications, band sawing was faster and cheaper.

Example 922. Contour Sawing of a Large Plate (Fig. 45)

An aluminum alloy plate weighing 1440 lb and measuring 48 by 60 by 5 in. was rough machined in a milling machine to obtain the contour shown in Fig. 45. Milling required about 4½ hr. The same part was produced in 67 min in a contour band saw, cutting at a rate of 15 sq in. per min. The area cut was 1000 sq in.

Sawing was done with a high speed steel blade (hook tooth, raker set, 6 pitch, 1 in. wide, 0.035 in. thick), using a heavy-duty chemical solution as a cutting fluid. A dimensional tolerance of ±0.015 in. was maintained

Example 923. Fabrication of Aluminum Honeycomb Core for Bonded Aircraft Pod Fin (Fig. 46)

The core shown in Fig. 46 was made of 5052 alloy foil and expected production was 500 parts (not including parts scrapped or destructively tested). When a milling machine was employed, the time required for complete fabrication of one part was 40 hr, 12 hr of which was devoted exclusively to milling. The cost of milling, using a circular-knife cutter (so-called bologna slicer) and a depth of cut of 0.250 in. per pass, was $160.

When contour band sawing was employed, machining time was reduced to about 30 min

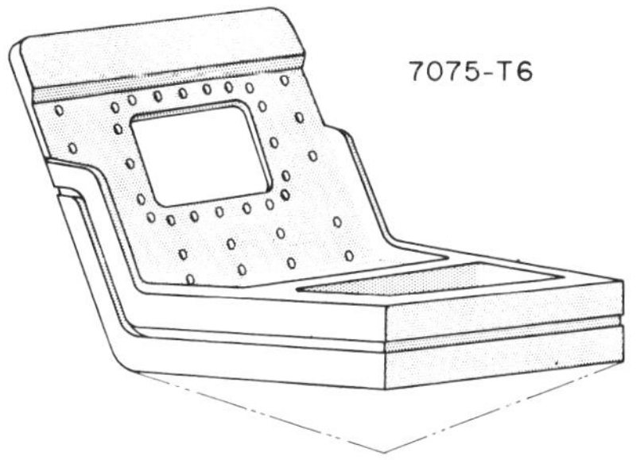

Fig. 44. Fitting in which distortion was eliminated by quenching from the solution-treating temperature in liquid nitrogen at −320 F before milling (Example 919)

(15 min per side) and machining cost was reduced to $4 per part. Details of the sawing process were as follows:

1 Precool fixture 1 hr before use by circulating a cold mixture of 60% ethylene glycol and 40% water through the fixture.
2 Load core into fixture.
3 Spray core cells with tap water so that each cell has 1/32 in. of water standing in the bottom.
4 Carefully lay lead weights on core to hold core firmly against fixture face.
5 Allow 3 to 5 min for water to freeze.
6 Remove weights.
7 Saw honeycomb with carbon steel band saw at speed of 10,000 sfm. (Blade: regular tooth, raker set, 14 pitch, 1 in. wide, 30⅓ ft long.)
8 After sawing, warm the fixture for 5 to 7 min by circulating warm mixture of 60% ethylene glycol and 40% water through it.
9 Remove core from fixture.
10 Repeat procedure for sawing other side, except that the sawed side is down on the second fixture.
11 After the second sawing operation, clean the core by spraying with tap water to remove all sawing particles, and blowing dry.

Power hacksawing is commonly done at 140 to 160 strokes per min with a feed of 0.015 in. per stroke (Table 25). The higher speed is recommended for sawing non-heat-treated cast aluminum alloys and the lower speed (140 strokes per min) for all other aluminum alloys.

Cutting Fluid. Although circular saws can be operated satisfactorily on aluminum alloys at moderate speeds and medium cuts without a cutting fluid, it is advisable to supply copious amounts of soluble-oil:water emulsion (1:20) for all high-speed cutting. The cutting fluid should flood the blade and workpiece under slight pressure, and should be filtered or settled before recycling. In some applications, the addition of a little kerosine or lard oil to the emulsion has been beneficial. Soap solutions can be substituted for oil emulsions.

For band saws, some cutting fluid is essential for all but the lightest cuts. A wide selection of compounds is available, ranging from tallow or grease sticks to kerosine-thinned mineral-base lubricating oil or emulsions of soluble oil and water. It is often more convenient to use a fluid lubricant, supplied generously through a recycling system.

For hacksawing, procedures are similar to those for band sawing.

Grinding

The harder, free-cutting aluminum alloys are comparatively easy to grind. The non-free-cutting alloys, particularly in their softer tempers, are likely

Table 25. Recommended Tooth Angles, Contours and Practice for Sawing Aluminum Alloys

Tool material	Feed control	Tooth angles and contours: Cutting angle	Top rake	Clearance angles: Primary	Secondary	Side	Side rake	Tooth spacing	Set	Speed, sfm	Feed, ipm
Circular Saws											
High speed steel	Hand	69° to 79°	5° to 12°	6° to 9°	25° to 35°	1° to 2°	0° to 15°	(a)	(b)	2000 to 7000	4 to 24(c)
	Power	61° to 74°	10° to 20°	6° to 9°	25° to 35°	1° to 2°	0° to 15°	(a)	(b)	2000 to 7000	4 to 24(c)
Carbide-tipped	Hand	76° to 83°	1° to 5°	6° to 9°	25° to 35°	1° to 2°	0° to 10°	(a)	(b)	10,000 to 15,000	4 to 24(c)
	Power	71° to 79°	5° to 10°	6° to 9°	25° to 35°	1° to 2°	0° to 10°	(a)	(b)	10,000 to 15,000	4 to 24(c)
Band Saws											
Spring temper or hard-tooth, flexible back	Hand	72° to 80°	5° to 10°	5° to 8°	30° to 40°	....	5° to 15°(d)	(e)	(f)	2500 to 7500(g)	2 to 24
	Power	62° to 75°	10° to 20°	5° to 8°	30° to 40°	....	5° to 15°(d)	(e)	(f)	2500 to 7500(g)	2 to 24
Hacksaws											
Hard-tooth, flexible back	Hand or power	55° to 75°	10° to 25°	5° to 10°	30° to 40°	....	....	(h)	(j)	140 to 160 strokes per min	0.015 in. per stroke

(a) Coarse; generally two or three teeth should be engaged at all times. (b) Alternate set or chip-breaker teeth. (c) Feed for hard alloys, to 17 ipm; for soft alloys, 17 to 24 ipm. (d) Resulting from alternate set. (e) Tooth spacing for heavy work, 4 to 5 per in.; for general work, up to 7 per in.; for thin stock, up to 11 per in. (f) Alternate set. (g) Speed for heavy work, up to 2500 sfm; for general work, 4000 to 5500 sfm; for thin stock, up to 7500 sfm. (h) For hand feed control, 10 to 15 per in.; for power feed, 5 to 10 per in. (j) Wavy set or alternate set.

Source: Metals Handbook, 8th Ed., Vol. 3, ASM

Table 26. Recommended Conditions for Circular Saws With Carbide Teeth

Blade diameter, in.	Number of teeth(a)	Blade speed, sfm	Power requirement, hp
84	60	480 to 10,500	250 at 900 rpm
54	36	15,000	75 at 1200 rpm
36	36	16,000	75 at 1750 rpm
24	36	10,600	75 at 1750 rpm
12	50, 70, 80	5,000	20 at 1750 rpm
10	190	9,000	5 at 3450 rpm

(a) Feed is normally about 0.001 in. per tooth.

Table 27. Conditions for Circular Sawing ¼-In. Plate of Alloy 7075-T6 With Carbide-Tipped Blades (Example 920)

Machine ......Special table saw (144 by 60 by ½ in.) with automatic saw feed and pneumatic plate clamping

Saw blade:
Material ....Carbide-tipped
Blade diameter ....10 in.
Number of teeth 60
Tooth thickness ....0.120 in.
Angles ....5° rake, 12° to 15° clearance

Operating Conditions

Speed ......1725 to 1825 rpm (4800 sfm max)
Feed ....60 ipm
Depth of cut ....0.250 in.
Length of cut ....144 in.
Cutting fluid ...Soluble-oil:water; spray mist
Cutting time ......2.4 min per plate (144 in.)
Setup time ....5 min
Tool life between grinds ....200 hr

to clog grinding wheels, and they do not finish to as bright and smooth a surface as the harder alloys.

Abrasive Wheels. For grinding aluminum alloys, a silicon carbide abrasive in a flexible base is generally preferred. Aluminum oxide is seldom recommended, except for piston grinding and in cutoff wheels. Wheels of medium hardness, about 30 grit size, and with a synthetic resin bond work best for roughing. For finishing, wheels of finer grit size (to about 54) and with a vitrified bond are generally used. Recommendations for wheels for several different types of grinding operations are given in Table 28. (For explanation of ASA system for identifying characteristics of grinding wheels, see Fig. 1 on page 258, in the article "Grinding".)

The following example describes specific grinding practice for pistons.

Example 924. Grinding Pistons (Fig. 47)

After extensive testing, an A-46-K5-V wheel was selected for grinding the skirt of permanent mold cast F132-T5 pistons. Requirements for the wheel were: (a) satisfactory performance without frequent redressing, (b) ability to hold the required profile, and (c) production of a 50-to-90-micro-in. finish. The A-46-K5-V wheel was capable of grinding 100 parts between redressings and met the other requirements.

A special hydraulic dresser, equipped with a profile bar, was used to dress the wheel. The dressing tool was a ¾-carat diamond that was turned in its holder after eight dressings to maintain a sharp point.

Details of this grinding operation are given in the table accompanying Fig. 47.

Cutoff Wheels. Abrasive cutoff wheels for aluminum are usually of aluminum oxide. For wet grinding, which is generally recommended, the bond is usually rubber. For dry grinding, either rubber or resinoid bond may be used. Typical specifications are A-20-U6-R (aluminum oxide, 20 grain size, U grade, 6 structure, rubber bond) and A-24-S7-B (aluminum oxide, 24 grain

size, S grade, 7 structure, resinoid bond). Width of wheels ranges from 0.003 to 0.156 in.; diameter varies from 1 to 30 in. These wheels cut to an accuracy of a few thousandths of an inch.

A typical specification for an abrasive cutoff wheel for aluminum bars is C/A-24-S6-B (silicon carbide/aluminum oxide combination, 24 grain size, S grade, 6 structure, resinoid bond).

For wet cutting of intricate extrusions, a recommended specification is C-46-S7-R or A-46-S7-R.

Reinforced (Flexible) Wheels. In cutting off gates and sprues from castings of irregular shape, excessive wheel breakage can occur because of very high pressure on the sides of the wheel. To eliminate this problem and provide for safe operation, special reinforced, flexible, abrasive wheels have been developed. These wheels are manufactured from laminated sheets of cotton fiber filled with abrasive grain, and are

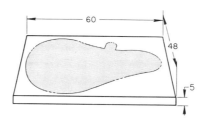

Fig. 45. Shape that was contour band sawed from aluminum plate (Example 922)

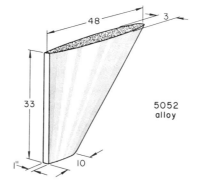

Fig. 46. Honeycomb core for aircraft pod fin (Example 923)

used for operations ranging from heavy grinding to light sanding: cutting off, sharpening, deburring, and finishing. Such wheels used for aluminum are C-24-O14-B to C-24-U14-B.

Speed. Typical wheel speeds for several types of grinding are given in Table 29. Sometimes, by adjusting the speed, a wheel that was previously unsuited for a particular operation can be made to grind satisfactorily. For example, if a wheel is too soft, increasing the speed will give a harder action.

Using the recommended speed for a wheel is important, not only from the standpoint of grinding results but also to insure safety. Stress from centrifugal force increases greatly as wheel velocity increases. The force tending to pull a wheel apart will be four times greater at 3600 rpm than at 1800 rpm.

Grinding Fluid. Neutral soluble-oil emulsions are satisfactory for grinding aluminum. Addition of a wetting agent (detergent) is sometimes helpful. Although an emulsion of 1 part soluble oil to 35 parts water is commonly used, a better cushioning effect, which also prevents clogging of the wheel, is obtained by using more oil and less water. One manufacturer, in grinding soft aluminum alloy castings, went progressively from a mixture of 1 part oil to 20 parts water to a mixture of 1 part oil to 6 parts water, before obtaining satisfactory results.

In rough grinding, where stock removal is the primary objective, generous application of wax or stick grease is often satisfactory. This type of lubricant is often used when the application of liquids is not feasible.

Belt Lubricant. Grinding fluids or stick lubricants improve the finish produced by a coated abrasive belt and prevent glazing of the belt. Lubricants used range from water to stick waxes, standard cutting oils and soluble-oil mixtures are often used in high-production belt machines.

Greases cushion the penetrating action of the abrasive into the work, and produce finer finishes than are obtained in dry grinding. Although the crest of each grain is free to cut, the grease prevents deep scratches.

Table 28. Recommended Wheels for Grinding Aluminum Alloys
(See Fig. 1, page 258, for explanation of wheel-classification system.)

Operation	Abrasive	Grain size	Grade and structure	Bond
General Grinding				
Centerless grinding	C	36	K8	V
Cylindrical grinding	C	36	K8	V
Surface grinding, cups and cylinders	C	24	J9	V-B
Surface grinding, disks	C or C/A	16 to 20	K19 to L4	B
Internal grinding	C	36	K19	V
Floor-stand grinders (5000 to 6500 sfm) ...	C	24	O	V
Floor-stand grinders (7000 to 9500 sfm) ...	C	24	P	B
Portable grinders (5000 to 6500 sfm)	C	24	O	V
Portable grinders (7000 to 9500 sfm)	C	30	O	B
Cutoff grinding, dry (9000 to 16,000 sfm) ..	A	24	S7	B
Cutoff grinding, wet (7500 to 12,000 sfm) ..	A	46	S7	R
Cutoff grinding, foundry machines	A	24	S7	B
Snagging, low-speed	C	24	O4	B
	A	24	O7	B
	C/A	24	O4	B
Snagging, high-speed	A	16	O7	B
Piston Grinding				
Cylindrical grinding	C	36 to 46	I to K8	V
Centerless grinding	C	36 to 46	I to K8	V
	C	60	J6	V
Regrinding	A or C	46	I to K8	V

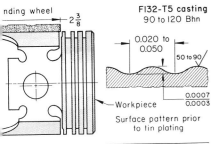

F132-T5 casting
90 to 120 Bhn

Surface pattern prior to tin plating

...hine ......Cylindrical grinder, 6 by 18 in., with automatic infeed electric-cycle control and semiautomatic profile dresser
...eel A-46-K5-V
...ze ....20 by 2⅜ by 12 in.
...fe per dressing ....100 pieces

Operating Conditions

...eel speed ....1300 rpm (6800 sfm)
...k speed ....96 rpm
...d per pass ....0.016 to 0.018 in.
...nding fluid ....Soluble-oil:water (1:25)
...duction rate ....106 pieces per hour
...e per pass(a) ....20 sec
...face finish ....50 to 90 micro-in.

(a) Infeed set with automatic timer

...ig. 47. Permanent mold cast piston that ...as ground in a single pass, removing ...0.016 to 0.018 in. of stock (Example 924)

...reases are used for offhand grind-...g of aluminum die castings. Where ...ck removal is the primary objective, ... ight grease should be used, prevent-... the belt from loading but permit-...g a maximum amount of abrasive ...netration into the metal being ...ound. For a good finish, a heavy ...ease should be used.

...ome operations use two types of ...ease, side by side, on the same abra-...e belt. One side is used for a high ...te of stock removal, and the other ... a finer finish. If the belt becomes ...ded despite the use of grease, an ap-...cation of kerosine will free the belt ...embedded particles.

...Liquid lubricants are used primarily ... prevent belt glazing. When water is ...ed, a rust inhibitor should be added. ...Soluble oil mixed with water is effec-...ve in grinding aluminum if stock re-...oval is the primary objective.

Honing

...Aluminum alloys are honed by meth-...s similar to those used for other ...etals (see the article "Honing", which ...gins on page 288). Resin-bond ...rasives are preferred; sulfurized ...ineral-base oil or lard oil mixed with ...rosine is used to flush the abrasive ...icks clean and to carry away heat.

...Honing is used to finish anodized ...uminum surfaces, primarily the bores ... some small aluminum engine blocks, ...d most aircraft hydraulic cylinders. ...he example that follows describes the ...chnique and conditions employed in ...oning of main bearing bores in alumi-...um engine blocks. The aluminum ...locks and the gray iron bearing caps ...ere honed simultaneously with a sili-...on carbide abrasive, even though, ...hen honed separately, gray iron and ...luminum would be honed with differ-...nt abrasives.

Example 925. Simultaneous Honing of Aluminum and Gray Iron (Fig. 48)

...Main-bearing bores in six-cylinder, die-cast ...uminum engine blocks were honed with ...ay iron bearing caps bolted in place, as

---

Table 29. Typical Wheel Speeds for Grinding Aluminum Alloys

Operation	Speed, sfm
Cylindrical grinding	5500 to 6500
Internal grinding	2100 to 6000
Snagging(a)	7000 to 9500
Surface grinding	4000 to 5000
Offhand grinding (large wheels)	4000 to 5000
Cutoff(b)	9000 to 16000

(a) Rubber and resinoid bonds. (b) Rubber, resinoid and shellac bonds.

shown in Fig. 48. The blocks were fixtured for honing and were held in position by a light clamping force on the head faces. Each block was held securely so that it could resist torsional forces from the honing tool, but adjustment of clamping force was critical, because excessive force would distort the block. Hydraulic cone expanders automatically fed out the single bank of six carbon-bonded silicon carbide stones (2 by ¼ in., 120 grit). Fifteen fiber guides, each 3 by ¼ in., were incorporated in the honing tool. Processing details are given in the table with Fig. 48.

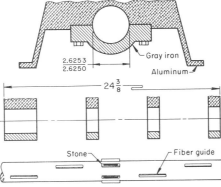

2.6253 / 2.6250 — Gray iron

Aluminum

24⅜

Stone — Fiber guide

Speed	900 rpm (620 sfm)
Spindle reciprocation rate	60 strokes per min
Hone speed	70 ft per min
Stock removed	0.0015 to 0.020 in.
Honing time	25 sec
Cutting fluid	Mineral seal oil
Size-control method	Air gage
Stone life, per set (avg)	300 assemblies
Production rate	75 pieces per hour
Bore alignment before honing ..	0.002 in.
Bore alignment after honing ..	0.0007 in.
Specified tolerance	±0.0003 in.
Specified finish	20 to 25 micro-in.

Fig. 48. Die-cast engine block that was honed with gray iron bearing caps in place, and honing tool (bottom) used (Example 925)

Long anodized aluminum tubes that are components of in-flight refueling apparatus are finished by manual honing. The tubes are chucked in a lathe and the honing tool is moved manual-ly. The oil supply is attached to the honing tool in such a manner that flow of oil is directed where most needed. This method of honing is also used for finishing connecting-rod journals or crankshafts in aircraft-overhaul shops.

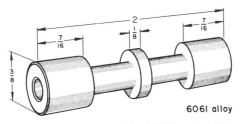

6061 alloy

Fig. 49. Part from which 0.0002 in. of metal was removed by lapping to smooth the surface to 1 micro-in. (Example 926)

Lapping

The same methods are used for lapping aluminum as for other metals (see the article "Lapping", which begins on page 298). However, because similar finishes often can be produced by other methods at less cost, lapping is seldom used. In the example that follows, an extremely smooth finish of 1 micro-in. on an anodized part was produced by two methods of lapping.

Example 926. Lapping Hard-Anodized Alloy 6061 (Fig. 49)

The hard-anodized aluminum part (surface hardness equivalent to Rockwell C 65) shown in Fig. 49 required removal of 0.0002 in. from the three lands, to produce a finish of 1 micro-in. Diamond abrasive (8000-mesh) in a paste vehicle was used for both centerless roll lapping and lapping in a two-plate machine. The roll lapper, at a rotation speed of 100 rpm (large roll) and a stroke speed of 2 ipm, produced ten parts per hour. The two-plate machine, which had upper and lower cast iron laps 16 in. in diameter and 3 in. thick, lapped 1000 parts per hour.

Chemical Machining

Chemical contour machining (chemical milling), discussed in detail on pages 245 to 249, is used to etch pre-formed aerospace parts to obtain increased strength-to-weight ratio. Examples 465(a) and 466 on page 247 describe the application of chemical machining to parts made of aluminum alloys 7072 and 2024. In the latter example, etching was assisted by an auxiliary anodic current.

Figure 50 (below) presents a typical curve for choosing the most economical method (chemical vs mechanical) for removing metal from flat parts on which large areas having complex or wavy peripheral outlines are to be reduced in thickness. Fillet ratio and thickness of metal to be removed are used as the basis for evaluation. Metal thicknesses greater than 0.250 in. should be removed mechanically; thicknesses less than 0.125, chemically. Between these two values, choice depends on fillet ratio, which governs the weight penalty.

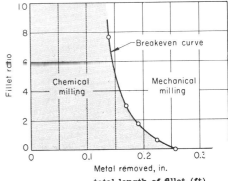

Breakeven curve

Chemical milling

Mechanical milling

Metal removed, in.

$$\text{Fillet ratio} = \frac{\text{total length of fillet (ft)}}{\text{total area of part (sq ft)}}$$

Fig. 50. Breakeven between chemical and mechanical milling. Choice between them depends on fillet ratio and depth of cut.

Other Examples of Machining Aluminum

205

Machining Aluminum

Lathes, drills, milling cutters and other metal-removal machines commonly found in metalworking shops are routinely used to shape aluminum alloys. For maximum cutting efficiency, the tooling and operating conditions should always be adjusted to suit the machining characteristics of the specific metal stock to be worked.

For aluminum, cutting speeds are generally much higher than for other metals; the cutting force required is low, the as-cut finish is generally excellent, the dimensional control is good, asd the tool life is outstanding.

Although many other metals have machinability ratings based in tool life vs. cutting speed, for aluminum the chip characteristics, Figure 4-1, and surface finish provide the most satisfactory basis for rating machinability. This is due to the fact that tool life for cutting most aluminum alloys is so long, even at the higher speeds employed, that tool wear is not a useful "machinability" rating basis.

Machinability of Aluminum

Correct tooling for machining a given aluminum alloy depends upon its machinability rating, designated as A, B, C, D or E. As shown in Table 4-1, nearly all of the principal wrought aluminum alloys machine satisfactorily with recommended tooling. While alloy 2011 is the most free-cutting and is therefore rated "A," many other alloys in the 2xxx series, and several in the 7xxx also have excellent machining characteristics and are given a "B" rating. Machinability ratings of the principal aluminum casting alloys are given in Table 4-2.

Power Consumption—Although power is consumed at a higher rate when machining aluminum, because of the high speeds employed, the *total* power consumption for a given cut or job is lower than that for cutting other common metals. For example, for each unit of power consumed, about three times the amount of metal will be removed when machining aluminum alloy 2017-T4 than when machining hot-rolled, low-carbon steel of about the some tensile strength.

Layout Lines

Layout lines should be made on machining stock at room temperature, out of direct rays of the sun or other radiant heat because of aluminum's relatively high coefficient of thermal expansion. Grease pencil is not accurate enough for most layout work and scribing is the common layout method.

Tooling—Recommended cutting tools for short production runs are high-speed steel, hardened to Rockwell C65. For cutting high-silicon aluminum alloys, or for high-production jobs using other alloys, carbide-tipped tools should be used. Diamond tools are finding increased acceptance in machining aluminum to produce optimum surface finish.

Well polished cutting tool surfaces reduce metal pickup; large clearance angles and flute areas aid chip removal. All cutting tools should have sharp cutting edges.

Temper of Stock—Where large amounts of metal are to be removed, the metal supplier should be consulted. It is often possible to furnish metal in a suitable initial temper to reduce distortion during machining. Also rough machining may be done prior to heat treatment, as in the case of castings. Subsequent relatively light finish machining will not generate sufficient heat to cause a significant loss of temper. Distortion also is minimized by light chucking, which is adequate for most aluminum parts, because cutting forces are generally low. Heavy flows of coolant are essential where it is necessary to minimize expansion during machining.

Turning, Boring, Planing, Shaping

Single-point tools, Figure 4-2, are used for turning, boring, planing and shaping. In turning and boring, the work generally is rotated, while the cutting tool remains stationary; however, when boring is done on a milling machine, or boring mill, the tool rotates and the work is stationary. In planing, the work moves and indexes, while the tool is stationary; in shaping, the work is fixed and the tool moves.

Turning and *boring* aluminum alloys are best done at fast speeds and the machines should be selected for rigid construction, high-speed drives, and for rapid acceleration and braking, the latter to take advantage of the short cutting times required; fast stops after one piece is completed help shorten turn around time for starting a new piece, thus increasing production.

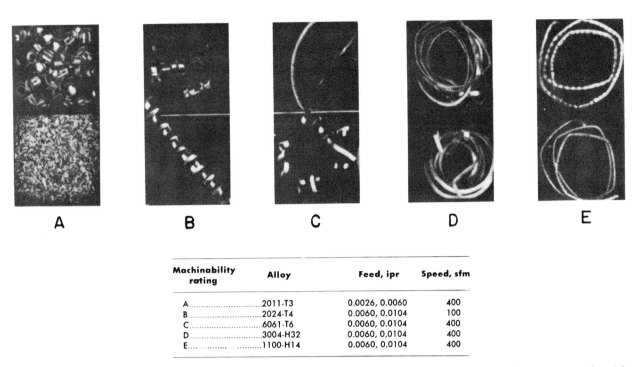

Machinability rating	Alloy	Feed, ipr	Speed, sfm
A.....................2011-T3		0.0026, 0.0060	400
B.....................2024-T4		0.0060, 0.0104	100
C.....................6061-T6		0.0060, 0.0104	400
D.....................3004-H32		0.0060, 0,0104	400
E............ ....1100-H14		0.0060, 0.0104	400

Fig. 4-1. Typical chips, feeds and speeds for aluminum alloy machinability ratings. All chips were made with a 20°-rake angle tool, at a 0.100 in. depth of cut.

TABLE 4-1
Machinability Ratings of Principal
Wrought Aluminum Alloys

Alloy(a)	Tempers(a)	Rating(b)	Alloy(a)	Tempers(a)	Rating(b)
1100	O, H112, H12	E	5454	O, H112, H311	D
1100	H14 to H18	D	5454	H343	C
1350	O, H111, H112, H12	D	5456	O, H112, H311	D
1350	H14 to H19	D	5456	H343	C
2011	T3, T4, T6, T8	A			
			5457	O	D
2014(c)	O	C	5457	H25, H28, H38	C
2014(c)	T3, T4, T6	B	5657	O	E
2017	O	C	5657	H25, H28, H38	D
2017	T4	B			
			6061(c)	O	D
2024(c)	T3, T4, T6, T8	B	6061(c)	T4, T6	C
2219	T3, T6, T8	B	6063	O, T4	D
2618	T6	B	6063	T5, T6, T8	C
3003(c)	O, H112, H12	E	6262	T4, T9	B
3003(c)	H14 to H18	D	6463	O	D
			6463	T4, T5, T6	C
3004(c)	O, H112, H32	D			
3004(c)	H34 to H38	C	7075(c)	T6, T73	B
5005	O. H112, H12, H32	E	7079	T6	B
5005	H14 to H18	D	7178(c)	T6	B
5005	H34 to H38	D			
5050	O, H112, H32	D			
5050	H34 to H38	C			
5052	O, H112, H32	D			
5052	H34 to H38	C			
5056	O	D			
5056	H18, H38	C			
5083	O, H112, H113, H32	D			
5083	H34	C			
5086	O, H112, H32	D			
5086	H34, H36	C			
5154	O, H112, H32	D			
5154	H34 to H38	C			

(a) Alloys and tempers are those commonly used. Alloy modifications designated by other second digits and temper variations designated by additional numerals will have the same ratings.

(b) A, B, C, D and E are relative ratings in increasing order of chip length and decreasing order of quality of finish, defined as follows:
A—Free cutting, very small broken chips and excellent finish
B—Curled or easily broken chips and good-to-excellent finish
C—Continuous chips and good finish
D—Continuous chips and satisfactory finish
E—Optimum tool design and machine settings are required to obtain satisfactory control of chip and finish.

(c) Includes alclad alloys and tempers.

To relate rating to speed see data beneath Fig. 4-1 above.

Source: Metalworking With Aluminum, 2nd Ed., Aluminum Assn., Inc.

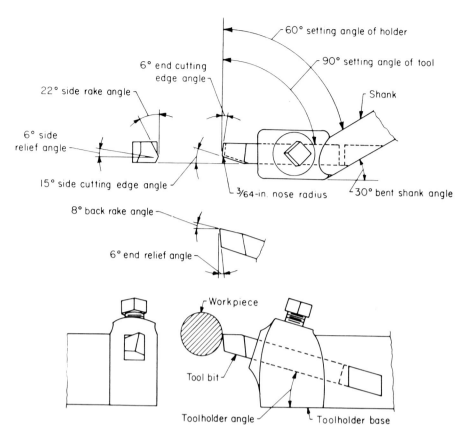

Fig. 4-2. Elements of a single-point tool.

Long pieces must be supported by adequate rollers when turning aluminum to minimize deflection. Depths of cuts in turning vary from 0.063 to 0.250 in. for small workpieces, up to 1.5 in. for large pieces. Rough-cut feeds range from 0.006 to 0.080 ipr; finishing cut feeds from 0.002 to 0.006 ipr. Suggested practices for turning aluminum on general-purpose equipment are given in Table 4-3.

Planing and shaping are done at top speed of the equipment; roughing cuts and feeds generally are large, to compensate for the slower tool speeds.

Details of tool design for turning, boring, shaping and planing are given in Figure 4-3.

Lubricants—Dimensional stability of the part and life of the cutting tool are both improved when cutting fluids are applied generously over the tool cutting point and entire workpiece, where practical. Choice of lubricant from available mineral oils, soluble oil emulsions and other aqueous chemical solutions depends upon specific conditions and operator preference for a particular machining job, but any of these compounded for aluminum will be satisfactory for general-run jobs.

Drilling, Reaming, Counterboring

Cutting speeds ranging from 600 to 1,000 sfm are used in drilling, reaming, and counterboring. To obtain these cutting speeds when small holes are being drilled very high spindle speeds are required. For example, a 0.125 (⅛) in. dia. drill cutting at 1,000 sfm is turning at a spindle speed of 30,000 rpm. For drilling small holes in aluminum, machines having spindle speeds up to 80,000 rpm are available. Feeds range from 0.010 ipr for a 0.125 in. drill to 0.020 ipr for drills over 0.313 in., when drilling an A-rated (machining) stock (alloy 2011).

Drilling—General-purpose, standard-helix drills are used for making shallow holes in medium and hard aluminum alloys. For deep holes (4 times drill diameter) and for soft alloys, a high-helix drill is recommended. For improved cutting and chip removal in very deep holes, oil-hole drills, or gun drills, are used.

Design features for twist drills are shown in Figure 4-4, which also include ASA standard terminology. General-purpose drills have a helix or spiral angle of 25 to 30°; high helix angle drills are 35 to 50°. High penetration rates achieved in drilling aluminum require large, highly polished flute surfaces to dispose of chips rapidly, preventing packing the hole being drilled.

A common drill-point angle of 118° is satisfactory for most jobs, but this should be increased to 130 to 140° for deep holes, because a narrower, more readily expelled chip is produced. Lip relief angles of 12 to 20° are used in drilling aluminum. The higher lip angles are used for the smaller drills and softer alloys, and lip relief angles generally are increased toward the center of the drill to hold the chisel-edge angle at 130 to 145°.

TABLE 4-2

Machinability Ratings of Principal Aluminum Casting Alloys

Alloy	Tempers(a)	Machinability Rating(b)
208.0	F	B
238.0	F	B
A240.0	F	A
242.0	T21, T571, T61, T77	B
295.0	T4, T6, T62	B
B295.0	T4, T6, T7	B
308.0	F	B
319.0	F	C
319.0	T5, T6	B
A332.0	T551, T65	C
F332.0	T5	C
333.0	F	C
333.0	T5, T6, T7	B
354.0	T61, T62	B
355.0	T51, T6, T61, T62, T7, T71	B
C355.0	T61	B
356.0	T51, T6, T7, T71	C
A356.0	T61	B
357.0	T6	B
A357.0	T61	B
359.0	T61, T62	B
360.0 F	F	C
A360.0	F	C
364.0	F, T5	C
380.0	F, T5	B
A380.0	F, T5	B
384.0	F	C
413.0	F	E
443.0	F	E
514.0	F	B
A514.0	F	B
F514.0	F	B
518.0	F	B
A535.0	F	B
520.0	T4	B
A712.0	F	B
C712.0	F	B
D712.0	F	B
850.0	T5	A
A850.0	T5	A
B850.0	T5	A

Notes (a) and (b), see footnotes for Table 4-1.

TABLE 4-3

Suggested Practices for Turning Aluminum on General-Purpose Equipment(a)

Variable	Condition	Suggested practice
Top rake		0 to 20°
Side rake	Machinability rating A	0 to 20°
	Machinability rating B	20°
	Machinability rating C	20 to 30°
	Machinability rating D, E	40°
Front clearance	High speed steel tool	8 to 15°
	Carbide tool	6 to 8°
Side clearance	High speed steel tool	8 to 15°
	Carbide tool	6 to 8°
End cutting-edge angle		5°
Side cutting-edge angle		5 to 15°
Nose radius	Rough cutting	0.031 to 0.125 in.
	Finish cutting	0.010 to 0.030 in.
Depth of cut	Small work	0.016 to 0.250 in.
	Large work	0.500 to 1.500 in.
Feed	Rough cutting	0.006 to 0.080 ipr
	Finish cutting	0.002 to 0.006 ipr
Speed	High speed steel tool	Up to 1000 fpm
	Carbide tool	Up to 15,000 fpm

(a) The suggested practices are those commonly used, but higher speeds, feeds and depths of cut may be employed in many applications (depending on the nature of the part, machine tool, tool design, lubrication and other cutting conditions) to increase production rates.

Source: Metalworking With Aluminum, 2nd Ed., Aluminum Assn., Inc.

A chisel edge is ground on the web at the drill point. This does no cutting but is an effective "plow," which pushes the metal out of the way. Because thickness of the web generally increases toward the shank end, the web must be thinned after a new point is ground in order to restore the chisel edge to its correct length.

Webs may be ground somewhat thinner for drilling aluminum than for most other metals. Several types of web thinning are used. It is important that thinning extend up the flute an average distance of one-quarter to one-half of drill diameter to assure that thinning is not too abrupt. Grinding must not extend into the *margin*.

Reaming—Commercially available reaming tools having large, highly polished flutes are used for general aluminum reaming jobs. A typical straight-fluted reamer for aluminum having proper tool angles is illustrated in Figure 4-5. Under ideal conditions, helical-flute reamers have less tendency to develop chatter. Feeds and speeds should be determined by trials. As a guide, commonly used feeds for straight holes range from 0.007 to 0.020 ipr, and speeds from 600 to 1,000 sfm; for tapered holes, feed ranges are 0.002 to 0.005 ipr and speeds 600 to 1,000 sfm.

Reamed holes tend to be somewhat larger than the reamer. This is normally compensated in reamer diameter for the tool is made only 0.0005 to 0.001 in. less than the hole diameter; the small reduction in tool size is due to contraction upon cooling. Holding close tolerances in reaming also is dependent upon a cleanly cut hole. The roughing tool used prior to reaming must be kept sharp to avoid work hardening of the hole sidewalls, which condition causes rapid reamer wear and resulting hole size variations.

Counterboring—Flat-bottomed, stepped, or tapered holes are produced by counterboring. Speeds are in the range of 600 to 1000 sfm and feeds are the same as for drilling. Adequate chip clearance and rapid chip removal are obtained through use of tools having minimum number of flutes; for small holes, a two-fluted tool is used. A typical "average-size" counterbore is shown in Figure 4-6.

Lubricants—Light cutting fluids such as kerosene/lard oil mixtures or soluble oil emulsions are used in drilling, reaming and counterboring to cool the work, reduce tool wear and facilitate chip movement out of the holes and off the workpiece.

Tapping and Die Threading

Tapping—Standard taps can be used for aluminum and are available from tool suppliers. Special taps may be used on aluminum with maximum efficiency obtained when proper cutting and rake and a minimum number of deep, wide flutes provide maximum chip clearance and free-running characteristics. Other tap design features which facilitate cutting by minimizing heat generation and torque are the use of tap lands just wide enough to support the tap in the hole. Hole size should be as large as specifications will permit.

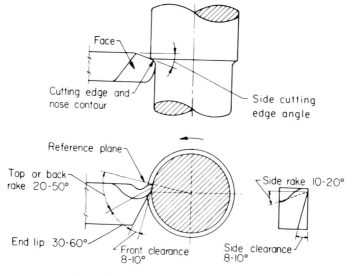

Face

Cutting edge and
nose contour

Side cutting
edge angle

Reference plane

Top or back
rake 20-50°

Side rake 10-20°

End lip 30-60°

Front clearance
8-10°

Side clearance
8-10°

Typical Lathe Tool for Turning Aluminum

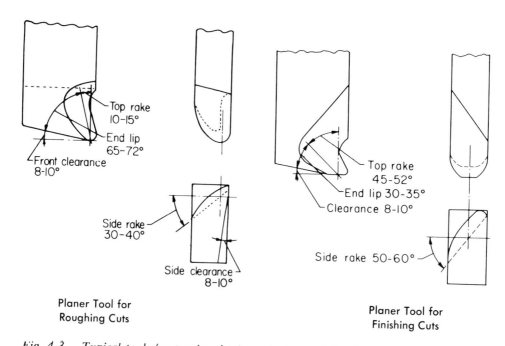

Top rake
10-15°

End lip
65-72°

Front clearance
8-10°

Side rake
30-40°

Side clearance
8-10°

**Planer Tool for
Roughing Cuts**

Top rake
45-52°

End lip 30-35°

Clearance 8-10°

Side rake 50-60°

**Planer Tool for
Finishing Cuts**

Fig. 4-3. Typical tools for turning, boring, planing and shaping aluminum alloys.

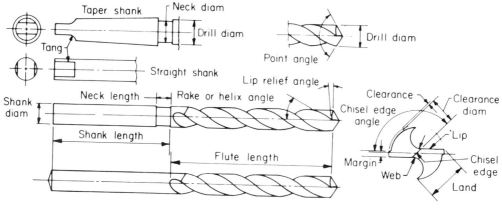

Taper shank

Neck diam

Drill diam

Tang

Drill diam

Straight shank

Point angle

Shank
diam

Neck length

Rake or helix angle

Lip relief angle

Clearance

Chisel edge
angle

Clearance
diam

Shank length

Flute length

Margin

Web

Lip

Chisel
edge

Land

Fig. 4-4. Elements of twist drills.

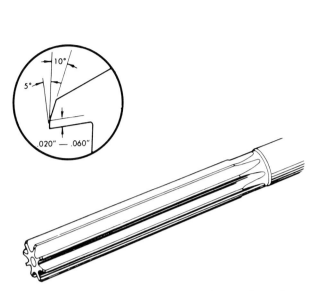

Fig. 4-5. Representative values for tool angles on reamers used for aluminum.

Straight taps are normally used for medium-to-thin material and helical-taps for deep holes in ductile alloys. As in reaming, all good tapping starts with holes properly made with sharp tools, which leave no work-hardened or uneven surfaces. Representative tool angles for tap elements are given in Figure 4-7. Tapping speeds for aluminum range from 100 to 200 sfm.

Die Threading—Dies for threading include *solid circular, tangent* (flat, rectangular), and *circular chasing tools* (see Figure 4-8). The solid dies for aluminum have undercut lands, similar to those of taps. Top rake on the leading edge ranges from 25 to 45° and is about 10° on the trailing edge.

Starting ends of the lands are chamfered to 30°. Land faces of the first three or four die threads or teeth should be relieved to 8 or 10° to give them some side rake, as these cutting edges do the most work. Self-opening diehead chasers are ground in the same way, except that no back-rake is required.

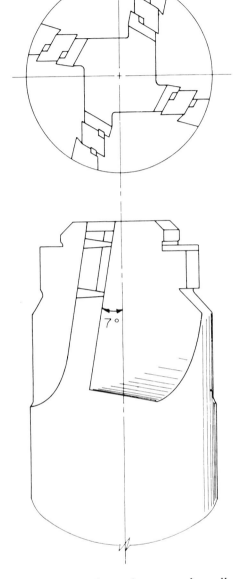

Fig. 4-6. Positive rake angles are used on all counter-bores for all aluminum alloys except 2011, which has a 0° rake.

Cutting Angle	Rake Angles		Included Angle D		Spiral Angle
A	Top B	Back C	Two Flutes	Three Flutes	
40-45°	45-50°	8° maximum	36-72°	24-48°	28-40° (a)

Hole Type		Thread Type	
Blind Spiral fluted and bottoming taps	Semi-blind (b) or through, Spiral pointed ("gun") taps	General Rounded or truncated thread contour	Soft alloys Staggered or interrupted thread

(a) For special flute. For "gun" tap, grind a lead spiral extending one full thread beyond chamber.
(b) Holes having sufficient depth to permit chips to collect in bottom.

Fig. 4-7. Tool-surface angles for tapping aluminum.

Source: Metalworking With Aluminum, 2nd Ed., Aluminum Assn., Inc.

TABLE 4-4

Approximate Feeds for Aluminum on Multi-Operation Machines

For tool speeds of 600-1000 sfm, using high-speed tools.[a]

Tool	Width or Depth of Cut, in	Hole Diameter, in	Feed, ipr	
			Alloy 2011	Alloys 2017,2024 6061,6262
Cut-Off Tools	1/64-1/16		0.0035	0.003
	1/32-1/8		0.004	0.0035
	5/32-3/16		0.0045	0.004
	3/16-1/4		0.005	0.045
Form Tools	1/8-1/4		0.0015-0.0035	—
	3/8-1/2		0.0012-0.0025	0.002-0.003
	5/8-3/4		0.001-0.002	0.001-0.002
	1.000		0.001-0.002	0.0008-0.0012
Box Tools (combined)	1/32(b)		0.008	0.007
	1/32(c)		0.012	0.010
	1/32(d)		0.015	0.012
	1/16(b)		0.007	0.006
	1/16(c)		0.010	0.009
	1/16(d)		0.012	0.010
	1/8(c)		0.009	0.007
	1/8(d)		0.010	0.008
	3/16(d)		0.009	0.007
Facing Tools	Wide Cuts		0.001-0.003	0.001-0.003
Drills		1/16	0.0036	0.003
		3/32	0.0084	0.007
		1/8	0.012	0.010
		5/32	0.013	0.011
		3/16	0.014	0.012
		7/32	0.016	0.013
		1/4	0.017	0.014
		9/32	0.018	0.015
		5/16	0.019	0.016
		over 5/16	0.020	0.017
Reamers, Straight		1/8 and less	0.007-0.010	0.007-0.010
		over 1/8	0.010-0.020	0.010-0.020
Reamers, Tapered		all sizes	0.002-0.005	0.002-0.005

(a) For long runs use carbide tools at the maximum speeds possible with the cutting equipment.
(b) For finished diameters 1/16-1/8 inch.
(c) For finished diameters 1/8-1/4 inch.
(d) For finished diameters over 1/4 inch.

Lubricants—Cooling and lubricating compounds are the same as those used for drilling and reaming although special tapping lubricants are available.

Turret Lathes and Screw Machines

Multi-operation machining is carried out in predetermined sequence on turret lathes, automatic screw machines and similar equipment. Speeds and feeds are generally near or at upper limits for each type of cutting, with each new operation following in rapid sequence the one just completed.

While nearly all alloys are machined in this manner, the most popular are 2011, 2017, 2024, 6061 and 6262. Most widely used is alloy 2011, because of its A-rated machinability. Representative design features for tools most generally used on automatic, multiple operation machines are illustrated in Figure 4-8.

High-speed steel cutting tools operate at speeds of 550 to 700 sfm, and carbide tools from 1,000 to 1,500 sfm. Approximate feeds for machining various alloys on multi-operation equipment are given for principal types of tools in Table 4-4.

Automatic screw machines mass produce round solid and hollow parts (threaded and/or contoured) from continuously fed bar or rod, employing up to eight or more successive (and some simultaneous) operations on a variety of complexly tooled turrets, cross-slides, cutting attachments and stock-feeding devices. "Swiss-type" screw machines have certain advantages over conventional types in that they are capable of producing long, slender parts to close tolerances. Stock is fed (while rotating) through an adjustable guide bushing, into the cutting heads, which are cam-indexed around the rotating workpiece.

Most operations on these machines are essentially the same as turning, boring and drilling, but a number of special tools are employed; these are typified by those shown in Figure 4-8.

Lubrication—Low-viscosity mineral oils or soluble-oils are used in generous quantities.

Milling

Aluminum is one of the easiest metals to shape by milling. High spindle speeds and properly designed cutters, machines, fixtures and power sources can make

Turning Tools (Box Tools)

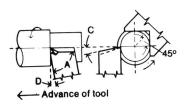

Tool Element	Tool Angle
Side rake, C	0–5°
Cutting angle, A	82°
Clearance angle, D	8°

Circular Form Tools

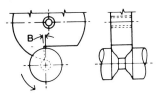

Tool Element	Tool Angle
Top rake, B	0–3°

Dovetail Form Tools

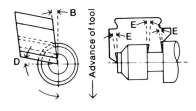

Tool Element	Tool Angle
Top rake, B	0–3°
Front clearance, D	10–15°
Side clearance, E	½ °

Facing Tools

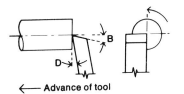

Tool Element	Tool Angle
Top rake, B	10–15°
Clearance angle, D	8–12°

Fig. 78
Tool angles for cutting alloy 2011 on multi-operation machines.

Cut-off Tools

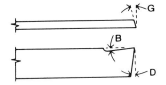

Tool Element	Tool Angle
Front angle, G	8–23°
Front clearance, D	8–12°
Top rake, B	0–3°
Side clearance	0–4°

Drills

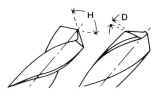

Drill Element	Tool Angle
Point angle, H	118°
Helix angle	20–25°
Clearance angle, D	12–20°
Flutes	Polished
Web thickness	Thinner than that used for other metals

Fig. 4-8.   Representative tools for machining aluminum on multi-operation equipment. Tool angles shown are for cutting alloy 2011. (Continued on next page.)

cuts in rigid aluminum workpieces at rates as high as 15,000 sfm with carbide cutters; 5,000 sfm with high-speed steel cutters; and 600 sfm with carbon-steel cutters.

Milling cutters rotate and are multipoint (two or more) tools, having concentric straight or helical teeth. Some helical cutters have curve teeth for profile milling. A variety of end-mill, side-mill and facing cutters have teeth in two planes at 90°—one set parallel to cutter axis and the other on the end of the cutter, perpendicular to the axis.

Milling cutter nomenclature is given in Figure 4-9. Representative milling cutters and typical spiral-cutter angles for aluminum are shown in Figure 4-10. Suggested feeds-per-tooth are given in Table 4-4

for milling aluminum alloys on general-purpose equipment.

Milling machines range in size from small, pedestal-mounted types to spar and skin mills having multiple cutting heads, with individual motor drives, mounted on gantries which run on ways the entire 200 to 300 ft length of the machines' beds, Figure 4-11. These latter machines are tape-controlled and are capable of complex contour milling while holding remarkably close tolerances over entire lengths of the part.

Lubricants—Various viscosities of mineral oil and soluble oil emulsions are used for milling aluminum depending upon type and depth of cut, tool, speed and alloy.

Source: Metalworking With Aluminum, 2nd Ed., Aluminum Assn., Inc.

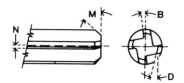

Reamers

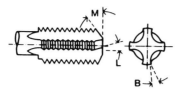

Taps

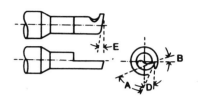

Recess Tools

Reamer Element	Tool Angle
Top rake, B	5–10°
Clearance angle, D	10°
Chamfer angle, M	45°
Flutes	Polished
Land, N	⅟₆₄–⅟₁₆ in

Tap Element	Tool Angle
Top rake, B	10–15°
Chamfer angle, M	20–45°
Lip hook, L	10–15°
Flutes	Polished

Tool Element	Tool Angle
Top rake, B	0–5°
Side clearance, E	½–5°
Cutting angle, A	85–75°
Front clearance, D	5–10°

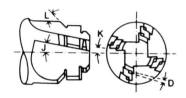

Counter Bores

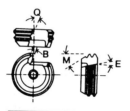

Circular Chasers

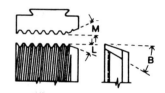

Tangent Chasers

Counter Bore Element	Tool Angle
Longitudinal rake, J	7–10°
Radial rake, K	5°
Lip angle, L	59°
Clearance angle, D	12–15°
Land	⅟₃₂–⅟₁₆ in

Chaser Element	Tool Angle
Top rake, B	25°
Chamfer angle, M	20–22°
Face angle, Q	20–25°
Clearance angle, E	10°

Chaser Element	Tool Angle
Top rake, B	30°
Chamfer angle, M	20–22°
Lip hook, L	5–10°

Fig. 4-8 (Concluded)

Broaching

Broaching employs graduated multi-tooth round or rectangular cutting tools which progressively make rough, semi-finished and finished cuts in a single pass as they are pulled or pushed through the metal.

A typical round, internal broach used for producing holes is shown in Figure 4-12. Standard broaches are used on aluminum, but for most jobs cutting speeds can be more than tripled when a broach is made specifically for the aluminum job. The cut-per-tooth is normally increased over that for steel or cast iron; tooth pitch is relatively coarse for aluminum, with only two or three teeth cutting at a given time.

As in single point tools, rake angles should be 10 to 20°. For external broaching, side rake angle should be 5 to 20° to produce smooth cutting and good finish.

Smalls clearance angles help to maintain tool dimensions when sharpening is necessary. Clearances are about 2° for roughing teeth, reducing to 1° for finishing teeth.

It is important to avoid distortion when clamping work for broaching, and tools must be kept sharp. Speeds are 100 sfm or higher for aluminum, as compared with about 30 sfm for other metals.

Lubrication—Cutting and chip removal are improved and tool wear is reduced when mineral oil and kerosene mixtures, or soluble oils are employed as a general rule. Some broaching of aluminum is done dry.

Sawing, Shearing, Routing and Filing

Aluminum is easily cut with the full range of power-driven cut-off tools, including all types of saws,

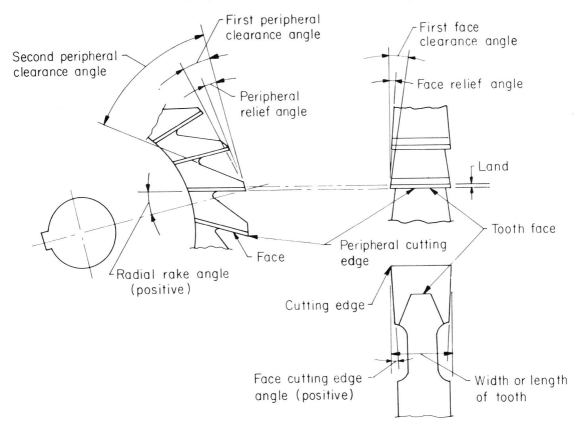

Fig. 4-9. Milling cutter nomenclature.

shears and routers. Hand-saws and files also are extensively used for working aluminum in the metalshop or in the field. In all cases, proper design of cutting edges produces smooth cuts at fast speeds.

Sawing—Circular saws having hollow ground, 15° alternate side rake, or those having alternate 45°-bevel chip-breaker and square finishing teeth, are best for sawing aluminum. Sturdy blades of sufficient diameter to permit the workpiece to be parted in a single cut should be used. Speeds range from 4,000 sfm for alloy tool steel blades; about 8,500 for high-speed steel teeth; to 15,000 for carbide-tipped blades.

Spring-tempered blades with 4 or 5 teeth per inch are best for bandsawing sheet; flexible, soft-back but hard-toothed bands having 6 or 8 teeth per inch cut heavy plate best on these machines. Where practicable, pitch of teeth should not exceed thickness of workpiece. Thin sheet may be cut with 14-teeth-per-inch blades. High-speed cutting of heavier stock demands fewer teeth, relatively coarse and with deep curved gullets; or skip-tooth or buttress-tooth design.

Lubricants—Soluble or mineral oils are recommended for use in cutting heavy material, or soft thin material; other work cuts well with application of paraffin wax, heavy grease, or stick lubricant compound.

Shearing—Padded hold downs and a clean shear bed are recommended for shearing aluminum. Light-gage sheet (particularly when cutting narrow strips of soft alloys) should be guillotine sheared using a top knife having a low rake (shearing) angle to reduce

twist. A between-blade clearance of 5 or 6% of sheet thickness is correct. Most medium-hard alloys require an 8 to 10% clearance, but the 7xxx alloys tend to "layer" and break with rough edges when sheared. For shearing plate of these alloys up to 3/16 in. thickness, an 8% clearance is recommended; for thicker gages, clearance should be about 0.012 in. Rake angle should be about 2°. Knives must be kept sharp.

Lubricants—Shearing is often done dry; paraffin wax may be used where lubrication is required.

Nibbling—Nibblers employ a rapidly reciprocating punch and die of circular or angular configuration to cut straight or curved edges in small successive "bites." A template is often used, but cutting may be done freehand. Capacities of hand-held nibblers range from thin sheet to about ⅜ in. thickness; larger pedestal mounted nibblers will cut aluminum plate 1½ in. thick.

Routing—Aluminum-type cutting tools used in routers resemble end-mills, with cutting edges on both the sides and ends. Routers used for machining aluminum have evolved from simlar equipment originally and currently used in woodworking. All types of metal working routers and some woodworking models are used on aluminum. These machines include portable hand routers, hinged and radial routers, and profile routers. Both plain and carbide-tipped high-speed steel tools, rotating at 20,000 rpm or more, are used.

Typical router cutters are shown in Figure 4-13. Feeds range from 10 to 30 ipm on stock up to ½ in. thick, and from 5 to 10 ipm for material up to 3 in. thick. The principal router applications for aluminum

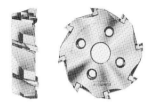

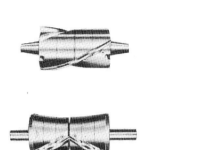

Courtesy, Goddard & Goddard

Fig. 4-10A. Various inserted-blade milling cutters designed to produce various profiles in aluminum. Cutter at top left has 8 cutting teeth or blades. The cutter shown top right is an inserted-carbide 12-section gang cutter that produces a 23 in. wide cut; each section has two blades. Cutter second from bottom is a two-flute, integral spar milling cutter. At bottom is a two-flute spar mill.

Tool Material	Spiral or Helix	Cutting Angle	Top Rake	Clearance Angles	
				Primary	Secondary
High speed steel	10-50°	67-48°	20-35°	3-7°	7-12°
Cemented carbide	—10 to +20°	97-68°	—10 to +15°	3-7°	7-12°

Fig. 4-10B.   Typical spiral-cutter angles for aluminum.

are for edge-profiling shapes from single or stacked sheet or plate, and for area removal of any volume of metal when router is used as a skin or spar mill.

Filing—Coarse, deeply cut curved teeth with a pitch of 10 teeth per inch are recommended for files which provide rapid metal removal for aluminum. The large clearance between teeth prevents loading of the teeth, and still produces a relatively smooth surface. Rasps and other double-cut tooth files produce rough surfaces and cut aluminum poorly. Finish filing, Figure 4-14, is best done with a long-angle file with a pitch of 14 to 20 teeth per inch for aluminum.

Grinding, Honing and Lapping

Metal removal by grinding is done in aluminum fabricating at much higher speeds than those used for ferrous materials. When proper wheel construction, shaft bearings, machine capacity and protective devices are employed, speeds range from a low of 2,000 to 6 rpm for internal grinding to a high of from 9,000 to 16,000 rpm for cutoff. General grinding wheel specifications for aluminum alloys are given in Table 4-5.

Close size and finish tolerances are obtained with grinding. Flatness within 0.002 in. is common for

disk and other surface grinders. Contact wheel belt grinders can hold dimension to 0.003 in. or less and finish within a 225 to 350 micro inch range.

Rough grinding is done with resin-bonded silicon carbide wheels of medium hardness and 24 to 30 grit. Wheels for finish grinding are generally softer, vitrified-bonded grit of somewhat smaller size.

Soft aluminum alloys clog abrasive materials; proper wheel type, speed and lubrication are used to control or improve this condition.

Lubrication—Grease sticks are used for grinding wheels, and belt lubrication is generally light-bodied grease. Wet grinding by belt or disk usually is lubricated with a soluble oil in water.

Honing—While the same equipment used to hone other metals is employed for aluminum, the surface-finishing mechanics are different. In most cases, honing is used to finish anodized aluminum surfaces (such as aircraft and automobile engine cylinder walls), smoothing without removing a significant amount of the hard aluminum oxide anodic coating. For non-anodized parts, desired finishes usually can be produced by other, less expensive machining methods.

Abrasives are in stick form and come in standard compositions, in grit types and sizes used for wheels

Fig. 4-11. *A 275 ft. skin mill equipped with six gantries, each with multiple motor-driven, tape-controlled cutting heads, is shown above (three of six gantries on this single giant mill are visible in this view).*

and belts. Resin-bonded sticks generally are used for aluminum.

Lubrication—Flushing and cooling is accomplished with a sulfurized mineral-base oil, or lard oil mixed with kerosene.

Lapping—Aluminum may be lapped with similar techniques used for other metals. However, this process is not generally used for aluminum parts because desired finish usually can be obtained by other machining methods at lower cost.

Machine Finishes

As contrasted with scratch brushing, sanding, tumbling, sand blasting, or buffing, *engine turning* and *knurling* are termed machine finishes.

Engine Turning—A wire-brush, or abrasive pad end-cutting tool, the brush having bristles parallel to its rotating shaft, is chucked in a drill press to produce circular scratch patterns on aluminum. A hand drill also may be used and the overall pattern may be in regular rows of spots, which in turn may be discrete or overlapping. Random spot patterns may also be produced.

Brush pattern texture may be varied slightly through use of lubricant. If abrasive pad is used, a lubricant is mandatory to keep abrasive free from aluminum particles. Disadvantages of the lubricated abrasive is that pattern is obscured, making it difficult to produce a uniform pattern where work or tool is being hand guided. Also, any lubricant must eventually be removed and the non-lubricated wire brush method is therefore generally preferred.

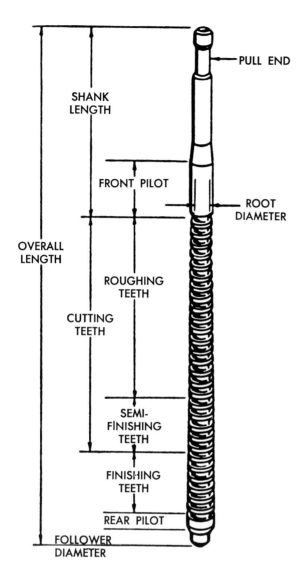

Fig. 4-12. Nomenclature of typical round, internal draw-broach.

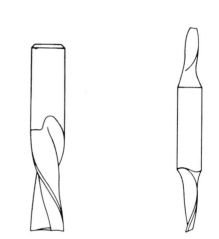

Fig. 4-13. Typical router cutters for aluminum.

Knurling—Knurling or other embossing rolls, properly fitted with adequate bearings, are used to produce patterns or legends in aluminum parts running on lathes or screw machines at the same speeds as other tools. Use of large-diameter knurling tools avoids excessive wear by minimizing bearing speeds. Roller bearings are used for work requiring high knurling pressure.

Cutting Fluids and Lubricants

Specific types of lubricants and cutting fluids have been recommended in the discussions of the several machining processes presented in this chapter. Some additional information on aluminum lubricants generally may prove helpful. This has been summarized in Table 4-6.

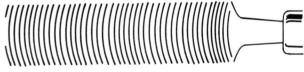

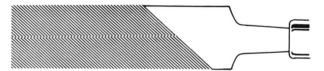

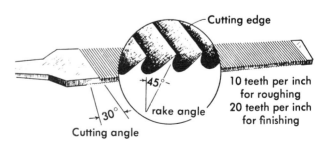

Fig. 4-14. Deep, curved, single-cut tooth files have proven most satisfactory for filing aluminum.

Chemical Milling

Chemical milling is a dimensional etching process for metal removal. In working aluminum, it is the preferred method of removing less than 0.125 in. from large, intricate surfaces. Sodium-hydroxide-base or other suitable alkaline solutions are generally used for chemical milling aluminum. Process is carried out at elevated temperatures. Metal removal (dissolution) is controlled by masking, rate of immersion, duration of immersion, and composition and temperature of the bath.

Dissolution of 0.001 in. thickness of aluminum per minute is a typical removal rate. Economics dictates removal of thickness above 0.250 in. by mechanical means. Choice of method between the aforementioned 0.125 and 0.250 in. metal-removal thicknesses depends on fillet ratio and weight penalty.

TABLE 4-5
General Specifications for Various Abrasive Wheel Grinding Machine Combination for Aluminum

Type of grinder	Wheel	Grit size
Centerless	Silicon carbide vitrified	60 to 80
Cylindrical	Silicon carbide vitrified	60 to 120
Surface	Segments: aluminum oxide vitrified	24 to 30
	Disk: silicon carbide resinoid	36 (dry)
Cutoff	Reinforced: aluminum oxide resinoid	20 to 24, R grade
	Reinforced: aluminum oxide MX	24
	Type 27: aluminum oxide resinoid	24
	Type 27: aluminum oxide MX	24
Snagging	Large wheels: silicon carbide resinoid YA-filled	163 to 203
	Large wheels: silicon carbide vitrified, YA-filled	24
	Portable: C3A resinoid, YA-filled	163 to 203
Mounted wheels	Silicon carbide vitrified (foundry)	30
	Aluminum oxide MX (aircraft)	54 to 320

TABLE 4-6
Cutting Fluids and Lubricants for Machining Aluminum

Type of Lubricant	Principal Ingredients	Viscosity Range for Aluminum	Applications & Maintenance	Relative Chip Flushing; Cutting; and Cooling Action	Necessary Precautions
Mineral Oils: (Fatty additive type preferred for aluminum.)	Mineral oil, lard or neat's-foot oil. Celic acid or butyl stearate.	40 SUS* at 100°F for high-speed cutting; 300 SUS for low speeds.	Generous flow at all cutting edges; keep recirculating fluid clean and cool.	Good chip flushing and lubrication; fair cooling action. Excellent finish because edge build-up is minimized.	Control air above oil where mist application endangers shop air. Remove oil from finished parts; also from chips to reclaim and reduce fire hazard.
Emulsions: (3 to 5% soluble oil in coater, for aluminum.)	Soluble oil, petroleum sulfonate emulsifying agents and water. Oil is added to water, which is the continuous phase (invert emulsion with oil as continuous phase not used for aluminum). Rust inhibitor to protect machine; germicidal; stain inhibitor to protect aluminum workpiece.	Generally low.	Generous flow at all cutting edges, keep recirculating fluid clean; cool when necessary.	Good chip flushing; adjustable lubrication. Excellent cooling action. Good finish.	For high-speed machinery, cooling is more important than lubrication. Where emulsion is applied as mist, keep oil content low as possible to reduce air and shop contamination.
Aqueous Chemical Solutions	Water; soluble (usually clear) synthetics; sometimes, fatty materials; rust inhibitors to protect machines; germicides.	Generally low.	Generous flow at all cutting edges; keep recirculating fluid clean; cool as required.	Good chip flushing; excellent cutting surface visibility, excellent coding action adjustable lubrication, good finish.	Keep oil content low; control mist; consider cost, which runs about three times that of soluble oil emulsions.
Stick Lubricants	Mineral compounds; animal fats; waxes; synthetics.	Various hardnesses.	Stick applied as required to blades, wheels, disks or files, or to workpiece.	Prevent loading of abrasive surfaces and saw and file teeth.	Application is intermittent but should be monitored and made as required throughout run.

* Saybolt Universal Seconds

Heat Treating of Aluminum Alloys

*By the ASM Committee on Heat Treating of Aluminum Alloys**

PROPERTY CHANGES accomplished in the heat treating of aluminum alloys are caused by solution and precipitation of hardening phases, as determined by solid solubilities.

The solubilities of several alloying elements in solid aluminum are much greater at elevated temperatures than at room temperature. Curve AB in Fig. 1 illustrates this relationship for copper in aluminum. If an aluminum alloy containing 5.25% Cu (line CD) is heated to 996 F (point E), all of the copper will be in solution. If the alloy is then rapidly quenched, it becomes supersaturated, containing almost 5.25% more copper in solution than it can retain under equilibrium conditions, and particles of an intermetallic aluminum-copper compound will precipitate. The final properties of the alloy will depend on the size and distribution of the precipitated particles, which in turn depend on the temperature at which precipitation occurs.

Solution Treating

To take advantage of the precipitation hardening reaction, it is necessary first to produce a supersaturated solid solution. The process by which this is accomplished is called solution treating. It consists of soaking the alloy at a temperature sufficiently high to achieve a nearly homogeneous solid solution and then quenching fast enough to retain the solute in solution.

Care must be exercised to avoid exceeding the initial eutectic melting temperature; on the other hand, the lower limit should be above the temperature at which complete solution occurs. In the 5.25% Cu alloy of Fig. 1, these temperatures would be 1018 and 996 F, respectively. However, under production conditions, a range of 999 to 1014 F would probably be used, to provide a 4 °F margin to safeguard against eutectic melting and a 3 °F cushion on the low side for increased solution and diffusion rates. The proximity of typical solution treating temperature ranges to eutectic melting temperatures of three common alloys is shown in the following table:

Alloy	Solution treating temperature, F	Eutectic melting temperature, F
2014	925 to 945	950
2017	925 to 945	955
2024	910 to 930	935

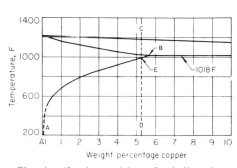

Fig. 1. Aluminum-rich end of the aluminum-copper equilibrium diagram. Line AB represents the increase in solubility of copper in solid aluminum with increasing temperature. See text for discussion.

If the eutectic melting temperature of the alloy is exceeded, grain boundary melting occurs (Fig. 2) and the material is rendered brittle and non-salvageable. This dangerous condition usually is not detectable visually or by nondestructive testing.

The shallow slope of the solubility line at its intersection with the composition line (typified by point E on line AB in Fig. 1) indicates that a slight decrease in temperature below point E will result in a large reduction in the concentration of the solid solution and a correspondingly significant decrease in final strength. The effect of solution treating temperature on the strength of two aluminum alloys is illustrated by the following data:

Solution treating temperature, F	Tensile strength, psi	Yield strength, psi
6061-T6 (sheet 0.064 in. thick)		
920	43,700	39,400
940	45,800	41,700
960	48,300	44,300
980	50,500	45,700
2024-T4 (sheet 0.032 in. thick)		
910	60,800	37,000
915	61,200	37,500
920	62,800	39,000
925	63,900	39,300

In the above tabulation, note especially the effect of small increments of temperature, within the normal range, on the properties of 0.032-in. 2024-T4 sheet.

Established solution treating temperatures and soaking times for

*R. H. GASSNER, *Chairman,* Assistant Chief Metallurgist, Aircraft Div., Douglas Aircraft Co.; C. H. AVERY, Research Specialist, Aircraft Div., Douglas Aircraft Co.; H. H. BLOCK, Chief Metallurgist, AiResearch Mfg. Co.; J. R. DOUSLIN, Airframe Product Sales Manager, Wyman-Gordon Co.

V. E. DRESS, Research Specialist — Metallurgy, Lockheed Aircraft Corp.; R. E. HUFFAKER, Manager of Manufacturing, Ladish Pacific Div., Ladish Co.; R. D. KESLER, General Dynamics/Astronautics; T. I.

McCLINTOCK, Chief Metallurgist, Vernon Works, Aluminum Co. of America; G. R. MOUDRY, Technical Director, Harvey Aluminum, Inc.

C. A. ROSELLEN, Materials Engineer, Hughes Aircraft Co.; R. SCHMIDT, Bureau of Naval Weapons, United States Department of the Navy; ELLIS STAIR, Supervising Engineer, Material Control Laboratory, Boeing Co.; M M. TILLEY, Kaiser Aluminum & Chemical Sales, Inc., J. C. WHITE Production Development Engineer, North American Aviation, Inc.

Alloy	Solution temperature, F(a)	Solution heat treatment By mill or user(b)	Solution heat treatment Post-quench mill processing	Quenchant temperature, F(c)	Temper after room temperature aging(d)	Precipitation treatment Time, hr(a)	Precipitation treatment Temperature, F	Temper after precipitation treatment (d)
Wrought Alloys Except Forgings								
2014	925 to 945	Mill	Coil or straighten	100 max	T4	9 to 11(e)	330 to 350	2014-T6
		Mill	Stress relief	100 max	T451x	9 to 11(e)	330 to 350	2014-T651x
		User	....	100 max (S)	T42	9 to 11(e)	330 to 350	2014-T62
2017	925 to 945	User	....	100 max	T4	....	....	2017-T4
2020	950 to 970	Mill	Stress relief	100 max	W(f)	17 to 19	310 to 330	2020-T651
		User	....	100 max	W(f)	17 to 19	310 to 330	2020-T6
2024	910 to 930(g)	Mill	1% cold work	100 max	T3	11 to 13	370 to 380	2024-T81
		Mill	1% cold work + stress relief	100 max	T351	11 to 13	370 to 380	2024-T851
		Mill	Coil	100 max	T4	16 to 18	370 to 380	2024-T6
		Mill	6% cold work	100 max	T36	7 to 9	370 to 380	2024-T86
		User	....	100 max (S)	T42	16 to 18	370 to 380	2024-T62
2117	925 to 950	User	....	100 max	T4	....	....	2117-T4
2219	985 to 1005	Mill	1% cold work	100 max	T31	17 to 19	340 to 360	2219-T81
		Mill	1% cold work + stress relief	100 max	T351	17 to 19	340 to 360	2219-T851
		Mill	7% cold work	100 max	T37	23 to 25	315 to 335	2219-T87
		User	....	100 max	T42	35 to 37	370 to 380	2219-T62
6053	965 to 985	User	....	100 max	T4	7 to 9(e)	340 to 360	6053-T6
		User	....	100 max	T4	6 to 8	350 to 370	6053-T651
6061	970 to 1000	Mill	Stress relief	100 max	T451	7 to 9(e)	340 to 360	6061-T651
		User	....	100 max (S)	T4	7 to 9(e)	340 to 360	6061-T6
6062	970 to 1000	Mill	Stress relief	100 max	T451x	7 to 9(e)	340 to 360	6062-T651x
		User	....	100 max	T4	7 to 9(e)	340 to 360	6062-T6
6063	970 to 1000	Mill	Press quench	100 max	T42	7 to 9(e)	340 to 360	6063-T5
		Mill	Press quench	100 max	T4	7 to 9(e)	340 to 360	6063-T6
6066	970 to 1000	Mill	Stress relief	100 max	T451x	7 to 9(e)	340 to 360	6066-T651x
		User	....	100 max	T4	7 to 9(e)	340 to 360	6066-T6
7075	860 to 880(h)	User	....	100 max	W(f)	23 to 28	240 to 260	7075-T6
		Mill	Stress relief	100 max	W(f)	23 to 28	240 to 260	7075-T651
7079	820 to 880	User	....	100 max	W(f)	(j)	(j)	7079-T6
		Mill	Stress relief	100 max	W(f)	(j)	(j)	7079-T651
7178	860 to 880	User	....	100 max	W(f)	23 to 28	240 to 260	7178-T6
		Mill	Stress relief	100 max	W(f)	23 to 28	240 to 260	7178-T651
Forgings								
2014	925 to 945	User	....	140 to 160	T4	9 to 11(e)	340 to 360	2014-T6
		User	....	212	T41	9 to 11(e)	340 to 360	2014-T61
		Mill	Stress relief	140 to 160	T452	9 to 11(e)	340 to 360	2014-T652
2017	925 to 945	User	....	140 to 160	T4	....	....	2017-T4
		Mill	Stress relief	140 to 160	T452	....	....	2017-T452
2018	940 to 960	User	....	140 to 160	T4	9 to 11	330 to 350	2018-T61
		User	....	140 to 160	T4	5 to 7	440 to 460	2018-T71
2218	940 to 960	User	....	212	T4	9 to 11	330 to 350	2218-T61
		User	....	212	T4	5 to 7	440 to 460	2218-T71
2219	985 to 1005	Mill	Stress relief	100 max	T352	9 to 11	340 to 360	2219-T852
		User	....	100 max	T4	17 to 19	365 to 385	2219-T6
2618	970 to 990	User	....	212	T41	19 to 21	385 to 395	2618-T61
4032	940 to 970	User	....	150 to 170	T4	9 to 11	330 to 350	4032-T6
		User	....	Air blast	T42	9 to 11	330 to 350	4032-T62
6053	960 to 980	User	....	100 max	T4	9 to 11(e)	330 to 350	6053-T6
		User	....	212	T41	9 to 11(e)	330 to 350	6053-T61
6061	975 to 995	User	....	100 max	T4	7 to 9(e)	340 to 360	6061-T6
6066	970 to 1010	User	....	160 to 180	T4	7 to 9(e)	340 to 360	6066-T6
6151	960 to 980	User	....	100 max	T4	9 to 11(e)	330 to 350	6151-T6
7075	870 to 890	User	....	140 to 160	W(f)	23 to 28	240 to 260	7075-T6
		Mill	Stress relief	140 to 160	W(f)	23 to 28	240 to 260	7075-T652
7076	860 to 880	User	....	212	W(f)	13 to 15	270 to 280	7076-T61
7079	820 to 880	User	....	100 max	W(f)	(j)	(j)	7079-T6
		Mill	Stress relief	100 max	W(f)	(j)	(j)	7079-T652

(a) Soaking time and maximum quench delay for solution heat treatment should be as shown in Table 2. Soaking times given for precipitation heat treatment apply to metal temperatures. (b) Material in any temper, heat treated by user or producer, will produce only the tempers following "User". Tempers following "Mill" can be obtained only by the mill and forge shop processes indicated. (c) Quenching by immersion in water at the temperature shown is required, except where otherwise noted. However, where the symbol (S) is shown, spray quenching of thin sections may be considered when substantiated by experimental data. See "Milder Quenching Mediums", page 274. (d) The symbol "x" indicates a fourth digit used for stress relieved extrusions. For example, T4510 would designate material stress relieved after room temperature aging that has not been straightened after stress relieving, and T4511 would indicate similar material straightened by minor cold work. (e) An alternate treatment

of 17 to 19 hr at 310 to 330 F is permissible, and may be required, to obtain satisfactory properties in thin sections. Heavy sections may be treated along with thinner material that requires the alternate treatment. (f) "W" indicates an unstable temper with properties continuously changing during exposure to room temperature. It is a specific designation only when the period of aging is indicated; for example, 2020-W (½ hr). (g) For heavy rolled rod, use lower side of solution heat treating range. (h) Sheet 0.050 in. thick and under must be solution treated at 910 to 930 F. Other sheet also may be solution heat treated at this higher temperature range. (j) Five days at room temperature followed by 48 to 50 hr at 230 to 250 F. Alloy 7079 may be given a double treatment of 6 to 10 hr at 190 to 200 F plus 23 to 28 hr at 240 to 260 F, which eliminates the five-day delay and permits mixing with 7075 and 7178 material for the final step.

(S) = spray; see note (c) above.   x = variable digit; see (d) above.

wrought aluminum alloys are included with data given in Tables 1 and 2. Solution treating temperatures and soaking times for aluminum casting alloys are given in Table 3.

The soaking times for wrought alloys (Table 2) take into account the normal thermal lag between furnace and part and the difference between surface and center temperatures for commercial equipment qualified to the standards of MIL-H-6088C. The rapid heating rates of salt baths permit all immersion time to be counted as soaking time unless the bath temperature drops below the minimum of the range. Even then, soaking time begins as soon as the bath temperature returns to the minimum. In air furnaces, soaking time does not begin until all furnace instruments return to their *original* set temperature, that is, the temperature reading before insertion of the load.

In air furnaces, thermocouples may also be attached to, or buried in, parts located in the load in such a manner as to represent the hottest and coldest temperatures in each zone. In this way it is possible to insure that adequate soaking is obtained.

Although, with most products, it is desirable to hold soaking time to a minimum for economy and to avoid detriment to the parts, assurance of adequate soaking for some loads requires extending the soaking time. However, the soaking time for parts made

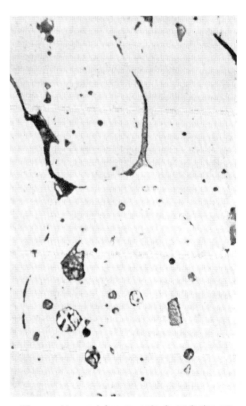

The rosettes and heavy grain boundaries are manifestations of material that melted during solution treating and resolidified during subsequent quenching. The as-cast structure in these areas is extremely brittle and, because of the nearly continuous grain boundary films, brittleness is imparted to the gross structure. Overheated material of this kind cannot be salvaged by reheat treating. Keller's reagent. 1000×.

Fig. 2. Microstructure showing eutectic melting caused by slight overheating in solution heat treating of 2024-T4 sheet

from alclad sheet must be held to a minimum, because the resulting diffusion of alloying elements into the cladding reduces corrosion resistance. For the same reason, it is common practice to prohibit reheat treatment of alclad sheet less than 0.030 in. thick and to limit the number of reheat treatments for sheet thicker than 0.030 in.

Special consideration is given also to establishing soaking time for hand and die forgings; soaking time in some specifications is extended to assure complete solution and homogenization in areas that received marginal reduction during forging. Considerable variation exists in the amount of soaking time added; some specifications call for an arbitrary addition, such as one hour, and others require the addition of one hour per inch of thickness of the original forging.

In air furnaces, careful attention should be given to arrangement of the load. Air flow and natural temperature distribution within the furnace should be known, and the parts should be arranged (a) to offer minimum resistance to air flow, (b) to produce the least disturbance in the natural temperature distribution, and (c) to afford constant replenishment of the envelope of air around each part. It is common practice to specify a minimum spacing of 2 in. between parts, but large complex shapes may require considerably greater spacing. Many operators have found conservative loading practices to be more economical in the long run than heavier loads, because heating rates are faster and fewer rejections and service failures are encountered.

Quenching

To avoid the type of precipitation detrimental to mechanical properties or corrosion resistance, the solid solution formed during solution treating must be rapidly cooled to produce a supersaturated solution at room temperature, the optimum condition for subsequent precipitation and hardening. This is usually accomplished by immersing the parts in cold water.

In order to avoid appreciable precipitation during cooling, two requirements must be satisfied. First, the transfer time from the furnace to the quenching medium must be short enough to preclude slow precooling into the temperature range (750 to 500 F) where very rapid precipitation takes place. Second, the volume of quenching medium, its capacity for absorbing heat, and its rate of flow past the parts must be such that little or no precipitation occurs during cooling through the 750 to 500 F range.

Quenching is normally controlled in practice by stipulating maximum quench delay time and maximum water temperature. The first requirement controls the cooling rate during transfer and, for high-strength alloys, is often based on the criterion of complete immersion before the metal cools below 775 F. The second requirement controls the cooling rate through the most critical range (750 to 500 F).

In Fig. 3, quenching rate is related to tensile properties. These data indicate that in quenching 7178 and 7075 alloys,

quenching rates of about 600 °F per sec or more are required in the temperature range of fast precipitation, to obtain maximum tensile and yield strengths after subsequent precipitation heat treatment.

Cooling rate through the 750 to 500 F range markedly affects the final corrosion resistance of the product, as well as its strength. In Fig. 4 the effect on corrosion resistance is shown by the percentage loss in tensile strength caused by corrosion, as well as the predominant type of corrosive attack (pitting or intergranular). These data were obtained on 2024 alloy in the solution treated (T4) condition and 7075 alloy in precipitation heat treated (T6) condition; they indicate that maximum

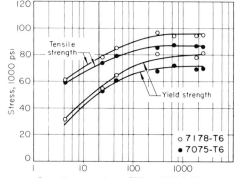

Fig. 3. Effect of quenching rate in the critical temperature range on the tensile and yield strengths of 7178-T6 and 7075-T6

Table 2. Soaking Times and Maximum Quench Delays for Solution Heat Treating Wrought Aluminum Alloys(a)

Thickness, in.(b)	Air furnace(c) Min	Air furnace(c) Max(e)	Salt bath(d) Min	Salt bath(d) Max(e)	Maximum quench delay, sec
0.016 or less	20	25	10	15	5
0.020	20	30	10	20	7
0.025, 0.032	25	35	15	25	7
0.040, 0.050, 0.063	30	40	20	30	10
0.071, 0.080, 0.090	35	45	25	35	10
0.100, 0.125	40	55	30	45	15
0.160, 0.180	50	60	35	45	15
0.250	55	65	35	45	15
0.251 to 0.500	65	75	45	55	15
For each additional ½ in. or fraction	+30	..	+20	..	15
Rivets (all)	60	..	30	..	5(f)

(a) See Table 1 for solution treating temperatures. (b) Minimum dimension of heaviest section. (c) Soaking times begin when all pyrometer instruments recover to original operating temperature. (d) Soaking time begins at time of immersion, except that, when a heavy charge causes bath temperature to drop below specified minimum, soaking time begins when bath regains minimum temperature. (e) Applicable to alclad materials only. (f) See text in regard to dump quenching.

Table 3. Solution and Precipitation Conditions for Aluminum Casting Alloys

Alloy and temper	Sand castings Solution(a) Temperature, F(b)	Solution(a) Time, hr(c)	Precipitation Temperature, F(b)	Precipitation Time, hr(c)	Permanent mold castings Solution(a) Temperature, F(b)	Solution(a) Time, hr(c)	Precipitation Temperature, F(b)	Precipitation Time, hr(c)
40E-T5	....	....	350	9 to 11	....	....	....	....
122-T551	....	....	....	....	....	....	340	18 to 22
122-T61	950	12 to 16	310	10 to 14	....	....	....	....
122-T65	....	....	....	....	940	4 to 8	340	7 to 9
A132-T551	....	....	....	....	....	....	340	14 to 18
A132-T65	....	....	....	....	960	8	340	14 to 18
F132-T5	....	....	....	....	....	....	400	7 to 9
142-T21	....	....	650	2 to 4	....	....	....	....
142-T571	....	....	340	22 to 26	....	....	340	22 to 26
142-T61	960	6	450	1 to 3	960	6	400	3 to 5
142-T77(a)	960	6	650	1 to 3	....	....	....	....
152-T524	....	....	....	....	....	....	525	5 to 7
195-T4	960	10 to 12	...	....	....	....	....	....
195-T6	960	10 to 12	310	3 to 6	....	....	....	....
195-T62	960	10 to 12	310	12 to 24	....	....	....	....
B195-T4	....	....	...	....	950	6 to 12	...	....
B195-T6	....	....	....	....	950	6 to 12	310	5 to 7
B195-T7	....	....	....	....	950	6 to 12	500	4 to 6
319-T5	....	....	400	7 to 9	....	....	....	....
319-T6	940	10 to 12	310	2 to 5	....	....	....	....
333-T5	....	....	....	....	....	....	400	7 to 9
333-T6	....	....	...	....	940	6 to 12	310	2 to 5
333-T7	....	....	...	....	940	6 to 12	500	4 to 6
355-T51	....	....	440	7 to 9	....	....	440	7 to 9
355-T6	980	10 to 12	310	3 to 5	980	6 to 12	310	3 to 5
355-T62	....	....	...	....	980	6 to 12	340	14 to 18
355-T7	980	10 to 12	440	3 to 5	980	6 to 12	440	4 to 6
355-T71	980	10 to 12	475	4 to 6	980	6 to 12	475	4 to 6
A355-T51	....	....	440	7 to 9	....	....	....	....
C355-T61	....	....	...	....	980	8 to 12	310	10 to 12
356-T51	....	....	440	7 to 9	....	....	....	....
356-T6	1000	10 to 12	310	3 to 5	1000	6 to 12	310	3 to 5
356-T7	1000	10 to 12	400	3 to 5	1000	6 to 12	440	7 to 9
356-T71	1000	12	475	2 to 4	....	....	....	....
A356-T61	....	....	...	....	1000	8 to 12	310	6 to 12
750-T5	....	....	430	7 to 9	....	....	430	7 to 9
A750-T5	....	....	430	7 to 9	....	....	430	7 to 9
B750-T5	....	....	430	7 to 9	....	....	430	7 to 9

(a) Except for 142-T77 sand castings, which are quenched in an air blast, solution treatment includes quenching in water at 150 to 212 F; a boiling water quench is recommended, because it minimizes quenching stresses and distortion. (b) Metal temperature should be maintained with as little variation as possible during soaking. (c) Exact time required is influenced by foundry variables and may have to be adjusted, on the basis of experience, to obtain desired properties

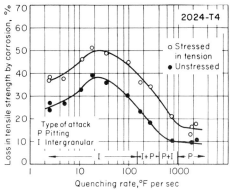

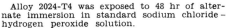

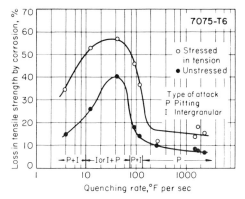

Alloy 2024-T4 was exposed to 48 hr of alternate immersion in standard sodium chloride – hydrogen peroxide solution.

Alloy 7075-T6 was exposed to three months of alternate immersion in 3.5% water solution of sodium chloride.

Fig. 4. Effect of quenching rate on pitting and intergranular corrosive attack and decrease in tensile strength of nonclad aluminum specimens 0.064 in. thick

corrosion resistance requires a rapid quenching rate, preferably not less than about 400 °F per sec. Note that the effect of slow quenches on corrosion resistance is magnified when a sustained tensile stress is imposed during corrosion.

Delay in Quenching. Whether the transfer of parts from the furnace to the quench is performed manually or mechanically, it must be completed in less than the specified maximum time. The maximum allowable transfer time or "quench delay" varies with the temperature and velocity of the ambient air and the mass and emissivity of the parts. From cooling curves such as those illustrated in Fig. 5, maximum quench delays (see table accompanying Fig. 5) can be determined which will assure complete immersion before the parts cool below 750 F. MIL-H-6088C specifies maximum quench delays for high-strength alloys of 5, 7, 10, and 15 sec for thickness ranges of (a) up to 0.016 in., (b) 0.017 to 0.031 in., (c) 0.032 to 0.090 in., and (d) over 0.090 in., respectively. Quench delay is conservatively defined as commencing "when the furnace door begins to open or the first corner of a load emerges from

a salt bath" and ending "when the last corner of the load is immersed in the water quench tank". However, exceeding the maximum delay times is permitted if temperature measurements of the load prove that all parts are above 775 F when quenched.

It is relatively easy to control quench delay in day-to-day operations by using a stopwatch or, if necessary, by attaching thermocouples to parts. However, although the cooling rate between 750 and 500 F is most critical and must be extremely high for many high-strength alloys (see Fig. 6 and 7), it cannot be directly measured in production operations. It is usual to rely on standardized practices, augmented by results of tension tests and tests of susceptibility to intergranular corrosion.

For water immersion quenching, MIL-H-6088C specifies that, except for forgings and castings, the temperature of the water after completion of quenching shall not exceed 100 F. This requirement controls both the quench water temperature before immersion and the ratio of the mass of load and rack to the volume of water. However, to assure adequate quenching effectiveness, it is necessary also that the cooling fluid flow past all surfaces of each part during the first few seconds after immersion. Before parts enter the furnace, their placement in racks or baskets should be compatible with this requirement. During the first few seconds of quenching, agitation of the parts or the water should be sufficient to prevent local temperature rise.

In one application, it was found that 2024-T4 plates (½ by 30 by 30 in.), quenched singly into a large volume of still water, were quite susceptible to intergranular corrosion. This susceptibility disappeared completely when the quenching practice was modified by adding sufficient agitation to break up the insulating blanket of steam that formed on the surface of the hot metal. Quenching practices for small parts such as fasteners and hydraulic fittings have been modified for the same reason. Dumping in bulk from baskets has been replaced by methods, such as the use of shaker hearth furnaces or special racking, which permit quenching the parts singly. Similarly, it has been found worthwhile to quench heavy plate by flushing with high-velocity,

high-volume jets of cold water, rather than by immersion, in order to reduce susceptibility to intergranular corrosion. Massive articles cannot possibly be quenched rapidly enough to be completely free of such susceptibility.

Milder Quenching Mediums. Although cold water immersion or flushing is most common because it produces the most effective quench (and is required by MIL-H-6088C for 2014, 2017, 2117, 2024, 7075 and 7178 alloys except forgings), milder quenching mediums are sometimes employed to reduce distortion and residual stresses. The most common of these are hot water (140 to 180 F), boiling water, water spray, air blast, and "fog". Quenching of forgings in hot water and castings in boiling water is standard practice, reflected in design allowables. The use of even milder quenches is restricted to alloys whose properties are relatively insensitive to quenching rate.

Indiscriminate use of the milder quenches can have catastrophic effects. However, when their use is based on sound engineering judgment and a metallurgical knowledge of the effects on the specific alloy, significant cost savings or performance improvements

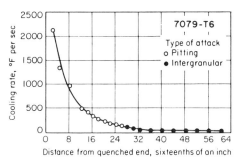

Fig. 6. Effect of cooling rate on the type of corrosion of 7079-T6 alloy. Observations were made on a modified end-quench specimen similar to that used for testing the hardenability of steel.

can be realized. The most frequent advantage is the reduction in costly straightening operations and resultant uncontrolled residual stresses. For example, one aircraft manufacturer utilizes water spray and air blast quenching on weldments and complex formed parts made from 6061, an alloy whose corrosion resistance is insensitive to quenching rate. Straightening requirements are negligible and, by careful control of racking and coolant flow, the decrease in mechanical properties is minimized, as shown by the data in Fig. 8. Similarly, in the ground transportation and building industries, partial solution heat treatments are obtained by rapid air cooling of freshly extruded lengths and press quenching or die quenching of forgings.

Although reduction of warpage is the most common reason for using quenches of moderate severity, a lower level of residual tensile stress is sometimes an attendant benefit. Lower tensile stresses reduce the likelihood of premature fatigue or stress-corrosion failure at points where a more drastic quench would produce high tensile stresses. They also alleviate warpage tendencies during subsequent machining opera-

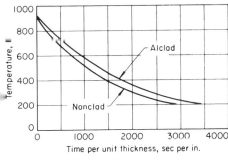

Air temperature, 80 F. Tabulated values of quench delay (maximum delay before the material being quenched has cooled below 750 F) were determined from cooling curves shown.

Thickness, in.	Maximum quench delay, sec	
	Alclad	Nonclad
0.016	6.4	4.4
0.020	8.0	5.5
0.025	10.0	6.8
0.032	12.8	8.8
0.040	20.0	11.0

Fig. 5. Cooling curves for alclad and nonclad aluminum products that were cooled from 920 F in air moving at 450 ft per min

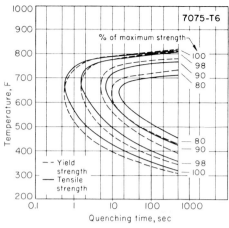

Fig. 7. Effect of time at constant temperature in the quenching range on tensile properties of 7075-T6 alloy. Note also effect on corrosion indicated in Fig. 6.

tions when, as metal is removed, residual stresses are redistributed.

Minimizing Warpage. Even in the same load, symmetry of cooling usually varies significantly between identical parts and the resultant inconsistent warpage usually requires costly hand straightening. Consequently, m u c h effort has been devoted to reducing or eliminating warpage by changing racking positions to achieve symmetry of cooling. For machined parts, the best material properties are obtained when finish machining precedes heat treatment, but thinner sections are more likely to warp during quenching; on the other hand, thicker sections are more likely to warp during subsequent machining. Frequently, the best solution is to rough machine to within about 1/8 in. of final dimensions, then heat treat and finish machine. This practice is most successful when the excess stock remaining after rough machining is the minimum amount that will permit correction of heat treat warpage in finish machining.

For sheet metal parts, one manufacturer uses a double screen floor in the quenching rack to reduce the force of initial contact between water and parts. Others allow parts to "free fall" from rack to quench tank. Spacing and positioning on the rack are carefully controlled so that parts will enter the water with minimum impact. With this technique, water turbulence must be avoided, as it will often cause parts to float for a few seconds, greatly reducing their cooling rate.

Treatments Prior to Precipitation Heat Treating

Immediately after quenching, most aluminum alloys are nearly as ductile as in the annealed condition. Consequently, it is often advantageous to form or straighten parts in this temper. Because precipitation hardening will occur at room temperature, forming or straightening usually follows as soon after quenching as possible.

In some alloys, notably those of series 2000, cold working of freshly quenched material greatly increases its response to later precipitation heat treatment. Mills take advantage of this

phenomenon by applying a controlled amount of rolling (sheet and plate) or stretching (extrusion, bar and plate) to produce higher mechanical properties. However, if the higher properties are used in design, reheat treatment must be avoided.

Forming and Straightening. These operations vary in degree from minor corrections of warpage to complete forming of complex parts from solution treated flat blanks. Particular value is gained when enough forming can be done at this stage of processing to eliminate the distortion caused by quenching. However, production operations must be adjusted so that most of the plastic deformation is accomplished before an appreciable amount of precipitation hardening takes place.

Residual stresses in parts formed in the freshly quenched condition will be somewhat higher than those receiving no deformation after solution treatment. Consequently, this procedure should be used judiciously for parts critical in fatigue or stress corrosion (Fig. 9). However, straightening is usually necessary to correct quenching warpage of parts formed in the annealed temper, and this nonuniform operation will often prove more detrimental than forming in the freshly quenched condition.

Refrigeration. Precipitation characteristics at room temperature and at lower temperatures vary from alloy to alloy with respect to both initiation and rate of change in mechanical properties (Fig. 10). It is usual to attempt to complete forming and straightening before precipitation and the change in mechanical properties commence. (This condition is often called "AQ" or "as quenched".) Therefore, refrigeration is often required to retard hardening. Unanticipated difficulties may arise as a result of failure to control refrigerator or part temperature closely. Too-frequent opening of the cold box to insert or remove parts has been known to result in exceeding the cooling capacity of the refrigerator. At times, the cooling rate of heavy-gage parts in a still-air cold box has been found insufficient. This problem has been solved in one plant by immersing parts in a solvent at −40 F before placing them in the refrigerator.

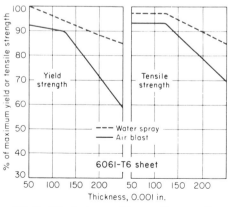

Fig. 8. Effect of quenching medium on the strength of 6061-T6 aluminum alloy sheet. A water immersion quench equals 100%. Control of coolant flow will minimize decrease in mechanical properties.

Precipitation Hardening

In some alloys, sufficient precipitation occurs in a few days at room temperature to yield stable products with properties adequate for many applications. These alloys are sometimes precipitation heat treated to provide increased strength. Other alloys with slow precipitation reactions at room temperature are always precipitation heat treated before use.

Choice of time-temperature cycles for precipitation heat treatment should receive careful consideration. Larger particles of precipitate result from longer times and higher temperatures; however, the larger particles must, of necessity, be fewer in number with greater distances between them. The objective is to select the cycle that produces optimum precipitate size and distribution pattern. Unfortunately, the cycle required to maximize one property, such as tensile strength, is usually different from that required to maximize others, such as yield strength or

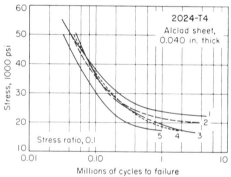

1 Not bent
2 Bend radius, 1/8 in. Flattened in annealed temper.
3 Bend radius, 1/8 in. Flattened in as-quenched condition after 3 days' storage at 0 to 10 F.
4 Bend radius, 1/8 in. Flattened in as-quenched condition after 14 days' storage at 0 to 10 F.
5 Bend radius, 1/16 in. Flattened in as-quenched condition after 3 days' storage at 0 to 10 F.

Fig. 9. Effect of flattening on fatigue characteristics of 0.040-in.-thick clad sheet previously bent 90° in the annealed temper

corrosion resistance. Consequently, the cycles used represent compromises that provide the best combinations of properties (Table 1).

Precipitation Hardening at Room Temperature. The curves in Fig. 10 show that hardening of 2024 alloy at room temperature is essentially complete (T4) in about four days; the alloy is frequently used in that condition. Other alloys sometimes used in the T4 temper are 2014 and 6061; their properties are usually considered fairly stable after about one month (Fig. 10). Most other alloys exhibit hardening characteristics at room temperature similar to those shown in Fig. 10 for 7079 and 7075; that is, their strength continues to rise at an appreciable rate for years after quenching. Such alloys are always precipitation heat treated to the T6 temper before use, whereas the other alloys are used in both the T4 and T6 tempers.

Precipitation heat treatments are generally low-temperature, long-time processes. Temperatures range from 240 to 375 F; times vary from 5 to 48 hr.

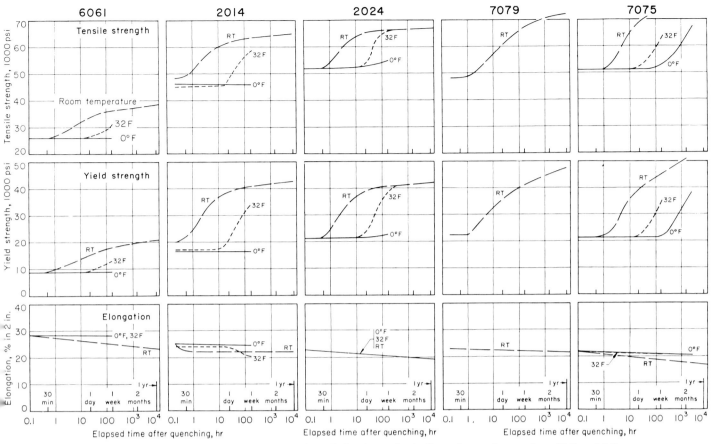

Fig. 10. *Precipitation hardening characteristics of aluminum sheet alloys at room temperature, 32 F and 0 F*

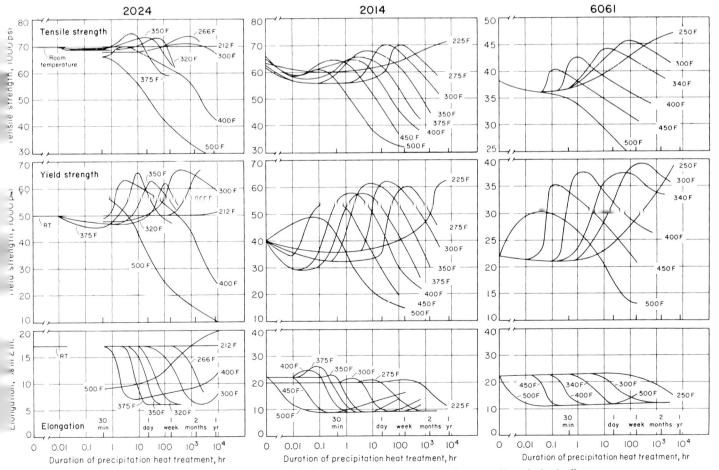

Fig. 11. *Typical effects of precipitation heat treatments on tensile properties of sheet alloys*

The optimum treatments are given in Table 1. Selection of the particular time-temperature cycle for each alloy is the result of a series of compromises. From the families of curves in Fig. 11, it may be seen that maximum tensile and yield strengths require different cycles. Further compromises are often dictated when effects on corrosion resistance are considered.

Soaking time in precipitation heat treating is not difficult to control; the specified times carry rather broad tolerances. Heavier loads with parts racked closer together, and even nested, are not abnormal. The principal hazard is undersoaking due to gross excesses in loading practices.

Temperature control and uniformity present essentially the same problems in precipitation heat treating as they do in solution heat treating. Tolerances on temperature are ±10 °F, except for 2024 alloy; the tolerance for this alloy is ±5 °F. Furnace radiation effects are seldom troublesome except in those few furnaces used for both solution and precipitation heat treating. The heat capacity needed for the higher temperatures is somewhat difficult to control at normal aging temperatures.

Hardening Cast Alloys

In hardening cast alloys, selection of a specific cycle that will produce the optimum combination of properties in all configurations is not possible. Foundry practice (chills, type of mold, and gating) plays an important role in the response of a casting, or a portion of a casting, to heat treatment. Furthermore, alterations of the precipitation heat treatment can produce significant differences in the magnitudes of, and the relation between, strength and ductility; the relative importance of each of these characteristics for the specific part is also a factor in selecting the cycle. Hence, the heat treating practice used for each casting is usually based on preliminary tests.

In general, the principles and procedures for heat treating wrought and cast alloys are similar. The major differences between solution treating conditions for castings and wrought products are found in soaking times and quenching mediums. Solution of the relatively large microconstituents present in castings requires longer soaking periods than those used for wrought products (Table 3). Reduction of quenching stresses and distortion dictate the use of boiling water, and sometimes milder, quenches.

Among precipitation treatments unique to castings are those resulting in the T5 and T7 tempers. The T5 temper is produced merely by applying a precipitation treatment to the as-cast casting, without previous solution treatment. A moderate increase in strength is achieved without warpage and subsequent straightening costs. The second treatment, which results in the T7 temper, is called stabilization and is employed to minimize dimensional changes during service. Precipitation temperatures higher than those used for T6 are utilized to obtain partial stress relief as well as precipitation; thus the strength is lower than T6.

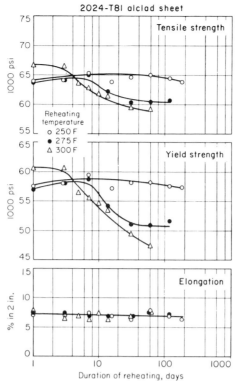

Fig. 12. Effect of reheating on the tensile properties of 2024-T81 alclad sheet

Effects of Reheating

The precipitation characteristics of aluminum alloys must frequently be considered when evaluating the effects of reheating on mechanical properties and corrosion resistance. Such evaluations are necessary when determining standard practices for manufacturing operations, such as hot forming and straightening, adhesive bonding, and paint and dry film lubricant curing, and when evaluating the effects of both short-term and long-term exposure to elevated temperatures in service.

The stage of precipitation present in the alloy at the time of reheating plays a significant role in the effects of reheating. Consequently, it is extremely dangerous to reheat material in a solution heat treated temper without first carefully testing its effects. In one such test, 2024-T4 sheet was found very susceptible to intergranular corrosion when subjected to a 15-min drying operation at 300 F during the first 8 hr after quenching; no susceptibility was evident when the same drying operation was performed more than 16 hr after quenching. In another test, the strengths of 7075-T6 bar and plate were found to be reduced by 10 to 25%

when the material was reheated for hot forming in the solution heat treated temper at 350 F for 20 min. Similar reheating of T6 material for up to 1 hr at 350 F produced no detrimental effect. In this test, times at room temperature after quenching were 0.17, 2, 6, 12, 23, 96, 288, and 600 hr. The shorter time periods produced the greater effects.

If reheating is performed on material in the solution treated condition, its effect can be estimated from families of precipitation heat treating curves such as those in Fig. 11. Such curves can also be used for reheating of precipitation heat treated material at the precipitation heat treating temperature. For reheating at other temperatures, other data may be needed (Fig. 12). The heat treating and reheating curves may be used as the basis for limitations on reheating (Table 4).

Annealing

Annealing treatments are of two types, usually termed "stress relief annealing" and "full annealing". These treatments are used when a softer product is desired. If the purpose of annealing is merely to remove the effects of strain hardening, heating to about 650 F will usually suffice. If it is necessary to remove the hardening effects of a heat treatment or of cooling from hot working temperatures, a treatment designed to produce a coarse, widely spaced precipitate is employed. This usually consists of soaking at 775 to 825 F, followed by slow cooling (50 °F per hr max) to about 500 F. The high diffusion rates existing during soaking and slow cooling permit maximum coalescence of precipitate particles and result in minimum hardness.

When only moderate forming is to follow, a stress relief anneal can sometimes be used for heat treated material, to reduce costs. Full annealing may be similarly used to soften work-hardened materials when furnace schedules make this economically desirable.

Stress relief annealing is accomplished by heating to 650 ± 15 F (or 750 ± 15 F for 3003 alloy) and cooling to room temperature. No appreciable holding time is required. However, it is important to assure that the proper temperature is reached in all portions of the load; therefore, it is common to specify a soaking period of at least 1 hr. The maximum annealing temperature is moderately critical; it is advisable not to exceed 775 F, because of oxidation and grain growth. The heating rate is not critical, except for 3003 alloy, which usually requires rapid heating to prevent grain growth. Rela-

Table 4. Reheating Conditions for Wrought Aluminum Alloys(a)

Alloy and temper	Reheating time at						
	300 F	325 F	350 F	375 F	400 F	425 F	450 F
2014-T4(b)	....	....	....	....	....	....	....
2014-T6	20 to 50 hr	8 to 10 hr	2 to 4 hr	½ to 1 hr	5 to 15 min	(c)	(c)
2024-T3(b), -T4(b)	....	....	....	....	....	....	....
2024-T81, -T86	20 to 40 hr	....	2 to 4 hr	1 hr	½ hr	15 min	5 min
6061-T6, 6062-T6,							
6063-T6	100 to 200 hr	50 to 100 hr	8 to 10 hr	1 to 2 hr	½ hr	15 min	5 min
7075-T6, 7178-T6	10 to 12 hr	1 to 2 hr	1 to 2 hr	½ to 1 hr	5 to 10 min	(c)	(d)

(a) Conditions that normally will not decrease strength more than 5%. (b) Reheating not recommended; it reduces corrosion resistance. (c) Bring to temperature. (d) Not recommended.

tively slow cooling, in still air or in the furnace, is recommended for all alloys, to minimize distortion and avoid partial solution treatment.

Full annealing usually consists of soaking at 775 to 825 F for 2 hr and furnace cooling at a maximum rate of 50 °F per hour to at least 500 F. As a result of this treatment, partial solution occurs in series 7000 alloys, and a second treatment (soaking at 450 ± 10 F for 2 hr) is required. When the need arises for small additional improvements in formability, cooling at 50 °F per hour should be extended to 450 F, and the material should be soaked at 450 F for 6 hr. The effects of eliminating or prolonging the 450 F second step on the ductility of 7075-O sheet are compared with the standard treatment in Table 5.

Although material annealed from the precipitation hardened condition will usually have sufficient ductility for most forming operations, ductility is frequently slightly less than that of material in which no prior heat treatment has occurred — that is, material annealed at the producing source. Therefore, when maximum ductility is required, annealing a heat treated product is sometimes unsuccessful.

Annealing Alclad Products. When alclad aluminum products are subjected to full annealing, precautions should be observed to avoid excessive diffusion of alloying elements into the cladding. This entails limiting the soaking time and the repetition of treatment to the minimum necessary to achieve the desired results.

Temperature control for full annealing is somewhat more critical than for stress relief annealing; the temperatures and times specified are selected to produce a precipitate of maximum size. Cooling rate must be closely controlled. Allowing the load to cool with the furnace may give an excessively fast rate. Similarly, lowering the furnace control instrument by 50 °F each hour may produce stepped cooling, which is not satisfactory for severe forming operations. For maximum softening, a continuous cooling rate of not more than 50 °F per hour is recommended.

Furnace Equipment and Accessories

Both molten salt baths and air chamber furnaces are suitable for solution heat treating of aluminum alloys. The choice of furnace equipment depends largely on the alloys and the configuration of the parts to be processed. Both heating mediums have advantages and disadvantages. Oil and gas-fired furnaces, in designs that allow the products of combustion to come in contact with the work, are usually unsatisfactory because they promote high-temperature oxidation.

Salt baths heat the work faster (see Table 2) than air furnaces, provided the amount of work introduced at any one time is controlled to prevent the temperature of the bath from falling below the desired range. If the temperature is permitted to fall below the minimum limit, much of the advantage of the salt bath is lost, because of the necessity for reheating the large mass of salt.

Salt baths are also more readily adapted to the introduction, at any time, of small amounts of work requiring different soaking periods. (Economical utilization of air furnaces usually dictates accumulation of a good sized load of parts of similar thickness before charging.) Also, the buoyant effect of the salt reduces distortion during heating, and the large reservoir of heat facilitates temperature control and uniformity.

Salt bath operation entails special housekeeping requirements. Dragout is costly and unsightly. Because residual salt on parts may result in corrosion, all salt must be completely removed, including that from crevices and blind holes. In addition, salt residue from the quench water must be kept to a minimum by a constant water overflow or by providing a fresh water rinse for all parts after quenching. When these provisions are impractical, corrosion can be inhibited by adding ½ oz of sodium or potassium dichromate to each 100 lb of the molten salt.

Precautions. Molten salt baths are potentially hazardous and require special precautions. Operators must be protected from splashing and dripping of the hot salt. Because heated nitrates are powerful oxidizing agents, they must never be allowed to come in contact with combustibles and reducing agents, such as magnesium and cyanides. Most authorities advise against inserting aluminum alloys containing more than a few percent of magnesium into molten nitrate. To avoid exposure of personnel to nitrous fumes produced during decomposition of nitrates, good ventilation is essential.

When molten nitrates are being used, the possibilities of explosions resulting from both physical and chemical reactions must be avoided. The former result from rapid expansion of gases entrapped beneath the surface of the bath. Hence, parts entering the bath must be clean and dry; they must also be free of pockets or cavities that contain air or other gases. Chemical reaction explosions result from rapid breakdown of the nitrates because of overheating or reaction with the pot material. Stainless steel pots (preferably of type 321 or 347 steel) are more resistant to scaling than those made of carbon steel or cast iron and therefore present a lower probability of local overheating. Sludge or sediment accumulations in bottom-heated pots can also lead to local overheating. Overheat controls are essential to insure against temperatures exceeding 1100 F.

It is vitally important that water be kept away from a nitrate tank. In controlling a nitrate fire, *do not use water or any fire extinguisher containing water.* The best extinguisher is dry sand, a supply of which should be kept near the tank.

Extra sacks of salt should be stored in a dry place, distant from the tank. If the fresh salt being added to the bath is even slightly damp, it should be added very slowly or when the bath is frozen.

Air furnaces are used more widely than salt baths because they permit greater flexibility in operating temperature. When production schedules and the variety of alloys requiring heat treatment necessitate frequent changes in temperature, the time and cost of adjusting the temperature of a large mass of salt makes the use of an air furnace almost mandatory. However, waiting periods are often required to allow the walls of air furnaces to stabilize at the new temperature before parts are introduced. Otherwise, parts may radiate heat to colder walls or absorb radiant heat from hotter walls, and the temperature indicated by the control instrument will not reflect actual metal temperature in the usual manner. Air furnaces are also more economical when the product mix includes a few rather large parts; holding the temperature of a large volume of salt in readiness for an occasional large part is far more expensive than heating an equal volume of air.

High-Temperature Oxidation

High-temperature oxidation of the work due to atmosphere contaminants (particularly moisture or sulfur compounds) is a potential hazard in air furnaces. Its most common manifestation is surface blistering, but occasionally the only manifestations are internal discontinuities or voids, which can be detected only by careful ultrasonic inspection or metallographically.

It is important to recognize that the symptoms of high-temperature oxidation are identical to those of unsoundness or high gas content in the original ingot or of other improper mill practice. Blisters resulting from ingot defects, improper extrusion or improper rolling may be lined up in the direction of working. However, it is usually impossible to distinguish among defect sources, and therefore the possibility that a contaminated atmosphere is the cause of the defects must be checked.

Moisture in contact with aluminum at high temperature serves as a source of nascent hydrogen, which diffuses into the metal. Foreign materials, such as sulfur compounds, function as decomposers of the natural oxide surface film, eliminating it as a barrier either

Table 5. Effects of Annealing Treatments on Ductility of 7075-O Sheet

	Elongation in tension, %(a) Thickness, in.			Bend angle, degrees(b) Thickness, in.		Elongation in bending, %(c) Thickness, in.	
	0.020	0.064	0.102	0.064	0.102	0.064	0.102
Treatment 1(d)	12	12	12	82	73	48	50
Treatment 2(e)	14	14	14	91	76	58	57
Treatment 3(f)	16	16	..	92.5	84	56	60

(a) Uniform elongation of gridded tension specimens. (b) Bend angle at first fracture. (c) Elongation in bend test for 0.05-in. gage spanning fracture. (d) Soak at 775 F ± 25 F for 2 hr; furnace cool at 50 °F per hr to 500 F and air cool. (e) Soak at 800 F for 2 hr and air cool. (f) Soak at 800 F for 1 hr; furnace cool at 50 °F per hr to 450 F; soak at 450 F for 6 hr and air cool.

between the moisture and the aluminum or between the nascent hydrogen and the aluminum.

All alloys and forms are not equally vulnerable to this type of attack. The series 7000 alloys are most susceptible, followed by the series 2000 alloys. Extrusions undoubtedly are the most susceptible form; forgings are probably second. Low-strength alloys and alclad sheet and plate are relatively immune to high-temperature oxidation. (The blistering of alclad material as a result of inadequate bonding is not the same as the blistering caused by high-temperature oxidation.)

If the protective oxide film formed during mill operations is removed from the mill product by a subsequent conditioning operation, such as sanding, the conditioned surface is more susceptible to high-temperature oxidation than those from which the film was not removed.

Moisture can be minimized by thoroughly drying parts and racks before they are charged. Drain holes are often needed in racks of tubular construction, to avoid entrapment of water. Another common requirement is adjustment of the position of the quench tank with respect to furnace doors and air intake. Because it is unlikely that all moisture can be eliminated from the atmosphere in a production heat treating furnace, it is extremely important to eliminate all traces of other contaminants from both the parts and the furnace atmosphere.

The most virulent contaminants in attacking aluminum are sulfur compounds. Residues from forming or machining lubricants or from a sulfur dioxide protective atmosphere used in prior heat treatment of magnesium are potential sources of sulfur contamination. In one plant, surface contamination resulted from sulfur-containing materials in tote boxes used to transport parts. In another, an epidemic of blistering was cured by rectifying a "sour" degreaser. In a third instance, it was found that a vapor degreasing operation was not completely removing a thin, hard waxy residue and an alkaline cleaning operation was added.

Very often, the source of contamination is obscure and difficult to detect, and the problem must be combated in another way. The most common of the alternative methods is use of a protective fluoborate compound in the furnace. Such a compound is usually effective in minimizing the harmful effects of moisture and other undesirable contaminants because it forms a barrier layer or film on the aluminum surface. The additive is not a panacea; in some applications, high-temperature oxidation has occurred even though a fluoborate compound was employed. Also, the use of such compounds, particularly ammonium fluoborate, may present a hazard to personnel if used in poorly sealed furnaces or in furnaces that discharge their atmospheres into enclosed areas.

Protective fluoborate compounds accentuate the staining or darkening of the parts being heat treated. (At times, this attack, particularly on parts located near the protective compound

container during heat treatment, has been severe enough to be termed "corrosion".) Although this minor nuisance might be considered a small price to pay for curing a problem of high-temperature oxidation, the residual compound in the furnace dissipates slowly. Therefore, subsequent loads of alloys and forms that require bright surfaces, and that are not susceptible to high-temperature oxidation, may be detrimentally affected.

Successful use of fluoborate protective compounds appears to depend on specifying the right amount for each furnace; this must be established on a trial-and-error basis. One aircraft manufacturer adds 0.004 oz per cubic foot of furnace chamber to each load. Another adds one pound per shift to a metal container hung on the furnace chamber wall, thus avoiding loss of the compound during quenching.

A second method of combating high-temperature oxidation is to anodize the work before it is heat treated. The resultant aluminum oxide film prevents attack by contaminants in the furnace atmosphere. The only deterrents to the use of anodizing are its cost (in money and time) and the slight surface frostiness which results from the subsequent stripping operation.

Usually the objection to the blistered surface produced by high-temperature oxidation is its unsightly appearance. This can often be improved (for salvage purposes) by applying local pressure to flatten each blister and then finishing by a mechanical process such as polishing, buffing, sanding or abrasive blasting. In general the effect of the oxidation on static properties and fatigue strength is slight. However, if a void resulting from oxidation is located close to another stress concentration, such as a hole, much greater degradation of fatigue strength is likely.

Temperature Control

The importance of close temperature control in solution treating has been noted in a previous section of this article.

Each control zone of each furnace should contain at least two thermocouples. One thermocouple, with its instrument, should act as a controller, regulating the heat input; the other should act independently as a safety cutoff, requiring manual reset if its set temperature (usually the maximum of the specified range) is exceeded during the solution treating cycle.

Safety cutoffs are mandatory for salt baths, to guard against explosions, and have often paid for themselves in air furnaces by saving a load of parts or even the furnace itself. It is important, however, that they be tested periodically (by deliberately overshooting the empty furnace) to guard against "frozen" or corroded contacts resulting from prolonged periods of idleness.

At least one of the instruments for each zone should be of the recording type and both instruments should have restricted scales — for instance, 800 to 1200 F, rather than 0 to 1200 F. This is required for maximum accuracy because manufacturers' guarantees are specified in terms of percent of scale.

In the placement of instruments, exposure to extremes in ambient temperature, humidity, vibration, dust and corrosive fumes should be avoided. Ambient temperatures between 40 and 120 F are satisfactory, but temperature changes of 10 °F or more per hour should be avoided. It is also essential that instruments and thermocouple circuits be shielded from electromagnetic fields commonly associated with the leads of high-amperage furnace heating elements.

Temperature-sensing elements must be capable of responding more rapidly to temperature changes than the materials being processed. Therefore, thermocouple wire diameter should not exceed 1½ times the thickness of the minimum gage material to be heat treated, and in no case should it exceed 14 gage. Thermocouples for salt baths should be enclosed in suitable protection tubes. Air furnace thermocouples should be installed in open-end protection tubes, with the thermocouple junction extending sufficiently beyond the tube to assure no loss in sensitivity.

Temperature-sensing elements should be located in the furnace work chamber, not in ducts and plenums, and should be as close as possible to the working zone. Specification MIL-H-6088C restricts distance between the sensing element and the working zone to a maximum of 4 in. The safety cutoff thermocouple should be located in a position to reflect the highest temperature in the working zone. The control thermocouple should be located in a position where it will read a temperature approximately halfway between the hottest and coldest temperatures.

Probe Checks. After the temperature measurement equipment is properly installed, it must be checked frequently for accuracy. This is accomplished by inserting a calibrated probe thermocouple into the furnace adjacent to each furnace thermocouple and comparing its reading on a calibrated test potentiometer to that indicated by the furnace instrument. Correction factors should be applied to the furnace instruments after each probe check, but if the correction required exceeds 5 °F, the source of the deviation should be corrected. MIL-H-6088C recommends that this check be made weekly, but many operators make the check as frequently as once each shift.

Temperature Uniformity Surveys. In controlling the temperature of parts that are being heat treated it must first be determined that the temperature indicated by the furnace instruments truly represents the temperature of the nearby air or salt. Second, the uniformity of temperature within the working zone must be shown to be within a 20 °F range (10 °F for precipitation heat treatment of 2024 alloy). This is accomplished by measuring the temperature at several test locations using calibrated test thermocouples and a calibrated test potentiometer, and reading furnace instruments nearly simultaneously. MIL-H-6088C recommends monthly surveys with one test location per 40 cu ft (25 cu ft for air furnaces on initial survey), but with a minimum of nine test locations distributed as shown in Fig. 13. Despite the large size of some furnaces, rather surprising temperature uniformities have been reported. In one case, the initial survey of an air furnace measuring 41 by 4 by 10 ft showed maximum temperature variations of +3, −2 °F. When a partition (1 ft thick) was lowered, converting the furnace to two chambers 20 by 4 by 10 ft each, the spread was +2, −1 °F in one section and +1, −2 °F in the other.

In salt baths, uniformity surveys are usually made by holding a probe thermocouple in each location until thermal equilibrium is reached; in air furnaces, a mock heat treating cycle is required. First, the air furnace is stabilized at the test temperature. Then a rack containing the test thermocouples is inserted into the furnace. By using multiple switches or a multipoint recording instrument, all test thermocouples and furnace instruments are read every 5 min. As the temperature approaches the test range, it is advisable to increase the frequency of readings to detect possible overshooting. After thermal equilibrium is reached, readings should be continued until the recurrent temperature pattern is established.

Surveys of salt baths are generally considered acceptable whether they are made while the bath is empty or filled with work. It is controversial whether surveys of air furnaces should be made with or without a load. Undoubtedly, recovery overshoots are most likely to occur with a very light load and these would not be detected if a heavier load were used. Certainly, if all loads are essentially alike, surveys should be made with typical loads. With widely varying loads the optimum approach is to make several surveys initially, including one with an empty furnace, and then to make succeeding surveys with an empty furnace to insure against changes in furnace characteristics. If any changes are made in the furnace that might affect temperature distribution, such as repair of vanes or louvers, the several surveys should be repeated.

Another aspect of the temperature control problem in air furnaces is assuring that the temperature of the parts is the same as that of the surrounding air. Furnace components whose temperature differs from the air temperature must be suitably shielded to prevent radiation to or from the parts being heat treated. In a furnace used to solution heat treat rivets, unshielded heating elements have been known to produce part temperatures as much as 35 °F higher than the control temperature, resulting in eutectic melting and rivet cracking. In two other instances, reradiation through inadequate shielding produced as much as a 20 °F radiation effect. One of these problems was solved by painting the shield with reflective aluminum paint and the other by adding a ½-in. thickness of asbestos to the 1/16-in. stainless steel shield.

Furnace wall temperatures that differ appreciably from the temperature of the parts must be guarded against also. Consequently, when the operating temperature of an air furnace is changed, waiting periods are required after the furnace instrument indicates stability,

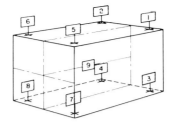

Rectangular furnace

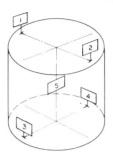 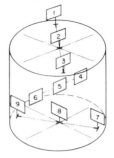

Cylindrical salt bath   Cylindrical air furnace

Fig. 13. Location of thermocouples for surveying temperature uniformity in the working zone of air furnaces and salt baths

to allow the furnace walls to stabilize at the new temperature. The magnitude of this limitation is directly proportional to the efficiency of the furnace as an insulated chamber, but possibilities of such radiation should be recognized even in thin-wall furnaces.

Radiation effects are potentially dangerous because they often cannot be detected by an ordinary thermocouple. Specially prepared radiation panels with thermocouples attached are used, and their readings are compared with adjacent free thermocouples. These panels are normally made of material representing the thinnest gage of parts to be heat treated and should have a single surface area of about 100 sq in. A thermocouple is attached to the center of the panel by welding or peening. In order to detect the maximum effect, surfaces of the panels should be darkened so that their emissivity is at least as high as that of any material to be processed. During the test, the panel surfaces should be parallel to the suspected source or recipient of radiation. As an example of the number of panels required several aerospace companies specify one panel for every five linear feet of furnace wall.

Instrument Calibration. All instruments and thermocouples must be accurately calibrated, and it is essential that the calibrations be traceable directly to the National Bureau of Standards. The chain of traceability should consist of not more than four links for sensing elements and three links for measuring elements. To illustrate, if the article calibrated by the National Bureau of Standards is called a primary standard, then the chain of traceability of measuring elements should consist of primary standard, test potentiometer, and furnace instrument. Similarly, the chain for sensing elements should consist of primary standard, secondary standard, test thermocouple, and furnace thermocouple. Every effort should be made to

insure that the temperature indicated by the furnace instruments is as close as possible to the actual temperature. To achieve this, it is necessary to apply correction factors obtained during calibration to the next lower echelon of accuracy. Even then, if all errors inherent in the chain are in the same direction, considerable difference will exist between the measured and actual temperatures. Therefore, it is advisable to operate as close to the mean of the desired range as possible.

Grain Growth

Many of the aluminum alloys in common use are subject to grain growth during solution treatment or annealing. This phenomenon appears to occur during recrystallization of material that has been subjected to a critical amount of prior cold work. It is usually manifested by surface roughening during subsequent fabrication operations and frequently results in rejections for appearance or functional reasons. Less frequently, some deterioration of mechanical properties is suspected, and this is undesirable regardless of surface roughening effects.

Degree of susceptibility to grain growth varies from alloy to alloy and form to form. The critical range of cold work is ordinarily about 5 to 15%. Usually, temperatures of 750 F and above must be reached before grain growth occurs, but some growth has been encountered at temperatures as low as 650 F. The common symptom, indicating moderately large grained material, is roughening or "orange peel" on the external surfaces of bends. Severe growth of grains to fingernail size and larger is sometimes evident after stretch forming and similar operations. This type of grain growth is often detected during subsequent anodizing, etching, and chemical milling operations.

Another characteristic which may indicate that severe grain growth has occurred is cracking during welding or brazing. In such cases, cracks propagate along grain boundaries that provide little obstruction to their progress.

If the surface roughening is objectionable from either an appearance or functional aspect, the desirability of surface smoothing operations such as sanding or buffing, must be evaluated. If reductions in mechanical properties are suspected, these must usually be established by test and evaluated in relation to the anticipated service.

In one application, tensile and yield strengths in portions of a stretch formed part (made from 0.080-in.-thick 6061-T6 sheet) exhibiting severe grain growth were significantly lower than in portions having normal grain size:

Test	Tensile strength, psi	Yield strength, psi	Grain structure
Transverse			
1	38,500	35,800	Coarse
2	38,200	35,000	Coarse
3	45,100	37,800	Fine
Longitudinal			
1	37,600	35,300	Coarse
2	39,000	35,600	Coarse
3	44,200	39,100	Fine

In other similar investigations, no detrimental effects have been discovered, and in many cases such parts have served satisfactorily in critical applications.

When a grain growth problem is discovered, it is too late to change the condition of the parts in question, but several possible methods are available for preventing recurrence of the difficulty. The simplest of these is relieving the causative residual stress by interjecting a stress relief anneal into the manufacturing sequence immediately prior to the solution treating or full annealing cycle in which the grain growth occurred. This approach is usually successful and practical. Another possibility is to adjust the amount of residual stress present in the part immediately prior to the critical heat treatment so that the stress level is outside the critical range. This may be done by adding a cold working operation before forming, such as the pre-stretching of blanks, or by forming in multiple stages with a stress relief anneal before each stage.

A third method which is sometimes successful consists of increasing the heating rate during the critical heat treatment by reducing the size of furnace loads or by changing from an air furnace to a salt bath. In one application, severe grain growth was found during bending of rectangular 1100 alloy tubing. The roughening of the inside surface of the parts, which occurred during forming of the large-grained material, impaired their functioning as radar waveguides. Investigation disclosed that the material was procured in the strain hardened (H14) temper, to minimize handling marks, and stress relief annealed at 650 F immediately prior to forming. Grain growth occurred during stress relieving as a result of the moderate amount of cold work introduced at the mill. The problem was eliminated by changing the stress relieving operation to a 5-min heating period in an air furnace operating at 1000 F. The explanation advanced for the success of this treatment was that the rapid heating rate raised the temperature of the material to the recrystallization temperature of the less severely cold worked grains before the critically cold worked grains had time to grow appreciably.

Control of Residual Stress and Distortion

Residual stresses in heavy sections of aluminum alloys originate during the later stages of quenching as the still-warm central material contracts, pulling in the already-cooled outer shell. The magnitude of stresses increases with section size and severity of quench.

Stress Distribution. The distribution pattern of residual stresses (compression in the outer layers and tension in the central portion) is usually desirable in service. Compressive stresses inhibit failure by fatigue and stress corrosion, two mechanisms which initiate in the outer fibers. Unfortunately, metal removal operations required after heat treating often expose material that is stressed in tension. Also, metal removal operations that are asymmetrical (with

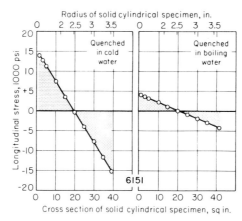

Fig. 14. Effect of quenching from 1000 F on residual stress in solid cylinders of 6151

respect to residual stresses) cause distortion by redistributing residual stress. When close-tolerance parts are being fabricated, the resulting warpage can be costly and difficult to correct.

Although service performance is sometimes a factor, the major incentive for reducing residual stresses usually has been the reduction of warpage during machining. A simple approach that is generally successful consists of rough machining to within 1/8 in. or less of finish dimensions before final heat treatment. This procedure is intended to reduce the cooling rate differential between surface and center by reducing thickness; other benefits that accrue if this technique is used to reduce or reverse surface tension stresses in finished parts are improvements in strength, fatigue life, and corrosion resistance, and reduced tendency to stress-corrosion cracking.

Several factors (especially quenching warpage) preclude general use of this procedure. The thinner and less symmetrical a section, the more it will warp during quenching, and the residual stresses resulting from straightening warped parts (plus straightening costs) are often less desirable than the quenching stresses. Holding fixtures and die quenching are sometimes helpful, but precautions must be taken to assure that they do not retard quenching rates excessively. Other factors that must be considered are the availability of heat treating facilities and whether the advantages of such a manufacturing sequence offset the delay and cost entailed in a double-machining setup.

Another approach to reducing the cooling-rate differential between surface and center is the use of a milder quenching medium, usually water that is hotter than normally used. The residual stress level decreases as the severity of the quench decreases, but boiling water is the slowest quenching medium used and it is seldom used because it lowers mechanical properties and corrosion resistance (Fig. 14).

Thermal Treatments for Relieving Stresses. Numerous attempts have been made to develop a thermal treatment that will remove, or appreciably reduce, quenching stresses. Normal precipitation heat treating temperatures are generally too low to provide appreciable stress relief and exposure to higher temperatures (at which stresses are re-

lieved more effectively) results in lower properties. However, such treatments are sometimes utilized when even a moderate reduction in residual stress levels is important enough so that some sacrifice in mechanical properties can be accepted. The T7 temper, mentioned previously, for castings is a typical example of this kind of treatment.

Other thermal stress relief treatments known as "subzero treatment" and "cold stabilization" involve the cycling of parts above and below room temperature. The temperatures chosen are those that can be readily obtained with boiling water and mixtures of dry ice and alcohol — namely, +212 and −100 F — and the number of cycles ranges from one to five. The maximum reduction in residual stress made possible by these techniques is about 25%. The maximum effect can be obtained only if the subzero step is performed first, immediately after quenching from the solution treating temperature while yield strength is low, and no benefit is gained from more than one cycle.

Although a 25% reduction in residual stress is sometimes sufficient to permit fabrication of a part that could not be made without this reduction, as much as 83% relief of residual stress is possible by increasing the severity of the "uphill quench", that is, more closely approximating the reverse of the cooling rate differential during the original quench. This may be accomplished by a patented process (U.S. Patent 2,949,-392) that involves extending the subzero step to −320 F and then very rapidly "uphill quenching" in a blast of live steam (Fig. 15). The rate of reheating is extremely critical and therefore, to apply the steam blast properly, a special fixture is usually required for each part.

This process will not solve all problems of warpage in machining. It may reduce warpage internally but increase warpage of the extreme outer layers, although in the opposite direction (Fig. 16). Also, the effect of the altered residual stress pattern on performance must be evaluated carefully for each part. This is particularly important for

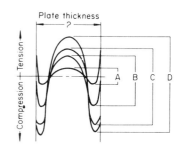

A Cooled to −320 F, then uphill quenched in a steam blast
B Cooled to −100 F, then uphill quenched in a steam blast
C Cooled to −100 or −320 F, then uphill quenched in boiling water
D Standard specimen, quenched and aged to T6 temper in conventional manner with no further treatment

NOTE: Uphill quenching treatments (single cycle only) were applied between ½ and 1½ hr after quenching from the recommended solution treating temperature. All specimens were aged to the T6 temper after uphill quenching

Fig. 15. Effectiveness of various uphill quenching treatments in reducing the magnitude of residual quenching stresses

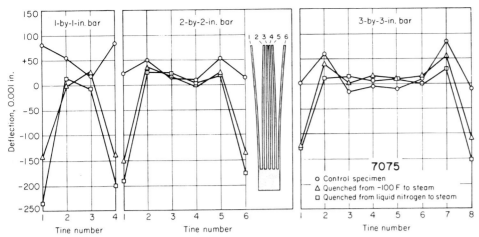

Fig. 16. *Effect of uphill quenching on deflection of tines. Six-tine specimen shown was machined from 2-by-2-in. bar. Similar specimens machined from 1-by-1-in. and 3-by-3-in. bars had four and eight tines, respectively.*

parts subject to cyclic loads or corrosive environments such as marine atmospheres, especially if the process is introduced after the start of production and original performance tests are not repeated. A further disadvantage is the cost and hazard involved in handling liquid nitrogen and live steam.

Mechanical Methods. At the mill level, controlled mechanical deformation is the most common method for reducing residual quenching stresses. Deformation consists of stretching (bar, extrusions and plate) or compressing (forgings) the product sufficiently to achieve a small but controlled

amount (1 to 3%) of plastic deformation. These processes are particularly useful when they eliminate, or greatly reduce, straightening by local deformation on "gag" presses. Residual stresses are aligned in the direction of working and stress differences are decreased in the thickness direction. Maximum effectiveness is obtained by working the metal immediately after quenching. If the benefits of mechanical stress relieving are needed, the user should refrain from reheat treating.

Figure 17 illustrates the beneficial effect of 3% permanent deformation in compression on a large forging.

These methods are most readily adaptable to mill and forge shop products and require equipment of greater capacity than that found in most manufacturing plants. Application of these methods to die forgings and extrusions usually requires construction of special dies and jaws. Stretching is generally limited to material of uniform cross section; however, it has been applied successfully to stepped extrusions and to a 10 by 47 ft aircraft wing skin roll-tapered to a thickness range of 0.280 to 0.125 in.

Effect of Heat Treatment on Corrosion Resistance

Maximum corrosion resistance requires that the heat treating cycle produce a precipitate that is essentially uniformly distributed across each grain, thus eliminating any electrochemical potential between grain boundaries and grain interiors. In practice, complete elimination of this potential is difficult to attain, and in heavy sections (because of their slower quench rates), virtually impossible. Because of the large size and wide separation of microconstituents in annealed alloys, such material is likely to corrode by pitting and therefore should not be exposed to corrosive environments.

Intergranular Corrosion. Less energy is required to form a particle of precipitate at a grain boundary than elsewhere in the matrix. Consequently, precipitation occurs first along grain boundaries. When such precipitation occurs in the high-strength alloys, either the precipitate itself, or the zone depleted in alloying element immediately adjacent to the boundaries, is anodic to the remainder of the material. If such material is exposed to a corrosive environment, such as salt water, an electric current will flow between the anodes (grain boundaries) and cathodes (grain centers). Corrosion will penetrate rapidly through the anodic grain boundaries, leaving the cathodic regions comparatively untouched. The insidious nature of this attack results from the fact that very little corrosion or corrosion product is visible on the surface. The grains usually remain mechanically locked together, although they are unbonded metallurgically; hence, a large reduction in strength may go undetected.

Susceptibility to intergranular corrosion must be carefully considered when heat treating cycles are being selected for high-strength alloys. It is usually advisable to incorporate all available practical measures to prevent or minimize anodic grain boundary zones. This may necessitate some sacrifice in mechanical properties, because maximum strength and maximum resistance to intergranular corrosion are not produced by the same precipitation heat treatment. Likewise, a drastic quench is essential (see Fig. 4), even though it may increase warpage, require straightening operations, and add to processing costs. Duration of precipitation heat treating is usually an important consideration, as indicated in Fig. 18.

The most common test for susceptibility to intergranular corrosion is described in the Appendix of this article.

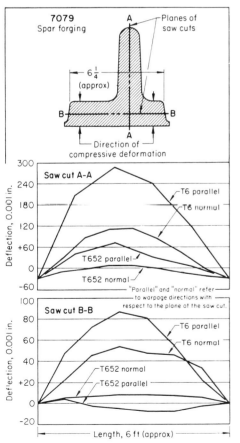

Fig. 17. *Effect of 3% permanent deformation in compression (T652 treatment) on the distribution of stress in a large forging*

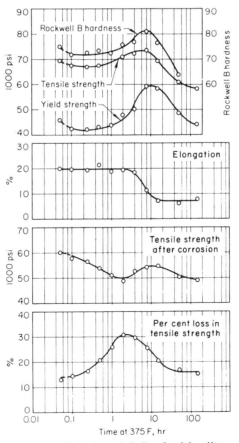

Fig. 18. *Effect of precipitation heat treating time on mechanical properties and on loss in strength after corrosion of 2024-T4 alloy*

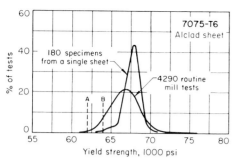

A is 95% probability that not more than 1% of all material will fall below this value.
B is 95% probability that not more than 10% of all material will fall below this value.

Fig. 19. Comparison of distribution of yield strength in heat treated 7075-T6 clad sheet product with distribution of yield strength in a single sheet. A and B refer only to curve representing 4290 routine mill tests.

Stress Corrosion. Susceptibility to stress-corrosion cracking is another factor that sometimes must be taken into account when selecting precipitation treating cycles. The high-strength alloys are susceptible to failure by this mechanism when they are subjected simultaneously to high sustained loads and corrosive environments, particularly if the loads are applied in the short transverse direction. Degree of susceptibility to such failure does not always correlate with susceptibility to intergranular corrosion; therefore, special cycles are sometimes used to increase resistance to stress corrosion.

For 2024 alloy, considerable improvement has been obtained by increasing the duration of precipitation heat treatment to 12 to 16 hr, the exact optimum time depending on product form. Virtual immunity to stress corrosion can be conferred on 7075 alloy by precipitation heat treating to the T73 temper, employing a proprietary process. However, the use of this process is not without penalty; it produces approximately 15% lower static strength than the normal T6 treatment. On the other hand, it does not affect fatigue strength adversely.

Appendix on Tests

Hardness tests are less valuable for acceptance or rejection of heat treated aluminum alloys than they are for steel. Nevertheless, hardness tests have some utility for process control. Typical hardness values for various alloys and tempers are given in Table 6.

Tension Tests. In general, the relatively constant relationships among various properties allow the use of tensile properties alone as acceptance criteria. The minimum guaranteed strength is ordinarily that value below which it can be predicted with 95% probability that not more than 1% of the material will fall. However, to provide this degree of assurance for each individual lot would require an economically prohibitive frequency of sampling. Also, the inherent variability within lots and among specimens from a given piece (Fig. 19) makes it impractical to rely solely on tension testing to eliminate subminimum material. Testing provides only a spot check for evidence of nonconformance; process capability and process control are the foundation for guaranteed values.

Published minimum guaranteed values are applicable only to specimens cut from a specific location in the product, with their axes oriented at a specific angle to the direction of working as defined in the applicable procurement specification. In thick plate, for example, the guaranteed values apply to specimens taken from a plane midway between the center and the surface, and with their

axes parallel to the width dimension (long transverse). Different properties should be expected in specimens taken from other locations, or in specimens whose axes were parallel to the thickness dimension (short transverse). However, the specified "referee" locations and orientations do provide a useful basis for lot-to-lot comparisons, and constitute a valuable adjunct to other process control measures.

A few random tension tests give little assurance of proper heat treatment. Nevertheless, tension tests can be used to evaluate the effects of changes in the process, provided specimens are carefully selected.

A variation in process that produces above-minimum properties on test specimens is not necessarily satisfactory. Its acceptability can be judged only by comparing the resulting properties with those developed by the standard process on identical specimens (preferably taken from adjacent positions) from the same lot of material. Finally, variations in heat treating procedure are likely to affect the relationships among tensile properties and other mechanical properties. In many applications, other properties are more important to the product than tensile properties.

Intergranular Corrosion Test. The most common test for susceptibility to intergranular corrosion is carried out as follows:

1 Use a sample having at least 3 sq in. of surface area.
2 Remove any cladding by filing or etching.
3 Clean the sample by immersing it for 1 min in a 5% concentrated nitric acid - 0.5% hydrofluoric acid solution at 200 F. Rinse in distilled water; immerse for 1 min in concentrated nitric acid at room temperature; rinse in distilled water.
4 Immerse the sample for 6 hr in a freshly prepared solution containing 57 g of sodium chloride and 10 ml of 30% hydrogen peroxide per liter at a temperature of 86 ± 9 °F. More than one sample may be corroded in a container provided that at least 30 ml of solution is used for each square inch of specimen surface and that

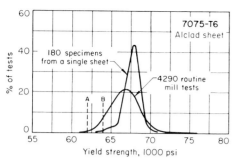

Severity of intergranular attack (schematic), as observed microscopically in transverse sections after test for susceptibility to intergranular corrosion. Top of each area shown is surface exposed to corrosive solution. See text.

Fig. 20. Intergranular attack

the specimens are electrically insulated from each other.
5 After the immersion period, wash the sample, using a soft bristle brush to remove any loose corrosion product. Cut a cross section specimen at least $\frac{3}{4}$ in. long through the most severely corroded area; mount and metallographically polish the specimen.
6 Microscopically examine the specimen at 100× and 500× both before and after etching with Keller's reagent.
7 Describe the results of microscopic examination in terms of severity of intergranular attack illustrated in Fig. 20 as "x areas of A severity, y areas of B severity, z areas of C severity", and so on.

Table 6. Typical Acceptable Hardness Values for Wrought Aluminum Alloys(a)

Alloy and temper	Form(b)	Rockwell hardness number B scale	E scale	H scale	15-T scale
2014-T3, -T4, -T42	All	65 to 70	87 to 95	....	....
2014-T6, -T62, -T65	Sheet(c)	80 to 90	103 to 110	....	....
	All others	81 to 90	104 to 110	....	....
2014-T61	All	....	100 to 109	....	....
2024-T3	Not clad(d)	69 to 83	97 to 106	111 to 118	82.5 to 87.5
	Clad, to 0.063 in.	52 to 71	91 to 100	109 to 116	80 to 84.5
	Clad, over 0.063 in.	52 to 71	93 to 102	109 to 116	....
2024-T36	All	76 to 90	100 to 110	....	85 to 90
2024-T4, -T42(e)	Not clad	69 to 83	97 to 106	111 to 118	82.5 to 87.5
	Clad, to 0.063 in.	52 to 71	91 to 100	109 to 116	80 to 84.5
	Clad, over 0.063 in.	52 to 71	93 to 102	109 to 116	....
2024-T6, -T62	All	74.5 to 83.5	99 to 106	....	84 to 88
2024-T81	Not clad	74.5 to 83.5	99 to 106	....	84 to 88
	Clad	....	99 to 106	....	....
2024-T86	All	83 to 90	105 to 110	....	87.5 to 90
6053-T6	All	....	79 to 87	....	74.5 to 78.5
6061-T4(e)	Sheet	....	60 to 75	88 to 100	64 to 75
	Extrusion; bar	....	70 to 81	82 to 103	67 to 78
6061-T6	Not clad, 0.016 in.	....	....	....	75 to 84
	Not clad, 0.020 in. and over	....	....	....	78 to 84
	Clad	47 to 72	85 to 97	....	78 to 84
6063-T5	All	....	84 to 96	....	....
6063-T6	All	....	55 to 70	89 to 97	62.5 to 70
6151-T6	All	....	70 to 85	....	....
7075-T6, -T65	Not clad(f)	85 to 94	91 to 102	....	....
	Clad:		106 to 114	....	87.5 to 92
	To 0.036 in.	....	102 to 110	....	86 to 90
	0.037-0.050 in.	78 to 90	104 to 110	....	....
	0.051-0.062 in.	76 to 90	104 to 110	....	....
	0.063-0.070 in.	76 to 90	102 to 110	....	....
	Over 0.070 in.	73 to 90	102 to 110	....	....
7079-T6, -T65	All(f)	81 to 93	104 to 114	....	87.5 to 92
7178-T6	Not clad(g)	85 min	105 min	....	88 min
	Clad:				
	To 0.036 in.	....	102 min	....	86 min
	0.037-0.062 in.	85 min	....	....	....
	Over 0.062 in.	88 min	....	....	....

(a) Acceptable hardness does not guarantee acceptable properties; acceptance should be based on acceptable hardness plus written evidence of compliance with specified heat treating procedures. Values higher than the maximums are acceptable, providing the material is positively identified as the correct alloy. (b) Minimum hardness values shown for clad products are valid up to and including 0.091-in. thickness. For heavier gages, cladding should be locally removed for hardness test, or test should be performed on edge of sheet. (c) Bhn, 126 to 158 (10-mm ball, 500-kg load). (d) Bhn, 100 to 130 (10-mm ball, 500-kg load). (e) Alloys 2024-T4, 2024-T42, and 6061-T4 should not be rejected for low hardness until they have remained at room temperature for at least three days after solution heat treatment. (f) Bhn, 136 to 164 (10-mm ball, 500-kg load). (g) Bhn, 136 min (10-mm ball, 500-kg load).

Cleaning and Finishing

Cleaning and Finishing of Aluminum and Aluminum Alloys

By the ASM Committee on Finishing of Aluminum*

VARIOUS types of finishes are applied to products made of aluminum or aluminum alloys, to enhance appearance or to improve the functional properties of the surfaces, or both. This article discusses the methods employed in cleaning and finishing.

Abrasive Blast Cleaning

One of the simplest and most effective methods for cleaning aluminum surfaces is by blasting with dry nonmetallic or metallic abrasives. Although this method as applied to aluminum is commonly associated with the cleaning of castings, it is also used to prepare surfaces of other product forms for subsequent finishes, such as organic coatings. In addition to being used for cleaning, blasting is employed to produce a matte texture for decorative purposes.

Abrasive blasting is most efficient in removing scale, sand, and mold residues from castings; it is readily adaptable to the cleaning of castings, because they are usually thick enough so that no distortion results from blasting.

Blast cleaning of parts with relatively thin sections is not recommended, because such parts are readily warped by the compressive stresses that are set up in the surface by blasting. The blasting of thin sections with coarse abrasive is not recommended either, because the coarse abrasive can wear through the aluminum. Typical conditions for dry blasting with silica abrasive are given in Table 1.

Washed silica sand and aluminum oxide are the abrasives most commonly used for blast cleaning of aluminum alloys; however, steel grit also is sometimes used. In fact, due to the fragmenting characteristics of silica, steel grit often is preferred, because its longer life lowers cleaning cost. However, when aluminum is blasted with grit, steel particles become embedded in the surface and, unless removed by a subsequent chemical treatment, will rust and stain the aluminum surface. When aluminum is blasted with No. 40 or 50 steel grit, a $3/8$-in.-diam nozzle and an air pressure of about 40 psi are commonly used. Organic mediums such as plastic pellets and crushed walnut shells also are used in blast cleaning aluminum, often for the removal of carbonaceous matter.

Steel shot is seldom used for cleaning aluminum surfaces; however, shot blasting is employed as a preliminary operation for developing a surface with a hammered texture. An attractive finish is produced when this textured surface is bright dipped and anodized. In addition, the varying degrees of matte texture that can be produced by blasting offer decorative possibilities. When a maximum diffuseness of re-flectivity is required, blasting can produce it. For example, aluminum army canteens are blasted as a final finish to reduce glare.

Sand blasting with a fine abrasive produces a fine-grained matte finish on wrought or cast aluminum products. For plaques, spandrels and related architectural decorative applications, sand blasting the background and polishing or buffing the raised portions of the surface produces an effect known as "highlighting".

The matte finish produced by abrasive blasting is highly susceptible to scratching, and to staining, as from fingerprints. Therefore, matte-finish surfaces usually are protected by an anodic coating or clear lacquer. Anodizing is the more popular protective treatment, because it reproduces the original texture of a surface. Clear lacquers smooth out the roughened surface and produce various degrees of gloss, which may be undesirable. When the blasted surface is anodized, a gray color results because of embedded abrasive particles in the aluminum surface. This color frequently is nonuniform, because of variations in blasting conditions such as nozzle-to-work distance, direction or movement of nozzle, and air pressure.

Close control of blasting conditions can be obtained by the use of specially designed equipment. Uniform move-

*WILLIAM C. SCHULTE, *Chairman*, Engineering Manager – Materials, Curtiss Div., Curtiss-Wright Corp.; B. W. BISCHOF, Staff Metallurgist, General Metallurgical Dept., Aluminum Co. of Canada, Ltd.; JACK CARROLL, Research Dept., Amchem Products, Inc.; CHARLES C. COHN, Technical Director, Technical Processes Div., Colonial Alloys Co.; WALTER O. DOW, JR., Finishing Superintendent, Sunbeam Corp.

EDWARD A. DURAND, Staff Engineer, Manufacturing Research Laboratory, General Products Div., International Business Machines Corp.; J. E. GAROL, Chief Materials and Process Engineer, Tulsa Div., Douglas Aircraft Co., Inc.; R. HUMPHREYS, Research Engineer, Production Development Laboratory, North American Aviation, Inc.; G. V. KINGSLEY, Director of Research, Bohn Aluminum and Brass Corp.; G. H. KISSIN,

Technical Assistant to the Director of Metallurgical Research, Kaiser Aluminum and Chemical Corp.; MATTIE F. McFADDEN, Manager, Materials and Processes, Missile Systems Div., Raytheon Co.; G. D. NELSON, Senior Research Chemist, Monsanto Chemical Co.; VITO PALOMBELLA, Materials Engineer, Grumman Aircraft Engineering Corp.; JACK W. PETERSEN, Chemist and Finishing Supervisor, Adams & Westlake Co.

C. A. ROSELLEN, Member of Technical Staff, Materials Technology Dept., Hughes Aircraft Co.; HARRY SOSSON, President, Aluminum Anodizing Div., Artcraft Plating, Inc.; ELMER P. TORKE, Chief Chemist, Mirro Aluminum Co.; R. V. VANDEN BERG, Manager of Finishes Div., Process Development Laboratories, Aluminum Co. of America; GILBERT G. WARREN, Materials Laboratory, Scintilla Div., Bendix Corp.

Table 1. Typical Conditions for Abrasive Blast Cleaning With Silica

Grit size, mesh	Nozzle diameter, in.(a)	Nozzle to work, in.(a)	Air pressure, psi
20-60 (coarse)	⅜-½	12-20	30-90
40-80 (medium)	⅜-½	8-14	30-90
100-200 (fine)	¼-½	8-14	30-75
Over 200 (very fine)..	½	8-12	45

(a) Nozzle approximately 90° to work

Table 2. Typical Applications for Abrasive Blast Cleaning of Aluminum Products(a)

Product, and size	Abrasive Type	Size mesh	Pieces per hr
Blasting to Prepare for Organic Coating			
Cake pan, 11 by 15 by 2 in...	Alumina	100	60
Frying pan, 10-in. diam ..	Alumina	100	260
Griddle, 10½-in. square ...	Alumina	100	225
Sauté pan, 8-in. diam	Alumina	100	250
Blasting for Appearance Produced			
Army canteen, 1 qt(b) ...	Steel	80	420
Cocktail-shaker body, 4-in. diam by 7 in.(c)...	Steel	80	375
Tray, 12-in. diam(c)	Steel	80	180

(a) Rotary automatic equipment with five nozzles used for blasting of all parts except cake pan, for which a hand-operated single-nozzle setup was used. (b) Blasted for reduction of light reflectivity. (c) Blasted for decorative effect.

Table 3. Cost Data for Abrasive Blast Cleaning (Example 1) (a)

Cost factor	Cost, or cost basis
Capital investment	$5000
Replacement parts.......	20¢ per machine-hr
Abrasive	87¢ per machine-hr
Total power requirement	40 hp
Direct labor........	1 man-hr per machine-hr
Indirect labor...	1/10 man-hr per machine-hr

(a) Data based on use of five-nozzle rotary automatic blasting machine for cleaning 10-in.-diam, 2-lb frying pans in preparation for organic coating, at rate of 260 pieces per hour, using 100-mesh alumina abrasive.

Table 4. Typical Conditions for Wet Blasting of Aluminum-Base Materials

(At nozzle-to-work distance of 3 to 4 in., operating pressure of 80 psi)

Operation	Abrasive Type	Size, mesh
Deburr and clean....	Alumina	220
Blend and grind.....	Silica flour	325
Lap and hone.......	Glass	1000
	Diatomite	625 to 5000

ment of the work on conveyors, established nozzle movement, constant velocity of the abrasive, and controlled size of grit contribute to better color uniformity of subsequently anodized surfaces.

The nonuniform appearance that results from blasting can be corrected by bleaching prior to anodizing. Bleaching is done by deep etching in a solution of 5% sodium hydroxide at 100 to 150 F to remove metal that contains embedded abrasive. Some trial and error may be necessary to determine etching time for specific conditions. If the surface is not etched deeply enough, a mottled appearance may result.

Table 2 lists some typical applications for abrasive blast cleaning of aluminum products, and indicates type and size of abrasive used and production rates. For one of these products — the 10-in.-diam frying pan — data relating to

costs of abrasive blast cleaning are given in the following example.

Example 1 (Table 3) lists actual costs, or bases for computing costs, for abrasive blast cleaning drawn aluminum frying pans 10 in. in diameter (weight, 2 lb apiece), in preparation for the application of an organic coating. As has been shown in Table 2, blasting was done with a five-nozzle rotary automatic machine, using 100-mesh alumina abrasive and at a rate of 260 pieces hourly.

Wet blasting combines a fine abrasive and water to form a slurry that is forced through nozzles. Abrasive grits from 100 to 5000 mesh may be used. Wet blasting is generally used when a fine-grained matte finish is desired for decorative purposes.

An attractive two-tone finish on appliance trim can be obtained by contrasting a buffed finish with a wet blasted finish. Also, aluminum firearm components and ophthalmic parts such as frames and temples are wet blasted to produce fine matte finishes. In these applications, anodic coatings, either plain or colored, are used to protect and reproduce the intended surface texture.

Typical wet blasting procedures are given in Table 4. Wet blasting is used also for graining lithographic plates and for preparing surfaces for organic or electroplated coatings.

Barrel Finishing

Many small aluminum stampings, castings and machined parts are cleaned, deburred and burnished by barrel finishing. In most instances, the main objective is deburring or burnishing or both, with cleaning being only an incidental benefit of the treatment. Barrel finishing is a low-cost method of smoothing off sharp edges, imparting a matte finish, and preparing surfaces for anodizing, painting or plating. Deburring sometimes is the final barrel operation, but more often it is followed by burnishing to obtain a smoother finish or one that is better suited to anodizing or plating. Parts that have been deburred only are often painted. Burnished parts are frequently anodized for protection.

Small aluminum parts are sometimes tumbled dry in mediums such as pumice and hardwood pegs, hardwood sawdust or crushed walnut shells to remove burrs and improve the finish. However, this method is relatively inefficient compared to the more widely used wet process.

All aluminum alloys can be safely finished by wet barrel methods. Limitations imposed by size and shape of workpieces are essentially the same as for steel and other metals. However, there are two general areas in which wet barrel finishing of aluminum parts is more critical than in processing similar parts made of steel. First, there is danger of surface contamination by ferrous metals, caused by the use of either a steel barrel or a steel medium. Second, pH of the compounds is more critical when processing aluminum, because the metal is susceptible to etching by both acids and alkalis, and because gas generated during chemical attack can build up pressure in the barrel and cause serious accidents. The

usual recommendation that barrels be vented is to be emphasized when processing aluminum. Compounds that are nearly neutral (pH of about 8) are recommended, although some alloys, especially those low in magnesium or silicon, can be safely processed in compounds having a pH as high as 9.

Barrels used for aluminum are basically the same as those used for processing steel. However, barrels made of steel or cast iron should be lined with rubber or similar material, to prevent contamination. A preferred practice is to use specific barrels for processing aluminum only.

Deburring is done by tumbling the work in a nonlubricating compound that contains abrasives. In most instances, mediums also are used, to cushion the workpieces and increase the abrasive action. Synthetic detergents mixed with granite fines or limestone chips are usually preferred as the compound for deburring aluminum; aluminum oxide and silicon carbide are not preferred, because they leave a smudge that is difficult to remove. High water levels (completely covering the mass) are used during deburring to assist in maintaining fluidity of the mass and to help prevent the medium from becoming glazed and losing cutting action.

Barrel burnishing is used to produce a smooth, mirrorlike texture on aluminum parts. Bright dipping immediately prior to burnishing will aid in producing a better finish. Other preliminary treatments also are helpful in specific instances, particularly for cast aluminum parts. One of these pretreatments entails etching the castings for 20 sec in an alkaline solution at 180 F and then dipping them for 2 to 3 sec in a solution consisting of 2 parts (by volume) nitric acid (36° Bé) and 1 part hydrofluoric acid at 70 to 75 F.

The principle of barrel burnishing is to cause surface metal to flow, rather than to remove metal from the surface. Burnishing compounds must have lubricating qualities. Soaps made especially for burnishing are usually used. They are readily obtainable, and most of them have a pH of about 8, which is preferred.

Control of pH is important when burnishing aluminum. It is accomplished by frequent titrations and by adding small amounts of borax or boric acid as required. Steel balls and shapes are the most commonly used burnishing mediums.

Several examples of conditions employed in barrel finishing applications are detailed in Table 5. It will be noted that deburring and burnishing are sometimes accomplished in a single operation. Data relative to the cost of burnishing a cast aluminum part are given in the following example.

Example 2 (Table 6) presents data on costs in one plant for burnishing cast aluminum parts in rubber-lined octagonal barrels (12 by 36 in., 2 cu ft in volume), each operated by a 1-hp motor. The parts are made of 380 alloy; each part weighs 1 lb and has a surface area of ½ sq ft. Each barrel burnishes 45 parts per hour; one employee operates five barrels, for a total production rate of 225 parts per hour. The burnishing medium consists of ⅜-in. steel double cones; 100 lb is used for five barrels. Soap is used as the burnishing compound, and each load requires ½ to ¾ lb of soap; sometimes, the soap is replenished after the first ½ hr of a 1-hr cycle.

Self-tumbling is an effective means of cleaning, deburring or burnishing small aluminum parts. Procedures for self-tumbling are not basically different from those for other methods of barrel finishing, except that mediums are not used (parts actually serve as the medium). Compounds for self-tumbling of aluminum should be of nearly neutral pH.

Size and shape of the parts usually determine whether self-tumbling is suitable. Parts larger than about 1 in. (maximum dimension) are usually impractical for self-tumbling. Interior surfaces receive little or no action during self-tumbling.

Vibratory finishing is a newer method used for deburring and burnishing metal parts. In the use of this method for aluminum parts, compounds and mediums are subject to the same restrictions as discussed previously for conventional barrel finishing.

Polishing and Buffing

Because aluminum is more easily worked than many other metals, few aluminum parts require polishing prior to buffing for final finish. In some instances, polishing may be required for the removal of burrs, flash or surface imperfections. Usually, however, buffing with a sisal wheel prior to final buffing is sufficient.

Polishing. Most polishing operations can be performed using either belts or setup wheels. Setup wheels may be superior to belts for rough cutting down when canvas wheels with a relatively crude setup can be employed. Also, for fine work, a specially contoured wheel may be more satisfactory than a belt for polishing aluminum. However, setup wheels have two main disadvantages, in comparison with belts: (a) time, skill and equipment are necessary for setting up wheels (even though the actual time required for setting up a wheel may be as short as 10 min, this time is spread over several hours, because of intermediate drying steps); and (b) wheels may cost as much as $120 each, and inventory thus becomes an important factor when wheels of several different types of abrasives or grit sizes are needed. Furthermore, greater operator skill is required for wheel polishing; unskilled labor may be used for belt polishing.

Typical conditions for polishing aluminum parts are given in the following:

Example 3 (Table 7) gives the conditions for wheel polishing die-cast aluminum soleplates for steam irons. The soleplates are made of alloy 380, and the sides are polished to remove holes or other surface defects. (Buffing follows, to produce the required mirror finish.) The polishing conditions given in Table 7 are based on a production rate of 115 pieces per hour per wheel. Each wheel has a service life of 5000 to 6000 pieces.

Example 4 (Table 8) relates to the conditions and sequence of operations for belt polishing die-cast steam-iron soleplates made of aluminum alloy 380. Ten polishing heads are employed to produce a bright finish on the sides and bottom of soleplates.

Example 5. Belt polishing was employed to produce a bright finish on the sides of frying pans die cast from aluminum alloy 360. Four polishing heads were used. The

contact wheel (2 by 12 in.) for each head was serrated 45° (7/16-in. land; groove, ⅜ by ⅜ in.) and had a hardness of 55 durometer. Belt speed for all polishing heads was 5400 sfm. Polishing oil was applied from one gun per head in the amount of 1 cu cm per shot, at the rate of 1 sec on time and 5 sec off time. The belts, 2 by 132 in., were made of cloth, and were coated with aluminum oxide abrasive (bond, resin over glue). The size of the abrasive grit for each successively used polishing head was as follows:

Head 1 .... 120 mesh
     2 150
     3 180
     4 240

Each belt cost $0.733 and had a service life of 800 to 1000 pieces.

Example 6. Frying pans made from wrought 3003 aluminum alloy were polished on the sides under the same operating conditions and with the same type of equipment as were used for the die-cast pans of Example 5. The size of the abrasive grit for each of the four heads successively used was as follows:

Head 1 .... 150 mesh
     2 180
     3 and 4 240

The cost and service life of each belt were the same as for the belts used in the operation described in Example 5.

Buffing. Selection of procedure for buffing depends mainly on cost, because it is usually possible to obtain the desired results by any one of several different procedures. For example, in hand buffing, combinations of the various influences might call for the use of equipment ranging from simple, light-duty machines to heavy-duty, variable-speed, double-control units. These machines represent a wide range in capital investment. A light-duty double-end lathe with a fixed-speed 2-hp motor would cost about $400. Double-end lathes with single-belt drive, but with variable speeds, would range in cost from about $900 (for 3 hp) to about $2000 (for 10 hp). A double-end 5-hp lathe having variable speeds (1500 to 2000 rpm) and compensation for buff wear would cost about $1200. A similar unit having 10 hp would cost about $2500. Double-end lathes having a double-motor and double-control arrangement (enabling the performance of different jobs at either end) would cost about $2400 for the 5-hp and $5000 for the 10-hp size.

Automatic buffing requires custom-made machinery or special fixtures on standard machinery. Size and complexity of the machinery are determined by the required production rates and by the size or shape of the workpieces. High production requires more stations, heavier equipment and more power. The configuration of the part may be so simple that one buff covers the total area to be finished, or it may

Table 5. Typical Conditions for Wet Barrel Finishing of Aluminum Products

Product	Number of pieces per— Pound	Number of pieces per— Load	Cycle time, min	Barrel speed, rpm
Clean, Deburr and Brighten(a)				
Percolator spout..	130	630	20	33
Measuring spoon..	48	750	20	33
Flame guard	91	1500	15	33
Leg	82	2700	30	33
Toy spoon	180	5000	17	33
Handle	226	5800	25	33
Deburr and Brighten(b)				
Handles, die-cast.	24	600	120	15
Burnish to High Gloss(c)				
Die-cast housing..	1	60	45	14

(a) Rubber-lined steel, single-compartment drum, 22 in. in diameter, 30 in. long. *Processing cycle:* Load drum with medium (50 lb of ⅛-in. steel balls per load), parts, and compound (5½ oz of burnishing soap per load); cover load with water (150 F); rotate drum for specified time; unload, rinse, separate parts from medium; tumble-dry parts in sawdust for 4 min. (b) Rubber-lined steel, double-compartment drum; each compartment 29 in. diameter, 36 in. long. *Processing cycle:* Load deburring compartment with parts, compound (5 lb of burnishing soap), and medium (800 lb of No. 4 granite chips), using hoist; cover load with cold tap water; rotate drum for 1 hr; unload, and rinse with cold water; separate parts and medium, and transfer parts to burnishing compartment; add burnishing compound (2 lb of burnishing soap) and medium (1500 lb of ⅛-in. steel balls); cover load with water (160 F) and rotate drum for 1 hr; separate parts and medium, and rinse parts in hot water and then in cold water; spin dry in a centrifugal hot-air drier. (c) Single-compartment drum, 5 ft long, 4 ft in diameter. *Processing cycle:* Load drum with parts (parts are fixtured, to prevent scratching), medium (4500 to 5000 lb of steel balls ⅛, ¼ and 5/16 in. in diameter, and 1/16-in. and ⅛-in. steel diagonals), and compound (12 lb of alkaline burnishing soap, pH 10); cover load with cold tap water; rotate drum for 22½ min in one direction, then 22½ min in reverse direction; rinse and unload; dip-rinse parts, and hand wipe.

Table 6. Cost Data for Barrel Burnishing (Example 2) (a)

Cost of each barrel.............$900 to $1000
Amortization ....8% per year
Cost of burnishing medium......23¢ per lb(b)
Cost of burnishing compound......15¢ per lb

(a) Based on burnishing 225 parts per hour. (b) Burnishing medium (⅜-in. steel double cones) is re-used many times, so that cost per load is negligible.

Table 7. Conditions for Wheel Polishing Die-Cast Aluminum Soleplates (Example 3)

Type of polishing wheel.............Felt(a)
Setup time........................10 min(b)
Wheel speed...1800-2000 rpm (6600-8400 sfm)
Lubricant ....Tallow grease stick

(a) Medium-hard felt wheel, 14 to 16 in. in diameter with a 5-in. face; surface of wheel double-coated with 240-mesh alumina abrasive bonded with hide glue. (b) Cumulative total; spread over several hours of operation.

Table 8. Conditions of Belt Polishing for Bright Finishing Die-Cast Soleplates (Example 4)

Operation	Area polished	Polishing head No.	Contact wheel Type	Contact wheel Size, in.	Hardness durometer	Belt(a) Size, in.	Belt(a) Abrasive size, mesh	Unit cost, $	Life, pieces
1......Side		1 and 2	Plain face	2 by 15	60	2 by 120	280(b)	$0.53	600
2......Side		3 and 4	Plain face	2 by 15	60	2 by 120	320(b)	0.53	600
3......Bottom		5	Serrated(c)	6 by 15	45	6 by 120	120(b)	1.55	1200
4......Bottom		6	Serrated(c)	6 by 15	45	6 by 120	150(b)	1.55	2000
5......Bottom		7	Serrated(c)	6 by 15	45	6 by 120	220(b)	1.55	2000
6......Bottom		8	Serrated(c)	6 by 15	45	6 by 120	280(b)	1.55	2000
7......Bottom		9	Plain face	6 by 15	60	6 by 120	320(b)	1.55	2000
8......Bottom		10	Plain face	6 by 15	60	6 by 120	320(d)	1.75	600

(a) Belt speed for all operations was 6900 sfm. All belts were cloth; bond, resin over glue. (b) Aluminum oxide abrasive. (c) 45° serration, ½-in. land, ⅜-in. groove. (d) Silicon carbide abrasive.

Table 9. Equipment and Operating Conditions for High-Luster Buffing of Aluminum Products

Product name (and size, in.)	Type of buffing machine	Buffing wheel Type	Diameter, in. Over-all	Center	Ply	Thread count	Wheel speed, sfm	Type of compound	Production, pieces per hour
Biscuit pan (13¼ by 9½)	Semiautomatic	Bias	14	5	16	86/93	8250	Bar	205
Burner ring (3 diam by ¾)	Continuous rotary (a)	Radial, vented	(b)	1⅛	20	64/64	297	(c)	Liquid
Cake-carrier base (11¼ diam by 1³⁄₁₆)	Continuous rotary (a)	Bias	Two 14	5	16	86/93	9550	Liquid	278
Cake pan (14 by 9½ by 2½)	Hand buffing (handles)	Bias	Two 13	3	2	64/68	8850	Liquid	
	Semiautomatic (sides)	Bias	13	3	2	64/68	7650	Bar	438
Cake pan (8 by 8 by 2)	Semiautomatic	Bias	14	5	16	86/93	8250	Bar	200
Cup (2⅜ diam by 2½)	Semiautomatic	Bias	14	5	16	86/93	8250	Bar	127
Pan bottom (11⅛ square)	Semiautomatic	Bias	14	5	16	86/93	8250	Bar	450
Pan cover (11¼ square)	Semiautomatics (d)	Bias (sides)	14	5	16	86/93	8250	Bar	106
		Loose, vented (top)	(e)	2	20	64/64	(f)	Bar	95
Toy pitcher (2½ diam by 3½)	Continuous rotary (g)	Bias	14	5	16	64/68	9550	Liquid	817
Toy tumbler (1⅞ diam by 2½)	Continuous rotary (g)	Bias	14	5	16	64/68	9550	Liquid	864

(a) Five-spindle machine; four buffing heads, one load-unload station. (b) Each of the four wheels used had one 13-in. and three 14-in. sections. (c) For 13-in. section, 8850 sfm; for 14-in., 9550 sfm. (d) Two machines, run by one operator. (e) Buff made up of 14, 15 and 16-in. sections. (f) 8250 sfm for 14-in. sections, 8800 for 15-in., and 9400 for 16-in. (g) Eight-spindle machine.

be so complex as to require the use of many buffs cammed and set at angles.

For example, a rotary table equipped with four spindles and three heads, for buffing small round aluminum parts, would cost about $6500 (exclusive of fixtures, guns, pumps, lines and ventilation). In contrast, a straight-line conveyor for buffing larger parts having several surfaces that must be cammed against the buff would cost about $156,000, exclusive of the same auxiliary components listed for the simpler machine. This latter machine would have 88 fixtures, 34 heads and 34 cams.

As a rule, polishing machines will cost about $500 more per head than buffing machines, because more power is needed for polishing.

A number of procedures that have proved successful for high-luster buffing of specific aluminum parts are summarized in Table 9; others are described in the following examples.

Example 7 (Table 10) relates to the conditions and sequence of operations for automatic buffing of wrought aluminum frying-pan covers. A specular finish was required.

Example 8. The sides of die-cast aluminum frying pans made from alloy 360 were buffed to a bright finish by an automatic machine with four buffing heads. The buffing wheel of each head consisted of a 14-ply, 16-spoke-sewed bias buff 17 in. in outside diameter, 9 in. in inside diameter, and with a 1¾-in.-diam arbor hole. Wheel speed was 1745 rpm (7700 sfm). Each buff was made up of four sections, which cost $1.79 each. A liquid buffing compound was applied by one gun per wheel at the rate of 3 grams per shot for the first wheel, 2.5 grams for the second and third wheels, and 1 gram for the fourth wheel. The gun operated for 0.1 sec on time and 5 sec off time. Service life of each buffing wheel was 1600 to 2100 pieces.

Example 9 (Table 11). Die-cast aluminum soleplates for steam irons were buffed to a bright finish on an automatic machine with eight buffing heads. The soleplates were made of alloy 380 and were prepolished with 320-mesh grit. A liquid buffing compound was applied by one gun per wheel for the first four heads and by two guns per wheel for the last four heads. The guns were on for 0.12 sec and off for 13 sec. Service life was 72,000 pieces for each buff of the first four heads, and 24,000 pieces for each buff of the last four heads.

A detailed cost analysis for polishing and buffing soleplates for steam irons is given in Example 10.

Example 10 (Table 12) relates to the cost of automatic polishing and buffing the sides and bottom of aluminum soleplates for steam irons. The operation consists of first breaking the edges and polishing the gate and then automatic polishing and buffing the sides and bottom. A double-end lathe is used for breaking the edges and polishing the gate. This machine costs $3500 (including tooling and ventilation) and employs canvas wheels with 150-mesh abrasive. Service life of a 5-in. canvas wheel for breaking the edges is 38,000 pieces; a 2-in. canvas wheel for polishing the gate has a service life of 3800 pieces. Labor for breaking the edges and polishing the gate consists of two employees, each handling 300 pieces per hour.

Satin Finishing

Mechanical satin finishing is an established method for obtaining an attractive surface texture on aluminum hardware items such as knobs, hinges, rosettes and drawer pulls. Satin finishes are used also for architectural, appliance, and automotive trim. The satin finish results from small, nearly parallel scratches in the metal surface, which give the surface a soft, smooth sheen of lower reflectivity than that of polished or buffed surfaces.

Satin finishes can be applied by fine wire brushing. Other methods utilize a greaseless abrasive compound in conjunction with a conventional buffing head, tampico brush, cord brush, string buff or brush-backed sander head. Abrasive-impregnated nylon disks mounted like buffs, and abrasive cloth sections mounted on a rotating hub are also used. All of these methods produce about the same type of finish, and the use of any particular one depends on the surface contour of the workpiece.

Surfaces of workpieces to be satin finished should be free of grease and oil, and low contact pressures should be used. Wire brushes must be kept free of oxide and accumulations of aluminum metal. This is accomplished by frequently bringing a pumice stone or soft brick in contact with the rotating brush. A combination of conditions commonly used in wire brushing consists of 0.015-in.-diam wire mounted on a 10-in.-diam wheel revolving at about 1600 sfm. Undue pressure on a rotating wire wheel will bend the wires and cause excessive tearing of the aluminum surface.

Stainless steel wires are recommended, because other metals such as brass or steel may become embedded in the aluminum surface and produce discoloration or corrosion. If brass or steel wire wheels are used, the particles embedded in the surface can be removed by immersing the work in a nitric acid solution (1 part water to 1 part acid by volume) at room temperature. The processes in which a greaseless abrasive compound is used are essen-

Table 10. Sequence and Conditions of Automatic Buffing Operations for Obtaining Specular Finish on Aluminum Frying-Pan Covers (Example 7)

Operation	Area buffed	Buffing head No.	Type	Diameter, in. Over-all	Center	Arbor hole	Ply	Thread count	Density	Sections Number	Cost, each	Speed, sfm	Life, pieces	Application of compound (a) Number of guns	Cycle, sec On	Off	Gram per shot
1	Sides (4)	1, 2, 3, 4	Bias, air cooled	17	7	1¾	..	86/93	2 and 4	20	$1.97	7750	40,000	3	0.1	7	0.5
2	Corners (2)	5, 6, 7, 8	Bias, 20-spoke sewed	17	7	1¾	16	86/93	4	4	2.17	7750	35,000	1	0.1	7	0.5
3	Sides (2)	9, 10, 11, 12	Bias, 20-spoke sewed	17	7	1¾	16	86/93	4	4	2.17	7750	50,000	1	0.1	7	0.5
4	Sides (2)	13, 14, 15, 16	Bias, 20-spoke sewed	17	7	1¾	16	86/93	4	4	2.17	7750	35,000	1	0.1	8	0.5
5	Top	17	Bias, 45° spoke sewed	17	7	1¾	16	86/93	4	15	2.49	7750	65,000	3	0.1	8	0.2
6	Top	18	Bias	17	7	1¾	12	86/93	8	18	1.72	7750	70,000	3	0.1	8	0.2
7	Top bias	19	Bias	17	7	1¾	12	86/93	8	18	1.72	7750	70,000	3	0.1	8	0.2
8	Top bias	20	Bias	16	5	1¾	14	64/68	2	19	1.35	7300	45,000	3	0.1	8	0.2
9	Corners (4)	21, 22, 23, 24	Bias	17	7	1¾	12	86/93	8	4	1.72	7750	65,000	1	0.1	10	0.5
10	Sides (4)	25, 26, 27, 28	Bias	17	7	1¾	12	86/93	8	4	1.72	7750	65,000	1	0.1	10	0.5
11	Top bias	29	Bias	16	5	1¾	14	64/68	2	15	1.35	4600	80,000	3	0.1	10	0.5
12	Sides (4)	30, 31 (b)	Domet flannel	17	7	2¾	20	(d)	(d)	40	1.61	4000	80,000	6	0.1	11	0.2
13	Top	32	Domet flannel (c)	17	7	1⅝	32	(d)	(d)	24	1.05	4900	80,000	3	0.1	11	0.2
14	Top	33	Domet flannel (c)	17	7	1⅝	32	(d)	(d)	24	1.05	3550	30,000	3	0.1	11	0.2

(a) Liquid tripoli compound applied to buffing heads No. 1 through 29; stainless steel buffing compound applied to heads No. 30 through 33. (b) Each head buffs two sides. (c) Domet flannel sections interleaved with 7-in.-diam disks of kraft paper. (d) Inapplicable to flannel buff.

Table 11. Automatic Bright-Finish Buffing of Aluminum Soleplates (Example 9)

Operation	Area buffed	Buffing head No.	Type	Buffing wheel Diameter, in.(a) Overall	Arbor hole	Sections Number	Cost, each	Speed, sfm	Life, pieces	Applying of compound (b) No. of guns	Grams per shot
1	Side	1, 2	Sisal, 3/8-in. spiral sewed	16	1¼	2	$1.60	7350	72,000	1	0.5
2	Side	3	Bias, 16-ply, 20-spoke sewed	17	1¾	2	2.17	7800	72,000	1	0.5
3	Side	4	Bias, 16-ply, 20-spoke sewed	17	1¾	2	2.17	7800	72,000	1	0.5
4	Top	5	Sisal, 3/8-in. spiral sewed	16	1¾	15	1.60	7350	24,000	2	3.0
5	Top	6	Sisal, 3/8-in. spiral sewed	16	1¾	15	1.60	7350	24,000	2	3.0
6	Top	7, 8	Bias, 16-ply, 20-spoke sewed	17	1¾	10	2.17	7800	24,000	2	3.0

(a) All wheels had 7-in.-diam centers. (b) Proprietary liquid compound was used. Cycle time: 0.12 sec on, 13.0 sec off.

tially dry. However, water is required for softening the binder in the abrasive compound so that it will adhere to the surface of the buff. After the binder dries, the buff is ready for operation. At this stage a lubricant, such as a buffing compound or tallow, may be used. Lubricants produce a higher sheen. Table 13 describes equipment and techniques employed in mechanical satin finishing processes. If the satin finished parts are to be anodized, etching or bright dipping should not precede anodizing, because the satin appearance will be lost. Cleaning treatments that do not etch (or that only slightly etch) the metal should be used before anodizing.

Chemical Cleaning

The degree and nature of cleanness required depend on the subsequent finishing operations. For example, the cleaning requirements for plating or for the application of chromate or other mild-reaction conversion coatings are more stringent than for anodizing.

When establishing a cleaning cycle or when testing different cleaners or cleaning conditions, it is desirable to test the cleanness of the processed surface. Wetting of an aluminum surface with water (the "water break" test) does not provide an indication of cleanness, because oxide-coated surfaces free of oil or grease can be wetted uniformly. Also, a surface that has been processed with a detergent containing a wetting agent can be wetted even though not thoroughly clean, because of the film of wetting agent remaining on the unclean surface. Two effective methods of testing aluminum for cleanness are as follows:

1 Spray or coat the work surface with, or dip a test panel into, an unheated aqueous solution containing 4 oz per gal of cupric chloride and 3.8 fl oz per gal of concentrated hydrochloric acid. Uniform gassing or a deposit of copper is an indication that the surface is chemically clean.
2 Spray or coat the work surface with, or dip a test panel into, an unheated chromate conversion coating bath of the acid type, until an orange-colored film is formed. A uniform orange film indicates a chemically clean surface.

Additional methods of testing for cleanness are discussed on page 316, in "Selection of Cleaning Process".

Solvent Cleaning. The primary function of solvent cleaners is the removal of oil and grease compounds. Organic solvents alone seldom provide sufficient cleaning to permit final finishing operations; solvents usually are used to remove excess amounts of organic contaminants to minimize overloading of the subsequently used alkaline cleaners.

Greases and oils vary as to solubility in specific solvents. Fish oils are more difficult to remove than oils of other types. When in a dried-out condition, some oxidizing oils, such as linseed oil, form a leathery film that is difficult to remove in any solvent.

Polishing and buffing compounds are readily removed by most solvents when cleaning is performed immediately after buffing. If the compounds are permitted to harden, however, they may be difficult to remove, and heated solutions, agitation or mechanical action (ultrasonics or physical force) may be required for satisfactory cleaning. To remove compounds burned in the surface, it is necessary to soak the parts in a liquid (not vapor) organic degreaser (trichlorethylene or methylene chloride) or in an inhibited alkaline cleaner.

If polishing and buffing compounds cannot be removed immediately after buffing, the application of a neutral mineral oil over the buffed surface will maintain the compounds in a more soluble condition for subsequent removal by a solvent. The sequence of operations usually required for buffed aluminum surfaces is as follows: solvent cleaning, nonetching alkaline detergent cleaning, rinsing, removal of surface oxides, rinsing, and finally the application of the desired finish. Some of these steps may be omitted, depending on the type and quality of the buffing compound, the quality of workmanship in buffing, and the quality of solvents and cleaners used.

Emulsifiable solvents also are used to clean aluminum. These are organic solvents, such as kerosine, Stoddard solvent and mineral spirits, to which small amounts of emulsifiers and surfactants are added. When applied to the work, this type of cleaner emulsifies the oil or grease on the surface. The soil and cleaner are removed with water, preferably spray applied.

This type of degreasing is satisfactory prior to anodizing, etching, removal of surface oxides, chemical conversion coating, plating and painting. In some instances intermediate treatments are required, such as the removal of surface oxides before etching.

The emulsifiable solvent should have a pH of 8 or less; otherwise, it will stain or corrode the aluminum if permitted to remain on the surface for a period of time prior to rinsing or additional cleaning. However, emulsifiable solvents with higher pH are more efficient cleaners, and can be used if the surfaces are rinsed or are cleaned by additional methods within 2 or 3 min after degreasing.

A lower-cost cleaning solution can be obtained by adding water to the emulsifiable solvent. This type of solution is less efficient than the concentrated emulsifiable solvent, however, and is limited to the removal of light oil and grease.

A more detailed discussion on cleaning with solvents is given in the articles on Solvent Cleaning, Emulsion Cleaning, and Vapor Degreasing, pages 326 to 340 in this volume.

Alkaline cleaning is the most widely used method for cleaning aluminum

Table 12. Costs for Automatic Polishing and Buffing of Soleplates (Example 10)

Cost factor	Cost
Machine and tooling	$ 87,400
Installation, guns, dust collector, and ventilation	22,600
Total initial investment	$110,000
Cost per soleplate for polishing belts:	
Heads 1, 2, 3 and 4 (total)	$0.0037(a)
Head 5	0.0014(b)
Heads 6, 7, 8 and 9 (total)	0.0033(c)
Head 10	0.0028(d)
Total	$0.0112
Cost per soleplate for buffing wheels:	
Heads 11 and 12 (total)	$0.00007(e)
Heads 13 and 14 (total)	0.00012(f)
Heads 15 and 16 (total)	0.00133(g)
Heads 17 and 18 (total)	0.00272(h)
Total	$0.00424

(a) $0.56 per belt × 4 heads ÷ 600 pieces per belt. (b) $1.64 per belt × 1 head ÷ 1200 pieces per belt. (c) $1.64 per belt × 4 heads ÷ 2000 pieces per belt. (d) $1.64 per belt × 1 head ÷ 600 pieces per belt. (e) $1.28 per section × 2 sections × 2 heads ÷ 120 hr × 600 pieces per hour. (f) $2.174 per section × 2 sections × 2 heads ÷ 120 hr × 600 pieces per hour. (g) $1.60 per section × 10 sections × 2 heads ÷ 40 hr × 600 pieces per hour. (h) $2.174 per section × 15 sections × 2 heads ÷ 40 hr × 600 pieces/hr.

Table 13. Methods, Equipment and Conditions for Mechanical Satin Finishing of Aluminum

Method	Suitable equipment Buffing lathe	Portable power head	Power required	Speed, sfm	Lubricant
Wire brushing(a)	Yes	Yes	(b)	1200 to 2250	None
Sanding with brush-backed head(c)	Yes	No	(d)	900 to 1800 rpm	Optional
Tampico or string brushing(e)	Yes	No	(b)	3000 to 6000	Pumice(f)
Finishing with abrasive-coated cloth(g)	Yes	Yes	(d)	6000 to 7000	Optional
Finishing with nylon disks(h)	Yes	Yes	(j)	4500 to 6500	Optional
Buffing with compounds(k)	Yes	Yes	(b)	3000 to 5000	(m)

(a) 12-in.-diam brush of stainless steel wire 0.005 in. in diameter. (b) 1 hp per inch of brush width. (c) Using 60 to 600-mesh abrasive cloth loadings. (d) 1 hp per head. (e) 12-in.-diam brush. (f) With oil or water; emery cake also may be used. (g) Cloth is mounted radially on rotating hubs; coated with 50 to 320-mesh emery abrasive. (h) Disks impregnated with silicon carbide abrasive, coarse to ultrafine. (j) ¼ hp per inch of disk width. (k) Greaseless satin-finishing compounds containing aluminum oxide abrasive (200 or 240 mesh) used with unstitched or loosely stitched buffs (14-in.) or with string brush. (m) Dry, or with buffing compound or grease stick.

and aluminum alloys. This method is easy to apply in production operations, and equipment costs are low.

Aluminum is readily attacked by alkaline solutions. Most solutions are maintained at a pH between 9 and 11, and they are often inhibited to some degree, to minimize or prevent attack on the metal. The most frequently used cleaner is the mildly inhibited type.

Cleaners of either the etching or the nonetching type have some ability to emulsify vegetable and animal oils or greases, but not mineral oils or greases. Therefore, they can sometimes remove fresh buffing compounds and the lard oils used in spinning operations.

The nonetching types of cleaners may be classified as silicated and nonsilicated cleaners. The silicated cleaners are based on aqueous solutions of sodium carbonate, trisodium phosphate, or other alkalis, to which small amounts of sodium silicate are added to inhibit etching. The main disadvantage of the silicated types, aside from their inability to emulsify and remove mineral oils, is that the silicate may react with the aluminum to form an insoluble aluminum silicate, especially when the temperature of the bath exceeds 180 F. (However, lower operating temperatures decrease the efficiency of the solution for the removal of certain soils.)

The nonsilicated cleaners are often based on the use of relatively large concentrations of surfactants. High operating temperatures are required, but some cleaners operated above 160 F can etch the aluminum surface. (Cleaners containing a large quantity of surfactants — particularly those types of surfactants that resist complete rinsing — must not be carried into baths used for bright dipping, anodizing, or chemical conversion coating.)

Neither the silicated nor the nonsilicated cleaners remove aluminum oxide uniformly. Because the removal of oxide is essential for the application of decorative or functional finishes, the best procedure is to clean with a solvent, remove oxide with an acid solution, and then proceed with finishing.

Nonetching cleaners may be used after solvent cleaning to produce water-wetted surfaces, or they may be used alone when soils are light and easily removed (after which the surfaces should be treated to remove oxides).

When silicates (ortho and meta) are used, the concentration of carbonates must be kept at a minimum to minimize the formation of floc, which may redeposit on the work. Unlike sodium hydroxide, the alkali silicates have good wetting, emulsifying and rinsing properties. The ratio of SiO_2 to Na_2O in the compound determines the effectiveness of the alkali silicates. The orthosilicate has good detergency and is effective in the cleaner at a ratio of 1 to 2, whereas metasilicate should be 1 to 1.

Agitation of the cleaner increases the cleaning action and is best created by pumps, propellers or movement of the work. Air agitation, although easier to install and most convenient to operate, has the following disadvantages:

1 It causes excessive foaming of those solutions containing wetting agents or surfactants. (Foaming of the solution may lead to dry-on problems.)
2 Air can reduce the solution temperature.

Table 14. Compositions and Operating Conditions of Alkaline Cleaners

Etching Cleaners

1 Sodium hydroxide	3 to 10 oz
Sodium phosphate	0.1 to 0.5 oz
Water	To 1 gal
Temperature of bath	140 to 180 F
Immersion time	30 sec to 10 min
2 Sodium hydroxide	0.25 to 0.75 oz
Sodium phosphate	1 to 8 oz
Sodium carbonate	1 to 8 oz
Water	To 1 gal
Temperature of bath	140 to 180 F
Immersion time	2 to 5 min

Nonetching Cleaners

1 Sodium pyrophosphate + sodium metasilicate	Total of 2 to 10 oz
Water	To 1 gal
Temperature of bath	140 to 160 F
Immersion time	2 to 5 min
2 Trisodium phosphate + sodium metasilicate	Total of 2 to 10 oz
Water	To 1 gal
Temperature of bath	140 to 160 F
Immersion time	2 to 5 min
3 Sodium carbonate	0.8 to 2.4 oz
Trisodium phosphate	0.8 oz
Water	To 1 gal
Temperature of bath	175 to 205 F
Immersion time	2 to 5 min
4 Sodium carbonate	1.6 to 6.4 oz
Sodium silicate	0.8 to 1.6 oz
Water	To 1 gal
Temperature of bath	140 to 160 F
Immersion time	2 to 5 min
5 Sodium carbonate	0.5 to 1 oz
Sodium metasilicate	0.5 to 1 oz
Water	To 1 gal
Temperature of bath	140 to 160 F
Immersion time	2 to 5 min

3 The additional oxygen may cause staining and tarnishing on some alloys.
4 It introduces carbon dioxide, which may increase the carbonate content.

Rinsing should be accomplished immediately after the work is removed from the alkaline bath, to prevent dry-on. Warm water is preferred.

Aluminum surfaces sometimes contain areas of localized corrosion, referred to as atmospheric etch and caused by contaminants in the air during storage. The corroded areas are more visible after alkaline cleaning or etching than before. When the corrosion spots are present, the work may be dipped in a sodium bisulfate solution (6 oz per gal), or in a cold 70% nitric acid solution, to minimize the effect of the subsequent alkaline cleaning.

During alkaline cleaning, especially if etching occurs, some alloys containing copper, iron, manganese or silicon develop a black smut on the surface.

Compositions and operating conditions of common alkaline cleaners are given in Table 14.

The reader is referred to the article "Alkaline Cleaning", page 317, for a more detailed discussion of this subject.

Electrocleaning is seldom used for cleaning aluminum and aluminum alloys, because this method often involves extensive attack on the metal. However, a few processes are used in production operations. These employ low-

Table 15. Compositions of Solutions for Electrocleaning of Aluminum(a)

1 Sodium orthosilicate	85%
Sodium carbonate (anhydrous)	10
Sodium resinate	5
2 Sodium carbonate (anhydrous)	46%
Trisodium phosphate	32
Sodium hydroxide	16
Rosin	6

(a) For typical operating conditions, see text.

voltage current, usually in the range of 6 to 12 volts.

Cathodic cleaning, in which the work is the cathode, is more common than anodic cleaning. Common practice is to reverse the current during the last 5 to 10 sec of the cleaning operation.

After removing the work from the cleaner, it is rinsed in warm or hot water, dipped in acid to neutralize any residual alkali, and finally rinsed in cold water. The work can then be finished as desired.

The composition of two solutions that are recommended for electrocleaning are given in Table 15.

Acid Cleaning. Acid cleaners may be used alone or in conjunction with other acid, alkaline, or solvent cleaning systems. Vapor degreasing and alkaline cleaning may be required for the removal of heavy oils and grease from workpieces before they are immersed in an acid bath. One of the main functions of an acid cleaner is the removal of surface oxides prior to resistance welding, painting, conversion coating, etching or anodizing.

A mixture of chromic and sulfuric acids is commonly used to remove surface oxides, burnt-in oil, water stains, or other films, such as the iridescent or colored films formed during heat treating. This acid mixture cleans and imparts a slightly etched appearance to the surface, preparing it for painting, caustic etching, conversion coating or anodizing.

Oxide films must be thoroughly removed before spot welding. A mixture of phosphoric and chromic acids is another solution that may be used for this purpose. Because of the corrosive nature of the chlorides and fluorides in welding fluxes, the fluxes should be removed as soon as possible after welding. Mixtures of nitric and hydrofluoric acids are best for removing fluxes. Most fluxes can also be satisfactorily removed by a dilute (5 to 20% by volume) nitric acid solution.

Proprietary nonetching acid cleaners are available for cleaning aluminum and aluminum alloys. Operating temperatures of these solutions range from 130 to 180 F, and the pH usually ranges from 4.0 to 5.7.

Compositions and operating conditions for typical acid cleaning solutions are given in Table 16.

Aluminum parts should be insulated from ferrous metal baskets or supports when immersed in acid cleaning solutions, because contact of these two metals can produce a galvanic action that causes corrosion. Materials such as vinyl plastisols, epoxy, polyethylene and polypropylene may be used for insulation. When practical, baskets or rods should be of the same (or similar) material as the workpieces.

Chemical Brightening (Polishing)

Chemical brightening (known also as "bright dipping" and "chemical polishing") smooths and brightens aluminum products by making use of the solution potential of the aluminum surface in the various baths employed and of the local differences in potential on the aluminum surface.

In general, chemical brightening baths are concentrated or dilute acid solutions containing oxidizing agents. The acids commonly used are sulfuric, hydrochloric, nitric, phosphoric, acetic and, to a lesser extent, chromic and hydrofluoric. Ammonium bifluoride is used when it is desirable to avoid the hazards that attend the use of hydrofluoric acid. Oxalic and citric acids may be used as alternates for acetic acid. Fluoboric and fluosilicic acids may be used as alternates for hydrofluoric acid. Nitric and chromic acids and, less often, ferric sulfate and hydrogen peroxide are used when oxidizing conditions are required.

Phosphoric-Nitric Acid Baths. Among the various types of concentrated baths, the phosphoric-nitric acid baths are the most widely used in the United States. Compositions and operating conditions for two commercial baths of this type are given in Table 17.

Alkali nitrates may be used as a substitute for nitric acid. Acetic acid, copper salts and other additives are used in some phosphoric-nitric acid baths. As content of the additives increases, control becomes more complex.

For economy, some phosphoric-nitric acid baths are operated with an aluminum phosphate content near the tolerable maximum of 10 to 12% (dissolved aluminum content, about 40 g per liter); this is close to the saturation point, at which precipitation of this compound on the work produces etch patterns.

The addition of surfactants suppresses the evolution of fumes, but at the same time increases the amount of metal removed under a given set of operating conditions. Acetic and sulfuric acids alter the physical property – composition relationship in the concentrated acid baths and also complicate control problems. Acetic acid also volatilizes rapidly from the bath.

Small concentrations of heavy metals in the bath enhance the brightening effect, particularly on alloys with negligible copper content. Dissolved copper can be introduced into the bath by one of three methods: (a) the direct dissolution of metallic copper; (b) the addition of a small amount of a copper compound, such as 0.01 to 0.02% cupric nitrate; or (c) the use of racks made of aluminum-copper alloys. Copper is added to the bath also when brightening aluminum alloys such as 2024 and 7075, which contain high percentages of copper. Excess copper can be plated out of the bath. In some baths, however, excess copper causes etching, and sometimes nickel or zinc is used instead of copper.

The phosphoric-nitric acid baths are not recommended for brightening alloys containing silicon, because excessive dissolution causes dispersion of undissolved silicon, which deposits on the work surfaces and is difficult to remove by rinsing. The gradual buildup of other metals in the bath from the aluminum alloys processed usually causes no difficulty unless the amount of aluminum dissolved exceeds the solubility limit. When this occurs, excess aluminum precipitates and causes coprecipitation of trace elements, which may be difficult to remove from the work.

Contamination of the bath by more than trace amounts of buffing or polishing compounds and other soils should be avoided. These compounds may cause the bath to foam excessively and

Table 16. Compositions and Operating Conditions of Acid Cleaners

```
1 Chromic acid ...................6 to 12 oz
  Sulfuric acid (66° Bé) .........1.2 to 1.5 pt
  Water .........................To 1 gal
  Temperature of bath .........110 to 180 F
  Immersion time ...............Up to 20 min
2 Nitric acid (42° Bé) .............4 to 6 pt
  Hydrofluoric acid (48%) .......3 to 24 fl oz
  Water .........................To 1 gal
  Temperature of bath ...........Room
  Immersion time ...............1 to 5 min
3 Sulfuric acid (66° Bé) ...........0.8 pt
  Hydrofluoric acid (48%) ........3 fl oz
  Chromic acid ...................5 oz
  Water .........................To 1 gal
  Temperature of bath .........150 to 160 F
  Immersion time ...............2 to 5 min
4 Nitric acid (42° Bé) ...........0.3 to 1 pt
  Sodium sulfate (hydrate) .......8 to 16 oz
  Water .........................To 1 gal
  Temperature of bath .........170 to 175 F
  Immersion time ...............4 to 8 min
5 Phosphoric acid ................9 fl oz
  Chromic acid ...................2.75 oz
  Water .........................To 1 gal
  Temperature of bath .........110 to 150 F
  Immersion time ...............1 to 5 min
```

may interfere with its polishing action. Food-grade or NF (National Formulary) phosphoric acid should be used. Lower grades contain fluorides, arsenic and other impurities that are deleterious to the process.

Close control of the nitric acid and water contents, necessary for optimum chemical brightening, is difficult because of the rapid volatilization of these liquids and because of the time required for chemical analysis of the bath. A control technique based on an electronic device that monitors the nitric acid content and on the physical measurement of specific gravity and viscosity has been described by G. D. Nelson and C. J. Knapp in *Modern Metals*, Sept 1961 (p 46 to 53).

Dragout is always a major factor in the cost of chemical brightening. The amount of solution and the weight of chemicals lost by dragout are related to the specific gravity and viscosity of the solution. Dragout may be minimized by operating the bath at higher temperatures, but this condition may increase the amount of transfer etch and the rates of aluminum dissolution and evaporation of nitric acid and water. However, transfer etch may be avoided by rapid transfer into the rinse, and the rate of aluminum dissolution can be minimized by a shorter period of immersion. In general, an operating

Table 17. Phosphoric Acid Baths for Chemical Brightening of Aluminum

Constituent or condition	Range
Phosphoric-Nitric(a)	
Phosphoric acid (85%) ....45 to 98% by wt(b)	
Nitric acid (60%) ....0.5 to 50% by wt(b)	
Water ....2 to 35% by wt	
Temperature ....190 to 230 F	
Immersion time ....½ to 5 min	
Phosphoric-Acetic-Nitric(c)	
Phosphoric acid (85%) ....80% by vol	
Acetic acid (glacial, 99.5%) ....15% by vol	
Nitric acid (60%) ....5% by vol	
Temperature ....190 to 230 F	
Immersion time ....½ to 5 min	

(a) U. S. Patent 2,729,551 (1956). (b) Recommended volumetric make-up consists of 93.5 parts of 85% phosphoric acid and 6.5 parts of 60% nitric acid. (c) U. S. Patent 2,650,157 (1953).

temperature in the range of 190 to 212 F is satisfactory, provided an optimum bath composition (including additives) is maintained. Also, evaporation of nitric acid and water is not excessive at this temperature. Acetic acid also reduces transfer etch, but this acid volatilizes rapidly from the bath.

Surfactants are employed in some baths to suppress the evolution of fumes; however, they may cause foaming and an increase in the amount of dragout. Surfactants also increase the rate of dissolution. The generation of heat accompanying high dissolution rates must be considered when providing for the control of bath temperature within the specified range.

Agitation is useful for maintaining a uniform temperature and composition throughout the bath, and for fast removal of reaction products and replenishment of reactants at the surfaces of the work. The most satisfactory method is mechanical agitation and movement of the work in an elliptical pattern. Air agitation is commonly used, but it must be properly controlled. Small air bubbles cause excessive loss of volatile acids by evaporation and an excess of nitrous oxide fumes. Large air bubbles sufficient to create uniform bath temperature provide satisfactory agitation.

The bath must be well vented to remove the noxious fumes; an exhaust of about 300 cu ft per min per square foot of bath surface is recommended. Fumes evolved during transfer of the parts to the first rinse tank should likewise be vented, and it is good practice also to vent the first rinse tank, for which an exhaust of about 200 cu ft per min per square foot of water surface is satisfactory. Water should be warm and air-agitated.

The fumes may be exhausted by fan or steam jet. Fume-separators are required when the fumes cannot be exhausted into the atmosphere.

Phosphoric and Phosphoric-Sulfuric Acid Baths. Concentrated solutions of phosphoric acid at operating temperatures above 175 F were the first baths employed for brightening aluminum. A more effective bath, which combines some smoothing or "polishing" with brightening action, is one containing (by volume) 75% phosphoric acid and 25% sulfuric acid. This bath, which is operated at 195 to 230 F, produces a diffuse but bright finish.

A white film of phosphate salts remains on the metal after treatment in either of these baths under some conditions of composition and bath temperature. The film must be removed, and this can be accomplished with a hot (140 to 160 F) aqueous solution of chromic and sulfuric acids. The composition of this acid solution is not critical, and may range, by weight, from 2 to 4% CrO_3 and 10 to 15% H_2SO_4.

Electrolytic Brightening (Electropolishing)

Electrolytic brightening (electropolishing) produces smooth and bright surfaces similar to those that result from chemical brightening. After pretreatment — which consists of buffing, cleaning in an inhibited alkaline soak cleaner, and thorough rinsing — the work is immersed in the electrobrightening bath, through which direct current is passed; the work is the anode.

Solution compositions and operating conditions for three commercial electrolytic brightening processes, as well as for suitable post-treatments, are given in Tables 18, 19 and 20. Operating conditions for electrolytes used in electrobrightening are selected to produce the desired selective dissolution, and they may vary for optimum results on different aluminum alloys.

Selection of Chemical and Electrolytic Brightening Processes

Chemical and electrolytic brightening are essentially selective-dissolution processes, in which the high points of a rough surface are attacked more rapidly than the depressions. An important feature of these processes is their ability to remove a surface skin of metal that is contaminated with oxides and with traces of residual polishing and buffing compounds, or other inclusions, while at the same time brightening the surface.

Metallurgical Factors. The composition, orientation and size of the individual grains have a direct effect on the uniformity of dissolution during brightening. Fine-grained material is the most desirable for chemical or electrolytic brightening.

Best results are obtained with alloys that are of uniform chemical composition and that do not precipitate constituents of different potential from the matrix during any necessary heating or heat treatment. Also, the alloys should be such that deformation in forming causes only relatively minor detrimental effects.

Mill operations must be controlled to produce material that can be brightened satisfactorily. It is important that the material be fine-grained and that surfaces be free of all imperfections, such as segregation, oxide inclusions, laps, die marks, and stains.

Optical Factors. In general, the highest total and specular reflectance of the brightened surface is obtained with pure aluminum having a fine grain structure. Both total and specular reflectance decrease with increasing amounts of alloying elements other than magnesium, which has a minor deleterious effect. The magnitude of effect of alloying elements varies greatly with different brightening processes.

In a few applications, chemically or electrolytically brightened surfaces are protected by a clear organic coating. However, most surfaces brightened by these methods are anodized to produce a clear, colorless, protective oxide coating. (For many decorative uses, the anodic coating is subsequently dyed.)

Applications of chemical and electrolytic brightening processes are functional and decorative, and include jewelry, razor parts, automotive trim, fountain pens, searchlight reflectors, natural-finished or brightly colored giftware, architectural trim, household appliances, and thermal reflectors for components of space vehicles.

Chemical and electrolytic brightening may be used to replace buffing, either completely or partly. Brightening may

Table 18. Fluoboric Acid Electrobrightening and Suitable Post-Treatments(a)

Electrobrightening(b)

Fluoboric acid .... 2.5% (wt)
Temperature of bath .... 85 F
Current density .... 10 to 20 amp per sq ft
Voltage .... 15 to 30 v
Immersion time .... 5 to 10 min
Agitation .... None

Smut Removal

Phosphoric acid .... 1.0% (wt)
Chromic acid .... 0.5% (wt)
Temperature of bath .... 190 to 200 F
Immersion time .... 30 sec

Anodizing

Sulfuric acid .... 7 to 15% (wt)
Current density .... 12 amp per sq ft
Temperature of bath .... 70 F
Immersion time .... 10 min

Sealing

Distilled water 100%
Temperature of bath .... 200 to 212 F
Immersion time .... 10 min

(a) Application of process: Specular and diffuse reflectors, and products made of superpurity aluminum (99.99%) in combination with up to 2% Mg, or of high-purity aluminum (99.7 to 99.9%). (b) U. S. Patent 2,108,603 (1938).

be employed before or after buffing, or as an intermediate operation. In processes where brightening is used to replace buffing completely, aluminum is dissolved at relatively rapid rates, and a mil or more of metal is removed. In processes where brightening is used as the final operation of the finishing sequence, metal is dissolved more slowly, and total metal removal usually ranges from about 0.1 to 0.5 mil. Such procedures are used primarily on superpurity aluminum with up to 2% Mg and on high-purity aluminum.

Chemical Versus Electrolytic Brightening. Because of recent improvements in chemical brightening processes, brightening results are equivalent to those obtained by the electrolytic proc-

Table 19. Sodium Carbonate Electrobrightening and Suitable Post-Treatments(a)

Electrobrightening

Sodium carbonate (anhydrous) ...... 15% (wt)
Trisodium phosphate................ 5% (wt)
pH 10.5
Temperature of bath .... 176 to 180 F
Current density .... 20 to 30 amp per sq ft
Voltage .... 9 to 12 v
Initial immersion without current...... 20 sec
Immersion time with current.......... 5 min
Agitation .... Work rod only

Smut Removal(b)

Sulfuric acid .... 10% (vol)
Temperature of bath.............. 70 to 80 F
Immersion time .... 15 to 30 sec

Anodizing(c)

Sodium bisulfate .... 20% (wt)
Temperature of bath .... 95 F
Current density .... 5 amp per sq ft
Voltage .... 10 v
Immersion time .... 15 min

Sealing

Distilled water 100%
Temperature of bath .... 185 F
Immersion time .... 20 min

(a) Application of process: Specular reflectors; automotive trim; decorative ware; jewelry; and products made of superpurity aluminum (99.99%) in combination with up to 2% Mg, of high-purity aluminum (99.7 to 99.85%), or of the following commercial alloys (in approximate order of decreasing quality of finish): 5457, 5357, 6463, 6063, 5052, 6363, 1100, 5005, 3003 and 6061. (b) Smut may also be removed mechanically. (c) The anodizing treatment listed in Table 18 may be used as an alternative.

esses, with the exception of reflector-type finishes on superpurity and high-purity aluminum.

Initial and operating costs for equipment are lower for chemical brightening than for electrolytic brightening, because electrical power and associated equipment are not required.

Electrobrightening processes can have low chemical costs, because the chemicals employed are less expensive, and because baths operate well at high levels of dissolved aluminum. Other advantages of some baths used in electrobrightening are chemical stability of the solution and the ability of the bath to operate continuously for long periods at optimum efficiency with relatively simple control.

Advantages Over Buffing. In performance and economy, chemical and electrolytic polishing processes offer the following advantages over buffing:

Performance

1 Contaminants are not introduced into the metal surface. Chemical or electrolytic processes *remove* trace amounts of contaminants initially present in the surface skin or embedded in the metal during preceding operations. Surfaces brightened by these processes have better total and specular reflectance.
2 Anodized and dyed surfaces that have been chemically or electrolytically brightened have a brilliance, clarity and depth not attainable with buffed surfaces. Anodizing reduces the reflectance values of chemically or electrolytically brightened surfaces less than it reduces the reflectance of buffed surfaces.
3 Chemical or electrolytic brightening of aluminum prior to electroplating provides better adhesion and continuity of the plated deposits. This improves corrosion resistance and serviceability.

Economy

1 Labor costs are lower than for buffing.
2 Processes are readily adaptable to high-production parts that, because of their shape, cannot be finished on automatic buffing machines, and to parts that require buffing of a large percentage of the total surface area. Also, modification of automatic buffing machines to accommodate parts of different configuration may be more expensive than changes in racking for chemical or electrolytic brightening of these parts.
3 Incorporation of processes into an automatic anodizing or electroplating line can result in economies in terms of space, equipment and operations, and may eliminate one or more cleaning or pickling operations in the pretreatment cycle. Deburring can sometimes be completely eliminated, because of the high rate of metal removal on edges and corners.

Electrolytic Brightening Processes

Chemical etching, employing either alkaline or acid solutions, produces a satin or matte finish on aluminum products. These processes may be used for final finishing, but are more often employed as intermediate treatments prior to lacquering, conversion coating, anodizing or other finishing treatments. Chemical etching also is used extensively in conjunction with buffing or chemical brightening.

Etching with alkaline or acid solutions prior to anodizing: (a) removes oxide films and embedded surface contaminants that would discolor the anodic coating if not removed; (b) roughens the surface slightly, to produce a less glossy anodized surface, and to minimize slight differences in the mill finish of different production lots; and (c) minimizes color-matching differences, which are more apparent with glossy or specular surfaces.

Wrought and cast alloys on which matte finishes are readily produced by chemical etching are listed in Table 21.

Cleaning prior to etching is recommended for attainment of the highest-quality finish. The need for prior cleaning, however, is determined by the amount and type of soil present on the surface of work being processed; in many instances, the etching solution serves both as a cleaner and as a finishing medium.

Post-Treatments. Subsequent treatments, such as anodizing or chromate conversion coating, are required for protection against corrosion, and to protect the soft, easily marred surface against mechanical damage.

Clear lacquer may be applied to protect the matte finish produced by the etching process. Before being lacquered, the work must be cleaned of etching smut, thoroughly rinsed in clean cold water, and dried in warm air. Lacquering (or painting) should be done as soon as possible, in a clean atmosphere.

Alkaline Etching

Alkaline etching reduces or eliminates surface scratches, nicks, extrusion-die lines, and other imperfections. However, some surface contaminants, if not removed before the work enters the etching solution, may accentuate these imperfections during etching.

Oxides, rolled-in dirt, and many other surface contaminants can sometimes be eliminated by treating the work with a 2 to 4% (by weight) chromic acid, 10 to 15% (by weight) sulfuric acid etchant at 140 to 160 F prior to alkaline etching. This treatment removes stains resulting from heat treating and other causes without removing much metal.

Solution Make-Up and Control. A hot (120 to 180 F) aqueous solution of sodium hydroxide, potassium hydroxide, trisodium phosphate or sodium carbonate is used for alkaline etching. The solution may contain more than one alkali.

Sequestrants, such as gluconic acid, sodium gluconate, the glucamines, and sorbitol, are added to alkaline solutions to prevent the formation of hydrated alumina. If permitted to form, this compound coats tank walls and heating coils with a difficult-to-remove scale. Sequestrants also increase the life of the bath by preventing the formation of scale, and by reducing the accumulation of sludge in the tank. They are added in concentrations of 1 to 5%.

Sodium hydroxide is the alkali most commonly employed. Its reaction with aluminum is exothermic, produces hydrogen gas and sodium aluminate, and may cause a rise in the temperature of the bath, depending on the relationship between rate of metal removal and tank volume. Uniform finishes thus may be more difficult to obtain with large loads or rapid dissolution rates in small tanks, because the increase in temperature causes faster etching and more rapid depletion of the chemical constituents in the bath.

Table 20. Sulfuric-Phosphoric-Chromic Acid Electrobrightening and Post-Treatments(a)

Electrobrightening(b)	
Sulfuric acid	4 to 45% (wt)
Phosphoric acid	40 to 80% (wt)
Chromic acid	0.2 to 9.0% (wt)
Trivalent metals	6% max (wt)
Temperature of bath	160 to 200 F
Viscosity of bath at 180 F	9 to 13 centipoises
Current density	25 to 950 amp per sq ft
Voltage	7 to 15 v
Agitation	Mechanical
Smut Removal	
Phosphoric acid	3.5% (wt)
Chromic acid	2.0% (wt)
Temperature of bath	190 to 200 F
Anodizing	
Sulfuric acid	7 to 15% (wt)
Current density	12 amp per sq ft
Temperature of bath	70 F
Immersion time	10 min
Sealing	
Distilled water	100%
Temperature of bath	200 to 212 F
Immersion time	10 min

(a) Application of process: Primarily for macrosmoothing to replace mechanical polishing in whole or in part; used on architectural trim, decorative ware, jewelry, and products made of commercial alloys. (b) U. S. Patent 2,550,544 (1951).

The concentration of sodium hydroxide in the etching solution usually ranges from 2 to 8 oz per gal. For most applications, a concentration of 4 to 6 oz per gal is adequate. The choice of concentration is influenced by the finish desired, operating temperature of the bath, quality of water, transfer time between the etchant and rinse, and the amount of dragout.

Solution control is maintained by regular titration of samples to determine free sodium hydroxide and sodium aluminate (aluminum). In a common method of operation, the concentration of free sodium hydroxide is not permitted to fall below 3.5 or 4 oz per gal when a uniform, medium-deep etch is required. The normal working concentration of aluminum is about 4 oz per gal, or about 2.5% by weight. When the aluminum content of the solution approaches 7 to 10 oz per gal and free sodium hydroxide about 5 oz per gal, the finish may become brighter and more reflective; this indicates that the solution is nearly exhausted and should be partly or completely replaced.

Determination of specific gravity also is useful in solution control. A solution that has a specific gravity of 1.15 to 1.18 while maintaining a free sodium hydroxide content of 4 to 5 oz per gal is considered to be approaching exhaustion. When this condition is reached, the finish being produced should be carefully observed for non-uniform etching and shiny appearance.

Table 21. Aluminum Alloys Commonly Chemically Etched for a Matte Finish

Wrought Alloys				
Sheet and plate			Extrusions	
1100	3003	5457	2014	6063
2014	5005	6061	2024	6463
2024	5052	7075	6061	7075
	5357		6062	

Casting Alloys			
142	214	B214	218
195	A214	F214	220

As the aluminum content of the solution increases, the solution becomes more viscous. This condition may result in poor rinsing and may increase the amount of dragout.

Equipment and Operating Procedures. Tanks and heating coils for alkaline etching may be made of mild steel. Ventilation is required for the etching tanks, because the mistlike fumes generated are a health hazard to personnel, and because alkali-contaminated air can corrode or etch unprotected aluminum in the work area, especially during periods of high humidity. Efficient venting should be provided also to exhaust the fumes and spray evolved during transfer of the parts to the first rinse tank.

Sometimes a blanket of foam on the solution is used to reduce the amount of mist. Foam is usually created by the addition of surface-active (wetting) agents to the bath. One or two inches of foam on the surface of the bath is usually adequate.

Work to be processed may be placed on appropriate racks or loaded in baskets for immersion in the etching solution. (Dipping is the method most often used for etching, although in some instances spray etching has been employed.) Workpieces to be bulk processed in baskets must be spaced to prevent the formation of air or gas pockets. For best results, it is desirable to agitate the solution by air or by movement of the work.

Racks and baskets are usually used when etching is followed by subsequent treatments, such as chemical brightening. Stainless steel is a suitable material for bulk-etching baskets, because it withstands the corrosive conditions of the various solutions used in these cleaning and finishing processes. Baskets for bulk etching cannot be used for anodizing, because an electrical contact cannot be made.

In general, bath temperatures range from 120 to 180 F. Specific operating temperature is determined by the final finish desired, the time cycle, available equipment, and the concentration of the bath constituents.

After etching, the work should be rinsed immediately. A high etching temperature and a long transfer time from the etching tank may cause dry-on of the etchant. This condition produces a nonuniform finish characterized by cloudy, pitted or stained areas.

A double rinse in cold water flowing in a countercurrent is recommended. This type of rinsing employs smaller tanks and less water, and produces better rinsing, than when warm water or only one rinse tank is used. (Warm water may cause staining as a result of postetching, especially when only one rinse tank is used.) The work should not remain too long in the first rinse tank following etching, because the first rinse tank usually contains sufficient residual sodium hydroxide to cause staining or a cloudy finish.

Spot welds, riveted areas, or folded edges may contain small cracks or crevices that entrap the alkaline solution. Rinsing may not remove the entrapped solution, with the result that the alkaline solution will bleed out and leave a residue of white powder after the finishing process is concluded. Bleed-out can occur also after subsequent anodizing of the work. Bleed-out is unattractive and can cause failure of organic films, such as lacquers and paints, applied for added protection.

Dimensional Changes. Etching in alkaline solutions can remove a considerable amount of metal. Figure 1 shows the dimensional changes that occurred when sheet materials of various aluminum-base alloys were etched for 1, 2 or 3 min in an air-agitated sodium hydroxide solution (5% NaOH by weight) operated at 160 ± 5 F.

The etching cycle must be carefully controlled when clad materials are being treated, to prevent loss of the cladding.

Desmutting. During the cleaning and etching operation, smut (a gray-to-black residual film) is deposited on the surface of the work. This deposit usually consists of iron, silicon, copper or other alloying constituents (in an aluminum-base material) that are insoluble in sodium hydroxide.

When etching is to be followed by anodizing, the smut can sometimes be removed by the anodizing solution (current flowing); this practice, however, generally cannot be controlled to produce a finish of uniform appearance. The recommended procedure is to remove the smut in a solution prepared specifically for this purpose.

A nitric acid solution (10 to 15% or more HNO_3 by volume) will remove smut. A solution containing 0.5 to 1% by weight chromic acid plus 4 to 6% by weight sodium bisulfate is similarly effective. Solutions of proprietary compounds are also used.

Fluorides are usually added to solutions to aid the removal of smut from high-silicon aluminum alloys. Good results have been obtained with a room-temperature solution of 3 parts nitric acid and 1 part hydrofluoric acid.

The following example describes the solution to a problem encountered in the desmutting of die castings of a high-silicon alloy that had been etched in a sodium hydroxide solution.

Example 11. The problem was to obtain an attractive, uniform finish on die castings of alloy A380. The difficulty was in desmutting, because of the high silicon content of this alloy (7.5 to 9.5% Si). A chromate-type desmutting solution had been used after etching in sodium hydroxide, but had not been entirely effective. The addition of an acid fluoride etch provided the desired finish. The sequence of operations now employed is as follows:
1 Soak in nonetching aluminum cleaner at 140 to 150 F for 5 to 10 min.
2 Rinse in cold water.

Table 22. Compositions and Operating Conditions for Acid Etching Baths

1 Nitric acid (conc) ....3 parts by vol
Hydrofluoric acid (conc).......1 part by vol
Temperature of bath............70 F max
Immersion time ....¼ to 1 min

2 Chromic acid ....10.5 oz
Sulfuric acid (conc) ....22.4 fl oz
Water ....To 1 gal
Temperature of bath ....140 to 160 F
Immersion time ....½ to 2 min

3 Chromic acid ....23.5 oz
Sulfuric acid (conc) ....2.5 fl oz
Water ....To 1 gal
Temperature of bath ....140 to 160 F
Immersion time ....½ to 2 min

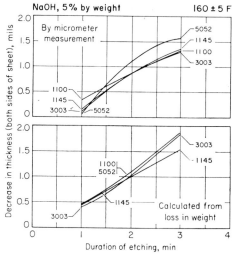

Fig. 1. Effect of time in alkaline etching solution on amount of metal removed from aluminum alloys

3 Etch for 60 to 90 sec in a sodium hydroxide etching solution at 140 to 150 F.
4 Rinse in cold water.
5 Remove part of smut by immersing in an air-agitated chromate-type desmutting solution at room temperature.
6 Rinse in cold water.
7 Rinse in hot deionized water.
8 Immerse in a room-temperature acid etching solution containing fluoride and nitric acid for 30 to 60 sec, to remove the remaining smut.
9 Rinse in cold water.

After being prepared in this manner, the castings are chromate conversion coated and dipped in lacquer.

Proprietary chromic-sulfuric acid desmutting solutions generally require a tank made of type 302 or 304 stainless steel, although some solutions may require type 316 or 347. They are usually operated at room temperature and normally do not require ventilation. This is an advantage over nitric acid solutions. A disadvantage of some proprietary solutions is the need for treatment of the wastes to remove the deleterious effects of chromium salts before the wastes are discharged from the plant. Local ordinances control the disposition of waste solutions.

Acid Etching

Acid solutions are commonly used for finishing castings, especially those made of high-silicon alloys. Hydrochloric, hydrofluoric, nitric, phosphoric, chromic and sulfuric acids are used in acid etching.

Combinations of these acids and mixtures of acids and salts are often used for specific applications. Sulfuric-chromic acid solutions remove heat treating stains with little etching of the metal; dilute hydrofluoric-nitric acid solutions produce bright, slightly matte-textured surfaces; and hydrochloric acid saturated with sodium

chloride or ferric chloride is used for deep etching of designs. Additions of cobalt and nickel salts to the hydrochloric acid solution accelerate etching, but do not affect the ability of the solution to produce a sufficiently smooth surface.

Compositions and operating conditions for three acid etching solutions are given in Table 22. Figure 2 shows a flow chart of the operations employed in acid etching.

Fumes from most acid etching solutions are corrosive, and the mist or spray carried up by the gases evolved constitutes a health hazard. Ventilation is required, even for the solutions operated at room temperature. Tanks are made of stainless steel or plastic, or are plastic lined; plastic or plastic-lined tanks are employed with solutions containing hydrochloric or hydrofluoric acid. Cooling coils may be required, because etching generates heat. Heating coils also are required for solutions operated at elevated temperature.

Acid etching is often used alone, but it may be used in conjunction with alkaline etching, either preceding or following it. It is usually used before alkaline etching when oxides are to be removed, and after alkaline etching when smut removal is a problem. Acid etching solutions, especially those containing fluorides, are excellent smut removers. After acid etching and thorough rinsing, the work is ready for further processing (Fig. 2).

Anodizing Processes

The basic reaction in all anodizing processes is the conversion of the aluminum surface to aluminum oxide while the part is made the anode in an electrolytic cell. Reasons for anodizing are:

1 **Increase corrosion resistance.** Aluminum oxide is corrosion resistant and impervious to atmospheric and salt water attack. The anodic coating protects the underlying metal by serving as a barrier to corrodents. The amorphous aluminum oxide produced by anodizing is sealed by treating in acidified hot water. (Sealing is discussed in a subsequent section.)

2 **Increase paint adhesion.** The tightly adhering anodic coating offers a chemically active surface for most paint systems. Anodic films produced in sulfuric acid baths are colorless and offer a base for subsequent clear finishing systems. Aluminum-base materials that are painted for service in severe corrosive environments are anodized before being painted.

3 **Permit subsequent plating.** The inherent porosity of the anodic film enhances electroplating. Usually, a phosphoric acid bath is used for anodizing prior to plating.

4 **Improve decorative appearance.** All anodic coatings are lustrous and have relatively good abrasion resistance. Therefore, these coatings are used as the final finishing treatment when the natural appearance of the aluminum is desired or when a mechanically induced pattern is to be preserved. The degree of luster of anodic

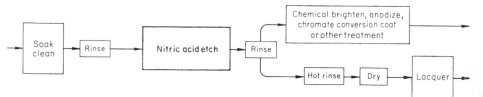

Fig. 2. Flow chart of operations employed in acid etching of aluminum and aluminum alloys

Table 23. Typical Products for Which Anodizing Is Employed in Final Finishing

Product (and size)	Alloy	Finishing before anodizing	Anodizing process	Post-treatment	Service requirement or environment
Auto headlamp (8½-in. diam, 1¼ in.)...	5557-H25	Buff, chemical brighten	Sulfuric acid(a)	Seal	Atmospheric exposure
Canopy track (30-in. T-extrusion)......	7075	Machine	Hard	None	Resist wear, sea air
Gelatin molds (6 to 8 in. over all)......	1100-O	Chemical brighten as-drawn	Sulfuric acid	Dye, seal	Food
Landing gear (8-in. diam by 4½ ft).....	7079-T6	(b)	Chromic acid	Paint	Corrosion resistance
Mullion (12 ft by 7 in. by 4 in.)(c).....	6063-T6	(d)	Sulfuric acid(e)	Seal, lacquer(f)	Urban atmosphere
Nameplates (various sizes)............	3003-H14	(g)	Sulfuric acid	Dye, seal	Atmospheric exposure
Percolator shell (5-in. diam by 6 in.)....	....	Buff, chemical brighten	Sulfuric acid	Seal	Coffee
Seaplane-hull skin (112 by 40 in.).....	Clad 2014-T6	(g)	Chromic acid	None	Erosion; corrosion(h)
Seat-stanchion tube (2-in. diam by 24 in.)	7075-T6	Machine	Hard	None	Wear resistance
Signal-cartridge container (7½ by 5½ by 6½ in.).....................	3003-O	As drawn	Chromic acid	Prime, paint	Marine atmosphere
Tray, household (17-in. diam)........	....	Butler	Sulfuric acid	Seal, buff	Food
Utensil covers (up to 2 sq ft total area)..	1100	Buff, chemical brighten	Sulfuric acid(j)	Dye, seal	Steam, cooked foods(k)
Voice transmitter (2-in. diam)........	5052-O	Burnish, alkaline etch	Sulfuric acid	Dye, seal(m)	Gas mask
Wheel pistons (up to 8 sq in. area).....	6151	Machine	Sulfuric acid(n)	Seal	Wear and corrosion(p)

(a) Anodic coating 0.3 mil thick. (b) Partially machine, clean with nonetching cleaner, and remove surface oxide. (c) 0.188 in. thick. (d) Lined finish (180-mesh grit) on 4-in. face; other surfaces alkaline etched. (e) Anodized for 80 min; minimum coating thickness, 1.2 mils. (f) Sealed for 20 to 30 min. Methacrylate lacquer, 0.3 mil minimum. (g) Clean with nonetching cleaner; remove surface oxide. (h) Maximum resistance required. (j) Anodic coating 0.2 mil thick. (k) Must not discolor during service. (m) Sealed in dichromate solution. (n) Anodized in sulfuric acid solution (30% H_2SO_4) at 70 F for 70 min at 25 amp per sq ft. (p) In presence of hydraulic brake fluids.

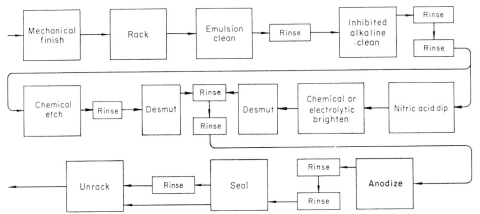

Fig. 3. Flow chart of operations typically employed in anodizing

coatings depends on the condition of the basis metal before anodizing. Dull etching decreases luster; bright etching, chemical or electrolytic brightening, and buffing increase luster, either diffuse or specular. Most of the aluminum used in architectural applications is anodized.

5 **Provide electrical insulation.** Aluminum oxide is a dielectric. The breakdown voltage of the anodic film varies from a few volts to several thousand volts, depending on the alloy and on the nature and thickness of the film.

6 **Permit application of photographic and lithographic emulsions.** The porosity of the anodic film offers a mechanical means of holding the emulsion.

7 **Increase emissivity.** Anodic films more than 0.032 mil thick increase the emissivity of the aluminum. When dyed black, the film has excellent heat absorption up to 450 F.

8 **Increase abrasion resistance.** The hard anodizing processes produce coatings from 1 mil to more than 4 mils thick. These coatings, with the inherent hardness of aluminum oxide, are thick enough for use in applications involving rotating parts where abrasion resistance is re-

quired. (Although all anodic films are harder than the substrate material, the coatings produced by chromic acid and some sulfuric acid baths are too thin or too soft to meet the requirements for abrasion resistance.)

9 **Detection of surface flaws.** A chromic acid anodizing solution can be used as an inspection medium for the detection of fine surface cracks. When a part containing a surface flaw is removed from the anodizing bath, then washed and dried quickly, chromic acid entrapped in the flaw seeps out and stains the anodized coating in the area adjacent to the flaw.

The three principal types of anodizing processes are (a) chromic, in which the active agent is chromic acid; (b) sulfuric, in which the active agent is sulfuric acid; and (c) hard — patented processes that use sulfuric and oxalic acids as the active agents. Other processes, used less frequently and for special purposes, employ sulfuric-oxalic, phosphoric, oxalic, boric, sulfosalicylic, or sulfophthalic acid solutions (J. M.

Kape, Unusual Anodizing Processes and Their Practical Significance, *Electroplating Metal Finishing*, Nov 1961). Except for those produced by hard anodizing processes, most anodic coatings range in thickness from 0.2 to 0.7 mil.

Table 23 describes a few applications in which anodizing is employed as a step in final finishing. The succession of operations typically employed in anodizing is illustrated in Fig. 3.

Surface Preparation. A chemically clean surface is a basic requirement for successful anodizing. The cleaning method is selected on the basis of the type of soils or contaminants that must be removed. Usually, the cleaning cycle consists of removing the major organic contaminants by vapor degreasing or solvent cleaning, and then making the surface chemically clean. The various types of cleaners used are discussed in the section on Chemical Cleaning in this article.

After cleaning, the work is etched or, when specular surfaces are required, treated in a brightening solution. The procedures for etching and for brightening have been discussed in the sections of this article on Chemical Etching, Alkaline Etching, Acid Etching, Chemical Brightening, and Electrolytic Brightening. After etching or brightening, desmutting usually is required, for the removal of heavy metal deposits resulting from the preceding operations. Desmutting is discussed in the section on Alkaline Etching.

Chromic Acid Process. The sequence of operations employed in this process depends on the type of part, the alloy to be anodized, and the principal objective for anodizing. Table 24 gives a typical sequence of operations that meets the requirements of military specification MIL-A-8625.

Chromic acid anodizing solutions contain from 3 to 10% CrO_3 by weight. A solution is made up by filling the tank about half full of water, dissolving the acid in the tank, and then adding water to adjust to the desired operating level.

A chromic acid anodizing solution should not be used unless:

1 The pH is between 0.5 and 1.0
2 The concentration of chlorides (as NaCl) is less than 0.02%
3 The concentration of sulfates (as H_2SO_4) is less than 0.05%
4 The total chromic acid content, as determined by pH and Baumé readings,

Table 24. Typical Sequence of Operations for Chromic Acid Anodizing

Operation	Solution	Solution temperature, F	Treatment time, min
1 Vapor degrease	Suitable solvent	....	....
2 Alkaline clean	Alkaline cleaner	(a)	(a)
3 Rinse(b)	Water	Ambient	1
4 Desmut(c)	HNO₃, 10 to 25% (vol)	Ambient	As required
5 Rinse(b)	Water	Ambient	1
6 Anodize	CrO₃, 5.25 oz/gal(d)	90 to 95	30(e)
7 Rinse(b)	Water	Ambient	1
8 Seal(f)	Water(g)	190 to 210	10 to 15
9 Air dry	....	225 max(h)	As required

(a) According to individual specifications. (b) Running water or spray. (c) Generally used in conjunction with alkaline-etch type of cleaning. (d) pH, 0.5. (e) Approximate; time may be increased to produce maximum coating weight desired. (f) Optional. (g) Water may be slightly acidulated with chromic acid, to a pH of 4 to 6. (h) Drying at elevated temperature is optional.

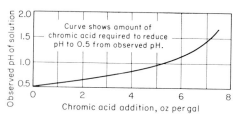

Fig. 4. Control of pH of chromic acid anodizing solutions

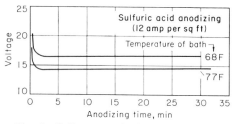

Fig. 5. Voltages required for maintaining a current density of 12 amp per sq ft at 68 and 77 F during sulfuric acid anodizing

Table 25. Voltage Required for Sulfuric Acid Anodizing at 12 Amp per Sq Ft

Alloy	Volts	Alloy	Volts
Wrought Alloys		6063	15.0
		6151	15.0
1100	15.0	7075	16.0
2011	20.0	**Casting Alloys**	
2014	21.0		
2017	21.0	13	26.0
2024	21.0	43	18.0
2117	16.5	142	13.0
3003	16.0	195	21.0
3004	15.0	214(a)	10.0
5005	15.0	218(a)	10.0
5050	15.0	319	23.0
5052	14.5	355	17.0
5056	16.0	356	19.0
5357	15.0	380	23.0
6053	15.5		
6061	15.0	(a) Current density, 9 amp per sq ft	
6062	15.0		

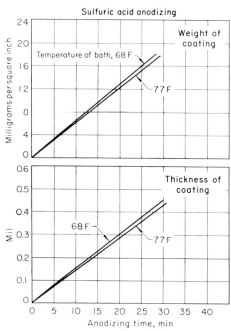

Data derived from aluminum-alloy automotive trim anodized in 15% sulfuric acid solutions at 68 and 77 F and at 12 amp per sq ft.

Fig. 6. Effect of anodizing time on weight and thickness of anodic coating

is less than 10%. (When this percentage is exceeded, part of the bath is withdrawn and is replaced with fresh solution.)

Figure 4 shows the amount of chromic acid that is required for reducing the pH from the observed value to an operating value of 0.5.

When the anodizing process is started, the voltage is controlled so that it will increase from 0 to 40 volts within 5 to 8 min. The voltage is regulated to produce a current density of not less than 1.0 amp per sq ft, and anodizing is continued for the specified time period (usually, 30 to 40 min). At the end of the cycle the current is gradually reduced to zero, and the part is removed from the bath within 15 sec and rinsed.

Sulfuric Acid Process. The basic operations for this process are the same as for the chromic acid process. Parts or assemblies that contain joints or recesses that could entrap the electrolyte should not be anodized in the sulfuric acid bath.

The concentration of sulfuric acid (sp gr, 1.84) in the anodizing solution is 12 to 20% by weight. A solution containing 9.5 gal of H_2SO_4 per 100 gal of solution is capable of producing an anodic coating that when sealed in a boiling dichromate solution, meets the requirements of MIL-A-8625.

A sulfuric acid anodizing solution should not be used unless:

1 The concentration of chlorides (as NaCl) is less than 0.02%
2 Aluminum concentration is less than 20 g per liter (2⅔ oz per gal)
3 Sulfuric acid content is between 165 and 200 g per liter (22.1 to 26.8 oz per gal).

At the start of the anodizing operation, the voltage is adjusted to produce a current density of 12 amp per sq ft. Figure 5 shows the voltage required to anodize at two different temperatures and a current density of 12 amp per sq ft. The voltage will increase slightly as the aluminum content of the bath increases. Table 25 gives the approximate voltage required for anodizing various wrought and cast aluminum alloys in a sulfuric acid bath.

When a current density of 12 amp per sq ft is attained, the anodizing process is continued until the specified weight of coating is produced, after which the flow of current is stopped and the parts are withdrawn immediately from the solution and rinsed. Figure 6 shows the effect of time on the weight and thickness of the coating developed on automotive trim that was anodized in 15% sulfuric acid solutions at 68 and 77 F; both solutions were operated at a current density of 12 amp per sq ft.

A flow chart and a table of operating conditions for operations typically employed in anodizing architectural parts

by the sulfuric acid process are presented in Fig. 7; similar information, for the anodizing of automotive bright trim, is given in Fig. 8.

Hard Anodizing. The primary differences between the sulfuric acid and hard anodizing processes are the operating temperature and the current density at which anodizing is accomplished. Hard anodizing produces a considerably heavier coating than conventional anodizing for a given length of time. Coating weights obtained as a function of time are compared for the two processes in Fig. 9.

The hard anodizing process employs a sulfuric acid bath containing 10 to 15% acid by weight, with or without additions. The operating temperature of the bath ranges from 32 to 50 F, and current density is between 20 and 36 amp per sq ft. Higher temperatures cause the formation of soft and more porous outer layers of the anodic coating. This change in coating characteristics reduces wear resistance significantly and tends to limit coating thickness. Excessive operating temperatures result in dissolution of coating and can burn and damage the work.

Proprietary processes also are commonly employed. One of the more common of these processes uses a solution containing 16 to 21 oz of sulfuric acid and 1.6 to 2.8 oz of oxalic acid ($H_2C_2O_4$) per gallon of water. This solution is operated at 50 ± 2 F and a current density of 25 to 36 amp per sq ft (voltage is increased gradually from zero to between 40 and 60 volts); treatment time is 25 min per mil of coating thickness.

Special Anodizing Processes. Table 26 gives the operating conditions for three anodizing baths that are used to produce an anodic coating with a hardness and porosity suitable for electroplating, or to produce anodic coatings of hardness or thickness intermediate to those obtainable from chromic acid, sulfuric acid and hard anodizing baths.

Process Limitations. Composition of the aluminum alloy, surface finish, prior processing, temper or heat treatment, and the use of inserts influence the quality of anodic coatings. The limitations imposed by each of these variables on the various anodizing processes are indicated below.

Alloy Composition. The chromic acid process should not be used to anodize aluminum casting alloys containing more than 5% Cu or more than 7.5% total alloying elements, because excessive pitting, commonly referred to as burning, may result. The sulfuric acid process can be used for any of the commercially available alloys, whereas the hard anodizing process is usually limited to alloys containing less than 3% Cu and 7% Si.

Two or more different alloys can be anodized at the same time in the same bath if the anodizing voltage requirements are identical. This condition is more critical for the

Table 26. Compositions and Operating Conditions of Solutions for Special Anodizing Processes

Type of solution	Composition (by weight)	Current density, amp/sq ft	Solution temperature, F	Treatment time, minutes	Use of solution
Sulfuric-oxalic	H_2SO_4, 15 to 20% + $H_2C_2O_4$, 5%	12	85 to 95	30	Thicker coating (a)
Phosphoric	H_3PO_4, 20 to 60% (vol)	3 to 12(b)	80 to 95	5 to 15	Prepare for plating
Oxalic	$H_2C_2O_4$, 3%	12	72 to 86	15 to 60(c)	Harder coating(d)

(a) Coating is intermediate in thickness between coating produced by sulfuric acid anodizing and coating produced by hard anodizing. (b) Potential, 5 to 30 volts. (c) Depends on coating thickness desired. (d) Hardness greater than by other processes except hard anodizing.

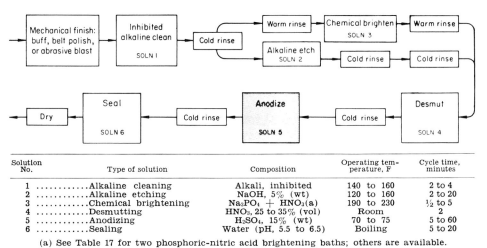

Solution No.	Type of solution	Composition	Operating temperature, F	Cycle time, minutes
1	Alkaline cleaning	Alkali, inhibited	140 to 160	2 to 4
2	Alkaline etching	NaOH, 5% (wt)	120 to 160	2 to 20
3	Chemical brightening	Na₃PO₄ + HNO₃(a)	190 to 230	½ to 5
4	Desmutting	HNO₃, 25 to 35% (vol)	Room	2
5	Anodizing	H₂SO₄, 15% (wt)	70 to 75	5 to 60
6	Sealing	Water (pH, 5.5 to 6.5)	Boiling	5 to 20

(a) See Table 17 for two phosphoric-nitric acid brightening baths; others are available.

Fig. 7. *Operations employed in sulfuric acid anodizing of architectural parts*

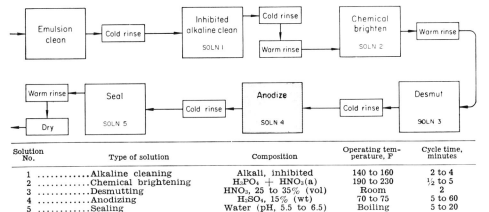

Solution No.	Type of solution	Composition	Operating temperature, F	Cycle time, minutes
1	Alkaline cleaning	Alkali, inhibited	140 to 160	2 to 4
2	Chemical brightening	H₃PO₄ + HNO₃(a)	190 to 230	½ to 5
3	Desmutting	HNO₃, 25 to 35% (vol)	Room	2
4	Anodizing	H₂SO₄, 15% (wt)	70 to 75	5 to 60
5	Sealing	Water (pH, 5.5 to 6.5)	Boiling	5 to 20

(a) See Table 17 for two phosphoric-nitric acid brightening baths; others are available.

Fig. 8. *Operations employed in sulfuric acid anodizing of automotive bright trim*

sulfuric acid process than for the chromic acid process. Table 25 indicates the commercial alloys that can be anodized together in a sulfuric acid bath.

Surface Finish. Anodic films accentuate any irregularities present in the original surface. However, surface irregularities are emphasized more by the chromic acid bath than by the sulfuric acid bath.

Sheet materials should be rolled from homogenized ingots from which surface oxides are removed prior to rolling. Clad sheet should be handled with care to prevent mechanical abrasion or exposure of the core material. Anodizing magnifies scratches, and if the core material is exposed it will anodize with a color different from that of the cladding.

Anodizing grade must be specified for extruded products so that mill operations are controlled to minimize longitudinal die marks and other surface blemishes.

Surface irregularities must be removed from forgings, and the surfaces of the forgings must be cleaned by a process that removes trapped and burned-in lubricants. Special attention is required when polishing the flash line, if this area is to appear similar to other areas of the forging after anodizing.

Castings can be anodized provided their composition is within the process limits described above under "Alloy Composition". From the standpoint of uniform appearance, however, anodizing usually is undesirable for castings, because of their nonuniform composition and their porosity. Improved results often can be obtained by soaking castings in boiling water after cleaning and before anodizing. This treatment, however, merely attempts to fill surface voids with water, so that voids do not entrap anodizing solution.

Usually, permanent mold castings have the best appearance after anodizing, then die castings, and finally sand castings. Permanent mold castings should be specified if an anodic coating of uniform appearance is required. Anodizing usually reveals the metal flow lines inherent in the die-casting process, and this condition is objectionable if uniform appearance is desired. In general, solution heat treatment prior to anodizing is beneficial for producing the most uniform and bright anodized finish obtainable on castings.

Regardless of the product form, rough

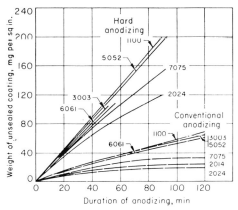

Hard anodizing solution contained (by weight) 12% H₂SO₄ and 1% H₂C₂O₄, was operated at 50 F and 36 amp per sq ft. Conventional anodizing solution contained 15% (wt) H₂SO₄, was operated at 70 F and 12 amp per sq ft.

Fig. 9. *Effect of anodizing time on weight of hard and conventional anodic coatings* (R. V. Vanden Berg, *Products Finishing*, Feb 1960)

finishing should be avoided when maximum corrosion resistance or uniformity of appearance of the anodic coating is desired. Rough surfaces, such as those produced by sawing, sand blasting and shearing, are difficult to anodize and should be strongly etched prior to anodizing to assure even minimal results.

The machined areas of castings or forgings may have an appearance different from that of the unmachined surfaces.

Prior Processing. Because of their effect on surface finish, welding, brazing and soldering affect the appearance of the anodic coating, for the reasons discussed above. In addition, the compositions of solders usually are not amenable to anodizing.

Spot, ultrasonic pressure or other types of welding processes where there is no introduction of foreign metal, fluxes or other contaminants do not affect the appearance of the anodic coating.

Temper or Heat Treatment. Differences in temper of non-heat-treatable alloys have no marked effect on the uniform appearance of the anodic coating.

The microstructural location of the alloying elements in heat treatable alloys affects the appearance of anodic coatings. Alloying elements in solution have little effect, but the effect is greater when the elements are precipitated from solid solution. The annealed condition should be avoided when maximum clarity of the anodic film is desired.

Inserts or attachments made of metals other than aluminum must be masked off, both electrically and chemically, to prevent burning and corrosion in surrounding areas. The masking must completely seal the faying surface between the insert and parent metal, to prevent adsorption of solution, which may result in corrosion and staining. Therefore, it is desirable to install inserts *after* anodizing.

Anodizing Equipment and Process Control

Chromic Acid Anodizing. Mild steel tanks are satisfactory for chromic acid baths. It is common practice to line up to half of the tank with an insulating material, such as glass, to limit the cathode area with respect to the expected anode area (a 1-to-1 ratio is normal). In nonconducting tanks, suitable cathode area is provided by the immersion of individual lead cathodes; however, these require the installation of additional busbars to the tanks for suspension of individual cathodes.

Provision must be made for heating the anodizing solution to 90 to 95 F; electric or steam immersion heaters are satisfactory for this purpose. Electric heaters are preferred, because they are easy to operate and do not contaminate the bath.

The anodizing process generates heat; therefore, agitation is required to prevent overheating of the bath and especially of the electrolyte immediately adjacent to the aluminum parts being anodized. Exhaust facilities must be adequate to trap the effluent fumes of chromic acid and steam.

Sulfuric Acid Anodizing. Tanks for sulfuric acid anodizing may be made of mild steel lined throughout with plasticized polyvinyl chloride and coated on the outside with corrosion-resistant synthetic-rubber paint. (Other suitable materials for tank linings are lead, rubber and acidproof brick.) Tanks made of special sulfuric-acid-resistant stainless steel (containing copper and molybdenum), or made entirely of an organic material, also may be used. The tank should have controls for maintaining temperature at between 68 and 85 F. Requirements for agitation and ventilation are the same as for chromic acid solutions.

The surface of the floor under the tank should be acid resistant. The bottom of the tank should be about 6 in. above the floor on acid-resistant and moisture-repellent supports.

A separate heat exchanger and acid make-up tank should be provided for sulfuric acid anodizing installations. This tank should be made of lead-lined steel. Lead is preferred over plastic for the lining because lead withstands the heat generated when sulfuric acid is added. Polyvinyl chloride pipes are recommended for air agitation of the solution and for the acid-return lines between the two tanks. Cooling coils should be made of chemical lead or antimonial lead pipe.

Hard Anodizing. Most of the hard anodizing formulations are variations of the sulfuric acid bath. The requirements for hard anodizing tanks are substantially the same as those for sulfuric acid anodizing tanks, except that cooling, rather than heating, maintains the operating temperature at 32 to 50 F.

Temperature-control equipment for all anodizing processes must regulate the over-all operating temperature of the bath and maintain the proper temperature at the interface of the work surface and electrolyte.

The operating temperature for most anodizing baths is controlled within ± 2 °F. This degree of control makes it necessary for the temperature-sensing mechanism and heat lag of the heating units to be balanced.

When electric immersion heaters are used, it is common practice to have high and low heat selection so that the bath can be heated rapidly to the operating temperature and then controlled more accurately on the low heat setting. Standard thermistor thermostats are used for sensing the temperature within the bath and activating the heating elements.

In steam heated systems, it is advantageous to have a throttling valve to prevent overheating. An intermediate heat exchanger is employed in some installations to prevent contamination of the electrolyte and the steam system by a broken steam line within the anodizing bath.

Agitation may be accomplished by stirring with electrically driven impellers, by recirculation through externally located pumps, or by air. In some installations the anode busbars are oscillated horizontally, thus imparting a stirring action to the work.

The two primary requirements of an agitation system are that it is adequate and that it does not introduce foreign materials into the solution. With air agitation, filters must be used in the line to keep oil and dirt out of the solution.

Power requirements for the principal anodizing processes are as follows:

Process	Voltage	Amp/ft²
Chromic	42	1 to 3
Sulfuric	24	6 to 24
Hard	100	25 to 35

Direct current is required for all processes. Some hard anodizing procedures also require a superimposed alternating current.

At present, most power sources for anodizing employ selenium or silicon rectifiers. Compared to motor generators, the selenium rectifiers have greater reliability, are lower in initial cost and maintenance cost, and have satisfactory service life.

Voltage drop between the rectifier and the work must be held to a minimum. This is accomplished by using adequate busbars or power-transmission cables.

Automatic equipment to program the current during the entire cycle is preferred. Manual controls can be used, but necessitate frequent adjustments of voltage. The presence of a recording voltmeter in the circuit insures that the time-voltage program specified for the particular installation is being adhered to by operating personnel. Current-recording devices also are advantageous.

Masking. When selective anodizing is required, masking is necessary for areas to be kept free of the anodic coating. Masking during anodizing may be required also for post-anodizing operations such as welding, for making an electrical connection to the basis metal, or for producing multicolor effects with dye coloring techniques.

Masking materials usually consist of pressure-sensitive tapes and stop-off lacquers. The tapes may have a metal or vinyl (or other plastic) backing. Stop-off lacquers provide satisfactory masking, but some types are difficult to remove. For effective masking when either type of material is employed, work surfaces should have a high degree of cleanness.

Racks for Anodizing

Anodizing racks or fixtures should be designed for efficiency in loading and unloading of workpieces. Important features that must be included in every properly designed rack are as follows:

1 **Current-carrying capacity.** The rack must be large enough to carry the correct amount of current to each part attached to the rack. If the spline of the rack is too slender for the number of parts that are attached to the rack, the anodic coating will be of inadequate thickness, or it will be burned or soft as the result of overheating.

2 **Positioning of parts.** The rack should enable proper positioning of the parts to permit good drainage, minimum gassing effects and air entrapment, and good current distribution.

3 **Service life.** The rack must have adequate strength, and sufficient resistance to corrosion and heat, to withstand the environment of each phase of the anodizing cycle.

The use of bolt and screw contacts, rather than spring or tension contacts, is a feature of racks designed for anodizing with the semihard-coat color processes. These processes require high current densities and accurate positioning of workpieces in the tank. Bolted contacts are used also on racks for conventional hard anodizing. However, bolting requires more loading and unloading time than tension contacts.

Materials for Racks. Aluminum and commercially pure titanium are the materials most commonly used for anodizing racks. Copper, brass, phosphor bronze, and steel (including stainless steel) can be used for their current-carrying ability, spring-tension properties, or strength, but these

materials must be insulated from the electrolyte by the application of a rack-coating compound. Aluminum alloys used for racks should contain not more than 5% Cu and 7% Si. Alloys such as 3003, 2024 and 6061 are satisfactory. Contacts must be of aluminum or titanium.

Racks made of aluminum have the disadvantage of being anodized with the parts. The anodic coating must be removed from the rack, or at least from contacts, before the rack can be re-used. A 5% solution of sodium hydroxide at 100 to 150 F, or an aqueous solution of chromic and phosphoric acids ($5\frac{1}{3}$ oz of CrO_3 and $5\frac{1}{3}$ fl oz of H_3PO_4 per gallon of water) at 170 to 190 F, can be used to strip the film from the rack. The chromic-phosphoric acid solution does not continue to attack the aluminum rack after the anodic film is removed.

Caustic etching (prior to anodizing) attacks aluminum spring or tension contacts, causing a gradual decrease in their strength for holding the parts securely. This condition, coupled with vibration in the anodizing tank (especially from agitation), results in movement and burning of workpieces.

On many racks, aluminum is used for splines, crosspieces and other large members, and titanium for the contact tips. The tips may be replaceable or nonreplaceable. Although replaceable titanium tips offer versatility in racking, the aluminum portions of the rack must be protected with an insulating coating. However, if the anodizing electrolyte penetrates the coating, the aluminum portion of the rack may become anodized and thus become electrically insulated from the replaceable titanium contact. A more satisfactory rack design employs nonreplaceable titanium contacts on aluminum splines that are coated with a protective coating. Titanium contacts that are welded to replaceable titanium crossbars offer a solution to many racking problems created by the variety of parts to be anodized. These crossbar members can be rapidly connected to the spline. Titanium should not be used in solutions containing hydrofluoric acid.

Plastisol (unplasticized polyvinyl chloride) is used as a protective coating for anodizing racks. This material has good resistance to chemical attack by the solutions in the normal anodizing cycle; however, it should not be used continuously in a vapor degreasing operation. Furthermore, if the coating becomes loose and entraps processing solution, the solution may bleed out and drip on the workpieces, causing staining or spotting.

Bulk Processing. Small parts that are difficult to rack are bulk anodized in perforated cylindrical containers made of fiber, plastic or titanium. Each container has a stationary bottom, a threaded spindle centrally traversing its entire length, and a removable top that fits on the spindle to hold the parts in firm contact with each other.

Anodizing Problems

Causes and the means adopted for correction of several specific problems in anodizing of aluminum are detailed in the following examples.

Example 12. Anodic coatings were dark and blotchy on 80 to 85% of a production run of construction workers' helmets made of alloy 2024. After drawing, these helmets had been heat treated in stacks, water quenched, artificially aged, alkaline etched (sodium hydroxide solution), anodized in sulfuric acid solution, sealed and dried. The dark areas centered at the crowns of the helmets and radiated outward in an irregular pattern.

Examination disclosed the presence of precipitated constituents and lower hardness in the dark areas. The condition proved to be the result of restricted circulation of the quench water when the helmets were stacked, which permitted precipitation of constituents because of slower cooling rate in the affected areas. The problem was solved by separating the helmets with at least three inches of space during heating and quenching.

Example 13. Part of a production lot of coupling nuts made of alloy 6061S that had been anodized by the hard process was found to have etched surfaces, which was cause for rejection. The problem was traced to the presence of moisture in the bottom of steel trays in which the nuts had been stored for a few days before being anodized, which had created a galvanic couple and thus corroded some of the pieces. The use of clean, dry storage trays solved the problem.

Example 14. Flux-coated rods were used in welding window frames fabricated from extrusions of alloy 6063. Before the frames were anodized, wire brushing, followed by alkaline etching, was used to remove the flux. After anodizing (in sulfuric acid electrolyte), there were several spots in welded areas where the ³⁄₈-in. section of the frames had been dissolved through completely. Not only had the frames been ruined, but the electrolyte had been contaminated with chlorides and fluorides to such an extent that it caused pitting when anodizing parts that had not been welded or brazed.

The problem was solved by replacing wire brushing and alkaline etching with a more effective method of flux removal. This method consisted of thoroughly soaking the frames in agitated hot water and then dipping them in a dilute solution of nitric and hydrofluoric acids. This completely converted the flux to soluble acids, which were then rinsed from the surface in clean running water. Hydrofluoric acid was used to dissolve some of the metal underlying the flux. This generated hydrogen, which broke up any accumulation of flux and accelerated its removal.

Example 15. Pieces of interior trim made from alloy 5005 sheet varied in color from light to dark gray after anodizing. Rejection was excessive, because color matching was required.

Investigation proved that the anodizing process itself was not at fault; the color variation occurred because the workpieces had been made of cutoffs from sheet stock obtained from two different sources of supply. To prevent further difficulty, two recommendations were made:

1 All sheet metal of a given alloy should be purchased from one primary producer, or each job should be made of material from one source. In the latter instance, all cutoffs should be kept segregated.

2 More rigid specifications should be established for the desired quality of finish. Most producers can supply a clad material on certain alloys that gives better uniformity in finishing.

Example 16. The problem was to improve the appearance of bright anodized automotive parts made of alloy 5357-H32. Deburring was the only treatment preceding anodizing.

An acceptable finish was obtained by changing to an H25 temper. The H25 had a better grain structure for maintaining a mirror-bright finish during anodizing.

Example 17. After alkaline etching, web-shaped extrusions made of alloy 6063-T6 exhibited black spots that persisted through the anodizing cycle. These extrusions were 11 ft long and had cross-sectional dimensions of 4 by 1½ in. and a web thickness of 3/16 in. Cleaning had consisted of treatment for 1 to 4 min in 15% sulfuric acid at 185 F and etching for 8 min in a sodium hydroxide solution (5 oz per gal) at 140 F.

The spots occurred only on the outer faces of the web. Affected areas showed subnormal

hardness and electrical conductivity. Metallographic examination revealed precipitation of magnesium silicide (Mg₂Si) there.

The defects were found to have occurred in areas where cooling from the extrusion temperature was retarded by the presence of insulating air pockets created by poor joints between the carbon blocks that lined the runout table. The extrusion had only to remain stationary on the runout table (end of extrusion cycle, flipped on side for sawing) for as little as 1 min for MgSi₂ to precipitate at locations where cooling was retarded. (This type of defect is not limited to a particular shape; it can result from a critical combination of size and shape of the extrusion, or from extrusion conditions and cooling rate.)

The solution to the problem was to provide uniform cooling of the extrusion on the runout table; this was accomplished by modifying the table and employing forced-air cooling.

Sealing of Anodic Coatings

When properly done, sealing partially converts the as-anodized alumina of an anodic coating to an aluminum monohydrate known as Boehmite. If the coating is to be colored, dyeing must precede sealing, because the anhydrous form of coating links more readily with the dyes than the monohydrate form.

The corrosion resistance of anodized aluminum depends largely on the effectiveness of the sealing operation. Sealing will be ineffective, however, unless the anodic coating is continuous, smooth, adherent, uniform in appearance, and free of surface blemishes and powdery areas.

After sealing, the stain resistance of the anodic coating also is improved. For this reason, it is desirable to seal parts subject to staining during service.

Tanks made of stainless steel or lined mild steel and incorporating adequate agitation and suitable temperature controls are used for sealing solutions.

Chromic acid anodized parts are sealed in slightly acidified hot water. One specific sealing solution contains 0.13 oz of chromic acid in 100 gal of solution. The sealing procedure consists of immersing the freshly anodized and rinsed part in the sealing solution at 175 ± 2 F for 5 min. The pH of this solution is maintained within a range of 4 to 6. The solution is discarded when there is a buildup of sediment in the tank or when contaminants float freely on the surface.

Sulfuric acid anodized parts also are sealed in slightly acidified water (pH, 4 to 6), at about 200 to 212 F. At temperatures below 190 F, the change in the crystalline form of the coating is not satisfactorily accomplished within a reasonable time.

One specific sealing solution contains 5 to 10% by weight potassium dichromate, and sufficient sodium hydroxide to maintain the pH at 5.0 to 6.0. This solution is prepared by adding potassium dichromate to the partly filled operating tank and stirring until the dichromate is completely dissolved. The tank is then filled with water to the operating level and heated to the operating temperature, after which the pH is adjusted by adding sodium hydroxide (which gives a yellow color to the bath).

For sealing, the freshly anodized and rinsed part is immersed in the solution at 210 ± 2 F for 10 to 15 min. After sealing, the part is air dried at a temperature no higher than 225 F.

Control of this solution consists of maintaining the correct pH and operating temperature. The solution is discarded when excessive sediment builds up in the tank or when the surface is contaminated with foreign material.

Sealing is not done on parts that have received any of the hard anodized coatings.

Water for sealing solutions can significantly affect the quality of the results obtained from the sealing treatment, as evidenced in the following:

Example 18. Strips for automotive exterior trim that were press formed from 5457-H25 sheet were found to have poor corrosion resistance after anodizing, even though appearance was acceptable.

The strips had been finished in a continuous automatic anodizing line incorporating the usual steps of cleaning, chemical brightening, desmutting, and anodizing in a 15% sulfuric acid electrolyte to a coating thickness of 0.3 mil. They had been sealed in deionized water at a pH of 6.0 and then warm-air dried. Rinses after each step had been adequate, and all processing conditions had appeared normal.

Investigation eliminated metallurgical factors as a possible cause, but directed suspicion to the sealing operation, because test strips sealed in distilled water showed satisfactory corrosion resistance. Although the deionized water used in processing had better-than-average electrical resistance (1,000,000 ohm-cm), analysis of the water showed that it contained a high concentration of oxidizable organic material. This was traced to residues resulting from the leaching of ion-exchange resins from the deionization column. The difficulty was remedied by the use of more stable resins in the deionization column.

Color Anodizing

Color anodizing consists of dyeing the anodized part, before sealing, with an organic or inorganic coloring material. The depth of dye absorption depends on the thickness and porosity of the anodic coating.

The dyed coating is transparent, and its appearance is affected by the basic reflectivity characteristics of the aluminum. For this reason, the colors of dyed aluminum articles should not be expected to match paints, enamel, printed fabrics or other opaque colors.

Shade matching of color anodized work is difficult to obtain. Single-source colors usually are more uniform than colors made by mixing two or more dye materials together. Maximum uniformity of dyeing is obtained by reducing all variables of the anodizing process to a minimum and then maintaining stringent control of the dye bath. Fresh dye baths should be made daily when shade matching is required.

Evaluation of Anodic Coatings

Table 27 lists the various ASTM methods that can be used to evaluate the quality of anodic coatings. In addition, the following methods are useful:

Coating Thickness

Metallographic Method. Measurement of a perpendicular cross section of the anodized specimen, using a microscope with a calibrated eyepiece, is the most accurate method for determining the thickness of coatings of at least 0.1 mil. This method is used to calibrate standards for other methods, and is the reference method in cases of dispute. Because of variations in the coating thickness, multiple measurements must be made and the results averaged.

Table 27. ASTM Methods for Evaluating Quality of Anodic Coatings

Method	ASTM designation
Coating Thickness	
Eddy current	B244
Gravimetric	B137
Sealing	
Dye test	B136
Corrosion Resistance	
Salt spray	B117
Acetic acid – salt spray	B287
Copper-accelerated acetic acid – salt spray	B368
Corrodkote	B380(a)
Abrasion Resistance	
Abrasive blast	D658
Falling sand	D968
Dielectric Strength	
Breakdown voltage	B110
Lightfastness	
Artificial weathering	D822; E42

(a) Although this method is designated by ASTM for use with decorative chromium plating, it is employed also for anodic coatings.

Table 28. Effect of Anodizing on Reflectance Values of Electrobrightened Aluminum

Thickness of anodic coating, mil(a)	Specular reflectance, % Electro-brightened	Electro-brightened and anodized	After removal of anodic coating(b)	Total reflectance after anodizing, %
99.99% Aluminum				
0.08......	90	87	88	90
0.2	90	87	88	90
0.4	90	86	88	89
0.6	90	85	88	88
0.8	90	84	88	88
99.8% Aluminum				
0.08......	88	68	83	89
0.2	88	63	85	88
0.4	88	58	85	87
0.6	88	53	85	86
0.8	88	57	85	84
99.5% Aluminum				
0.08......	75	50	70	86
0.2	75	36	64	84
0.4	75	26	61	81
0.6	75	21	57	77
0.8	75	15	53	73

Source: Aluminium Development Association

(a) Converted from microns. (b) Anodic coating removed in chromic-phosphoric acid.

Micrometer Method. Coating thickness of 0.1 mil or more can be determined by micrometrically measuring the thickness of a coated specimen, stripping the coating (using the solution described in ASTM B137), micrometrically measuring the thickness of the stripped specimen, and subtracting the second measurement from the first.

Scratch Method. This method employs an instrument with a sliding stylus that is advanced under increasing pressure until it penetrates the coating. Only coatings produced under similar conditions and on similar alloys can be compared reliably. Surface finish and direction of measurement affect results. Accuracy is approximately ±10%.

Effectiveness of Sealing

Sulfur Dioxide Method. This method comprises exposure of the anodic coating for 24 hr to attack by moist air (95 to 100% relative humidity) containing 0.5 to 2% (by volume) sulfur dioxide, in a special test cabinet. The method is very discriminative. Coatings that are incompletely or poorly sealed develop a white bloom.

Abrasion Resistance

Taber Abrasion Method. Abrasion resistance is determined by an instrument that, by means of weighted abrasive wheels, abrades test specimens mounted on a revolving turntable.

Abrasion resistance is measured in terms of either (a) weight loss of the test specimen for a definite number of cycles or (b) the number of cycles required for penetration of the coating. This procedure is covered by Method 6192 in Federal Test Method Standards No. 141.

Lightfastness

Fade-O-Meter Method. This is a modification of the artificial-weathering method described in ASTM D822 and E42, in that the cycle is conducted without the use of water. Staining and corrosion products thus cannot interfere with interpretation of results. A further modification entails the use of a high-intensity ultraviolet mercury-arc lamp and the reduction of exposure to a period of 24 to 48 hr.

Effects of Anodic Coatings on Surface and Mechanical Properties

As the thickness of an anodic coating increases, light-reflectance, both total and specular, decreases. This decrease is only slight for pure aluminum surfaces, but it becomes more pronounced as the content of alloying elements other than magnesium (which has little effect) increases.

The decrease in reflectance values is not strictly linear with increasing thickness of anodic coating; the decrease in total reflectance levels off when the thickness of the coating on superpurity and high-purity aluminum is greater than about 0.1 mil.

Data comparing the reflectance values of chemically brightened and anodized aluminum materials with those of other decorative materials are given in "Anodic Oxidation of Aluminium and Its Alloys", Bulletin No. 14 of the Aluminium Development Assn.

The effect of anodized coatings 0.08 to 0.8 mil (2 to 20 microns) thick on the reflectance values of electrobrightened aluminum of three degrees of purity is shown in Table 28. This table also includes specular reflectance values for surfaces after removal of the anodic coating. These data show that the degree of roughening by the anodizing treatment increases as the purity of the aluminum decreases. The reflectance values of the anodized surfaces are influenced also by the inclusion of foreign constituents or their oxides in the anodic coating.

Metallurgical factors have a significant influence on the effect of anodizing on reflectance. For minimum reduction in reflectance, the conversion of metal to oxide must be uniform in depth and composition. Particles of different composition do not react uniformly. They produce a nonuniform anodic coating and roughen the interface between the metal and the oxide coating. For a thorough discussion of this subject, see the paper by W. E. Cooke, "Factors Affecting Loss of Brightness and Image Clarity During Anodizing of Bright Trim Aluminum Alloys in Sulfuric Acid Electrolyte" (*Plating*, Nov 1962, p 1157-1164).

Anodizing Conditions. The composition and operating conditions of the anodizing electrolyte also influence the light reflectance and other properties of the polished surface.

The data in Fig. 10 show the effect of sulfuric acid concentration, temperature of bath, and current density on the specular reflectance of chemically brightened aluminum alloy 5457. These

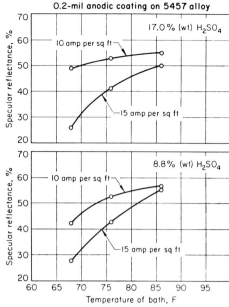

Fig. 10. Effect of anodizing conditions on specular reflectance of chemically brightened aluminum

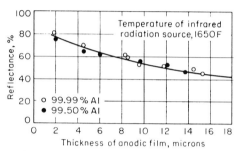

Fig. 11. Effect of anodic coating thickness on reflectance of infrared radiation (Aluminium Development Association)

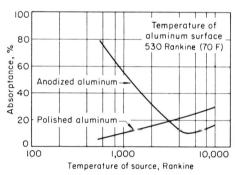

Fig. 12. Comparison between anodized aluminum and polished aluminum as to absorptance of blackbody radiation

data show that a particular level of specular reflectance can be produced by varying operating conditions.

Thermal Radiation. The reflectance of aluminum for infrared radiation also decreases with increasing thickness of the anodic coating, as shown in Fig. 11. These data indicate that the difference in purity of the aluminum is of minor significance.

A comparison between anodized aluminum surfaces and polished aluminum surfaces at 70 F with respect to absorptance when exposed to blackbody radiation from sources of different temperatures is presented in Fig. 12. Although

Table 29. Effect of Anodizing on Fatigue Strength of Aluminum Alloys(a)

| Alloy | Fatigue strength at 1,000,000 cycles, psi | |
	Not anodized	Anodized
Wrought Alloys		
2024 (bare)	19,000	15,000
2024 (clad)	11,000	7,500
6061 (bare)	15,000	6,000
7075 (bare)	22,000	9,000
7075 (clad)	12,000	10,000
Casting Alloys		
220	7,500	7,500
356	8,000	8,000

Source: F. J. Gillig, WADC Technical Report 53-151, P. B. 111320, 1953

(a) Sulfuric acid hard coatings, 2 to 4 mils thick, were applied using a 15% H_2SO_4 solution at 25 to 32 F and 10 to 75 volts dc.

Table 30. Applications Employing Chemical Conversion Coatings

Application	Aluminum alloy	Subsequent coating
Oxide Conversion Coatings		
Baking pans(a)	1100, 3003, 3004, 5005, 5052	Silicone resin
Phosphate Conversion Coatings		
Screen cloth	5056	Clear varnish
Storm doors	6063	Acrylic paint(b)
Cans	3004	Sanitary lacquer
Fencing	6061	None applied
Chromate Conversion Coatings		
Aircraft fuselage skins	7075 clad with 7072	Zinc chromate primer
Electronic chassis	6061-T4	None applied
Cast missile bulkhead	356-T6	None applied
Screen	5056 clad with 6253	Clear varnish
Extruded doubler	6061-T6	Clear lacquer

(a) Baking pans of these alloys may alternatively be chromate conversion coated prior to the application of silicone resin. (b) Thermosetting.

anodized aluminum is a better absorber of low-temperature radiation, as-polished aluminum is a more effective absorber of blackbody radiation from sources at temperatures exceeding 3300 Rankine (2840 F).

Fatigue Strength. Anodic coatings are hard and brittle, and will crack readily under mechanical deformation. (This is true for thin as well as thick coatings, even though cracks in thin coatings may be less easily visible.) Cracks that develop in the coating act as stress raisers and are potential sources of fatigue failure of the substrate metal. Typical fatigue-strength values for aluminum alloys before and after application of a hard anodic coating 2 to 4 mils thick are given in Table 29.

Chemical Conversion Coating

Chemical conversion coatings are adherent surface layers of low-solubility oxide, phosphate, or chromate compounds produced by the reaction of suitable reagents with the metallic surface. These coatings affect the appearance, electrochemical potential, electrical resistivity, surface hardness, absorption and other surface properties of the material. They differ from anodic coatings in that conversion coatings are formed by a chemical oxidation-reduction reaction at the surface of the aluminum, whereas anodic coatings are formed by an electrochemical reaction. The reaction that takes place in chemical conversion coating involves the removal of 0.01 to 0.1 mil of the material being treated.

Conversion coatings are excellent for: (a) corrosion retardation under supplementary organic finishes or films of oil or wax, (b) improved adhesion for organic finishes, (c) mild wear resistance, (d) enhanced drawing or forming characteristics, (e) corrosion retardation without materially changing electrical resistivity, and (f) decorative purposes, when colored or dyed.

Conversion coatings are used interchangeably with anodic coatings in organic finishing schedules. (One use of conversion coating is as a spot treatment for the repair of damaged areas in anodic coatings.)

The simplicity of the basic process, together with the fact that solutions may be applied by immersion, spraying, brushing, wiping or any other wetting method, makes conversion coating convenient for production operations. Some

applications employing chemical conversion coatings on various aluminum alloys are given in Table 30.

In most installations, conversion coating offers a cost advantage over electrolytic methods. Moreover, unlike some anodic coatings, chemical conversion coatings do not lower the fatigue resistance of the metal treated.

Procedure. The sequence of operations for applying a satisfactory conversion coating to aluminum-base materials is as follows:

1 Removal of organic contaminants
2 Removal of oxide or corrosion products
3 Conditioning of the clean surface to make it susceptible to coating
4 Conversion coating
5 Rinsing
6 Acidulated rinsing (recommended if supplementary coating is to be applied)
7 Drying
8 Application of a supplementary coating, when required.

Surface preparation entails the same procedures as are used in preparation for anodizing, which are described on page 621. However, the cleaning procedure for preparing aluminum for

Table 31. Oxide Conversion Coating

| Constituent or condition | Process | | |
	MBV(a)	EW(b)	Alrok
Solution Composition, Oz per Gal			
Sodium carbonate....	4	7.5	2.6
Sodium chromate	2	2.5	...
Sodium silicate	...	0.1-0.6	...
Potassium dichromate	...	...	0.66
Operating Conditions			
Bath temperature, F..	190-212	190-212	190-212
Treatment time, min.	3-5	8-10	20

(a) A modification, introduced about 1931, of the BV process described in German Patent 423,758 (1916). (b) German Patent 691,903 (1937).

Table 32. Phosphate Conversion Coating

Specific Formulation(a)

Each gallon of solution contains 10 to 20 oz of a mixture consisting of:

Ammonium phosphate ($NH_4H_2PO_4$).....61.7%	
Ammonium fluoride (NH_4HF_2).......22.9%	
Potassium dichromate ($K_2Cr_2O_7$).......15.4%	
Operating temperature..........110 to 120 F	
Treatment time ....1 to 5 min	

Desired Operating Range

Phosphate ion....2.6 to 13.2 oz per gal	
Fluoride ion............0.26 to 0.80 oz per gal	
Dichromate ion ....0.80 to 2.6 oz per gal	
Operating temperature ....65 to 120 F	
Treatment time ....1.5 to 5 min	

(a) U. S. Patent 2,494,910 (1950)

conversion coating is much more critical than for anodizing. After cleaning, removal of the natural oxide film is accomplished in any of the standard aqueous solutions, such as chromate-sulfate, chromate, or phosphate.

Pretreatment immediately prior to the coating operation is required for the development of extremely fine-grained conversion coatings. Solutions of either acid or alkaline type are used.

Subsequent to the above operations, the work is subjected to the conversion coating solution. The addition of a wetting agent, such as sodium alkyl aryl sulfonate, to the solution helps to produce a uniform and continuous coating. After coating, the work is thoroughly rinsed and dried. The final rinse is usually hot (140 to 180 F), to aid drying. Drying is important because it prevents staining. Drying at temperatures higher than 150 F usually dehydrates the coatings, and so increases hardness and abrasion resistance.

Supplementary coatings of oil, wax, paint or other hard organic coatings frequently are applied. If the conversion coating is intended to improve subsequent forming or drawing, the final supplementary coating may be soap or a similar dry-film lubricant.

Oxide Coating Processes. The modified Bauer-Vogel (MBV), Erftwerk (EW), and Alrok processes are the principal methods for applying oxide-type conversion coatings. Nominal compositions of the solutions used and typical operating conditions are given in Table 31.

The MBV process is used on pure aluminum, as well as on aluminum-magnesium, aluminum-manganese, and aluminum-silicon alloys. The coating produced varies from a lustrous light gray to a dark gray-black color.

The EW process is used for alloys containing copper. The film produced is usually very light gray.

The Alrok process is for general-purpose use with all alloys, and is often the final treatment for aluminum products. Coatings vary in color from gray to green, and are sealed in a hot dichromate solution.

Phosphate Coating Process. The range of operating conditions and a formula for a standard solution for phosphate coating are given in Table 32.

Phosphate coatings vary in color from light bluish-green to olive-green, depending on the composition of the aluminum-base material and operating conditions of the bath. The phosphate-chromate conversion coatings are used extensively on aluminum parts or assemblies employing components of different kinds of materials, such as bushings or inserts made of steel.

Chromate Coating Process. Solution compositions and operating conditions for two chromate conversion coating processes are given in Table 33.

Chromate coatings vary from clear and iridescent to light yellow or brown, depending on the composition of the aluminum-base material and on the thickness of the film. The chromate coatings are selected among the various conversion coatings when maximum resistance to corrosion is desired.

Chromate coatings exhibit low electrical resistivity. At a contact pressure of 200 psi, in a direct-current circuit, the resistivity of a normal chromate film varies from 200 to 2000 microhms per sq in. This resistivity is low enough so that a chromate coated article can be used as an electrical ground. The conductivity of the films at radio frequencies is extremely high. This permits the use of a chromate film on electrical shields and wave guides. Thus, chromate conversion coating is widely used for treatment of aluminum articles for the electronics industry.

Processing equipment, tanks and racks for conversion coating solutions must be made from acid-resistant materials. Tanks may be made of type 316 stainless steel, or of mild steel if lined with polyvinyl chloride or other suitably protective material. Tanks for solutions that do not contain fluorides may be made of acid-resistant brick or chemical stoneware.

Racks may be made of mild steel, but must be coated with acid-resistant compound. Heating coils or electrical immersion heaters should be made of stainless steel or stainless-clad material.

Some conversion coating solutions cause a sludge to form in the bottom of the tank. To prevent contact between the sludge and the workpieces, the tank may be equipped with a false bottom through which sludge can fall.

Adequate ventilation must be provided to remove vapors. The inhalation of fluoride vapors is dangerous. Solutions should not contact the skin, but if they do, the area affected should be washed immediately with running water. Respirators, goggles and gloves should be worn when handling all chemicals used to make up solutions.

When brushes are used for applying solutions, they should be made of natural bristles. Synthetic bristles are attacked by the solutions.

Control of Solution. Most users of conversion coating solutions purchase prepared formulations for make-up and solution adjustment. In general, the solutions require control of pH and of the concentration of the critical elements. Direct measurement of pH is made with a glass-cell electric pH meter. The percentage concentration of active ion is obtained by direct titration with a suitable base.

Solution control becomes more critical as the size of the bath decreases with respect to the amount of work treated. Experienced operators of a conversion coating process can detect

Table 33. Chromate Conversion Coating

Solution Composition, Oz per Gal

Process A(a)		Process B(b)	
Cr_2O_3 .... 0.79(c)		$Na_2Cr_2O_7 \cdot 2H_2O$	0.99(c)
NH_4HF_2 .... 0.35		NaF 0.132
$SnCl_4$ 0.58		$K_3Fe(CN)_6$ 0.66
		HNO_3 (48° Bé) .. 3 ml

Operating Conditions for Both Processes

Solution temperature .... 60 to 130 F	
Treatment time .... 5 sec to 8 min	
pH .... 1.2 to 2.2	

(a) U. S. Patents 2,507,956 (1950) and 2,851,385 (1958). (b) U. S. Patent 2,796,370 (1957). (c) Desired range of hexavalent chromium ion, 0.132 to 0.92 oz per gal.

Table 34. ASTM Test Methods Useful for Determining Quality of Chemical Conversion Coatings on Aluminum

Type of test	ASTM designation
Corrosion Resistance	
Salt spray B117	
Copper-accelerated acetic acid— salt spray (fog) B368	
Evaluation of painted or coated specimens subjected to corrosive exposure . D1654	
Resistance to Blistering	
Evaluation of blistering of paints...... D714	
Adherence	
Elongation of attached organic coatings with conical mandrel apparatus . D522	

Table 35. Electrolytic Potentials of Several Metals Against Pure Aluminum(a)

Metal	Potential, mv(b)
Magnesium	−850
Zinc	−350
Cadmium	−20 to 0
Aluminum (pure)	0
Aluminum-magnesium alloys...	+100
Aluminum-copper alloys	+150
Iron; mild steel	+50 to 150
Tin	+300
Brass	+500
Nickel	+500
Copper	+550
Silver	+700
Stainless steel	+400 to 700
Gold	+950

NOTE. Metals above aluminum in this list will protect it; those below cause aluminum to corrode preferentially. Cathode and anode polarization, however, can cause a reversal of these relationships.

(a) Source: *Metal Finishing*, Nov 1956. (b) In a 6% NaCl solution.

changes in the composition of the solution by observing the color and appearance of the treated work. A skilled operator often can control the bath by this method alone.

During use, coating solutions are depleted by consumption of the basic chemicals, and by drag-in and dragout. In one plant, drag-in of alkaline

cleaner into the conversion coating bath adversely affected the appearance of the conversion coating. Details of this problem and the method adopted for correcting it are given in Example 19.

Example 19. Aluminum screen cloth made from wires of alloy 5056 clad with alloy 6253 had a rejection rate as high as 3% because of the presence of "sparklers" on the product after chemical conversion coating. (Sparklers, known also as "shiners", are areas that have higher metallic reflectance than the rest of the conversion-coated surface; they are merely an appearance defect, and do not affect the adherence of organic coatings.) The following processing cycle was being used:

1 Alkaline cleaning for 1 min in an inhibited solution at 160 F
2 Rinsing for 30 sec in overflowing cold water
3 Conversion coating for 2½ min in a phosphate-chromate solution at 100 to 115 F (green coating)
4 Rinsing for 30 sec in overflowing cold water
5 Rinsing for 30 sec in overflowing cold water
6 Drying
7 Application of a clear varnish (baked at 275 F for 1½ to 2 min) or of a gray pigmented paint. (For material to be painted, conversion coating required only 1½ min.)

The coating defects were found to be caused by contamination (and neutralization) of the acid conversion coating solution by drag-in from the alkaline cleaner. Although the use of a rotating beater to shake droplets of cleaning solution out of the screen openings had reduced dragout from that bath, it did not eliminate it.

To prevent neutralization of the acid conversion coating solution by contamination with alkali from step 1, the slightly acid overflow from the rinse in step 4 was piped back into the rinse tank in step 2, thus keeping it on the acid side. Elimination of rejects resulted. This procedure also reduced the amount of overflow rinse water needed to operate the line.

Control of Coating Quality. A properly applied coating should be uniform in color and luster and should show no evidence of a loose or powdery surface. Poor luster or powdery surfaces are caused by low pH, improper cleaning and rinsing, excessive treatment temperature or treatment time, a contaminated bath, or insufficient agitation. Light and barely visible coatings are caused by high pH, low operating temperature, insufficient treatment time or high ion concentrations.

Usually, the quality of a conversion coating is established on the basis of its appearance, corrosion resistance, hardness and adherence. These qualities may be determined by the ASTM test methods listed in Table 34.

Electroplating

Aluminum-base materials are more difficult to electroplate than the common heavier metals, because:

1 Aluminum has a high affinity for oxygen.
2 Most metals used in electroplating are cathodic to aluminum; therefore, voids in

Table 36. Effect of Pretreatment on Zincate Deposit on Aluminum Alloy 1100-H28(a)

Treatment	Zincate deposit		
	Weight, mg/dm²	Zn content, %	Resistance, microhms(b)
Electrodeposited zinc	....	....	5
Solvent cleaned; zincated 30 sec	15.8	93.8	10
Alkaline cleaned; nitric acid dipped; zincated 30 sec (see Fig. 14)..	5.3	83.0	15
Alkaline cleaned; zincated 30 sec; nitric acid dipped; zincated 30 sec (see Fig. 16)	2.5	72.5	70

NOTE. Low contact resistance indicates a more uniform zinc film. However, although the coating produced by double zincating has the lowest zinc content, it is thin and more dense and thus a more desirable zinc coating for adhesion of subsequent electrodeposits.

(a) Source: Wernick and Pinner, *Metal Finishing*, Feb 1957, p 61-65. (b) Measured by a Kelvin bridge using 0.25-sq-in. contacts and 500-lb pressure.

Table 37. Applications Employing Electroplated Coatings on Aluminum Products

Product (and form)	Preplating treatment	Electroplating system (and thicknesses in mils)	Reason for plating
Automotive Applications			
Bearings (sheet)	None	Pb-Sn-Cu alloy (0.25 to 1.25)	Prevent seizing
Bumper guards (castings)	Buff and zincate	Cu (0.1) + Ni (2) + Cr (0.03)	Appearance; corrosion resistance
Lamp brackets; steering-column caps (die castings)	Polish and zincate	Cu (0.03) + Ni (0.8) + Cr (0.05)	Appearance; corrosion resistance
Tire molds (castings)	None	Hard Cr (2.0)	Appearance; corrosion resistance
Aircraft Applications			
Hydraulic parts; landing gears; small engine pistons (forgings)	Machine and zincate	Cu flash + Cu (0.1) + hard Cr (1 to 3)	Wear resistance
Propellers (forgings)	Conductive rubber coating	Ni (8.0)	Resistance to corrosion and erosion
Shell (extrusion)	Double zincate	Cu flash + Cd (0.3 to 0.5) (a)	Dissimilar-metal protection
Electrical and Electronics Applications			
Busbars; switchgears (extrusions) ...	Zincate	Cu flash + Cu (0.3) + Ag (0.2) (b)	Nonoxidized surface; solderability; corrosion resistance
Intermediate-frequency housings (die castings)	Zincate	Cu flash + Cu (0.5) + Ag (0.5) + Au (0.025) (c)	Surface conductivity; solderability; corrosion resistance
Microwave fittings (die castings)	Zincate	Cu flash + Cu (0.01) + Ag (0.5) + Rh (0.02)	Smooth, nonoxidized interior; corrosion resistance of exterior
Terminal platters (sheet)	Zincate	Cu flash	Nonoxidized surface; solderability; corrosion resistance
General Hardware			
Screws; nuts; bolts (castings)	Buff and zincate	Cd (0.5; 0.2 on threads)	Corrosion resistance
Die-cast spray guns and compressors	Buff and zincate	Hard Cr (2.0)	Appearance
Die-cast window and door hardware..	Barrel burnish and zincate	Brass (0.3) (d)	Appearance; low cost
Household Appliances			
Coffee maker (sheet)	Buff and zincate	Cr (0.2)	Appearance; cleanness; resistance to food contamination
Refrigerator handles; salad makers; cream dispensers (castings)	Buff and zincate	Cu (0.1) + Ni (0.5) + Cr (0.03)	Appearance; cleanness; resistance to food contamination
Personal Products			
Compacts; fountain pens (sheet)	Buff and zincate	Cu flash + brass (0.2)	Appearance; low cost
Hearing aids (sheet)	Zincate	Cu flash + Ni (0.75) + Rh (0.01)	Nonoxidizing surface; low cost
Jewelry (sheet)	Buff and zincate	Brass (0.3) + Au (0.01)	Appearance; low cost

(a) Chromate coating applied after cadmium plating. (b) Soldering operation follows silver plating. (c) Baked at 400 F after copper plating and after silver plating. Soldering operation follows gold plating. (d) Brass plated in barrel or automatic equipment.

the coating lead to localized galvanic corrosion. (Table 35 compares the electrolytic potentials of several common metals against pure aluminum.)

3 The thermal expansion of aluminum-base materials differs markedly from that of most of the metals used in plating. Because this difference may cause peeling of the plated metal, commercial use of plated aluminum has not progressed rapidly, despite the saving in weight and the potentially high resistance to corrosion offered by properly electroplated aluminum parts.

Prior to electroplating, the surface of the aluminum material must be carefully prepared, to obtain a void-free deposit and to minimize the effect of thermal stress between the deposit and the aluminum substrate. Surface preparation may be accomplished by mechanical means, after which numerous metals can be electrodeposited directly on the aluminum surface.

Surface preparation can be accomplished also by chemical means. The most versatile of these is zincating, which produces a thin, compact layer of zinc that provides a metallurgical bond for the deposit. Adhesion, however, is affected by the composition of the aluminum substrate material and by the pretreatment techniques employed prior to zincating. Table 36 shows how different pretreatments alter the characteristics of zincate deposits on alloy 1100-H28.

For good adhesion of the electrodeposit, it is generally preferable to zincate the aluminum and then, before applying other metals, to do one of the following: (a) copper strike the zincted aluminum, (b) brass strike it, or (c) plate it with electroless nickel.

Electrodeposits of cadmium, copper, tin, zinc, gold or silver are frequently used for solderability. A copper strike coated with cadmium and chromate or by flowed tin enables the soft soldering of electrical terminals to an aluminum chassis. Brass enhances the bonding of rubber to aluminum. Silver, gold and rhodium provide specific electrical and electronic surface properties. Examples of applications of plated aluminum and of the respective finishing sequences involved are given in Table 37.

Effect of Substrate Characteristics on Plating Results. Each aluminum alloy behaves differently from others during electroplating, depending on the metallurgical structure. Alloying elements may be in solid solution in the aluminum, or they may be present as discrete particles or as intermetallic compounds. These microconstituents have different chemical or electrochemical reactivities, and their surfaces do not respond uniformly to treatment. Also, variations in response occur between different lots or product forms of the same alloy.

In general, aluminum-copper alloys are the easiest to electroplate, because of their excellent response to surface

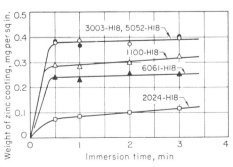

Fig. 13. Effect of immersion time on weight of zinc coating obtained on different wrought alloys given the same pretreatment

preparation by zincating. Aluminummagnesium and aluminum-silicon alloys are more difficult to electroplate, and require variations in procedure in order to obtain satisfactory results.

The electropotential of the alloy affects adhesion of the zinc coating. Purer aluminum alloys, such as 1100 and 3003, as well as alloys containing magnesium, have higher potential differences with respect to zinc than aluminum alloys containing heavier metals such as copper. Consequently, under identical conditions, a thicker, more porous, and less adherent deposit of zinc is obtained on the purer and magnesium-containing alloys than on copper-containing alloys. The thickness of zinc coating as a function of immersion time for several alloys is shown in Fig. 13.

Surface Preparation Methods. The three established methods for surface preparation prior to electroplating are surface roughening, anodizing, and zincating.

Surface roughening, which is accomplished either by mechanical abrasion or by chemical etching, assists in mechanically bonding the electrodeposits to the aluminum surface. Surface roughening is sometimes used in preparation for the application of hard chromium to aluminum engine parts such as pistons.

A water blast of fine quartz flour may be used to remove surface oxides and to abrade the surface. The adherent wet film protects the aluminum surface from further oxidation before plating. The quartz film is dislodged by the evolution of hydrogen that occurs during plating. Chemical etching produces undercut pits that provide keying action for the electrodeposited metal.

In general, mechanical bonding of electrodeposits is not reliable — especially for applications involving temperature variations. Therefore, preparation by surface roughening is not recommended.

Anodizing is sometimes used as a method of surface preparation prior to electroplating.

However, the adherence of the subsequent electrodeposit is limited, plated deposits over anodic films are highly sensitive to surface discontinuities, and the time, temperature and current density of the anodizing process are critical.

Phosphoric acid anodizing has been used for the aluminum alloys listed in Table 38; the sequence of operations is as follows:

1 Vapor degrease or solvent clean.
2 Mild alkaline clean.
3 Rinse.
4 Etch for 1 to 3 min in a solution containing sodium carbonate (3 oz/gal) and sodium phosphate (3 oz/gal), at 150 F.
5 Dip in nitric acid solution (50% HNO_3 by volume) at room temperature.
6 Rinse.
7 Phosphoric acid anodize according to the conditions given in Table 38; the anodic coating should not be sealed.
8 Rinse.
9 Electroplate in a conventional low-pH bath.

Zincating is the usual method of preparing aluminum surfaces for electroplating. It is simple and low in cost, but it is also critical with respect to surface pretreatment, rinsing, and strike sequence employed.

The principle of zincating is one of chemical replacement, whereby aluminum ions replace zinc ions in an aqueous solution of zinc salts. Thus, a thin, adherent film of metallic zinc deposits on the aluminum surface. Adhesion of the zinc film depends almost entirely on the metallurgical bond between the zinc and the aluminum. The quality and adhesion of subsequent electrodeposits depend on obtaining a thin, adherent and continuous zinc film.

Zincating Procedures. To obtain consistently good results with the zincating procedure, it is essential that cleaning and conditioning treatments produce a surface of uniform activity for deposition of the zinc film. Vapor degreasing or solvent cleaning followed by alkaline cleaning is employed for removing oil, grease and other soils. The alkaline cleaner may be a mild etching solution containing 3 oz of sodium carbonate and 3 oz of sodium phosphate per gallon of water. The solution temperature should range from 140 to 180 F, and the material should be immersed for 1 to 3 min, after which it should be thoroughly rinsed.

After cleaning, the material is further treated to remove the original oxide film and to remove any microconstituents that may interfere with the formation of a continuous zinc film or that may react with the subsequent plating solutions.

Castings present special problems, because their surfaces are more porous than those of wrought products. Solutions entrapped in pores are released during subsequent processing, and this results in unplated areas or in staining or poor adhesion of the electrodeposit. Sometimes the entrapped solutions become evident much later, during storage or further processing, such as heating for soldering. Furthermore, even if pores are free of solution, the deposit may not bridge them, thus creating a point of attack for corrosion of the basis metal. (This is of particular significance in the electroplating of aluminum, because the electrodeposited metal is electrolytically dissimilar to aluminum and hence every opening in a casting surface will be a source of electrolytic corrosion.) To avoid these problems, it is essential when preparing cast aluminum surfaces for electroplating that all processing steps be carefully controlled and that electroplating of cast surfaces that have excessive porosity be avoided.

Table 38. Anodizing Prior to Electroplating

Alloy(a)	Specific gravity	Tempera-ture, F	Volt-age	Time, minutes
1100	1.300	87	22	5
3003	1.300	85	22	5
5052	1.300	85	22	10
6061	1.300	85	22	7

(a) With special care, phosphoric acid anodizing may be used also for Al-Cu or Al-Si alloys (Witlock, *Tech Proc AES*, 48, 52; 1961). (b) Aqueous solution of 85% H_3PO_4.

Table 39. Zincating Solutions That May Be Substituted for Solution in Fig. 14, 15 and 16

Constituent or condition	Modified solution(a)	No. 1	No. 2
Solution Composition, Oz per Gal			
NaOH	70.0	6.7	16.0
ZnO	13.0	0.67	2.7
FeCl₃ crystals	0.13	0.27	0.27
Rochelle salt	1.3	6.7	6.7
NaNO₃	..	0.13	0.13
Operating Conditions			
Temperature, F	60-80	70-75	70-75
Time, sec	30-60	30 max	30 max

(a) U. S. Patent 2,676,916 (1954). (b) U. S. Patents 2,676,916 (1954) and 2,650,886 (1953).

The procedures used for removal of the original oxide film and for applying a film of zinc depend to a considerable degree on the aluminum alloy. Several methods are available for accomplishing this surface conditioning. Some alloys can be conditioned by more than one procedure. In these instances the order of preference follows the order of discussion of these procedures in the following paragraph.

Wrought alloys that do not contain interfering microconstituents and casting alloys containing high silicon are prepared for electroplating according to the procedure shown by the flow chart in Fig. 14. The flow chart in Fig. 15 represents the procedure for alloys that contain interfering microconstituents; this procedure is suitable for all wrought alloys, most casting alloys, and especially aluminum-magnesium alloys. Figure 16 indicates the procedure for treating most casting alloys, wrought alloys that contain less than about 3% Mg, and alloys of unknown identity.

Table 39 gives details of three zincating solutions that may be used alternatively to the solution indicated in the

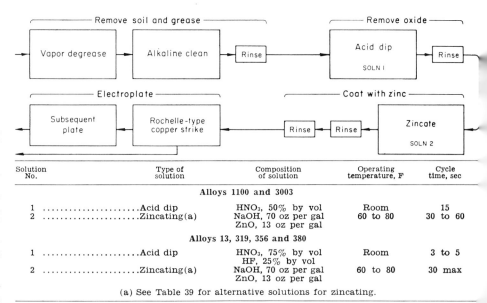

Solution No.	Type of solution	Composition of solution	Operating temperature, F	Cycle time, sec
Alloys 1100 and 3003				
1	Acid dip	HNO₃, 50% by vol	Room	15
2	Zincating(a)	NaOH, 70 oz per gal ZnO, 13 oz per gal	60 to 80	30 to 60
Alloys 13, 319, 356 and 380				
1	Acid dip	HNO₃, 75% by vol HF, 25% by vol	Room	3 to 5
2	Zincating(a)	NaOH, 70 oz per gal ZnO, 13 oz per gal	60 to 80	30 max

(a) See Table 39 for alternative solutions for zincating.

Fig. 14. Preplating surface preparation of alloys 1100 and 3003 (which have no interfering microconstituents), and of casting alloys 13, 319, 356, 380 and others containing high silicon

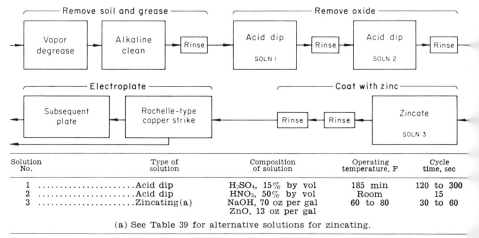

Solution No.	Type of solution	Composition of solution	Operating temperature, F	Cycle time, sec
1	Acid dip	H₂SO₄, 15% by vol	185 min	120 to 300
2	Acid dip	HNO₃, 50% by vol	Room	15
3	Zincating(a)	NaOH, 70 oz per gal ZnO, 13 oz per gal	60 to 80	30 to 60

(a) See Table 39 for alternative solutions for zincating.

Fig. 15. Preplating surface preparation for all wrought alloys, most casting alloys, and especially magnesium-containing alloys that have interfering microconstituents. (Examples are alloys 1100, 3003, 3004, 2011, 2017, 2024, 5052, 6053, 6061, 85, 108, 112, 195, 319 and 355.)

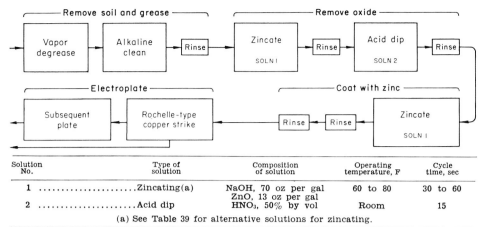

Solution No.	Type of solution	Composition of solution	Operating temperature, F	Cycle time, sec
1	Zincating(a)	NaOH, 70 oz per gal ZnO, 13 oz per gal	60 to 80	30 to 60
2	Acid dip	HNO₃, 50% by vol	Room	15

(a) See Table 39 for alternative solutions for zincating.

Fig. 16. Preplating surface preparation for most casting alloys and for wrought alloys containing less than about 3% Mg. (Examples are alloys 1100, 3003, 3004, 2011, 2017, 2024, 5052, 6053, 6061, 13, 43, 85, 108, 195, 319, 355 and 356.) This processing sequence is applicable also to alloys whose identity is not known.

tables accompanying Fig. 14, 15 and 16. The modified solution in Table 39 is recommended when double-immersion zincating (Fig. 16) is required; it is not essential for alloys 2024 and 7075. This solution produces more uniform coverage than the unmodified solution, and also provides the treated work with greater resistance to corrosion. Dilute solution No. 1 in Table 39 is recommended when there are problems in rinsing and dragout. Dilute solution No. 2 provides a greater reserve of zinc for high-production operations, but at a slight sacrifice in effectiveness of rinsing.

The weight of the deposit obtained for a given immersion time in zincating is affected by the alkalinity and the temperature of the solution, as shown in Fig. 17. The change in concentration of sodium hydroxide does not affect the concentration of zinc oxide. The operating temperature of a zincating bath should not exceed 80 F.

With correct procedure, the resulting zinc deposit is uniform and firmly adherent to the aluminum surface. The appearance of the surface, however, will vary with the alloy being coated, as well as with the rate at which the coating forms. The weight of zinc deposit should be from 0.1 to 0.3 mg per sq in. Generally, it is desirable to limit the deposit to 0.2 mg per sq in.

The thinner and more uniform zinc deposits are the most suitable for plating preparation and for the service performance of plated coatings. Heavy zinc deposits usually are spongy and less adherent, and undesirable from the standpoint of corrosion resistance.

Plating Procedures. Copper is one of the easiest metals to electrodeposit on zincated aluminum surfaces. For this reason, copper is used extensively as an initial strike over which other metals may be subsequently deposited. An advantage of the copper strike is that it protects the thin zinc film from attack by the plating solutions; penetration of the zinc film and attack of the underlying aluminum surface by the plating solutions result in a poorly bonded electrodeposit.

The copper strike bath should be a Rochelle-type copper cyanide solution. The composition (in ounces per gallon)

and operating conditions recommended for this bath are as follows:

Copper cyanide 5.5
Total sodium cyanide 6.5
Free sodium cyanide ....0.5 max
Sodium carbonate 4.0
Rochelle salt 8.0
Operating temperature ......100 to 130 F
pH ....Varies with alloy; see Table 40

Electrical contact should be made before the zincated aluminum is immersed in the electrolyte, and a high initial current density (24 amp per sq ft) should be used to achieve rapid coverage. After copper striking for about 2 min at 24 amp per sq ft, the current density may be reduced to 12 amp per sq ft and deposition continued for 3 to 5 min more (depending on thickness desired). The work can be transferred from the strike bath to other standard plating solutions as desired.

Table 40 gives operating conditions for electrodepositing different metals on zincated aluminum surfaces.

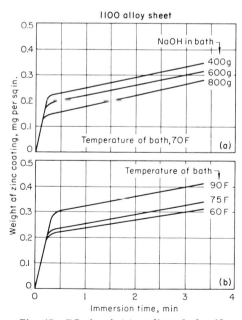

Fig. 17. Effects of (a) sodium hydroxide concentration of the zincating bath and (b) bath temperature on the weight of zinc deposited for a given immersion time on alloy 1100 (J Electrochem Soc, April 1950)

Immersion Plating

Immersion plating refers to processes in which another metal is deposited from solution on an aluminum surface under the influence of the potential that exists between the solution and the immersed aluminum material. An external potential is not required. Deposits produced by immersion plating are thin and of little protective value.

Zincating, the procedure employed for coating aluminum surfaces with zinc prior to electroplating (see the preceding section), is an example of immersion plating. Brass deposits may be produced by adding copper compounds to the sodium zincate solutions used in zincating.

Tin may be deposited from aqueous solutions based on potassium stannate, stannous chloride, or stannous sulfate-fluoride. The lubricating qualities of these tin deposits are desirable for piston and engine components made of aluminum alloys. Immersion tin coatings also are used to facilitate soft soldering and as a base coating for building up electrodeposits.

The composition and operating conditions of a successful immersion tin bath are given in Table 41.

Chemical Plating

Chemical plating refers to nonelectrolytic processes that involve chemical reduction, in which the metal is deposited in the presence of a reducing agent. Deposition may take place on almost any type of material, even the container of the solution.

For a variety of applications in the aircraft industry, nickel is chemically plated on aluminum parts of configurations for which electroplating is not practical. However, chemical plating is too expensive to be used when conventional electroplating is feasible. The composition and operating conditions of a bath for successfully depositing nickel are given in Table 42. The deposits produced contain about 6% phosphorus and usually are not considered suitable as a base for chromium plate.

Silver may be chemically plated on anodized aluminum-base materials. The procedure consists of first degreasing the anodized surface, and then dipping in dilute hydrochloric acid, water rinsing, and then immersing the material in the silvering solution.

A mixture of two solutions is required for silvering. The first consists of 3.33 ml of a 10% solution of silver nitrate to which a 7.5% (by volume) solution of ammonium hydroxide is added until the precipitate first formed just redissolves, after which an excess of 40 ml of ammonium hydroxide solution is added. The second solution is made up by adding 30 grams of Rochelle salt or 40 grams of potassium citrate to water to a total volume of 330 ml. Solutions are filtered and mixed immediately before they are to be used.

Painting

The difference between painting of aluminum and painting of iron and steel is primarily in the method of surface preparation. Therefore, the in-

Table 40. Typical Conditions for Electroplating Various Metals on Zincated Aluminum Surfaces

Electroplate	Minimum deposit, mils	Plating time, minutes	Bath temperature, F	Current density, amp per sq ft	Type of electrolyte
Copper strike(a)	0.3	2(b)	100 to 130	24(b)	Rochelle cyanide(c)
Brass strike(a)	0.3	2 to 3	80 to 90	5	Cyanide
Copper:					
1 Copper or brass strike (see top of table)					
2 Copper plate(d)	0.5	40 sec to 2 min	170 to 180	30 to 60	Hi-speed NaCN or KCN
Brass	0.5	3 to 5	80 to 90	10	Cyanide
Cadmium:					
1 Copper strike (see top of table)					
2 Cadmium plate	0.5	8 to 20	70 to 95	14 to 45	Cyanide
Chromium, decorative:					
1 Copper or brass strike (see top of table)					
2 Nickel undercoat	0.1 to 0.2	(e)	(e)	(e)	(e)
3 Chromium plate	0.01 to 0.02	10 to 12	110 to 115	0.7 to 1.5	Conventional
Chromium, decorative (direct on zincate)	0.03	5 to 10	65 to 70	0.7 to 1.5	Conventional
Chromium, hard:					
1 Copper strike (see top of table)					
2 Chromium plate	0.05	5	130	0.7 to 1.5	Conventional
Chromium, hard (direct on zincate)	0.05	10 to 20	65 to 70; then 130(f)	0.7 to 1.5; then 3(f)	Conventional
Chromium, hard (for corrosion protection):					
1 Copper or brass strike (see top of table)					
2 Nickel undercoat	1 to 2	(e)	(e)	(e)	(e)
3 Chromium plate	0.1 to 0.2	10 to 12	110 to 115	0.7 to 1.5	Conventional
Gold:					
1 Copper or brass strike (see top of table)					
2 Nickel undercoat	0.7	(e)	(e)	(e)	(e)
3 Gold plate	0.025	10 sec to 1 min	120 to 160	5 to 15	Potassium cyanide
Nickel (for minimum corrosion protection):					
1 Copper or brass strike (see top of table)					
2 Nickel plate	0.3 to 0.5	(e)	(e)	(e)	(e)
Nickel (for maximum corrosion protection):					
1 Copper or brass strike (see top of table)					
2 Nickel plate	1 to 2	(e)	(e)	(e)	(e)
Silver:					
1 Double silver strike	0.025	10 sec(g)	80(g)	15 to 25(g)	Cyanide(h)
2 Silver plate	0.05 to 0.1	18 to 35	80	5	Cyanide
Silver (alternative method):					
1 Copper strike (see top of table)					
2 Silver strike	0.02	10 sec	80	15 to 25	Cyanide(j)
3 Silver plate	0.05 to 0.1	18 to 35	80	5	Cyanide
Tin:					
1 Copper strike (see top of table)					
2 Tin plate(k)	0.7	15 to 30	200 to 210	45 to 65	Sodium stannate
Zinc:					
1 Copper strike (see top of table)					
2 Zinc plate	0.5	18 to 45	75 to 86	10 to 30	Pyrophosphate
Zinc (direct on zincate)	0.5	10	75 to 95	5 to 50(m)	Pyrophosphate

(a) An initial cyanide copper strike is generally used to achieve complete metal coverage of zincated aluminum parts prior to plating, because of the excellent throwing power of the copper electrolyte. A copper strike is not, however, recommended as the initial coating for alloys 5056, 214, 218 and others that contain substantial amounts of magnesium; these will achieve a better initial coverage in a brass strike. Neither copper strike nor brass strike should be used as a final finish; both should always have an electroplated top coat. (b) The copper strike is achieved during the first 2 min while the current density of the electrolyte is maintained at 24 amp per sq ft. Instead of being transferred from the strike bath to a high-speed sodium or potassium electrolyte for subsequent copper plating, the work may be allowed to remain (3 to 5 min) in the Rochelle-type electrolyte to be copper plated, provided the current density is lowered to 12 amp per sq ft.
(c) Colorimetric pH of electrolyte is 12.0 for all treatable alloys except 5052, 6061 and 6063, for which pH is 10.2 to 10.5. (d) Work for which copper strike plating may be used may be left in the copper strike for copper plating, instead of being transferred to the high-speed sodium or potassium cyanide electrolyte (see footnote c). (e) As discussed in the article "Nickel Plating" (page 432), various electrolytes are used, depending on the specific purpose of the plated deposit. If the nickel is to be deposited directly on the zincated surface, a bath must be selected that is suitable for application over zinc (examples of such baths are fluoborate and sulfamate nickel electrolytes). (f) The transition from low-temperature to high-temperature plating may be accomplished either by heating the electrolyte to 130 F after deposition has started at 65 to 70 F or by transferring the work (without rinsing) from an electrolyte at 65 to 70 F to one at 130 F and holding the work in the high-temperature electrolyte without current until the work reaches bath temperature. Current density is 0.7 to 1.5 amp per sq ft in the electrolyte at 65 to 70 F, 3 amp per sq ft at 130 F.
(g) Each bath. (h) First strike bath contains 1 g of AgCN and 90 g of NaCN per liter; second bath, 5.3 g of AgCN and 67.5 g of NaCN per liter. (j) Contains 5.3 g of AgCN and 67.5 g of NaCN per liter. (k) After the aluminum material has been copper strike plated, tin may be applied also by immersion for 45 min to 1 hr in a sodium stannate solution at 122 to 165 F (time and temperature depend on solution used). (m) Current is applied as work is being immersed in electrolyte.

formation on materials and methods of application in the article "Painting of Steel and Cast Iron" (page 548) is, in general, applicable to aluminum.

Aluminum is an excellent substrate for organic coatings if the surface is properly cleaned and prepared. For many applications (for example, indoor decorative parts) the coating may be applied directly to a clean surface. However, a suitable prime coat, such as a wash primer or a zinc chromate primer, usually improves the performance of the finish coat.

For applications involving outdoor exposure, or for indoor applications exposing the part to impact or abrasive forces, a surface treatment such as anodizing or chemical conversion coating is required prior to the application of a primer and a finish coat. These processes have been discussed in previous sections of this article.

Anodizing in sulfuric or chromic acid electrolytes provides an excellent surface for organic coatings. Usually, only thin anodic coatings are required as a prepaint treatment. Decorative parts for home appliances generally are anodized before painting to assure good paint adhesion over an extended period. Sulfuric acid anodic coatings are used when painting of only part of the surface is required for decorative effects; the anodic coating protects the unpainted portions of the surface.

Conversion coatings usually are less expensive than anodic coatings, provide a good base for paint, and improve the life of the paint by retarding corrosion of the aluminum substrate material. Adequate coverage of the entire surface by the conversion coating is important for good paint bonding.

Table 41. Tin Immersion Plating(a)

Solution Composition, Oz per Gal

Potassium stannate	13.40
Zinc acetate	0.27
m-Cresol sulfonic acid	4.40

Operating Conditions

Temperature of solution	140 F
Immersion time	2 min

(a) Degreasing is the only pretreatment required. Thickness of tin coating is about 0.05 mil; solution life, about 30 sq ft per gal.

Table 42. Nickel Chemical Plating

Solution Composition, Oz per Gal

Nickel chloride	4.00
Sodium hypophosphite	1.00
Sodium citrate	9.64
Ammonium chloride	6.43
Ammonium hydroxide (sp gr, 0.880)	1.74

Operating Conditions

pH	10
Temperature of solution	180 to 190 F
Immersion time(a)	1 hr

(a) For deposits 2 or more mils thick.

Porcelain Enameling

Aluminum products may be finished by porcelain enameling to enhance appearance, chemical resistance, and weather resistance. The wrought aluminum alloys that can be enameled are 1100 and 3003 (sheet), and 6061 (sheet and extrusions). Special designations of these alloys are commercially available that provide excellent response to porcelain enameling because of the compositional control used in fabrication. Castings made of alloys 43 and 356 can be porcelain enameled.

Before the porcelain enamel frit is applied, aluminum surfaces are prepared by being (a) cleaned in an alkaline cleaner, to remove soil; (b) etched in a solution of chromic and sulfuric acids, to remove surface oxide; and (c) dipped in a chromate solution, to apply a chromate-oxide film. Details of processing procedures for the application of porcelain enamel coatings on aluminum may be found in the article "Porcelain Enameling", page 573.

Standards for Aluminum Finishes

General Standard

MIL-F-7179A — Finishes and coatings; general specification for protection of aircraft and aircraft parts. (Covers finishing procedures for corrosion protection of aircraft and component parts. This specification is not applicable to the purchase of mill products but is a good reference for recommended finishes for aluminum.)

Anodic Coatings

ASTM test methods for the evaluation of various properties and qualities of anodic coatings are listed in Table 27 on page 626.
AMS 2468 — Hard coating of aluminum alloys
AMS 2470D — Anodic films, corrosion-protective for aluminum alloys. (Covers chromic acid anodizing of aluminum alloys.)
AMS 2471 — Anodic treatment for aluminum-base alloys. (Covers anodizing of aluminum alloys by the sulfuric acid process.)
AMS 7222C — Rivets, 2117-T4. (Covers 2117-T4 rivets that are to be anodized.)
AMS 7223 — Rivets, 2024-T4. (Covers 2024-T4 rivets that are to be anodized.)
MIL-A-8625A — Anodic coatings for aluminum alloys. (Covers the procedure and requirements for anodizing. Type I is a chromic acid coating, Type II a sulfuric acid coating.)
MIL-B-6812A (Amendment 2) — Aircraft bolts, 2024. (Covers aluminum alloy 2024-T4 anodized bolts.)
MIL-I-8474A — Anodizing process for inspection of aluminum parts. (Covers the use of chromic acid anodizing for the surface inspection of cracks and other defects.)
MIL-N-6034 (Amendment 1) — Aircraft nuts, 2024. (Covers aluminum alloy 2024-T4 anodized nuts.)
NAVORD OD 7837 — Hard anodizing of aluminum. (Covers the process for sulfuric acid anodizing.)

Chemical Conversion Coatings

ASTM test methods that may be employed for the evaluation of various properties and qualities of chemical conversion coatings are listed in Table 34 on page 628.
AMS 2473A — Chemical treatment for aluminum alloys; general purpose. (Covers the requirements for chemical films applied for increased corrosion resistance or for paint adhesion.)
AMS 2474 — Chemical treatment for aluminum alloys; low electrical resistivity. (Covers the requirements for chemical films applied for increased corrosion resistance or for paint adhesion where a conductive coating is required.)

MIL-C-5541 (Amendment 1) — Chemical films for aluminum and aluminum alloys. (Covers the minimum requirements for qualification of chemical films on aluminum applied to aid paint adhesion or corrosion resistance. Specific acceptable treatments are listed in the table of qualified products.)

Painting

ASTM test methods that may be employed for the evaluation of various properties and qualities of paints are listed in Table 17 on page 558 in the article "Painting of Steel and Cast Iron", in this volume.
MIL-C-15328A — Wash primer pretreatment. (Covers phosphoric acid wash primer to prepare aluminum surfaces for painting.)
MIL-P-6808A — Application of zinc chromate primer. (Covers the procedures in applying zinc chromate primer to aircraft.)
MIL-P-14504A — Primer coating, pretreatment. (Covers a primer coating for steel, aluminum, and magnesium surfaces. The primer consists of polyvinyl butyral resin, suitable solvents, phosphoric acid, pigment of rust-inhibitive chromate, and necessary extender pigments.)
MIL-P-15930A — Vinyl-zinc chromate primer. (Covers zinc chromate primer suitable for use on aluminum surfaces that have been treated with a wash primer conforming to MIL-C-15328A.)
MIL-S-5002 (Amendment 2) — Surface treatments for metal parts in aircraft. (Covers various treatments required for airframes prior to priming and painting.)
MIL-T-704C (Amendment 2) — Treatment and painting for construction and engineering equipment. (Covers finishing schedules for various metals, including aluminum.)

Electroplating

ASTM B253 — Recommended practice for preparation of and electroplating on aluminum alloys. (Covers practices for electroplating of gold, silver, tin and zinc on aluminum alloys.)
AMS 2420 — Plating aluminum for solderability. (Covers the zincate process for preparing aluminum parts for soldering.)

Porcelain Enameling

ASTM B244 — Method of measuring thickness of anodic coatings on aluminum with eddy-current instruments.
Other ASTM test methods for determining properties of porcelain enamel coatings are listed in Table 22, page 585, in the article "Porcelain Enameling", in this volume.
MIL-A-16994B — Porcelain enamel coated sheet. (Covers porcelain enameled 6061 sheet.)
PEI AL-2a (4th Edition) — Recommended processing methods for porcelain enamel on aluminum alloys. (Porcelain Enamel Institute, Inc.)
PEI ALS-105 (57) — Tentative specification for porcelain enamel on aluminum used for sign and architectural applications. (Porcelain Enamel Institute, Inc.)

Selected References

General Sources

S. Wernick and R. Pinner, "The Surface Treatment and Finishing of Aluminium and Its Alloys", Robert Draper Ltd, Teddington (England), 1959
G. H. Kissin, editor, "Finishing of Aluminum", Reinhold, New York, 1963.

Chemical Cleaning

When Cleaning Aluminum, *Mod Metals*, Sept 1959
W. B. Stoddard, Jr., U. S. Patent 3,041,259 (1962). [Cleaning of aluminum surfaces, with particular reference to a method of electrolytic alkaline cleaning.]

Chemical and Electrolytic Brightening

W. J. Tegart, "The Electrolytic and Chemical Polishing of Metals in Research and Industry", Pergamon Press, New York, 1959
N. P. Fedot'ev and S. Grilikhes, "Electropolishing, Anodizing, and Electrolytic Pickling of Metals", Moscow, 1957 [Translation by A. Behr, Robert Draper Ltd (England), 1959]
R. M. Rall and H. Yoshimoto, Radiant Cooling or Shielding, *Prod Eng*, Nov 14, 1960
F. A. Champion and E. E. Spillett, Super Purity Aluminium and Its Alloys, *Sheet Metal Ind*, Jan 1956
W. H. Tingle and F. R. Potter, New Instrument Grades Polished Metal Surfaces, *Prod Eng*, March 27, 1961
G. D. Nelson and C. J. Knapp, How to Control the Aluminum Bright Dipping Process, *Mod Metals*, Sept 1961
A. W. Brace, "The Electrolytic and Chemical Polishing and Brightening of Aluminium and Its Alloys", Aluminium Development Assn. RP 54; reprinted from *Metal Finishing J* (London), June and July 1955
W. R. Meyer and S. H. Brown, Cleaning, Etching, Chemical Polishing and Brightening of Aluminum, *Tech Proc Am Electroplaters' Soc*, 36, 163 (1949)
A. V. Davis, U. S. Patent 528,513 (1894). [Improving the surface of aluminum by treating with a mixture of hydrofluoric acid and nitric acid.]
J. C. Lum and others, U. S. Patent 2,428,464 (1947). [An acid composition, of essentially the R-5 formula, for etching of metals. The specification and some claims refer to copper, copper alloys and ferrous metals. The specification states that a bright surface free from pitting will be obtained, but there is no mention of heated baths.]
H. A. H. Pray and others, U. S. Patent 2,446,060 (1948). [A concentrated acid bath containing nitric, phosphoric and acetic acids and covering a broad range of concentrations, for chemically polishing metal surfaces. Metals given in some claims are nickel silver, copper, brass, nickel and Monel.]
F. H. Hesch, U. S. Patent 2,593,447 (1952). [A bath containing hydrogen, nitrate, fluoride, ammonium, and chromate ions.]
F. H. Hesch, U. S. Patent 2,593,449 (1952). [A bath containing hydrogen, nitrate, fluoride, chromate, and noble-metal ions.]
W. C. Cochran, U. S. Patent 2,613,141 (1952). [A bath for brightening aluminum in phosphoric acid and hydrogen peroxide.]
H. J. Reindl and S. Prance, U. S. Patent 2,614,913 (1952). [A dilute bath containing nitric acid, soluble fluorides and various additives.]
E. Shelton-Jones, U. S. Patent 2,650,156 (1953). [A process consisting of immersing aluminum in a bath of concentrated phosphoric and sulfuric acids.]
W. C. Cochran, U. S. Patent 2,650,157 (1953). [Nitric and phosphoric acids with or without acetic or sulfuric and acetic acids.]
J. T. Ferguson, U. S. Patent 2,671,717 (1954). [Method of brightening aluminum in a hot solution of alkali metal hydroxide and an alkali nitrate.]
E. R. DuFresne and others, U. S. Patent 2,673,143 (1954). [Forming a reflective surface on aluminum using a bath of sodium hydroxide, sodium gluconate and an oxidizing agent.]
R. C. Spooner, U. S. Patent 2,678,875 (1954). [Brightening of aluminum in hot concentrated phosphoric and nitric acids and silicic acid as an inhibitor.]
J. F. Jumer, U. S. Patent 2,705,191 (1955). [A solution for polishing aluminum, containing phosphoric acid, alkali metal nitrate and alkali metal sulfate.]
J. F. Murphy, U. S. Patent 2,719,079 (1955). [Bath containing complex fluoride ions, nitric acid and a noble metal.]
F. H. Hesch, U. S. Patent 2,719,781 (1955). [A simple fluoride bath containing nitric acid, fluoride ions and noble-metal ions.]
C. C. Cohn, U. S. Patent 2,729,551 (1956). [Method of treating aluminum with a broad range of phosphoric acid, nitric acid and water, or with phosphoric acid and water.]
W. Helling and others, U. S. Patent 2,746,849 (1956). [An Erftwerk type of bath.]

Chemical Etching

R. H. Elliott, Jr., U. S. Patent 2,882,135 (1959). [Composition and operating conditions for an alkaline etching solution.]

Anodizing

James H. Weaver, ASD-TDR-62-918, "Anodized Aluminum Coatings for Temperature

Control of Space Vehicles", Aeronautical Systems Div., Wright-Patterson AFB, 1963

F. J. Gillig, WADC Technical Report 53-151, 1953, P. B. 111320

J. Herenguel and R. Segond, *Rev Met (Paris)*, **46**, 377 (1949), and **42**, 258 (1945)

J. Herenguel, *Trans Inst Metal Finishing*, **31** (1954), Advance Copy No. 1

J. E. Bunch, Racks for Anodizing, *Metal Finishing*, July 1957, p 45

A. K. Graham and H. L. Pinkerton, "Electroplating Engineering Handbook", Reinhold, New York, 1955

"Anodic Oxidation of Aluminium and Its Alloys", Aluminium Development Assn. Bulletin No. 14

J. M. Kape, Unusual Anodizing Processes and Their Practical Significance, *Electroplating Metal Finishing*, Nov 1961

F. Howitt and I. H. Jenks, Improved Aluminum Alloys for Bright Anodizing, *Metal Progress*, Jan 1960

W. E. Cooke, Factors Affecting Loss of Brightness and Image Clarity During Anodizing of Bright-Trim Aluminum Alloys in Sulfuric Acid Electrolyte, *Plating*, Nov 1962

Electroplating

R. F. Hafer, Electroplating on Aluminum, *Metal Progress*, May 1955

S. Wernick and R. Pinner, Plating on Aluminum — Chemical Etching Processes, *Metal Finishing*, Nov 1956

S. Wernick and R. Pinner, Plating on Aluminum — Zinc Immersion Process, *Metal Finishing*, Feb and March 1957

S. Wernick and R. Pinner, Plating on Aluminum — the Vogt Process, *Metal Finishing*, April 1957

S. Wernick and R. Pinner, Plating on Aluminum — Hard Chromium and Non-Electrolytic Deposits, *Metal Finishing*, May 1957

S. Wernick and R. Pinner, Plated Aluminum — Tests, Corrosion, Applications, *Metal Finishing*, June 1957

R. Spooner and D. Seraphim, Nickel-Chromium Plated Aluminum Sheet, *Metal Finishing*, Jan 1961

"Metal Finishing Guidebook", 32nd Edition (1964), Metals and Plastics Publications, Inc., Westwood, N. J.

W. G. Zelley, Plating on Aluminum, Chapter 24 (p 556-564) in "Modern Electroplating" (Second Edition), Wiley, New York, 1963

H. Uhlig, "The Corrosion Handbook", Wiley, New York, 1948

"Recent Developments in the Plating of Aluminium", Aluminium Development Assn.

F. Keller and W. G. Zelley, Conditioning Aluminum Alloys for Electroplating, *J Electrochem Soc*, April 1950

F. Keller and W. G. Zelley, Plating on Aluminum Alloys, *Tech Proc Am Electroplaters' Soc*, **36**, 149-162 (1949)

H. V. Wittrock, Nickel-Chromium Plating Upon Anodized Aluminum, *Tech Proc Am Electroplaters' Soc*, **48**, 52 (1961)

Painting

R. I. Wray, Painting of Aluminum and Magnesium, *Metal Progress*, Dec 1954

R. Burns and W. Bradley, "Protective Coatings for Metals", Reinhold, New York, 1955

M. Hess, "Paint Film Defects", Reinhold, New York, 1952

U. S. Govt Spec MIL-F-18264 B(-1), "Finishes; Organic, Aircraft; Application and Control of", 22 Jan 1958, Washington, D. C.

Porcelain Enameling

E. A. Farrell, Glass on Aluminum, *Mod Metals*, Oct 1956

N. H. Stradley, Porcelain Enamels for Aluminum and Magnesium, *Am Ceram Soc Bull*, Aug 1959

F. L. Church, Porcelain on Aluminum, *Mod Metals*, June 1962

D. Lamarche, Porcelain Enameling of Aluminum Alloys, *J Can Ceram Soc*, **31** (1962)

A. L. Sopp and others, Chemical and Weather Resistance of Porcelain Enamels on Aluminum, *Ceram Age*, April 1960

Other Finishing Processes

A. Cahne, U. S. Patent 2,944,917 (1960). [Method of Coating a Metal Base With Polytetrafluoroethylene.]

C. A. MacNeill, Gas Plating — an Introduction, *Metal Finishing*, July 1963, p 40-44, 47

The Aluminum Association
Designation System for Aluminum Finishes

The many proprietary designations that have been introduced for finishes on aluminum have created a great deal of confusion and have made it difficult for users to specify finishes so that suppliers know what to furnish. To remedy this situation, The Aluminum Association, through its Technical Committee, has developed a system of designations that is broad enough to cover all types of finishes now being used on aluminum products and to meet anticipated future needs as new finishes are developed.

Almost all finishes used on aluminum may be subdivided into three major categories:

1. Mechanical Finishes
2. Chemical Finishes
3. Coatings

Coatings may be further subdivided into the following categories:

Anodic Coatings
Resinous and Other Organic Coatings
Vitreous Coatings
Electroplated and Other Metallic Coatings
Laminated Coatings

In The Aluminum Association System, mechanical and chemical finishes and each of the five classes of coatings are designated by a letter. The various finishes in each class are designated by two-digit numerals. Specific finishes of the various types thus are designated by a letter followed by a two-digit numeral as shown in the tables.

Conversion coatings are listed under "Chemical Finishes" (Table II) because they are produced by chemical processes and frequently are used as pretreatments with other coatings.

A single designation may be used alone where only a simple finish is involved, or two or more designations may be combined into a single composite designation to identify a sequence of operations covering all of the important steps leading to a final complex finish.

When designations for chemical coatings are used alone, it is understood that other processing steps normally used ahead of these finishes are at the option of the processor. Where a finish requires two or more treatments of the same class, the class letter is repeated, each being followed by the appropriate two-digit numeral.

The "Examples of Methods of Finishing" given in the tables are intended for illustrative purposes and not as specifications. Alternatives to the examples of methods of obtaining a final finish can be used provided that an equivalent finish is produced. Many equipment and process variations and limitations exist in the finishing industry which may require modifications of example procedures.

Designations for specific coatings have been developed for only the first of the five classes of these finishes listed above—the Anodic Coatings (Table III). For the present, coatings of the other four classes may be tentatively designated by the respective letters assigned for them (Table IV to VII, inclusive). Detailed designations for these four categories may be developed and added to the system later.

System Can Be Expanded

In the event that additional finishes require the use of all of the two-digit numbers available in a given group, the system may be expanded by adding a third digit to the numbers. For example, under Mechanical Finishes—Directional Textured, if new entries are made requiring the use of all the numbers between M35 and M39, the system will be expanded by the use of three-digit numbers M301, M302, etc., as required. This will provide for 90 more designations. While the need for designations beyond these cannot be foreseen at present, the system could be expanded still further by adding a fourth digit if this should ever become necessary.

How The System Works

The following examples show how the Aluminum Association Designation System for Aluminum Fin-

Source: Designation System for Aluminum Finishes, 6th Ed., Aluminum Assn., Inc.

257

ishes is used (each designation is preceded by the letters AA to identify it as an Aluminum Association designation):

Example 1—Smooth Specular Finish

A finish obtained by polishing aluminum with an aluminum oxide compound according to the following schedule: Begin with grits coarser than 320; follow with 320 grit and a peripheral wheel speed of 6,000 feet per minute; complete polishing by buffing with aluminum oxide buffing compound at peripheral speeds of 7,000 feet per minute; the designation for this finish is:

AA—M21

AA—Aluminum Association
M21—Mechanical finish—bright smooth specular appearance (Table I)

Example 2—Architectural Building Panel

If an architect wished to designate a matte anodized finish for a building such as that produced by giving aluminum a matte finish, then chemical cleaning followed by architectural Class II natural anodizing, he would designate it as follows:

AA—M32C12A31

AA—Aluminum Association
M32—Mechanical finish—medium satin appearance (Table I)
C12—Chemical treatment — inhibited chemical cleaning (Table II)
A31—Anodic Coating — architectural, class II (0.4 to 0.7 mil thick) clear (Table III)

Example 3—Architectural Aluminum with Anodized Integral Color

If an architect wished to specify an anodized panel with an integral color for architectural application, the designation would be:

AA—M10C21A42

AA—Aluminum Association
M10—Unspecified as fabricated finish (Table I)
C21—Chemically etched fine matte finish (Table II)
A42—Anodic Coating—architectural, class I (0.7 mil thickness and greater) integral color (Table III)

Example 4—Automotive Trim Finish Designation

AA—M11C11C31A21

AA—Aluminum Association
M11—As fabricated specular (Table I)
C11—Degreased, nonetched cleaned (Table II)
C31—Highly specular chemical brightening (Table II)
A21—Protective and decorative clear anodic coating less than 0.4 mil thick (Table III)

Example 5—Chromium-Plated Aluminum Panel

The finish for a chromium-plated aluminum panel which is first given a smooth specular mechanical finish, then a nonetch chemical cleaning, followed by a thin anodic coating produced in phosphoric acid, and finally direct chrome plating would be designated as follows:

AA—M21C12A1XE1X

AA—Aluminum Association
M21—Smooth specular — produced by polishing with aluminum oxide compound (Table I)
C12—Inhibited chemical cleaning (Table II)
A1X—Specify exact anodizing process (Table III)
E1X—Specify exact chrome-plating procedure (Table VI)

The publication of typical examples of finishing processes in the Designation System by The Aluminum Association does not constitute authority to use the process nor does it imply endorsement of a particular process by The Aluminum Association.

NUMERICAL LISTING OF DESIGNATIONS

MECHANICAL FINISHES (M)

As Fabricated
M10—Unspecified
M11—Specular as fabricated
M12—Nonspecular as fabricated
M1X—Other (to be specified)

Buffed
M20—Unspecified
M21—Smooth specular
M22—Specular
M2X—Other (to be specified)

Directional Textured
M30—Unspecified
M31—Fine satin
M32—Medium satin
M33—Coarse satin
M34—Hand rubbed
M35—Brushed
M3X—Other (to be specified)

Nondirectional Textured
M40—Unspecified
M41—Extra fine matte
M42—Fine matte
M43—Medium matte
M44—Coarse matte
M45—Fine shot blast
M46—Medium shot blast
M47—Coarse shot blast
M4X—Other (to be specified)

CHEMICAL FINISHES (C)*

Nonetched Cleaned
C10—Unspecified
C11—Degreased
C12—Inhibited chemical cleaned
C1X—Other (to be specified)

Etched
C20—Unspecified
C21—Fine matte
C22—Medium matte
C23—Coarse matte
C2X—Other (to be specified)

Brightened
C30—Unspecified
C31—Highly specular
C32—Diffuse bright
C3X—Other (to be specified)

Chemical Conversion Coatings
C40—Unspecified
C41—Acid chromate-fluoride
C42—Acid chromate-fluoride-phosphate
C43—Alkaline chromate
C4X—Other (to be specified)

*Includes chemical conversion coatings, electrochemical brightening and cleaning treatments.

COATINGS, (A, R, V, E, L)

Anodic Coatings (A)

General
A10—Unspecified
A11—Preparation for other applied coatings
A12—Chromic acid anodic coatings
A13—Hard, wear and abrasion resistant coatings
A1X—Other (to be specified)

Protective and Decorative
(Coatings less than 0.4 mil thick)
A21—Clear
A22—Integral color
A23—Impregnated color
A24—Electrolytically deposited color
A2X—Other (to be specified)

Architectural Class II**
(0.4-0.7 mil coating)
A31—Clear
A32—Integral color
A33—Impregnated color
A34—Electrolytically deposited color
A3X—Other (to be specified)

Architectural Class I**
(0.7 mil and thicker anodic coatings)
A41—Clear
A42—Integral color
A43—Impregnated color
A44—Electrolytically deposited color
A4X—Other (to be specified)

**Aluminum Association Standards for Anodized Architectural Aluminum.

Resinous and Other Organic Coatings (R)***
R10—Unspecified
R1X—Other (to be specified)

Vitreous Coatings (Porcelain and Ceramic Types) (V)***
V10—Unspecified
V1X—Other (to be specified)

Electroplated and Other Metal Coatings (E)***
E10—Unspecified
E1X—Other (to be specified)

Laminated Coatings (L)***
(Includes veneers, plastic coatings and films bonded to aluminum)
L10—Unspecified
L1X—Other (to be specified)

***These designations may be used until more complete series of designations are developed for these coatings.

All designations are preceded by the letters AA to identify them as Aluminum Association designations.

Source: Designation System for Aluminum Finishes, 6th Ed., Aluminum Assn., Inc.

259

TABLE I—MECHANICAL FINISHES (M)

TYPE OF FINISH	DESIG-NATION*	DESCRIPTION	EXAMPLES OF METHODS OF FINISHING
As Fabricated	M10 M11 M12 M1X	Unspecified Specular as fabricated Nonspecular as fabricated Other	To be specified.
Buffed	M20 M21	Unspecified Smooth specular	Polished with grits coarser than 320. Final polishing with a 320 grit using peripheral wheel speed of 6,000 feet per min. Polishing followed by buffing, using aluminum oxide buffing compound and peripheral wheel speed of 7,000 feet per min.
	M22	Specular	Buffed with aluminum oxide compound using peripheral wheel speed 7,000 feet per min.
	M2X	Other	To be specified.
Directional Textured	M30	Unspecified	
	M31	Fine satin	Wheel or belt polished with aluminum oxide grit of 320 to 400 size; peripheral wheel speed 6,000 feet per min.
	M32	Medium satin	Wheel or belt polished with aluminum oxide grit of 180 to 220 size; peripheral wheel speed 6,000 feet per min.
	M33	Coarse satin	Wheel or belt polished with aluminum oxide grit of 80 to 100 size; peripheral wheel speed 6,000 feet per min.
	M34	Hand rubbed	Hand rubbed with stainless steel wool lubricated with neutral soap solution. Final rubbing with No. 00 steel wool.
	M35	Brushed	Brushed with rotary stainless steel wire brush (wire diameter 0.0095 in.; peripheral wheel speed 6,000 feet per min) or various proprietary satin finishing wheels or satin finishing compounds with buffs.
	M3X	Other	To be specified
Nondirectional Textured	M40	Unspecified	
	M41	Extra fine matte	Air blasted with finer than 200 mesh washed silica or aluminum oxide. Air pressure 45 pounds, gun 8-12 inches at 90° angle.
	M42	Fine matte	Air blasted with 100 to 200 mesh silica sand if darkening is not a problem; otherwise aluminum oxide type abrasive. Air pressure 30 to 90 pounds (depending upon thickness of material); gun distance one foot from work at angle of 60° to 90°.
	M43	Medium matte	Air blasted with 40 to 50 mesh silica sand if darkening is not a problem; otherwise aluminum oxide type abrasive. Air pressure 30 to 90 pounds (depending upon thickness of material); gun distance one foot from work at angle of 60° to 90°.
	M44	Coarse matte	Air blasted with 16 to 20 mesh silica sand if darkening is not a problem; otherwise aluminum oxide type abrasive. Air pressure 30 to 90 pounds (depending upon thickness of material); gun distance one foot from work at angle of 60° to 90°.
	M45	Fine shot blast	Shot blasted with cast steel shot of ASTM size 70-170 applied by air blast or centrifugal force. To some degree, selection of shot size is dependent on thickness of material since warping can occur.
	M46	Medium shot blast	Shot blasted with cast steel shot of ASTM size 230-550 applied by air blast or centrifugal force. To some degree, selection of shot size is dependent on thickness of material since warping can occur.
	M47	Coarse shot blast	Shot blasted with cast steel shot of ASTM size 660-1320 applied by air blast or centrifugal force. To some degree, selection of shot size is dependent on thickness of material since warping can occur.
	M4X	Other	To be specified.

The complete designation must be preceded by AA—signifying Aluminum Association.

TABLE II—CHEMICAL FINISHES (C)

TYPE OF FINISH	DESIG-NATION*	DESCRIPTION	EXAMPLES OF METHODS OF FINISHING
Nonetched Cleaned	C10	Unspecified	
	C11	Degreased	Organic solvent treated.
	C12	Inhibited chemical cleaned	Inhibited chemical type cleaner used.
	C1X	Other	To be specified.
Etched	C20	Unspecified	
	C21	Fine matte	Trisodium phosphate, 3-6 oz per gal used at 140-160 F for 3 to 5 min.
	C22	Medium matte	Sodium hydroxide, 4-6 oz per gal used at 130-150 F for 5 to 10 min.
	C23	Coarse matte	Sodium fluoride, 1½ oz plus sodium hydroxide 4-6 oz per gal used at 130-150 F for 5 to 10 min.
	C2X	Other	To be specified.
Brightened	C30	Unspecified	
	C31	Highly specular	Chemical bright dip solution of the proprietary phosphoric-nitric acid type used, or proprietary electrobrightening or electropolishing treatment.
	C32	Diffuse bright	Etched finish C22 followed by brightened finish C31.
	C3X	Other	To be specified.
Chemical Conversion Coatings	C40	Unspecified	
	C41	Acid chromate-fluoride	Proprietary chemical treatments used producing clear to typically yellow colored surfaces.
	C42	Acid chromate-fluoride-phosphate	Proprietary chemical treatments used producing clear to typically green colored surfaces.
	C43	Alkaline chromate	Proprietary chemical treatments used producing clear to typically gray colored surfaces.
	C4X	Other	To be specified.

*The complete designation must be preceded by AA—signifying Aluminum Association.

Source: Designation System for Aluminum Finishes, 6th Ed., Aluminum Assn., Inc.

261

TABLE III—ANODIC COATINGS (A)

TYPE OF FINISH	DESIG-NATION*	DESCRIPTION	EXAMPLES OF METHODS OF FINISHING
General	A10	Unspecified	
	A11	Preparation for other applied coatings	0.1 mil anodic coating produced in 15% H_2SO_4 at 70 F$\pm$2 F at 12 amp per sq ft for 10 min.
	A12	Chromic acid anodic coatings	To be specified.
	A13	Hard, wear and abrasion resistant coatings	To be specified.
	A1X	Other	To be specified.
Protective & Decorative (Coatings less than 0.4 mil thick)	A21	Clear coating	Coating thickness to be specified. 15% H_2SO_4 used at 70 F$\pm$2 F at 12 amp per sq ft.
	A211	Clear coating	Coating thickness—0.1 mil minimum. Coating weight—4 mg/in^2 minimum.
	A212	Clear coating	Coating thickness—0.2 mil minimum. Coating weight—8 mg/in^2 minimum.
	A213	Clear coating	Coating thickness—0.3 mil minimum. Coating weight—12 mg/in^2 minimum.
	A22	Coating with integral color	Coating thickness to be specified. Color dependent on alloy and process methods.
	A221	Coating with integral color	Coating thickness—0.1 mil minimum. Coating weight—4 mg/in^2 minimum.
	A222	Coating with integral color	Coating thickness—0.2 mil minimum. Coating weight—8 mg/in^2 minimum.
	A223	Coating with integral color	Coating thickness—0.3 mil minimum. Coating weight—12 mg/in^2 minimum.
	A23	Coating with impregnated color	Coating thickness to be specified. 15% H_2SO_4 used at 70 F$\pm$2 F at 12 amp per sq ft followed by dyeing with organic or inorganic colors.
	A231	Coating with impregnated color	Coating thickness—0.1 mil minimum. Coating weight—4 mg/in^2 minimum.
	A232	Coating with impregnated color	Coating thickness—0.2 mil minimum. Coating weight—8 mg/in^2 minimum.
	A233	Coating with impregnated color	Coating thickness—0.3 mil minimum. Coating weight—12 mg/in^2 minimum.
	A24	Coating with electrolytically deposited color	Coating thickness to be specified. 15% H_2SO_4 at 70 F$\pm$2 F at 12 amp per sq ft, followed by electrolytic deposition of inorganic pigment in the coating.
	A2X	Other	To be specified.
Architectural Class II ** **(0.4 to 0.7 mil coating)**	A31	Clear coating	15% H_2SO_4 used at 70 F$\pm$2 F at 12 amp per sq ft for 30 min, or equivalent.
	A32	Coating with integral color	Color dependent on alloy and anodic process.
	A33	Coating with impregnated color	15% H_2SO_4 used at 70 F$\pm$2 F at 12 amp per sq ft for 30 min, followed by dyeing with organic or inorganic colors.
	A34	Coating with electrolytically deposited color	15% H_2SO_4 at 70 F$\pm$2 F at 12 amp per sq ft for 30 min, followed by electrolytic deposition of inorganic pigment in the coating.
	A3X	Other	To be specified.
Architectural Class I ** **(0.7 mil and greater coating)**	A41	Clear coating	15% H_2SO_4 used at 70 F$\pm$2 F at 12 amp per sq ft for 60 min, or equivalent.
	A42	Coating with integral color	Color dependent on alloy and anodic process.
	A43	Coating with impregnated color	15% H_2SO_4 used at 70 F$\pm$2 F at 12 amp per sq ft for 60 min, followed by dyeing with organic or inorganic colors, or equivalent.
	A44	Coating with electrolytically deposited color	15% H_2SO_4 at 70 F$\pm$2 F at 12 amp per sq ft for 60 min, followed by electrolytic deposition of inorganic pigment in the coating.
	A4X	Other	To be specified.

*The complete designation must be preceded by AA — signifying Aluminum Association.

** Aluminum Association Standards for Anodized Architectural Aluminum.*

TABLE IV—RESINOUS AND OTHER ORGANIC COATINGS (R)

Designations for these coatings will consist of the letter R followed by a two-digit number. For the present the following two designations can be used until a more complete system is developed:

R10—Unspecified Resinous or Other Organic Coating

R1X—To be specified

TABLE V—VITREOUS COATING (PORCELAIN AND CERAMIC TYPES) (V)

Designations for these coatings will consist of the letter V followed by an appropriate two-digit number. For the present the following two designations can be used until a more complete system is developed:

V10—Unspecified Vitreous Coating

V1X—To be specified

TABLE VI—ELECTROPLATED AND OTHER METAL COATINGS (E)

Designations for these coatings will consist of the letter E followed by an appropriate two-digit number. For the present the following two designations can be used until a more complete system is developed:

E10—Unspecified Electroplated or Other Metal Coating

E1X—To be specified

TABLE VII—LAMINATED COATINGS (L)

Designations for these coatings, which include veneers, plastic coatings and bonded films, will consist of the letter L followed by an appropriate two-digit number. For the present the following two designations can be used until a more complete system is developed:

L10—Unspecified Laminated Coating

L1X—To be specified

Source: Designation System for Aluminum Finishes, 6th Ed., Aluminum Assn., Inc.

263

Section X: Welding

Arc Welding of Aluminum Alloys

By the ASM Committee on Welding of Aluminum Alloys*

GAS METAL-ARC and gas tungsten-arc welding have almost entirely replaced other arc welding processes for aluminum alloys. These gas-shielded arc welding processes result in optimum weld quality and minimum distortion, and they require no flux. As a result, difficult-to-reach places and completely inaccessible interiors of welded assemblies are left free from flux residues that could be a potential source of corrosion. Furthermore, welding can be done in all positions, because there is no slag to be worked out of the weld by gravity or by puddling.

Visibility is good. The gas envelope around the arc is transparent, and the weld puddle is clean. A welder doing a hand welding job can make a neat, sound weld because he does not have to contend with smoke and fumes and can see what he is doing.

Base Metals

Most aluminum alloys can be joined by either gas metal-arc or gas tungsten-arc welding, and the weldabilities of aluminum alloys are essentially the same for both processes. The most common alloys are grouped by weldability rating in Table 1; nominal compositions are given in Table 2.

Wrought alloys most easily welded by gas-shielded arc processes are those of the non-heat-treatable $1xxx$, $3xxx$ and $5xxx$ series; the alloys in the heat treatable $6xxx$ series are also easily welded. Alloys of the $4xxx$ series and of the high-strength, heat treatable $2xxx$ series can also be arc welded, but special techniques may be required and somewhat lower ductility may be obtained. Of the high-strength heat treatable $7xxx$ series, alloys 7075, 7079 and 7178 are weldable, but have brittle heat-affected zones, and therefore welding is usually not recommended, but alloys 7005 and 7039 were developed specifically for welding and have good weldability. Alloys 7005 and 7039 are of special interest for large structures in which the welds must be of high strength, because welds will age

naturally to 70 to 90% of the strength of the heat treated base metal (depending on the chemical composition of the weld deposit) within 30 to 90 days after welding.

The heat of welding removes part or all of the effects of strain hardening; in consequence, the yield strength of the heat-affected zone of a weld in a non-heat-treatable alloy may not exceed that of the annealed alloy. The size of the low-strength zone will depend primarily on the speed of welding and the amount of strain hardening. On the whole, weldments exhibit good joint efficiency and ductility.

Table 1. Weldability of Aluminum Alloys by the Gas Metal-Arc and Gas Tungsten-Arc Processes (a)

Readily Weldable

Wrought alloys(b):
  Pure aluminum, EC, 1060, 1100
  2219
  3003, 3004
  5005, 5050, 5052, 5083, 5086, 5154, 5254, 5454, 5456, 5652
  6061, 6063, 6101, 6151
  7005, 7039
Casting alloy: 43

Weldable in Most Applications
(May require special techniques for some applications)

Wrought alloys: 2014, 4032
Casting alloys:
  13, 108, A108
  214, A214, B214, F214
  319, 333, 355, C355, 356
  A612, C612, D612

Limited Weldability
(Require special techniques)

Wrought alloy: 2024
Casting alloys: 138, 195, B195

Welding Not Recommended

Wrought alloys: 7075, 7079, 7178
Casting alloys: 122, 142, 220

(a) Wrought alloys are listed here by Aluminum Association designations; casting alloys, by industry designations. See Table 2 for nominal compositions of all alloys listed, and for Aluminum Association designations of casting alloys. (b) See Table 14 on page 877 in Volume 1 of this Handbook for strength and ductility of gas metal-arc welded joints in many of these alloys and combinations of these alloys, using various filler metals.

When a heat treated alloy (T4 or T6 condition) is arc welded, its strength in the as-welded condition is slightly less than that of the unwelded alloy in the T4 condition. This decrease in strength is attributed to the comparative weakness of the heat-affected zone. The zone normally consists of an area of solution-annealed material adjacent to the weld, an area where partial annealing has occurred, and an overaged area. Because of the high strength of the base metal and the low strength of the heat-affected zone, weldments of alloys in the T6 condition have a low as-welded joint efficiency and often a lack of ductility. Solution heat treatment and aging after welding may restore much of the strength, but little improvement in ductility occurs. After postweld aging alone, the strength may be no higher, and the ductility can be lower, than those of some non-heat-treatable alloys. To obtain optimum properties of weldments, it may be preferable to weld in the annealed condition, and to solution heat treat and age afterward.

There is little difference between the strengths of welded and unwelded heat treatable and non-heat-treatable alloys in the annealed condition.

Casting Alloys. Most casting alloys can be gas-shielded arc welded if they are given the correct edge preparation. Aluminum sand and permanent mold castings are welded to repair foundry defects, to repair items broken in service, or to join cast fittings to wrought members. Formerly, die-cast fittings were seldom used where welded construction was required, because they often contained porosity, but recent advances in casting technique, such as vacuum die casting, have resulted in improved quality; die castings are now satisfactorily welded for some applications, such as irrigation tubing.

Filler Metals

Classifications and compositions of filler metals for gas metal-arc and gas tungsten-arc welding of aluminum al-

*CARSON L. BROOKS, *Chairman*, Director, Research Technology and Applied Science, Metallurgical Research Div., Reynolds Metals Co.; F. R. BAYSINGER, Senior Research Associate, Center for Technology, Kaiser Aluminum & Chemical Corp.; CHARLES E. CATALDO, Materials Engineer, Marshall Space Flight Center, NASA; VERNE CLAIR, JR., Manager, Koldweld Div., Utica Turbine Parts Div., Kelsey-Hayes Co.; ALLAN ENIS, Project Engineer, Linde Div., Union Carbide Corp.; DON R. FYLLING, Senior Staff Engineer, Ordnance Engineering Div., FMC Corp.

JOHN J. HOFFER, Metallurgist, Kodak Apparatus Div., Eastman Kodak Co.; G. O. HOGLUND· (retired), formerly Manager, Joining and Metalworking Div., Alcoa Process Development Laboratories, Aluminum Co. of America; FRANK W. HUSSEY (deceased), formerly Chief, Metal Joining, Frankford Arsenal; H. A. JAMES, Assistant to the President, Sciaky Bros., Inc.; W. R. JEBSON, Plant Manager, Infilco Div., Westinghouse Electric Corp.; A. J. KISH (formerly Supervisor, Metal-

lurgical Engineering, Albuquerque Div., ACF Industries Inc.); FLORENCE R. MEYER, Aeroprojects Inc.; W. C. RUDD, Director, AMF Thermatool Inc., American Machine & Foundry Co.; Z. P. SAPERSTEIN, Chief Engineer, American Welding and Manufacturing Co. (formerly Group Engineer, Advanced Joining Technology, Missile & Space Systems Div., Douglas Aircraft Co., Inc.).

H. L. SAUNDERS, Welding Engineer, Alcan Research and Development Limited; WARREN F. SAVAGE, Professor and Director of Welding Research, Department of Materials Engineering, Rensselaer Polytechnic Institute; E. R. SEAY, Group Engineer, Manufacturing Research, Lockheed-Georgia Co. Div., Lockheed Aircraft Corp.; E. S. TYMINSKI, Chief Metallurgist, Air Products and Chemicals Inc.; N. E. WHEELER, Welding Engineer, Truck and Coach Div., General Motors Corp.

Some of the examples presented in this article were contributed by members of other Metals Handbook welding committees. References to examples that appear elsewhere in this volume are given on page 336.

Table 2. Nominal Compositions of Aluminum Alloys

Alloy	Composition, %	Alloy	Composition, %	Alloy	Composition, %
Wrought Aluminum Alloys(a)		5456	0.8 Mn, 5.1 Mg, 0.12 Cr	138 (238.0)	10.0 Cu, 4.0 Si, 0.3 Mg
1060	99.60 Al (min)	5652	2.5 Mg, 0.25 Cr	142 (242.0)	4.0 Cu, 1.5 Mg, 2.0 Ni
EC	99.45 Al (min)	6061	0.6 Si, 0.27 Cu, 1.0 Mg, 0.2 Cr	195 (295.0)	4.5 Cu, 0.8 Si
1100	0.12 Cu, 99.00 Al (min)	6063	0.4 Si, 0.7 Mg	B195 (B295.0)	4.5 Cu, 2.5 Si
2014	0.8 Si, 4.4 Cu, 0.8 Mn, 0.5 Mg	6101	0.5 Si, 0.6 Mg	214 (514.0)	3.8 Mg
2024	4.4 Cu, 0.6 Mn, 1.5 Mg	6151	0.9 Si, 0.6 Mg, 0.25 Cr	A214 (A514.0)	3.8 Mg, 1.8 Zn
2219	6.3 Cu, 0.3 Mn, 0.18 Zr, 0.1 V	7005	0.45 Mn, 1.4 Mg, 0.13 Cr, 4.5 Zn	B214 (B514.0)	1.8 Mg, 3.8 Si
3003	0.12 Cu, 1.2 Mn	7039	0.27 Mn, 2.8 Mg, 0.2 Cr, 4.0 Zn	F214 (F514.0)	0.5 Si, 3.8 Mg
3004	1.2 Mn, 1.0 Mg	7075	1.6 Cu, 2.5 Mg, 0.3 Cr, 5.6 Zn	220 (520.0)	10.0 Mg
4032	12.2 Si, 0.9 Cu, 1.1 Mg, 0.9 Ni	7079	0.6 Cu, 0.2 Mn, 3.3 Mg, 0.2 Cr, 4.3 Zn	319 (319.0)	3.5 Cu, 6.0 Si
5005	0.8 Mg	7178	2.0 Cu, 2.7 Mg, 0.3 Cr, 6.8 Zn	333 (333.0)	3.8 Cu, 9.0 Si
5050	1.4 Mg			355 (355.0)	1.3 Cu, 5.0 Si, 0.5 Mg
5052	2.5 Mg, 0.25 Cr	**Aluminum Casting Alloys(b)**		C355 (C355.0)	1.3 Cu, 5.0 Si, 0.5 Mg, 0.2 Fe max
5083	0.6 Mn, 4.45 Mg, 0.15 Cr	13 (413.0)	12.0 Si	356 (356.0)	7.0 Si, 0.3 Mg
5086	0.45 Mn, 4.0 Mg, 0.15 Cr	43 (443.0)	5.0 Si	A612 (A712.0)	0.5 Cu, 0.7 Mg, 6.5 Zn
5154	3.5 Mg, 0.25 Cr	108 (208.0)	4.0 Cu, 3.0 Si	C612 (C712.0)	0.5 Cu, 0.35 Mg, 6.5 Zn, 1.0 Fe
5254	2.5 Mg	A108 (308.0)	4.5 Cu, 5.5 Si	D612 (D712.0)	0.6 Mg, 5.3 Zn, 0.5 Cr
5454	0.8 Mn, 2.7 Mg, 0.12 Cr	122 (222.0)	10.0 Cu, 0.2 Mg		

(a) Wrought alloys are identified by Aluminum Association designations. (b) Casting alloys are identified first by industry designations, and then parenthetically by Aluminum Association designations.

loys are given in Table 3. In addition, filler metals having the same composition as the base-metal alloy are often used for repairing casting defects.

Selection of Filler Metal. Common criteria to be considered in selecting a filler metal are ease of welding, strength, ductility, resistance to corrosion of the filler metal – base metal combination, color match with the base metal after anodizing, and service at elevated temperature. The filler metals listed in Table 3 have been developed to satisfy these requirements. A guide for selection of the filler metal that gives the optimum combination of these criteria for general welding of a selection of alloy combinations is shown in Table 4. Tables 5 and 6 rate filler metals for specific welding criteria — namely, ease of welding, as-welded joint strength and ductility, corrosion and heat resistance, and color match after anodizing.

Joint Design and Edge Preparation

In general, joint design for aluminum alloys is similar to that for steel (see the illustrations in the article on Recommended Proportions of Grooves for Arc Welding, beginning on page 148 in this volume). The fact that the fluidity of aluminum during welding is higher than that of steel makes for some differences: for example, in thin sheet, the root opening is smaller. Recommended butt-joint designs for gas-shielded arc welding are shown in Fig. . When using straight-polarity direct-current gas tungsten-arc welding, the root face can be thicker and the grooves narrower. Some butt-joint designs used for gas metal-arc welding are shown in Fig. 6 and Table 9.

Lap joints are used more often for aluminum alloys than for most other metals. The efficiency of lap joints is 60 to 80%, depending on the alloy and temper. Lap joints offer the advantages of no edge preparation being required and ease of fit-up, but have the disadvantage that inspection of the weld is difficult. Preferred types of lap joints are shown in Fig. 2.

T-joints are also widely used. Beveling is seldom required, but it is used on thick material to reduce welding costs and to minimize distortion.

Welding a lap joint or a T-joint on one side only is not recommended. It is better to use a small continuous fillet weld on each side of the joint.

Edge Preparation and Assembly. Material up to about ⅜ in. thick can be sheared to a reasonably square edge that can be cleaned readily. Shear blades should be kept free of oil and foreign material; the aluminum should be degreased before shearing if there is excessive lubricant on the surface.

Band sawing, using a stick-wax lubricant, can be employed for edge preparation of metal several inches thick. After sawing, all lubricant should be removed from the sawed surface.

Usually, no lubricant is used when machining joint edges. When a lubricant must be used, sharp cutting tools of correct design should be employed. Dull or improperly designed tools result in prepared edges that can trap lubricant, which can cause weld porosity.

The extra time needed to ensure a close fit is often less than the extra time required in welding an improperly prepared assembly. Better fit and uniformity of the joint are required for automatic and out-of-position welding than for semiautomatic and flat-position welding. Automatic gas tungsten-arc welding of aluminum less than ⅛ in. thick requires that joint fit-up should be held within 0.003 to 0.010 in., depending on metal thickness. A very close fit of the edges is also essential when gas tungsten-arc welding without the addition of filler metal.

Aluminum alloy extrusions are sometimes produced with edge designs that facilitate welding. Besides edge preparation, the design may include (a) self-aligning mechanical fitting (see Example 294); (b) integral weld backing (see Example 311 and section F-F in Fig. 36); or (c) an increase in section thickness at the joint area to make welding easier, or (as in Example 319) to compensate for the lower unit strength of the weld area than of the base metal — which is especially valuable in butt welds in heat treatable alloys used in structures too large for most furnaces used for postweld heat treating.

Preweld Cleaning

Preweld cleaning of aluminum is essential for optimum weld quality. Precleaning requirements are especially stringent prior to straight-polarity direct-current gas tungsten-arc welding, because under such conditions the arc exerts no cleaning action. However, the highest-quality welds are not always needed. Where service requirements permit, many aluminum parts are welded with no preweld cleaning at all.

Surface contaminants that should be removed from the base metal include dirt, metal particles, oil and grease, paint, moisture, and heavy oxide coatings. Another source of contamination is oxide film on the filler metal. Base metals such as 1100 and 3003 have a relatively thin oxide coating as-fabricated, and the $5xxx$ and $6xxx$ series al-

Table 3. Compositions of Consumable Electrodes and Filler Metals for Gas Metal-Arc and Gas Tungsten-Arc Welding of Aluminum Alloys (AWS A5.10-69) (a)

AWS classification	Composition, %
ER1100	1.0 Si+Fe, 0.05-0.20 Cu, 0.05 Mn, 0.10 Zn, 99.00 Al (min)
ER1260	0.40 Si+Fe, 0.04 Cu, 0.01 Mn, 99.60 Al (min)
ER2319	0.20 Si, 0.30 Fe, 5.8-6.8 Cu, 0.20-0.40 Mn, 0.02 Mg, 0.10 Zn, 0.10-0.20 Ti
ER4043	4.5-6.0 Si, 0.8 Fe, 0.30 Cu, 0.05 Mn, 0.05 Mg, 0.10 Zn, 0.20 Ti
ER4047	11.0-13.0 Si, 0.8 Fe, 0.30 Cu, 0.15 Mn, 0.10 Mg, 0.20 Zn
ER4145	9.3-10.7 Si, 0.8 Fe, 3.3-4.7 Cu, 0.15 Mn, 0.15 Mg, 0.15 Cr, 0.20 Zn
ER5039	0.10 Si, 0.40 Fe, 0.03 Cu, 0.30-0.50 Mn, 3.3-4.3 Mg, 0.10-0.20 Cr, 2.4-3.2 Zn, 0.10 Ti
ER5183	0.40 Si, 0.40 Fe, 0.10 Cu, 0.50-1.0 Mn, 4.3-5.2 Mg, 0.05-0.25 Cr, 0.25 Zn, 0.15 Ti
ER5356	0.50 Si+Fe, 0.10 Cu, 0.05-0.20 Mn, 4.5-5.5 Mg, 0.05-0.20 Cr, 0.10 Zn, 0.06-0.20 Ti
ER5554	0.40 Si+Fe, 0.10 Cu, 0.50-1.0 Mn, 2.4-3.0 Mg, 0.05-0.20 Cr, 0.25 Zn, 0.05-0.20 Ti
ER5556	0.40 Si+Fe, 0.10 Cu, 0.50-1.0 Mn, 4.7-5.5 Mg, 0.05-0.20 Cr, 0.25 Zn, 0.05-0.20 Ti
ER5654(b)	0.45 Si+Fe, 0.05 Cu, 0.01 Mn, 3.1-3.9 Mg, 0.15-0.35 Cr, 0.20 Zn, 0.05-0.15 Ti
R-C4A(c)	1.5 Si, 1.0 Fe, 4.0-5.0 Cu, 0.35 Mn, 0.03 Mg, 0.35 Zn, 0.25 Ti
R-CN42A(c)	0.7 Si, 1.0 Fe, 3.5-4.5 Cu, 0.35 Mn, 1.2-1.8 Mg, 0.25 Cr, 1.7-2.3 Ni, 0.35 Zn, 0.25 Ti
R-SC51A(c)	4.5-5.5 Si, 0.8 Fe(d), 1.0-1.5 Cu, 0.50 Mn(d), 0.40-0.60 Mg, 0.25 Cr, 0.35 Zn, 0.25 Ti
R-SG70A(c)	6.5-7.5 Si, 0.6 Fe, 0.25 Cu, 0.35 Mn, 0.20-0.40 Mg, 0.35 Zn, 0.25 Ti

(a) Single values are maximums, except for aluminum content of ER1100 and ER1260. (b) ER5654 replaces ER5154, ER5254 and ER5652. (c) For repair of castings. (d) If iron exceeds 0.45%, manganese should be equal to one-half the iron content.

Table 4. Filler Metals Suitable for General-Purpose Gas-Shielded Arc Welding of Various Combinations of Aluminum Alloy Base Metals

NOTE: All filler metals shown here are covered by AWS specification A5.10-69, prefixed by the letters "ER". Throughout this table, the prefix has been omitted, to conserve space. Filler metals 5356, 5556 and 5654 are not recommended for sustained service at temperatures higher than 150 F. Other service conditions, such as immersion in fresh or salt water or exposure to specific chemicals, may also limit the choice of filler metal. Where no filler metal is listed, the base-metal combination is not recommended for welding.

Base metals to be welded (in column below, and in column heads at right)	1060, EC	1100, 3003, alclad 3003	2014, 2024	2219	3004, alclad 3004	5005, 5050	5052, 5652a	5083	5086	5154, 5254a	5454	5456	6061, 6063, 6101, 6151	7005, 7039, A612, C612, D612	214, A214, B214, F214	13, 43, 356	319, 333, 355, C355
1060, 1100, 3003, alclad 3003	1260bf	1100b	4145	4145	4043c	1100b	4043c	5356b	5356b	4043c,e	4043c,e	5356b	4043c	4043c	4043c,e	4043c,d	4145b,c
2014, 2024		1100b	4145	4145	4043e	4043e	4043c	5356b	5356b	4043c,e	4043c,e	5356b	4043c	4043c	4043c,e	4043c,d	4145b,c
2219			4145g	4145g	4043	4043e	4043c	4043	4043	4043c	4043c	4043	4145	4145	4043	4145	4145g
3004, alclad 3004				2319b,c,d	4043e	4043	4043c,e	5356e	5356e	5654h	5654h	5356e	4043c,d	4043c	5654h	4043c	4145b,c,g
5005, 5050					4043e,f	4043	4043c,e	5356e	5356e	5654h	5654h	5356e	4043h	5356e,k	5654h	4043c	4043c
5052, 5652a						5654a,b,h	5356e	5356e	5654h	5356e	5356e	4043h	5356b,k	5356e	4043c,h	4043c
5083							5183e	5356e	5356h	5356h	5183e	5356e	5356b,h	5356b,k	5654h	5356b,c,e
5086								5356e	5356h	5356h	5356h	5356b,h	5356b,h	5356e	5654h	5356e,k
5154, 5254a									5654a,h	5356h	5356h	5356e	5356b,h	5356b,h	5356e	5356b,c,e
5454										5554h	5356h	5356e	5356e	5356e	5654h	4043c,h
5456											5556	5356e	5356e	5356e	5356b	5356b,c,e
6061, 6063, 6101, 6151												4043c,h	5356b,c,h,k	5356b	4043c,h	5356b,c
7005, 7039, A612, C612, D612													5039e	4043c	4043c,h	4043c
214, A214, B214, F214														5654h,j	4043c	5356h,k
13, 43, 356															4043c	4043c
319, 333, 355, C355																4145b,c,f
5554	5554 is suitable for service at elevated temperature.																

(a) Base metals 5254 and 5652 are used for hydrogen peroxide service. Filler metal 5654 is used for welding both alloys for service at temperatures of 150 F and below. (b) 4043 may be used for some jobs. (c) 4047 may be used for some jobs. (d) 2319 may be used for some jobs. (e) 5183, 5356, 5554, 5556 and 5654 may be used. In some cases they provide improved color match after anodizing treatment, highest weld ductility, and higher weld strength. Filler metal 5039 may be used for some jobs. (f) 1100 may be used for some jobs. (g) 4145 may be used for some jobs. (h) 5183, 5356, 5554, 5556 and 5654 may be used for some jobs. (j) Filler metal of the same composition as the base metal is sometimes used. (k) 5039 may be used for some jobs.

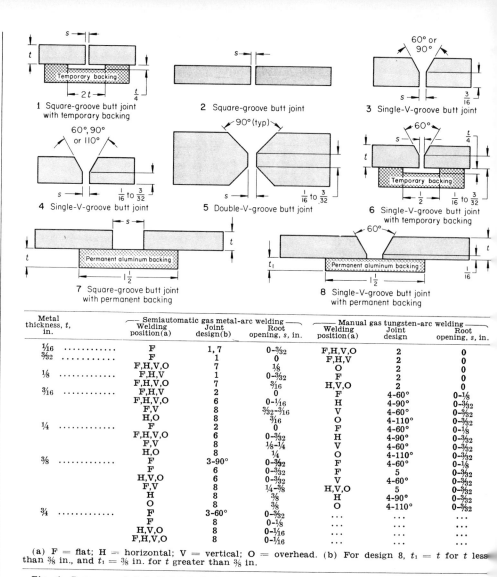

Metal thickness, t, in.	Semiautomatic gas metal-arc welding			Manual gas tungsten-arc welding		
	Welding position(a)	Joint design(b)	Root opening, s, in.	Welding position(a)	Joint design	Root opening, s, in.
1/16	F	1, 7	0-3/32	F,H,V,O	2	0
3/32	F	1	0	F,H,V	2	0
	F,H,V,O	7	1/8	O	2	0
1/8	F,H,V	1	0-3/32	F	2	0
	F,H,V,O	7	3/16	H,V,O	2	0
3/16	F,H,V	2	0	F	4-60°	0-1/8
	F,H,V,O	6	0-1/16	H	4-90°	0-3/32
	F,V	8	3/32-3/16	V	4-60°	0-3/32
	H,O	8	3/16	O	4-110°	0-3/32
1/4	F	2	0	F	4-60°	0-1/8
	F,H,V,O	6	0-3/32	H	4-90°	0-3/32
	F,V	8	1/8-1/4	V	4-60°	0-3/32
	H,O	8	1/4	O	4-110°	0-3/32
3/8	F	3-90°	0-3/32	F	4-60°	0-1/8
	H,V,O	6	0-3/32	F	5	0-3/32
	F,V	8	1/4-3/8	H,V,O	5	0-3/32
	H	8	3/8	H	4-90°	0-3/32
	O	8	3/8	O	4-110°	0-3/32
3/4	F	3-60°	0-3/32	...	...	...
	O	8	0-1/8	...	...	...
	F,H,V,O	8	0-1/16	...	...	...

(a) F = flat; H = horizontal; V = vertical; O = overhead. (b) For design 8, $t_1 = t$ for t less than 3/8 in., and $t_1 = 3/8$ in. for t greater than 3/8 in.

Fig. 1. Recommended butt-joint designs for the gas metal-arc welding (dcrp) and gas tungsten-arc welding (ac) of aluminum alloys. Joints 2, 3, 4, 5 and 6 should be back gouged to solid weld metal before applying a pass on the root side.

loys generally have a thick, dark oxide coating. The thicker the oxide, the greater its adverse effect on weld-metal flow and solidification and the greater the risk of porosity. Any foreign material that remains on the surfaces to be welded is a potential source of unsound welds. For best results, all cleaning and oxide removal should be done immediately before welding.

First, the work-metal surface should be cleaned of contaminants. The following manual cleaning methods can be used for small production runs. Dirt can be removed easily by washing and scrubbing with a detergent solution; an effective drying procedure is necessary to ensure that no moisture is present on the surfaces to be welded. Removal of grease and oil can be accomplished by swabbing with solvent-soaked cloths. Suitable solvents include

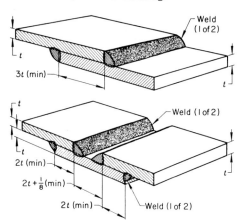

Fig. 2. Preferred types of lap joints for arc welding of aluminum alloys

Footnotes for Table 5

(a) Rating applies particularly to fillet welds. All filler alloys rated will develop presently specified minimum strengths in butt welds.

(b) Rating based on continuous or alternate immersion in fresh or salt water. (c) Rating based on free-bend elongation of weld.

(d) Filler alloy 5183 has the same ratings as 5556, except that welds made with 5183 are slightly more ductile and, in cases where the filler metal controls the weld strength, slightly less strong than welds made with 5556. Because of its lower strength, 5183 filler metal is not recommended for welding 5456.

(e) Filler-metal alloys 5356 and 5556 are not recommended for corrosion resistance in welding alloy 1100, 3003 or 3004 to bare alloy 3003 or 3004, but are rated B for corrosion resistance in welding alloy 1100 or 3003 to alclad 3003 or 3004, and rated C for corrosion resistance in welding alloy 3004 to alclad 3004. (f) Ratings do not apply when heat treated after welding

Table 5. Filler Metals Commonly Used in Arc Welding Combinations of Aluminum Alloys

(Ratings are relative, in decreasing order of merit, and apply only within a given block. Combinations having no rating are not recommended.)

	Filler alloy(d)																																			
	Ease of welding						Strength of welded joint (as-welded)(a)						Corrosion resistance(b)						Service at sustained temp above 150 F						Color match after anodizing						Ductility(c)					
Alloys to be welded	1100	4043	5654	5356	5554	5556	1100	4043	5654	5356	5554	5556	1100	4043	5654	5356	5554	5556	1100	4043	5654	5356	5554	5556	1100	4043	5654	5356	5554	5556	1100	4043	5654	5356	5554	5556
To weld alloy 1100 to:																																				
1100	B	A	–	C	–	C	B	A	–	A	–	A	A	A	–	–	–	–	A	A	–	–	–	–	A	–	–	B	–	B	A	D	–	B	–	C
3003, alclad 3003	A	A	–	B	–	B	B	A	–	A	–	A	A	A	–	(e)	–	(e)	A	A	–	–	–	–	A	–	–	B	–	B	A	D	–	B	–	C
3004, alclad 3004	C	A	–	B	–	B	B	A	–	A	–	A	A	A	–	(e)	–	(e)	A	A	–	–	–	–	A	–	–	B	–	B	A	D	–	B	–	C
5005, 5050	B	A	–	B	–	B	B	A	–	A	–	A	A	A	–	–	–	–	A	A	–	–	–	–	A	–	–	B	–	B	A	D	–	B	–	C
5052, 5154, 5454	–	–	–	–	–	–	–	–	–	–	–	–	–	–	–	–	–	–	–	–	–	–	–	–	–	–	–	–	–	–	–	–	–	–	–	–
5083, 5086, 5456	–	–	–	–	–	–	–	–	–	–	–	–	–	–	–	–	–	–	–	–	–	–	–	–	–	–	–	–	–	–	–	–	–	–	–	–
6063(f), 6101(f)	–	A	–	B	–	B	–	A	–	A	–	A	–	A	–	–	–	–	–	A	–	–	–	–	–	–	–	A	–	A	–	C	–	A	–	B
6061(f)	–	A	–	B	–	B	–	A	–	A	–	A	–	A	–	–	–	–	–	A	–	–	–	–	–	–	–	A	–	A	–	C	–	A	–	B
To weld alloy 3003 to:																																				
3003, alclad 3003	A	A	–	B	–	B	C	B	–	A	–	A	A	A	–	(e)	–	(e)	A	A	–	–	–	–	A	–	–	B	–	B	A	D	–	B	–	C
3004, alclad 3004	–	A	–	B	–	B	–	B	–	A	–	A	–	A	–	(e)	–	(e)	–	A	–	–	–	–	–	–	–	A	–	A	–	C	–	A	–	B
5005, 5050	B	A	–	B	–	B	C	B	–	A	–	A	A	A	–	–	–	–	A	A	–	–	–	–	A	–	–	B	–	B	A	D	–	B	–	C
5052	–	A	–	B	–	B	–	B	–	A	–	A	–	A	–	–	–	–	–	A	–	–	–	–	–	–	–	A	–	A	–	C	–	A	–	B
5154	–	A	C	B	C	B	–	B	A	A	A	A	–	C	A	B	A	B	–	–	–	–	–	–	–	–	B	A	A	A	–	C	A	A	A	B
5454	–	A	–	B	C	B	–	B	–	A	A	A	–	C	–	B	A	B	–	A	–	–	A	–	–	–	–	A	A	A	–	C	–	A	A	B
5083, 5086, 5456	–	A	–	A	–	A	–	B	–	A	–	A	–	B	–	A	–	A	–	–	–	–	–	–	–	–	–	A	–	A	–	C	–	A	–	B
6063(f), 6101(f)	–	A	–	B	–	B	–	B	–	A	–	A	–	A	–	–	–	–	–	A	–	–	–	–	–	–	–	A	–	A	–	C	–	A	–	B
6061(e)	–	A	–	B	–	B	–	B	–	A	–	A	–	A	–	–	–	–	–	A	–	–	–	–	–	–	–	A	–	A	–	C	–	A	–	B
To weld alclad 3003 to:																																				
Alclad 3003	A	A	–	B	–	B	C	B	–	A	–	A	A	A	–	B	–	B	A	A	–	–	–	–	A	–	–	B	–	B	A	D	–	B	–	C
3004, alclad 3004	–	A	–	B	–	B	–	B	–	A	–	A	–	A	–	B	–	B	–	A	–	–	–	–	–	–	–	A	–	A	–	C	–	A	–	B
5005, 5050	B	A	–	B	–	B	C	B	–	A	–	A	A	A	–	B	–	B	A	A	–	–	–	–	A	–	–	B	–	B	A	D	–	B	–	C
5052	–	A	–	B	–	B	–	B	–	A	–	A	–	A	–	B	–	B	–	A	–	–	–	–	–	–	–	A	–	A	–	C	–	A	–	B
5154	–	A	C	B	C	B	–	B	A	A	A	A	–	C	A	B	A	B	–	–	–	–	–	–	–	–	B	A	A	A	–	C	A	A	A	B
5454	–	A	–	B	C	B	–	B	–	A	A	A	–	C	–	B	A	B	–	A	–	–	A	–	–	–	–	A	A	A	–	C	–	A	A	B
5083, 5086, 5456	–	A	–	A	–	A	–	B	–	A	–	A	–	B	–	A	–	A	–	–	–	–	–	–	–	–	–	A	–	A	–	C	–	A	–	B
6063(f), 6101(f)	–	A	–	B	–	B	–	B	–	A	–	A	–	A	–	B	–	B	–	A	–	–	–	–	–	–	–	A	–	A	–	C	–	A	–	B
6061(f)	–	A	–	B	–	B	–	B	–	A	–	A	–	A	–	B	–	B	–	A	–	–	–	–	–	–	–	A	–	A	–	C	–	A	–	B
To weld alloy 3004 to:																																				
3004, alclad 3004	–	A	C	B	C	B	–	D	C	B	C	A	–	A	B	(e)	B	(e)	–	A	–	–	A	–	–	–	B	A	A	A	–	C	A	A	A	B
5005, 5050	–	A	–	B	–	B	–	B	–	A	–	A	–	A	–	–	–	–	–	A	–	–	–	–	–	–	–	A	–	A	–	C	–	A	–	B
5052	–	A	–	B	–	B	–	C	–	B	–	A	–	A	–	–	–	–	–	A	–	–	–	–	–	–	–	A	–	A	–	C	–	A	–	B
5154	–	A	C	B	C	B	–	D	C	B	C	A	–	C	A	B	A	B	–	–	–	–	–	–	–	–	B	A	A	A	–	C	A	A	A	B
5454	–	A	–	B	C	B	–	D	–	B	C	A	–	C	–	B	A	B	–	A	–	–	A	–	–	–	–	A	A	A	–	C	–	A	A	B
5083, 5086, 5456	–	A	–	A	–	A	–	C	–	B	–	A	–	B	–	A	–	A	–	–	–	–	–	–	–	–	–	A	–	A	–	C	–	A	–	B
6063(f), 6101(f)	–	A	–	B	–	B	–	C	–	B	–	A	–	A	–	–	–	–	–	A	–	–	–	–	–	–	–	A	–	A	–	C	–	A	–	B
6061(f)	–	A	–	B	–	B	–	C	–	B	–	A	–	A	–	–	–	–	–	A	–	–	–	–	–	–	–	A	–	A	–	C	–	A	–	B
To weld alclad 3004 to:																																				
Alclad 3004	–	A	C	B	C	B	–	D	C	B	C	A	–	A	B	C	B	C	–	A	–	–	A	–	–	–	B	A	A	A	–	C	A	A	A	B
5005, 5050	–	A	–	B	–	B	–	B	–	A	–	A	–	A	–	B	–	B	–	A	–	–	–	–	–	–	–	A	–	A	–	C	–	A	–	B
5052	–	A	–	B	–	B	–	C	–	B	–	A	–	A	–	B	–	B	–	A	–	–	–	–	–	–	–	A	–	A	–	C	–	A	–	B
5154	–	A	C	B	C	B	–	D	C	B	C	A	–	C	A	B	A	B	–	–	–	–	–	–	–	–	B	A	A	A	–	C	A	A	A	B
5454	–	A	–	B	C	B	–	D	–	B	C	A	–	C	–	B	A	B	–	A	–	–	A	–	–	–	–	A	A	A	–	C	–	A	A	B
5083, 5086, 5456	–	A	–	A	–	A	–	C	–	B	–	A	–	B	–	A	–	A	–	–	–	–	–	–	–	–	–	A	–	A	–	C	–	A	–	B
6063(f), 6101(f)	–	A	–	B	–	B	–	C	–	B	–	A	–	A	–	B	–	B	–	A	–	–	–	–	–	–	–	A	–	A	–	C	–	A	–	B
6061(f)	–	A	–	B	–	B	–	C	–	B	–	A	–	A	–	B	–	B	–	A	–	–	–	–	–	–	–	A	–	A	–	C	–	A	–	B
To weld alloy 5005 or 5050 to:																																				
5005, 5050	C	A	–	B	–	B	–	B	–	A	–	A	A	A	–	–	–	–	A	A	–	–	–	–	A	–	–	B	–	B	A	D	–	B	–	C
5052	–	A	–	B	–	B	–	B	–	A	–	A	–	A	–	–	–	–	–	A	–	–	–	–	–	–	–	A	–	A	–	C	–	A	–	B
5154	–	A	C	B	C	B	–	B	A	A	A	A	–	C	A	B	A	B	–	–	–	–	–	–	–	–	B	A	A	A	–	C	A	A	A	B
5454	–	A	–	B	C	B	–	B	–	A	A	A	–	C	–	B	A	B	–	A	–	–	A	–	–	–	–	A	A	A	–	C	–	A	A	B
5083, 5086, 5456	–	A	–	A	–	A	–	B	–	A	–	A	–	B	–	A	–	A	–	–	–	–	–	–	–	–	–	A	–	A	–	C	–	A	–	B
6063(f), 6101(f)	–	A	–	B	–	B	–	B	–	A	–	A	–	A	–	–	–	–	–	A	–	–	–	–	–	–	–	A	–	A	–	C	–	A	–	B
6061(f)	–	A	–	B	–	B	–	B	–	A	–	A	–	A	–	–	–	–	–	A	–	–	–	–	–	–	–	A	–	A	–	C	–	A	–	B
To weld alloy 5052 to:																																				
5052	–	A	B	A	C	A	–	D	C	B	C	A	–	C	B	–	B	–	–	A	–	–	B	–	–	–	A	A	B	B	–	C	A	A	A	B
5154	–	A	B	A	C	A	–	D	C	B	C	A	–	C	A	B	A	B	–	–	–	–	–	–	–	–	A	A	B	B	–	C	A	A	A	B
5454	–	A	B	A	C	A	–	D	C	B	C	A	–	C	B	B	A	B	–	A	–	–	A	–	–	–	B	A	A	A	–	C	A	A	A	B
5083, 5086, 5456	–	–	–	A	–	A	–	–	–	B	–	A	–	–	–	A	–	A	–	–	–	–	–	–	–	–	–	A	–	A	–	–	–	A	–	B
6063(f), 6101(f)	–	A	C	B	C	B	–	B	A	A	A	A	–	A	B	–	B	–	–	A	–	–	A	–	–	–	B	A	A	A	–	C	A	A	A	B
6061(f)	–	A	C	B	C	B	–	D	C	B	C	A	–	A	B	–	B	–	–	A	–	–	A	–	–	–	A	A	B	B	–	C	A	A	A	B
To weld alloy 5083 or 5456 to:																																				
5154	–	–	B	A	B	A	–	–	C	B	C	A	–	–	A	A	A	A	–	–	–	–	–	–	–	–	B	A	A	A	–	–	A	A	A	B
5454	–	–	–	A	B	A	–	–	–	B	C	A	–	–	–	B	A	B	–	–	–	–	–	–	–	–	–	A	A	A	–	–	–	A	A	B
5083, 5086, 5456	–	–	–	A	–	A	–	–	–	B	–	A	–	–	–	A	–	A	–	–	–	–	–	–	–	–	–	A	–	A	–	–	–	A	–	B
6063(f), 6101(f)	–	A	B	A	B	A	–	B	A	A	A	A	–	A	A	A	A	A	–	–	–	–	–	–	–	–	B	A	A	A	–	C	A	A	A	B
6061(f)	–	A	B	A	B	A	–	D	C	B	C	A	–	A	A	A	A	A	–	–	–	–	–	–	–	–	B	A	A	A	–	C	A	A	A	B
To weld alloy 5086 to:																																				
5154	–	–	B	A	B	A	–	–	C	B	C	A	–	–	A	A	A	A	–	–	–	–	–	–	–	–	B	A	A	A	–	–	A	A	A	B
5454	–	–	–	A	B	A	–	–	–	B	C	A	–	–	–	B	A	B	–	–	–	–	–	–	–	–	–	A	A	A	–	–	–	A	A	B
5086	–	–	–	A	–	A	–	–	–	B	–	A	–	–	–	A	–	A	–	–	–	–	–	–	–	–	–	A	–	A	–	–	–	A	–	B
6063(f), 6101(f)	–	A	B	A	B	A	–	B	A	A	A	A	–	A	A	A	A	A	–	–	–	–	–	–	–	–	B	A	A	A	–	C	A	A	A	B
6061(f)	–	A	B	A	B	A	–	D	C	B	C	A	–	A	A	A	A	A	–	–	–	–	–	–	–	–	B	A	A	A	–	C	A	A	A	B
To weld alloy 5154 to:																																				
5154	–	–	B	A	B	A	–	–	C	B	C	A	–	–	A	–	A	–	–	–	–	–	–	–	–	–	A	A	B	B	–	–	A	A	A	B
5454	–	–	B	B	B	A	–	–	C	B	C	A	–	–	A	B	A	B	–	–	–	–	–	–	–	–	B	A	A	A	–	–	A	A	A	B
6063(f), 6101(f)	–	A	C	B	C	B	–	B	A	A	A	A	–	A	B	–	B	–	–	–	–	–	–	–	–	–	B	A	A	A	–	C	A	A	A	B
6061(f)	–	A	C	B	C	B	–	D	C	B	C	A	–	A	B	–	B	–	–	–	–	–	–	–	–	–	A	A	B	B	–	C	A	A	A	B
To weld alloy 5454 to:																																				
5454	–	–	B	A	B	A	–	–	C	B	C	A	–	–	B	B	A	B	–	–	–	–	A	–	–	–	B	A	A	A	–	–	A	A	A	B
6063(f), 6101(f)	–	A	C	B	C	B	–	B	A	A	A	A	–	B	B	–	A	–	–	A	–	–	A	–	–	–	B	A	A	A	–	C	A	A	A	B
6061(f)	–	A	C	B	C	B	–	D	C	B	C	A	–	B	B	–	A	–	–	A	–	–	A	–	–	–	B	A	A	A	–	C	A	A	A	B
To weld alloy 6061 to:																																				
6063(f), 6101(f)	–	A	C	B	C	B	–	B	A	A	A	A	–	A	B	C	B	C	–	A	–	–	B	–	–	–	B	A	A	A	–	C	A	A	A	B
6061(f)	–	A	C	B	C	B	–	D	C	B	C	A	–	A	B	C	B	C	–	A	–	–	B	–	–	–	B	A	B	B	–	C	A	A	A	B
To weld alloy 6063 or 6101 to:																																				
6063(f), 6101(f)	–	A	C	B	C	B	–	B	A	A	A	A	–	A	B	C	B	C	–	A	–	–	B	–	–	–	B	A	A	A	–	C	A	A	A	B

For footnotes, see facing page.

Source: Metals Handbook, 8th Ed., Vol. 6, ASM

butyl alcohol, naphtha, acetone, carbon tetrachloride, and trichlorethylene. Butyl alcohol, naphtha and acetone must be used with care, because they are flammable; carbon tetrachloride and trichlorethylene should be used only with effective ventilation, and well away from the welding area, because they decompose and produce toxic fumes when contacted by the arc.

Next, heavy oxide layers should be mechanically removed with a wire brush, steel wool, mill file, portable milling tool, or a scraper. The use of abrasive paper or grinding disks alone is not recommended, because particles of the abrasive may become embedded in the aluminum and, unless subsequently removed, can cause inclusions in the weld. Wire brushes should have sharp bristles and should be kept free of oil and other foreign material; bristles preferably should be 0.012 to 0.016 in. in diameter and of stainless steel, to minimize iron oxide pickup.

Motor-driven wire brushes should be used carefully. If excessive pressure is applied, a burnishing action in which the oxide is rolled into the freshly exposed surface will result, and the weld may be of poorer quality than one made without wire brushing. However, enough pressure has to be used to cause the sharp bristles to break the oxide from the surface of the aluminum alloy.

Chemical removal of oxides can be accomplished by immersion in solutions of the butyl alcohol–phosphoric acid type. After the chemical treatment, the parts should be washed thoroughly with water and dried with hot air.

For thick and persistent oxide coatings, immersion in a 5% sodium hydroxide solution at 150 F for 30 sec is recommended. This treatment leaves a dark smut on the surface. To remove the smut, the treatment should be followed by a cold water rinse, immersion in a solution containing equal parts of commercial nitric acid and water at room temperature, a final water rinse (preferably hot) and hot air drying. Heavy-etching caustic solutions are not recommended, because the rough surface that they produce is likely to collect hydrocarbons and foreign material.

It is preferable that degreasing and chemical cleaning be done before the parts are assembled for welding. Cleaning after assembly can result in retention of foreign material and solutions between abutting edges and lapped areas of the joint, and porosity and dross entrapment in the weld are likely to result.

Freshly machined and freshly filed surfaces are the cleanest and are often specified when the ultimate in weld quality is demanded.

Occasionally, special precleaning methods are used to solve a specific problem, as in the following example:

Example 293. Preweld Cleaning of Parts for Fuel-Storage Tanks (Fig. 3)

Preweld cleaning required special attention in the fabrication of fuel-storage tanks for M-60 combat tanks from 80 individual parts, because the welded joints had to have optimum ductility and fatigue strength to withstand the severe vibrational stress to which the fuel-storage tanks were subjected in service.

Original preweld cleaning practice called for: (a) vapor degreasing (when necessary) to remove most of the foreign matter; (b) dipping in a caustic etching solution; (c) rinsing; (d) dipping in a nitric acid deoxidizing solution; and (e) rinsing. This method of cleaning, however, was unsatisfactory because:

1 The metal surfaces reoxidized after a few hours, which necessitated the recleaning of many parts and subassemblies during the welding of a tank.
2 During the caustic etch, the amount of metal removed from threaded parts was enough to cause the threads to be out of tolerance.
3 Use of nitric acid created a safety hazard.

A special chemical cleaning method consisting of five steps was therefore developed. The process is shown in Fig. 3 and described in the accompanying table. Parts with drawing compound or heavy soils were vapor degreased prior to step 1.

To prevent contamination of the chemical solutions, back rinsing was not permitted. Solution strengths were checked daily by titration and were kept in the composition ranges listed in the table.

Work metal was $\frac{1}{8}$-in.-thick alloy 5086-H32 sheet, alloy 5083-H112 extrusions, and alloy 6061-T6 fittings. The design of the vehicle utilized every available cubic inch of space between the engine and the tank hull, and in consequence the left-hand and right-hand fuel tanks, composed of 50 subassemblies (80 parts), were of dissimilar and complex shapes. Although the irregular shapes were formed, wherever possible, by bending, approximately 20 ft of gas metal-arc tack welding and 200 ft of gas tungsten-arc welded seams were required per fuel tank. The details for tack welding are given in Example 305; joint-welding details are given in Example 311.

The special precleaning method produced a more stable surface on the aluminum alloy parts, which permitted a longer elapsed time between cleaning and welding, and permitted, under normal conditions,

Table 6. Guide to Selection of Filler-Metal Alloys for Arc Welding Various Combinations of Heat Treatable Aluminum Alloys

(Ratings are relative, in decreasing order of merit, and apply to a given base-metal combination and postweld condition. The use of base metals as filler metals, or of combinations indicated here by dashes as having no ratings, is not recommended.)

Alloys to be welded(a)	Postweld condition(b)	Ease of welding — Filler alloys						Strength(c) — Filler alloys						Ductility(d) — Filler alloys						Corrosion resistance(e) — Filler alloys					
		2319	4043	4145	5039	5556(f)	5554(g)	2319	4043	4145	5039	5556(f)	5554(g)	2319	4043	4145	5039	5556(f)	5554(g)	2319	4043	4145	5039	5556(f)	5554(g)
To weld 2014 or 2024 to:																									
2014, 2024 or 2219	X	C	B	A	–	–	–	A	B	A	–	–	–	A	A	B	–	–	–	A	B	B	–	–	–
	Y	C	B	A	–	–	–	A	C	B	–	–	–	A	B	B	–	–	–	A	B	B	–	–	–
To weld 2219 to:																									
2219	X	A	A	A	–	–	–	A	B	B	–	–	–	A	B	B	–	–	–	A	B	B	–	–	–
	Y or Z	A	A	A	–	–	–	A	C	B	–	–	–	A	B	B	–	–	–	A	B	B	–	–	–
To weld 6061, 6063 or 6101 to:																									
1100	X	–	A	–	–	B	–	–	A	–	–	A	–	–	B	–	–	A	–	–	A	–	–	B	–
2014 or 2024	X	–	B	A	–	–	–	–	A	A	–	–	–	–	A	B	–	–	–	–	A	A	–	–	–
2219	X	–	A	A	–	–	–	–	A	A	–	–	–	–	A	A	–	–	–	–	A	A	–	–	–
3003, 3004, 5005 or 5050	X	–	A	–	–	B	–	–	B	–	–	A	–	–	B	–	–	A	–	–	A	–	–	B	–
5052, 5154 or 5454	X	–	A	–	–	B	C	–	C	–	–	A	B	–	B	–	–	A	A	–	A	–	–	B	A
5083, 5086 or 5456	X	–	–	–	–	A	B	–	–	–	–	A	B	–	–	–	–	B	A	–	–	–	–	A	A
6061, 6063 or 6101	X	–	A	–	–	B	C	–	C	–	–	A	B	–	B	–	–	A	A	–	A	–	–	C	B
	Y or Z	–	A	–	–	(h)	B	–	A	–	–	(h)	B	–	B	–	–	(h)	A	–	A	–	–	(h)	B
To weld 7005 or 7039 to:																									
5052, 5154 or 5454	X	–	A	–	A	A	B	–	D	–	A	B	C	–	B	–	A	A	A	–	B	–	A	A	A
5083, 5086 or 5456	X	–	–	–	A	A	–	–	–	–	A	B	–	–	–	–	A	A	–	–	–	–	A	A	–
6061 or 6063	X	–	A	–	A	A	B	–	D	–	A	B	C	–	B	–	A	A	A	–	A	–	A	A	A
	Y or Z	–	A	–	A	(h)	B)	–	C	–	A	B	C	–	B	–	A	(h)	A	–	A	–	A	(h)	A
7005 or 7039	X	–	–	–	A	A	–	–	–	–	A	B	–	–	–	–	A	A	–	–	–	–	A	A	–
	Y or Z	–	–	–	A	(h)	–	–	–	–	A	(h)	–	–	–	–	A	(h)	–	–	–	–	A	(h)	–
To weld 7075 or 7178 to:																									
7075 or 7178	X	–	A	A	B	B	–	–	C	C	A	B	–	–	B	B	A	A	–	–	B	B	A	A	–
	Y or Z	–	A	A	B	(h)		–	B	B	A	(h)		–	B	B	A	(h)		–	A	A	B	(h)	

(a) Ratings for both bare and alclad materials are the same. (b) X = naturally aged for 30 days or longer; Y = postweld solution heat treated and artificially aged; Z = postweld artificially aged. (c) Ultimate strength from cross-weld tensile test. (d) Ratings based on free-bend elongation of weld. (e) Ratings based on continuous or alternate immersion in fresh or salt water. (f) 5183 and 5356 have the same ratings as 5556. (g) Filler alloy 5554 is suitable for welding 6061, 6063 and 7005 prior to brazing. (h) Filler alloy not recommended because of possible susceptibility to stress-corrosion cracking when postweld heat treated.

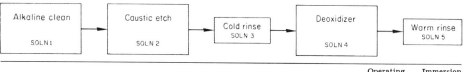

Number	Solution Type	Composition	Operating temperature, F	Immersion time, minutes
1	Nonsilicated alkaline cleaner	3 to 4 oz/gal of water	140 to 150	5 to 10
2	Caustic soda etch	3 to 4 oz/gal of water	145 to 150	4 to 6
3	Cold water rinse	Water(a)	70	1 to 3
4	Chromic acid deoxidizer	11 to 13 oz/gal of water	70 to 90	6 to 10
5	Warm water rinse	Water(b)	135 to 145	1(c)

(a) Rinse should be overflowing, with air agitation. (b) Rinse should be overflowing, to remove the acid and warm the part for quick drying. (c) Minimum.

Fig. 3. Flow chart for five-step cleaning process used for parts to be welded to make a fuel-storage tank (Example 293)

complete welding of an assembly without recleaning. Solution 2 was bypassed when parts that were to be cleaned contained threads (as the etchant affected thread dimensions) and when recleaning was required for dusty parts and parts whose welding had been delayed.

Chemical recleaning could not be used on the subassemblies before final welding of the assembly because capillary action would have caused entrapment of reagents in the seams on some of the parts, which would have caused sputtering during welding. Therefore, these joints were recleaned mechanically with power brushes having stainless steel wire bristles.

Preheating

In gas-shielded arc welding of aluminum alloys, preheating of parts to be welded is normally employed only when the temperature of the parts is below 15 F or when the mass of the parts is such that the heat is conducted away from the joint faster than the welding process can supply it. Preheating may be advantageous for gas tungsten-arc welding with alternating current of parts thicker than about 3/16 in. and gas metal-arc welding of parts thicker than about 1 in. Gas tungsten-arc welding with reverse-polarity direct current is limited to thin material, and preheating is not necessary with this process. It is also not necessary to preheat thick parts when gas tungsten-arc welding using straight-polarity direct current, because of the high heat input provided to the work.

Preheating can also reduce production costs because the joint area will reach welding temperature faster, thus permitting higher welding speeds.

Various methods can be employed to preheat the entire part or assembly to be welded, or only the area adjacent to the weld can be heated by use of a gas torch. In mechanized welding, local preheating (and drying) can be done by gas or tungsten-arc torches installed ahead of the welding electrode.

The preheating temperature depends on the job. Often 200 F is sufficient to ensure adequate penetration on weld starts, without readjustment of the current as welding progresses. Preheating temperature for wrought aluminum alloys seldom exceeds 300 to 400 F, because the desirable properties of certain aluminum alloys and tempers may be adversely affected at higher temperatures. Aluminum-magnesium alloys containing 4.0 to 5.5% Mg (5083, 5086 and 5456) should not be preheated to between 200 and 450 F, because their resistance to stress-corrosion cracking will be reduced by this treatment.

Large or intricate castings should be preheated to approximately 800 F to minimize thermal stresses and to facilitate attainment of the welding temperature. After welding, such castings should be cooled slowly to minimize the danger of cracking. Castings that are to be used in the heat treated condition should be welded before heat treatment or should be reheat treated after welding. Preheating (and the heat of welding) may affect the corrosion resistance of some alloys — for instance, alloy 220 — unless welding is followed by heat treatment.

Preheating for weld repair of a plate is described in Example 307, and for a casting on page 318.

Fixtures

Design of fixtures is based on the expectation that dimensional changes in welding aluminum alloys will be twice as great as in the welding of steel. The coefficient of expansion of aluminum is about twice that of steel, and its melting point is about half that of steel. Thus, the change in dimensions from welding heat is in the same range as that for steel. However, the thermal conductivity of aluminum is greater. In general, the amount of expansion is inversely proportional to the speed of welding.

When butt welding aluminum sheet, the fixture should enable the sheet to be clamped with a uniform force of approximately 200 lb per linear inch of

Table 7. Typical Conditions for Welding Corner Joints by the Semiautomatic Gas Metal-Arc Process

Metal thickness, in.	Welding position(a)	Electrode wire Diameter, in.	Electrode wire Used per 100 ft, lb	Argon flow, cfh	Current (dcrp), amp	Arc Voltage, v	Welding Speed, ipm	Number of passes
1/8	F	3/64	2	30	110	20	30	1
	H, V	3/64	2	30	100	20	24	1
	O	3/64	2	40	100	20	24	1
3/16	F	3/64	4½	30	170	20	30	1
	H, V	3/64	4½	35	150	20	24	1
	O	3/64	4½	40	160	20	24	1
1/4	F	1/16	7	40	200	25 to 29	30	1
	H, V	1/16	7	45	170	25 to 29	24	1
	O	1/16	7	50	180	25 to 29	24	1
3/8	F	1/16	17	50	250	25 to 29	30	3
	H, V	1/16	17	50	170	25 to 29	24	3
	O	1/16	17	60	180	25 to 29	24	3
1/2	F	3/32	30	50	290	25 to 31	16	3
	H, V	1/16	30	50	190	25 to 29	12	3
	O	1/16	30	70	200	25 to 29	18	5
3/4	F	3/32	66	60	310	25 to 29	16	4
	H, V	1/16	66	60	220	25 to 29	8	4

(a) F = flat; H = horizontal; V = vertical; O = overhead

Table 8. Typical Conditions for Welding T and Lap Joints by the Semiautomatic Gas Metal-Arc Process

Metal thickness, in.	Welding position(a)	Electrode wire Diameter, in.	Electrode wire Feed, ipm	Electrode wire Used per 100 ft, lb	Argon Flow, cfh	Argon Used per 100 ft, cu ft	Current (dcrp), amp	Arc Voltage, v	Time per 100 ft, hr(b)	Welding Speed, ipm	Number of passes
1/8	F	3/64	190	2	30	31	125	20	1.04	30	1
	H, V	3/64	180	2	30	33	115	20	1.10	24	1
	O	3/64	175	2	40	45	110	20	1.13	24	1
3/16	F	3/64	255	4½	30	55	190	20	1.75	24	1
	H, V	3/64	230	4½	35	70	165	20	1.94	20	1
	O	3/64	245	4½	40	75	180	20	1.82	20	1
1/4	F	1/16	195	7	40	80	225	25 to 29	2.01	24	1
	H, V	1/16	170	7	45	105	200	25 to 29	2.30	20	1
	O	1/16	170	7	50	115	200	25 to 29	2.30	20	1
3/8	F	1/16	275	17	50	175	300	25 to 29	3.45	30	3
	H, V	1/16	170	17	50	280	200	25 to 29	5.59	24	3
	O	1/16	195	17	60	290	220	25 to 29	4.87	24	3
1/2	F	3/32	145	30	60	305	340	25 to 31	5.09	16	3
	H, V	1/16	200	30	60	505	225	25 to 29	8.39	12	3
	O	1/16	205	30	60	655	230	25 to 29	8.18	18	5
3/4	F	3/32	160	66	60	610	375	25 to 31	10.15	16	4
	H, V	1/16	235	66	60	945	260	25 to 29	15.71	8	4
	O	1/16	250	66	80	1180	275	25 to 29	14.76	18	10
1	F	3/32	180	120	60	985	425	25 to 31	16.40	8	4
	H, V	1/16	235	120	80	1715	260	25 to 29	28.56	6	6
	O	1/16	265	120	80	2025	290	25 to 29	25.31	18	14

(a) F = flat; H = horizontal; V = vertical; O = overhead.
(b) Based on 100% arc efficiency at electrode-wire feed shown.

Table 9. Typical Conditions for Welding Edge Joints by the Semiautomatic Gas Metal-Arc Process

Joint design	Metal thickness, in.	Welding position(a)	Electrode wire Diameter, in.	Electrode wire Used per 100 ft, lb	Argon flow, cfh	Current (dcrp), amp	Arc Voltage, v	Welding Speed, ipm	Number of passes
Joint Design A									
	1/8	F	3/64	4	30	110	20	30	1
		H, V	3/64	4	30	100	20	24	1
		O	3/64	4	40	100	20	24	1
	3/16	F	3/64	8	30	170	20	30	1
		H, V	3/64	8	35	150	20	24	1
		O	3/64	8	40	160	20	24	1
	1/4	F	1/16	15	40	200	25 to 29	30	1
		H, V	1/16	15	45	170	25 to 29	24	1
		O	1/16	15	50	180	25 to 29	24	1
Joint Design B									
	3/8	F	1/16	34	50	250	25 to 29	30	3
		H, V	1/16	34	50	170	25 to 29	24	3
		O	1/16	34	60	180	25 to 29	24	3
	1/2	F	3/32	60	50	290	25 to 31	16	3
		H, V	1/16	60	50	190	25 to 29	12	3
		O	1/16	60	70	200	25 to 29	18	5

(a) F = flat; H = horizontal; V = vertical; O = overhead.

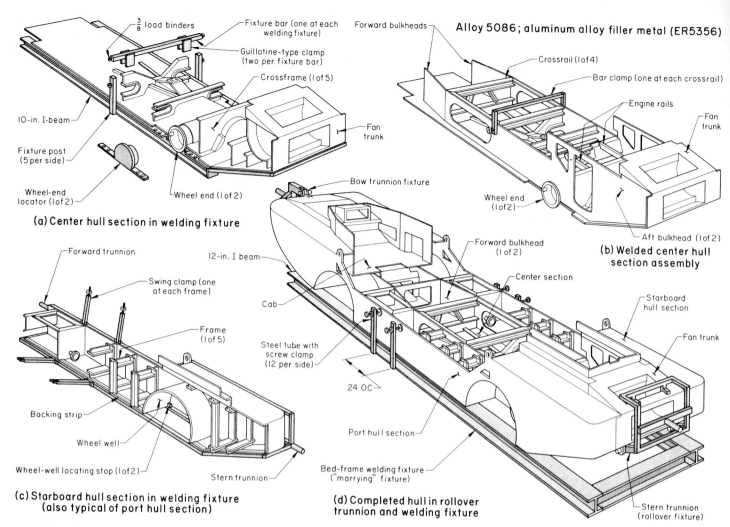

(a) Center hull section in welding fixture

(b) Welded center hull section assembly

(c) Starboard hull section in welding fixture (also typical of port hull section)

(d) Completed hull in rollover trunnion and welding fixture

Fig. 4. Fixtures used for welding center hull section of an amphibious lighter to port and starboard hull sections (see also Example 297)

seam. This amount of force will usually ensure against movement of the sheet during welding. To guard against deflection of the arc, nonmagnetic materials, such as austenitic stainless steel, copper and aluminum, should be used for those parts of a fixture within 4 in. of the arc, and must be used for fixture parts within 2 in. of the arc.

Although rigid clamping reduces distortion, the inability of the weldment to contract, caused by the restraint, may induce residual stress as high as the yield strength of the base metal and may also result in cracking. To keep distortion to the minimum, the joint should be designed with minimum separation between members, and welding should be done in the minimum number of passes.

The several fixtures required for welding a 418-in.-long amphibious lighter are shown in Fig. 4. The fixtures included guillotine-type clamps for use with load binders, bar clamps, multiple swinging clamps, rollover trunnion adapters, I-beam bed plates with steel tubes around the outside edge (the basic "marrying" fixture), and screw clamps. The rollover feature was adopted to avoid out-of-position welding, as when a weld had to be made on the outside of the bottom of the hull. (Welding the center hull section to the port and starboard sections is described in Example 297.)

A fixture used in welding long pipelines is described in Example 298.

Because many aluminum alloy weldments incorporate extruded products, self-fixturing can often be employed. In the following example, the extrusions were designed so that the joints were self-aligning, thereby reducing both the assembly time and the cost of fixtures.

Example 294. Use of Extruded Shapes for Self-Alignment of Parts for Welding (Fig. 5)

By the use of self-aligning extruded shapes throughout, the modular instrument enclosure shown in Fig. 5 could be made as cheaply from aluminum as from steel. In this application, strength and seal-tightness were not important. Material costs were 60% higher for aluminum than for steel, but welding costs and overhead costs were lower, and less welding skill was needed. In addition, aluminum enclosures were lighter, required less maintenance, and had better corrosion resistance.

The enclosures were made of alloy 6061-T6. The roof, sides, base and doors were subassembled by means of interlocking mechanical joints, and then were assembled and welded only in strategic places, as shown in Fig. 5. The interlocking joints along the sides of the panel extrusions were left unwelded. The joints in the roof were calked with sealant, to make them dust-tight.

The self-aligning feature of the design can be seen in the corner detail in Fig. 5. A blank plate was used to maintain square alignment of the door opening.

Welding was done by the gas metal-arc process, using an electrode holder having an integral wire-feed drive from a 1-lb spool. The electrode holder, control unit, and power supply were a coordinated package. Initial voltage was set by the operator, and further adjustment was made by a wire-feed-rate dial on the electrode holder, which automatically adjusted welding current to the proper level. Additional information is given in the table with Fig. 5.

In later production, the original electrode holder was replaced by one having a pull-type wire feed from a 10-lb spool that was separate from the electrode holder. By using 10-lb spools instead of 1-lb spools, wire cost was reduced by approximately $1 per pound.

Electrode-wire selection was important from the standpoint of color match, because completed enclosures were not painted. ER4043 and some other electrode wires darkened in service. Preferred electrode was ER5154 wire having a bright finish, but ER5356 also met the color-match requirements and was used later.

Precleaning was not required, because the material was sufficiently clean and free of oil in the as-received condition.

Gas Metal-Arc Welding

The ability of gas metal-arc welding to deposit large quantities of weld metal in a short period of time has played a large part in the increased use of aluminum since the late 1940's. Typical conditions for gas metal-arc welding of aluminum alloys are given in Tables 7 through 10. Figure 6 shows butt-joint designs for the conditions given in Table 10.

Thicknesses of aluminum alloys commonly joined by gas metal-arc welding range from $\frac{1}{8}$ in. up to the maximum plate thickness available (several inches). In this thickness range, gas metal-arc welding is capable of high-quality weld deposits — for example, those meeting requirements of the ASME Boiler and Pressure Vessel Code. With the use of pulsed-current power supplies, some types of joints can be gas metal-arc welded in aluminum as thin as 0.030 to 0.040 in.

Welding speeds up to 55 in. per minute are obtained with semiautomatic welding, and speeds for machine and automatic welding can be as high as 180 in. per minute. Maximum welding speeds commensurate with the application are always desirable when welding aluminum alloys. The rapid cooling after welding, which results from high welding speeds, produces fine-grain weld deposits and retards the formation of low-melting constituents at the grain boundaries.

Power Supply and Equipment. Only reverse-polarity direct current (electrode positive), which gives good penetration and a cathodic cleaning action at the work surface, is used in gas metal-arc welding of aluminum alloys. The steady and pulsed direct-current power supplies, and the wire-feed systems, electrode holders, and control systems used for gas metal-arc welding of aluminum alloys, are the same as those used for gas metal-arc welding of other metals (see the article on Gas Metal-Arc Welding, on page 78). Push-type wire-feed systems can handle aluminum wire down to 0.045 in. in diameter, but for smaller wires, a pull-type or a push-pull system must be used. Grooved drive rolls are preferred; knurled rolls and serrated rolls are likely to chip off small particles of metal, which can enter the wire conduit and slow down or stop wire feed. Wire conduits, inlet guides, guide liners, and bushings for aluminum electrode wire should be of all-nylon or all-Teflon construction.

Shielding Gases for Gas Metal-Arc Welding

Argon, helium, and mixtures of the two, are used as shielding gases in gas metal-arc welding of aluminum alloys. Table 11 lists the preferred gases for various thicknesses of aluminum alloy to be welded.

Argon is generally preferred when welding thinner metal, mainly because of its lower arc heat. In addition, argon results in a smoother and more stable arc than helium, and thus much less weld spatter is obtained.

Helium, because of its greater arc heat, is capable of producing the deep penetration desirable in weld deposits in thicker metal. The bead profile with helium shielding is wider and less convex than with argon shielding, and the penetration pattern has a broader underbead. Welding with pure helium produces welds of darker appearance with some spatter. Helium is lighter than argon, requires higher flow rates,

and it is more expensive. Therefore, helium is seldom used alone. However, in some jobs the use of higher currents, higher welding speeds and fewer passes can more than compensate for the higher cost of helium.

Argon-Helium Mixtures. To take advantage of the higher arc heat of helium without the disadvantages associated with using the pure gas, mixtures of argon and helium are usually used for out-of-position welding and in joining thick metal. Although users have individual preferences, mixtures ranging between 25 and 75% helium are most widely used. A helium-rich mixture, such as 75% helium and 25% argon, is frequently employed when welding workpieces more than 2 in. thick and is usually employed for out-of-position gas metal-arc welding. For workpieces more than 3 in. thick, helium-rich mixtures will maximize weld penetration and minimize porosity. When welding workpieces 1 to 3 in. thick in the flat position, increasing the current or voltage, or both, enables the helium content to be decreased.

Oxygen Additions. Small percentages of oxygen are sometimes added to pure argon or to argon-helium mixtures. For some jobs they have been found to improve arc stability and make out-of-position welding easier. For example, in out-of-position welding thin sheet of

alloys 1100 and 3003, a small amount of oxygen added to the argon shielding gas was found to improve solidification of the weld puddle. A drawback to the addition of oxygen to the shielding gas is that the welds are likely to contain a larger amount of entrapped oxide.

Nitrogen shielding gas plus a small amount of argon introduced separately through the contact-tube bore of the electrode holder results in an extremely hot, penetrating arc and has been used to produce welds of lowest cost and adequate strength and quality in EC electrical bus conductor.

Flow Rates. Typical shielding-gas flow rates for gas metal-arc welding of aluminum and aluminum alloys are given in Table 12. Note that helium requires about twice the flow of argon. The rate should not be greater than that which will have laminar flow.

Arc Characteristics in Gas Metal-Arc Welding

Increasing the welding current from low to high changes the arc from one producing short-circuiting metal transfer to one producing globular metal transfer and then to one producing spray metal transfer (see Fig. 2, page 79, in the article on Gas Metal-Arc Welding). Spray transfer produced by

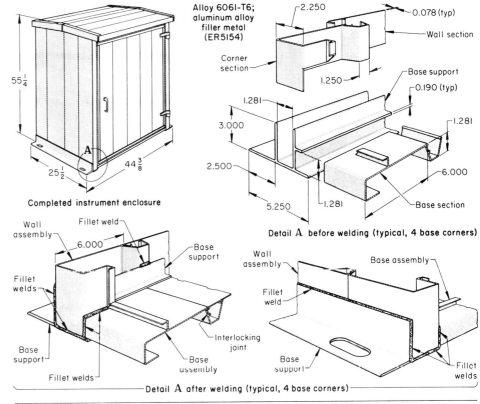

Completed instrument enclosure

Detail A before welding (typical, 4 base corners)

Detail A after welding (typical, 4 base corners)

Conditions for Semiautomatic Gas Metal-Arc Welding

Joint types .... T, lap	Electrode wire .... 0.035-in.-diam ER5154(a)
Weld type .... Fillet	Shielding gas .... Argon, at 20 cfh
Power supply .... 200-amp, constant-voltage transformer-rectifier	Electrode stickout .... $\frac{1}{4}$ in.
Wire-feed system .... Adjustable speed	Current .... 130 amp, dcrp
Electrode holder .... 200 amp, air cooled	Voltage .... 24 v
	Number of passes .... One

(a) ER5154 is a former AWS classification that has been replaced by ER5654. ER5356, which met color-match requirements as well as ER5154, was used in later production.

Fig. 5. Modular instrument enclosure fabricated of extruded aluminum shapes. Note the self-aligning feature of the assembly. (Example 294)

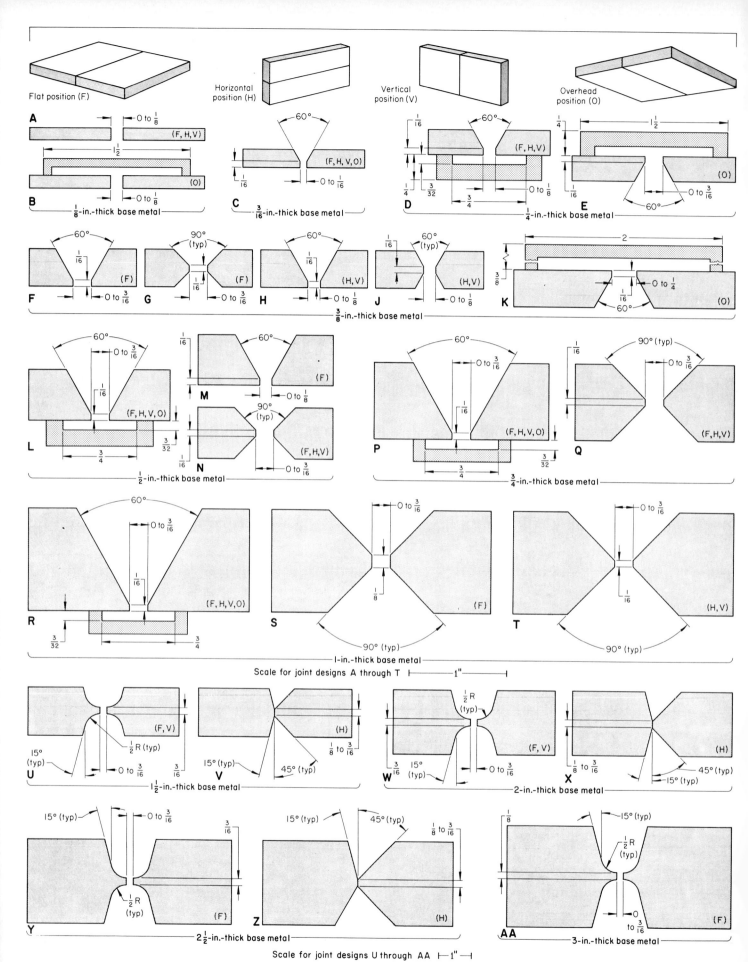

Fig. 6. Butt-joint designs for which applicable welding conditions are given in Table 10

either a steady-current arc or by a pulsed-current arc is used for almost all gas metal-arc welding of aluminum alloys. In some special applications, globular transfer and steady current are used instead.

To obtain spray metal transfer from steady-current arcs requires extremely high current densities when welding aluminum alloys. It is not uncommon to employ current densities ranging from 50,000 to 300,000 amp per square inch of electrode cross section. In contrast, current densities for gas tungsten-arc welding of aluminum alloys and for gas metal-arc welding of steel are about 10,000 amp per square inch.

The steady-current and current-density ranges in which the transition from globular to spray transfer takes place depend on the electrode size and the arc voltage employed. For a 3/64-in.-diam electrode and 22 to 31 volts, the change in type of transfer occurs at about 120 amp, or about 70,000 amp per square inch. Increasing the electrode diameter to 3/32 in. increases the transition current to about 220 amp, but decreases the current density to about 30,000 amp per square inch. When electrode diameters are larger than standard, the current density for the transfer transition is further reduced. The steady currents and wire-feed rates at which transfer transition takes place for electrodes of standard sizes are shown in Fig. 7. Pulsed currents must be used in order to achieve spray transfer at lower average currents and wire-feed rates.

Spray Transfer. Two of the notable characteristics of the spray-transfer arc are its stiffness and its narrowness; these advantages are described below:

Arc Stiffness for Deep Penetration. There is no lack of weld penetration when using spray transfer. Even in the low range of welding currents, the use of high current density and small-diameter electrode wire establishes a stable arc column with a well-defined pattern on the workpiece. To ensure fusion at the root of a butt joint, a minimum amount of root reinforcement is required, usually 1/32 to 3/16 in., depending on metal thickness and joint design.

Arc Stiffness for Out-of-Position Welding. When using spray transfer, the transfer follows the direction in which the electrode wire is pointed, which makes this type of transfer suitable for out-of-position welding. It can be an advantage when complicated parts require welding in several positions, such as in Examples 297 and 305. Spray transfer is also used to make a circumferential weld around a part too large to rotate, such as the welding of pipeline in Example 298.

Arc Narrowness for Small Fillet Welds. The spray arc has a narrow stable core, which concentrates the heat. This property enables fully fused small fillet welds to be made in relatively thick material.

In one application, corner joints having a minimum amount of weld metal and a minimum heat-affected zone were welded in thick alloy 5083 plate at minimum welding cost. Two basic joints were developed for near-minimum penetration (Fig. 8). Either a constant-current or a constant-voltage heavy-duty power supply was used, along with a heavy-duty wire-feed system and a water-cooled electrode holder. The electrode wire was 3/32-in.-diam ER5356. This wire size was chosen because the base metal was thick enough to prevent melt-through, it cost less per pound than smaller-diameter wire, and it was the largest diameter that could be deposited in all positions with semiautomatic equipment.

Table 10. Typical Conditions for Semiautomatic Gas Metal-Arc Welding of Butt Joints of Designs Shown in Fig. 6

Metal thickness, in.	Joint design (see Fig. 6)(a)	Welding position (b)	Electrode wire Diameter, in.	Electrode wire Feed, ipm	Electrode wire Used per 100 ft, lb	Argon Flow rate, cfh	Argon Used per 100 ft, cu ft	Arc Current (dcrp), amp	Arc Voltage, v	Time per 100 ft, hr(c)	Welding Speed, ipm	Welding Number of passes
1/8	A	F	3/64	175	2	30	34	110	20	1.14	24	1
	A	H,V	3/64	170	2	30	35	100	20	1.17	24	1
	B	O	3/64	170	2½	40	58	105	20	1.46	24	1
3/16	C	F	3/64	235	4½	30	57	170	20	1.90	24	1
	C	H,V	3/64	215	4½	35	75	150	20	2.08	20	1
	C	O	3/64	225	5	40	90	160	20	2.21	18	1
1/4	D	F	1/16	170	8	40	105	200	25	2.63	24	1
	D	H,V	1/16	150	8	45	255	170	25	2.98	24	3
	E	O	1/16	160	10	50	175	180	29	3.49	24	3
3/8	F	F	1/16	265	18	50	190	290	25	3.80	24	2
	G	F	1/16	250	15	50	170	275	29	3.35	24	2
	H	H,V	1/16	160	18	50	315	190	25	6.29	24	2
	J	H,V	1/16	150	15	50	280	170	29	5.29	24	2
	K	O	1/16	170	23	50	380	200	25-29	7.56	24	5
1/2	L	F	3/32	130	31	50	295	290	25-31	5.87	16	2
	M	F	3/32	140	30	50	265	320	25-31	5.27	16	2
	N	F	3/32	130	29	50	275	300	25-31	5.49	16	3
	L	H,V	1/16	...	31	50	...	215	25-29	...	12	2
	N	H,V	1/16	160	29	50	505	190	25-29	10.13	12	3
	L	O	1/16	200	31	80	695	225	25-29	8.66	18	8
3/4	P	F	3/32	150	62	60	610	350	25-29	10.17	16	4
	Q	F	3/32	145	72	60	735	330	25-29	12.22	16	4
	P	H,V	1/16	225	62	60	925	250	25-29	15.47	8	4
	Q	H,V	1/16	215	72	60	1125	240	25-29	18.71	8	4
	P	O	1/16	225	62	80	1235	250	25-29	15.42	18	12
1	R	F	3/32	170	105	60	910	400	25-31	15.20	12	4
	S	F	3/32	165	85	60	760	380	25-31	12.68	12	6
	R	H,V	1/16	225	105	60	1565	250	25-29	26.11	6	4
	T	H,V	1/16	215	95	60	1480	240	25-29	24.69	6	6
	R	O	1/16	250	105	80	1880	275	25-29	23.48	18	15
1½	U	F	3/32	180	200	80	2185	425	25-31	27.33	12	10
	V	H	1/16	255	105	80	1840	280	25-31	23.02	24	24
	V	H	3/32	150	105	80	1380	350	25-31	17.22	24	14
	U	V	1/16	225	200	80	3980	260	25-31	49.73	24	20
	U	V	3/32	145	200	80	2715	330	25-31	33.93	24	12
2	W	F	3/32	180	335	80	3665	425	25-31	45.79	12	12
	X	H	1/16	215	185	80	3845	245	25-31	48.08	24	30
	X	H	3/32	170	185	80	2140	425	25-31	26.78	24	24
	W	V	1/16	215	300	80	6240	240	25-31	77.97	20	26
	W	V	3/32	150	300	80	3935	350	25-31	49.19	20	15
2½	Y	F	3/32	180	350	80	3825	425	25-31	47.83	12	14
	Z	H	1/16	215	270	80	5615	245	25-31	70.18	24	32
	Z	H	3/32	150	270	80	3540	350	25-31	44.27	24	26
3	AA	F	3/32	190	500	80	5180	450	25-31	64.77	20	30

(a) Letters refer to joint designs in Fig. 6. When joint designs V, X and Z are used in the horizontal welding position, the 15° bevel should be on the bottom plate. (b) F = flat; H = horizontal; V = vertical; O = overhead. (c) Based on 100% arc efficiency at electrode-wire feed shown.

Very small fillet welds can be made in thinner workpieces, such as between the 1/4-in.-thick liner ring and the 1/8-in.-thick truncated cone shown in Fig. 9. In this application, using 3/64-in.-diam ER5183 electrode wire, it was not difficult for the welding operator to maintain a small weld bead and thus to hold to a minimum any distortion that could have taken place had the weld been larger.

Arc Narrowness for Square-Groove and Narrow-Groove Butt Joints (High-Current-Density Welding). The concentrated heat of the spray arc can also be used to weld butt joints with square or narrow grooves, thus reducing the amount and cost of the electrode wire required to make the joint.

Techniques have been developed to extend the usable current densities into the high range (to 300,000 amp per square inch), to take advantage of the very narrow penetrating arc. (At these high current densities, the characteristic hissing noise of the arc is replaced by a crackling noise.) These techniques are especially suitable

Table 11. Shielding Gases and Gas Mixtures Commonly Used for Gas Metal-Arc Welding of Aluminum Alloys

Work-metal thickness, in.	Shielding gas or mixture
0 to 3/4	100% argon
3/4 to 2	100% argon
	75% argon, 25% helium
	50% argon, 50% helium
2 to 3	50% argon, 50% helium
	25% argon, 75% helium
Over 3	25% argon, 75% helium

Table 12. Typical Shielding-Gas Flow Rates for Gas Metal-Arc Welding of Aluminum Alloys (a)

Shielding gas	Flow rate, cfh(b)
100% argon	30 to 70
75% helium, 25% argon	50 to 110
100% helium	60 to 140

(a) Using 1/16-in.-diam electrode wire. (b) The lower rates are more suitable for indoor work and moderate welding current. The higher rates are more suitable for high current, maximum speed, and outdoor welding.

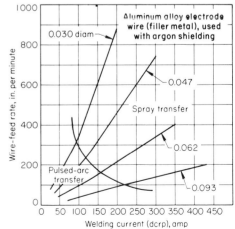

Fig. 7. Effect of wire-feed rate and welding current for various sizes of electrode wires in gas metal-arc welding. Note transition from pulsed-arc to spray transfer.

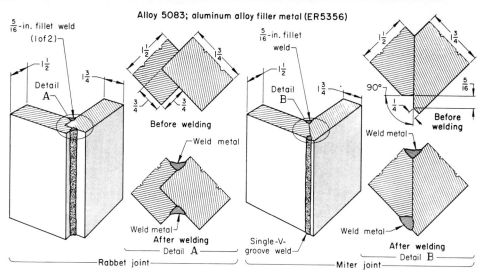

Alloy 5083; aluminum alloy filler metal (ER5356)

Fig. 8. Corner joints with small fillet and groove welds made by gas metal-arc welding

Table 13. Typical Conditions for High-Current-Density Welding of Square-Groove Butt Joints by the Automatic Gas Metal-Arc Process

Plate thickness, in.	Electrode wire Diameter, in.	Feed (approx), ipm	Argon flow, cfh	Arc Current (dcrp), amp	Voltage, v	Welding Speed, ipm	Number of passes
¼	³⁄₃₂	170	80	370	24	23	1
¼	¹⁄₁₆	240	60	280	23 to 24	35	2
⅜	³⁄₃₂	200	80	420	24 to 25	18	1
⅜	³⁄₃₂	155	80	350	24 to 25	28 to 30	2
½	³⁄₃₂	210	100	450	25	14 to 15	1
½	³⁄₃₂	205	80	430	25	23	2
½	⅛	125	100	450	25	14 to 15	1
⅝	³⁄₃₂	205	80	430	25	18	2
¾	³⁄₃₂	210	100	450	25 to 26	16	2
¾	⅛	125	100	450	25 to 26	16	2
1	³⁄₃₂	240	100	500	25 to 26	10 to 12	2
1	⅛	135	100	500	25 to 26	10 to 12	2
1¼	⅛	145	100	550	26	8 to 10	2
1½	⁹⁄₆₄	130	100	590	26	8	2

when making square-groove butt joints in base metal from ¼ to ⅝ in. thick. Welding is often accomplished in two passes, one from each side, at a much greater speed than is possible at lower current densities. Back gouging is rarely required, and welding in one pass instead of several stringer-bead passes greatly reduces the total heat input. The reduction in heat input results in less distortion and, in heat treatable alloys, produces better as-welded properties. Most welds made with the "square-butt" and "high-current" techniques are of better quality than standard radiographic requirements demand.

Thicknesses greater than ⅝ in. can also be welded with a square-groove butt joint, but the amount of reinforcement may be excessive. Where reinforcement must be minimized, V-grooves can be machined in both sides of the joint to the amount required. Figure 10 shows how two 1¾-in.-

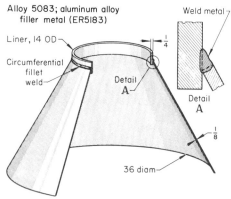

Alloy 5083; aluminum alloy filler metal (ER5183)

Fig. 9. Cone and liner ring that were joined by a small fillet weld to minimize distortion

thick plates of alloy 5083 were joined, using only one pass from each side, with 450-amp welding current, 28 volts, 100 cu ft per hour of argon for shielding, and ¹⁄₁₆-in.-diam ER5356 electrode wire.

The degree of bevel required with high-current-density welding is considerably less than with conventional welding. The root face is quite thick — usually about half the thickness of the plate. Joint preparation is not critical; machining need not be as accurate as for conventional joints.

Good results can be achieved with either a constant-current or a constant-voltage power supply. Argon should be supplied at 60 to 100 cu ft per hour, without excessive turbulence. The electrode holder and welding machine must have suitable current-carrying capacity. At present, high-current-density welding is normally used for automatic welding in the flat position where the welding conditions can be closely controlled. See Table 13 for conditions.

Table 14 presents the results obtained in tension and bend tests on single-V-groove joints made by conventional methods and typical square-groove butt joints made by high-current-density methods. The economic advantage of high-current-density welding with square grooves is evident.

Pulsed-arc transfer is a type of spray transfer that occurs in pulses at regularly spaced intervals. In the time interval between pulses, the welding current is reduced and no metal transfer occurs. The low average current and low heat input associated with pulsed-arc welding have allowed the advantages of spray transfer to be extended to the welding of sections thinner than can be spray-transfer welded using conventional steady-current power supplies. (Previously, short-circuiting

transfer was used to gas metal-arc weld sheet of this lower thickness.)

In addition to enabling the spray-transfer welding of aluminum 0.030 to 0.125 in. thick, pulsed-arc transfer offers other advantages. One is the option of using larger-diameter electrode wires, which cost less per pound, are easier to feed, have fewer current-transfer problems in the contact tube, and have a lower probability of weld porosity from surface contamination on the wire because of the lower surface-to-volume ratio of the larger wire.

Another advantage is that sheet can be welded to heavier plate, even when the joint has a poor fit. A layer of metal is progressively built up on the thicker section until the gap is bridged.

Well-formed root beads and finishing beads are easily made on thin aluminum with pulsed-arc welding, whereas the beads made by short-circuiting transfer have high crowns, which consume more filler metal, can cause distortion due to the unbalanced cross section of single-pass welds, and have poor appearance. Also, adjusting welding conditions to obtain good fusion with short-circuiting transfer is difficult. This type of transfer has been largely replaced by pulsed-arc transfer.

Globular Transfer. The type of arc that produces metal transfer by a large drop of molten metal is seldom used when welding aluminum alloys because with conventional steady-current power supply the transfer is likely to be erratic. But, because the arc penetration is shallower and the heat input is lower at the current densities that produce this type of transfer, globular transfer has occasionally been used when welding metal thinner than that normally welded with spray transfer and steady current (⅛ in. and less).

Globular transfer was successfully employed in joining the side of about 1200 ft of 1-in.-OD, 0.065-in.-wall alloy 3003 tubing to the surface of ⅛-in.-thick alloy 3003 sheet with a single-flare bevel-groove weld. A steady current of 120 to 130 amp and a voltage of 19 to 19½ volts were used with a constant-voltage power supply, a shielding-gas mixture of 75% argon and 25% helium, and 0.020-in.-diam ER4043 electrode wire. Welding speed was 15 in. per minute, using manual manipulation of the electrode holder. Only two

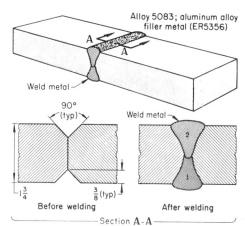

Alloy 5083; aluminum alloy filler metal (ER5356)

Fig. 10. Edge preparation for high-current-density welding of aluminum plate 1¾ in. thick, with one pass from each side

eaks, both caused by excessive melt-through, needed to be repaired.

Electrode Wires for Gas Metal-Arc Welding

Classifications and compositions of electrode wires are given in Table 3. Standard wire sizes are available in 1-lb and 10-lb spools in sizes from 0.030-in. to 0.040-in. diam and in 1-lb and 15-lb spools in sizes from $\frac{3}{64}$-in. to $\frac{1}{8}$-in. diam. Deposition and wire-feed rates obtained with two common electrodes in the standard sizes are shown in Fig. 11 for various welding conditions.

Electrode-wire feed should be selected so that the wire is consumed as fast as it emerges from the electrode holder, without extending more than $\frac{3}{8}$ in. beyond the shielding-gas nozzle. The electrode holder is tilted not more than 10° forehand. The arc length that should be used is governed by the metal thickness, the type of joint, and the welding current. When making small fillet welds and welding narrow-groove butt joints, a short arc is preferred. Arc length is usually $\frac{1}{8}$ to $\frac{3}{8}$ in.

The wire size chosen for each application depends on the requirements and welding conditions for that application. The following example describes the successful semiautomatic gas metal-arc welding of one of the aluminum-copper alloys, using a fairly small-diameter electrode wire and a special joint design.

Example 295. Semiautomatic Gas Metal-Arc Welding of $\frac{1}{4}$-In. 2014-T6 Plate, Using a "Step-Down" Joint and $\frac{3}{64}$-In.-Diam Electrode Wire (Fig. 12)

Alloy 2014-T6 plate $\frac{1}{4}$ in. thick was butt welded in two passes by semiautomatic gas metal-arc welding, using a special step-down joint, an electrode wire of smaller diameter, a helium-argon atmosphere, and a special backing insert.

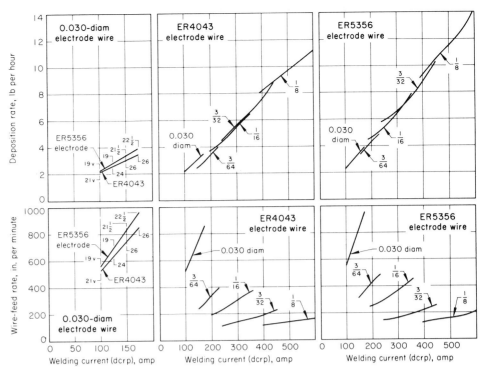

Fig. 11. Typical deposition rates and wire-feed rates for gas metal-arc welding with ER4043 and ER5356 electrode wire, under argon shielding

The purpose of the step-down joint (Fig. 12) was to ensure uniform root penetration and a smooth contour on the root surface. This joint was superior to a V-groove joint because the arc produced by the conventional power supply used might have wandered on the groove face of a V-groove joint; this undesirable wandering does not occur in a step-down joint. A further advantage was the ease with which a uniform land could be machined into the plate edges. Use of the $\frac{3}{64}$-in.-diam electrode wire, rather than the $\frac{1}{16}$-in.-diam wire normally used with $\frac{1}{4}$-in. plate, allowed a lower welding current while maintaining a high current density and a uniform metal transfer (spray type). The step-down joint enabled a relatively low welding current to be

used for the root pass to avoid melt-through. The smaller-diameter wire also resulted in a more concentrated plasma cone and faster welding, which helped to reduce the width and severity of the heat-affected zone. The $\frac{3}{64}$-in.-diam wire was used for both passes. ER4043 filler metal was chosen for its low crack sensitivity.

A 75% helium, 25% argon gas mixture was used for shielding, primarily so that the cover pass would be wider and the weld could be completed in two passes.

The weld backing bar contained a grooved insert that was made of either a metal with low thermal conductivity (such as stainless steel) or one with high thermal conductivity (such as copper), depending on the heat flow encountered in each

Table 14. Typical Test Results and Cost Factors for Gas Metal-Arc Welds in $\frac{1}{2}$-In. Alloy 5356 Plate

Alloy 5356, $\frac{1}{2}$-in. thick; aluminum alloy filler metal (ER5356)

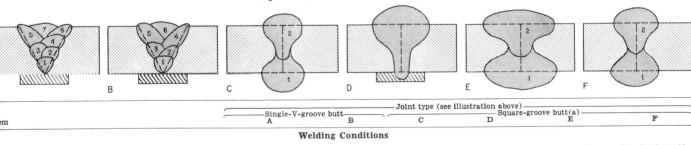

Item	Single-V-groove butt A	B	Square-groove butt(a) C	D	E	F
Welding Conditions						
Operation	Automatic	Automatic	Automatic	Automatic	Automatic	Semiautomatic
Electrode wire	ER5356	ER5356	ER5356	ER5356	ER5356	ER5356
Electrode diameter, in.	$\frac{1}{16}$	$\frac{1}{16}$	$\frac{3}{32}$	$\frac{3}{32}$	$\frac{3}{32}$	$\frac{1}{16}$
Shielding gas	75% He, 25% A	Argon	Argon	Argon	75% He, 25% A	Argon
Current (dcrp), amp	275	290	400	450	400	350
Number of passes	7	6	2	1	2	2
Properties of Welds						
Tensile strength, psi	42,200	42,900	43,200	41,100	40,900	43,500
Elongation in 2 in., %	12.5	13.5	11.0	13.0	14.0	14.5
Bend test (number passed, number tested)(b):						
$4t$ test	3 of 3	3 of 3	0 of 4	3 of 3	3 of 4	3 of 3
$6\frac{2}{3}t$ test	4 of 4	1 of 1	1 of 1	....	....	....
Cost Factors						
Shielding gas, cu ft/ft of weld	7.9	2.7	1.4	1.3	4.1	1.4
Arc time, min/ft of weld	3.8	3.3	1.0	1.0	1.4	1.7
Electrode wire, lb/ft of weld	0.24	0.23	0.13	0.14	0.16	0.16

(a) High-current-density welding. (b) Standard is $6\frac{2}{3}t$.

Source: Metals Handbook, 8th Ed., Vol. 6, ASM

individual welding job. Use of a low-conductivity metal insert was likely to produce a smoother contour at the root surface than use of the high-conductivity metal insert. However, the risk of melt-through was somewhat greater when using the low-conductivity insert, and the cooling of the weld area was slower, which somewhat increased the width and severity of the heat-affected zone.

Before assembly for welding, joint surfaces were chemically cleaned by brush application of a commercial cleaner, wiping the joint clean, and then drying it with a clean cloth. After completion of the root pass, the face of the weld was cleaned with a rotary stainless steel wire power brush, in preparation for the cover pass.

Conditions for welding are given in the table that accompanies Fig. 12.

[In addition to the technique described above, pulsed-arc welding may be used with a V-groove joint to join ¼-in.-thick alloy 2014-T6 plate.]

As a rule, electrode wires from 0.030 to ³⁄₃₂ in. in diameter are used with semiautomatic and automatic welding. The ⅛-in.-diam size is normally used only with automatic welding, as in the following application.

Example 296. Use of ⅛-In.-Diam Electrode Wire and Automatic Welding To Decrease Welding Time for Large Heat Exchangers (Fig. 13)

Several heat exchangers, 6 ft in diameter and 80 ft long, were constructed by welding 2-in.-thick alloy 5083-O formed plate sections by the gas metal-arc process. Because of the size of the heat exchangers and the thickness of the metal, welding conditions that would keep welding time to the minimum were desirable.

Double-U grooves were machined on the plates for longitudinal welds, where welding could be done from both sides, and single-U grooves were machined for circumferential welds, where welding could be done from one side only. The single-U grooves were permanently backed with aluminum rings. Design of the two types of grooves is shown in Fig. 13.

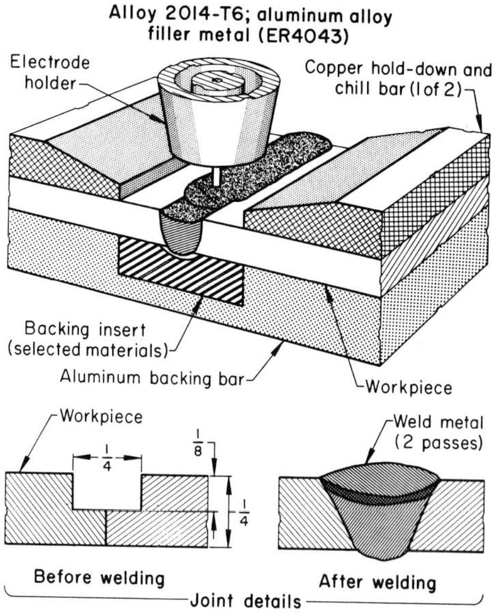

The double-U grooves were filled with fairly small beads by making five passe one side, back gouging the root and m ing all nine passes on the other side then making the last four passes on first side; the single-U grooves were f in 23 passes. The small size of the ind ual beads resulted in a weld having ductility, but because of the high wel speed used the total welding time was more than would have been needed to the grooves by using fewer passes and ducing larger weld beads.

The flow rate of the 75% argon, helium gas was great enough (60 cfh ensure adequate shielding at all times; creasing the flow would not have been essary had field erection been required.

Use of ⅛-in.-diam electrode wire, inst of the ³⁄₃₂-in.-diam wire often used to v 2-in. plate, reduced the number of pa that were needed by about one-half, fully automatic welding permitted hig welding speeds. Use of automatic wel also ensured good control of v quality. No peening or other in-pro treatment was required during weld and porosity was at an acceptable le Welding conditions were the same for b types of joints and are given in the ta that accompanies Fig. 13.

Welding With Large-Diameter El trode Wires.

The current density quired for spray transfer with stea current is reduced for electrode si larger than standard. Current densit of 12,000 to 30,000 amp per square in are used for welding with ⁵⁄₃₂, ³⁄₁₆, ⁷⁄₃₂-in.-diam electrode wires, compa with 30,000 to 100,000 amp per squa inch for welding with ³⁄₆₄ to ⅛-in.-di wires. Using the larger-diameter wir deposition rates of 15 lb per hour a readily obtained, compared with 5 to lb per hour for standard sizes of wi making this a method for low-c welding of thick aluminum plate in t flat position. Most gas metal-arc equi ment is designed for use with electro wires not exceeding ⅛ in. in diamet and this equipment may not be su able for welding with large-diame wires. However, suitable equipment c usually be made by converting su merged-arc equipment. Constant-cu rent motor-generator power suppli are preferred, although rectifiers ha been used.

When welding with large-diamet electrodes, somewhat different tec niques are required to ensure 100% f sion to the sidewalls of grooves. general, double-V grooves with fair wide included angles (45° to 90°) a preferable to deep, narrow groove Shorter arc lengths, which give mo fusion at the sidewalls, must be use The arc should be shortened until th characteristic hissing disappears and replaced by a popping sound. Th welding speed should always be lo enough to allow the arc to impinge o the molten puddle. Although 100 argon can be used for most applica tions, the addition of helium to the argon increases penetration. Condition for welding butt joints in metal thick nesses from ¾ through 3 in. are give in Table 15; Table 16 summarizes cor ditions for welding corner joints wit fillets sized from ½ through 1½ i Every procedure listed in the table has met the requirements of Sectio IX of the ASME Boiler and Pressu Vessel Code. Thick-wall spheres, larg cranes and other massive structure have been welded by this method.

Alloy 2014-T6; aluminum alloy filler metal (ER4043)

Semiautomatic Gas Metal-Arc Welding

Joint type	Butt
Weld type	Step-down groove
Joint tolerances	0.025-in. max root opening; ±0.005-in. max mismatch
Welding position	Flat
Power supply	500 amp, constant voltage
Fixtures	Copper hold-down and chill bars; aluminum backing bar with grooved insert
Electrode holder	500 amp, water cooled
Electrode wire	³⁄₆₄-in.-diam ER4043
Shielding gas	75% helium, 25% argon, at 100 cfh
Number of passes	Two

	First pass	Second pass
Current (dcrp), amp	215	140
Voltage, v	28	30
Welding speed, ipm	29	15

Fig. 12. Welding setup, showing special step-down joint design and backing bar with insert for varying cooling effect (Example 295)

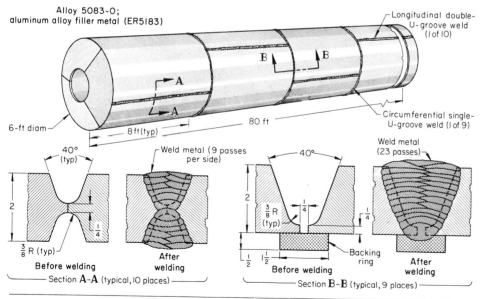

Conditions for Automatic Gas Metal-Arc Welding

Joint type	Butt	Shielding gas	75% A, 25% He, at 60 cfh
Weld type:		Welding position (all welds)	Flat
Longitudinal welds	Double-U groove	Current	460 to 480 amp, dcrp
Circumferential welds	Single-U groove	Voltage	35 v
Power supply	1000 amp, constant voltage	Welding speed	18 to 20 ipm
Electrode holder	800 amp, water cooled	Number of passes, longitudinal welds	18
Electrode wire	⅛-in.-diam ER5183	Number of passes, circumferential welds	23

Fig. 13. Heat exchanger that was welded by automatic gas metal-arc welding, joint design, and welding-pass sequence (Example 296)

Weld Backing for Gas Metal-Arc Welding

Backing bars are commonly used for gas metal-arc welds in butt joints, as this permits welding to be accomplished at higher speed, with less operator skill and with less control of welding conditions, especially when using spray transfer for joining thin sections. Steel is the material most commonly used for temporary backing of welds in aluminum alloys. Carbon steel is often used, but stainless steel is used when lower thermal conductivity is required in the backing. Copper and aluminum may be used when higher thermal conductivity is needed. Backing made of magnetic material sometimes deflects the arc and interferes with welding. When this occurs, nonmagnetic materials such as austenitic stainless steel, copper and aluminum should be used instead.

Austenitic stainless steel backing bars have reasonable life against arc damage and do not produce arc blow; their use minimizes the possibility of iron or rust pickup in the root bead. When copper backing is used, copper pickup must be prevented. Local deposition of copper or copper-aluminum alloy can result in corrosion in service. Life of copper backing is somewhat less than that of stainless steel, especially under direct arc impingement. Chromium plating of copper backing has been used to reduce copper pickup and increase backing life. Aluminum backing with a hard anodic coating will provide adequate chilling; an added advantage is that the arc will not strike the aluminum backing and cause damage, because the anodic coating is an excellent dielectric.

Backing bars may be temporary, permanent, or integral. Temporary aluminum backing is removed by chipping after welding. It is not necessary that a butt weld be completely fused to the temporary aluminum backing, provided that the root pass is back gouged to sound metal after the backing bar has been removed. Temporary backing should be grooved to allow the root surface of the weld to protrude beyond the plane of the back surface of the workpiece, thereby ensuring adequate penetration. This groove should be shallow (0.010 to 0.030 in.) and wider than the width of the root surface of the weld. Too wide a groove will give insufficient support to the metal under the hold-down clamps.

Although the chilling effect of the backing bar may be advantageous at times, at other times it may be a disadvantage, and then it is common practice to place sheets of asbestos between the backing bar or clamps, and the work metal. The asbestos sheets should not be placed directly beneath the joint. Properly placed strips of asbestos will provide a backing groove and will eliminate the need for a groove in the backing bar.

Temporary backing bars may be seen with the butt welds in Fig. 6. Example 295 describes how backing inserts of different metals can be used to slow down or accelerate the cooling of a joint during welding.

When permanent aluminum backing is used, it is necessary to obtain complete fusion between the backing, the root faces and the root layer of the weld. This is facilitated by using a greater root opening than is employed with temporary backing. Mechanical and magnetic oscillation can be used to help achieve fusion to both root faces in a single pass. Permanent backing bars are shown with the five welds in Table 17. Service conditions do not always permit the use of permanent backing, but by eliminating the back gouging required when temporary backing is used, the use of permanent backing (when permitted) can reduce costs, as in the following example.

Example 297. Use of Permanent Backing Strips for Sounder Welds and Savings in Labor (Fig. 14)

Permanent backing strips were used in joining the starboard and port hull sections to the center hull section of an amphibious lighter made of 3/16-in.-thick alloy 5086 sheet. The strips, 1 in. wide by 3/16 in. thick, were tack welded to the inside seam edge of both the starboard and port hull sections while they were still in the subassembly fixture (Fig. 4c). The tack welds were 2 in. long on 6-in. centers. The starboard and port hull sections were then hoisted into the final assembly fixture (see Fig. 4d), and tack welded to the center section. Bulkheads and braces were welded in place and the bow was joined to the hull. Finally, the trunnions were fastened in place and the hull was turned over in the fixture

Table 15. Typical Butt Joints and Conditions for Gas Metal-Arc Welding With Large-Diameter Electrode Wires

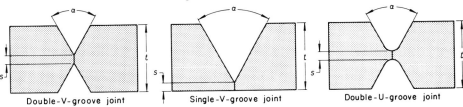

Double-V-groove joint   Single-V-groove joint   Double-U-groove joint

Plate thickness, t, in.	Groove type	Groove angle, α, deg	Root face, s, in.	Pass	Electrode-wire diameter, in.	Shielding gas	Gas flow, cfh	Arc current (dcrp), amp	Arc voltage(a), v	Welding speed, ipm
¾	Double-V	90	¼	....	1, 1st side	5/32	Argon	100	450	28	16
				2, 2nd side	5/32	Argon	100	500	28	16
¾	Double-V	90	¼	....	1, 1st side	3/16	Argon	100	450	32	15
				2, 2nd side	3/16	Argon	100	500	32	15
1	Double-V	70	3/16	...	1, 1st side	5/32	Argon	100	450	28	10
				2, 2nd side	5/32	Argon	100	500	28	10
1	Double-V	70	1/8	...	1, 1st side	3/16	Argon	100	500	26.5	12
				2, 2nd side	3/16	Argon	100	500	26.5	12
1¼	Double-V	70	3/16	...	1, 1st side	3/16	Argon	100	550	26.5	10
				2, 2nd side	3/16	Argon	100	550	26.5	10
1¼	Single-V	45	¼	....	1, 1st side	5/32	Argon	100	500	25	10
				2, 1st side	5/32	Argon	100	500	27	10
				3, back	5/32	Argon	100	500	26	12
1 5/16	Double-V	70	¼	....	1, 1st side	3/16	Argon	100	550	29	8
				2, 2nd side	3/16	Argon	100	575	29	8
1½	Double-V	70	3/16	...	1, 1st side	7/32	Argon	100	650	27	8
				2, 2nd side	7/32	Argon	100	675	27.5	8
1½	Double-V	70	3/16	...	1, 1st side	3/16	Argon	100	550	26	10
				2, 2nd side	3/16	Argon	100	575	27	10
				3, 1st side	3/16	Argon	100	600	29	10
				4, 2nd side	3/16	Argon	100	600	29	10
1¾	Double-V	70	3/16	...	1, 1st side	3/16	Argon	100	600	28	10
				2, 2nd side	3/16	Argon	100	600	28	10
				3 to 6, alternate	3/16	Argon	100	500	27	14
1¾	Double-V	70	1/8	....	1, 1st side	7/32	Argon	100	650	26	10
				2, 2nd side	7/32	Argon	100	650	26	10
				3, 1st side	7/32	Argon	100	600	27	10
				4, 2nd side	7/32	Argon	100	600	27	10
1¾	Single-V	45	¼	....	1, 1st side	3/16	Argon	100	600	28	10
				2, 1st side	3/16	Argon	100	600	28	10
				3, 1st side	3/16	Argon	100	550	30	14
				4, 1st side	3/16	Argon	100	550	30	14
				5, back	3/16	Argon	100	550	30	10
2	Double-V	70	3/16	...	1, 1st side	3/16	75 He, 25 A	120	550	31	10
				2, 2nd side	3/16	75 He, 25 A	120	550	33	10
				3, 1st side	3/16	75 He, 25 A	120	550	32	10
				4, 2nd side	3/16	75 He, 25 A	120	550	33	10
2	Double-V	70	1/8	...	1, 1st side	7/32	Argon	100	600	26	10
				2, 2nd side	7/32	Argon	100	600	30	10
				3, 1st side	7/32	Argon	100	600	30	10
				4, 2nd side	7/32	Argon	100	600	30	10
2	Single-V	45	¼	....	1, 1st side	3/16	Argon	100	600	28	10
				2, 1st side	3/16	Argon	100	600	28	10
				3 to 7, 1st side	3/16	Argon	100	500	26	14
				8, back	3/16	Argon	100	550	28	10
3	Double-V	70	¼	....	1, 2 (b)	3/16	75 A, 25 He	100	600	25	9
				3, 4 (b)	3/16	75 A, 25 He	100	500	23	11
				5, 6 (b)	3/16	75 A, 25 He	100	625	26	9
				7 to 12 (b)	3/16	75 A, 25 He	100	600	27	9
3	Double-V	70	3/16	...	1, 2 (b)	7/32	75 A, 25 He	100	650	25	9
				3, 4 (b)	7/32	75 A, 25 He	100	500	23	10
				5, 6 (b)	7/32	75 A, 25 He	100	650	26	9
				7 to 10 (b)	7/32	75 A, 25 He	100	625	27	9
3	Double-U	30(c)	½	....	1, 2 (b)	7/32	75 He, 25 A	120	650	29	10
				3 to 6 (b)	7/32	75 He, 25 A	120	650	31	10

(a) Voltages are measured from contact tube to test plate. Somewhat higher readings will result if drops in welding and ground leads are included. (b) The first side receives odd-number passes; the second side, even-number passes. (c) Radius of groove, ¼ in.

Source: Metals Handbook, 8th Ed., Vol. 6, ASM

Table 16. Typical Corner Joints and Conditions for Gas Metal-Arc Welding With Large-Diameter Electrode Wires(a)

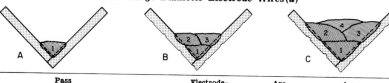

Fillet size, in.	Pass type (see above)	Pass number	Electrode-wire diameter, in.	Arc current (dcrp), amp	Arc voltage(b), v	Welding speed, ipm
½	A	1	5/32	525	22	12
½	A	1	3/16	550	25	12
5/8	A	1	5/32	525	22	12
¾	A	1	5/32	600	25	10
¾	A	1	3/16	625	27	8
¾	A	1	7/32	625	22	8
1	B	1	5/32	600	25	12
		2, 3	5/32	555	24	10
1	B	1	3/16	625	27	8
		2, 3	3/16	550	28	12
1	A	1	7/32	675	23	6
1¼	B	1	5/32	600	25	10
		2, 3	5/32	600	25	10
1¼	B	1	3/16	625	27	8
		2, 3	3/16	600	28	10
1¼	B	1	7/32	625	22	8
		2, 3	7/32	625	22	10
1½	C	1	7/32	650	23	6
		2 to 4	7/32	650	23	10

(a) Argon shielding gas, at 100 cu ft per hour. (b) Measured from contact tube to test plate.

to make the longitudinal weld on the outside. One welding pass was needed for one-third of the length and two passes for the other two-thirds. The placement of the backing strip and the welding sequence for attachment of the strip are shown in Fig. 14. The welding conditions are given in the table that accompanies Fig. 14.

The procedure originally used involved no backing strips. The first weld was made on the inside of the hull, the assembly was rotated, the root of the weld was back gouged by grinding, and two more passes were made on the outside of the joint.

The use of backing strips resulted in a saving of 8 hr of welding and back-gouging time at a cost of ½ hr to install the backing strips and an added material cost of $5.00. Because the welds using the improved method were subject to less rework based on the results of radiographic inspection, there was an added saving in reduced repair time. These improvements led to improved material flow, eliminated the need for one of the two trunnion fixtures, thus gaining 200 sq ft of floor space, and freed two machines for other welding.

Warpage was a serious imperfection, irrespective of the welding method and was never completely eliminated. Welding with a wandering sequence was helpful, but was at the discretion of the operator.

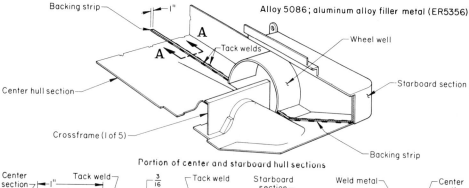

Portion of center and starboard hull sections

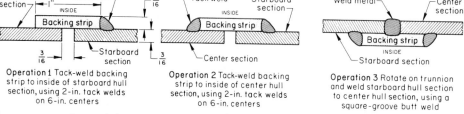

Operation 1 Tack-weld backing strip to inside of starboard hull section, using 2-in. tack welds on 6-in. centers

Operation 2 Tack-weld backing strip to inside of center hull section, using 2-in. tack welds on 6-in. centers

Operation 3 Rotate on trunnion and weld starboard hull section to center hull section, using a square-groove butt weld

Section A-A (also typical for welding port hull section to center hull section)

Conditions for Semiautomatic Gas Metal-Arc Welding

Joint type	Butt
Weld type	Square groove
Welding positions	Flat, vertical
Power supply	300-amp, constant-voltage transformer-rectifier
Fixtures	Assembly and clamping, mechanical shield jigs, permanent backing strip (see Fig. 4)
Precleaning	Wire brush, wipe with acetone
Electrode holder	Manual, water cooled
Electrode wire	3/64-in.-diam ER5356
Shielding gas	Argon, at 35 to 45 cfh
Current	220 to 250 amp, dcrp
Voltage	26 to 27 v
Welding speed	About 14 ipm
Number of passes	One, for flat position; two, for vertical position

Fig. 14. Section of amphibious lighter, showing use of backing strip for joining starboard and port sections to center hull section (Example 297)

Butt joints in extrusions can be designed so that the weld backing is an integral part of the extrusion. Integral backing is not recommended in environments where the nonwelded portion of the backing can promote crevice type corrosion.

Multiple-Pass Gas Metal-Arc Welding

When welding joints in thin-wall vessels, it is sometimes desirable to use two passes rather than one, to avoid leakage due to porosity; gases can escape more easily from the smaller weld puddles, the second pass can fill some of the porosity that may exist in the first-pass weld bead, and there is little probability that any remaining pore in the first-pass bead will line up with a pore in the second-pass bead to produce a through hole.

For butt welding sections 3/8 in. thick or thicker, common practice is to weld from both sides when possible. Whether or not the first weld penetrates to the underside, the bead should be back gouged into sound fused weld metal before depositing the backing bead. Back gouging removes entrapped oxide film at the base of the weld bead. Proper depth is attained by gouging to the point where the chip no longer splits along the oxide film entrapped at the original face of the joint. Back gouging can be accomplished by a pneumatic hammer and knife-edge chisels of proper design, or by machining. Oil should not be used when back gouging, or it should be removed prior to welding. Disk grinders should not be used. Portable back gouging equipment that employs shaped milling cutters is available. Regardless of method, the back-gouging groove should be of uniform shape with no torn metal, sharp corners, or crevices from which oil or foreign material cannot be removed.

It is advisable to check that all defects extending to the gouged surface have been removed before depositing the backing bead. This check may be done by dye-penetrant inspection or for the ultimate in weld quality, by radiographic inspection (as in Example 307) or ultrasonic inspection.

The shells of most aluminum vessels are thick enough to require at least two welding passes. In the feed-gas cooler shown in Fig. 15, 45 passes, made in the horizontal welding position, were required to complete the joining of a 3-in.-thick tube sheet to a 1½-in.-thick by 18-in.-OD pipe, both made from alloy 5083-O plate. In order to facilitate welding, the cooler was placed on turning rolls and rotated. Two welders worked simultaneously on the job; one at the 12 o'clock position and the other at the 6 o'clock position. The electrode holders were hand held, but were provided with supports to minimize operator fatigue. A constant-voltage power supply, a shielding-gas mixture of 75% argon and 25% helium, and ER5183 electrode wire were selected. A 1/16-in. diam wire was used, allowing maneuverability of the electrode holder. None of the welded coolers failed the mass spectrometer leak test.

Conditions for making multiple-pass welds in butt, corner and T-joints in ¼ and ⅜-in.-thick alloy 6061-T6 are given in Table 17. A multiple-pass technique was used in Example 298, for welding of pipe, and in Example 306, where leaktight joints were required.

Automatic Gas Metal-Arc Welding

When the size of the production run warrants the installation cost and setup time, the use of automatic gas metal-arc welding equipment offers several advantages, among which are better quality on a more consistent basis and higher welding speed than can be obtained with manual manipulation of the electrode holder. An application where the higher welding speed greatly reduced welding time is described in the following example.

Example 298. Use of Automatic Gas Metal-Arc Welding of Pipe To Greatly Reduce Welding Time (Fig. 16)

Joining lengths of alloy 6351-T4 pipe in the field by automatic gas metal-arc welding was found to be economical for lengths of five miles or more for a 6-in.-diam pipe (Fig. 16).

The U-groove joint with ends butted tightly, as shown in Fig. 16, was essential for the process. After cleaning the joint by wiping with solvent, alignment and backing for the root bead were accomplished by an internal tool that could be expanded and collapsed manually by means of an extension handle. Use of the alignment tool made tack welding unnecessary. The alignment tool was withdrawn as soon as the root bead was completed; it was used to align the next joint while welding of the previous joint was continued.

Welding was accomplished with an air-cooled electrode holder (with electrode-wire spool attached) mounted on a machine that rotated it around the pipe. In this way, a six-pass weld was finished without

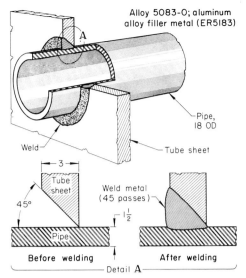

Alloy 5083-O; aluminum alloy filler metal (ER5183)

Fig. 15. Leak-free joint between tube sheet and pipe in an aluminum feed-gas cooler

stopping. Welding began near the top of the pipe and continued until the six passes were completed (Fig. 16). The electrode holder was adjusted for bead location and depth, and the direction of rotation was reversed after passes 2 and 5 without extinguishing the arc, to ensure adequate penetration and fusion, and correct weld-bead shape. Welding speed was fairly high (100 ipm), welding current was high (200 amp), and an electrode wire of small diameter (0.035 in.) was used. Welding conditions are given in the table with Fig. 16.

The estimated production rate, allowing for normal downtime, was 12 welds per hour per machine. The estimated production rate for welding with a manually manipulated electrode holder was five welds per hour per operator.

In the next example, the cost savings made possible by the higher welding speed helped overcome the high raw

material cost of using aluminum rather than steel for the application.

Example 299. Automatic Gas Metal-Arc Welding of Three Joints at a Time (Fig. 17)

By automatic gas metal-arc welding of three joints simultaneously, which reduced welding time to about one third of that for welding one joint at a time, aluminum alloy pressure cylinders of the type shown in Fig. 17 were made competitive with steel cylinders, despite the considerably higher cost of the aluminum alloys (5154-O, 6061-T1 and 6063-T42). Originally, a few aluminum alloy cylinders had been produced when the higher cost of aluminum was outweighed by its superior compatibility with the product being contained.

Designs for the various joints to be welded are shown in sections A-A, B-B, and C-C in Fig. 17. Before being assembled, the components were cleaned by (a) immersing them in a caustic etch-cleaner at 145 to 155 F for 4 to 6 min; (b) rinsing in warm water (100 to 120 F) for 1 min, in a bath that was overflowing and air agitated; (c) deoxidizing in an acid bath at 70 F maximum for 8 to 10 min; and (d) rinsing in warm water (125 to 145 F) for 1 min, in an overflowing bath.

The straight-side upper shell was pressed over the offset lower shell, this subassembly was placed in a welding lathe together with the collar and foot ring, and the parts were clamped by means of an air cylinder in the lathe tailstock. The assembly was rotated by means of a variable-speed drive.

Three electrode holders and wire drives were attached on side-beam carriages behind the lathe, which allowed for adjustment for cylinders of a variety of sizes. The welding controls included an adjustable weld timer to ensure correct overlap at the ends of the welds and provision for preflow and postflow of shielding gas. All of the controls were in one console.

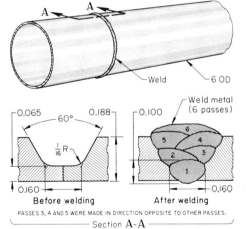

Alloy 6351-T4; aluminum alloy filler metal (ER5254)

PASSES 3, 4 AND 5 WERE MADE IN DIRECTION OPPOSITE TO OTHER PASSES.
— Section A-A —

Automatic Gas Metal-Arc Welding

Joint type	Butt
Weld type	Single-U groove
Root opening	None
Welding position	Horizontal-fixed pipe
Power supply	300-amp engine-driven generator
Fixture	Expandable mandrel
Electrode holder	Mechanized, air cooled
Electrode wire	0.035-in.-diam ER5254(a)
Shielding gas	Argon, at 60 cfh
Current	200 amp, dcrp
Voltage	20 to 24 v
Welding speed	100 ipm
Arc time per joint	80 sec
Number of passes	Six
Production rate per machine	12 welds per hour

(a) Chosen because it is compatible with all common aluminum alloys used for pipe and pipe fittings. ER5254 is a former AWS classification that has been replaced by ER5654.

Fig. 16. Large pipe that was automatic gas metal-arc welded (Example 298)

Table 17. Conditions for Multiple-Pass Welding by the Semiautomatic Gas Metal-Arc Process

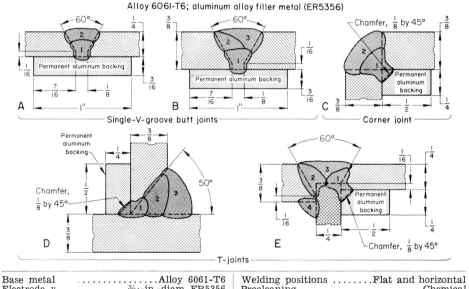

Alloy 6061-T6; aluminum alloy filler metal (ER5356)

Single-V-groove butt joints — Corner joint — T-joints

Base metal	Alloy 6061-T6
Electrode wire	3/64-in.-diam ER5356
Shielding gas	75% He, 25% A; 50 cfh
Welding positions	Flat and horizontal
Precleaning	Chemical
Interpass cleaning	None

Item	Welding conditions for joints illustrated above				
	A	B	C	D	E
Joint type	Butt	Butt	Corner	T	T
Current (dcrp), amp	180 to 200	180 to 200	180 to 200	190 to 220	180 to 210
Voltage, v	22 to 24	22 to 24	22 to 24	22 to 25	22 to 24
Welding speed, ipm	25 to 30	25 to 30	25 to 30	20 to 28	25 to 30
Number of passes	2	3	2	3	4

Source: Metals Handbook, 8th Ed., Vol. 6, ASM

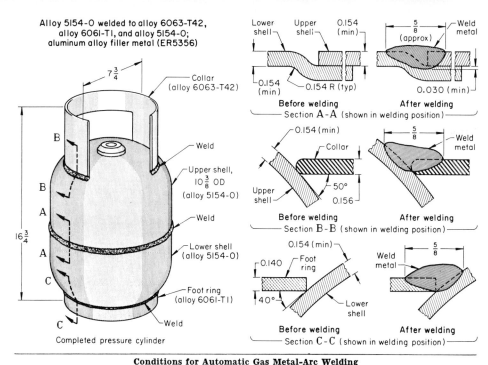

Alloy 5154-O welded to alloy 6063-T42, alloy 6061-T1, and alloy 5154-O; aluminum alloy filler metal (ER5356)

Completed pressure cylinder

Before welding / After welding — Section A-A (shown in welding position)

Before welding / After welding — Section B-B (shown in welding position)

Before welding / After welding — Section C-C (shown in welding position)

Conditions for Automatic Gas Metal-Arc Welding

Joint and weld types ....See figure	Shielding gas ....Argon, at 50 cfh	
Welding position ....Horizontal-rolled pipe	Number of passes ....One	

	Section		
	A-A	B-B	C-C
Electrode-wire diam, in. ..	$\frac{1}{16}$	$\frac{3}{64}$	$\frac{3}{64}$
Current (dcrp), amp	290	200	190
Voltage, v	24	25	25
Wire-feed rate, ipm	240	325	310
Welding speed, ipm	45	34.7	42

Power supply: Three 500-amp transformer-rectifiers; adjustable slope and voltage control
Mechanization ......Lathe with variable-speed drive, three electrode holders
Wire-feed system ....Variable speed
Electrode holder ....Mechanized, 700 amp, water cooled
Electrode wire ER5356

Fig. 17. Pressure cylinder on which three welds were made simultaneously by automatic gas metal-arc welding (Example 299)

After alignment of electrode holders had been checked, all three welds were started simultaneously by pushing a master start button. Welding equipment and conditions are given in the table that accompanies Fig. 17. There was no postweld heat treatment, but all parts were postweld cleaned in hot dilute phosphoric acid.

All welds had to be free of undercutting on the sidewalls of the welding groove and the adjoining base metal, and it was specified that any crack, leak or other defect that appeared on the surface on a weld bead could be repaired only in accordance with a repair welding procedure for the weld in question.

Each cylinder was proof tested to 480 psig, and checked for leaks while under pressure. One cylinder from each lot of 200 cylinders or less was subjected to a series of tests. The first was a tension test across the girth weld (section A-A in Fig. 17), where minimum tensile strength required was 30,000 psi, and the minimum tensile strength calculated on the minimum wall thickness had to be at least the wall stress calculated for 960 psig. A weld-root bend test was also required. Two samples of the base metal were tension tested and both were required to meet the following requirements: tensile strength exceeding the wall stress calculated for 960 psig, yield strength not exceeding 80% of the tensile strength, and elongation in 2 in. of at least 7%. The chemical composition of the base metal was also verified.

One cylinder of each lot of 1000 cylinders was hydrostatically tested to destruction by bursting. Minimum pressure at failure was required to be 960 psig.

All pressure testing was conducted hydrostatically. Cylinders were filled with water and connected to an air-operated hydraulic pump. The low compressibility of water minimized the stored energy in the cylinder and the hazards that attended the bursting test.

Cylinders with valves, for liquefied petroleum gas service, were pressurized with 150 psig dry air after valves were attached. The entire assembly was submerged in a tank of water (with added wetting agent). Leaks showed as a stream of fine bubbles.

The production rate for automatically making three welds simultaneously was about the same as would have been expected for welding the girth joint alone, and there was no extra handling time.

In the example that follows, the reduced welding time and reduced distortion that resulted from the high welding speed obtained by automatic welding were important advantages.

Example 300. Reduction in Welding Time and Distortion by Changing From Semiautomatic to Automatic Gas Metal-Arc Welding (Fig. 18)

Originally, the four continuous welds along the full 96-ft length of the alloy 5083-H11 overhead-crane girder shown in Fig. 18 were made as fillet welds in square-groove joints by semiautomatic gas metal-arc welding. By changing to the single-bevel-groove weld with fillet weld reinforcement shown in section A-A in Fig. 18, and to fully automatic gas metal-arc welding, welding time was reduced by 80%. The 60° groove provided by beveling the web plates contributed to the reduction in welding time by allowing a 33% decrease in weld metal, at no sacrifice in joint strength. Welding current was increased from 260 to 375 amp.

The girders were tack welded at 15-in. centers on the inside to hold them in place for fillet welding. The continuous machine fillet welds were made in the horizontal position.

Other benefits of machine welding were a significant reduction in distortion, better

joint appearance, and elimination of the defects associated with weld starts and stops. Welding conditions and a comparison of semiautomatic and automatic welding are given in the table with Fig. 18.

Production Examples of Gas Metal-Arc Welding

For the welding of aluminum, the gas metal-arc process affords welding speeds equal to or greater than those of other arc welding processes. This has led to other advantages, such as lower cost and less distortion. The previous section described some advantages of automatic gas metal-arc welding, most of which relate to the welding speed realized with this method.

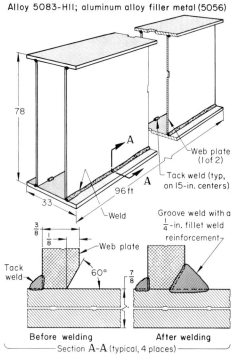

Alloy 5083-H11; aluminum alloy filler metal (5056)

Before welding / After welding — Section A-A (typical, 4 places)

Automatic Gas Metal-Arc Welding

Joint type ....T
Weld type ....Single-bevel-groove fillet
Root opening ....None
Welding position ....Horizontal
Power supply ....500-amp, constant-current transformer-rectifier
Wire-feed system ....Constant speed
Electrode holder .....Mechanized, water cooled
Electrode wire ....$\frac{1}{16}$-in.-diam alloy 5056(a)
Shielding gas ....Argon, at 60 cfh
Current ....See below
Voltage ....26 v
Wire-feed rate ....410 ipm
Welding speed ....See below
Number of passes ....One

Comparison of Semiautomatic and Automatic Gas Metal-Arc Welding

	Semi-automatic	Fully automatic
Current (dcrp), amp	260	375
Welding speed, ipm	12	20
Duty cycle per joint, %	$33\frac{1}{3}$	100
Welding time per joint, min .	288	58
Shielding-gas consumption per joint, cu ft	64	60
Electrode consumption per joint, lb	12	8

(a) This electrode wire has been discontinued. See the footnote in the table that accompanies Fig. 22.

Fig. 18. Overhead-crane girder, the welding of which was changed from semiautomatic to automatic gas metal-arc to reduce welding time and distortion (Example 300)

Cost Savings. Higher welding speed usually results in a higher production rate per man-hour, and the lower labor cost per weld significantly affects the cost of a fabricated part. In the example that follows, a continuous-bead weld produced by gas metal-arc welding replaced a joint made by resistance spot welding and brazing, at a cost saving and with an improvement in the quality of the product.

Example 301. Gas Metal-Arc Welding of a Dust-Tight Box Cover at 60% Lower Labor Cost (Fig. 19)

When the joining process was changed from resistance spot welding plus torch brazing to continuous-bead semiautomatic gas metal-arc welding, the alloy 6061-T6 box cover shown at top left in Fig. 19 was produced not only to required dust-tightness (not attainable by spot welding plus brazing), but also at a 60% cost saving. The resistance spot welds had been placed on 1-in. centers, which permitted dust to penetrate between them during service. Torch brazing had been used at the corner gaps.

The fixture used for gas metal-arc welding was an angle-iron table with side-edge and front-edge stops, as shown in the upper right-hand corner of Fig. 19. With the parts in the position shown in the two middle views in Fig. 19, each of the ends was tacked to the cover at four places with fillet welds (lap joints), and the butt joints at the four mitered corners of the flange were tacked with square-groove welds. The square-groove tack welds, which extended to within $\frac{1}{16}$ in. of the edge of the flange, were made with a minimum of weld-metal buildup. A copper bar served as a positioner and heat sink for the square-groove tack welds.

After the cover had been tack welded, it was turned over (see upper right-hand view in Fig. 19). Gaps between the ends and the cover were hammer closed and tack welded where needed. A copper backing vise gripped the back edge of the cover, a copper spatter shield was placed over the end, and the joint was welded from the apex of the cover to the back edge. The workpiece was reclamped and the joint from the apex to the front edge was welded. The second end was welded on in the same manner. A contoured arm rest assisted in electrode-holder guidance. After welding, the weld surfaces were wiped clean with a cloth and rough spots on the weld were hammered smooth. Welding conditions are given in the table with Fig. 19.

The following example describes an application in which the replacement of riveting by gas metal-arc welding resulted in a cost saving and an improvement in the product.

Example 302. Reduction in Cost and Rejection Rate by the Use of Gas Metal-Arc Welding Instead of Riveting (Fig. 20)

The truck-radiator grill frame shown in Fig. 20, an assembly of alloys 5052 and 6063 components, was originally joined by riveting with a hand-operated air gun, using rivet sets and a bucking bar. Cutouts were needed in the clamping fixture around each rivet, to allow use of the gun and bucking bar. These cutouts weakened the fixture, and the assemblies became twisted, resulting in a 12% rejection rate. Some assemblies also were out-of-square, as the joints could not be held tight and flush before riveting.

By changing from riveting to gas metal-arc welding, it was possible to use clamps that held the assemblies more securely in position during joining. Completed assemblies had more accurate dimensions and improved rigidity. Other advantages were a reduction of rejects to 1% and a 50% saving in labor time.

The assemblies were manually loaded in the welding fixture, toggle-clamped, welded in a single pass (with ER4043 filler metal, for maximum ease of welding and corrosion resistance), unclamped, and then manually unloaded. The weld passes were horizontal and vertical-up. Intermittent welding was used for all joints over 1 in. long, the procedure being to weld 1 in. and skip 4 in. Conditions for semiautomatic gas metal-arc welding are given in the table that accompanies Fig. 20.

All welds had good penetration, and weld buildup was kept to a minimum. Typical penetration was 30 to 50% of the $\frac{3}{16}$-in. lower channel thickness and 40 to 60% of the $\frac{1}{8}$-in. thickness of the other parts.

Minimizing Distortion. High welding speed results in less heat being absorbed by the metal being welded, which in turn results in less thermal expansion, less residual stress and less distortion. In the following example, when resistance spot welding proved unsuitable because of the inaccessibility of joints, gas metal-arc welding was selected because it caused less distortion than the other arc welding processes, although more than resistance spot welding. Close dimensional control was achieved with proper fixturing.

Example 303. Use of Gas Metal-Arc Welding in the Final Assembly of a Frame for a Truck Cab Door (Fig. 21)

Both gas metal-arc welding and resistance spot welding were used in making the alloy 6061 military-truck-cab doorframe shown in Fig. 21. The resistance spot welding is described in Example 419, in the article on Resistance Welding of Aluminum Alloys. Because some of the doorframe joints were inaccessible for resistance spot welding, or had limited accessibility (see detail A, Fig. 21), gas metal-arc welding was selected as the best alternative — its high welding speed caused less distortion than the lower welding speed of gas tungsten-arc welding. However, it was advisable to hold the gas metal-arc welds to a minimum for two reasons: (a) Because the heat input was greater than in resistance spot welding, the probability of distortion in the highly stressed, tempered and cold worked material was greater; and (b) the larger mass of the weld metal produced greater residual stress during contraction in cooling.

An important requirement of the military truck was that it be able to float

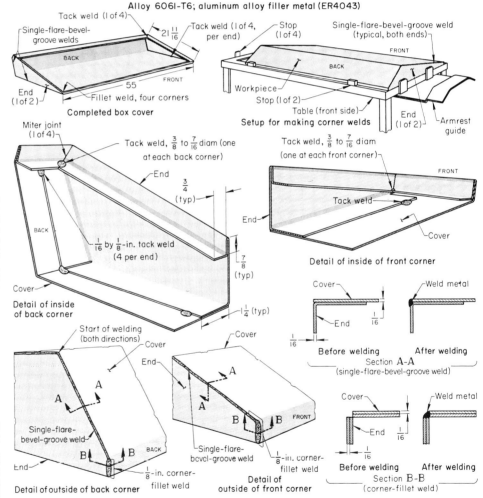

Conditions for Semiautomatic Gas Metal-Arc Welding

Joint types	Butt, lap, corner
Weld types	Square groove, fillet, single-flare-bevel groove
Welding positions	Flat, vertical
Power supply	500-amp, constant-voltage transformer-rectifier
Wire-feed system	Variable speed(a), automatic current-voltage control
Fixtures	Clamping, copper backing bar, copper spatter shield
Electrode holder	Air cooled
Electrode wire	0.030-in.-diam ER4043
Shielding gas	Argon, at 30 cfh
Current	90 to 100 amp, dcrp
Voltage	17 to 18 v
Number of passes	One

(a) Wire was fed from a 1-lb spool that was mounted on the electrode holder.

Fig. 19. Box cover that was gas metal-arc welded to ensure dust-tightness (Example 301)

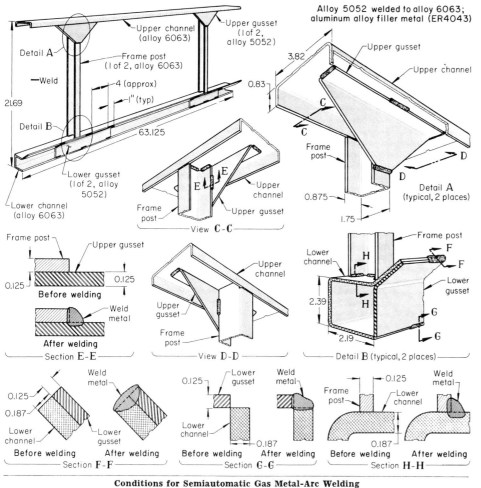

(swim) when fully loaded, the tractor portion being given buoyancy by a watertight cab. In order that the doors be watertight, the frames had to be built to close dimensional tolerances, so that they would fit snugly in their openings. Both fixturing and welding were critical in maintaining dimensions.

Gas metal-arc welding was done without removing the frame from the same rigid fixture (see Fig. 21) used for resistance spot welding. Welding conditions are given in the table that accompanies Fig. 21. After welding, the frame was allowed to cool and was removed from the fixture to check dimensions and shape. The weldment was then furnace heated at 380 F for 6 hr to T6 condition, and tested for hardness. One frame per week of production (400 doors) was strength tested to destruction.

Final checking of dimensions and shape of each frame occurred after it was incorporated in a completed door assembly, and the latter had been installed in a truck cab. The cabs were then tested for watertightness by immersing them in water to within 4 in. of the freeboard of the truck. The first cab of a production lot was permitted a door fit that leaked one quart in 6 hr. All other cabs of the lot were required to show no visible leakage after 2 min of immersion.

Often, the welding sequence may be arranged so that only a minimum amount of fixturing is needed. This is illustrated in the following example.

Example 304. Welding Alloy 5083-H11 Plate by the Semiautomatic Gas Metal-Arc Process (Fig. 22)

Transverse joints in 7/8-in.-thick alloy 5083-H11 flange plates for overhead-crane girders were welded in ten passes by the gas metal-arc process. Although welding time could have been reduced by using a fully automatic procedure, the amount of welding did not justify the cost of obtaining and setting up the necessary equipment, so semiautomatic welding was used.

The edges of the plates were prepared as shown in Fig. 22. The joints were then tack welded, starting and runoff tabs were attached, and welding was begun. After the third pass, the plates were turned over, the joint was back gouged to remove root defects, and three weld passes were made on this side of the joint. In order to check

Conditions for Semiautomatic Gas Metal-Arc Welding

Joint types	Corner, T, lap, edge	Shielding gas	Argon, at 35 cfh
Weld types	Square groove, fillet	Number of passes	One
Welding positions	Horizontal, vertical up	Current	115 amp, dcrp
Power supply	300-amp three-phase rectifier	Voltage	20 v
Wire-feed system	Electric push – air pull	Wire-feed rate	450 ipm
Electrode wire	0.035-in.-diam ER4043	Welding speed	24 ipm

Fig. 20. Truck-radiator grill frame that was gas metal-arc welded at an improvement in quality and reduction in costs over riveted assembly (Example 302)

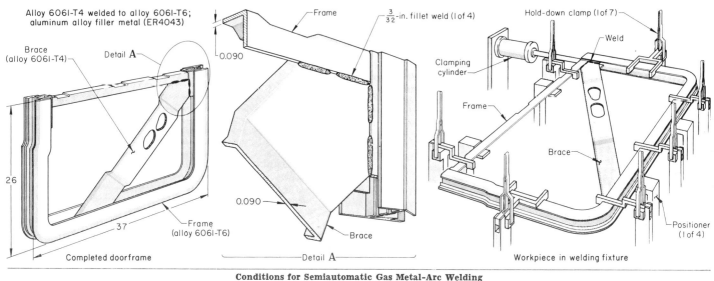

Conditions for Semiautomatic Gas Metal-Arc Welding

Joint type	Lap	Wire-feed system	Variable speed(a)
Weld type	Fillet	Fixtures	Clamps
Welding position	Horizontal	Electrode holder	100 amp, air cooled
Power supply	200-amp, constant-voltage transformer-rectifier	Electrode wire	0.030-in.-diam ER4043
		Shielding gas	Argon, at 30 cfh

Current	110 amp, dcrp
Voltage	19 v
Wire-feed rate	180 ipm
Welding speed	12 ipm
Number of passes	One

(a) Wire was fed from a 1-lb spool that was mounted on the electrode holder.

Fig. 21. Truck-cab doorframe on which the gas metal-arc process was used to make the fillet welds shown (Example 303)

distortion, the plate was turned over three times during welding. The last two passes on each side were made with a longer arc, in order to obtain the required weld contour. About 1¾ lb of electrode wire was used for each 33-in.-long weld. Further welding details are given in the table that accompanies Fig. 22.

Gas metal-arc welding is often used for making tack welds when final welding is to be done by the gas tungsten-arc process, as in the following example.

Example 305. Use of the Semiautomatic Gas Metal-Arc Process for Tack Welding Aluminum Fuel-Tank Assemblies (Table 18)

For tack welding the 50 subassemblies and the final assembly of a fuel-storage tank for an M-60 combat tank, gas metal-arc welding was selected in preference to gas tungsten-arc welding, for these reasons: (*a*) the higher welding speed of the gas metal-arc process resulted in less distortion; (*b*) the faster welding reduced welding cost; (*c*) the electrode holder was easier to manipulate in the various welding positions; (*d*) the penetration obtained in the ⅛-in.-thick metal was excellent; (*e*) the cleaning action of the reverse-polarity direct current ensured oxide-free welds.

The parts were clamped in fixtures and tacked with 1-in.-long welds on approximately 4-in. centers, using the equipment and settings listed in Table 18. To keep distortion to a minimum, tack welding sequences for each subassembly were developed. Because of the variety of shapes, these sequences were arrived at by trial-and-error, but in general they were based on working outward from the center of joints and assemblies.

To facilitate manipulation of the electrode holder, the electrode wire was fed from a 1-lb spool mounted on the holder. Quality control of the electrode wire was necessary. In addition to the requirement that the wire meet military specification MIL-E-16053, samples of wire were tested periodically for cleanness, as described in Example 311. The wire was ordered in a very hard (H19) temper so that the small knurled drive wheels used in the wire feed would not allow the wire to slip. When softer wire was used, the knurled drive wheels would sometimes "mill" the wire, which caused it to slip and produce a burnback.

Example 293 describes preweld cleaning of the alloy 5083-H112, alloy 5086-H32, and alloy 6061-T6 components of the subassemblies, and Example 311, final seam welding.

Soundness of Welds Made by Gas Metal-Arc Welding

The five principal defects encountered in gas metal-arc welding of aluminum alloys are transverse weld-metal cracking, longitudinal weld-metal cracking, crater cracking, porosity, and inadequate penetration. In addition, inclusions and cold laps are occasionally encountered.

Transverse and longitudinal weld-metal cracking are usually associated with the higher-strength aluminum alloys of the 2*xxx* and 7*xxx* series. In particular, cracks are likely to originate at the starting and stopping points of the arc, because craters caused by normal shrinkage occur in these areas. Therefore, it is good practice to use starting and runoff tabs and not to start or break the arc on the workpiece.

In one application, consistency of weld quality in ¾-in. alloy 2219-T87 plate was improved by replacing a dou-

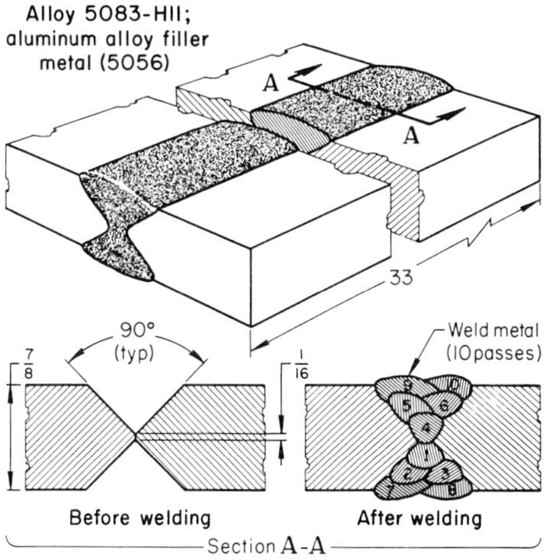
Alloy 5083-H11; aluminum alloy filler metal (5056)
A
A
33
90° (typ)
7/8
1/16
Weld metal (10 passes)
Before welding
After welding
Section A-A

Semiautomatic Gas Metal-Arc Welding

Joint type	Butt
Weld type	Double-V groove
Welding position	Flat
Power supply	500-amp, constant-current transformer-rectifier
Wire-feed system	Constant speed
Electrode holder	Water cooled
Electrode wire	1/16-in.-diam alloy 5056(a)
Shielding gas	Argon, at 40 cfh
Current	260 to 270 amp, dcrp
Voltage	25 v
Welding speed	16 to 25 ipm
Number of passes	Ten
Total welding time per joint (33⅓% duty cycle)	45 min

(a) Alloy 5056 electrode wire has been discontinued and has been replaced by ER5356, which has the same chemical composition except for lower limits on silicon and iron and the addition of a small amount of titanium. The titanium addition refines the grains and reduces tendency for hot-short cracking. For general-purpose welding, ER5183 (which gives greater ductility) is often used. For higher-strength welds, ER5556 is used. All three electrode types can be used with the welding conditions listed above.

Fig. 22. Double-V-groove weld in an alloy 5083-H11 flange plate for an overhead-crane girder (Example 304)

ble-V-groove weld that required eight passes (four from each side) with a double-U-groove weld that required only three passes. First, the ⅛-in. root face of the double-U groove was welded, and then a facing pass was made on each side of the groove with the electrode holder oscillating from side to side to fill the remainder of the groove completely. (Mechanical and magnetic equipment is available to produce an oscillation in which both frequency and amplitude are adjustable.) The weld was used to join two

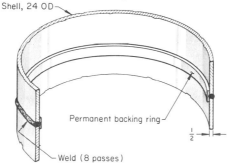

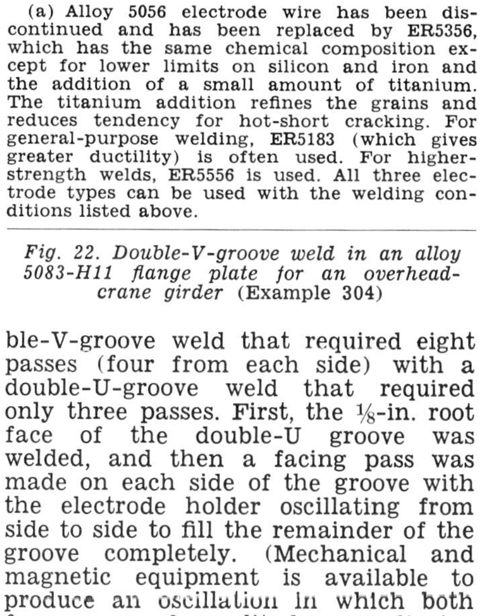
Alloy 5083; aluminum alloy filler metal (ER5183)
Shell, 24 OD
Permanent backing ring
1/2
Weld (8 passes)

Fig. 23. Subcooler shell in which porosity was eliminated by increasing the arc voltage to produce a stiffer arc column in gas metal-arc welding

Table 18. Materials, Equipment and Operating Conditions for Tack Welding Fuel-Tank Subassemblies and Assemblies (Example 305)

(See Example 293 for a description of preweld cleaning and Fig. 36 for a view of the tank and some specific joints.)

Base metals	⅛-in.-thick alloy 5086-H32 sheet, alloy 5083-H112 extrusions, alloy 6061-T6 fittings
Welding process	Semiautomatic gas metal-arc
Equipment	
Power supply	200-amp transformer-rectifier, 60% duty cycle
Electrode holder	200 amp, air cooled
Electrode wire	3/64-in.-diam ER5356
Shielding gas	Argon, at 30 to 40 cfh
Gas nozzle	⅝-in. diam
Fixtures	Clamps
Welding Conditions	
Joint types	Butt, lap, T, corner
Weld types	Square-groove, V-groove, fillet
Welding positions	Flat, vertical, horizontal
Current	160 to 180 amp, dcrp
Voltage	18 to 22 v
Wire feed	280 to 320 ipm
Number of passes	One

barrel sections to form a space-launch booster tank. Welding position was vertical.

Weld-cracking problems can often be attributed to restrained shrinkage of the weld metal. Process variables that produce coarse-grain weld-metal deposits and large heat-affected zones are additional causes. For example, longitudinal weld-metal cracking in a square-groove butt joint in ⅛-in. alloy 5083 sheet was eliminated in one application by sufficiently relieving hold-down clamp pressure to allow slight transverse movement of the workpieces during welding. In addition, weld reinforcement was increased by reducing the welding speed, thereby creating a larger weld cross section that withstood the higher shrinkage stresses without cracking.

In another application, transverse weld-metal cracking in a square-groove butt joint in 3/16-in. alloy 5083 sheet was eliminated by increasing the solidification rate of the weld puddle. This was accomplished by reducing the arc voltage from 28 to 24 volts and the welding current from 280 to 185 amp, and increasing the welding speed from 18-to-25 to 27-to-30 in. per minute. The lower arc voltage resulted in a narrow, deeply penetrating weld and allowed the welding speed to be increased. In addition, the power supply was changed from the constant-voltage type to the conventional drooping-voltage type. The electrode diameter remained at 1/16 in. and the number of passes at two.

Sound, porosity-free welds meeting radiographic and mass-spectrometer leak-test requirements can be made in aluminum alloys by the gas metal-arc process, but careful attention must be given to the selection and use of welding equipment, materials, conditions and techniques.

Hydrogen contamination is the cause of virtually all weld porosity in aluminum alloys. Solidification shrinkage is of minor significance as a contributor to weld porosity. Hydrogen has high solubility in molten aluminum but very low solubility in solid aluminum (a small fraction of the solubility in solid

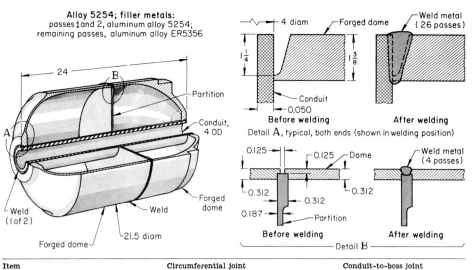

Alloy 5254; filler metals:
passes 1 and 2, aluminum alloy 5254;
remaining passes, aluminum alloy ER5356

Detail A, typical, both ends (shown in welding position)

Detail B

Fig. 24. Pressure vessel that formed part of the fuel system of a naval torpedo, showing details of two principal joints (Example 306)

Item	Circumferential joint	Conduit-to-boss joint
Conditions for Automatic Gas Metal-Arc Welding		
Joint type	T	Corner
Weld type	See detail B	Single-J groove
Position	Flat	Flat
Power supply	500-amp, constant-voltage transformer-rectifier	500-amp, constant-voltage transformer-rectifier
Fixtures	Clamping jig, rotating positioner	Clamping jig, rotating positioner
Electrode holder	Water cooled	Water cooled
Gas-nozzle diameter ..	¾ in., all passes	Passes 1 to 4: ⅝ in.; passes 5 to 26: ¾ in.
Electrode wire(a)	Passes 1 and 2: 1/16-in.-diam 5254 Passes 3 and 4: 1/16-in.-diam ER5356	Passes 1 and 2: 1/16-in.-diam 5254 Passes 3 to 26: 1/16-in.-diam ER5356
Shielding gas	75% helium, 25% argon, at 30 cfh	75% helium, 25% argon, at 30 cfh
Current	1st pass: 180 to 190 amp, dcrp Passes 2 to 4: 190 to 200 amp, dcrp	200 to 210 amp, dcrp (all passes)
Voltage	27 to 27½ v, all passes	27 to 27½ v, all passes
Welding speed	29 ipm	29 ipm
Number of passes	4	26 (approx)

(a) Electrode wires conformed to military specification MIL-E-16053. The 5254 electrode wires (no longer an AWS classification; replaced with ER5654) were selected for strength, and the ER5356 electrode wires, for better corrosion resistance.

steel and titanium). Hydrogen dissolved in the molten weld puddle during welding is released during solidification. The high freezing rate associated with gas metal-arc welding can prevent the evolved hydrogen from rising to the surface of the weld puddle, with the result that porosity occurs. An extremely small amount of hydrogen source can cause significant amounts of porosity.

The major sources of hydrogen are hydrated oxide, oil and other hydrocarbon contaminants on the surface of the electrode wire. Other sources are moisture, oil, grease and hydrated oxide on the work-metal surface and moisture in the shielding gas. Factors that can contribute to porosity from contamination are insufficient gas flow, excessive distance from the gas nozzle to the work metal, leakage in the shielding-gas hose or fittings, and erratic electrode-wire feed.

When weld porosity is encountered, the electrode wire should be checked, first to determine whether it is clean, and then to determine whether it is capable of depositing sound metal. In some instances, a radiograph of a weldment made in the overhead position with the wire in question can be obtained from the producer of the wire. Also, a check weld (butt or fillet) can be made, broken open and examined. If the wire will produce sound welds on one machine but not another, the source of the porosity is elsewhere than the wire. One way to make sure

the wire is not a source of hydrogen is to use shaved wire.

Next, conditions for gas metal-arc welding that will bring about a slower solidification rate should be selected. Welding in the flat or vertical position also aids escape of gases.

Correct voltage and arc length can reduce porosity in a weld, such as the one in the subcooler shown in Fig. 23. This vessel was fabricated from ½-in.-thick alloy 5083 by gas metal-arc welding in the vertical-pipe position. A constant-voltage power supply and 1/16-in.-diam ER5183 electrode wire were used with a welding current of 280 to 290 amp, a welding speed of 18 to 20 in. per minute, and 75% argon, 25% helium shielding gas. Eight passes were required. Severe porosity was encountered. After a thorough re-evaluation of the procedure, it was concluded that welding position had little effect on the porosity but that raising the arc voltage from the 24-to-26-volt range to the 28-to-29-volt range brought about a stiffer type of spray transfer that resulted in a dense, sound weld.

Another factor that contributes to gross porosity is incorrect or erratic wire feed, which results in an unstable arc. In general, the arc should be manipulated in a reciprocating fashion to obtain the maximum amount of stirring action in the weld puddle and so to assist gases to escape. Porosity can also be reduced by using a shielding-gas mixture containing a large proportion of helium.

A small amount of porosity scattered uniformly throughout a weld has little effect on the strength of the welded joint. Clusters of porosity and gross porosity can adversely affect weld strength. Various welding codes limit the amount and distribution of acceptable porosity.

Multiple-pass welding helps prevent leakage due to porosity, as explained in the section of this article on Multiple-Pass Gas Metal-Arc Welding. In the following example, leaktight welds were obtained in joints designed so that complete penetration was obtained; four passes were used for one type of joint and about 26 passes for the other type. (Leak-free joints can also be made in one pass, as described in Example 299.)

Example 306. Producing Leaktight Welds in a Pressure Vessel (Fig. 24)

The major components of the pressure vessel shown in Fig. 24 were two closed-die-forged domes, a central partition, and an axial conduit — all made of alloy 5254. The domes were joined by a single circumferential weld that also incorporated the partition as backing (Fig. 24, detail B). The conduit was welded to the vessel at both ends. Internal baffles and fittings (not shown in Fig. 24) completed the vessel structure, which later was shrink fitted into the 4340 steel shell of a naval torpedo, the vessel forming part of the fuel system. Joint designs and welds used to join the major components of the pressure vessel are shown in Fig. 24, details A and B. The principal conditions for automatic gas metal-arc welding of both joints are given in the table that accompanies Fig. 24.

The centrally located partition and the two dome sections were welded simultaneously (Fig. 24, detail B), in four passes. To ensure weld soundness, joints between the conduit and the 1⅜-in.-thick bosses were designed for full-penetration single-J-groove welds, and were completed in about 26 passes. These joints were economical to make and had a high degree of reproducibility. The welds were of excellent quality, showing "water clear" on x-ray plates.

After edge preparation (machining) and cleaning of joint areas, internal baffles and fittings (not shown in Fig. 24) were installed in the dome sections. These sections, together with the center partition, were then assembled in an alignment fixture, clamped, mounted (axis horizontal) under a fixed electrode holder and welded. The welding area was carefully shielded from drafts. During welding, the workpiece was rotated without stopping, except to change electrode wire, and the welds were wire brushed during rotation. The conduit was then inserted and similarly welded, with the axis of the assembly vertical. After welding, the vessel and welds were machined. Welds were inspected by liquid-penetrant methods and the vessel was subjected to a mass-spectrometer leak-rate test.

Mechanical problems, such as burnback of the electrode wire into the contact tube, snagging of the electrode wire either on the wire spool or in the flexible cable joining the spool to the electrode holder, and inability of the wire to maintain a constant arc length during welding (hunting), also occur. These are almost always associated with malfunctions of equipment (especially, wire-feeding equipment), rather than with process or material limitations. All of these difficulties with gas metal-arc welding, and several others are listed in Table 19, along with their usual causes.

Repair Welding by the Gas Metal-Arc Process

Welding is widely used for repairing defects in both cast and wrought parts. The techniques for making such repairs vary, depending on the type of defect and the properties and condition of the part to be repaired. One repair technique used on plate is described in the example that follows.

Example 307. Repair Welding Alloy 5083-O Plate (Fig. 25)

A welding technique for repairing cracks (resulting from forming) in 1⅛-in.-thick alloy 5083-O plate included trepanning a circular plug, containing the cracks, from the plate and then welding in a plug of sound metal. The plug of sound metal was machined to fit the 5-in.-diam trepanned hole with a maximum radial clearance of 0.020 in., as shown in Fig. 25. The plug was inserted in the hole and held in place by three 2-in.-long tack welds spaced 120° apart. Next, the joint region was preheated locally to 200 F with an oxyacetylene flame and the first pass was made on the side opposite the tack welds, special care being taken to avoid melt-through. Passes 2 and 3 (Fig. 25) were then made, the tack welds were ground out, and the weld was inspected radiographically. The root pass was back gouged to a depth of about ³⁄₃₂ in. and the next four passes were made. The remaining passes were deposited as shown in the welding-pass sequence in Fig. 25.

Each of the 14 welding passes was made in two parts, each part through approximately 180° of the joint. Upon completion of each part of a pass, the arc was diverted to a runoff tab and broken there instead of in the repair weld to avoid the possible formation of crater cracks in the

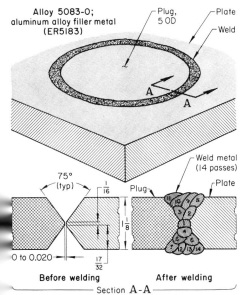

Alloy 5083-O; aluminum alloy filler metal (ER5183)

Plug, 5 OD — Plate — Weld

Weld metal (14 passes) — Plate

75° (typ) — ¹⁄₁₆ — Plug — 1⅛ — 0 to 0.020 — ¹⁷⁄₃₂

Before welding — After welding

Section A-A

Semiautomatic Gas Metal-Arc Welding

```
Joint type .............................Butt
Weld type ..................Double-V groove
Welding position .....................Flat
Power supply ........500 amp, constant voltage
Electrode wire ...........¹⁄₁₆-in.-diam ER5183
Shielding gas ..75% helium, 25% argon, at 100
     cfh, plus 99% argon, 1% oxygen, at 10 cfh
Current ......................300 amp, dcrp
Voltage ...............................32 v
Preheat ..............................200 F
Interpass temperature .........150 to 200 F
Number of passes .....................14
Welding time ........Approx 1½ min per pass
```

Fig. 25. Plate in which a crack was repaired by removing the cracked area by trepanning and then welding a sound plug in the hole (Example 307)

Table 19. Common Problems With Gas Metal-Arc Welding and Their Usual Causes

Porosity

1. Gas entrapment from poor shielding, shielding gas, air
2. Hydrogen from moisture, unclean wire surface, oil on base metal
3. Excessive cooling rate of weld puddle
4. Erratic electrode-wire feed (see causes in item 2 under "Arc-Length Fluctuations")
5. Erratic arc transfer, caused by incorrect current

Transverse Weld-Metal Cracking

1. Excessive longitudinal restraint
2. Slow solidification of weld puddle
3. Absorption of halogen compound in weld puddle
4. Incorrect combination of base metal and filler metal

Longitudinal Weld-Metal Cracking

1. Excessive transverse restraint
2. Concave, instead of convex, root-pass weld bead
3. Insufficient cross section of root-pass bead
4. Excessive current for electrode-wire size

Inadequate Penetration

1. Insufficient back gouging
2. Improper edge preparation for arc characteristics (groove too narrow)
3. Insufficient current
4. Excessive voltage
5. Welding speed too high

Incomplete Fusion

1. Improper edge preparation for arc characteristics
2. Arc too long
3. Dirty workpieces or electrode wire
4. Insufficient current

Undercutting

1. Excessive current
2. Welding speed too low
3. Improper electrode-holder angle

Arc-Starting Difficulty

1. Wrong polarity (electrode should be positive)
2. Incomplete welding circuit
3. Inadequate flow of shielding gas
4. Wrong electrode-wire feed rate or welding current

Arc-Length Fluctuations

1. Poor condition of contact tube (rough inner walls, sharp shoulders, contamination by weld spatter)
2. Erratic electrode-wire feed, caused by:
   - Kinked wire (electrode wire should be evenly wound and free of kinks)
   - Excessive or erratic friction in electrode conduit or electrode holder (conduit should be in good condition and of the correct size and length)
   - Clogged contact tubes
   - Unbalance of wire spool
   - Maladjustment of wire-spool brake
   - Poor operation of wire-feed motor or wire straightener
   - Sharp bends in electrode conduit (suspend equipment overhead)
   - Fluctuations in line voltage to wire-feed unit
   - Poor ground connection or burned governor control in wire-feed motor
   - Slippage or insufficient pressure of drive rolls in wire-feed unit

Burnbacks(a)

1. Erratic electrode-wire feed (see causes in item 2 under "Arc-Length Fluctuations")
2. Poor condition of contact tube (see item 1 under "Arc-Length Fluctuations")
3. Incorrect power-supply settings
4. Poor functioning of cooling equipment
5. Poor contact between voltage pickup lead and work

(a) A burnback occurs when electrode wire fuses to the copper contact tube and wire feed is stopped. It happens when the wire feed is insufficient for the current being used, which causes the arc to lengthen until it overheats the end of the contact tube. An inexperienced welder may get burnbacks while establishing the correct welding conditions.

Inadequate Cleaning Action by the Arc

1. Wrong polarity (electrode should be positive)
2. Inadequate gas shielding because of:
   - Insufficient gas flow
   - Spatter on inside of gas nozzle
   - Contact tube off-center in relation to gas nozzle
   - Wrong nozzle-to-work distance
   - Incorrect electrode-holder position (see item 3)
   - Drafty environment (work should be shielded)
3. Incorrect electrode-holder position (should be 7° to 15° forehand)

Dirty Weld Bead(b)

1. Dirty workpieces or electrode wire
2. Impurities in shielding gas (because of air or water leakage)
3. Wrong forehand angle
4. Damaged or dirty gas nozzle
5. Wrong gas-nozzle size (should be smallest possible)
6. Insufficient shielding-gas flow
7. Drafty environment (work should be shielded)
8. Incorrect arc length
9. Contact tube recessed too far (should not be more than ⅛ in. inside gas nozzle)

Rough Weld Bead

1. Unstable arc
2. Improper electrode-holder manipulation
3. Improper current
4. Welding speed too low

Too Narrow Weld Bead

1. Insufficient current
2. Welding speed too high

Too Wide Weld Bead

1. Excessive current
2. Welding speed too low
3. Arc too long

Poor Visibility of Arc and Weld Puddle(c)

1. Wrong position of work
2. Wrong work angle or forehand angle
3. Small, dirty or wrong lens in helmet (a No. 10 or 12 lens should be used)
4. Wrong gas-nozzle size (should be smallest size)

Overheating of Power Supply(d)

1. Excessive power demand (two similar welding machines can be used in parallel if the capacity of one is insufficient)
2. Poor functioning of cooling fan
3. Dirty rectifier stacks (regular maintenance)

Overheating of Cables

1. Loose or faulty connections
2. Cables too small

Overheating of Electrode-Wire Feed Motor

1. Excessive friction between electrode wire and conduit
2. Wrong gear ratio of wire-feed unit
3. Poorly adjusted wire-spool brake
4. Incorrect alignment of gears and rolls in wire-feed unit
5. Worn brushes on wire-feed motor
6. Inadequate capacity of wire-feed motor (high welding rates and large wire sizes require motor of adequate power)
7. Worn or arced governor controls

Operator Fatigue

1. Wrong position of work (weld in flat position whenever possible)
2. Inadequate seating for welder
3. Lack of ventilation
4. Disregard of safety rules in respect to head shield, lens, gloves
5. Weight of cables (reduce by suspending cables overhead)
6. Too many auxiliary operations, such as cleaning and chipping

(b) The appearance of small amounts of black smut in welding with the aluminum-magnesium alloys is not a fault.
(c) The welder must be able to see the arc and the weld puddle at all times.
(d) High demand can damage the power supply by overheating. Overheating is particularly serious with rectifiers.

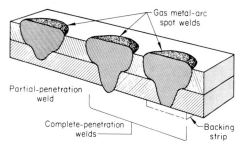

Fig. 26. Shapes of typical gas metal-arc spot welds

weld area. (Starting tabs were not used.) Between passes, the surface of the previously deposited bead was cleaned with a stainless steel wire brush. Interpass temperature was maintained between 150 and 200 F. The tensile strength of the weld repair was essentially the same as that of the original base metal.

Repair welding of castings is more common than repair welding of wrought metal. Most casting repair is done to correct foundry defects or to repair parts broken in service. For example, an alloy 355-T6 piston, 42 in. in diameter and 31 in. high with a thickness that varied from 1 to 3 in., had a large broken area on the top surface and broken areas on the skirt near the compression ring. For repair, the defective areas were chipped to sound unbroken metal, and all surfaces were washed with a solvent cleaner. The casting was then placed in an insulated box and preheated to 300 F by wrapping it with a bead-type resistance heater. For the welding operation, a constant-voltage power supply, a shielding-gas mixture of 75% argon and 25% helium, and a ⅟₁₆-in.-diam ER1100 electrode wire were used. Each area of repair was welded without interruption. Adequate weld reinforcement was provided so that the repaired area could be ground flush after cooling. The repairs, five in all, were made with no evidence of cracking, and radiographic inspection showed that they were satisfactory.

Spot Welding by the Gas Metal-Arc Process

Spot welding by the gas metal-arc process is a quick and reliable method of joining aluminum alloy sheet and extrusions. Normally, only enough force is required to hold parts in intimate contact, and only one side of the joint need be accessible. Aluminum alloys can be arc spot welded satisfactorily at high speed (12 or more spots per minute) by unskilled operators.

The cost of gas metal-arc spot welding is approximately half that of riveting, and the spots can develop shear strength and bearing strength equal to or better than those obtained with ⁵⁄₃₂-in. 2117-T6 rivets. In addition, fatigue strength is higher than that of riveted joints and resistance spot welded joints. Weld strength and appearance can be varied to suit the job by proper selection of degree of penetration, base-metal alloy and thickness, filler-metal alloy, joint design, fit-up and shielding.

Gas metal-arc spot welding can be used to join all of the arc weldable

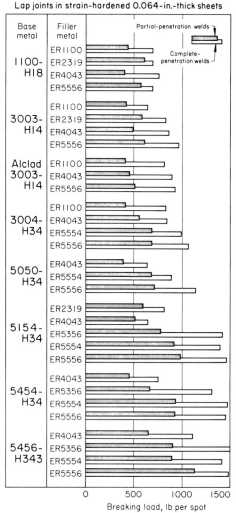

Fig. 27. Tensile-shear breaking loads for gas metal-arc spot welded 0.064-in. sheet

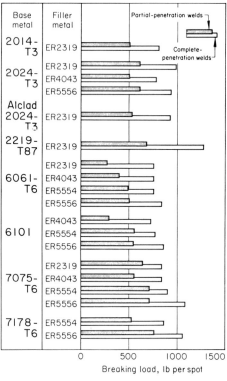

aluminum alloys and some (for example, 7075 and 7079) whose welding by other arc processes is not recommended (Table 1). A guide to filler-metal selection is given in Table 20. The process is also useful for welding aluminum alloys to steel or copper.

For spot welding, the nozzle assembly on the conventional gas metal-arc welding electrode holder is changed and circuitry is added to provide automatic control of feed, arc, and gas time. After adjusting the current, wire feed and other operating conditions in keeping with the thickness of metal and penetration required, the nozzle is brought into contact with the first member and sufficient pressure is applied to hold the two members in contact. The welding process is started and the electrode wire feeds forward, initiating the arc, which melts through the first member into the second member and forms the spot weld. Crater filling is automatically controlled to obtain a shrink-free spot of the correct shape. The weld usually is made in one second or less.

Reverse-polarity direct current is employed, with argon, helium or argon-helium gas shielding. A pull-type wire feed with a slow run-in control is recommended, to ensure reliable arc starting. A time-lag control between wire-feed shutoff and breaking the welding current prevents the electrode wire from freezing in the weld puddle when the power is cut off.

Constant-voltage power supplies, of either the motor-generator or rectifier type, with adjustable slope control, have been found to give the best results. They are capable of delivering the high current surge required for arc initiation. Constant-current power supplies are not recommended because aluminum electrode wire is likely to ball up on the end when the arc is extinguished.

Gas metal-arc spot welding necessitates the minimum amount of preweld cleaning. Removal of normal oxides

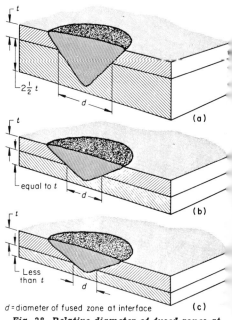

d = diameter of fused zone at interface

Fig. 28. Relative diameter of fused zones at sheet interface for three combinations of sheet thicknesses

and mill finishes is not necessary unless the ultimate in weld quality is demanded, but anodic and chemical-dip oxide finishes, and lacquers and other insulating coatings, must be removed. Solvent wiping is recommended for the removal of grease and die compounds. Alcohol and toluol are the preferred cleaning agents. Chlorinated solvents such as carbon tetrachloride and trichlorethylene should be used only with thorough ventilation and in an area far remote from the welding area, because they decompose and yield toxic fumes when in the vicinity of an electric arc.

Helium shielding is preferred when welding thin sheet (less than 0.040 in. thick) because its use results in a less sharply pointed weld cone than the use of argon shielding, thus permitting a larger fused area to be made at the faying surfaces. Drawbacks to the use of helium are: it is less readily available than argon, it is more costly, it has a higher level of spatter, and it results in a rougher weld surface. Low gas-flow rates — approximately 20 cu ft per hour — are possible because the spot welding nozzle provides an almost complete enclosure. Gas hoses should be purged with shielding gas before making the first weld in a series. A 5-sec purge is usually sufficient, but a longer purge may be needed at the beginning of the day's work. Once the gas nozzle is purged, successive welds can be made as quickly as the electrode holder can be repositioned.

Aluminum in thicknesses from 0.020 to ¼ in. can be joined by gas metal-arc spot welding. When the first member (usually, the top member) is ⅛ in. thick or less, no special preparation is needed, but if the first member is ⅛ to ¼ in. thick a pilot hole is required. The second member should preferably be at least as thick as the first member, and ideally two to three times as thick. Minimum thickness for the second member is generally 0.030 in. using solid backing; otherwise, it is 0.050 in. Use of chilled or massive backing allows complete penetration through the second member, to achieve maximum nugget diameter and strength.

Spot welds look like slightly crowned buttons on the surface closest to the electrode holder. In cross section, they should be cone-shape and penetrate through, or almost through, the second member. Figure 26 shows the shapes of diametral sections through typical spot welds. For sheets of nearly equal thickness, weld strength is highest when the weld penetrates through the second member. When made against a flat, clean metal backing plate, the spots are flush and uniform, leaving a mark resembling a resistance spot weld. For consistent results, clamping may be necessary to ensure uniform contact at the faying surfaces and between the work and backing. Partial-penetration spot welds show no mark at all on the back surface, and stiffeners and brackets can be welded to the back of architectural panels and other products where appearance is of prime importance, without any marring of the opposite surface.

Gas metal-arc spot welding of aluminum alloys is covered in Table 21.

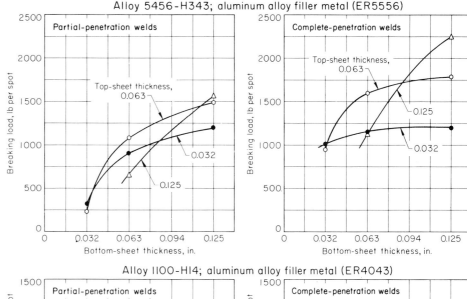

Alloy 5456-H343; aluminum alloy filler metal (ER5556)

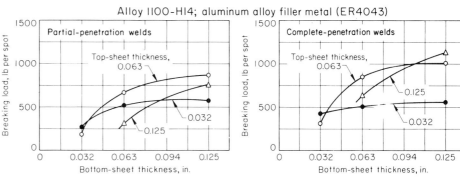

Alloy 1100-H14; aluminum alloy filler metal (ER4043)

Fig. 29. Effect of sheet thicknesses on tensile-shear breaking load for partial-penetration and complete-penetration gas metal-arc spot welds

The strength of a spot weld is a function of the alloy and the area of the nugget at the interface. Figure 27 shows tensile-shear breaking loads for 0.064-in. sheet of various aluminum alloys with partial-penetration and complete-penetration spot welds. Welds in alloys of the 5xxx series have the highest strength. The higher base-metal strength of the heat treatable alloys of series 2xxx, 6xxx and 7xxx is not reflected in the as-spot-welded strength. The combination of alloy 5456 sheet and ER5556 filler metal produces the highest tensile-shear strength per spot weld at a given thickness.

Table 20. Guide to the Choice of Filler-Metal Alloys for Gas Metal-Arc Spot Welding(a)

Aluminum base-metal alloys	Good filler-metal alloys(b)			Usable filler-metal alloys(b)		
1060, 1100, EC	ER1100,	ER4043,	ER5556	...		
2014, 2024, 2219	ER2319,	ER4043,	ER4145	...		
3003	ER1100,	ER4043,	ER5556	...		
5005, 5050	ER4043,	ER5356,	ER5556	...		
5052, 5083, 5086, 5154, 5456	ER5356,	ER5556		ER5554		
5454	ER5356,	ER5554,	ER5556	...		
6061, 6063, 6101	ER4043,	ER5356,	ER5556	ER5554		
7075, 7178	ER4043			ER5039,	ER5554,	ER5556

(a) Based on weld cracking resistance. (b) ER5183 can be used in place of ER5556.

Table 21. Typical Conditions for Gas Metal-Arc Spot Welding of Various Thicknesses of Aluminum Alloy Sheet(a)

Sheet thickness, in.		Partial-penetration welds			Complete-penetration welds		
Top	Bottom	Open circuit voltage, v	Wire feed, ipm(b)	Welding time, sec	Open circuit voltage, v	Wire feed, ipm	Welding time, sec
0.020	0.020	...	...	...	27	250	0.3
0.020	0.030	...	...	...	28	300	0.3
0.030	0.030	25.5	285	0.3	28	330	0.3
0.030	0.050	25.5	330	0.3	31	430	0.3
0.030	0.064	30	360	0.3	31	450	0.3
0.050	0.050	31	385	0.4	32	450	0.4
0.050	0.064	32	400	0.4	32	500	0.4
0.064	0.064	32	420	0.4	32	550	0.5
0.064	0.125	32.5	650	0.5	34.5	675	0.5
0.064	0.187	35	700	0.5	39	700	0.5
0.064	0.250	39	775	0.5	41	800	0.5
0.125	0.125	39.5	800	0.5	41	850	0.6
0.125	0.187	41	850	0.75	41	900	0.75
0.125	0.250	41	900	1.0	...	...	...

(a) Overlap joints; electrode, 0.047-in.-diam ER5554. (b) Welding current (dcrp), in amperes, is approximately equal to one-half wire feed, in inches per minute, of 0.047-in.-diam electrode wire.

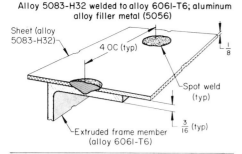

Alloy 5083-H32 welded to alloy 6061-T6; aluminum alloy filler metal (5056)

Semiautomatic Gas Metal-Arc Spot Welding

Joint type ....Lap
Welding position ....Flat
Power supply ....500-amp, constant-voltage
transformer-rectifier
Fixtures ....Clamping (when needed)
Electrode holder ....500 amp, water cooled
Gas nozzle ....¾-in. diam
Electrode wire ....¹⁄₁₆-in.-diam alloy 5056(a)
Shielding gas ....Argon, at 60 cfh
Electrode stickout ....½ in.
Current ....610 amp, dcrp
Voltage ....32 v
Arc time ....58 cycles per spot
Shielding-gas
consumption ....7 to 10 cu ft/100 spots
Electrode consumption ...0.3 to 0.4 lb/100 spots
Production rate ....7 to 10 min/100 spots

(a) This electrode wire has been discontinued. See footnote in table with Fig. 22 for information on alternative wires.

Fig. 30. Roof sheet and frame members that were joined by semiautomatic gas metal-arc spot welding (Example 308)

Maximum strength is obtained when the bottom sheet is at least twice the thickness of the top sheet, as the interface will be nearer to the face of the weld nugget and therefore larger (Fig. 28a). When the bottom sheet is about 2½ times thicker than the top sheet, the area of the weld nugget does not vary greatly with small variations in penetration. If the two sheets are of equal thickness (Fig. 28b) or if the top sheet is thicker (Fig. 28c) and if complete penetration cannot be tolerated, the same percentage variation in depth of penetration produces much greater variation in the weld-nugget interface area. If the surface of the bottom sheet is completely penetrated, less variation results in the interface area.

Figure 29 shows the effect of various combinations of top and bottom sheet thicknesses on tensile-shear breaking load per spot, for partial-penetration and complete-penetration spot welds made in alloy 5456-H343 with ER5556 electrode wire and in alloy 1100-H14 with ER4043 electrode wire.

Thicknesses being joined, and strength and appearance requirements, should be considered in determining whether control should be set to produce welds with partial or complete penetration. Welding conditions are easier to establish for complete-penetration welds, and the welds produced will have more uniform strength and appearance. Variability in partial-penetration welds will be reduced if the weld area of the second member is rigidly supported to ensure that the pressure on the first member by the electrode holder will hold the two members in contact.

The two examples that follow describe the use of gas metal-arc spot welding. In the first example, welding was semiautomatic and partial-penetration welds were made through thinner

metal into thicker metal. In the second example, welding was automatic and complete-penetration welds were made through thicker metal into backed-up thinner metal.

Example 308. Use of Semiautomatic Gas Metal-Arc Spot Welding for Joining Flat Roofs to Extruded Frame Members (Fig. 30)

In the manufacture of covered railway hopper cars, ⅛-in.-thick 5083-H32 flat roof sheet was laid over ³⁄₁₆-in.-thick 6061-T6 extruded frame members and welded. Originally, fillet welds were deposited either intermittently or continuously from below, by semiautomatic gas metal-arc welding, but this method was costly and difficult to use on thin material in this position.

Gas metal-arc spot welding was tried. The surfaces to be welded were precleaned by degreasing, and spot welding was done in the flat position through the ⅛-in. roof sheet into the frame member. The pressure of the nozzle of the hand-held electrode holder was usually enough to ensure no gap between the surfaces, but clamping was used when needed to ensure closure.

After spot welding was completed, the perimeter of the roof sheet was manually fillet welded to the car frame to seal against moisture. In addition to their structural functions, the spot welds held the roof sheet firmly in place for the fillet welding. Welding conditions for gas metal-arc spot welding are given in the table that accompanies Fig. 30.

Example 309. Use of Automatic Equipment for Making 700 Spot Welds per Hour by Gas Metal-Arc Welding (Fig. 31)

Gas metal-arc spot welding was used to attach stiffeners to sidewalls and roofs in the welding of 30-ft-long cargo containers for shipboard transportation. Other subse-

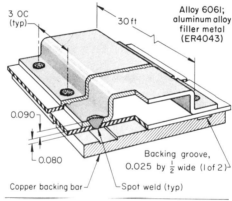

Automatic Gas Metal-Arc Spot Welding

Joint type ....Lap
Welding position ....Flat
Power supply ....500-amp, constant-voltage
transformer-rectifier, with variable slope
and inductance
Fixtures ....Pneumatic clamping; copper
backing bar
Electrode-holder clamping pressure .....400 psi
Electrode holder ....500 amp, water cooled
Gas nozzle ....1-in. diam, copper
Electrode wire ....¹⁄₁₆-in.-diam ER4043
Shielding gas ....75% helium, 25% argon,
at 50 cfh
Electrode stickout ....⅝ in.
Current ....325 amp, dcrp
Voltage ....28 v
Arc time ....About 30 cycles(a)
Shielding-gas consumption ....About
1 cu ft/100 spots
Electrode consumption ....About
0.0743 lb/100 spots
Production rate ......About 700 spots/hour(b)

(a) Depending on the metal thickness being joined. (b) Includes indexing of gantry and loading and unloading of work.

Fig. 31. Joining stiffeners to panels for a cargo container by automatic gas metal-arc spot welding (Example 309)

quent welding operations were required to join the wall and roof panels to floor assemblies, siderails, and corner posts to make a leakproof container.

Joining the stiffeners (extrusions) to the roof (sheet) by resistance spot welding was impractical, because the large size of the roof panels would have necessitated the provision of a welding machine with an excessively deep throat. Joining by riveting would have been expensive and would have required the sealing of each rivet hole. The cost of gas metal-arc spot welding, including labor, consumable supplies, and amortization of equipment, was estimated to be about half the cost of joining by riveting.

Wall and roof panels were made of 0.060 to 0.080-in.-thick 6061-T6 sheet; the stiffeners were hat-shape extruded sections, 0.080 to 0.090 in. thick, of 6061-T6. Because more than 4200 spot welds were to be made on each container and many containers were to be made, special mechanized welding equipment and controls were constructed. A gantry-type assembly that housed 14 spot welding electrode holders rode over the work on two siderails. An operator indexed it over a stiffener and then the control unit automatically actuated groups of four electrode holders in a predetermined sequence designed to minimize distortion of the panel. The electrode holders applied 40 psi pressure to the work to clamp the extrusions and sheet together. After a stiffener was welded in place, the gantry assembly was indexed about 18 in. to the next stiffener and the operation was repeated.

A 75% helium, 25% argon shielding-gas mixture and ¹⁄₁₆-in.-diam ER4043 electrode wire were selected to prevent weld crater cracking. No precleaning was required.

Copper backing bars with a relief groove under the welds were used to ensure good metal-to-metal contact during welding and to allow controlled full penetration for maximum strength. The backing bar was also essential because the thicknesses of the two pieces of metal being welded were unequal and because welding was being done through the thicker piece into the thinner piece, which is more difficult than the opposite arrangement.

All penetration nuggets were ground off to meet interior-smoothness requirements (no retention of any particle larger than 300 mesh). Shear strength in excess of 700 lb per spot was consistently obtained. Other processing data are given in the table that accompanies Fig. 31.

Gas Metal-Arc Spot Welding Aluminum to Other Metals. In gas metal-arc spot welding of aluminum alloys to other metals, the brittle intermetallic compounds formed at the periphery of the welds have little effect on strength and ductility in shear loading, which permits fusion spot welding of metal combinations that cannot be welded along seam joints without the use of special techniques.

When the other metal is thin, the weld can be made by melting through it with the arc. The in-rushing aluminum alloy filler metal and the force of the arc push the other metal away from the center of the weld so that the core and crown are composed of relatively ductile aluminum. The maximum thickness of the other metal that can be handled in this way is about 0.030 in. A pilot hole (about ¼ in. in diameter) through the nonaluminum member improves performance by providing a path for the filler metal, so that it remains undiluted and ductile. Pilot holes are essential when the other metal is more than 0.030 in. thick.

With a filler metal suitable for fusion welding the other metal, joints can be made in which the bottom member is the other metal. These filler metals usually have higher melting points than aluminum, though, and a superior joint is obtained if the aluminum is sandwiched between two pieces of the other metal. Three-layer joints of this type, with copper outer members and aluminum in the middle (see Fig. 32), are useful in making permanent connections in electrical applications.

Two or more pieces of aluminized steel can be joined by gas metal-arc spot welding, using an aluminum alloy filler metal and a backing strip of aluminum beneath the bottom steel sheet. In this joint, only the aluminum is exposed to the environment.

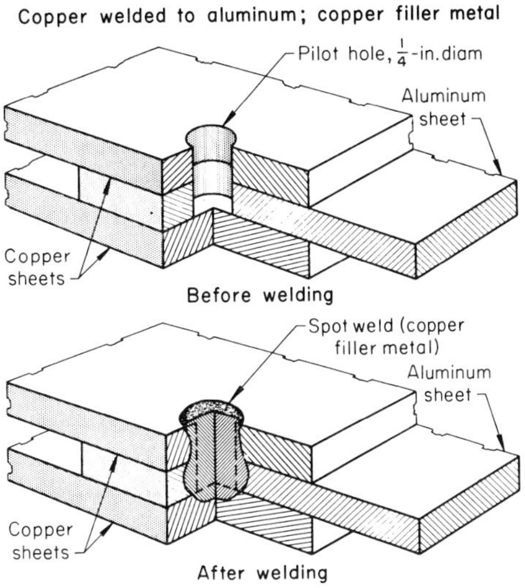

Gas Tungsten-Arc Welding

The advantages of welding aluminum alloys by the gas tungsten-arc process are the same as for other metals, as discussed in the article on Gas Tungsten-Arc Welding, which begins on page 113 of this volume.

Welding can be done with or without filler metal, but because filler metal is often used, there must be access at the joint for both torch and filler metal.

Thicknesses of aluminum alloys commonly welded by the gas tungsten-arc process range from 0.040 to ⅜ in. for manual welding and from 0.010 to 1 in. for automatic welding. Gas tungsten-arc welding is especially suitable for the automatic welding of thin workpieces that require the utmost in quality or finish, because of the precise heat control possible and the ability to weld with or without filler metal. Metal thicker than ⅜ in. can be manually welded; however either gas metal-arc or automatic tungsten-arc welding is preferred.

Power Supply and Equipment. For joining aluminum alloys, gas tungsten-arc welding utilizes either alternating or direct current. Both straight and reverse polarity are used with direct-current welding. The same power supplies, arc-stabilization accessories, torches, and control systems as are used for gas tungsten-arc welding of other metals are used for aluminum (see the article on Gas Tungsten-Arc Welding, page 113). Single-phase alternating current welding transformers should have an open-circuit voltage of 80 to 100 volts.

The oxide layer on the surface of aluminum alloys gives rise to some arc rectification during the reverse-polarity half of the alternating-current cycle. This arc rectification, either partial or complete, is undesirable, because it results in poor arc stability and possible overheating of the transformer; it can be overcome by the use of condensers in the welding circuit or preferably by placing a battery bias in series with the welding circuit. Battery power of 6 to 8 volts is usually sufficient to balance the current. The positive terminal should be in the direction of the electrode. About 100 amp-hr of storage-battery capacity should be used with every 100 amp of welding current. If two or more batteries are needed to obtain the required ampere-hour electrical capacity, they should be connected in parallel.

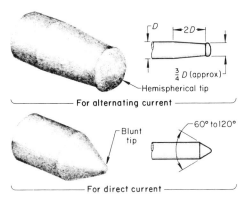

Fig. 32. Gas metal-arc spot weld with copper filler metal joining copper-aluminum-copper sandwich

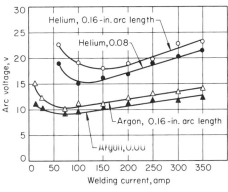

Fig. 33. Electrode tips used for gas tungsten-arc welding of aluminum alloys

Fig. 34. Arc-voltage characteristics of argon and helium shielding gas in gas tungsten-arc welding of aluminum alloys

Electrodes for Gas Tungsten-Arc Welding

For alternating-current gas tungsten-arc welding, unalloyed tungsten and tungsten-zirconium electrodes are recommended. Zirconiated electrodes are less likely to be contaminated by aluminum and have a slightly higher current rating. Unalloyed tungsten electrodes minimize inclusions in the weld bead and current unbalance.

Electrodes of 1% thoriated tungsten, which have higher current capacity than unalloyed tungsten and cost less

than zirconiated electrodes, are also used; their main disadvantage for alternating-current welding is a slight tendency to drip. This drip will result in some tungsten inclusions in the weld metal. With a skilled operator and good equipment, the inclusions are small and well dispersed. For best results with 1% thoriated electrodes, the electrode should have a ground surface. Electrodes of 2% thoriated tungsten are not generally used for alternating-current welding of aluminum alloys.

When gas tungsten-arc welding aluminum with alternating current, the tip of the electrode should be hemispherical, as shown in Fig. 33. The tip is prepared by using an electrode one size larger than required for the welding current, taper grinding the tip and forming the hemispherical end by welding for a few seconds with a current 20 amp higher than needed, holding the electrode vertically up.

Thoriated tungsten electrodes are normally used for direct-current gas tungsten-arc welding of aluminum. The tip of the electrode should be ground to a blunt conical point, having an included angle between 60° and 120° as shown in Fig. 33, to attain maximum penetration.

When an electrode becomes contaminated with aluminum, it must be replaced or cleaned. Minor contamination can be burned off by increasing the current while holding the arc on a piece of scrap metal. Severe contamination can be removed by grinding or by breaking off the contaminated portion of the electrode and re-forming the correct electrode contour on a piece of scrap aluminum.

Shielding Gases for Gas Tungsten-Arc Welding

Argon, helium, and mixtures of argon and helium are used as shielding gases in the gas tungsten-arc welding of aluminum alloys. The selection is somewhat dependent on the type of current used.

Welds made with alternating current show little difference in soundness or strength whether made with argon or helium shielding. With helium shielding, penetration is deeper; hence helium is sometimes employed with higher speeds and for thicker sections. Also, the welds develop slightly higher mechanical properties. However, argon is used more, for the following reasons:

1 It is more readily available and costs less than helium.
2 It affords better control of the weld puddle.
3 It gives a smoother, quieter arc, greater arc cleaning action, and easier arc starting.
4 Less gas is required for a specific application.
5 It has better cross-draft resistance than helium.
6 There is less clouding, and the metal stays brighter. The operator can see the weld puddle more easily.

With argon shielding, the arc voltage is lower for a given current value and arc length, as shown in Fig. 34. The lower arc-voltage characteristic of argon is essential to the successful manual alternating-current welding of

Table 22. Typical Conditions for Manual Gas Tungsten-Arc Welding of Butt Joints, Using Alternating Current(a)

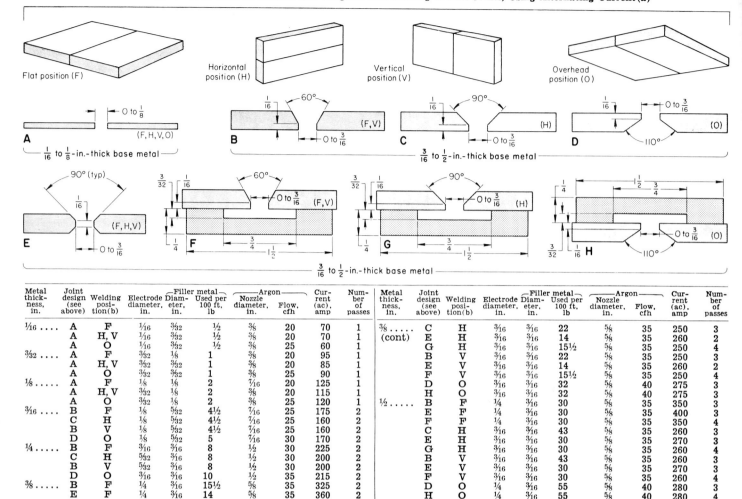

Metal thickness, in.	Joint design (see above)	Welding position(b)	Electrode diameter, in.	Filler metal Diameter, in.	Filler metal Used per 100 ft, lb	Argon Nozzle diameter, in.	Argon Flow, cfh	Current (ac), amp	Number of passes
1/16	A	F	1/16	3/32	1/2	3/8	20	70	1
	A	H, V	1/16	3/32	1/2	3/8	20	70	1
	A	O	1/16	3/32	1/2	3/8	25	60	1
3/32	A	F	3/32	1/8	1	3/8	20	95	1
	A	H, V	3/32	3/32	1	3/8	20	85	1
	A	O	3/32	3/32	1	3/8	25	90	1
1/8	A	F	1/8	1/8	2	7/16	20	125	1
	A	H, V	3/32	1/8	2	3/8	20	115	1
	A	O	3/32	1/8	2	3/8	25	120	1
3/16	B	F	1/8	5/32	4½	7/16	25	175	2
	C	H	1/8	5/32	4½	7/16	25	160	2
	B	V	1/8	5/32	4½	7/16	25	160	2
	D	O	1/8	5/32	5	7/16	30	170	2
1/4	B	F	3/16	3/16	8	1/2	30	225	2
	C	H	5/32	3/16	8	1/2	30	200	2
	B	V	5/32	3/16	8	1/2	30	200	2
	D	O	3/16	3/16	10	1/2	35	215	2
3/8	B	F	1/4	3/16	15½	5/8	35	325	2
	E	F	1/4	3/16	14	5/8	35	360	2
	F	F	1/4	3/16	15½	5/8	35	325	3
3/8 (cont)	C	H	3/16	3/16	22	5/8	35	250	3
	E	H	3/16	3/16	14	5/8	35	260	2
	G	H	3/16	3/16	15½	5/8	35	250	4
	B	V	3/16	3/16	22	5/8	35	250	3
	E	V	3/16	3/16	14	5/8	35	260	2
	F	V	3/16	3/16	15½	5/8	35	250	4
	D	O	3/16	3/16	32	5/8	40	275	3
	H	O	3/16	3/16	32	5/8	40	275	3
1/2	B	F	1/4	3/16	30	5/8	35	350	3
	E	F	1/4	3/16	30	5/8	35	400	3
	F	F	1/4	3/16	30	5/8	35	350	4
	C	H	3/16	3/16	43	5/8	35	260	3
	E	H	3/16	3/16	30	5/8	35	270	3
	G	H	3/16	3/16	30	5/8	35	260	3
	B	V	3/16	3/16	43	5/8	35	260	3
	E	V	3/16	3/16	30	5/8	35	270	3
	F	V	3/16	3/16	30	5/8	35	260	3
	D	O	1/4	3/16	55	5/8	40	280	3
	H	O	1/4	3/16	55	5/8	40	280	4

(a) Welding speed is 8 in. per minute for all metal thicknesses except 1/8 and 3/16 in., for which it is 10 in. per minute. Preheat is not required for metal through 3/16 in. thick; it is optional for 1/4-in.-thick metal; for welding 3/8-in.-thick metal in the flat position, it is up to 400 F; for welding 3/8-in.-thick metal in the other positions and for welding 1/2-in.-thick metal in all positions, it is up to 600 F. (b) F = flat; H = horizontal; V = vertical; O = overhead.

extremely thin material, because it decreases the probability of burn-through. This same characteristic is advantageous in vertical and overhead welding, because the molten metal is less likely to sag or run.

In special applications, where a balance of characteristics is desired, a mixture of argon and helium is used with alternating-current welding.

Argon is preferred for reverse-polarity direct-current welding because it establishes an arc more easily and provides better arc control.

Helium or an argon-helium mixture is always used with straight-polarity direct-current welding of aluminum. It assists in providing the deep, narrow penetration essential for the best properties and a minimum heat-affected zone. Helium shielding also prevents development of the rippled surface typical of argon shielding and straight-polarity direct-current welding.

When aluminum is welded with alternating current or reverse-polarity direct current, a white band of varying width appears alongside the weld bead. This white band, disclosed by one analysis to be aluminum oxide, never occurs when welding is done with straight-polarity direct current, and it

is believed to be caused by the emission of electrons from the surface of the aluminum when it is on the cathode side of the arc (dcrp). The electrons leave the aluminum through the aluminum oxide, thus serving to detach the oxide from the surface.

When the white band alongside the weld is of hairline width immediately adjacent to the weld bead itself, the flow of shielding gas is adequate for proper shielding of the tungsten arc. Any increase in gas flow will cause widening of the band, indicating that gas is being wasted.

Filler Metals for Gas Tungsten-Arc Welding

Gas tungsten-arc welding can be done with or without filler metal. Sometimes the joint design permits the base metal to provide the weld metal. In some square-groove butt joints, the weld metal comes from the straight sides of the groove, or extra metal may be provided on a corner or flange that is melted to form the weld. If restraint is likely to cause cracking, best results are achieved by the addition of separate filler metal.

Usually, filler metal is added in the form of a bare rod for manual welding or as a coil of wire for automatic feeding. The filler-metal alloys used for gas-shielded arc welding of aluminum are discussed earlier in this article (see page 296) and are listed in Table 3. Suitability of the various filler metals for use with different aluminum alloys, and for different properties, is given in Tables 4, 5 and 6.

Filler-metal rod and wire comes in a wide range of sizes. Straight lengths of rod (36 in. long), packaged in tubes containing 5 lb of filler metal, are available in diameters of 1/16, 3/32, 1/8, 5/32, 3/16 and 1/4 in. from regular stock, and rod in diameters of 0.030, 0.035, 0.040, and 3/64 is available on special order. Wire is available in 1-lb and 10-lb spools in sizes from 0.030 to 0.040 in. in diameter and in 1-lb and 15-lb spools in sizes from 3/64 to 1/8 in. in diameter.

Weld Backing in Gas Tungsten-Arc Welding

Backing bars are commonly used when butt welds are made from one side only, but they are usually not necessary in automatic straight-polarity direct-current welding of square-groove butt joints from one side only.

Temporary backing bars are shown with the butt welds in Table 22. Permanent backing bars like those shown in Table 17 and described in Example 297 (for gas metal-arc welding) are also applicable to gas tungsten-arc welding. For additional discussion of backing bars, see the section on Weld Backing for Gas Metal-Arc Welding.

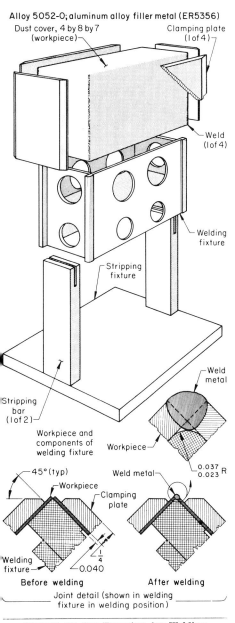

Alloy 5052-0; aluminum alloy filler metal (ER5356)

Fig. 35. Module can made of 0.040-in.-thick alloy 5052-O that was welded with negligible distortion because of careful fixturing and process control (Example 310)

Manual AC Gas Tungsten-Arc Welding

Joint type	Corner
Weld type	Fillet
Welding position	Flat
Power supply	40 v, 320 amp, high-frequency stabilization
Fixtures	Internal fixture, clamping plates, clamps
Torch	Water cooled
Electrode	$\frac{3}{32}$-in.-diam EWTh-2
Filler metal	$\frac{1}{16}$-in.-diam ER5356
Shielding gas	Argon, at 20 cfh
Current	170 amp, ac
Number of passes	One
Production rate	3 cans per hour

Table 23. Typical Conditions for Manual AC Gas Tungsten-Arc Welding of Corner Joints

Metal thickness, in.	Welding position (a)	Electrode diameter, in.	Filler metal Diameter, in.	Filler metal Used per 100 lb	Argon Nozzle diameter, in.	Argon Flow, cfh	Current (ac), amp	Welding Preheat	Welding Speed, ipm	Number of passes
$\frac{1}{16}$	F	$\frac{1}{16}$	$\frac{3}{32}$	$\frac{1}{2}$	$\frac{3}{8}$	20	60	None	10	1
	H, V	$\frac{1}{16}$	$\frac{3}{32}$	$\frac{1}{2}$	$\frac{3}{8}$	20	60	None	10	1
	O	$\frac{1}{16}$	$\frac{3}{32}$	$\frac{1}{2}$	$\frac{3}{8}$	25	60	None	10	1
$\frac{3}{32}$	F	$\frac{3}{32}$	$\frac{1}{8}$	1	$\frac{3}{8}$	20	90	None	10	1
	H, V	$\frac{3}{32}$	$\frac{1}{8}$	1	$\frac{3}{8}$	20	90	None	10	1
	O	$\frac{3}{32}$	$\frac{1}{8}$	1	$\frac{3}{8}$	25	90	None	10	1
$\frac{1}{8}$	F	$\frac{1}{8}$	$\frac{1}{8}$	2	$\frac{3}{8}$	20	115	None	10	1
	H, V	$\frac{3}{32}$	$\frac{1}{8}$	2	$\frac{3}{8}$	20	115	None	10	1
	O	$\frac{3}{32}$	$\frac{1}{8}$	2	$\frac{3}{8}$	25	115	None	10	1
$\frac{3}{16}$	F	$\frac{1}{8}$	$\frac{5}{32}$	$4\frac{1}{2}$	$\frac{7}{16}$	25	160	None	10	1
	H, V	$\frac{1}{8}$	$\frac{5}{32}$	$4\frac{1}{2}$	$\frac{7}{16}$	25	160	None	10	1
	O	$\frac{1}{8}$	$\frac{5}{32}$	$4\frac{1}{2}$	$\frac{7}{16}$	30	170	None	10	1
$\frac{1}{4}$	F	$\frac{5}{32}$	$\frac{3}{16}$	7	$\frac{1}{2}$	30	210	Optional	8	2
	H, V	$\frac{5}{32}$	$\frac{3}{16}$	7	$\frac{1}{2}$	30	200	Optional	8	1
	O	$\frac{3}{16}$	$\frac{3}{16}$	7	$\frac{1}{2}$	35	215	Optional	8	1
$\frac{3}{8}$	F	$\frac{3}{16}$	$\frac{3}{16}$	17	$\frac{5}{8}$	35	280	Optional	8	2
	H, V	$\frac{3}{16}$	$\frac{3}{16}$	17	$\frac{5}{8}$	35	250	Optional	8	2
	O	$\frac{3}{16}$	$\frac{3}{16}$	17	$\frac{5}{8}$	40	260	Optional	8	3
$\frac{1}{2}$	F	$\frac{3}{16}$	$\frac{3}{16}$	30	$\frac{5}{8}$	35	290	Optional	8	3
	H, V	$\frac{3}{16}$	$\frac{3}{16}$	30	$\frac{5}{8}$	35	260	Optional	8	3
	O	$\frac{3}{16}$	$\frac{3}{16}$	30	$\frac{5}{8}$	40	280	Optional	8	3

(a) F = flat; H = horizontal; V = vertical; O = overhead

Table 24. Typical Conditions for Manual AC Gas Tungsten-Arc Welding of T and Lap Joints

Metal thickness, in.	Welding position (a)	Electrode diameter, in.	Filler metal Diameter, in.	Filler metal Used per 100 ft, lb	Argon Nozzle diameter, in.	Argon Flow, cfh	Current (ac), amp	Preheat temperature, F	Welding Speed, ipm	Number of passes
$\frac{1}{16}$	F	$\frac{1}{16}$	$\frac{3}{32}$	$\frac{1}{2}$	$\frac{3}{8}$	20	80	None	8	1
	H, V	$\frac{1}{16}$	$\frac{3}{32}$	$\frac{1}{2}$	$\frac{3}{8}$	20	80	None	8	1
	O	$\frac{1}{16}$	$\frac{3}{32}$	$\frac{1}{2}$	$\frac{3}{8}$	25	70	None	8	1
$\frac{3}{32}$	F	$\frac{1}{8}$	$\frac{3}{32}$	1	$\frac{3}{8}$	20	120	None	8	1
	H, V	$\frac{3}{32}$	$\frac{3}{32}$	1	$\frac{3}{8}$	20	100	None	8	1
	O	$\frac{3}{32}$	$\frac{3}{32}$	1	$\frac{3}{8}$	25	110	None	8	1
$\frac{1}{8}$	F	$\frac{1}{8}$	$\frac{1}{8}$	2	$\frac{7}{16}$	20	150	None	10	1
	H, V	$\frac{3}{32}$	$\frac{1}{8}$	2	$\frac{3}{8}$	20	120	None	8	1
	O	$\frac{3}{32}$	$\frac{1}{8}$	2	$\frac{3}{8}$	25	135	None	8	1
$\frac{3}{16}$	F	$\frac{5}{32}$	$\frac{5}{32}$	$4\frac{1}{2}$	$\frac{1}{2}$	25	215	None	8	1
	H, V	$\frac{1}{8}$	$\frac{5}{32}$	$4\frac{1}{2}$	$\frac{7}{16}$	25	180	None	8	1
	O	$\frac{5}{32}$	$\frac{5}{32}$	$4\frac{1}{2}$	$\frac{7}{16}$	30	190	None	8	1
$\frac{1}{4}$	F	$\frac{3}{16}$	$\frac{3}{16}$	7	$\frac{1}{2}$	30	260	Optional	8	1
	H, V	$\frac{3}{16}$	$\frac{3}{16}$	7	$\frac{1}{2}$	30	235	Optional	8	1
	O	$\frac{3}{16}$	$\frac{3}{16}$	7	$\frac{1}{2}$	35	240	Optional	8	1
$\frac{3}{8}$	F	$\frac{1}{4}$	$\frac{3}{16}$	17	$\frac{5}{8}$	35	345	Up to 400	8	2
	H, V	$\frac{3}{16}$	$\frac{3}{16}$	17	$\frac{5}{8}$	35	290	Up to 600	8	2
	O	$\frac{3}{16}$	$\frac{3}{16}$	17	$\frac{5}{8}$	40	290	Up to 600	8	3
$\frac{1}{2}$	F	$\frac{1}{4}$	$\frac{3}{16}$	30	$\frac{5}{8}$	35	375	Up to 600	8	3
	H, V	$\frac{1}{4}$	$\frac{3}{16}$	30	$\frac{5}{8}$	35	300	Up to 600	8	3
	O	$\frac{1}{4}$	$\frac{3}{16}$	30	$\frac{5}{8}$	40	310	Up to 600	8	3

(a) F = flat; H = horizontal; V = vertical; O = overhead

Table 25. Typical Conditions for Manual AC Gas Tungsten-Arc Welding of Edge Joints

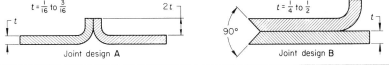

Metal thickness, t, in.	Welding position (a)	Electrode diameter, in.	Filler metal Diameter, in.	Filler metal Used per 100 ft, lb	Argon Nozzle diameter, in.	Argon Flow, cfh	Current (ac), amp	Preheat	Welding Speed, ipm	Number of passes
Joint Design A										
$\frac{1}{16}$	F	$\frac{1}{16}$	$\frac{3}{32}$	$\frac{3}{4}$	$\frac{3}{8}$	20	55	None	10	1
	H, V	$\frac{1}{16}$	$\frac{3}{32}$	$\frac{3}{4}$	$\frac{3}{8}$	20	55	None	10	1
	O	$\frac{1}{16}$	$\frac{3}{32}$	$\frac{3}{4}$	$\frac{3}{8}$	25	55	None	10	1
$\frac{3}{32}$	F	$\frac{3}{32}$	$\frac{1}{8}$	2	$\frac{3}{8}$	20	85	None	10	1
	H, V	$\frac{3}{32}$	$\frac{1}{8}$	2	$\frac{3}{8}$	20	80	None	10	1
	O	$\frac{3}{32}$	$\frac{1}{8}$	2	$\frac{3}{8}$	25	85	None	10	1
$\frac{1}{8}$	F	$\frac{3}{32}$	$\frac{1}{8}$	4	$\frac{3}{8}$	20	110	None	10	1
	H, V	$\frac{3}{32}$	$\frac{1}{8}$	4	$\frac{3}{8}$	20	100	None	10	1
	O	$\frac{3}{32}$	$\frac{1}{8}$	4	$\frac{3}{8}$	25	100	None	10	1
$\frac{3}{16}$	F	$\frac{1}{8}$	$\frac{5}{32}$	8	$\frac{7}{16}$	25	150	None	10	1
	H, V	$\frac{1}{8}$	$\frac{5}{32}$	8	$\frac{7}{16}$	25	150	None	10	1
	O	$\frac{1}{8}$	$\frac{5}{32}$	8	$\frac{7}{16}$	30	160	None	10	1
Joint Design B										
$\frac{1}{4}$	F	$\frac{5}{32}$	$\frac{5}{32}$	15	$\frac{1}{2}$	30	200	Optional	8	1
	H, V	$\frac{5}{32}$	$\frac{5}{32}$	15	$\frac{1}{2}$	30	190	Optional	8	1
	O	$\frac{5}{32}$	$\frac{5}{32}$	15	$\frac{1}{2}$	35	200	Optional	8	1
$\frac{3}{8}$	F	$\frac{3}{16}$	$\frac{3}{16}$	33	$\frac{5}{8}$	35	270	Optional	8	1
	H, V	$\frac{3}{16}$	$\frac{3}{16}$	33	$\frac{5}{8}$	35	230	Optional	8	2
	O	$\frac{3}{16}$	$\frac{3}{16}$	33	$\frac{5}{8}$	40	250	Optional	8	3
$\frac{1}{2}$	F	$\frac{3}{16}$	$\frac{3}{16}$	60	$\frac{5}{8}$	35	275	Optional	8	3
	H, V	$\frac{3}{16}$	$\frac{3}{16}$	60	$\frac{5}{8}$	35	240	Optional	8	3
	O	$\frac{3}{16}$	$\frac{3}{16}$	60	$\frac{5}{8}$	40	260	Optional	8	3

(a) F = flat; H = horizontal; V = vertical; O = overhead

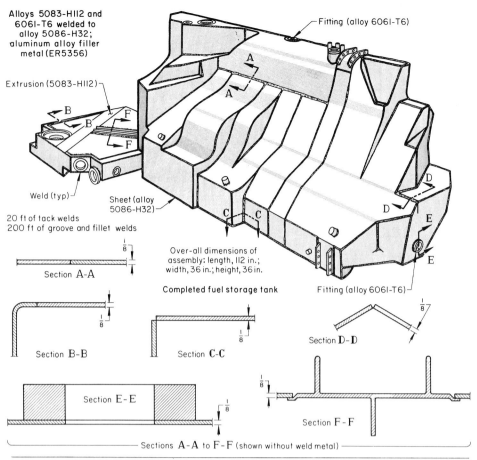

Alloys 5083-H112 and 6061-T6 welded to alloy 5086-H32; aluminum alloy filler metal (ER5356)

Extrusion (5083-H112)

Weld (typ)

Sheet (alloy 5086-H32)

Fitting (alloy 6061-T6)

20 ft of tack welds
200 ft of groove and fillet welds

Section A-A

Over-all dimensions of assembly: length, 112 in.; width, 36 in.; height, 36 in.

Completed fuel storage tank

Fitting (alloy 6061-T6)

Section B-B

Section C-C

Section D-D

Section E-E

Section F-F

Sections A-A to F-F (shown without weld metal)

Conditions That Were the Same for All Joints(a)

Welding process .. Manual gas tungsten-arc (ac)
Power supply .. 200-amp transformer, continuous high-frequency stabilization, 60% duty cycle
Torch .... 200 amp, water cooled
Gas nozzle .... 7/16-in. diam

Electrode 3/32-in.-diam EWTh-1
Filler metal 1/8-in.-diam ER5356
Shielding gas .... Argon, at 15 to 20 cfh
Voltage .... 20 to 26 v
Number of passes .... One

Conditions That Varied With Joint

Joint	Type	Weld	Welding position(b)	Current (ac), amp	Alloys joined
A-A, B-B	Butt	Square groove	F, V	100-140	5086 to 5086
C-C	Corner	Fillet	F, H, V	110-160	5086 to 5086
D-D	Corner	V-groove	F	100-140	5086 to 5086
E-E	T	Fillet	H	110-160	5086 to 6061
F-F	Butt	Single-bevel groove	F, V	120-160	5086 to 5083

(a) For precleaning and tack welding procedures, see Examples 293 and 305, respectively.
(b) F = flat; H = horizontal; V = vertical.

Fig. 36. Fuel tank for an M-60 combat tank, and types of welded joints (Example 311)

Alternating-Current Gas Tungsten-Arc Welding

Almost all manual and automatic gas tungsten-arc welding of aluminum alloys 0.040 through 3/8 in. thick is done with balanced-wave alternating-current high-frequency-stabilized power supplies, argon shielding gas, and un-alloyed tungsten electrodes. Zirconiated tungsten electrodes and helium and argon-helium shielding-gas mixtures are also used with alternating-current welding for reasons discussed earlier, in the sections on Electrodes for Gas Tungsten-Arc Welding and on Shielding Gases for Gas Tungsten-Arc Welding. Adequate gas shielding is indicated by the bright silvery band bordering each side of the weld bead (also discussed earlier) and a shiny bead.

Usually, alternating-current welding provides the optimum combination of current-carrying capacity, arc controllability, and arc cleaning action for the welding of aluminum alloys. A short arc length must be maintained in order to obtain sufficient penetration and to prevent undercutting, excessive width of weld bead, and consequent loss of control of penetration and weld contour. Arc length should be about equal to the diameter of the tungsten electrode. On fillet welds, a short arc and adequate current are needed to prevent bridging the root. A short arc also ensures that the inert gas completely surrounds the weld as it forms.

Manual Welding. Typical conditions for manual alternating-current gas tungsten-arc welding are given in Tables 22 to 25. Metal that is more than 1/8 in. thick is grooved to ensure complete penetration. A single-V groove with an included angle of 60° to 90° is the most often used. Under certain conditions, a double-V groove may be advantageous for metal more than 1/4 in. thick. If the operator has difficulty in maintaining a very short arc, a larger included angle or joint spacing may be

required in order to allow a longer arc to be used.

The arc should not be started by touching the tungsten electrode to the aluminum workpiece, because this may mark the work or result in aluminum being picked up on the electrode, which is likely to cause a wild, uncontrollable arc and a dirty weld. The initial arc should be struck on a starting block to heat the electrode to its operating temperature. (The arc should never be struck on a piece of carbon, as this will contaminate the electrode.) The arc is then broken and reignited at the joint. This technique reduces the likelihood of forming tungsten inclusions at the start of the weld, which can happen when a cold electrode is used to start the weld.

The arc is struck like striking a match — by swinging the electrode holder in a pendulum-like motion toward the starting place. With superimposed high-frequency current for arc stabilization, there is no need to touch the work with the electrode as the arc will start when the electrode tip is brought close to the work surface. Some machines apply the high frequency only when starting; others have it on continuously, or have a switch that permits the operator to cut it on or off at will. The arc is held at the starting point until the metal liquefies and a weld puddle is established. Establishment and maintenance of a suitable weld puddle is important and welding must not proceed ahead of the puddle. A separate foot-operated heat control, available with certain power supplies, is highly advantageous in preventing uneven penetration by permitting the current to be adjusted as the work becomes hotter. Breaking the arc also requires special care, to prevent the formation of shrinkage cracks in the weld crater. Several techniques are used. The arc can be gradually lengthened while filler metal is added to the crater; the arc can be quickly broken and restruck several times while adding filler metal to the crater; or a foot control can be used to reduce current at the end of the weld. Crater-filling devices may be used if properly adjusted and timed.

By using these techniques, and adequate fixturing, weld joints can be made manually in aluminum alloys down to 0.040 in. thick, without excessive distortion. This is shown in the following example.

Example 310. Maintaining Close Dimensional Tolerances During Manual Gas Tungsten-Arc Welding of Thin Aluminum Sheet (Fig. 35)

The open-end module can shown in Fig. 35, which served as a dust cover and a heat sink for electronic gear, was made from a single sheet of 0.040-in. aluminum alloy 5052-O by brake bending the bottom corners and manually welding the four vertical corner joints. Tolerances of ±0.01 to ±0.02 in. were necessary to ensure close fit over components for heat-sink efficiency.

To meet the tolerances, alternating-current gas tungsten-arc welding and ER5356 filler metal were selected, and a box-shape fixture was constructed that consisted of four 1/2-in.-thick steel plates joined so as to match the internal dimensions of the can. The fixture was tapered so that the can was slightly under dimension at the closed end, and slightly over dimension at the open end.

The sequence of operations for welding was as follows:

1. After the can was formed and chemically cleaned, the fixture was inserted.
2. Four ¼-in.-thick plates of a size to leave access for welding the four vertical corners of the can were placed against the outer surfaces of the four sides of the can and clamped to the fixture through the end.
3. The corner joints were welded in the flat position (slightly downhill) on a welding table by the manual gas tungsten-arc process. (Welding conditions are given in the table that accompanies Fig. 35.)
4. The clamping plates were removed, leaving the can held on the fixture by shrinkage.
5. The can and fixture were placed on raised supports, the can was heated with an oxyacetylene torch, the can expanded, and the fixture dropped free.

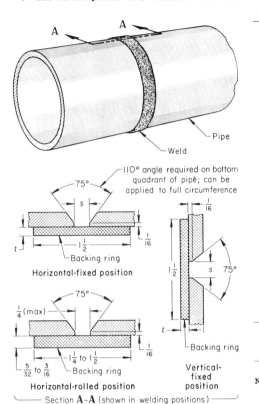

Root opening, s, is zero with no backing ring or with a removable backing ring, and ¼ in. max with an integral backing ring. For thickness of backing ring (t) for fixed-position welding, see Table 26.

Fig. 37. Edge preparation for fixed-position pipe welding using the typical conditions given in Table 26

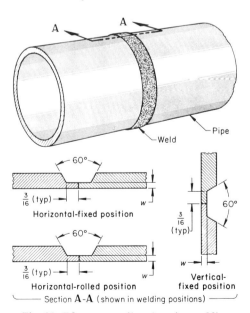

Fig. 38. Edge preparation for pipe welding using the conditions and root-face widths (w) given in Table 27

Table 26. Typical Conditions for Fixed-Position Pipe Welding by the Manual Alternating-Current Gas Tungsten-Arc Process, Using Joint Designs Shown in Fig. 37

Nominal pipe size, in.	Wall thickness, in.	Thickness of backing ring (t in Fig. 37), in.	Electrode diameter, in.	Filler-metal diameter, in.	Gas-nozzle diameter, in.	Argon flow, cfh	Current (ac), amp	Number of passes(a)
Horizontal-Fixed Position								
1	0.133	0.072	⅛	³⁄₃₂	½	30 to 80	90 to 110	1 to 2
1¼	0.140	0.072	⅛	⅛	½	30 to 80	100 to 120	1 to 2
1½	0.145	0.072	⅛	⅛	½	30 to 80	110 to 130	1 to 2
2	0.154	0.093	⅛	⅛	½	30 to 80	120 to 140	1 to 2
2½	0.203	0.093	⅛	⅛	½	30 to 80	130 to 150	2
3	0.216	0.093	⅛	⅛	½	30 to 80	145 to 165	2
3½	0.226	0.093	⅛	⅛	½	30 to 80	150 to 170	2
4	0.237	0.125	³⁄₁₆	⅛ to ³⁄₁₆	½	35 to 80	160 to 180	2
5	0.258	0.125	³⁄₁₆	⁵⁄₃₂ to ³⁄₁₆	½	35 to 80	180 to 190	2
6	0.280	0.187	³⁄₁₆	⁵⁄₃₂ to ³⁄₁₆	½	50 to 80	195 to 205	2
8	0.322	0.187	³⁄₁₆	⁵⁄₃₂ to ³⁄₁₆	½	50 to 80	210 to 220	2 to 3
10	0.365	0.187	³⁄₁₆	⁵⁄₃₂ to ³⁄₁₆	½	50 to 80	230 to 240	2 to 3
12	0.406	0.187	³⁄₁₆	⁵⁄₃₂ to ³⁄₁₆	½	50 to 80	245 to 255	2 to 3
Vertical-Fixed Position								
1	0.133	0.072	⅛	³⁄₃₂	⁷⁄₁₆	25 to 50	95 to 115	1 to 2
1¼	0.140	0.072	⅛	⅛	⁷⁄₁₆	25 to 50	105 to 125	1 to 2
1½	0.143	0.072	⅛	⅛	⁷⁄₁₆	25 to 50	115 to 135	1 to 2
2	0.154	0.093	⅛	⅛	⁷⁄₁₆	30 to 60	125 to 145	2 to 3
2½	0.203	0.093	⅛	⅛	⁷⁄₁₆	30 to 60	135 to 155	3 to 5
3	0.216	0.093	⅛	⅛	½	40 to 60	150 to 170	3 to 5
3½	0.226	0.093	⅛	⅛	½	40 to 60	155 to 175	3 to 5
4	0.237	0.125	³⁄₁₆	⅛ to ⁵⁄₃₂	½	40 to 60	165 to 185	3 to 5
5	0.258	0.125	³⁄₁₆	⁵⁄₃₂ to ³⁄₁₆	½	50 to 60	185 to 205	3 to 5
6	0.280	0.187	³⁄₁₆	⁵⁄₃₂ to ³⁄₁₆	½	50 to 60	200 to 220	3 to 5
8	0.322	0.187	³⁄₁₆	⁵⁄₃₂ to ³⁄₁₆	½	60 to 80	215 to 235	5 to 8
10	0.365	0.187	³⁄₁₆	⁵⁄₃₂ to ³⁄₁₆	½	60 to 80	235 to 255	5 to 8
12	0.406	0.187	³⁄₁₆	⁵⁄₃₂ to ³⁄₁₆	½	70 to 80	250 to 270	6 to 8

(a) For horizontal-fixed position, more passes are required for the bottom quadrant of the joint.

Table 27. Typical Conditions for Pipe Welding by the Manual Alternating-Current Gas Tungsten-Arc Process, Using Joint Designs Shown in Fig. 38

Nominal pipe size, in.	Wall thickness, in.	Root-face width (w in Fig. 38), in.	Electrode diameter, in.	Filler-metal diameter, in.	Gas-nozzle diameter, in.	Argon flow, cfh	Current (ac), amp	Number of passes
Horizontal-Fixed Position								
1	0.133	¹⁄₁₆	⅛	³⁄₃₂	½	30 to 80	90	3 to 4
1¼	0.140	¹⁄₁₆	⅛	⅛	½	30 to 80	100	3 to 4
1½	0.145	¹⁄₁₆	⅛	⅛	½	30 to 80	110	3 to 4
2	0.154	¹⁄₁₆	⅛	⅛	½	30 to 80	120	3 to 4
2½	0.203	¹⁄₁₆	⅛	⅛	½	30 to 80	130	3 to 4
3	0.216	³⁄₃₂	⅛	⅛	½	30 to 80	145	3 to 4
3½	0.226	³⁄₃₂	⅛	⅛	½	30 to 80	150	3 to 4
4	0.237	³⁄₃₂	³⁄₁₆	⅛ to ⁵⁄₃₂	½	35 to 80	160	3 to 4
5	0.258	³⁄₃₂	³⁄₁₆	⁵⁄₃₂ to ³⁄₁₆	½	35 to 80	180	3 to 4
6	0.280	³⁄₃₂	³⁄₁₆	⁵⁄₃₂ to ³⁄₁₆	½	50 to 80	195	3 to 4
8	0.322	³⁄₃₂	³⁄₁₆	⁵⁄₃₂ to ³⁄₁₆	½	50 to 80	210	3 to 4
10	0.365	³⁄₃₂	³⁄₁₆	⁵⁄₃₂ to ³⁄₁₆	½	50 to 80	230	3 to 4
12	0.406	³⁄₃₂	³⁄₁₆	⁵⁄₃₂ to ³⁄₁₆	½	50 to 80	245	3 to 4
Vertical-Fixed Position								
1	0.133	¹⁄₁₆	⅛	³⁄₃₂	½	25 to 50	90	3 to 4
1¼	0.140	¹⁄₁₆	⅛	⅛	½	25 to 50	100	3 to 4
1½	0.145	¹⁄₁₆	⅛	⅛	½	25 to 50	110	3 to 4
2	0.154	¹⁄₁₆	⅛	⅛	½	30 to 60	120	4 to 5
2½	0.203	¹⁄₁₆	⅛	⅛	½	30 to 60	130	4 to 5
3	0.216	³⁄₃₂	⅛	⅛	½	40 to 60	145	4 to 5
3½	0.226	³⁄₃₂	⅛	⅛	½	40 to 60	150	4 to 5
4	0.237	³⁄₃₂	³⁄₁₆	⅛	½	40 to 60	160	4 to 5
5	0.258	³⁄₃₂	³⁄₁₆	⁵⁄₃₂ to ³⁄₁₆	½	50 to 60	180	4 to 5
6	0.280	³⁄₃₂	³⁄₁₆	⁵⁄₃₂ to ³⁄₁₆	½	50 to 60	195	5 to 6
8	0.322	³⁄₃₂	³⁄₁₆	⁵⁄₃₂ to ³⁄₁₆	½	60 to 80	210	5 to 6
10	0.365	³⁄₃₂	³⁄₁₆	⁵⁄₃₂ to ³⁄₁₆	½	60 to 80	230	5 to 6
12	0.406	³⁄₃₂	³⁄₁₆	⁵⁄₃₂ to ³⁄₁₆	½	70 to 80	240	5 to 6
Horizontal-Rolled Position								
1	0.133	¹⁄₁₆	⅛	³⁄₃₂	⁷⁄₁₆	25 to 40	90	1 to 2
1¼	0.140	¹⁄₁₆	⅛	⅛	⁷⁄₁₆	25 to 40	100	1 to 2
1½	0.145	¹⁄₁₆	⅛	⅛	⁷⁄₁₆	25 to 40	110	1 to 2
2	0.154	¹⁄₁₆	⅛	⅛	⁷⁄₁₆	25 to 40	120	3 to 4
2½	0.203	¹⁄₁₆	⅛	⅛	⁷⁄₁₆	30 to 40	130	3 to 4
3	0.216	³⁄₃₂	⅛	⅛	½	30 to 40	145	3 to 4
3½	0.226	³⁄₃₂	⅛	⅛	½	30 to 40	150	3 to 4
4	0.237	³⁄₃₂	³⁄₁₆	⅛	½	30 to 40	160	3 to 4
5	0.258	³⁄₃₂	³⁄₁₆	⁵⁄₃₂	½	30 to 40	180	3 to 4
6	0.280	³⁄₃₂	³⁄₁₆	⁵⁄₃₂ to ³⁄₁₆	½	35 to 40	195	3 to 5
8	0.322	³⁄₃₂	³⁄₁₆	⁵⁄₃₂ to ³⁄₁₆	½	35 to 40	210	3 to 5
10	0.365	³⁄₃₂	³⁄₁₆	⁵⁄₃₂ to ³⁄₁₆	½	35 to 40	230	3 to 5
12	0.406	³⁄₃₂	³⁄₁₆	⁵⁄₃₂ to ³⁄₁₆	½	35 to 40	245	3 to 5

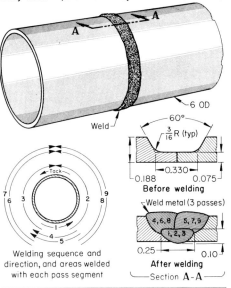

Alloy 6351-T4; aluminum alloy filler metal (ER5254)

60°
$\frac{3}{16}$ R (typ)

6 OD
Weld

0.188   0.075
0.330
Before welding

Weld metal (3 passes)
4,6,8 5,7,9
1,2,3
0.25   0.10
After welding
Section A-A

Welding sequence and
direction, and areas welded
with each pass segment

Manual AC Gas Tungsten-Arc Welding

Joint type ....Butt
Weld type ....Single-U groove
Joint spacing ....None
Welding position ....Horizontal-fixed pipe
Power supply ..400-amp engine-driven generator
Fixtures ....External alignment clamp
Torch ....Water cooled
Electrode .....$\frac{3}{16}$-in.-diam EWZr, taper ground
Filler-metal wire ..$\frac{1}{8}$-in.-diam alloy ER5254(a)
Shielding gas ....Argon, at 25 cfh
Current ....190 amp
Arc time per joint ....7 min
Number of passes ....Three
Hourly production per welder(b) ....5 joints

(a) Chosen because it is compatible with all common aluminum alloys used for pipe and pipe fittings, ER5254 is a former AWS classification that has been replaced by ER5654. (b) Includes allowance for downtime.

Fig. 39. Welding large-diameter aluminum pipe for a pipeline (Example 312)

The can, welding fixture, clamping plates, stripping fixture, and joints are shown in Fig. 35. The inside radii of the welded corners were established by the corner radii of the fixture. The outside radii were dressed as needed to maintain a 0.04-in. maximum radius.

Tack welding before final welding is helpful in controlling distortion. Tack welds should be of ample size and strength, and preferably should be chipped out or tapered at the ends before welding over them. Alternating-current gas tungsten-arc welding is less suitable for tack welding than straight-polarity direct-current gas tungsten-arc welding, or than gas metal-arc welding (in which reverse-polarity direct current is used). Gas metal-arc welding (with dcrp) was used for tack welding during assembly of fuel tanks as described in Example 305; for final welding of the joints in these tanks, as described in the example that follows, manual alternating-current gas tungsten-arc welding was selected, because of the high weld quality that could be obtained with this process.

Example 311. Manual AC Gas Tungsten-Arc Welding of Fuel Tanks (Fig. 36)

Manual gas tungsten-arc welding, with alternating current, was used for making the 200 ft of groove welds and fillet welds required in the fabrication of the aluminum alloy fuel-storage tank shown in Fig. 36. The various butt, T and cor-

ner joints involved in welding the final assembly are also shown in Fig. 36. It was essential that the fuel tanks be leaktight, so the gas tungsten-arc process was selected for making these final welds because the ease with which the weld puddle could be controlled helped to ensure high weld quality.

The special preweld cleaning required for the components of this tank is described in Example 293. Tack welding of the components into 50 subassemblies, and tack welding of the subassemblies for final welding, were done by gas metal-arc welding, as described in Example 305, because the faster welding speed of that process reduced distortion and cost.

Before gas tungsten-arc welding, the tack welds and joints were mechanically cleaned with a stainless steel wire power brush. To avoid accumulation of dirt on the cleaned surfaces, final welding was done within 24 hr of the wire brushing.

Alloy 5086-H32 sheet, $\frac{1}{8}$ in. thick, was welded to itself and to 5083-H112 extrusions, which served as stiffeners and attachment flanges, and also formed an integral part of the fuel-tank wall. Bosses and fittings were of alloy 6061-T6. The parts were assembled and welded in a fixture.

As shown in the table that accompanies Fig. 36, many of the welding conditions were the same for all joints. Current varied according to joint design and welding position. Complete-penetration welds were deposited in single continuous passes. Tack welds were not removed. When the operator encountered a tack weld, he proceeded at about the same speed but added only enough filler metal to maintain proper weld contour. This procedure completely re-fused the tack welds.

After welding, the fixtured assembly was stress relieved in a furnace at 450 F for 2

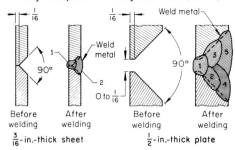

Alloy 5083; aluminum alloy filler metal (E5356)

Weld metal

Weld metal
90°
1
2
0 to $\frac{1}{16}$

90°
3 5
1
2
4

Before   After
welding   welding
$\frac{3}{16}$-in.-thick sheet

Before   After
welding   welding
$\frac{1}{2}$-in.-thick plate

Manual AC Gas Tungsten-Arc Welding

Joint type ....Butt
Weld type ....Single-V groove
Welding position ....Horizontal
Power supply ....Stabilized
Weld backing ....None
Torch ....Manual, water cooled
Electrode:
 $\frac{3}{16}$-in. sheet ....$\frac{1}{8}$-in.-diam EWZr
 $\frac{1}{2}$-in. plate ....$\frac{1}{4}$-in.-diam EWZr
Filler metal:
 $\frac{3}{16}$-in. sheet ....$\frac{5}{32}$-in.-diam ER5356
 $\frac{1}{2}$-in. plate ....$\frac{3}{16}$-in.-diam ER5356
Shielding gas ....Argon, at 35 cfh
Current:
 $\frac{3}{16}$-in. sheet ....160 amp, ac
 $\frac{1}{2}$-in. plate ....300 amp, ac
Preheat:
 $\frac{3}{16}$-in. sheet ....None
 $\frac{1}{2}$-in. plate ....200 F
Interpass temperature ....200 to 400 F
Number of passes:
 $\frac{3}{16}$-in. sheet ....Two
 $\frac{1}{2}$-in. plate ....Five

Results of Qualification Tests

Tensile strength ....26,805; 27,400 psi(a)
Failure ....Ductile failure, in weld metal
Guided bend tests (4) ......Results acceptable

(a) Results of two tests in reduced-section tensile specimens 0.750 by 0.487 in. and 0.751 by 0.474 in.

Fig. 40. Welds in $\frac{3}{16}$-in. sheet and $\frac{1}{2}$-in. plate, made in the horizontal position by the gas tungsten-arc process (Example 313)

hr, furnace cooled to 200 F, and then cooled in air to room temperature while still in the fixture.

Testing Procedures. Weld quality was checked by visual inspection based on workmanship samples, and the fuel tanks were tested for leaktightness by two different tests. In one test, the openings were plugged, the tanks were internally pressurized to 3 psi, and a liquid soap solution was flowed over all the welds. Leaks showed as a stream of fine bubbles. In the second test, the tanks were filled to 75% of capacity with a 0.25-to-0.50% aqueous solution of a detergent and a water-soluble dye, the remaining air space was pressurized to 3 psi, and the tanks were placed in a fixture and spun at 3 rpm for 3 min and 10 rpm for 7 min. The tanks were required to pass both tests with no leaks. If a leak occurred, which was unusual, repair was made by gas tungsten-arc welding.

Cleanness of Filler-Metal Wire. Because cleanness of the materials used to make the fuel tanks was of utmost importance (see Example 293), quality control of the filler-metal wire was necessary. In addition to the requirement that the wire meet Federal Specification QQ-R-566, samples of wire were tested periodically for cleanness by the following procedure. Using gas tungsten-arc equipment and settings (see the table that accompanies Fig. 36), an arc was struck near one edge of a clean coupon of alloy 5086 ($\frac{1}{8}$ in. thick by 4 in. wide by 6 in. long). Without adding filler metal, the arc was moved across the coupon, fusing well into it. If all conditions were correct, the weld puddle was clean and quiet. Next, some suspect filler metal was added to the puddle. Clean filler metal caused only a slight agitation of the puddle when added, and no dirt was seen floating on the molten puddle or on the weld bead afterward. Dirty filler metal caused violent action of the puddle and resulted in dirt floating on the surface. This was seen during the test through the proper shade of filter lens. After the test was completed, dirt could be seen on the surface of the weld bead.

Because gas tungsten-arc welding with alternating current affords close control of the weld puddle in all positions, it is often used for the welding of pipe joints. Typical welding conditions are given in Tables 26 and 27, and joint edge preparations are shown in Fig. 37 and 38.

Manual alternating-current gas tungsten-arc welding is an economical process for joining pipe up to fairly long lengths. The equipment required is less expensive than that for gas metal-arc welding and it needs less maintenance, a desirable feature when field welding. The suitability of this process for welding aluminum pipe is described in the following example, in which the importance of joint design is also discussed.

Example 312. Welding Pipe in the Horizontal-Fixed Position by the Gas Tungsten-Arc Process (Fig. 39)

The 6-in.-OD, 0.188-in.-wall alloy 6351-T4 pipe shown in Fig. 39 was welded economically in lengths up to five miles (for use in a pipeline) by the manual gas tungsten-arc process. Because the pipe was fixed in the horizontal position, it was necessary to be able to control the weld puddle in all positions. The gas tungsten-arc process was therefore chosen. The joint was a single-U-groove butt with no root opening, as shown in Fig. 39. Joint surfaces were precleaned by wiping with solvent, an external clamp was used to align the joint, and the joint was tack welded. After tack welding, the clamp was removed and the joint was welded in three passes, each consisting of three segments. By remelting starts and stops of each segment when restriking the arc, potential defects were avoided. The weld passes are shown in section A-A in Fig. 39, and the sequence and direction of the segments of each weld pass are shown at lower left in Fig. 39. Segments 1, 4 and 5 were made in the overhead position, with the welder lying under the pipe, and the remainder of the segments were made in the vertical-up position, with the welder kneeling. Welding conditions are given in the table that accompanies Fig. 39.

Preheating parts thicker than about ³⁄₁₆ in. may be advantageous when gas tungsten-arc welding with alternating current. The preheating temperature depends on the thickness of the base metal and the particular problems associated with the job. Often 200 F is a sufficient preheat temperature for material up to ½ in. thick, as in the following example, in which the use of preheat and careful selection of electrode material helped in obtaining the necessary mechanical properties.

Example 313. Use of Preheat in Welding ½-In.-Thick Alloy 5083 Plate (Fig. 40)

Figure 40 shows the joint designs and the buildup sequences used in manual gas tungsten-arc welding of ³⁄₁₆-in.-thick sheet and ½-in.-thick plate, both of alloy 5083. In welding the ½-in. plate, preheating to 200 F was found helpful in producing a weld puddle fluid enough for welding in the horizontal position; the ³⁄₁₆-in. sheet could be welded without preheat. Both the sheet and the plate were welded with EWZr electrodes, which resulted in clean weld metal, with minimum tungsten contamination.

The edges to be welded were grooved by machining or grinding, or both. All grease, oil, and oxide were removed by solvent cleaning and brushing with a stainless steel wire brush before welding. It was essential that the welding current and method of depositing the weld metal be such that there was no undercutting. All cracks and blowholes that appeared on the surface of a bead were removed by chipping or grinding before depositing the next bead. Production data and results of welding-procedure qualification tests are summarized in the table that accompanies Fig. 40.

Automatic Welding. The gas tungsten-arc process can be mechanized either with or without the addition of filler metal. If filler metal is used, it is normally added mechanically by cold-wire feed units. Automatic gas tungsten-arc welding usually employs a shorter arc length, and higher welding current and welding speed, and results in deeper penetration than manual welding. Typical conditions for the automatic alternating-current gas tungsten-arc process, for butt joints and metal thicknesses from ¹⁄₁₆ to ½ in., are given in Table 28.

Joint fit-up, joint cleanness and filler-metal cleanness are especially important with automatic welding. Joint-edge cleaning must be thorough and should immediately precede welding. Additional torches can be installed ahead of the main welding torch for cleaning and preheating.

Automatic alternating-current gas tungsten-arc welding has been used in the aerospace industry for joining relatively thin aluminum. High-strength high-quality welds can be made without excessive distortion, and the quantities are usually large enough to warrant mechanization. Two such applications of the automatic gas tungsten-arc process are described in Examples 314 and 315, which follow.

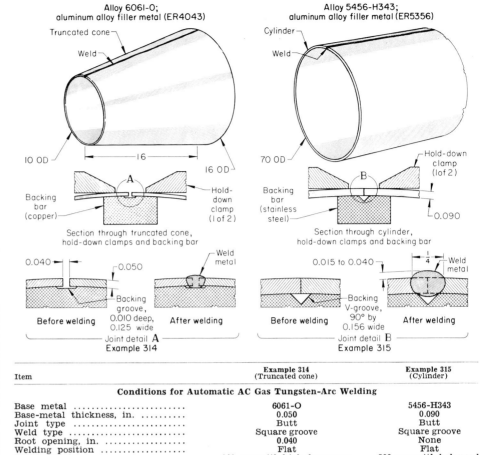

Item	Example 314 (Truncated cone)	Example 315 (Cylinder)
Conditions for Automatic AC Gas Tungsten-Arc Welding		
Base metal	6061-O	5456-H343
Base-metal thickness, in.	0.050	0.090
Joint type	Butt	Butt
Weld type	Square groove	Square groove
Root opening, in.	0.040	None
Welding position	Flat	Flat
Power supply	300 amp with high-frequency stabilization	300 amp with balanced wave
Mechanization and fixtures	Automatic welding machine with segmented hold-down fingers	
Backing	Copper bar	Stainless steel bar
Torch	Water cooled	Water cooled
Electrode	⅛-in.-diam EWP	⁵⁄₃₂-in.-diam EWP
Filler metal	¹⁄₁₆-in.-diam ER4043	0.045-in.-diam ER5356
Shielding gas	Argon, at 16 cfh	Argon, at 22 cfh
Current (ac), amp	100	185
Voltage, v	40	10 to 11
Filler-metal feed, ipm	22	112
Welding speed, ipm	24	21
Number of passes	One	One

Fig. 41. A truncated cone and a cylinder that were automatic gas tungsten-arc welded, and hold-down devices, backing-groove designs, and joint details (Examples 314 and 315)

Examples 314 and 315. Welding Aerospace Parts by the Automatic Alternating-Current Gas Tungsten-Arc Process (Fig. 41)

Example 314 — Truncated Cone (Fig. 41). Because the welded truncated cone (alloy 6061-O) shown at the left in Fig. 41 served as a blank to be explosively formed into a streamlined (ballistic ogive) shape, the welded joint had to be ductile enough to undergo considerable distortion without rupturing. The 0.010-in. by 0.125-in. groove in the backing bar provided for complete joint pen-

Table 28. Typical Conditions for Automatic Gas Tungsten-Arc Welding of Butt Joints, Using Alternating Current(a)

Metal thickness, in.	Electrode diameter, in.(b)	Argon flow, cfh	Welding current (ac), amp(c)	Number of passes
¹⁄₁₆	¹⁄₁₆	15	60 to 80	1
⅛	³⁄₃₂	20	125 to 145	1
³⁄₁₆	⅛	20	190 to 220	1
¼	³⁄₁₆	25	260 to 300	2
⅜	¼	30	330 to 380	2
½	¼	30	400 to 450	4

(a) Power supply: alternating current with superimposed high-frequency current, balanced wave. (b) Unalloyed tungsten electrodes are recommended. (c) Current ranges are averages for butt welds with square edges. For metal ¼ in. thick or more, edges are usually beveled.

etration, but with limited reinforcement to help ensure ductility of the weld. After welding, but before forming, the weld bead was roll planished. After forming, welds were checked for cracks by liquid-penetrant inspection. The joints made using the conditions listed in the table that accompanies Fig. 41 consistently had acceptable ductility, and they were crack-free after forming.

Example 315 — Cylinder (Fig. 41). The alloy 5456-H343 shown at the right in Fig. 41 was part of a missile fuel tank. The 0.156-in.-wide 90° V-groove in the backing bar was used to provide the maximum root reinforcement allowed. The weld bead face was ¼ in. wide and had a reinforcement of about 30%. Welding was done under the conditions given in the table that accompanies Fig. 41. The square-groove butt joint had zero root opening. The edges were drawfiled and scraped to remove surface oxides prior to welding.

Welds had acceptable radiographic quality and tensile properties — 31,820 psi yield strength, 50,620 psi tensile strength, and 5.5% elongation. Gas metal-arc welding was also tried for this part, and although welding speed was about twice that for gas tungsten-arc welding, rejections because of cracks and porosity were numerous.

Another application in which automatic alternating-current gas tungsten-arc welding was used to join relatively thin aluminum was the fillet welding of an 0.087-in.-thick alloy 5456-H343 extruded T-ring stiffener to the inside surface of a 0.071-in.-thick alloy 5456-H343 sheet cylinder, as shown in Fig. 42. The fillet welds were made using an oscillating torch, which was mounted on a boom that reached inside the cylinder. Welding was done in the horizontal-rolled position, with the cylinder being rotated by a precision positioner. The torch had arc-voltage control. A 300-amp balanced-wave power supply and 0.030-in.-diam ER5556 filler-metal wire were used.

The assembly was part of a fuel tank. Manual welding of the stiffeners had been tried, but it resulted in excessive distortion, defects requiring repair, and excessive production time. Automatic welding reduced the number of out-of-tolerance parts by 90%, weld defects by 30%, and welding time per tank by 200 man-hours.

As the thickness of the metal to be welded increases, power requirements increase. When the power requirement exceeds the capacity of the power supply, maximum welding speed cannot be attained and one of the advantages of mechanization is not realized. For single-pass square-groove butt welding, the advantage of higher welding speed is lost when the thickness of the material reaches 3/16 to 1/4 in. For example, when welding the circumferential seam of a manifold sump in 0.190-in.-thick alloy 5052-H32, the current was raised from 210 amp, which is normally used for automatic gas tungsten-arc welding of this thickness of aluminum, to 310 amp (the upper limit of the power supply) and the welding speed was raised to only 8 in. per minute, about the same as for manual welding. The weld joint and the conditions for welding are shown in Fig. 43. The filler metal was smaller in diameter than often used, to improve control of the weld puddle. Although the welding speed was slow, the welds did meet requirements — namely, uniform bead width, very smooth bead surface, radiographic quality to class II (MIL-R-45774), and weld-metal yield strength of 14,150 psi, tensile strength of 29,300 psi, and elongation of 14%.

For butt welds in material thicker than 3/16 to 1/4 in., the edges of the joint are usually beveled to a single or double V-groove for multiple-pass welding. An alternative process would be gas tungsten-arc welding with straight-polarity direct current, which can make square-groove welds in material up to 3/4 in. thick without difficulty.

Repair welding can be done by the alternating-current gas tungsten-arc process. In the following example, filler metal was not added until a clean weld puddle was well established, which was helpful in obtaining clean weld metal on a resin-impregnated casting.

Example 316. Repair of Spotfacing Error in Resin-Impregnated Aluminum Alloy Casting (Fig. 44)

A spotfacing error in an attachment boss (Fig. 44) used for bolting together the two halves of an aircraft-engine crankcase casting made of alloy 355-T7 reduced the height of a boss below tolerance. The casting was salvaged by weld repair, which was permitted because the service load in the

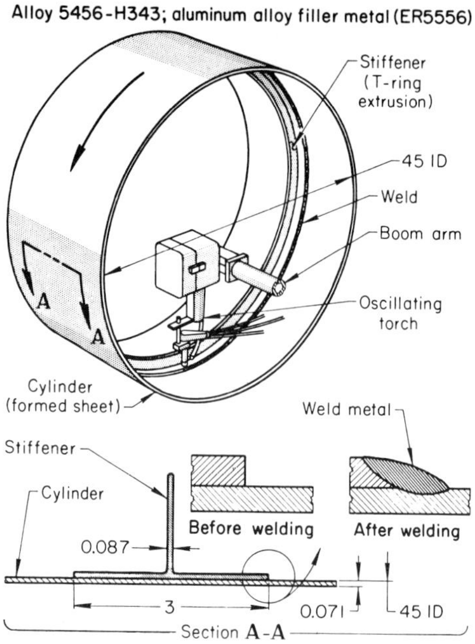

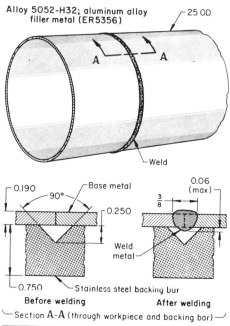

Fig. 42. *Automatic ac gas tungsten-arc welding, with an oscillating torch, of an extruded stiffener to a fuel-tank cylinder, which was rotated in a precision positioner during welding*

Automatic AC Gas Tungsten-Arc Welding

Joint type ....Butt
Weld type ....Square groove
Root opening ....None
Welding position ....Horizontal-rolled pipe
Power supply ....300 amp, balanced wave
Fixtures ....Clamps, stainless steel backing bar(a), rotating positioner
Torch ....Water cooled
Electrode ....3/16-in.-diam EWP
Filler metal 0.045-in.-diam ER5356
Shielding gas ....Argon, at 20 cfh
Current ....310 amp, ac
Voltage ....11 to 12 v
Filler-metal feed ....88 ipm
Welding speed ....8 ipm
Number of passes ....One

(a) The segmented backing bar (25 in. in diameter, with a 90° V-groove 0.250 in. deep) was hydraulically expanded to align the joint edges against an external clamping fixture.

Fig. 43. *Square-groove butt weld that represents practical thickness limit for automatic alternating-current gas tungsten-arc welding in one pass*

boss area was relatively low. The equipment and welding conditions, as listed in the table that accompanies Fig. 44, were conventional for gas tungsten-arc welding. However, deposition of the weld bead required careful manipulation to avoid development of porosity and to obtain complete fusion, because the casting had been impregnated with a polyester resin.

The casting had been cleaned by blasting at the foundry, but required vapor degreasing and stainless steel wire brushing of the boss and surrounding area. Preheat and postheat were considered unnecessary because the service load was not a critical factor in this portion of the casting.

To remove the impregnated resin, an arc was struck and manipulated over a small area until a puddle of clean metal was obtained. This puddle was then extended to cover the entire area to be welded; no filler metal was used at this stage. After the puddle solidified, the area was wire brushed. The arc was restruck and a thin layer of filler metal was deposited in crescent-shape beads to cover the area. This layer was wire brushed, and a second bead was similarly deposited, bringing the buildup to a height sufficient for re-spotfacing to correct size.

After visual inspection and machining, the welded area was radiographed to check for cracks and porosity. The repair operation proved satisfactory.

Reverse-Polarity Direct-Current Gas Tungsten-Arc Welding

Although gas tungsten-arc welding of aluminum with reverse-polarity direct current (electrode positive) is seldom used, this process offers certain advantages in the joining or repairing of thin-wall heat exchangers, tubing and similar assemblies with sections up to about 3/32 in. thick.

The process is characterized by shallow penetration, ease of arc control and good arc cleaning action. However, reverse-polarity direct current causes most of the heat of the arc to be generated at the electrode, which necessitates the use of large-diameter electrodes and decreases arc efficiency. If practical electrode sizes are to be used, work must be thin. For example, a 1/4-in.-diam electrode is needed in order to carry a 125-amp current. This would weld aluminum up to about 1/8 in. thick.

Reverse-polarity direct-current welding is useful for small shops because it can be used with almost any general-purpose power supply. Thoriated tungsten electrodes are normally used, and argon shielding is preferred, because it facilitates arc starting and arc control. Table 29 gives typical conditions for welding butt joints in metal up to 0.050 in. thick with reverse-polarity direct current.

Reverse-polarity direct-current welding was used in constructing from 0.020-in.-thick alloy 1100 sheet reflectors that required a high-quality mirror finish after buffing. Riveting could not be used as it resulted in distortion and polishing difficulties. Spot and seam resistance welding were ruled out by the shape of the parts, and the material was too thin to be joined by gas metal-arc welding. Therefore, gas tungsten-arc welding had to be used, and reverse-polarity direct current was selected because its shallow penetration reduced the risk of burn-through.

The reflectors weighed about 1 lb each and required butt, corner and lap joints. The joint areas were precleaned by sandblasting, and the parts were lightly clamped and tack welded.

Direct current was supplied by a rectifier of 200-amp capacity, adjustable to as low as 10 amp. A standard water-cooled torch was used, with a ceramic gas nozzle, argon shielding gas, a $\frac{3}{16}$-in.-diam thoriated tungsten electrode, and ER1100 filler metal. Reflectors of satisfactory quality were made without difficulty.

Reverse-polarity direct current was also used in welding an open box to be used as a housing. The housing was required to be both rigid and lightweight. Sand casting could not be used because the walls were too thin, and the design and the low total production ruled out die casting. Therefore, the housing was designed as a weldment in 0.050-in.-thick alloy 6061-T6 sheet, with stiffeners and numerous bosses, up to $\frac{1}{4}$ in. thick, welded on. The housing weighed about 3 lb.

Resistance spot welding of the housing joints was unsuitable because of the shape of the components and the combination of thin and thick sections. Gas metal-arc welding was ruled out because of the short joint lengths, the need for frequent repositioning of the assembly, and the thinness of the metal. Therefore, gas tungsten-arc welding was used and reverse-polarity direct current was selected because of its shallow penetration.

The parts were vapor degreased, and tack welded in standard clamps. They were then removed from the clamps and were welded without preheating. The current was supplied by a 200-amp rectifier. A special foot switch was used to break the arc at the end of the seam, to prevent the formation of craters. A standard water-cooled torch was used, with a ceramic gas nozzle, argon shielding, a $\frac{3}{32}$-in.-diam thoriated tungsten electrode, and ER4043 filler metal. After welding, the housing was re-aged, which gave it sufficient rigidity and dimensional stability, and critical dimensions were machined.

Straight-Polarity Direct-Current Gas Tungsten-Arc Welding

With straight-polarity direct current (electrode negative), the heat is generated at the workpiece surface, producing deep penetration and permitting higher welding currents for a given electrode size than can be used with reverse polarity. As a result, smaller electrodes can be employed with a given welding current, which helps to keep the weld bead narrow. Because of the narrow and deep penetration obtained, less edge preparation and less filler metal are needed, and welding is faster than when using reverse polarity. Because of the high heat generated on the workpiece surface, melting is rapid, no preheat is required, even of thick sections, and there is little distortion of the base metal.

The process has been used for years on as-received material to make irrigation tubing in high-speed tube mills, at speeds up to 50 ft per minute. It is the process employed in almost all of the highly automatic coil-joining welders

Table 29. Typical Conditions for Manual Gas Tungsten-Arc Welding of Square-Groove Butt Joints, Using Reverse-Polarity Direct Current(a)

Metal thickness, in.	Electrode diameter, in.(b)	Filler-metal diameter, in.	Argon flow rate, cfh	Current (dcrp), amp(c)
0.020	$\frac{1}{8}$ to $\frac{5}{32}$	0.020	15-20	40-55
0.030	$\frac{3}{16}$	0.020 or $\frac{3}{64}$	15-20	50-65
0.040	$\frac{3}{16}$	$\frac{3}{64}$	25-30	60-80
0.050	$\frac{3}{16}$	$\frac{3}{64}$ or $\frac{1}{16}$	25-30	70-90

(a) Single-pass welds made in the flat position. Use of a backing bar having a generous groove is recommended. (b) Thoriated tungsten electrodes. (c) Higher currents with larger electrodes may be used for automatic welding.

used on continuous process lines in the aluminum industry. Perhaps more lineal feet of welds in aluminum alloys have been made by this process than by any other process.

Straight-polarity direct-current gas tungsten-arc welding is also especially suitable for joining thick sections and has been used on aluminum up to 1 in. thick. It is well suited for tack welding and produces welds of good contour and high quality. Butt joints are characteristically narrow and flat, and buildup can be controlled by varying the size and amount of filler wire. Fillet welds characteristically have a concave or flat face. Fillet size can be regulated easily by varying the size of the filler wire. The shape of the weld is generally uniform, and the concentrated heat of the arc gives good fusion at the root of the joint.

The mechanical properties of welds made by this method are equal to or better than those made with alternating current. The welding heat is more

Table 30. Typical Conditions for Manual Gas Tungsten-Arc Welding of Butt Joints, Using Straight-Polarity Direct Current, Thoriated Tungsten Electrodes, and Helium Shielding

Metal thickness, in.	Groove design	Electrode diameter, in.	Filler-metal diameter, in.	Helium flow rate, cfh	Current (dcsp), amp	Voltage, v	Welding speed, ipm	Number of passes
0.030	Square	0.040	$\frac{3}{64}$	20	20	21	17	1
0.040	Square	0.040	$\frac{1}{16}$	20	26	20	16	1
0.060	Square	0.040	$\frac{1}{16}$	20	44	20	20	1
0.090	Square	$\frac{1}{16}$	$\frac{3}{32}$	30	80	17	11	1
0.125	Square	$\frac{1}{16}$	$\frac{1}{8}$	20	118	15	16	1
0.250	Square	$\frac{1}{8}$	$\frac{5}{32}$	30	250	14	7	1
0.500	90° single V, $\frac{1}{4}$-in. root face	$\frac{1}{8}$	$\frac{5}{32}$	40	310	14	$5\frac{1}{2}$	2
0.750	90° double V, $\frac{3}{16}$-in. root face	$\frac{1}{8}$	$\frac{5}{32}$	50	300	17	4	2
1.000	90° double V	$\frac{1}{8}$	$\frac{1}{4}$	50	360	19	$1\frac{1}{2}$	5

Table 31. Typical Conditions for Manual Gas Tungsten-Arc Welding of T and Lap Joints, Using Straight-Polarity Direct Current, Thoriated Tungsten Electrodes, and Helium Shielding

Metal thickness, in.	Welding position	Fillet size, in.	Electrode diameter, in.	Filler-metal diameter, in.	Helium flow rate ($\frac{1}{2}$-in. nozzle), cfh	Current (dcsp), amp	Voltage, v	Welding speed, ipm
0.090	Horizontal	$\frac{1}{8}$	$\frac{3}{32}$	$\frac{3}{32}$	40	130	14	21
0.125	Horizontal	$\frac{1}{8}$	$\frac{3}{32}$	$\frac{3}{32}$	40	180	14	18
0.250	Horizontal	$\frac{3}{16}$	$\frac{1}{8}$	$\frac{5}{32}$	40	255	14	15
	Vertical	$\frac{3}{16}$	$\frac{1}{8}$	$\frac{5}{32}$	40	230	14	10
0.375	Horizontal	$\frac{5}{16}$	$\frac{1}{8}$	$\frac{1}{4}$	50	290	14	7
	Horizontal	$\frac{3}{16}$	$\frac{1}{8}$	$\frac{5}{32}$	50	335	14	14
0.500	Horizontal	$\frac{5}{16}$	$\frac{1}{8}$	$\frac{1}{4}$	50	315	16	7
	Vertical	$\frac{5}{16}$	$\frac{1}{8}$	$\frac{1}{4}$	50	315	16	6

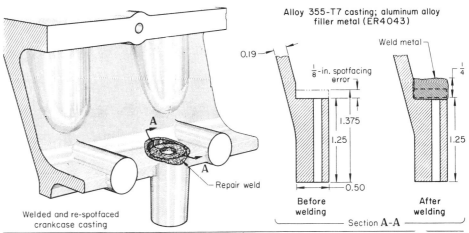

Welded and re-spotfaced crankcase casting

Alloy 355-T7 casting; aluminum alloy filler metal (ER4043)

Conditions for Manual AC Gas Tungsten-Arc Repair Welding

Weld type ....Surfacing	Torch ....300 amp, water cooled
Welding position ....Flat	Gas nozzle ....$\frac{1}{2}$-in. diam, ceramic
Power supply ..40-v, 300-amp transformer, with high-frequency oscillator, 60% duty cycle	Electrode ....$\frac{1}{8}$-in.-diam EWP
	Filler metal ....$\frac{3}{32}$-in.-diam ER4043
Special equipment ....Foot control for frequency, current, and delayed start and shutoff of gas and water; automatic voltage regulation	Shielding gas ......Argon, at 25 cfh (flowmeter control)
	Current ....150 amp, ac (foot control for 40 to 150 amp)
	Voltage ....Automatically regulated

Fig. 44. Portion of an aircraft-engine crankcase casting, showing repair weld (Example 316)

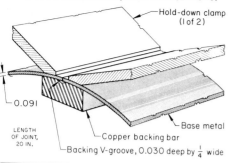

Alloy 6061; aluminum alloy filler metal (ER4043)

- Hold-down clamp (1 of 2)
- Base metal
- Copper backing bar
- Backing V-groove, 0.030 deep by ¼ wide
- 0.091
- LENGTH OF JOINT, 20 IN.

Automatic Gas Tungsten-Arc Welding (dcsp)

Joint type ....Butt
Weld type ....Square groove
Power supply ..200 amp, with drooping output
Mechanization ....Cold wire feeder; torch mounted on a carriage
Fixtures ....Hold-down clamps; grooved copper backing bar
Torch ....Water cooled
Electrode ....3⁄32-in.-diam EWP
Filler metal ....1⁄16-in.-diam ER4043
Shielding gas ....Helium, at 50 cfh; argon, at 5 cfh
Current ....200 amp, dcsp
Filler-metal feed ....50 ipm
Welding speed ....25 ipm
Number of passes ....One

Fig. 45. Arrangement for gas tungsten-arc welding a 20-in.-long longitudinal joint in a cylinder, showing hold-down clamps and grooved backing bar (Example 317)

concentrated, the heat-affected zone is smaller and, because preheating is not needed and only a few weld passes are customary, residual tensile stress is low. Also, cold worked alloys retain their temper. These are important advantages when joining heavy sections of alloys such as the 5xxx series.

As surface oxides on aluminum are not removed during straight-polarity direct-current welding, thorough preweld cleaning is necessary to ensure that oxide will not be trapped in the molten weld puddle. Normal practice in the aerospace industry is to clean chemically and to scrape or file the joint area. However, many commercially acceptable welds have been made with no preweld cleaning.

The surfaces of the welds are not as bright as those made with alternating current because they are coated with an oxide film. The film does not indicate any lack of fusion or the presence of porosity or inclusions and is easily removed by a light wire brushing.

Because of the highly penetrating nature of the straight-polarity direct-current arc, melting occurs the instant the arc is struck. Care should be taken to strike the arc within the weld area to prevent undesirable marking of the workpiece. Although a high-frequency

sparking current is not required to stabilize the arc during direct-current welding, it is useful for starting the arc without marking the workpiece or causing tungsten inclusions. A starting tab of scrap aluminum can be used for touch starting if a high-frequency circuit is not available.

Because continuous high-frequency and wave-balancing circuits are not used in direct-current welding, performance can be duplicated easily by using standardized arc voltages and amperages, even on different machines. Normally, thoriated tungsten electrodes are employed, with helium shielding.

Manual Welding. Typical conditions for welding by the manual straight-polarity direct-current gas tungsten-arc process are given in Tables 30 and 31. Metal thicker than ¼ in. is grooved (single-V or single-U) to ensure complete joint penetration. A double-V or double-U groove may be advantageous for metal more than ½ in. thick.

Table 32. Typical Conditions for Automatic Gas Tungsten-Arc Welding of Square-Groove Butt Joints, Using Straight-Polarity Direct Current(a)

Metal thickness, in.	Electrode diameter, in.(b)	Filler metal Diameter, in.	Filler metal Feed, ipm	Helium flow rate, cfh	Arc Current (dcsp), amp	Arc Voltage, v	Welding speed, ipm
0.025	3⁄64	3⁄64	60	60	100	10	60
0.031	3⁄64	3⁄64	76	60	110	10	60
0.040	3⁄64	3⁄64	68	60	125	10	60
0.051	3⁄64	3⁄64	64	60	150	12	60
0.062	3⁄64	3⁄64	99	60	145	13	60
0.080	3⁄64	3⁄64	100	60	290	10	60
0.125	1⁄16	1⁄16	55	30	240	11	40
0.250	1⁄16	1⁄16	40	30	350	11	15
0.375	1⁄16	1⁄16	30	40	430	11	8

(a) Single-pass welds made in the flat position. (b) Thoriated tungsten electrodes.

Table 33. Typical Conditions for Automatic Gas Tungsten-Arc Welding of Square-Groove Butt Joints, Using Straight-Polarity Direct Current(a)

Metal thickness, in.	Welding position (b)	Filler-metal (1⁄16-in. diam) feed, ipm	Helium flow rate, cfh	Arc Current (dcsp), amp	Arc Voltage, v	Welding Speed per pass, ipm	Welding Number of passes
Alloy 5083							
¼	F	30	100	250	11	25	Two, one each side
¼	V	None	50	260	10	20	Two, one each side
3⁄8	F, V	None	80	300	12	14	Two, one each side
3⁄8	F	12	100	360	10	10	Two, one each side
½	F, V	None	100	400	10	15	Two, one each side
½	F	12	100	390	10	8	Two, one each side
¾	F, V	None	100	500	9	5	Two, one each side
Alloy 2219							
¼	F, V	36	100	145	12	8	Two, one side
¼	H	36	100	135	12	10	Two, one side
3⁄8	F, V	32	120	220	12	8	Two, one side
3⁄8	H	32	120	180	12	10	Two, one side
½	H, V	10	100	250	12	8	Two, one each side
5⁄8	H, V	5-7	120	300	12	7	Two, one each side
¾	H, V	5-7	125	340	12	6	Two, one each side
⅞	H, V	4-6	125	385	12	5	Two, one each side
1	H, V	3-5	120	425	12	4	Two, one each side
Alloy 7039							
¼	F, V, H	None	100	265	10	18	Two, one each side
¼	F	40	120	250	14	20	Two, one each side
3⁄8	F, V	None	50	300	10	12	Two, one each side
½	F, V	None	100	390	10	15	Two, one each side
¾	F, V	None	100	450	9	6	Two, one each side
¾	F	48	100	390	10.5	4	Two, one each side

(a) Thoriated tungsten electrodes: 1⁄8-in.-diam electrodes with 0.100-in.-diam tip for metal ¼ to ¾ in. thick; 5⁄32-in.-diam electrodes with 0.125-in.-diam tip for metal ⅞ in. thick; 3⁄16-in.-diam electrodes with 0.156-in.-diam tip for metal 1 in. thick. (b) F = flat; H = horizontal; V = vertical.

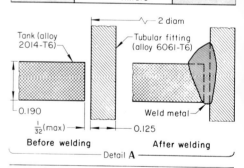

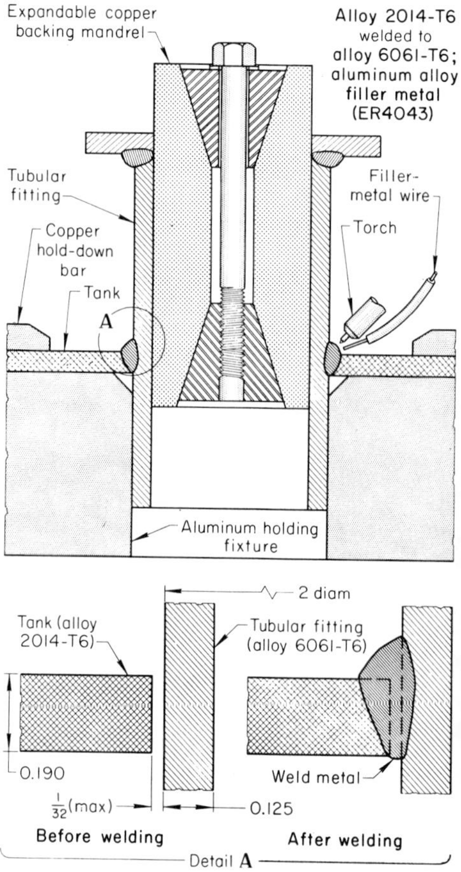

Alloy 2014-T6 welded to alloy 6061-T6; aluminum alloy filler metal (ER4043)

- Expandable copper backing mandrel
- Tubular fitting
- Copper hold-down bar
- Tank
- A
- Aluminum holding fixture
- Filler-metal wire
- Torch

- Tank (alloy 2014-T6)
- Tubular fitting (alloy 6061-T6)
- Weld metal
- 0.190
- 1⁄32 (max)
- 0.125
- 2 diam
- Before welding
- After welding
- Detail A

Semiautomatic Gas Tungsten-Arc Welding (dcsp)

Joint type ....Circumferential T
Weld type ....Fillet
Power supply ..500 amp, with constant voltage and high-frequency start
Mechanization ....Automatic torch rotation, automatic workpiece rotation
Fixtures ....Expanding backing mandrel, copper hold-down bars, holding fixture
Torch ....Mechanically held, pencil type, water cooled
Electrode ....3⁄32-in.-diam EWTh-2
Filler metal ....1⁄16-in.-diam ER4043
Shielding gas ....Helium, at 75 cfh
Current ....160 amp, dcsp
Voltage ....15 v
Filler-wire feed ....110 ipm
Welding speed ....12 ipm

Fig. 46. Welding a tubular fitting into the wall of a tank (Example 318)

The welder must use care in maintaining a suitable short arc length. In addition to the standard techniques (runoff tabs and striking plates) for preventing and filling craters, foot-operated heat controls are used. These controls are also advantageous for adjusting the current as the workpiece heats up and as section thickness changes. The arc is moved steadily forward and filler metal is fed into the leading edge of the weld puddle or laid on the joint and melted by the arc. Bead size can be controlled by varying filler-metal size.

Automatic Welding. Straight-polarity gas tungsten-arc welding is readily adaptable to mechanization, which is desirable in order to maintain the required short arc lengths. The result is improved weld quality, as discussed in the following example, which describes the automatic butt welding of relatively thin alloy 6061 sheet.

Example 317. Welding 0.091-In.-Thick Sheet by the Automatic Straight-Polarity Direct-Current Gas Tungsten-Arc Process (Fig. 45)

A 20-in.-long butt weld (see Fig. 45) used to complete a cylinder formed from 0.091-in.-thick alloy 6061 sheet was required to be defect-free under radiographic inspection. Automatic gas tungsten-arc welding was chosen, a clamping fixture and a grooved copper backing bar were used, and the process variables were closely controlled (see the table that accompanies Fig. 45).

The joint was cleaned chemically and by draw filing. To facilitate arc initiation and adjustment, starting and runoff tabs were attached at the joint. The welding torch was adjusted to give a very short arc — from below the original workpiece surface to about 0.015 in. above, and on the verge of short circuiting. To ensure accurate weld placement, the carriage with the welding torch mounted on it was aligned with the joint to within ±0.005 in. for the entire 20-in. length of the weld. Helium with a small amount of argon added was the shielding gas.

Sound, defect-free welds were produced. Production rate varied from 20 to 40 pieces per shift (including cleaning and setup time), depending on operator skill.

Mechanization is useful in preventing crater cracking by eliminating all but one start and stop. This is illustrated in the following example, which describes the fillet welding of alloy 6061 tubing to alloy 2014 sheet.

Example 318. Semiautomatic Welding of 0.125-In.-Wall Tubular Fittings in a 0.190-In.-Thick Tank Wall (Fig. 46)

When manual gas tungsten-arc and gas metal-arc welding the alloy 6061 tubular fittings shown in Fig. 46 to alloy 2014 tank walls, several repositionings of the workpieces were required, necessitating several starts and stops. Weld crater cracking became a problem, and so it was decided to change to semiautomatic gas tungsten-arc welding, which could be done continuously and with close control. Straight-polarity direct current was selected because of the deep penetration that could be obtained by using it.

During welding, either the workpieces were rotated and the torch was stationary, or the torch was rotated and the workpieces were stationary — depending on workpiece size and the tooling available. Auxiliary wire feed was used to obtain the required fillet size. Some designs required fillet welds on both sides of the joint. Precise tooling was needed to align the electrode and the filler wire with the joint. Copper

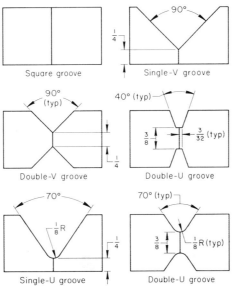

Fig. 47. Typical joint designs for making butt welds by the automatic straight-polarity direct-current gas tungsten-arc process

backing mandrels and copper hold-down bars promoted rapid cooling and faster welding. As a result, the size of the heat-affected zones was restricted and good weld strength was obtained.

Various methods were used to minimize crater cracking, the preferred method being automatic sequencing of welding variables so as to add filler-metal wire after travel had stopped, while gradually increasing arc voltage and decreasing current.

Preweld cleaning consisted of manual brushing, wiping with commercial cleaners, and wiping dry with clean cloths. Welding conditions and equipment data are shown in the table that accompanies Fig. 46.

For best results, a fully mechanized automatic setup should be employed. With a fully automatic setup, welds are made in aluminum alloys from 0.010 in. thick to more than 1 in. thick. Because this process allows precise control of weld penetration, it is often selected for joining aluminum in the thickness range from 0.010 to ⅛ in.

Typical conditions for making square-groove butt welds with automatic straight-polarity direct-current gas tungsten-arc welding in aluminum up to ⅜ in. thick are given in Table 32. Automatic welding has also been used to weld square-groove butt joints in aluminum up to 1¼ in. thick, but V-groove and U-groove edge preparations are often used on thick sections. Mechanical and magnetic oscillation can be used to spread the filler metal and to aid fusion when groove welding with this process. Typical edge preparations are shown in Fig. 47.

Because square-groove butt welding using the automatic straight-polarity direct-current gas tungsten-arc process results in narrow weld beads, low dilution with filler metal, and excellent weld strength, this process is used for joining rather thick sections of high-strength aluminum alloys. Conditions for welding three such alloys (5083, 2219 and 7039) are given in Table 33.

Two examples of this type of weld in 0.406-in.-thick and 1.000-in.-thick alloy 2219 plate follow.

Example 319. Making Aerospace-Quality Arc Welds in Alloy 2219 Plate (Fig. 48)

In producing the large cylindrical shell shown in Fig. 48 for part of a rocket-propellant tank, it was necessary to weld four segments together. Alloy 2219-T87 was cho-

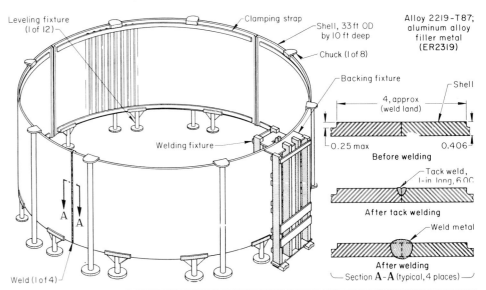

Conditions for Automatic Gas Tungsten-Arc Welding (dcsp)

Joint type ....Butt	Gas nozzle ....⅝-in. diam, copper
Weld type ....Square groove	Electrode ....⅛-in.-diam EWTh-2, with tip
Root opening ....None	taper ground to 0.090-in. diam
Welding position ....Vertical up	Filler metal 1/16-in.-diam ER2319
Power supply ......600 amp, constant current,	Shielding gas ....Helium, at 125 cfh
controlled to 1% variation; 100% duty cycle	Electrode stickout ....⅜ in.
Mechanization ......Welding head mounted on	Current ....225 amp, dcsp
progressive welding boom, with	Voltage ....11 to 13 v
vertical up-and-down travel	Filler-metal feed ....22 ipm
Fixtures ....Twelve leveling fixtures; eight	Welding speed ....6 ipm
chucks; clamping straps;	Setup time ....8 hr
welding fixture	Weld time ....30 to 40 min
Torch ....Water cooled	Number of passes ....One

Fig. 48. Welded aluminum cylindrical shell, showing fixtures, and joint before and after welding (Example 319)

Table 34. Aging Treatments, Properties Obtained in Transverse-Weld Specimens, and Welding Conditions for Alloy 7075 and 7079 Plate (Example 321)

Alloy 7075-T6; aluminum alloy filler metal (ER5183)

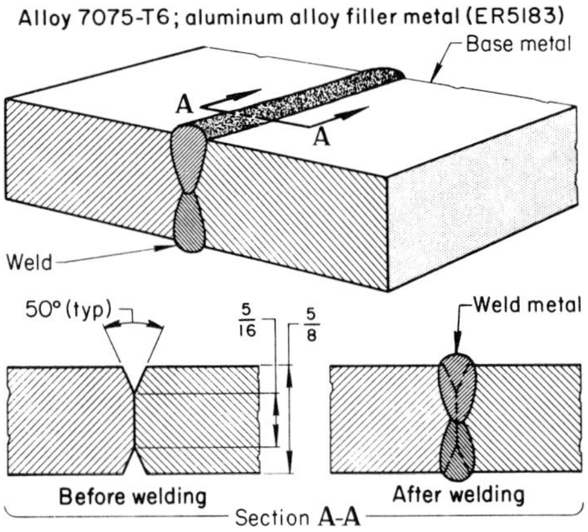

Section A-A

Alloy 7079-T6; special high-zinc aluminum alloy filler metal

Section B-B

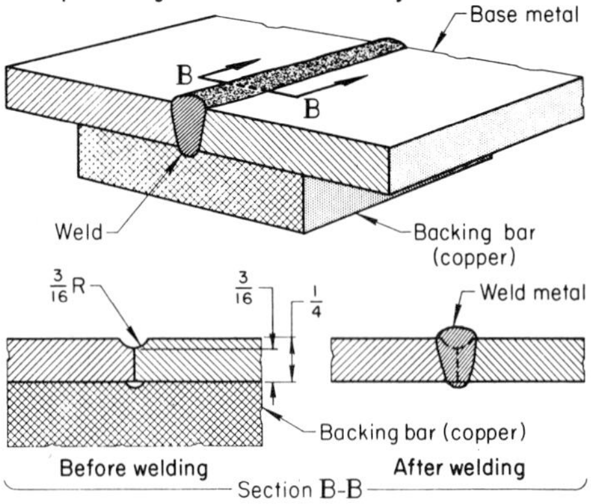

Time at aging temperature	Tensile strength, psi	Yield strength, psi	Elongation in 2 in., %
Alloy 7075 Plate, ⅝ In. Thick(a)			
4 hr	63,300	53,600	6.0(b)
Alloy 7079 Plate, ¼ In. Thick			
Aged at room temperature			
8 hr	42,400	28,900	4.0
1 wk	50,200	35,800	3.0
2 wk	51,400	35,900	3.0
3 wk	52,800	37,300	3.0
4 wk	52,900	37,400	4.5
6 wk	52,300	36,600	4.0
12 wk	53,600	38,100	3.5
Aged at 200 F			
4 hr	50,600	36,700	3.0
8 hr	51,400	37,500	3.5
12 hr	51,100	37,800	3.0
24 hr	52,400	38,900	3.0
48 hr	54,500	43,600	2.0
Aged at 225 F			
4 hr	49,500	36,000	2.5
8 hr	51,300	38,400	3.0
12 hr	51,200	38,100	3.5
24 hr	54,400	42,400	2.5
48 hr	54,900	42,600	2.5

Item	Alloy 7075	Alloy 7079
Semiautomatic Gas Tungsten-Arc Welding		
Joint type	Butt	Butt
Weld type	Double-V	Single-U
Welding position .	Flat	Flat
Weld backing	None	Copper bar
Filler metal	ER5183	(c)
Filler-metal diam .	1/16 in.	1/16 in.
Shielding gas	Helium	Helium
Gas-flow rate	75 cfh	100 cfh
Current (dcsp) ...	270 amp	205 amp
Filler-metal feed .	30-40 ipm	30-33 ipm
Welding speed	10-12 ipm	6 ipm
Number of passes .	Two	One

(a) Average of values after aging for 4 hr at 200, 250 and 315 F. (b) Elongation in 1.4 in. (c) 4.4% Zn, 2.8% Mg, 1.0% Cu, remainder Al.

Table 35. Common Problems With Gas Tungsten-Arc Welding and Their Usual Causes

Arc-Starting Difficulty

1 Incorrect adjustment of high-frequency spark gap
2 Incomplete welding circuit

Inadequate Cleaning Action by the Arc

1 Incorrect adjustment of high-frequency unit or battery bias
2 Open-circuit voltage too low
3 Inadequate gas shielding, caused by:
   Insufficient gas flow
   Spatter on inside of gas nozzle
   Contact tube off-center in relation to gas nozzle
   Wrong nozzle-to-work distance
   Incorrect position of welding torch
   Drafty environment

Dirty Weld Bead

1 Insufficient shielding-gas coverage, caused by:
   Insufficient gas flow
   Damaged or dirty gas nozzle
   Wrong nozzle-to-work distance
   Incorrect position of welding torch
   Contact tube off-center in relation to gas nozzle
   Wrong nozzle size (use smallest possible)
   Drafty environment
   Impurities in shielding gas, due to air or water leakage
2 Poor cleaning action by the arc (see causes listed under the heading "Inadequate Cleaning Action by the Arc", above)
3 Unstable arc (use battery bias)
4 Electrode contamination
5 Dirty workpieces or filler metal

Electrode Contamination by Aluminum

1 Improper manipulation of torch
2 Excessive electrode extension
3 Wrong electrode material (use zirconiated electrode with alternating current)

Incorrect Electrode Contour

1 Incorrect electrode size for current
2 Incorrect contouring of electrode end before welding
3 Wrong electrode material (use zirconiated electrode with alternating current)

Weld-Bead Contamination by Electrode

1 Electrode size too small for current
2 Improper manipulation of torch
3 Wrong electrode material (use zirconiated electrode with alternating current)

Rough Weld Bead

1 Unstable arc
2 Improper manipulation of torch
3 Incorrect current

Weld Bead Too Wide

1 Excessive current
2 Welding speed too low
3 Arc too long
4 Electrode stickout too short
5 Incorrect position of welding torch

Inadequate Penetration

1 Wrong edge preparation for the arc characteristics (groove too narrow)
2 Excessive filler metal in weld puddle
3 Insufficient current
4 Arc too long
5 Welding speed too high

Difficulty in Adding Filler Metal

1 Improper manipulation of welding torch or filler metal, or both
2 Incorrect current, welding speed or filler-metal size
3 Incorrect adjustment of high-frequency unit
4 Poor insulation on high-frequency unit or leads
5 Incorrect operation of battery bias (connections may be reversed)

Poor Visibility of Arc and Weld Puddle

1 Wrong position of work
2 Incorrect position of welding torch
3 Small or dirty lens helmet
4 Wrong size of gas nozzle (use smallest possible)

Overheating of Power Supply

1 Excessive power demand (two similar welding machines can be operated in parallel if the capacity of one is insufficient)
2 Poor functioning of cooling fan
3 Poor grounding of high-frequency unit
4 Poor functioning of bypass capacitor
5 Poor functioning of battery bias
6 Dirty rectifier stacks (regular maintenance required)

Overheating of Welding Torch, Leads and Cables

1 Loose or faulty connections
2 Welding torch, leads or cables too small
3 Inadequate cooling-water flow

Welder Fatigue

1 Wrong position of work (weld in flat position whenever possible)
2 Inadequate seating arrangement for welder
3 Lack of ventilation
4 Disregard of safety rules regarding head shield, lens, gloves
5 Weight of cables (reduce by suspending cables overhead)
6 Too many auxiliary operations, such as cleaning and chipping (provide additional help)

---

sen for this application because of its combination of good base-metal strength at elevated temperature, good weld strength, and good weldability compared to other high-strength, heat treatable aluminum alloys. High-quality welds were required.

The four segments were produced from plates 120 in. wide by 311 in. long and 2 in. thick by curving them in the long direction to a 16½-ft radius and mechanically milling the concave side to various final thicknesses. Vertical stiffening ribs 2 in. thick, top and bottom rims, and 2-in.-wide lands 0.406 in. thick (and thus with root faces 0.406 in. wide) were left on the plates. Other areas of the plates were machined to various thicknesses up to 0.25 in., which was the thickness that adjoined the weld lands. The extra thickness of the weld lands was designed to compensate for the lower unit strength of the weld area compared with that of the base metal.

The procedure for making the welds was as follows:

1 Clean the areas to be welded, both chemically and mechanically.
2 Place shell segments on leveling fixtures and against chucks to form the cylinder. Position clamping straps inside the top rim and clamp in place. Clamp welding fixture in place with two vacuum chucks, one on either side of the joint.
3 Check joint alignment and spacing.
4 Manually weld aluminum runoff tabs, 6 in. square, top and bottom of each joint.
5 Make 1-in. tack welds manually on 6-in. centers.
6 Check equipment.
7 Automatically weld four 10-ft-long joints in one pass each, on inside of cylinder.
8 Inspect visually and radiographically.
9 Remove runoff tabs.

With the machine settings used, it was not necessary to use a backing bar, but the back of the weld was cooled with excess helium gas from the welding operation. The weld was made in one pass, with only minor distortion. If the weld lands had been thicker, thus providing wider root faces, or if less distortion than the minor amount obtained had been required, a double-welded joint with one pass from each side would have been used, as discussed in the following example. Welding conditions are shown in the table that accompanies Fig. 48.

Example 320. Automatic Straight-Polarity Direct-Current Gas Tungsten-Arc Welding of 1-In.-Thick Alloy 2219 (Fig. 49)

A Y-shape ring machined from a rectangular forging was used as a transition fitting between the large-diameter cylindrical shell and the bulkhead of a rocket-propellant tank, as shown in Fig. 49. Welding of the alloy 2219-T87 cylinder is described in Example 319. In welding the Y-ring to the cylinder, the 1.000-in. wall thickness required two weld passes, one from each side.

The workpieces were alkaline cleaned and deoxidized, and the joint edges were mechanically scraped to bare metal before welding. They were then mounted on a rotating table powered by a 3-hp-drive motor with proportional and integral servo-amplifier speed control. Two welding units were used: one outside and one inside the cylinder. The unit inside the cylinder was placed so that its weld puddle lagged approximately 4 ft behind the weld puddle of the outside unit. Both welding units were equipped with sequence control for programing starts and stops and were also equipped with a cold filler-wire feed driven by a closed-loop velocity servo system.

Tack welds 2 in. long were made on 6-in. centers around the full circumference of the cylinder. Penetration was established before rotation of the workpiece started. Welding was done simultaneously from both sides using the "buried-arc" technique in which fairly low arc voltage and a high current were used, the electrode following the concave molten weld puddle below the original workpiece surface. With this technique, deep penetration and narrow welds were obtained at fairly high welding speed. Weld-quality requirements were severe; virtually no porosity or defect was allowed.

Setup time was about 8 hr, and welding time was 5 hr per joint.

Although the welding of some of the high-strength heat treatable alloys, such as 7075 and 7079, is not recommended, they can be gas tungsten-arc welded with straight-polarity direct current by skilled welders using special techniques. A welding technique that will ensure retention of the high strength of the base metal, and that will prevent cracking of the weld metal and allow development of maximum weld-metal strength is imperative. Full postweld heat treatment (solution heat treatment, quenching, and aging) results in the highest strength, but solution heat treatment and quenching often causes excessive warping of the part, and thick sections are difficult to quench effectively. A combination of welding conditions and postweld aging that produced good results in one application is noted in the next example:

Example 321. Welding Plate of High-Strength Alloys 7075 and 7079 (Table 34)

Butt welds between two plates of alloy 7075-T6, 5/8 in. thick, and two plates of alloy 7079-T6, 1/4 in. thick, were made by the gas tungsten-arc process. The joint design for the 7075 plates was a double-V groove with a 5/16-in. root face, and for the thinner 7079 plates, a single-U groove with a 3/16-in. root face. The large root faces and small grooves for both welds favored substantial alloying of the base metal in the weld metal, as shown in the table below:

Element	Base metal	Filler metal(a)	Weld metal
Welding Alloy 7075 Plate			
Zinc, %	5.1-6.1	0.25 max	4.10
Magnesium, %	2.1-2.9	4.3-5.2	2.50
Copper, %	1.2-2.0	0.10 max	1.20
Welding Alloy 7079 Plate			
Zinc, %	3.8-4.8	4.4	4.75
Magnesium, %	2.9-3.7	2.8	2.50
Copper, %	0.4-0.8	1.0	1.10

(a) Filler metal ER5183 was used in welding the alloy 7075 plate, and a special high-zinc alloy of the composition shown was used in welding the alloy 7079 plate.

The weld metal in both joints had about the same zinc and magnesium contents as alloy 7039 (3.5 to 4.5% Zn, 2.3 to 3.3% Mg), which is readily arc weldable and is strengthened by natural aging.

The postweld aging treatments and the properties obtained in the weld metal for both alloys are shown in Table 34, along with the welding conditions.

Problems in Gas Tungsten-Arc Welding of Aluminum Alloys

Many of the problems that are encountered in gas metal-arc welding of aluminum alloys are also present in gas tungsten-arc welding. Common problems and their causes are summarized in Table 35.

Dirty workpieces and filler metal can result in a dirty weld bead and an unsound weld. Preweld cleaning of workpieces is described in the section on page 297 of this article. An effective test for cleanness of filler metal is described in Example 311 on page 326.

Improper fixturing can also result in weld defects. For instance, when a rough and uneven weld bead with excessive porosity and areas of incomplete fusion was encountered on a corner weld in alloy 6061, investigation showed that the magnetic field surrounding the arc had been deflected by the nearby carbon steel fixturing, which had caused arc instability. Changing to a nonmagnetic fixturing material ended the trouble. Aluminum fixturing was tried, but it became loose on heating. Austenitic stainless steel proved satisfactory.

In other applications, excessive spatter of tungsten was ended by changing from an unalloyed tungsten electrode to a thoriated tungsten electrode; complete penetration was obtained when the 1/8-in.-diam filler-metal wire was replaced with a 1/16-in.-diam wire.

Gas Metal-Arc Welding vs Gas Tungsten-Arc Welding

The uses of gas metal-arc and gas tungsten-arc welding overlap to some extent. The general merits of the two

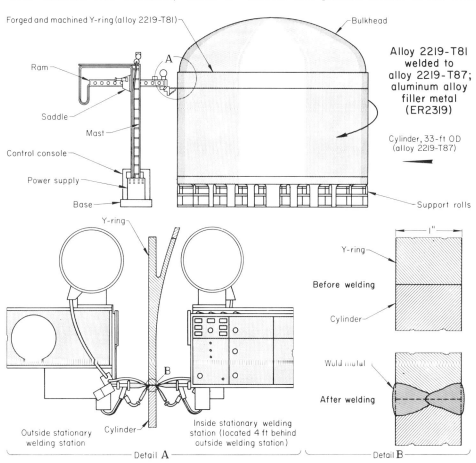

Forged and machined Y-ring (alloy 2219-T81)

Bulkhead

Alloy 2219-T81 welded to alloy 2219-T87; aluminum alloy filler metal (ER2319)

Cylinder, 33-ft OD (alloy 2219-T87)

Ram

Saddle

Mast

Control console

Power supply

Base

Support rolls

Y-ring

Before welding

Cylinder

Weld metal

After welding

Outside stationary welding station

Cylinder

Inside stationary welding station (located 4 ft behind outside welding station)

Detail A

Detail B

Conditions for Automatic Gas Tungsten-Arc Welding (dcsp)

Joint type .... Butt
Weld type .... Square groove
Welding position .... Horizontal
Power supply .... 600 amp, constant current, controlled to 1% variation; 100% duty cycle
Mechanization ... Automatic arc-voltage control to 0.1% variation; wire-feed system; 360° rotation of work on motor-drive table
Wire-feed system .... 1 to 100 ipm, controlled to 1% variation

Torch .... Water cooled
Gas nozzle .... 5/8-in. diam
Electrode 5/32-in.-diam EWTh-2
Filler metal .... 1/16-in.-diam ER2319(a)
Shielding gas .... Helium, at 120 cfh
Voltage .... 11.5 to 12.5 v
Filler-metal feed .... 1 in. of wire per inch of travel
Welding speed .... 2 to 5 ipm
Number of passes .... Two

(a) Wire was stored in a hermetically sealed container before use, and was fed from dustproof containers during welding.

Fig. 49. Automatic gas tungsten-arc welding of a forged and machined Y-ring to a 33-ft-diam cylinder, showing placement of welding heads for making welds on the inside and outside of the cylinder and ring (Example 320)

Table 36. Comparison of the Gas Metal-Arc and the Gas Tungsten-Arc Processes for Welding Aluminum Alloys

Application considerations	Relative rating(a)	
	Gas metal-arc	Gas tungsten-arc
Cost Factors		
Cost of equipment	B	A
Maintenance of equipment	B	A
Operating factor (output)	A	B
Volume of metal deposited	A	B
Welding rate	A	B
Versatility		
Welding with filler metal	A	B
Welding without filler metal ...	NA	A
Welding metal thinner than $\frac{1}{8}$ in.	A	A
Welding metal thicker than $\frac{1}{8}$ in.	A	B
Out-of-position welding	A	B
Making short welds	B	A
Making welds having abrupt changes in contour	B	A
Low welding speed possible	B	A
Weld Quality		
Strength	A	A
Ductility	A	A
Corrosion resistance	A	A
Absence of defects	A	A
Penetration	A	A
Distortion	A	A
Welding of Castings		
General reclamation	B	A
Reclamation to specification ...	B	A
Repair welding	B	A
Fabrication with castings	A	B

(a) An A rating is better than a B rating. NA indicates process is not applicable.

processes are compared in Table 36. Individual applications should be considered in detail, with reference to Table 36 and the following factors.

Advantages of Gas Metal-Arc Welding. Most of the advantages of gas metal-arc welding over gas tungsten-arc welding stem from the fact that in gas metal-arc welding reverse-polarity direct current is used at a high current density. This is possible because the electrode is consumable and is melted during the welding, whereas in gas tungsten-arc welding the current is limited by the melting temperature of the electrode. Heat transfer by the arc is very efficient.

High Welding Rate. Welding speeds two to three times those obtainable by manual gas tungsten-arc welding are possible, particularly when welding metal more than $\frac{3}{8}$ in. thick. When machine welding thinner metal, the welding speed is about the same for the two processes.

In manual gas tungsten-arc welding, the length of welding is somewhat limited by the length of filler-metal rod that the welder can conveniently handle; he usually cannot make a weld longer than 12 in. without breaking the arc.

The gas metal-arc process and the automatic gas tungsten-arc process share the feature that the filler metal is added mechanically, and the operator is usually able to weld at least 24 in. without having to break the arc and change position. Therefore, with these latter processes less time is lost in starting and stopping, which results in fewer weld craters and more feet of weld per hour. They are also less fatiguing than the manual gas tungsten-arc process because the operator does not have to coordinate the movement of both hands, and he can continue welding for a greater length of time, a factor that contributes to higher welding rates.

Lower Welding Cost on Metal More Than $\frac{1}{4}$ In. Thick. The equipment used for gas metal-arc welding is more expensive than that used for gas tungsten-arc welding, but on thick sections requiring multiple-pass welding (generally more than $\frac{1}{4}$ in. thick), the higher welding rates of the gas metal-arc process generally result in lower welding cost.

Low Distortion. Because of the high welding speed, which results in rapid chilling of the weld area, distortion is generally low. The distortion produced on aluminum with the gas metal-arc process is no more, and is usually less, than that produced on steel of the same thickness when it is welded with flux-cored electrodes. As soon as the arc is established, filler metal is added to the joint, which aids in preventing distortion when sheet is being welded to thicker framing members.

Good Weld Quality. The quality of welds produced by the gas metal-arc process using spray transfer is of a very high order.

Good Out-of-Position Welding. Because the appreciable arc force projects the weld metal across the arc at a high velocity, not affected by gravity, welding can be done in any position.

High Deposition Rate. Where a high rate of filler-metal deposition is required, as in welding heavy sections or in building up a surface, the gas metal-arc process has a considerable advantage. High rates of metal deposition are easy to obtain with the large-diameter filler wires (up to $\frac{7}{32}$ in. in diameter) when they are used with high welding currents.

Readily Adapted to Machine Welding. Because of its semiautomatic nature, the gas metal-arc process can be readily adapted to automatic welding for metal from 0.030 in. thick to the thickest commercially available. Automatic gas tungsten-arc welding requires good control of joint fit-up, usually within 0.003 to 0.010 in., depending on material thickness, but gas metal-arc welding is less sensitive to variations in fit-up.

Freedom From Radio Interference. Gas metal-arc welding employs direct current, and so it is not necessary to use high-frequency current for arc stabilization, which means that there is no radio interference as there may be when using high-frequency current with gas tungsten-arc welding.

Table 38. Pounds per Foot, and Feet per Pound, of Various Diameters of Aluminum Alloy Filler-Metal Wire(a)

Wire diam, in.	Pounds per foot	Feet per pound
0.030	0.000848	1180
0.035	0.001153	867
0.040	0.001508	664
$\frac{3}{64}$	0.00207	484
$\frac{1}{16}$	0.00368	272
$\frac{3}{32}$	0.00828	121
$\frac{1}{8}$	0.01473	68
$\frac{5}{32}$	0.0230	44
$\frac{3}{16}$	0.0332	30
$\frac{7}{32}$	0.0451	22
$\frac{1}{4}$	0.0589	17

(a) Based on a density of 0.100 lb per cubic inch. For correction factors for alloys of other densities, see Table 39.

Advantages of Gas Tungsten-Arc Welding. Most of the advantages of gas tungsten-arc welding stem from the fact that the filler metal is introduced separately into the arc, which allows the welding current and wire speed to be independently adjusted.

Lower Welding Costs on Metal Less Than $\frac{1}{8}$ In. Thick. In automatic welding, where attainable welding speed is nearly equal to that used in gas metal-arc welding, greater economy is usually realized with the gas tungsten-arc process, because welding current and wire speed can be independently adjusted to reduce the consumption of filler metal to the minimum. However, in semiautomatic welding, greater economy is generally realized with the gas metal-arc process because welding speed is two to three times faster than that obtainable with the gas tungsten-arc process.

The equipment used for gas tungsten-arc welding is less expensive than that used for gas metal-arc welding, and needs less maintenance.

Very Thin Material Can Be Welded. Using a pulsed arc, the gas metal-arc process can be used to weld metal as thin as 0.040 in., but metal as thin as 0.010 in. can be welded by the gas tungsten-arc process, provided the workpieces are correctly aligned and held.

Butt Welds Can Be Made in Small Shapes. Because filler metal is added manually to the weld in manual gas tungsten-arc welding, the welder has complete control of the weld puddle at all times. This is a definite advantage in butt welding small and medium angles and other shapes in which heat requirement at the toe of the angle is less than at the heel.

Welds Can Be Made Without Filler Metal. This is important in fusing together the edges of a butt joint or the edge of a lap joint, to make smooth welds that require little grinding or cleaning.

Excellent Weld Quality. The quality of welds made by the gas tungsten-arc process is of a very high order, and the process offers excellent reliability. When welding thick material by the gas tungsten-arc process, the filler metal need not be added to the weld until the base metal has been well penetrated; with the gas metal-arc process, filler metal is added as soon as the arc is struck, which sometimes prevents penetration and causes cold starts. Preheating thick material to 200 to 250 F ensures satisfactory starts when gas metal-arc welding; otherwise, cold starts must be chipped out and rewelded.

Cost of Welding. The over-all cost of welding comprises capital expenditure for equipment, the actual welding expenses, and the cost of material preparation and finishing (edge preparation, cleaning, fitting, assembling, handling, and surface finishing). The actual welding expenses are the cost of filler-metal wire, gas, overhead, labor, and maintenance of welding equipment. Ordinarily, the process that enables a

Table 37. Approximate Costs of Gas Metal-Arc and Gas Tungsten-Arc Welding Equipment

Electrode-wire diameter, in.	Welding unit(a)	Power supply	Total	Thicknesses to be welded, in.
Gas Metal-Arc Welding Equipment				
0.030 to $\frac{3}{32}$	$2200	$900 to $1350	$3100 to $3550	0.040 to over 3

Machine capacity, amp	Alternating-current unit(b)	Welding torch	Total	Thicknesses to be welded, in.
Gas Tungsten-Arc Welding Equipment				
200	$ 800 to $ 900	$200	$1000 to $1100	0.020 to $\frac{3}{16}$
300	950 to 1050	200	1150 to 1250	0.020 to $\frac{5}{16}$(c)
400	1000 to 1100	200	1200 to 1300	0.020 to $\frac{3}{8}$(c)
500	1100 to 1200	200	1300 to 1400	0.020 to $\frac{1}{2}$(c)

(a) Including wire feeder, control panel, welding torch, and secondary contactor. (b) Including high-frequency unit and water and gas controls. (c) Being able to weld 0.020-in.-thick metal depends on ability to reduce current output of machine below normal rated output.

Table 39. Correction Factors for Density of Aluminum Filler-Metal Alloys

Filler alloy	Density, lb/cu in.	Factor(a) Lb/ft	Factor(a) Ft/lb
ER1100	0.098	0.98	1.02
ER1260	0.098	0.98	1.02
ER2319	0.103	1.03	0.97
ER4043	0.097	0.97	1.03
ER4047	0.097	0.97	1.03
ER4145	0.101	1.01	0.99
ER5039	0.097	0.97	1.03
ER5183	0.096	0.96	1.04
ER5356	0.095	0.95	1.05
ER5554	0.097	0.97	1.03
ER5556	0.095	0.95	1.05
ER5654	0.096	0.96	1.04
R-C4A	0.101	1.01	0.99
R-CN42A	0.102	1.02	0.98
R-SC51A	0.098	0.98	1.02
R-SG70A	0.097	0.97	1.03

(a) Multiply value in Table 38 by this factor.

weldment to be made in the minimum time is the most economical.

The amount of welding, and whether or not it is repetitive, influence the selection of a welding process and auxiliary equipment. Large amounts of welding will usually justify a considerable investment in welding equipment, jigs and fixtures.

In computing welding costs, it is usually assumed that the arc is maintained for only 33% of the time — that is, the operator welds for only 20 min of each hour. On certain production jobs where fast-operating jigs are employed, the operating factor may exceed 33%, and on those where a large amount of time for fit-up is required, or where only one assembly is being made, the operating factor may be much less than 33%.

In selecting a welding process, cost of equipment should be weighed against its advantages, because often the cost of an expensive piece of equipment can be offset by increased production and a higher-quality product. For a small production lot, high equipment cost can be justified only if the equipment is required for special reasons of quality or accessibility, or if future high-production use is anticipated. Table 37 gives the approximate costs of equipment for gas tungsten-arc welding and gas metal-arc welding. The gas tungsten-arc units described are standard alternating-current arc welding machines having a built-in high-frequency unit and gas and water controls. The machines can be converted for the welding of steel by operating a switch to bypass the high-frequency unit and gas and water controls.

Weights of aluminum welding wire of various diameters and correction factors for alloys are given in Tables 38 and 39, respectively.

Selection of Process. Availability of equipment may determine the process to be used for a given application, but generally selection is based on the capability of a process to meet joint requirements, and on cost. When the thickness of aluminum sheet reaches about ³⁄₁₆ in., the use of the automatic gas tungsten-arc process with alternating current for single-pass butt welding becomes prohibitively slow, although joint quality is excellent. The same joints in this thickness and above can be single-pass welded at a much higher speed using gas tungsten-arc

welding with straight-polarity direct current, because of the narrower and deeper penetration obtained, but more careful edge cleaning is needed to ensure high joint quality. Both processes are capable of producing welds to high quality standards, and joint thickness becomes a consideration when deciding which to use.

Aluminum sheet ³⁄₁₆ in. or more in thickness can also be welded by the gas metal-arc process using spray transfer and at much higher speeds. Because reverse-polarity direct current is used, edge cleaning is less critical than for gas tungsten-arc welding with straight-polarity direct current. Joint quality is good and easily meets commercial requirements.

In Table 40, these three processes are roughly compared for mechanized welding of butt joints in ¼-in.-thick aluminum alloy plate, using hold-down clamps and a grooved backing bar. The illustration in Table 40 shows the two most commonly used types of edge preparation for these joints — square grooves and single-V grooves.

The use of gas tungsten-arc welding with alternating current, as indicated

in Table 40, would necessitate edge preparation in the form of a single-V groove to obtain complete penetration. The welding speed of this process is relatively low, and the effective welding speed for the joint is only half the actual welding speed, because two passes are needed to fill the joint. Sound weld metal is produced.

Gas tungsten-arc welding with straight-polarity direct current can be done at a relatively high welding speed, and deep penetration is obtained. Although the square-groove edge preparation shown in Table 40 to be applicable for this process does not entail beveling, to obtain optimum weld-metal soundness joint edges must be cleaned chemically and mechanically (by filing or scraping) before welding. Starts and stops must be regulated by current-control devices, or must be eliminated completely by means of starting and runoff tabs.

Gas metal-arc welding of the joints shown in Table 40 can be accomplished at high welding speed, depending on the quality and reliability demanded of the weld, but it is more difficult to establish and maintain precise control

Table 40. Comparison of Three Arc Welding Processes for Welding Butt Joints in ¼-In.-Thick Aluminum Alloy Plate

Welding process	Edge preparation (weld type)	Shielding gas	No. of passes	Typical welding speed, ipm	Suitability of process
Gas tungsten-arc (ac)	Single-V groove	Argon	2	4 to 8	(a)
Gas tungsten-arc (dcsp) ..	Square groove	Helium	1	12 to 20	(b)
Gas metal-arc (dcrp)	Square or single-V groove	Argon(c)	1 or 2	10 to 50	(d)

Butt joint prepared for square-groove weld

Butt joint prepared for single-V-groove weld

(a) Suitable for nuclear and aerospace applications, but too slow. (b) Suitable for nuclear and aerospace applications. (c) Helium additions up to 80% improve radiographic quality. (d) Suitable for commercial applications — both code (pressure vessel, piping) and noncode applications.

Table 41. Comparison of the Gas Tungsten-Arc and the Gas Metal-Arc Processes for Welding of Butt Joints in 0.160-In.-Thick Alloy 5456 Sheet(a)

Item	Automatic gas metal-arc welding	Automatic gas tungsten-arc welding
Welding Conditions		
Current, amp	160, dcrp	260, ac
Voltage, v	24	12
Shielding gas	Argon-helium, at 60 cfh(b)	Argon, at 25 cfh
Welding speed, ipm	22	15
Costs per Lineal Foot of Weld		
Labor and burden(c) ...	$0.237	$0.280
Gas	0.087	0.054
Cleaning(d)	0.022	...
Total	$0.346	$0.334
Weld Quality		
X-ray standard(e)	Class II	Class I
Appearance	Uniform bead width and contour, rough penetration, excessive spatter on weld-face side	Very uniform bead width, excellent surface appearance, smooth penetration, well-fused edges
Mechanical properties:		
Yield strength, psi	23,300	24,450
Tensile strength, psi ..	47,700	49,800
Elongation, %	6	9.5

(a) Single-pass welds in square-groove butt joints. (b) 30 cfh of argon and 30 cfh of helium. (c) Includes wages of operator, based on 50% welding time, and administrative, general overhead, and amortization costs. (d) Includes removal of spatter and discoloration, and dressing of rough starts. (e) Class standards as defined by MIL-R-45774.

over welding variables in gas metal-arc welding than in gas tungsten-arc welding. For example, arc length, burnoff rate, wire-feed speed, and current and voltage are directly related in gas metal-arc welding. The butt joints in Table 40 could be welded in a single pass with high reinforcement if square-groove edge preparation were used, or in two passes with limited reinforcement if single-V-groove edge preparation were used. Although argon is normally used in gas metal-arc welding of metal up to ¾ in. thick, radiographic quality of the weld metal can be improved by the addition of up to 80% helium.

For welding the joints shown in Table 40, the first process, gas tungsten-arc welding with alternating current, is too costly; it would be used only if no other process were available. As between gas tungsten-arc welding with straight-polarity direct current and gas metal-arc welding, weld-quality requirements would be the deciding factor. Gas tungsten-arc welding is capable of meeting the highest standards of nuclear and aerospace applications; gas metal-arc welding is capable of meeting the requirements of pressure-vessel and piping codes, as well as other commercial standards, where high dep-osition rates are more important than in nuclear and aerospace applications.

When the aluminum sheet thickness is less than ³⁄₁₆ in., the gas tungsten-arc process becomes competitive with gas metal-arc welding. The costs for making a single-pass square-groove butt weld in 0.160-in.-thick alloy 5456 sheet by the gas tungsten-arc and gas metal-arc processes are compared in Table 41. Although the power supply and tooling costs are roughly the same for both processes, the other equipment costs for gas metal-arc welding can be $2000 more. This adds to the amortization costs and lessens the advantage of the lower labor and burden costs. In Table 41, the higher costs for shielding gas and postweld cleaning more than offset the lower labor and burden costs of making the weld by the gas metal-arc process, so that the over-all cost of producing the welded joint was less for the gas tungsten-arc process. In addition, gas tungsten-arc welding produced a weld that had better quality, needed less repair welding and developed higher mechanical properties.

In the following example, both the automatic gas tungsten-arc and the automatic gas metal-arc processes were found acceptable for making fillet welds between ¼ and ½-in. stock. The welding speeds were similar enough so that the welding cost differences became less important than the availability of equipment.

Example 322. Approval of Both Automatic Gas Tungsten-Arc and Automatic Gas Metal-Arc Processes for Welding Alloy 6061 (Fig. 50)

For joining the alloy 6061-T6 aircraft bypass fitting shown in Fig. 50, several processes were considered. Oxyacetylene welding was tried, but without success. The heat was dissipated too rapidly, and the resulting weld was not up to the standard required. The assembly could have been furnace brazed, but this method was unacceptable because: (a) in order to make the part to close tolerances to provide close fits, the tooling would have had to be changed; and (b) there was no brazing furnace available in the plant and so brazing would have had to be subcontracted, which would have added to the cost.

The part was successfully welded by the gas tungsten-arc process. Manual welding, using alternating current, was tried first. This met all aircraft standards and engineering requirements, but it was very slow, even though small turntables were used to rotate the part. Automatic gas tungsten-arc welding made fully satisfactory welds. A voltage-controlled contour welding machine with automatic wire feed was combined with an adjustable torch-holding carriage and a turntable that were already available. A welding fixture (see Fig. 50) was designed to fit on the turntable. The use of automatic welding resulted in the required increase in welding speed.

Although gas metal-arc welding was not extensively used in the plant, because most aluminum alloy parts welded were too thin for the process, it was tried for the bypass fitting, in which sections were fairly thick (¼ and ½ in.). The same fixture, turntable and carriage as those used for automatic gas tungsten-arc welding were used for automatic gas metal-arc welding. The results were good. Etching and face-bending tests met the requirements for the assembly.

Welding time was slightly less for gas metal-arc welding than for gas tungsten-arc welding, but both automatic processes were approved and used. This was one of the few assemblies for which both processes were permitted.

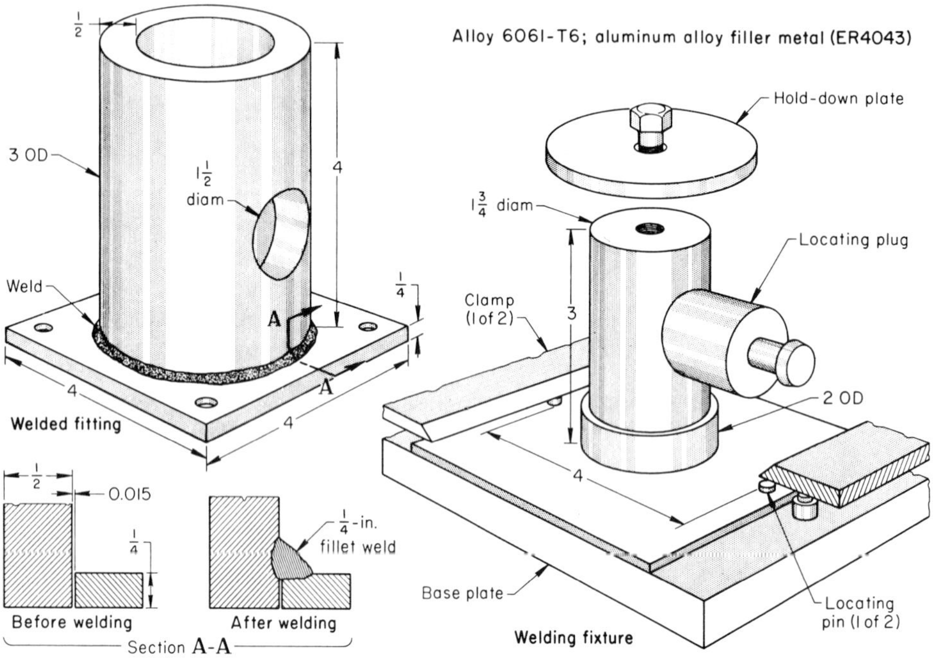

Other Arc Welding Processes

In addition to being welded by the gas metal-arc and gas tungsten-arc processes, aluminum alloys are sometimes joined by shielded metal-arc, stud, and percussion welding.

Shielded metal-arc welding is used primarily in small shops for miscellaneous repair work in noncritical applications. A flux-covered aluminum alloy electrode is used. The flux combines with aluminum oxide to form a slag. The slag must be removed after each weld pass. Weld soundness and surface smoothness are poor. The process is limited to butt welds in ⅛-in. and thicker aluminum. AWS A5.3-69 includes two covered electrodes: one with core wire corresponding to ER1100 and one to ER4043.

Stud welding of aluminum alloys is generally accomplished by the capacitor-discharge method, rather than the arc method. Examples 169, 172 and 174 in the article on Stud Welding (page 167) are illustrations of the stud welding of aluminum alloys.

Percussion welding of aluminum alloys is used principally for joining wire to wire. Numerous dissimilar metal joints, including aluminum to copper and to steel are made.

Alloy 6061-T6; aluminum alloy filler metal (ER4043)

Item	Automatic gas tungsten-arc welding	Automatic gas metal-arc welding
Joint type	Corner	Corner
Weld type	Fillet	Fillet
Root opening, in.	0.015	0.015
Welding position	Flat	Flat
Power supply	300-amp transformer-rectifier	300-amp transformer-rectifier
Mechanization	Turntable	Turntable
Filler-wire feed system	Automatic, push	Automatic, push
Fixtures	Assembly, clamping	Assembly, clamping
Edge preparation	Deburring	Deburring
Torch or electrode holder ...	Water cooled, held at 40° angle	Air and gas cooled
Filler metal	³⁄₆₄-in.-diam ER4043-H18	³⁄₆₄-in.-diam ER4043-H18
Shielding gas	Helium, at 20 cfh	Argon, at 20 cfh
Electrode stickout, in.	½	⅜
Current, amp	200, dcsp	Dcrp; amperage not recorded
Voltage, v	15	40
Filler-metal feed, ipm	230	240
Welding speed, ipm	14	15
Number of passes	One	One

Fig. 50. An aircraft bypass-fitting assembly that could be welded by either the automatic gas tungsten-arc or the automatic gas metal-arc process in approximately the same welding time, both producing welds that met quality standards, and the fixture used for welding by both processes (Example 322)

Resistance Welding of Aluminum Alloys

*By the ASM Committee on Welding of Aluminum Alloys**

ALUMINUM ALLOYS, both the non-heat-treatable and heat treatable types, either wrought or cast, can be resistance welded, some more readily than others. Aluminum alloys have comparatively high thermal and electrical conductivity, a relatively narrow plastic range (about 200 to 400 F temperature differential between softening and melting), considerable shrinkage during cooling, a troublesome surface oxide, and an affinity for copper electrode materials.

Resistance spot and seam welding of aluminum alloys are used in the manufacture of cooking utensils, tanks (both for seams and for securing baffles), bridge flooring, and many aircraft components. Resistance welding of aluminum aircraft components such as wing-skin sections, deck sections, brackets and cowling usually involves making many high-quality welds in one structure, and may require elaborate and expensive equipment for cleaning, welding and control of weld quality. In many commercial applications, resistance welding of aluminum is done with less cleaning and a lower level of acceptable weld quality.

*For committee list, see page 296.

Weld Strength. The strength of resistance welds in aluminum alloys varies with the alloy and its thickness. Resistance welds should be located so that the weld is under shear loading. For tensile or combined loading, the tensile strength of the welded joint is only about 25% of the shear strength. Nuggets with diameters equal to two thicknesses of base metal plus 0.06 in. should have shear strengths greater than the values given in Table 1.

The heat of resistance welding decreases the strength and hardness of strain hardened and of solution treated and precipitation hardened aluminum alloys, depending on the temperature attained and the length of time that a temperature of 400 F or more is maintained during welding.

Base Metals

Although all aluminum alloys can be resistance spot and seam welded, some alloys or combinations of alloys have higher as-welded properties than others. Melting ranges, electrical and thermal conductivities, and resistance weldability of some wrought alloys and casting alloys are given in Table 2.

Resistance welding is also done on alclad products made by roll cladding some of the alloys listed in Table 2 with a thin layer of aluminum, or an aluminum alloy, that is anodic to the core alloy and thus provides electrochemical protection for exposed areas of the core. Alclad alloys 2219, 3003, 3004, 6061 and 7075 have a cladding of alloy 7072, which contains 1% zinc; alclad alloy 2014 has a cladding of alloy 6006, or sometimes of alloy 6053, both of which contain about 1.2% magnesium; and alclad alloy 2024 has a cladding of alloy 1230, which contains a minimum of 99.3% aluminum.

The hardness of an alloy affects its weldability. Any alloy in the annealed condition (O temper) is more difficult to weld than the same alloy in a harder temper. In general, alloys in the softer tempers are much more susceptible to excessive indentation and sheet separation, and to low or inconsistent weld strength. Greater deformation under the welding force causes an increase in the contact area and variations in the distribution of current and pressure. Therefore, welding of aluminum alloys in the annealed condition or in the softer tempers either requires special electromechanical or electronic controls or else is not recommended.

High-strength alloys such as 2024 and 7075 are easy to resistance weld, but they may require special welding techniques because they are more susceptible to cracking and porosity than the lower-strength alloys. Sheet separation in welding high-strength alloys is low, and weld strength is consistent. Alloys clad with alloy 1230 or 7072 are less easily resistance welded than bare alloys of the same composition, because of the low electrical resistance and high melting point of the cladding at the contacting interfaces.

Although the strength of welds made in low-strength alloys such as 1100 and 3003 may vary, these alloys can be resistance welded readily in most applications. High welding current or low electrode force may be needed to compensate for the low electrical resistance of these alloys.

Shrinkage cracks in the weld metal are confined almost exclusively to welds made in the copper-bearing and zinc-bearing alloys such as 2024 and 7075. Such high-strength alloys, as well as the chromium-bearing alloys such as 5052 and 6053, may develop some porosity in the weld metal, particularly when they are welded in the hardened condition.

In joining dissimilar aluminum alloys, those with similar electrical conductivities and melting temperatures are easiest to weld together; those pairs with the greatest difference in electrical conductivity and melting temperature are the most difficult to weld together.

Wrought aluminum alloys are frequently spot welded to permanent mold, sand and die castings made from aluminum alloys. Of these types, permanent mold castings are easiest to weld, because the thickness is more nearly uniform. Such castings are sound, and have smooth surfaces and a low as-cast surface resistance, if welded within a reasonable time after casting. Die castings also are dimensionally accurate, but may require special cleaning to prepare the surface for welding, and sometimes special dies and foundry practice are needed to ensure the soundness of the metal in the region to be welded.

Spot and seam welds in non-heat-treatable alloys such as 1100, 3003 and 5052 are not selectively attacked by corrosion, but have the same corrosion resistance as the unwelded metal. Welds in heat treatable magnesium-silicon alloys such as 6061 and 6063 also have good corrosion resistance.

Welds in unclad 2xxx and 7xxx series alloys may be attacked preferentially under severely corrosive conditions and, therefore, weldments made from these alloys should not be used in a corrosive environment unless properly protected. However, when these same alloys are resistance welded to aluminum-clad parts of corresponding composition, the cladding electrochemically protects the unclad base metal at the interface and thus improves the over-all resistance to corrosion at the joint. Maximum resistance to corrosion at the welded joint is achieved when each of the parts being welded is an alclad alloy.

Factors Affecting Resistance Welding of Aluminum Alloys

Because of the inherent characteristics of aluminum alloys, resistance welding of these alloys requires procedures different from those used for resistance welding of steel. Included among these characteristics are high electrical and thermal conductivities, low melting-temperature ranges and low strengths at elevated temperatures, narrow plastic ranges, high shrinkage during solidification and the presence of natural oxide coatings.

Electrical and Thermal Conductivities. Aluminum alloys are much higher in electrical conductivity than most metals that are commonly resistance welded. For example, the electrical conductivity of alloy 2024 (one of the low-conductivity aluminum alloys) is more than twice that of low-carbon steel. This high electrical conductivity necessitates the use of high-capacity welding machines capable of supplying high welding currents, because high current density is needed to generate enough heat to melt the aluminum alloy and produce the weld. The high thermal conductivity of aluminum alloys necessitates rapid welding to avoid dissipation of heat into the workpieces.

Effect of Melting Temperature. As the temperature is increased during resistance welding, aluminum alloys soften more rapidly and at lower temperatures than does steel. Low-inertia welding-machine heads are needed so that electrodes can make the rapid movements necessary for maintenance of weld force and workpiece contact. Although these movements are small, they must take place during an interval of about 2 to 5 milliseconds.

The plastic range in which a weld can be made is very narrow for aluminum alloys. Therefore, the energy input to the weld must be precisely controlled to bring the metal up to, but not above, its plastic range.

Effect of Shrinkage During Cooling. Aluminum alloys exhibit considerable shrinkage during cooling from the liquidus temperature to room temperature. This property is most pronounced in the high-strength heat treatable alloys such as 2024 and 7075, and can result in cracking. The non-heat-treatable alloys and the 6xxx series alloys are less likely to crack as a result of shrinkage of the nugget.

Porosity and cracking can result from shrinkage unless the electrodes can maintain proper pressure on the nugget until solidification is completed. Machines for welding aluminum alloys generally have, in addition to low-inertia heads, a means of increasing the electrode force as the nugget solidifies. This permits forging of the nugget, and thus improves weld soundness.

Effect of Surface Oxide. Aluminum combines almost instantaneously with oxygen in the atmosphere to produce an aluminum oxide coating that has a high and somewhat erratic electrical resistance, which in turn affects the amount of heat produced in the metal beneath during resistance welding. Therefore, for aircraft-quality welds, this oxide film should be removed or changed to a film of uniform electrical resistance before welding.

Commercial spot or seam welding often can be done on aluminum without cleaning or oxide removal, but electrode pickup increases, electrode life decreases, and welds will be lower in shear strength, variable in quality and erratic in shape. The amount of sur-

Table 1. Minimum Shear Strength of Resistance Spot Welds in Aluminum Alloys

Thickness of thinnest sheet, in.	Minimum shear strength, lb per spot, for alloy:			
	1100-H14 1100-H18	3003-H12 3003-H18 5052-O	5052-H32 5052-H38 6061-T4 6061-T6 5050-H34	2024-T3, alclad 2024-T3, 7075-T6, alclad 7075-T6
0.016	40	70	98	108
0.020	55	100	132	140
0.025	70	145	175	185
0.032	110	210	235	260
0.040	150	300	310	345
0.051	205	410	442	480
0.064	280	565	625	690
0.081	420	775	865	1050
0.102	520	950	1200	1535
0.125	590	1000	1625	2120

SOURCE: "Welding Alcoa Aluminum", Aluminum Co. of America, Pittsburgh, 1969

Table 2. Melting Ranges, Electrical and Thermal Conductivities, and Resistance Weldability of Common Aluminum Alloys(a)

Alloy and temper	Melting range, F	Electrical conductivity, % IACS (b)	Relative thermal conductivity, % (c)	Resistance weldability(d)
Non-Heat-Treatable Wrought Aluminum Alloys				
EC-H19 ...1195-1215		62	60	ST
1060-H18 ..1195-1215		61	57	ST
1100-H18 ..1190-1215		57	55	RW
3003-H18 ..1190-1210		40	39	RW
3004-H38 ..1165-1205		42	42	RW
5005-H38 ..1170-1205		52	51	RW
5050-H38 ..1160-1205		50	49	RW
5052-H38 ..1100-1200		35	35	RW
5083-H321 ..1065-1180		29	30	RW
5086-H34 ..1084-1184		31	32	RW
5154-H38 ..1100-1190		32	32	RW
5454-H34 ..1115-1195		34	34	RW
5456-H321 ..1060-1180		29	30	RW
Heat Treatable Wrought Aluminum Alloys				
2014-T6 ... 950-1180		40	39	ST
2024-T36 ... 935-1180		30	31	ST
2219-T37 ..1010-1190		28	29	ST
6061-T6 ..1100-1200		43	43	RW
6063-T6 ..1140-1210		53	51	RW
6101-T6 ..1140-1205		57	55	RW
7075-T6 ... 890-1180		33	33	ST
Aluminum Casting Alloys				
13-F 1065-1080		31	32	LW
43-F 1065-1170		37	37	RW
A108-F 970-1135		37	37	ST
138-F 945-1110		25	26	LW
A214-F 1075-1180		34	34	ST
220-T4 840-1120		21	22	NR
333-T6 960-1085		29	30	ST
C355-T61 ..1015-1150		39	38	ST
356-T6 1035-1135		39	38	ST
C612-F 1120-1190		40	39	LW

(a) In this table, wrought alloys are identified by Aluminum Association designations, and casting alloys by industry designations. For Aluminum Association designations of casting alloys, see Table 2 on page 297 in the article on Arc Welding of Aluminum Alloys. (b) International Annealed Copper Standard, volume basis at 68 F. For comparison, copper alloy 102 (oxygen-free copper) is 101% and low-carbon (1010) steel about 14%. (c) Based on copper alloy 102 as 100%, which has a thermal conductivity of 226 Btu/sq ft/ft/hr/°F at 68 F. Low-carbon steel has a thermal conductivity of about 13% on this relative scale. (d) RW, readily weldable; ST, weldable in most applications but may require special techniques for specific applications; LW, limited weldability and usually requires special techniques; NR, welding not recommended.

face preparation needed depends on the strength and quality requirements of the welded product and on the alloy being welded.

Resistance Welding Machines

Aluminum alloys can be resistance welded with single-phase direct-energy, three-phase direct-energy, and stored-energy machines. Best results are obtained by using a machine that has the following features:

1 Ability to handle high welding currents for short weld times
2 Synchronous electronic controls for weld time and welding current
3 A low-inertia welding head for rapid follow-up of electrode force
4 Slope control (for single-phase welding machines)
5 A multiple-electrode-force system to permit proper forging of the weld nugget, and re-dressing of electrodes.

The three types of machines are discussed briefly in the following paragraphs. For additional information, see the article on Resistance Spot Welding, beginning on page 401 in this volume.

Single-Phase Machines. Single-phase direct-energy machines have high intermittent kva demand and low power factor, and may disturb other electrical equipment. A wide variation in line voltage can cause nonuniformity in welding. However, adequate transformers or substations reduce the variation.

The addition of upslope and downslope control to a single-phase machine is recommended for spot welding of aluminum (see discussion headed "Slope control", below).

Three-Phase Machines. Three-phase direct-energy machines, of either the frequency-converter or the dry-disk-rectifier types, produce excellent resistance welds in aluminum because of their partial control of the shape of the welding-current wave. The gradual increase in current at the beginning of the weld cycle and the decay at the end of the cycle are similar to the upslope and downslope used with single-phase machines.

Stored-Energy Machines. Electrostatic stored-energy machines use a three-phase full-wave rectifier to charge a capacitor bank to a predetermined voltage. The weld is made by discharging the bank of capacitors through a suitable welding transformer. The use of these machines has been largely superseded by three-phase direct-energy machines.

Synchronous controls for weld time and welding current are recommended for resistance welding of aluminum alloys because they provide precise control of short weld times and high welding currents. Magnetic and mechanical controls generally are not suitable.

Slope control permits adjustment of the rate of rise and fall of the welding current. Upslope control causes the welding current to increase gradually during the first few cycles of the weld time. The maximum current level is not reached until the electrode face has seated itself into the softened aluminum; therefore, excessively high currents do not normally occur at localized points. Overheating of metal at the interface of the electrode and the workpiece is reduced, which results in

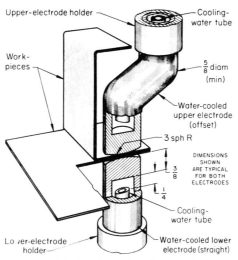

Fig. 1. Details of construction of straight and offset radius-face electrodes used in resistance spot welding of aluminum alloys

increased weld quality and electrode life and in better surface appearance.

Downslope control tapers the current off gradually, which prevents rapid chilling of the nugget. Downslope also permits better forging, which results in finer grain structure, eliminates cracks and voids in the nugget, and permits wider variations in amount and time of application of forging force. Figure 16(b) on page 414 in the article on Resistance Spot Welding shows upslope and downslope in a weld cycle.

Multiple-electrode-force cycles usually consist of three stages. In the first stage, a high precompression force is exerted to seat the electrodes firmly on the work metal and to establish good electrical contact. The electrode force is then reduced to increase contact resistance while the weld is being made. After the nugget has formed, the force is again increased to forge the nugget. Figure 16(d) on page 414 in the article on Resistance Spot Welding shows a multiple-electrode-force cycle incorporated in the welding cycle.

A low electrode force for welding permits the use of a lower welding current and minimizes sheet separation. Use of high forging force reduces cracking. Multiple-electrode-force cycles make the accuracy of the machine settings less critical and increase the range in which high-quality welds can be produced.

Some welding machines can also produce an electrode force of 100 to 200 lb for use in re-dressing the electrodes with a paddle-type dresser.

Electrodes and Electrode Holders

Selection of electrode material and face shape, maintenance of the face and cooling of the electrode are important in producing consistent spot and seam welds in aluminum alloys.

Copper alloy electrodes, RWMA classes 1 and 2 (Table 2, page 409 in the article on Resistance Spot Welding), are used when welding aluminum alloys. These electrode materials have high electrical and thermal conductivities — which, together with adequate cooling, help to keep the temperature of the electrode below the relatively

low point at which aluminum will alloy with copper, causing electrode pickup.

Design of Spot Welding Electrodes. Both straight and offset electrodes are suitable for spot welding of aluminum. However, straight electrodes should be used whenever possible, because deflection and skidding may occur with offset electrodes under similar welding conditions. If offset electrodes are used, the amount of offset should be the minimum permitted by the shape of the assembly being welded. Only electrodes that have the cooling-water hole within $\frac{3}{8}$ in. of the face surface should be used. Fluted cooling-water holes provide more cooling surface than round holes. Construction details for both straight and offset electrodes suitable for spot welding of aluminum are shown in Fig. 1.

Face Contour. The face of at least one electrode must be shaped so that the current is highly concentrated at the weld. For most spot welding applications, an RWMA type F electrode, with a face having a spherical radius greater than the diameter of the electrode, is used on one or both sides of the workpieces. A radius face provides easy alignment and minimum sheet separation, concentrates the welding current, and is easier to clean and to maintain than is a flat face. One flat-face (RWMA type C) electrode can be used to minimize indentation on one workpiece, although higher joint strength usually is obtained by using equally radiused electrodes in joining workpieces of approximately equal thickness. (Types of electrode faces are described and shown in the section on Electrode Design, page 409, in the article on Resistance Spot Welding.)

Electrode-face radii for a variety of metal thicknesses and tempers are given in Table 3. When workpieces of dissimilar thickness are being welded, a radius-face electrode of correct dimensions should be used in contact with the thinner member; good-quality welds are more difficult to make if an electrode with too large a face radius or a flat-face electrode is used against the thinner workpiece.

Electrode Maintenance. Correct maintenance of electrode faces is essential if spot welds of uniform size and shape are to be made. The quality of resistance welds in aluminum alloys is more dependent on the contour, surface finish and cleanliness of the electrode face than is the quality of welds made in other metals and alloys. The faces should be regularly redressed and periodically replaced or remachined to their original shapes with properly designed tools when they show signs of wear or an appreciable change in contour. (Shaping of electrode faces by hand with a file is inaccurate and should be avoided.)

In the spot welding of aluminum alloys, electrode life is determined by metal pickup on the electrode face, and not deformation, as in the welding of steel. The copper-aluminum alloy formed on the electrode face by pickup is of low electrical conductivity and, if welding is continued, the electrodes will stick to the work metal and the surface of the work metal will melt. Aluminum must be removed from the electrode face by periodic hand dressing to avoid marking the surfaces of succeeding welds and to maintain the original condition of the face.

Recommended practice is to clean the electrode when the center portion of the spot weld appears either dirty or crusty, or when work metal begins to adhere to the electrode. Less frequent cleaning will cause rapid electrode deterioration and poor weld quality. Electrode pickup can be minimized by proper preparation of the work-metal surface prior to welding, use of adequate electrode force, and avoidance of excessive welding current.

The cleaning operation must remove all the aluminum pickup, but must not change the face contour by removing an appreciable amount of electrode material. To maintain the original shape of radius-face electrodes, a dressing tool in the shape of a paddle with two depressions contoured to match the desired face radius should be used. The two depressions are faced with No. 240, or finer, abrasive cloth.

The dressing tool is clamped between the electrodes with a force of 100 to 200 lb and is rotated a few times to remove the copper-aluminum alloy. The faces are then cleaned, using a cloth dampened with a solvent, to remove any clinging abrasive dust, and then wiped dry. Abrasive grit or deep scratches in the electrode face caused by coarse grit can be transferred to the workpiece during welding, and thus should be avoided. A rubber block and two pieces of abrasive cloth can be used instead of a metal dressing tool.

Electrode Cooling. An adequate means of cooling the electrode face must be provided. This is usually done by a flow of water or refrigerated coolant through the inside of the electrode. Electrodes with either round or fluted water holes are available. Fluted holes provide more cooling surface than round holes. For continuous welding, each water-cooled electrode should be operated at a cooling-water flow rate of at least 1 gallon per minute, and preferably 1½ to 2 gallons per minute. The cooling water should be brought to within ¼ to ⅜ in. of the electrode face, and the inner cooling-water tube should extend to within ¼ in. of the bottom of the cooling-water hole to provide good circulation (see Fig. 1). The end of the cooling-water tube should be cut at an angle, so that if it bottoms in the cooling-water hole in the electrode, the water flow will not be stopped.

Cooling-water temperature should be 60 F or less, and should not vary more than 10 F. If the water temperature is above 60 F, or if it varies widely, the use of a refrigerated coolant may be helpful in improving electrode life and weld consistency. By cooling the electrodes with refrigerated coolant at temperatures of 38 to 40 F, the number of spot welds made between face cleanings can be increased appreciably. When a refrigerated coolant is used, however, condensation of water on the electrodes and electrode holders may present a problem.

Electrode Holders. The commercially available electrode holders are suitable for use in welding aluminum alloys.

Table 3. Face Radii for Resistance Spot Welding Electrodes or Seam Welding Electrode Wheels for Use on Aluminum Alloys of Various Thicknesses(a)

Condition of work metal	Radius, in., for work-metal thickness of:				
	Up to 0.020 in.	0.021 to 0.032 in.	0.033 to 0.064 in.	0.065 to 0.094 in.	0.095 to 0.125 in.
Annealed or as-extruded	2	3	4	4	...
Intermediate tempers of non-heat-treatable alloys	2	3	3	4	6
Heat treated	1	2	3	4	6

(a) Spherical radii for faces of spot welding electrodes and transverse radii for edges of seam welding electrode wheels. When a flat surface is needed on one side of the workpiece, one electrode is made to the above radius, and the electrode that contacts the surface to be flat is either flat or has a 10-in.-radius face or edge. [Source of table: Same as Table 1]

Offset electrode holders sometimes are required for spot welding assemblies not accessible to straight holders and are preferred to offset electrodes because they are more rigid and less likely to cause skidding of electrodes.

Seam welding electrode wheels are from ⅜ to 1 in. thick and from 6 to 12 in. or more in diameter. An electrode wheel less than 6 in. in diameter sometimes is required, depending on the configuration or accessibility of the parts being welded. Electrode wheels usually have two curvatures — the radius of the wheel, which changes only slightly when the wheel is dressed, and the transverse radius of the crown on the edge of the wheel. Transverse radii of electrode wheels used for welding aluminum alloys of various thicknesses and tempers are given in Table 3. Electrode wheels with flat faces or with crowns 10 in. or more in radius can be used against work-metal surfaces to avoid marking or indentation.

Maintenance practices for seam welding electrodes are essentially the same as for spot welding electrodes. Electrode pickup can be removed from the face of an electrode wheel by dressing with a suitable grade of abrasive cloth. A moderately coarse grade of cloth produces a rough surface that prevents slippage between the wheel and the work metal. Some form of a medium-fine grade of abrasive held against the wheel under a load of 5 to 10 lb can be used for continuous dressing of electrode wheels. Knurl-driven electrode wheels should not be used because they roughen the surface of the wheel excessively, mark the aluminum work metal and cause electrode pickup.

Electrode wheels usually are cooled by a flow of water directed against the periphery of the wheel at the weld and sometimes are cooled internally.

Preweld Surface Preparation

Although welds satisfactory for some purposes can be made without any preweld surface preparation, welds free from cracks, porosity, and sheet separation and having maximum strength, symmetry, and consistency and that are economical are obtained only with correct procedures for cleaning and for reduction or removal of oxide film. Adequate surface preparation also reduces electrode contamination.

Commercial spot and seam welding of aluminum alloys such as 1100, 3003 and 5052 can be accomplished with only a degreasing and cleaning operation for surface preparation. However, consistency in commercial welding of the more highly alloyed compositions generally requires additional mechanical or chemical cleaning. Aircraft construction, regardless of the alloy used, demands the utmost in cleaning and oxide removal and requires continual checking of surface resistance.

Oxide can be removed by either mechanical or chemical methods. Usually, the length of time tolerable between oxide removal and welding varies from 48 hours to several days, depending on methods of oxide removal and handling and on storage environment.

Cleaning begins with the removal of any stencil identification marks with alcohol, paint thinner or other suitable solvent. Then parts heavily soiled with dirt, oil, grease, or lubricants from forming operations are cleaned with commercial solvents by wiping, dipping, washing, spraying, or vapor degreasing, depending on the size and quantity. Vapor degreasing with an acceptable chlorinated solvent generally is used whenever a large number of parts is involved. If only a few parts are to be cleaned, they can be immersed in or wiped with acceptable chlorinated solvents or acetone. Cleaning of metal with these chemicals should be done in a well ventilated area.

Degreasing is often followed by treatment with a nonetching alkaline cleaner specially formulated to produce low, consistent surface resistance on aluminum (see Alkaline Cleaning, page 615 in Volume 2 of this Handbook). After the cleaning operations, the work-metal surface should be able to support a water film without a break. Lightly soiled workpieces can be alkaline cleaned without degreasing.

Mechanical removal of oxides is primarily a hand operation and its effectiveness depends on the skill of the operator. The contact resistance of surfaces cleaned by this method sometimes is lower than that of surfaces cleaned by a chemical method. The cleaning action must be severe enough to cut through the hard oxide film, yet gentle enough not to form an excessively rough surface in the comparatively soft metal underneath.

When welding is confined to a small area and the oxide film is thin, mechanical methods provide quick and complete removal of the oxide film over that portion of the surface where the welds are to be made, with little investment for equipment, and without danger of subsequent formation of a high-resistance film. Mechanical cleaning can be done immediately preceding welding. Also, mechanical methods are useful for removing oxide from work pieces that are too large to be dipped and rinsed. After the workpieces have been degreased, the oxide film can be removed with a fine grade of abrasive cloth, a fine stainless steel wool or a motor-driven brush made of fine stain less steel wire. Glass brushes and aluminum wool have also been used. Carbon or low-alloy steel brushes or steel wool should not be used.

Chemical Removal of Oxides. An acid dip is used after heavy oxide removal or directly after cleaning, to obtain uniform surface resistance. A typical solution contains 12% (by volume) concentrated nitric acid, 0.4% (by volume) hydrofluoric acid and 0.2% (by weight) wetting agent, and is used at a temperature of 70 to 80 F. Immersion time in this solution is 2 to 6 min. This is followed by rinsing in clear water and drying.

Forgings, castings, extrusions or similar parts having thick oxide accumulation may need an alkaline etch before the acid dip. A commonly used alkaline-etch treatment is immersion in an aqueous solution of 5% sodium hydroxide at 150 to 160 F for 20 to 50 sec, followed by rinsing in cold water. The alkaline-etch solution may contain additives to prevent the formation of scale in the tank.

Aluminum alloys 1060, 1100 and 3003 and aluminum-clad alloys frequently are immersed for 1½ to 3 min in a warm (190 F) solution containing 10% (by volume) concentrated nitric acid, 6 oz sodium sulfate per gallon and 0.1% (by weight) wetting agent. The parts are then rinsed in cold running water for 5 min and dried rapidly. Heat treatable alloys such as 6061 are immersed for 1½ to 3 min in a warm (185 F) solution containing 15% (by volume) concentrated nitric acid, 13 oz sodium sulfate per gallon and 0.1% (by weight) wetting agent. The parts are then rinsed in cold running water for 5 min and dried rapidly. For more detailed information on cleaning and etching of aluminum alloys, see the article on Cleaning and Finishing of Aluminum and Aluminum Alloys, page 611 in Volume 2 of this Handbook.

To ensure satisfactory preparation of the surfaces for spot and seam welding, it must be determined that the cleaning and deoxidizing procedures are adequate and that the strength of the solutions is correct. This determination should be made by measuring the surface contact resistance after surface treatment of small coupons of the material to be welded; visual inspection is not a satisfactory control method. Measurement of contact resistance should be made also on each batch of workpieces being welded. Corrections in the procedures or additions to the solutions should be made as required to maintain the contact resistance of the control samples and of the workpieces at the desired value.

Occasionally, special surface-preparation methods are used to solve particular problems. For instance, in Example 293 in the article on Arc Welding of Aluminum Alloys, a method is described that met the exacting requirements of gas metal-arc and gas tungsten-arc welding on that job, and that could be adapted easily to preparation for resistance welding.

Contact-Resistance Test. A standard test can be used to determine the electrical resistance of an interface between aluminum alloy samples or workpieces. The two samples or workpieces are placed between two spot welding electrodes ⅝ in. in diameter with faces 3 in. in spherical radius, and are clamped under a static force of 600 lb. A 50-milliamp (ma) direct current is transmitted through the electrodes, and the resistance between the workpieces is determined with a suitable instrument.

The tests must be performed under identical conditions of force, applied current, and electrode size and contour. The measurement is sensitive to small changes in test procedure, and values are usually obtained by averaging at least 2 or 3 readings on each of the four possible interface combinations of a pair of specimens. Movement of either specimen after the electrode pressure is applied breaks the oxide coating and causes false low readings. The presence of burrs on the specimens also causes low readings.

The contact resistance of well cleaned aluminum alloys is from 10 to about 200 microhms, while that of unclean stock can be 1000 microhms or more. For noncritical welding, contact resistance of 200 to 500 microhms is satisfactory. For best results (as required for military applications), contact resistance should be about 50 microhms. A narrow spread in readings generally is preferable to low average values with an occasional high reading.

Seam Sealants. Elastic materials have been used between members of resistance welded joints to make containers fluid-tight and to limit interface corrosion, especially in high-hu-

Table 4. Typical Conditions for Resistance Spot Welding of Aluminum Alloy Sheets in 60-Cycle Single-Phase Direct-Energy Welding Machines

Thickness of thinnest sheet, in.	Electrode diameter, in.	Face radius, in. Upper electrode	Lower electrode	Electrode force, lb	Weld time, cycles	Welding current, amp	Diameter of nugget, in.
0.016	⅝	1	Flat	320	4	15,000	0.110
0.020	⅝	1	Flat	340	5	18,000	0.125
0.025	⅝	2	Flat	390	6	21,800	0.140
0.032	⅝	2	Flat	500	6	26,000	0.160
0.040	⅝	3	Flat	600	8	30,700	0.180
0.051	⅝	3	Flat	660	8	33,000	0.210
0.064	⅝	3	Flat	750	10	35,900	0.250
0.072	⅝	4	4	800	10	38,000	0.275
0.081	⅞	4	4	860	10	41,800	0.300
0.091	⅞	6	6	950	12	46,000	0.330
0.102	⅞	6	6	1050	15	56,000	0.360
0.125	⅞	6	6	1300	15	76,000	0.425

SOURCE: Same as Table 1

Table 5. Typical Conditions for Resistance Spot Welding of Aluminum Alloy Sheets in 60-Cycle Three-Phase Direct-Energy Welding Machines

Thickness of thinnest sheet, in.	Electrode diameter, in.	Electrode face radius, in.	Electrode force, lb Weld	Forge	Time, cycles Weld	Postheat	Current, amp Weld	Postheat	Diameter of nugget, in.
Three-Phase Rectifier-Type Machines									
0.016	⅝	3	440	1000	1	None	19,000	None	0.110
0.020	⅝	3	520	1150	1	None	22,000	None	0.125
0.032	⅝	3	670	1540	2	None	28,000	None	0.160
0.040	⅝	3	730	1800	3	None	32,000	None	0.180
0.051	⅝	8	900	2250	4	4	37,000	30,000	0.210
0.064	⅝	8	1100	2900	5	5	43,000	36,000	0.250
0.072	⅝	8	1190	3240	6	7	48,000	38,000	0.275
0.081	⅞	8	1460	3800	7	9	52,000	42,000	0.300
0.091	⅞	8	1700	4300	8	11	56,000	45,000	0.330
0.102	⅞	8	1900	5000	9	14	61,000	49,000	0.360
0.125	⅞	8	2500	6500	10	22	69,000	54,000	0.425
Three-Phase Frequency-Converter-Type Machines									
0.020	⅝	3	500	None	½	None	26,000	None	0.125
0.025	⅝	3	500	1500	1	3	34,000	8,500	0.140
0.032	⅝	4	700	1800	1	4	36,000	9,000	0.160
0.040	⅝	4	800	2000	1	4	42,000	12,600	0.180
0.051	⅝	4	900	2300	1	5	46,000	13,800	0.210
0.064	⅝	6	1300	3000	2	5	54,000	18,900	0.250
0.072	⅝	6	1600	3600	2	6	61,000	21,350	0.275
0.081	⅞	6	2000	4300	3	6	65,000	22,750	0.300
0.091	⅞	6	2400	5300	3	8	75,000	30,000	0.330
0.102	⅞	8	2800	6800	3	8	85,000	34,000	0.360
0.125	⅞	8	4000	9000	4	10	100,000	45,000	0.425

SOURCE: Same as Table 1

Table 6. Typical Conditions for Resistance Spot Welding of Aluminum Alloy Sheets in Capacitor-Type Stored-Energy Welding Machines

Thickness of thinnest sheet, in.	Electrode diameter, in.	Electrode face radius, in.	Electrode force, lb Weld	Forge	Condenser capacity, mfd	Condenser charge, volts	Transformer ratio	Total energy, watt-sec	Diameter of nugget, in.
0.020	⅝	3	376	692	240	2150	300:1	555	0.125
0.032	⅝	3	580	1300	240	2700	300:1	875	0.160
0.040	⅝	3	680	1580	360	2550	300:1	1172	0.180
0.051	⅝	3	890	2100	600	2560	300:1	1952	0.210
0.064	⅝	3	1080	2680	720	2700	300:1	2622	0.250
0.072	⅝	3	1230	3150	960	2750	450:1	3630	0.275
0.081	⅞	3	1550	4000	1440	2700	450:1	5250	0.300
0.091	⅞	3	1830	4660	1920	2650	450:1	6750	0.330
0.102	⅞	3	2025	5100	2520	2700	450:1	9180	0.360

SOURCE: Same as Table 1

midity environments. For instance, welds of military quality can be made through gun-grade caulking compounds, which consist of finely divided aluminum powder in a special elastic binder, with no significant change in machine settings. Some tapes and paints provide equally good results.

Resistance Spot Welding

All of the commercial aluminum alloys that are produced as sheet, extrusions or castings can be spot welded; the combined maximum thickness with ordinary equipment is between ½ and ¾ in. Process control is much more critical than for spot welding of low-carbon steel, and the range of permissible welding-machine settings is narrower for a given work-metal thickness. Also, the condition of the work-metal surface is extremely important for production of satisfactory welds.

Figure 2 shows a typical spot weld between two 0.102-in.-thick sheets of alclad alloy 2024-T4 (alloy 1230 cladding; 99.3% min Al). In the center of this spot weld is an oval zone with an equiaxed grain structure. Surrounding this zone is a zone made up of a dendritic (or columnar) type of grain structure. The area of these two zones constitutes the spot weld nugget. Each is essentially a cast structure. The large size of the dendritic zone is the result of a welding technique that employed a postweld heat treatment permitting grain growth.

Surrounding the dendritic zone is a band of light color that consists of a layer of metal that has been heated close to the melting point, and in which segregation of eutectic material has occurred in the base metal. Forcing of this eutectic material into adjacent base metal results in a dark-color ring immediately surrounding the lighter ring. The cladding at the interface was completely absorbed with the base metal into the nugget. Indentation was not severe and the outer surfaces of the work metal in contact with the electrodes show no effect of heating.

Welding Current. As the thermal and electrical conductivities of aluminum alloys are about two to four times those of low-carbon steel, the heat for welding, and thus the welding current, must be greater than that used for welding steel of equivalent thickness. Tables 4, 5 and 6 list typical conditions for spot welding aluminum alloys in single-phase direct-energy, three-phase direct-energy, and capacitor-type stored-energy welding machines. These values are starting points and should be adjusted to suit the particular alloy and job requirements.

The higher the current, the more rapidly the nugget is formed. Also, the longer the duration of current flow, the greater the penetration of the nugget into the base metal. If the current is too low, the nugget forms too slowly, and excess heating and warping occur in the surrounding area. If the current is too high, formation of gas pockets and expulsion of metal result, causing sheet separation and weak welds.

Weld time is the actual time that the welding current flows through the workpieces, and must be sufficient to

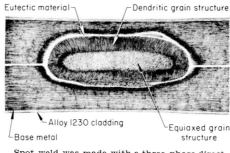

Alclad alloy 2024-T4, 0.102 in. thick

Spot weld was made with a three-phase direct-energy resistance welding machine, using forging pressure and postheating. See text for discussion. (Source: RWMA Bulletin 18)

Fig. 2. Typical spot weld nugget made in a heat treated alclad aluminum alloy

form the weld without excessively heating the remainder of the weld area. As work-metal thickness increases, longer weld times are required, as shown in Tables 4 and 5.

Within a narrow range of weld time, weld strength is approximately proportional to weld time. Using weld time beyond this range produces no appreciable further increase in weld strength.

Electrode force used for spot welding of aluminum alloys generally is greater than that needed for spot welding of steel of equivalent thickness. Low-strength aluminum alloys usually need lower electrode force than high-strength alloys.

Use of insufficient electrode force can result in expulsion of weld metal, internal defects, surface burning and excessive electrode pickup. Use of excessive electrode force can result in extreme indentation, sheet separation, work distortion, and asymmetrical welds. When a low electrode force is used, high contact resistance is developed at the interface, requiring a low welding current; when a high electrode force is used, contact resistance is reduced, and a higher current is needed.

A multiple-electrode-force cycle, in which the weld is made at a low electrode force followed by application of a higher force during hold time, is used to provide forging action during solidification of the nugget. In minimizing internal defects, timing of the application of forging force is important. If the forging force is applied before completion of weld time, the contact re-

Table 7. Suggested Minimum Joint Overlap, Weld Spacing and Distance Between Rows for Resistance Spot Welds in Aluminum Alloys

Thickness of thinnest sheet, in.	Minimum joint overlap, in.(a)	Minimum weld spacing, in.(b)	Minimum distance between rows, in.(c)
0.016	5/16	3/8	1/4
0.020	3/8	3/8	1/4
0.025	3/8	3/8	5/16
0.032	1/2	1/2	5/16
0.040	9/16	1/2	3/8
0.051	5/8	5/8	3/8
0.064	3/4	5/8	3/8
0.072	13/16	3/4	7/16
0.081	7/8	3/4	1/2
0.091	15/16	7/8	1/2
0.102	1	1	1/2
0.125	1⅛	1¼	5/8

(a) Minimum edge distance is equal to one half of minimum overlap. (b) Measured from center to center. (c) For rows of staggered welds at minimum weld spacing. [Source of table: Same as Table 1]

sistance is decreased excessively, and welds may be unsound. If forging force is applied too late, after the weld has solidified, forging will be ineffective.

Spacing of Spot Welds. When rows of spot welds are made, each successive weld can be affected by shunting of part of the welding current through the preceding welds. The shunting effect increases as spot spacing, work-metal thickness and electrical resistance of the alloy being welded decrease. Also, the shunting effect increases as the contact resistance between the workpieces increases.

In order to eliminate most of the shunting effect, the minimum spacing of spot welds made in aluminum alloy sheets normally should be no less than eight times the sheet thickness (8t), and preferably not less than the values given in Table 7. Where it is necessary to space welds at less than 8t, the current can be increased after making the first spot weld to offset the loss from shunting. An alternative is to use two or more rows of spot welds with the welds in each row spaced apart by at least 8t. Table 7 gives the suggested minimum distance between rows of staggered spot welds.

If a spot weld is made too close to the edge of a workpiece, the metal between the weld and the edge may bulge out or split, and molten metal may be expelled from the joint. The minimum distance a spot weld should be from the edge of a workpiece is one half the minimum joint overlap given in Table 7. If more than a single row of spot welds is made, the minimum overlap must be increased by the distance between rows.

Welding Practice. Use of the welding conditions given in Tables 4, 5 and 6 should produce welds having shear strengths exceeding those given in Table 1. Larger welds with proportionately higher shear strengths sometimes can be obtained with stored-energy equipment. Smaller welds with strengths lower than those given in Table 1 should be avoided. Settings that result in small-diameter welds in aluminum are likely to cause a substantial percentage of unacceptable welds under production conditions.

Although the welding conditions given in Tables 4, 5 and 6 are good starting points, optimum conditions must be determined by making and testing welds in sample setups of the job, and adjusting the given conditions accordingly. During production, it is necessary to test welds frequently to ensure that optimum conditions are maintained.

Welding conditions optimum for a specific application may vary substantially from those given in Tables 4, 5 and 6. For instance, in welding a 0.102-in.-thick handle flange to a 0.125-in.-thick frying pan (Fig. 3), both made of alloy 3003, using a three-phase frequency converter welding machine, an electrode force of 1440 lb was used and a welding current of 70,000 amp was applied in two 5-cycle weld pulses separated by a 2-cycle off time for cooling the electrodes. With these conditions, output was 600 assemblies in 8 hours.

In welding workpieces of unequal thickness, the thinner workpiece governs the welding conditions that should be used and the diameter of the resulting nugget.

Three or more thicknesses of aluminum alloy can be spot welded simultaneously. Conductivity of the alloy welded and thickness of the outside sheets govern the choice of machine settings. Because of the added resistance of the additional interfaces, electrode pressures are higher than those used for welding two sheets.

When spot welded aluminum assemblies must have smooth outer surfaces for purposes of aerodynamics or appearance, a flat-face electrode can be used on one side of the joint and a radius-face electrode on the other. Indentation will occur primarily on the side that contacts the contoured electrode, but some indentation results from shrinkage of the nugget. However, higher joint strength usually is achieved when electrodes of the same contour are applied to both sides of the joint, provided that the sheet thicknesses are about equal.

Preweld positioning of components by means of fixtures, clamps, spring fasteners or tack welds is recommended. Otherwise, some of the electrode force may be expended in bringing the components into contact, thus affecting the quality of the weld, especially if the effective electrode force varies. Mating parts should fit together so that the surfaces to be joined are in contact with each other, or can be readily pressed into contact with each other, at the weld area. All tooling that is in the throat of the machine during the welding operation should be nonmagnetic; aluminum, fiberglass and various types of plastics are often used.

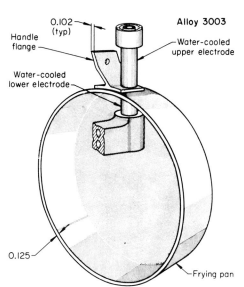

Fig. 3. Spot welding of a handle flange to an aluminum alloy frying pan

In the following example of spot welding for a military application, both fixturing and welding procedures were critical. In this example, as in spot welding of the frying pan shown in Fig. 3, the welding conditions finally selected differed substantially from those given in Tables 4 and 5.

Example 419. Resistance Spot Welding of Truck-Door Frames Using Both Press-Type and Portable Equipment (Fig. 4)

Structural frames for doors of military truck-tractors were made of alloy 6061-T6 extrusions and alloy 6061-T4 sheet, all 0.090 in. thick (see Fig. 4). The truck-tractors were designed to float in water through buoyancy of the all-aluminum cab, and the die-formed and unmachined mating surfaces between door and cab had to be accurately aligned to make watertight joints. Welding the heat treated and cold worked aluminum alloy gave rise to distortion difficulties, because the welding heat relieved high residual stresses. Welded construction was necessary, however, to meet the production demand of 400 frames per week.

A typical frame was held together by mechanical fasteners, as well as by welds at seven major joints. Five of the joints were resistance spot welded, by two different methods. The two other joints were gas metal-arc welded, as described in Example 303, in the article on Arc Welding of Aluminum Alloys.

Cleaning for both methods of spot welding was the same; proprietary cleaners and oxide-removal solutions were applied to reduce the electrical resistance of joint surfaces to a range of 150 to 250 microhms. Prior to welding, the surfaces were wiped with oxide-removal solution.

Each of two corner brackets was attached to the extruded frame with four spot welds, as shown in detail A in Fig. 4. The brackets, aligned in a hand-held fixture, were welded in a press-type spot welding machine under the conditions given in the table with Fig. 4.

Then the subassembly was removed from the hand-held fixture and was placed in a floor fixture for the addition of two braces. A portable spot welding gun was used to weld a joint between the two braces and to weld two of four joints between the braces and the frame. The locations of the 11 spot welds at these joints are shown in the views at right in Fig. 4. Welding conditions for this operation are given in the table with Fig. 4.

Toggle clamps were used to hold the braces in alignment in the floor fixture, as shown in Fig. 4, and to prevent distortion of the formed outer-frame extrusion. A mandrel was inserted in one leg of the outer frame to serve as an alignment reference for the assembly.

Both the press-type welding machine and the portable gun had controls that enabled

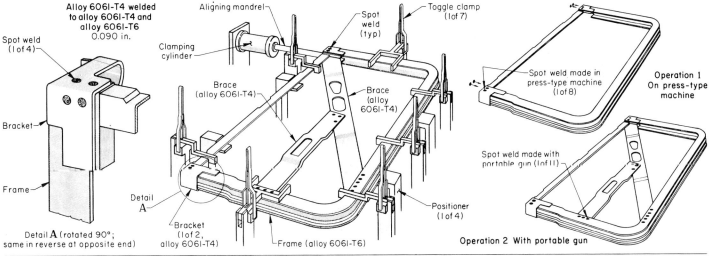

Item	Welding of brackets	Welding of braces	Item	Welding of brackets	Welding of braces
Equipment Details			**Conditions for Resistance Spot Welding**		
Welding machine	Press type, 440 v, 60 cycle, 3-phase freq. converter(a)	Heavy-duty portable, 440 v, 60 cycle, single-phase(b)	Welding current, amp	46,980	36,200
Transformer	Series-parallel, no tap switch	Series-parallel, 4-step tap switch	Transformer connection	Parallel	Parallel and No. 4 tap
Rating at 50% duty cycle ..	100 kva	250 kva	Heat-control setting, %	87	90
Welding controls	Synchronous, full and half cycle(c); phase-shift heat control	Nonsynchronous solid state, with slope control	Electrode force, lb	1200	1000
			Squeeze time, cycles	20	12
			Weld time, cycles	3	25
Electrodes	RWMA class 1, 7/8-in. diam, type F face (4-in. radius)	RWMA class 1, 5/8-in. diam, type F face (4-in. radius)	Hold time, cycles	25	12
			Nugget diameter, in.	0.25	0.25
			Weld spacing (approx), in. ..	1.5	1.5

(a) With 30-in. throat, air-operated low-inertia head, and electrode-dressing pressure. (b) With 6-in. throat, and electrode-dressing pressure. (c) Unipolarity and alternate polarity.

Fig. 4. Truck-door frame that was fabricated by resistance spot welding of brackets in a press-type machine, and by resistance spot welding of braces (using the fixturing shown) with a portable gun (Example 419)

the electrodes to be re-dressed in the machine, using a low-pressure contact on a paddle-type electrode dresser. The electrodes used in the press-type welding machine were dressed after making 80 to 100 welds, and those in the portable gun were dressed after 40 to 70 welds.

The order in which spot welds are made in a multiple-weld assembly is important in controlling warpage of the assembly and maintaining the strength of the spots. Making a spot weld produces slight lateral expansion of the work metal, and therefore spot welding preferably should be started from the center of the sheet and made in succession at the desired spacing toward the ends. Additional spot welds should not be made between two existing welds because shunting through adjacent spot welds could result in poor welds; also, expansion or warpage could prevent good contact of the sheets during welding. If three or more rows of welds are being made, the center row or rows should be made first.

Roll Resistance Spot Welding

Roll resistance spot welds can be made in conventional seam welding machines either with continuously rotating electrode wheels or with intermittent-motion electrode wheels. With intermittent motion, better surface appearance and better weld quality are obtained in welding aluminum alloys. Weld spacing is obtained by proper adjustment of electrode speed, or indexing time, and of the hold time. The individual roll resistance spot welds are essentially the same as resistance spot welds made in the conventional manner, except that shorter hold times are employed. With continuously rotating electrode wheels, heat times are usually shorter than those normally used for spot welding. The high current employed sometimes requires the use of high electrode force. Also, nuggets made by continuously rotating electrode wheels are usually elongated because of electrode travel.

Extruded or roll-formed sections frequently are roll spot welded to sheets. For instance, 0.060-in.-thick alloy 2024-T3 roll-formed Z-sections were attached to 0.060-in.-thick alloy 2024-T3 sheets to serve as stiffeners (see Fig. 5). The electrode wheels were stationary during welding (intermittent motion), and the electrode force was increased from 1500 lb for welding to 3600 lb for forging the nugget as it contracted during cooling, thereby producing high-quality, crack-free welds. The weld current of 55,000 amp was supplied from a 60-cycle three-phase frequency-converter welding machine in a single impulse of 2 cycles of heat time and 6 cycles of current decay. The 6-cycle current-decay time was an advantage because it served to decrease the cooling rate of the weld.

Resistance Seam Welding

The overlapping spot welds produced in resistance seam welding result in a continuous gastight and liquid-tight seam. The welding current can be applied either when the wheels are moving or while they stop momentarily.

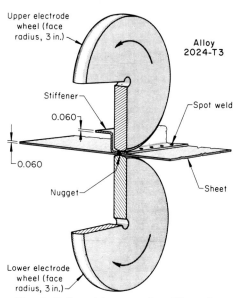

Fig. 5. Roll resistance spot welding of a Z-section longitudinal stiffener to a sheet, using intermittent electrode motion, a welding force and a forging force

Intermittent motion results in better surface appearance and better weld quality in aluminum alloys, and is ordinarily used for work of military quality when the work metal being seam welded is 0.080 in. or more in thickness.

Seam welding of aluminum alloys with continuously rotating electrodes was used in the assembly of the integral leading-edge wing fuel tank shown in Fig. 6. In this application, 0.040-in.-thick alloy 6061-T6 sheet was joined to 0.081-in.-thick alloy 2014-T6 clad sheet. Nylon rollers were used for guiding and supporting the workpieces and for easily moving the assembly between the electrode wheels without marring the work-metal surface. The welding force was 2800 lb. The weld current of 58,000 amp was supplied from a three-phase frequency-converter welding machine in a single impulse of 2 cycles preheat time and 4 cycles heat time, with 6 cycles cool time. The overlapping spot welds were made 12 to the inch at a rate of 25 in. per minute.

Typical conditions for seam welding alloy 5052-H34 using a conventional single-phase direct-energy seam welding machine are given in Table 8. Data in this table also can be used as a basis for developing conditions for welding other alloys or tempers. The maximum heat time should be between one fifth and one third the total time. Use of a heat time shorter than one fifth the total time helps to reduce electrode pickup, but also reduces nugget size. Electrode force, welding current, heat time, cool time and welding speed are adjusted to produce the desired spacing and weld width. Width of a seam weld should be twice the thickness of the sheet being welded plus 0.06 in. $(2t + 0.06 \text{ in.})$.

Quality control for seam welding is the same as for spot welding except that an additional test, such as the pillow test, may be required for determining gastightness or liquid-tightness.

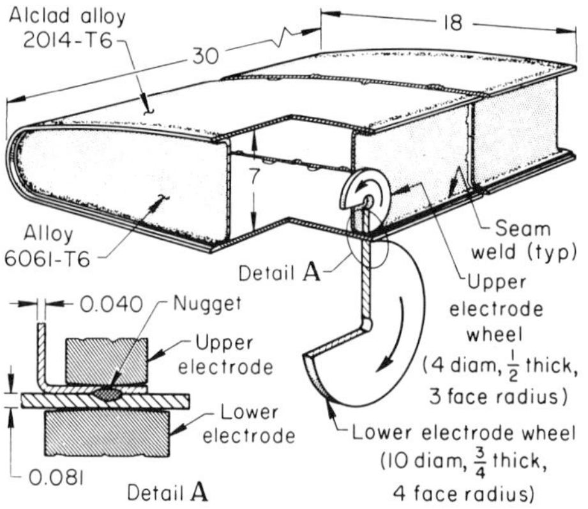

Projection Welding

Aluminum alloys are seldom projection welded, because extremely close control is needed in order to produce acceptable welds. Embossed projections like those used in low-carbon steel sheet, if made in aluminum alloy sheet, would collapse prematurely, and therefore are not used. Projections that have been coined in aluminum alloy workpieces are stronger and better able to resist collapse than are embossed projections, and are preferred.

Because of the narrow plastic range of aluminum alloys, the quality of projection welds is less uniform than that of spot welds of equivalent size.

Cross-Wire Welding

Aluminum alloy wires, round and in other shapes, can be cross-wire welded to make racks, grills or screens. Press-type resistance spot welding machines with low-inertia heads and fast follow-up are needed to maintain proper welding force on the joint as the wires deform and melt. Each cross-wire weld must be made individually; multiple-wire welding with bar electrodes has been unsatisfactory on aluminum alloys.

Selection of alloy and temper is the same as for spot welding. All aluminum alloy wires from about $\frac{1}{16}$ to $\frac{3}{8}$ in. in diameter can be cross-wire welded. Wires of equal diameters, or of unequal diameters in ratios up to 2 to 1, are readily weldable. Low-strength ring-type welds can result if the ratio of wire diameters is greater than 2 to 1.

Wire can be welded to a tube if the thickness of the tube wall is equal to or greater than the diameter of the wire. Wire can be welded to extruded aluminum alloy angles, or to other structural shapes, that have elongated projections extending at right angles to the wire direction. For optimum results, the cross-sectional radius of the projection should be approximately equal to the radius of the wire.

Optimum welding conditions are established by twist tests and by measuring setdown. Twist tests are made by twisting the wires so as to tear the area between wires. Tests of properly made cross-wire welds usually result in base-metal fracture outside the weld.

Setdown is the difference in the combined height of both wires before

Alloy 6061-T6 welded to alclad alloy 2014-T6

Fig. 6. Resistance seam welding of an aircraft integral wing fuel tank, using continuous electrode motion

Table 8. Typical Conditions for Making Gastight Resistance Seam Welds in Alloy 5052-H34 Sheets With 60-Cycle Single-Phase Direct-Energy Welding Machines(a)

Sheet thickness, in.	Spots per inch	Total weld time, cycles(b)	Wheel speed, fpm(c)	Heat time, cycles(d) Min	Max	Electrode force, lb(e)	Welding current, amp(e)	Width of weld, in.
0.010	25	3½	3.4	½	1	420	19,500	0.08
0.016	21	3½	4.1	½	1	500	22,000	0.09
0.020	20	4½	3.3	½	1½	540	24,000	0.10
0.025	18	5½	3.0	1	1½	600	26,000	0.11
0.032	16	5½	3.4	1	1½	690	29,000	0.13
0.040	14	7½	2.9	1½	2½	760	32,000	0.14
0.051	12	9½	2.6	1½	3	860	36,000	0.16
0.064	10	11½	2.6	2	3½	960	38,500	0.19
0.081	9	15½	2.1	3	5	1090	41,000	0.22
0.102	8	20½	1.8	4	6½	1230	43,000	0.26
0.125	7	28½	1.5	5½	9½	1350	45,000	0.32

(a) Electrode wheels and work metal must be cooled with 2 to 3 gallons of water per minute. (b) Heat time plus cool time. (c) Wheel speed is adjusted to give desired number of spots per inch. (d) Heat time must be set at full-cycle setting if total time is set at full-cycle setting. (e) Electrode force and welding current are adjusted to give desired width of weld. Values are for 5052-H34 aluminum alloy. Lower forces should be used for 5052-O and 3003-H14 aluminum alloys. [Source of table: Same as Table 1]

and after welding. For joints between wires of equal diameter, setdown should be 25 to 35% of the combined height before welding. For joints between wires of unequal diameter, setdown should be 25 to 35% of twice the diameter of the smaller wire. The quality of cross-wire welds is usually consistent when, during a production run, the variation in setdown does not exceed ±5% of the nominal value.

Flash Welding

All wrought aluminum alloys can be joined by flash welding. The process is particularly suitable for making butt and miter joints between two workpieces of similar cross-sectional shape. Aluminum alloy bars and tubes can be flash welded to copper bars and tubes.

Machines for flash welding of aluminum alloys require much larger transformer capacity than is needed for flash welding of steel. For best results, the welding machine must be capable of supplying a current density of 100,000 amp per sq in. while the workpieces are held in firm contact, without arcing. A secondary voltage of 2 to 20 v is required. Upsetting pressures are 8,000 to 40,000 psi.

Copper alloy clamping dies, RWMA classes 1 and 2, are used when flash welding aluminum alloys if a long die life is required. Hard-drawn copper may be used instead if a limited number of pieces are to be welded.

Initial die spacing varies according to work-metal thickness. About ⅛ in. of initial die spacing is suitable for thin-wall tubing and for thin sheets or extrusions, and about 1 in. is needed for flash welding a ¾-in.-diam bar.

Pinch-off dies provide the best weld quality in flash welding of aluminum alloys. These dies are made of hardened steel and are sharpened to a cutting edge. They are used to trim the upset metal or flash from the joint at the end of the upsetting stroke.

For additional information, see the article on Flash Welding, page 485 in this volume. Examples 432 and 434 in that article present applications of flash welding of aluminum alloys.

Inspection and Testing

Peel, twist or tear tests are common methods of determining the quality of resistance welds made in aluminum alloys. To meet commercial requirements, a button of metal having a diameter at least twice the thickness of the thinnest workpiece plus 0.06 in. ($2t + 0.06$ in.) should be pulled from one of the workpieces at each weld. To meet military standards, the button diameter should be equal to or exceed the nugget diameter given in Tables 4, 5 and 6. Spot welds in aluminum alloys 2014, 2024, 6061 and 7075, either bare or clad, will not always pull buttons completely through the sheet when the work-metal thickness is greater than about 0.080 in. In these alloys and metal thicknesses, the weld is peel tested and the diameter of the fractured area is determined.

When peel testing indicates that welds of the proper size are being produced, test welds can be made for use in determining shear strength. Welds also can be sectioned for metallographic examination to determine nugget diameter, penetration and microstructure. Radiographic examination can be used to determine the soundness of test welds.

During production, visual examination can be used to detect electrode pickup, surface burning, cracks, skidding, expulsion of molten metal, and excessive indentation. Radiographic inspection can, in some alloys, be used to detect internal defects such as cracks, porosity, and segregation, and to evaluate the size and shape of the nugget and the structure of the weld metal. In general, radiographic examination is used principally in the establishment of optimum welding conditions, and not as a production-control method. Other inspection methods sometimes used are eddy current, ultrasonic and sonic.

Indentation of the base metal can be determined by measuring the thickness of the weld with ball-tip micrometers, or by determining the difference in height between the weld and the surrounding area using a dial-indicator depth gage. Sheet separation can be measured with feeler gages.

Causes and Prevention of Weld Defects

Resistance weld defects most common in aluminum alloys include electrode pickup, cracks and porosity, expulsion of molten metal, indentation and sheet separation, and irregular-shape and unfused welds.

Electrode pickup, or alloying of the work metal with the electrode material, is usually the result of excessive heating at the interface between the electrode and the work metal. In severe cases, there is actual melting or burning of the work-metal surface.

Electrode pickup can be minimized by using adequate electrode force during welding, or by not using excessive welding current or weld time. Pickup may be caused by improper cleaning of work metal or electrodes, by use of improper electrode material, size, or contour, by inadequate cooling of the electrodes, or by skidding. Electrode pickup can occur with all types of welding equipment, but it usually occurs sooner when welding is done with the use of single-phase alternating-current equipment.

Cracks and porosity in the weld metal may result from too-rapid heating of the weld metal, an excessively high cooling rate, or inadequate or incorrect application of electrode force during or after welding. Spot welds in some high-strength alloys such as 2024 and 7075 are subject to cracking if welding current is too high or electrode force during welding is too low. Cracking may also result from too-rapid quenching of the weld metal after the welding current has been turned off. Changes in the downslope of the current or the use of postheating may eliminate cracking. On machines with dual electrode force, readjustment of the forge-starting time may also eliminate cracking.

Expulsion of molten metal from the weld area by flashing or arcing can usually be eliminated by use of better cleaning methods or by a slight reduction in welding current. Another cause of expulsion is an initial electrode force that is too low, followed by excessive forging pressure.

Indentation and sheet separation generally occur together. One of the major causes of these defects is the use of work metal of too soft a temper. These defects sometimes can be minimized by decreasing the electrode force, increasing the face radius of the electrode, or reducing the welding current or time. Sheet separation also can be caused by lack of flatness of the sheets being welded.

Welds with irregular shape and incomplete fusion are caused by incorrect fit-up of workpieces, incorrect electrode alignment, skidding of the electrodes, inadequate surface preparation, or an irregular electrode contour.

Inadequately fused welds in clad sheet may have some unfused cladding metal in the nugget. This defect can usually be avoided by a moderate increase in welding current.

Burning of holes through the workpieces can result from: (a) insufficient electrode force to squeeze the metal effectively; (b) the presence of foreign material such as paper or steel wool between the workpieces; (c) emery dust or emery cloth adhering to one or both electrodes; and (d) attempts to spot weld at points where there are screws, projections, or drilled holes. If none of these appear to be the cause of the difficulty, the welding machine and its controls should be inspected.

Brazing of Aluminum Alloys

BRAZING of aluminum alloys was made possible by the discovery of fluxes that disrupt the oxide film on aluminum without harming the underlying metal, and by the development of filler metals (aluminum alloys) with suitable melting ranges and other properties.

The aluminum-base filler metals used for brazing aluminum alloys have liquidus temperatures much closer to the solidus temperature of the base metal than do those for brazing most other metals. For this reason, close temperature control is required in brazing aluminum. The brazing temperature should be approximately 70 F below the solidus temperature of the base metal, but if temperature is accurately controlled and the brazing cycle is short, it can be as close as 10 F. Aluminum alloys, depending on composition, can be brazed with commercial filler metals from 1020 to 1180 F. Most brazing is done at temperatures between 1040 and 1140 F.

Much of the equipment and many of the techniques used to prepare, braze and inspect aluminum alloys are the same as those used for other metals; the reader may refer to the articles on Furnace Brazing, Torch Brazing, Resistance Brazing and Dip Brazing of Steel in Molten Salt in this volume for general information.

Base Metals

The non-heat-treatable wrought alloys that have been brazed most successfully are the 1xxx and 3xxx series, and low-magnesium members of the 5xxx series. The alloys containing a higher magnesium content are more difficult to braze by the usual flux methods, because of poor wetting by filler metal and excessive penetration. Filler metals are available that melt below the solidus temperatures of most commercial wrought non-heat-treatable alloys.

Of the heat treatable wrought alloys, those most commonly brazed are the 6xxx series. The 2xxx and 7xxx series of aluminum alloys are low melting and, therefore, not normally brazeable, with the exception of 7072 (used as a cladding material only) and 7005.

Alloys that have a solidus above 1100 F are easily brazed with commercial binary aluminum-silicon filler metals. Stronger, lower-melting alloys can be brazed with proper attention to filler-metal selection and temperature control, but the brazing cycle must be short to minimize penetration by the molten filler metal. Sand and perma-

nent mold casting alloys with a high solidus temperature are brazeable; the most commonly brazed are 43, 356 and 612. Formerly, aluminum die castings were not brazed because of blistering due to high gas content, but recent advances in casting technique have resulted in improved quality.

Some common wrought and cast aluminum alloys, along with their melting temperature ranges and brazeability ratings, are listed in Table 1.

Brazing of aluminum is generally limited to parts more than 0.015 in. thick, but dip brazing and fluxless vac-

uum brazing have been done successfully on aluminum as thin as 0.006 in.

Filler Metals

Commercial filler metals for brazing aluminum are aluminum-silicon alloys containing 7 to 12% Si. Lower melting points are attained, with some sacrifice in resistance to corrosion, by adding copper and zinc. The compositions and melting ranges of the most commonly used brazing filler metals for aluminum are given in Table 2.

The optimum brazing-temperature range for an aluminum-base filler metal not only is determined by the melting range of the filler metal and by the amount of molten filler metal needed to fill the joint, but also is limited by the mutual solubility between the filler metal and the base metal being brazed. The brazing-temperature ranges of some filler metals are related to those of some base metals in Fig. 1.

Filler metals to be applied separately from the base metal to be brazed are available as wire and sheet (thin-gage shim stock). The manufacture of filler metal in sheet and wire forms becomes more difficult as the silicon content increases. Only filler metals BAlSi-2 (alloy 4343), BAlSi-4 (alloy 4047), and alloy X4003 are available as sheet.

Most filler metals are used for any of the common brazing processes and methods, but one (alloy X4003, which contains an addition of magnesium and has a brazing-temperature range of approximately 1110 to 1130 F) has been developed exclusively for use in fluxless vacuum brazing. Another, a proprietary mixture of filler metal BAlSi-4 (alloy 4047) in powder form and a chemical compound, is used exclusively with dip

Table 1. Melting Ranges and Brazeability of Some Common Aluminum Alloys

Alloy	Melting range, F	Brazeability(a)
Non-Heat-Treatable Wrought Alloys		
EC	1195 to 1215	A
1100	1190 to 1215	A
3003 (b)	1190 to 1210	A
3004	1165 to 1205	B
5005	1170 to 1205	B
5050	1160 to 1205	B
5052	1100 to 1200	C
Heat Treatable Wrought Alloys		
6053	1100 to 1205	A
6061	1100 to 1200	A
6063	1140 to 1210	A
6951 (c)	1140 to 1210	A
7005	1125 to 1200	B
Casting Alloys(d)		
43	1065 to 1170	B
356	1035 to 1135	B
A612	1105 to 1195	B
C612	1120 to 1190	A

(a) A, generally brazeable by all commercial procedures; B, brazeable with special techniques or in specific applications that justify preliminary trials or testing to develop the procedure and to check the performance of brazed joints; C, limited brazeability. (b) Used both plain and as the core of brazing sheet. (c) Used only as the core of brazing sheet. (d) Sand and permanent mold castings only.

Figures 1 through 8, Tables 4, 7 and 8, portions of Tables 2 and 3, and much of the text of this article are based on Chapter 13, by M. A. Miller and A. S. Russell, in Volume III of "Aluminum", American Society for Metals, 1967, p 487-524. Examples and other information were contributed by members of various Metals Handbook welding and brazing committees. The manuscript was reviewed by the ASM Committee on Welding of Aluminum Alloys.

Table 2. Compositions and Melting Ranges of Brazing Filler Metals for Use on Aluminum Alloys

AWS-ASTM class	Alloy	Product form	Principal alloying elements, %				Approximate melting range, F
			Si	Cu	Mg	Zn	
BAlSi-2	4343	Sheet, cladding	7.5	...	...	...	1070 to 1135
BAlSi-3	4145	Wire, flattened wire	10	4	...	...	970 to 1085
BAlSi-4	4047	Wire, sheet	12	...	...	...	1070 to 1080
BAlSi-5	4045	Cladding	10	...	...	...	1070 to 1095
...	X4003	Wire, sheet, cladding	7.5	...	2.5	...	1010 to 1110
...	4245	Wire	10	4	...	10	960 to 1040

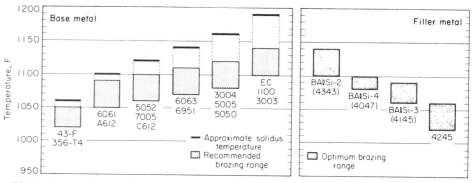

Fig. 1. *Brazing-temperature ranges of some aluminum alloy base metals compared with those of four aluminum alloy brazing filler metals*

Table 3. Compositions and Brazing-Temperature Ranges of Aluminum Brazing Sheets

Brazing sheet(a)	Sides clad	Core alloy	Cladding alloy	Cladding on each side, % of sheet thickness	Optimum brazing range, F
X3	2	3003	X4003	15% for 0.024 in. and less 10% from 0.025 in. to 0.062 in. 7½% for 0.063 in. and over	1120 to 1130 ... ...
11	1	3003	4343	10% for 0.063 in. and less 5% for 0.064 in. and over	1100 to 1140 ...
12	2	3003	4343	10% for 0.063 in. and less 5% for 0.064 in. and over	1100 to 1140 ...
X5	2	6951	X4003	15% for 0.024 in. and less 10% from 0.025 in. to 0.062 in. 7½% for 0.063 in. and over	1110 to 1115 ... ...
21	1	6951	4343	10% for 0.090 in. and less 5% for 0.091 in. and over	1100 to 1120 ...
22	2	6951	4343	10% for 0.090 in. and less 5% for 0.091 in. and over	1100 to 1120 ...
23	1	6951	4045	10% for 0.090 in. and less 5% for 0.091 in. and over	1080 to 1120 ...
24	2	6951	4045	10% for 0.090 in. and less 5% for 0.091 in. and over	1080 to 1120 ...

(a) Designations registered with the Aluminum Association

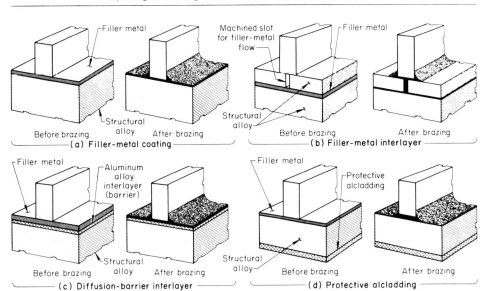

Fig. 2. Four types of aluminum brazing sheet, shown in joints with a vertical member

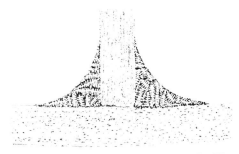

Fig. 3. Section showing fillets obtained with 0.040-in.-thick No. 22 brazing sheet as the vertical member in a T-joint with alloy 3003 as the horizontal member. Keller's etch. 15×.

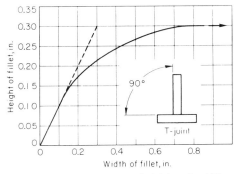

Fig. 4. Relation between height and width of fillets obtained in 90° T-joints with 0.040-in.-thick No. 22 brazing sheet as the vertical member and alloy 3003 as the horizontal member

brazing. This mixture can be brushed or extruded onto the joints and can be applied to parts in all positions. The mixture stays in place because it is baked onto the metal surface during preheating. It may be employed in brazing overhead joints in wave-guide assemblies and in applications where a small, controlled flow of aluminum alloy filler metal is desired.

Brazing Sheet

Brazing sheet consists essentially of one or more coatings or interlayers of filler metal (usually an aluminum-silicon alloy) roll bonded to one or more sheets of structural aluminum alloy. Brazing sheet provides a more convenient method of supplying the filler metal than wire, shims or powder; it is particularly convenient for mass-produced, complex assemblies. However, the choice to use brazing sheet instead of filler metal in other forms is based on cost in a given application. Brazing sheet can be subjected to drawing, bending or any other forming process that does not break the bond between the filler metal and the structural alloy that compose the sheet.

Four types of brazing sheet are shown in Fig. 2. The most common type (Fig. 2a) has filler metal on one or both sides. The compositions and brazing-temperature ranges of commercially available brazing sheets of this type are listed in Table 3.

The three other types of brazing sheet shown in Fig. 2 are available only on special order. The type shown in Fig. 2(b) has structural alloy sheets on both sides of an interlayer of filler metal; a slot is machined into the structural alloy sheet on the joint side, to permit flow of filler metal. The brazing sheet shown in Fig. 2(c) has an interlayer of aluminum alloy to act as a diffusion barrier between the high-silicon filler metal and the core sheet of structural alloy (see discussion headed "Silicon Diffusion", on page 678). The brazing sheet shown in Fig. 2(d) has filler metal on the joint side of the structural alloy and is alclad, for corrosion resistance, on the opposite side.

The structural alloys commonly used in brazing sheet are 3003, which is resistant to sagging at brazing temperatures, and 6951, which is heat treatable after brazing and is used where higher strength is desired. Some of the commercially available filler metals are used as cladding of brazing sheet.

Fluxes

Conventional brazing, performed in air or other oxygen-containing atmosphere, requires the use of a chemical flux. Fluxes, which become active before brazing temperature is reached, and which are molten over the entire brazing range, penetrate the film of oxide, exclude air, and promote wetting of the base metal by the filler metal. A satisfactory flux must (a) begin to melt at a temperature low enough to minimize oxidation of the parts, (b) be essentially molten at the time the filler metal melts, (c) flow over the joint and the filler metal to shield them from oxidizing gases, (d) penetrate the oxide films, (e) lower the surface tension between the solid and liquid metals to encourage wetting, (f) remain liquid until the filler metal has solidified, and (g) be relatively easy to remove after brazing is complete.

A superior flux for furnace and torch brazing will melt at a temperature only slightly lower than the melting temperature of the filler metal, ensuring uniform wetting and flow of filler alloy in minimum time. A flux to be used as a dip brazing bath is compounded to be molten and stable at the melting temperature of the filler metal. In addition, a flux for use in dip brazing should form only minimum quantities of solid particles or sludge that sink to the bottom of the bath or collect in joint interstices. Since the parts are totally immersed in flux during dip brazing and oxygen cannot reach the surfaces of the parts to re-form oxide, less active fluxes can be employed for dip brazing than for torch or furnace brazing. Physical properties of typical fluxes are given in Table 4.

Fluxes for use in brazing aluminum alloys usually consist of mixtures of alkali and alkaline earth chlorides and fluorides, sometimes containing aluminum fluoride or cryolite ($3NaF \cdot AlF_3$). The compositions are adjusted to give a favorable balance between melting range, density, chemical activity, etching characteristics, and cost. Small amounts of one or more of the chlorides of antimony, cadmium, chromium, cobalt, copper, iron, lead, manganese, nickel, silicon, tin, zinc, precious metals, or rare earths improve the performance of fluxes. Absence of fluoride prevents effective oxide removal, but too high a concentration results in an undesirably high melting range.

Flux is received in dry powder form in sealed, moistureproof containers. It can be stored for long periods if the seal is maintained. Once a flux container is opened, the utmost care must be taken to prevent contamination of the flux. Flux containers should be of perfectly clean aluminum, glass or earthenware — *never* of steel.

Aluminum brazing fluxes can be applied dry, or they can be mixed with tap water or alcohol and be applied by painting, spraying or dipping. Dry flux can be sprinkled on the work, or a heated filler rod can be dipped into the dry flux. Although flux can be mixed with tap water to form a paste, the use of alcohol may be preferred in some applications. Where vapor pressure from drying flux may cause dislocation of the filler metal or the assembly, the use of alcohol will minimize this effect.

Although 45 minutes can be considered as the maximum time lapse between the application of flux and subsequent brazing, it is recommended that the flux be applied immediately prior to brazing. When wet flux mixtures are used, they should be freshly prepared (at least once in each shift).

The wetting action of a flux can be improved considerably by the use of a wetting agent. A mixture of two-thirds flux and one-third water by weight usually is satisfactory for painting. Spraying or dipping will require a thinner consistency with more water being added. The amount of water needed to suit the spray gun used is best determined by trial.

Flux Stop-Offs. Sometimes it is desirable to take positive action to prevent filler metal from flowing beyond a certain area. Stop-offs suitable for this purpose usually consist of a mixture of equal parts by weight of a medium-heavy engine oil (SAE 30), finely powdered graphite, and benzene or naphtha (mineral spirits). Often, a mark made by a soft graphite pencil is an effective stop-off. Proprietary, commercial stop-off compounds are also available. Some of these may be applied in paste form without being baked, and later may be removed by brushing.

Furnace and dip brazing frequently require the use of a stop-off to prevent the jigs and fixtures from being brazed to the work. The mixture is brushed or sprayed on the areas to be stopped off and then baked at 400 to 600 F to carbonize the oil. One application will usually last for several brazing cycles. Stop-offs for fluxless vacuum brazing are usually refractory oxides, which are sprayed on the jigs and fixtures, or are formed on them by heating to high temperature in an air atmosphere.

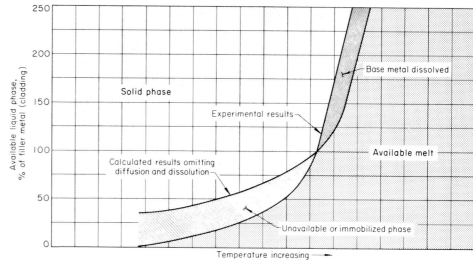

Fig. 5. *Effect of temperature on availability of liquid phase from aluminum brazing sheet. See text for discussion.*

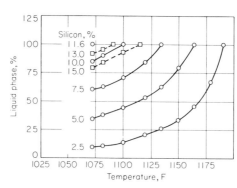

Fig. 6. *Effect of temperature and silicon content on percentage of liquid phase available, for aluminum-silicon alloys (calculated)*

Such coatings generally last until mechanically damaged. In torch brazing, the use of stop-offs is not required, because the operator has adequate control over the flow of filler metal.

Fillet Formation

The major requirement of brazing is to adjust conditions so that gravity and capillarity cause molten brazing filler metal to flow through the full length of the joint and form fillets. The effects of gravity are often influenced by the buoyant action of molten flux, as in dip brazing. The density of the molten flux is usually only slightly less than that of molten filler metal.

In an inert gas or in vacuum, the surface tension of some aluminum brazing alloys is about 850 dynes per centimeter; in the presence of a brazing flux, it is about 650 dynes per centimeter. The addition of metallic wetting agents, such as the magnesium that is alloyed in X4003 filler metal, will effectively lower the surface tension to the range of 500 to 700 dynes per centimeter, without the presence of a brazing flux.

The microsection shown in Fig. 3, taken through a T-joint in which the vertical member was No. 22 brazing sheet (both sides clad with filler metal), shows the two fillets of filler metal to have the shape of almost perfect arcs of a circle. In an experiment on T-

Table 4. Physical Properties of Typical Fluxes for Brazing Aluminum Alloys

Property of flux	Dip brazing (Flux 33)	Torch and furnace brazing (Flux 34)
Solidus temperature, F	900	915
Liquidus temperature, F	1035	1115
Density at 1100 F, lb per cu ft	104	107
Specific heat, Btu per lb per °F (approximate)	0.2	(a)
Heat of fusion, Btu per lb (approximate)	168	(a)
Heat requirement, Btu to heat 1 lb of flux from solid at 70 F to liquid at 1150 F (approximate)	385	(a)
Resistivity, ohm-cm at:		
1080 F	0.43	(a)
1130 F	0.36	(a)
1150 F	0.33	(a)
1180 F	0.29	(a)

(a) These properties are not pertinent to torch and furnace brazing.

joints of this kind, fillet heights and widths were measured; the results are plotted in Fig. 4. As Fig. 4 shows, fillet heights and widths were equal up to approximately 0.15 in.; beyond that point, as the width increased, the height approached a maximum value of 0.30 in., which agrees with the value calculated from the surface tension.

In another experiment, T-joints in which the *horizontal* member was brazing sheet, clad on the joint side with filler metal, were heated to various temperatures, and the amount of flow of filler metal was measured. The results are shown in Fig. 5, together with the results of calculations based on the known character of the filler metal. These experimental data show that at a certain temperature, 100% of the filler metal (cladding) will flow. This is the point at which the dissolution of the base metal by the filler metal is equal to the absorption of filler metal by the base metal. As the temperature rises above this point, the molten filler metal dissolves more base metal from the brazing sheet, causing an increase in the amount of molten phase until at the melting point of the base metal all of the brazing sheet is molten.

As the temperature is lowered from the point indicating 100% flow, more and more of the molten phase is immobilized by capillary forces in the increasing number of solid particles, and the flowability of the molten phase decreases. The temperature of 100% flow depends on composition and thickness of filler-metal cladding and base-metal core, specific flux used, type of joint to be brazed, length of the flow path, and time at temperature.

Figure 6 gives the calculated percentage of liquid phase available at several temperatures for aluminum-silicon filler-metal alloys of various silicon contents. The amount of liquid phase, of course, increases with silicon concentration up to the eutectic composition (11.6%), and with temperature. Although the eutectic composition at first appears to be optimum for filler metal, commercial practice usually employs a lower-silicon filler metal. This permits control of fillet size by temperature control, as the amount of filler metal melted depends on temperature. Figure 7 shows the amount of filler metal that flows from the interlayer of a sheet. Although from Fig. 6 all of an Al-10Si filler metal should be available for flow at 1100 F, only 25% flow was actually found in the experiment.

Silicon Diffusion. A limitation to the general application of brazing sheet is imposed by diffusion between the core metal and the coating of filler metal. Long heating times increase diffusion of silicon from the coating into the core, which can lower the mechanical properties of the core and can reduce the amount of filler metal available for flow. Figure 8 shows temperature and duration of heating for the production of 0.0005 and 0.0015-in. silicon-depleted zones in coatings of alloys Al-7.5Si and Al-12Si on brazing sheet. Brazing sheet clad with Al-7.5Si heated at 1040 F for 9 hr is shown as having a depleted zone of 0.0015 in. Thus, in theory, 0.015-in. No. 11 and 12 brazing sheets, which have a nominal cladding of 0.0015 in., could not be brazed if subjected to this temperature for this long a time, because all the silicon would have diffused into the core. When a No. 12 brazing sheet was heated for 3 hr at 1065 F, the measured thickness of the silicon-depleted zone was 0.0011 in. For Al-7.5Si cladding, Fig. 8 predicts 0.0014 in.

To restrict diffusion, the brazing cycle should be as short and at as low a temperature as possible. Core alloys must be selected to prevent formation of harmful intermetallic compounds. Under conditions where the core material is aggressively penetrated by the coating alloy, an intermediate protective layer of commercial-purity aluminum or of an alloy not easily penetrated by the coating can be used.

Joint Design

Joints to be brazed with the use of flux must be designed to permit application of the flux to the joint surfaces before assembly or to permit entry of the flux between the components after assembly. In addition, provision must be made for the flux to flow out; entrapped flux is a potential source of corrosion. Joint design must also permit the escape of gas and allow subsequent penetration by the filler

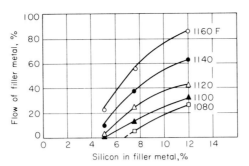

Fig. 7. Flow of filler metal from interlayer of brazing sheet (measured)

metal, and must ensure the complete distribution of filler metal in the joint. (See the section on Joint Fit and Design on page 607 in the article on Furnace Brazing.)

Assemblies to be brazed may be designed with many types of joints. For brazing processes that require a flux, joint strength equal to the strength of the base metal can be obtained with lap joints. The designs of six lap joints for brazing are contrasted with counterpart butt, T and corner joints used for welding in Fig. 31 in the article on Furnace Brazing (see page 610). Lap joints that require the filler metal to flow long distances should be designed so it flows in one direction only, because filler metal flowing from both edges of such joints may entrap flux. (The need for flow in joints having wide laps is nullified by using brazing sheet as one of the members.)

Butt and scarf joints will not usually be as strong as the base metal, but when correctly designed, such joints may give satisfactory service. For fluxless brazing processes, joints having narrow or line contact are preferred to joints having wide contact.

Joints of short length or line contacts are highly desirable during any aluminum brazing process, whether torch, furnace or dip. For long lap joints, corrugations can be used to provide an outlet for molten flux, and the final result is the same as when line contacts are used.

In joints for furnace and torch brazing, capillary rise is limited to about ¼ in. and must be considered in the design of the joint. In joints for dip brazing, capillary rise is seldom a limiting factor in design.

During brazing of aluminum, base metal and filler metal are mutually soluble. This causes the filler metal to change progressively in composition as it flows in joints, which progressively raises the liquidus temperature of the filler metal and reduces the ability of the filler metal to wet and flow. Clearances must be sufficient to prevent premature solidification of the filler metal in small capillary spaces, which entraps flux and causes porosity. The longer the distance the filler metal must flow, the greater the clearance must be.

In dip brazing with preplaced filler metal, joint clearance at room temperature ranging from 0.002 to 0.004 in. may suffice for narrow laps (¼ in. or less). Wider laps may require clearances up to 0.010 in. For furnace and torch brazing, clearance ranging from

0.004 to 0.010 in. is required for narrow laps (¼ in. or less), and as much as 0.025 in. for wider laps. With brazing sheet, clearances may be smaller. To ensure formation of a continuous fillet in fluxless vacuum brazing with brazing sheet, clearances normally should not exceed 0.003 in., but in some applications continuous fillets have been formed in joints with clearances as great as 0.009 in.

Tube-to-tube joints to be torch or furnace brazed require that the outer tube be flared 10° to 12° to produce sound joints. In joining fittings to a tube, knurling of the tube or fitting will permit complete penetration through the joint to be achieved.

When not employing brazing sheet, the correct preplacement of the filler metal is of utmost importance. Gravity is usually sufficient to keep the filler metal in place for fixed-position furnace brazing. In dip brazing, the filler may have to be held in place, because of the buoyancy of the molten flux.

Prebraze Cleaning

Oil and grease must be removed from components of assemblies to be brazed. For non-heat-treatable alloys, vapor or solvent cleaning is usually adequate, although chemical cleaning may be required for components that have been severely formed, as by spinning. For the heat treatable alloys, chemical cleaning is usually necessary, to reduce the amount of tenacious oxide film. (Chemical cleaning is not normally required for fluxless vacuum brazing.) Scrubbing with steel wool, abrasive cloth or a power-driven wire brush (preferably with stainless steel bristles) can also be used before brazing. Burrs should be removed before brazing.

Chemical cleaning methods used prior to brazing include nitric acid, hydrofluoric acid, or nitric-hydrofluoric acid mixtures at room temperature. A widely used method is immersion for about 30 sec in a solution containing equal parts of commercial nitric acid and water, followed by rinsing in clean water (preferably hot) and drying in hot air.

Aluminum-silicon alloys require a special etchant, because the silicon constituent is not attacked readily by many alkaline or acid solutions. For these alloys, a room-temperature solution of 3 parts concentrated nitric acid and 1 part concentrated hydrofluoric acid is employed. This solution requires a tank lined with an inert material such as carbon brick or certain types of plastic. The presence of fluorides necessitates caution in handling and special waste-disposal procedures. For thick and resistant oxide coatings, immersion for about 30 sec in a warm (150 F) aqueous solution of 5% sodium hydroxide is recommended. To remove the surface smut produced by this treatment, the treatment should be followed by a cold-water rinse, immersion in a room-temperature solution containing equal parts of commercial nitric acid and water, a final water rinse (preferably, hot), and hot-air drying.

Chemical cleaning of aluminum provides excellent surfaces for brazing. Cleaning in a caustic solution is particularly effective, although residues from caustic solutions can interfere with brazing — probably because of the large amounts of aluminum oxide formed. Nitric, sulfuric and phosphoric acid residues may prevent brazing entirely. To eliminate the possibility of harmful residues, chemical treatments should be followed by a hot water rinse, after which the components are dried. Hydrofluoric acid residues are not detrimental to brazing, but hydrofluoric acid is ineffectual for removing oil and grease and thus is useful only on components that have been degreased by a solvent or emulsion cleaner.

For best results, brazing should be done immediately after cleaning, or at least within 48 hr. However, if precautionary measures are taken to prevent their contamination, adequately cleaned components do not lose brazing qualities even in several weeks.

See pages 611 to 616 in Volume 2 of this Handbook for more information on methods for cleaning aluminum alloys.

Assembly

Components to be brazed must be correctly located during assembly and be held in position by some type of jigging. Correct jigging is of particular importance in dip brazing, where the displacement of air and the buoyancy of the flux must be considered. Self-jigging, when possible, offers an economic advantage over the cost of design, maintenance and replacement of jigs. Several methods of self-jigging are described and illustrated in the article on Furnace Brazing. Another method (tabs and mating slots) is described in Example 632, on the next page.

Mating surfaces of brazing sheet should not be spot welded for self-jigging, because they can separate in the flux bath. Jigs that may be required to hold the parts in correct alignment must be resistant to the highly reactive molten flux. Low-carbon steel fixtures may have sufficiently long life for a specific job. Aluminum-coated steel has longer useful life.

Because of differential thermal expansion, the aligning jig should be designed with spring relief. Stainless steel and Inconel X-750 are both good materials for such springs; Inconel X-750 will retain more of its spring characteristics at brazing temperatures. Inconel X-750 also has better resistance to corrosion, not only during brazing, but also in postcleaning operations.

Dip Brazing

The best method of heating and fluxing aluminum joints simultaneously is to immerse the entire assembly in a bath of molten flux. This is known as dip brazing, or flux bath brazing. Dip brazing has been used successfully in the manufacture of complex, multiple-joint heat exchangers.

Immersing the entire assembly into molten flux has many advantages. Heat is applied to all parts simultaneously and uniformly. Air is replaced by a buoyant and surface-active environment, promoting brazing filler-metal flow. The uniform temperature permits production assembly of parts with di-

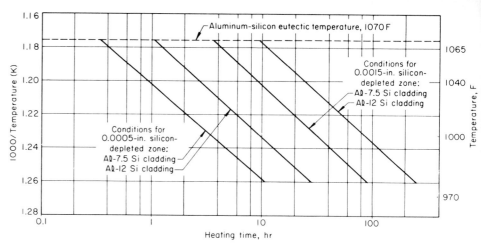

Fig. 8. *Effect of heating time, temperature and original silicon content on thickness of silicon-depleted zone in filler-metal cladding*

mensional tolerances as low as ±0.002 in. or even less.

Heat-transfer units assembled from alternate corrugated and flat aluminum brazing sheets or from various crimped and formed pieces are examples of the type of work that dip brazing can handle advantageously. Units weighing up to 20,000 lb have been joined by dip brazing. Certain designs have to withstand a service pressure of 650 psi. Brazing sheet is essential to this type of work, reducing assembly and brazing costs. The rapid and even heating and flux buoyancy minimize distortion.

For assemblies designed with components in close proximity, flux removal can be tedious and expensive. For instance, when components such as those of a heat-exchanger matrix are spaced closer than 1/8 in., the flux holds to the surfaces by surface tension and capillary action; it will not drain from the components freely. This is not as great a problem with spacings greater than 1/8 in. between components of normal length; wider spacing of long components is desirable.

Equipment for dip brazing may be as simple as a heat-resistant glass beaker inside a resistance-heated furnace, or as complex as a large steel vessel lined with high-alumina, acid-proof brick. For adequate resistance to flux, the alumina content of lining brick should be at least 40%. The molten bath is usually heated by low-voltage alternating current passing through the flux between wrought nickel, Inconel 600, or carbon electrodes. These show less attack than copper or copper-bearing electrodes, and cause minimum contamination of the flux. Attack at the electrode-flux-air interface has led to preference for submerged electrodes. The bath temperature should be controlled within ±5 F.

Technique. The amount of flux to fill the bath is about 100 lb per cubic foot. Approximately 385 Btu per pound is required to melt and heat the flux. Thermocouples enclosed in protective tubes should be used to determine the bath temperature, which is the actual temperature of the assembly. There should be enough flux so that the temperature does not drop more than 5 to 10 F when parts are immersed. The specific heat of dip brazing flux, approximately

0.2 Btu per pound per °F, is about the same as that of aluminum. For assemblies that have been preheated to 1000 to 1050 F before immersion in the salt bath, there should be about 16 lb of molten flux per pound of aluminum. With this ratio, the bath temperature may drop 2 to 5 F, and it should be possible to braze four to six loads per hour.

The composition of the flux in the bath should be adjusted periodically by fluoride and chloride additions. Proprietary additive mixtures are available for this purpose. Even when the molten bath is idle, side reactions reduce its activity. Because molten flux may contain water, it should be dehydrated periodically with aluminum to minimize the formation of hydrogen when the assemblies are dipped. The aluminum used for dehydrating the bath may conveniently be a loose coil of alloy 1100 or alloy 3003. When hydrogen stops burning at the surface of the bath, dehydration is essentially complete. Initial dehydration should be conducted for 4 to 48 hr, depending on bath size. Insertion of aluminum in the bath before the brazing operation is begun will also remove heavy-metal impurities such as nickel, copper, iron and zinc. The heavy-metal deposit on the aluminum coil is removed by quenching the coil in water, dipping it in nitric acid, and giving it a thorough water rinse. The coil should be dried before being reused.

These operations, as well as the actual brazing, produce a sludge containing oxides from the brazed parts and the brickwork, and insoluble fluoride complexes. After settling, the sludge should be ladled out at periodic intervals with a perforated tool.

Flux will be removed by dragout on the parts being brazed, and must be replaced. When an assembly is dip brazed, there will be approximately 0.5 oz of flux dragout per square foot of flat surface. With heat exchangers having complex and devious passages, this amount may be larger, because of capillary forces holding the flux. For a specific unit, dragout may vary as much as threefold, depending on the melting point and viscosity of the flux.

Before immersion in the flux bath, all moisture must be removed from the assembly and from any fixture used with it. Even a slight amount of mois-

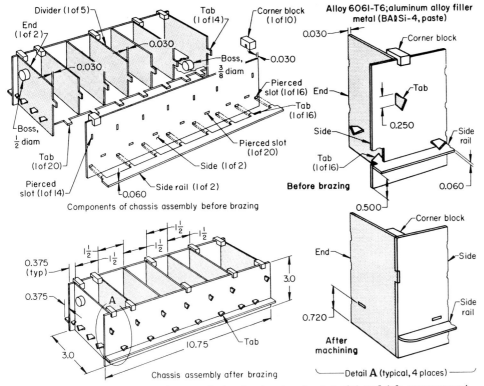

Labels in figure:
Divider (1 of 5)
Tab (1 of 14)
Corner block (1 of 10)
End (1 of 2)
0.030
0.030
Boss, 3/8 diam
0.030
Alloy 6061-T6; aluminum alloy filler metal (BAlSi-4, paste)
0.030
Corner block
Pierced slot (1 of 16)
End
Tab
0.250
Boss, 1/2 diam
Tab (1 of 16)
Side
Side rail
Tab (1 of 20)
Pierced slot (1 of 20)
Side (1 of 2)
Tab (1 of 16)
0.060
Pierced slot (1 of 14)
0.060
Side rail (1 of 2)
Before brazing

Components of chassis assembly before brazing

0.375 (typ)
0.375
1 1/2
1 1/2
1 1/2
1 1/2
A
3.0
3.0
10.75
Tab
Chassis assembly after brazing

0.500
Corner block
End
Side
0.720
Side rail
After machining
Detail A (typical, 4 places)

Fig. 9. Dip brazed assembly for an electronic chassis, showing slot-and-tab arrangement for self-jigging (Example 632)

ture can cause spattering in contact with molten flux. Drying by preheating is recommended. The use of preheated assemblies decreases the drop in temperature of the salt bath, shortening brazing time. Large or complex assemblies should be preheated to 1000 to 1050 F, usually in an air-recirculating furnace, at a rate that provides a suitable compromise between distortion from fast heating and diffusion during slow heating. Methods and advantages of preheating are discussed further in the article on Dip Brazing of Steel in Molten Salt, pages 655 to 660.

After being preheated, parts are immediately immersed in the flux bath for the scheduled period. This period will depend somewhat on the mass of the assembly, but immersion is usually only of 1/2 to 3-min duration. For large assemblies, such as a cryogenic heat exchanger that may weigh more than 1000 lb, immersion time may be as long as 20 min. Time in the bath should be no longer than is required to obtain melting and complete flow of the filler metal. After being preheated, the self-jigged assembly in the following example was dip brazed in only 20 sec.

Example 632. Use of Dip Brazing To Join a Complex Assembly (Fig. 9)

The chassis assembly shown in Fig. 9 was used for airborne electronic equipment. Casting was not a practical method for production of this chassis, because it was a large, thin-wall structure of complex design and the production quantities were small. Resistance spot welding, arc welding and torch brazing were ruled out by the need for a continuous metal surface, close dimensional tolerances and the presence of hidden joints in the design. Dip brazing was selected as the joining method best fulfilling the design requirements.

The dip brazed assembly was made of alloy 6061-T6 as follows. The two ends, two sides, five dividers, two side rails and the bottom were blanked and pierced in a numerically controlled press. The ten corner blocks and the two round bosses were machined from bar stock. Self jigging of the 24 components was achieved by providing the sheet-metal components with slots and mating tabs; the tabs were inserted in the slots, and hand twisted after assembly to hold the components in place. After brazing, the tabs and other extraneous material were machined off (see lower right view in Fig. 9).

This type of assembly allowed brazing with no external fixturing and permitted the use of assembly-line techniques, thus effecting savings of an estimated one fourth to one half of the cost of purchasing the assembly from an outside supplier. Total processing cost (excluding cost of material) was approximately 10¢ per inch of joint, or about $10.00 per assembly.

After burrs larger than 0.005 in. were removed from the sheet-metal components, the chassis was assembled and then cleaned by degreasing followed by immersion in either a caustic bath or a phosphoric acid etching solution. Brazing paste containing BAlSi-4 filler metal was applied to one side of each joint, to ensure against flux entrapment. The assembly was preheated for 20 to 30 min in an electric furnace operating at 1000 F, and then was dipped for 20 sec in a bath of proprietary brazing flux electrically heated to 1400 F.

After brazing, the assembly was cooled to about 500 F by an air blast (to minimize distortion) before being quenched in hot water and washed to remove flux. (The heating for brazing, followed by the air-blast cooling and the hot-water quench, put the 6061 alloy in a condition that yielded a T4 temper after natural aging for several days.)

After the self-jigging tabs and other extraneous metal had been removed by machining, the brazed chassis assembly was inspected visually. Parts were held within 0.015-in. total tolerance of warp over the 10-in. dimension, and angularity of 1° in 3 in. Fillet radii were held within 0.030 to 0.060 in. at junctures of two parts and within 0.030 to 0.090 in. at junctures of three parts. Fluorescent-dye or radiographic inspection was used in special cases. The rejection rate for this chassis was only 2% from all causes.

Furnace Brazing

Brazing in an atmosphere furnace is a high-production process that requires minimum training and skill of operators. Production rates can be considerably higher, and costs can be lower, than for torch brazing. Aircraft hot air ducts are furnace brazed in as little as one twentieth of the time required to torch braze similar parts. Mass-production assemblies, such as refrigerator evaporators, are brazed at about 500 pieces per hour in continuous furnaces.

Equipment. Heating methods for furnace brazing include electrical heating elements, direct combustion tubes and radiant tubes. Direct combustion furnaces are inexpensive, but the furnace gases may cause undesirable metallurgical effects during brazing of the heat treatable alloys — for example, the 6xxx series. Furnaces are generally refractory lined, although such linings become saturated with flux components. Heat-resistant steels, which are normally not recommended because of flux attack, are satisfactory for furnace linings if kept clean, and particularly if aluminum coated.

Whatever the type of furnace, the temperature in the brazing zone must be uniform within ±10 F, and preferably within ±5 F. Circulation of atmosphere, preferably with appropriate baffles, is required, to prevent local heat variations and to obtain the maximum rate of temperature rise.

Technique. Flux slurry may be applied to the parts by dipping, brushing or spraying. Tap, distilled or deionized water can serve as a vehicle; tap water should be free of heavy metals, because these can cause subsequent corrosion. Because hydrogen may be evolved when wet flux is heated on aluminum parts, closed assemblies must be vented. Gas generation can be reduced by drying the flux on the part prior to brazing. Mixing the flux with alcohol instead of water will speed the drying, but the explosive fumes from the alcohol must be dissipated.

Ambient air or chemically inert gas is normally used as the furnace atmosphere. A dry atmosphere (dew point of −40 F) consisting of the products of combustion of fuel can sometimes reduce the amount of flux needed. For brazing aluminum to other metals, an inert, dry atmosphere is particularly beneficial.

Continuous furnace brazing requires furnaces divided into several progressive heating zones to improve heating rate and joint quality and to reduce warpage. A furnace cycle of 15 min or less is desirable. In automated operations, the brazing zone usually requires a travel time of 2 to 3 min for assemblies of moderate size. Because the flux loses its activity in about 30 min, aluminum assemblies large enough and heavy enough to require heating times exceeding this limit should not be furnace brazed.

Beyond the heating portion of the furnace, from 1 to 5 min of conveyor travel should be in an unheated zone to allow the filler metal to solidify. Directly following should be an air blast, a hot-water spray (180 to 212 F), or a boiling-water quench, which begins the

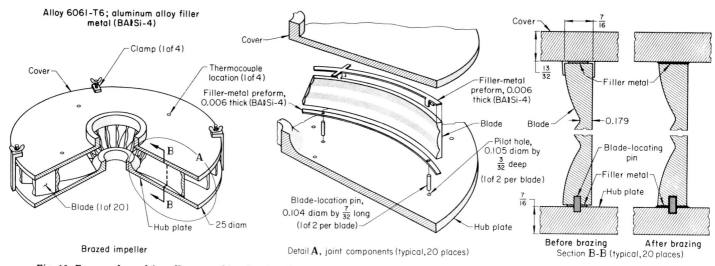

Alloy 6061-T6; aluminum alloy filler metal (BAlSi-4)

Clamp (1 of 4)

Cover

Thermocouple location (1 of 4)

Filler-metal preform, 0.006 thick (BAlSi-4)

B A

B

Blade (1 of 20)

Hub plate

25 diam

Brazed impeller

Cover

Filler-metal preform, 0.006 thick (BAlSi-4)

Blade

Pilot hole, 0.105 diam by $\frac{3}{32}$ deep (1 of 2 per blade)

Blade-location pin, 0.104 diam by $\frac{7}{32}$ long (1 of 2 per blade)

Hub plate

Detail A, joint components (typical, 20 places)

Cover

$\frac{7}{16}$

$\frac{13}{32}$

Filler metal

0.179

Blade

Blade-locating pin

Filler metal

Hub plate

$\frac{7}{16}$

Before brazing

After brazing

Section B-B (typical, 20 places)

Fig. 10. Furnace brazed impeller assembly, showing the locating pins used to hold the blades in position during brazing (Example 633)

flux-removal process. For the heat treatable alloys, a water quench after brazing will permit improvement in the mechanical properties, especially if the parts are subsequently given an aging treatment.

Batch furnaces are also used for brazing aluminum alloys, as described in the following example.

Example 633. Use of Furnace Brazing To Join an Impeller Assembly (Fig. 10)

Impellers like the one shown in Fig. 10 were used in radial-flow turbo-compressors to increase the recoverable energy content of the gas passing through the compressor. Speeds of various models of impellers ranged from 3000 to 30,000 rpm. More than 80 different sizes of impellers were made. Aluminum was used for impellers that, depending on size and speed, were to run at temperatures up to about 400 F.

The casting of impellers, which was done for some other applications, would have been expensive because of the large investment required for a multiplicity of patterns, the need to make new patterns for design changes and to store the old patterns for replacement orders, the high cost of developing the casting techniques, and expensive inspection requirements.

Brazed impellers were found to be easily manufactured with a large saving in capital cost. The initial capital outlay for producing 80 different sizes of brazed impellers was about 5% of the investment that would have been required for production of the impellers as castings. Design changes were made easily without the need to change equipment. A standard hub plate and cover were used for a number of impeller sizes; only the blade size was changed. Manufacturing cost (exclusive of savings in initial investment) was 1% lower than for casting. Inspection was easier, and the rejection rate of brazed impellers was only one-fourth that of cast impellers. In addition, brazed impellers were salvageable.

Aluminum alloy 6061-T6 plate was selected for the parts of the assembly because of its strength, brazeability and availability. Although brazing destroyed the T6 temper and it was necessary to reheat treat after brazing, the plate was purchased in this temper to avoid possible mixup with other 6061-T6 plate used in the plant, and there was no cost premium for the temper. Blades were cut from a cylinder made by curving the plate on a three-roll former, gas metal-arc welding the longitudinal seam, and stress relieving. The blades were then finish machined to size and shape, and holes for locating pins were drilled on one edge.

The blades, the hub plate (machined and stress relieved), and the cover, together with 0.006-in.-thick BAlSi-4 filler-metal preforms, were cleaned in the following sequence of operations.

1 Immerse in emulsion cleaner at 150 F. The emulsion was a mixture (2 to 3 oz per gallon of water) of alkaline salts combining complex phosphates and sulfates with anionic surface-active agents of the aryl-alkyl sulfonic type.
2 Rinse in cold running water.
3 Immerse in alkaline etching cleaner solution (2 to 3 oz per gallon of water) at 150 to 160 F.
4 Rinse in cold running water.
5 Immerse in nitric acid solution (30 to 40% by weight) at room temperature until all stains or smudges are removed.
6 Rinse in cold running water.
7 Rinse in hot running water.
8 Dry with air blast.

The impeller components and filler-metal preforms were assembled in a clean, air-conditioned room. The hub plate was placed on a rigid baseplate fixture made of type 316 stainless steel. Flux was mixed within 4 hr prior to being used, from 3 parts by volume of a proprietary powder (aluminum fluorides and chlorides) to 1 part of clean water. Aluminum blade-locating pins were inserted in the hub plate and covered with flux. The lower filler-metal preforms were fluxed on both surfaces and put in position over the pins. The blades were fluxed and put in position (located by the pins). The upper filler-metal preform strips were fluxed and placed on the blades.

Tabs were bent down over the blades to hold the filler-metal strips in position. Flux was brushed onto the joint side of the cover. The cover was placed in position over the blades, concentric with the hub plate, and held there by four locating clamps fastened to the cover at 90° intervals and extending down to the bottom of the outside edge of the hub plate.

The cover had been drilled with four $\frac{1}{8}$-in.-deep holes on the top surface to accommodate thermocouple beads. For small assemblies, only the holes at the front and back positions during brazing were used. For large assemblies, the holes at the side positions in the furnace also had thermocouple beads peened into them. Care was taken to avoid pickup of foreign metal when making the thermocouple joints and also to avoid contaminating the thermocouple wires with flux.

A box-type furnace, electrically heated on all interior surfaces, was used. The assembly was placed in the furnace, which had been preheated to 1200 F (120 to 130 F above the brazing temperature), and the temperature of the assembly was checked with the thermocouples at regular intervals. When any thermocouple reading was within 50 F of the brazing temperature of 1070 to 1080 F, readings were taken every minute. When the assembly reached brazing temperature, the furnace was opened, and the assembly was removed to cool in air to room temperature. The brazed as-

sembly was washed in hot water to remove flux and then cleaned by the same procedure as used before brazing.

After cleaning, the impeller was solution heat treated, quenched and aged to regain the T6 temper and again was given the same sequence of cleaning operations as before, to remove the slight surface oxidation that formed during heat treatment.

Final inspection included visual examination, dye-penetrant inspection and a hardness check. In addition, the brazed assemblies were inspected for deformation and brazing failure after the impeller was test run 20% over design speed for two minutes in vacuum. Assemblies that showed porosity in a brazed joint were salvaged by recleaning, refluxing, positioning small clips of additional filler metal where needed, and rebrazing. If cracks were found in a joint, the hub plate and cover were salvaged for reuse by cutting apart the assembly. (The used blades were discarded.)

Fluxless Vacuum Brazing

Furnace brazing in a vacuum with the use of no flux offers several advantages. The possibility of flux inclusions is eliminated. Blind cavities, tortuous paths, and small passageways can be designed into the assembly without regard to flux removal or entrapment after brazing. Fluxless brazing also eliminates the cost of flux and its application, the need for cleaning the assembly after brazing, and potential corrosion of equipment and pollution of air and water by flux residues or flux reaction products.

With correct techniques, alloys of the $1xxx$, $3xxx$, $5xxx$, $6xx$ and $7xxx$ series can be vacuum brazed using X3 and X5 brazing sheets, which are clad with X4003 filler metal. (When additional filler metal is required, X4003 in wire and sheet form also can be introduced.) The joint designs used for brazing with flux can be used for fluxless vacuum brazing.

Equipment. Cold-wall vacuum furnaces with electrical-resistance radiant heaters are recommended for aluminum vacuum brazing. Both batch-type and semicontinuous furnaces are used. The vacuum pumping system should be capable of evacuating a conditioned chamber to a moderate vacuum (about 10^{-5} torr) in 5 min. For most applications, rectangular chambers made of hot rolled steel are suitable. The temperature distribution within the work

320

Metal thickness, in.	Oxyacetylene brazing			Oxy-hydrogen brazing		
	Orifice diameter, in.	Oxygen pressure, psi	Acetylene pressure, psi	Orifice diameter, in.	Oxygen pressure, psi	Hydrogen pressure, psi
0.020	0.025	0.5	1	0.035	0.5	1
0.025	0.025	0.5	1	0.045	0.5	1
0.032	0.035	0.5	1	0.055	0.5	1
0.040	0.035	0.5	1	0.065	1	2
0.051	0.045	1	2	0.075	1	2
0.064	0.055	1	2	0.085	1	2
0.081	0.065	1.5	3	0.095	1.5	3
0.102	0.075	1.5	3	0.105	1.5	3
0.125	0.085	2.0	4	0.115	1.5	3

being brazed should be reasonably uniform, ideally within ±5 F. For many applications, wider ranges are used.

Technique. Components are cleaned, usually by vapor degreasing with a common solvent such as perchlorethylene (ordinarily, chemical cleaning is not required), assembled, and clamped in a suitable fixture made of thin stainless steel sheet. The use of dry cotton gloves is recommended for assembling by hand. Heating of the assembly is started simultaneously with pumpdown of batch-type furnaces. Average time for heating to brazing temperature is about 15 min. The assembly is then held at brazing temperature (see optimum brazing ranges, Table 3) for about 1 min. After backfilling the chamber with chemically inert gas, the assembly is removed at approximately 1000 F. Heat treatable alloys can then be quenched; non-heat-treatable alloys are air cooled. The clean, dry brazed assembly is ready for use or further processing as soon as it is cool.

Torch Brazing

Torch brazing is used for either manual or automatic fabrication, and for repair operations. The uses of torch brazing range from rather simple tube-to-tube joints to more complex and mechanized assemblies. Some of the more common commercial applications are tubular joints in refrigerator coils, miter joints in extruded window frames, and joints between electric heating elements and structures.

Equipment. Oxyacetylene, oxy-hydrogen and oxy-natural gas are employed commercially for torch brazing. It is possible also to use gasoline blow-torches, and all types of gas burners.

Torch brazing is similar to gas welding, in that the heat to effect the joint is applied locally. The torch-tip sizes used are also similar to those for gas welding. The choice of tip size and gas pressures depends on the thickness of the parts and should be determined by trial, using the values in Table 5 as starting points.

With the generally employed fillers, BAlSi-3 (alloy 4145) and BAlSi-4 (alloy 4047), close temperature control is needed, especially for torch brazing of alloys having low solidus (wrought alloys 5052, 6053, 6061 and 7005, and the casting alloys listed in Table 1). Since aluminum alloys show no color when hot, even melting without a color change, it is necessary to have some means for determining when the parts are reaching brazing temperature. The flux used should be one that melts at a slightly lower temperature than the filler metal and thus serves as a temperature indicator. Aligning jigs should be insulated to avoid excessive heat conduction.

Technique. After the components of an assembly to be torch brazed have been suitably cleaned, the joint areas and the filler metal are painted with a slurry of brazing flux, and the components assembled and (if required) jigged. The assembly is then brazed by directing a soft, slightly reducing flame over the entire joint area. The filler metal can be preplaced, or it can be face fed (flowed into the joint when touched against the heated work). The brazed joint should have a smooth fillet, usually requiring little or no finishing. All flux should be removed.

Specialized Brazing Processes

The various processes described in this section are not currently in wide use. For some of these processes, the basic art, knowledge and materials are available, but the applications to date are meager. For others, the technology is not fully developed.

Modifications of Dip Brazing. In one modification of dip brazing, mixtures of filler-metal powder and one of the active components of the flux, such as a fluoride, are applied to the areas to be brazed and are dried, and then the assembly is dipped into a less-active molten flux vehicle.

Another modification is useful when, because of joint design, it is desirable to supply filler metal from a molten bath. This is done in either of two ways: (a) assemblies coated with flux (by spraying or dipping) and thoroughly dried are placed into the molten filler metal; or (b) the assembly is dipped into a molten flux bath and then dipped into the molten filler metal. In either method, the molten filler metal flows into the capillary spaces at the joints to effect a braze.

Resistance brazing of aluminum alloys most often involves joining of small parts: making connections in electric motor windings is a typical application. Usually, the work is clamped for heating between two carbon blocks held in a tong arrangement. For some jobs, it is clamped in a resistance welding machine.

Alloy Brazing. This fluxless process achieves a braze by first heating the joint area with an interposed shim to form a liquid phase, then extruding this liquid along with surface oxides from the joint cross section. Because of rate of alloying, fluidity, melting temperature, and availability as foil, the preferred shim material is copper.

The extreme brittleness of the aluminum-copper intermetallic compounds is no deterrent, because the compounds are entirely displaced by extrusion.

Many types of heating are used for alloy brazing; resistance heating is commonest. Clamping pressure between the carbon blocks is generally 1200 to 2000 psi, based on the overlap area. Current densities of 2500 to 4000 amp per square inch with an operating potential of 9 to 13 volts are satisfactory.

This process is used in the electrical industry, because the electrical conductivity of the brazed joints is essentially the same as the parent aluminum conductor, and the process is low in cost. In addition to simple overlap and butt joints, multiple-ply overlap, thin-to-thick, and round-to-flat joints have been brazed. The simple, inexpensive, fluxless features also make this process attractive for brazing narrow sheet and plate members, butt joining round and square aluminum rod, and sealing the ends of thin-wall tubing. Alloys such as EC, 1060, 1100 and 3003, with solidus temperatures considerably above 1018 F (aluminum-copper eutectic temperature), are the most readily brazed. The 5xxx and 6xxx alloys with lower solidus temperatures can be brazed if close temperature control is provided.

Motion brazing includes both vibration brazing and flow brazing. As might be expected, vibration of low or ultrasonic frequency has a pronounced beneficial effect in brazing aluminum, particularly when brazing sheet is used. Brazed joints can be made with brazing-sheet parts in the absence of flux and in air. The brazing-sheet surfaces are held together at a temperature preferably above the liquidus of the brazing alloy. A relative movement between the brazing sheets displaces the oxide film on the semiliquid contact surfaces.

In flow brazing, simple joints can be brazed between brazing sheets or even plain aluminum parts. The part to be brazed or the molten filler metal is moved rapidly with respect to the other, causing a mechanical removal of oxide film and the mating of liquid-liquid or solid-liquid interfaces. For simple shapes, this can be done in air; for more difficult shapes, in an inert gas. No flux is used. Vibration is helpful. The total time must be short.

The motion brazing concept has certain obvious limitations. Parts are restricted to rather elementary structures because of the requirements of directional vibration, rate and type of motion, supply of premelted filler alloy to the joint, shape of part, precleaning, and other complicating factors.

Brazing to Other Metals

Aluminum can be brazed to many other metals. In specific applications, painting or other suitable coating may be required after brazing, to minimize subsequent galvanic corrosion of the joint area. Stresses from nonuniform expansion must also be considered.

Aluminum to Ferrous Alloys. Steel should be protected from oxidation during preheating and brazing to aluminum. In dip brazing, oxidation can be prevented by dipping unheated parts into molten flux, but this procedure has limited application because it is likely to cause warping and misalignment of the components.

Plated or coated steel can be brazed to aluminum more readily than can bare steel. Copper, nickel or zinc electroplates and aluminum, silver, tin or hot dip zinc coatings are used to promote wetting of the steel and to minimize formation of brittle aluminum-iron constituents, thus producing a more ductile joint.

The furnace brazing of plated steel liners or sleeves in aluminum alloy cylinder blocks, as well as steel valve seats in aluminum alloy cylinder heads, has been done experimentally.

Aluminum-coated steels can be torch brazed readily to aluminum, using aluminum filler metals and fluxes. The procedure is the same as in brazing aluminum to aluminum except that preheating should be rapid and brazing time must be minimized, in order to avoid the formation of brittle aluminum-iron phases at the interface. Tube-to-tube joints, with a nominal clearance of about 0.010 in., and laps varying from 0.50 to 2.50 in., have shown shear strengths of 10,000 to 15,000 psi.

In certain complex applications, a multiple-step joining procedure must be employed to permit flux removal. For instance, a section of steel tube was hot dip coated with aluminum at one end, and the aluminum-coated end was dip brazed to a section of aluminum tube. After thoroughly cleaning the brazed subassembly to remove residual brazing flux, the aluminum tube portion was welded to an aluminum container that had been furnace brazed and cleaned in separate operations. The completed assembly was vacuum tight.

Aluminum to Copper. It is difficult to braze aluminum to copper, because of the low melting temperature (1018 F) of the aluminum-copper eutectic and its extreme brittleness. By heating and cooling rapidly, however, reasonably ductile joints are made for applications such as copper inserts in aluminum castings. The usual filler metals and fluxes for brazing aluminum to aluminum can be used, or the silver alloy filler metals BAg-1 and BAg-1a can be used if heating and cooling are rapid (to minimize diffusion). Pretinning the copper surfaces with solder or silver alloy filler metal improves wetting and permits shorter time at brazing temperature. A more practical way to braze aluminum to copper is to braze one end of a short length of aluminum-coated steel tube to the aluminum, and then silver braze the other end of the tube to the copper.

Aluminum to Other Nonferrous Metals. Aluminum-silicon filler metals are unsuitable for brazing aluminum to uncoated titanium because of the formation of brittle intermetallic compounds, but titanium can be hot dip coated with aluminum, after which it can be brazed to aluminum with the usual aluminum filler metals.

Under correct conditions, nickel and nickel alloys are no more difficult to braze to aluminum than are ferrous alloys. They can be brazed directly or precoated with aluminum. Although Monel alloys can be wetted directly, brazed joints are likely to be brittle, and Monel alloys are thus preferably precoated with aluminum.

Beryllium can be wetted directly by aluminum brazing alloys. Magnesium alloys can be brazed to aluminum, but the brazed joints have limited usefulness because of the extremely brittle aluminum-magnesium phases that form at the interface.

Flux Removal

Fluxes used in brazing aluminum alloys can cause corrosion if allowed to remain on the parts. It is therefore essential to clean joints after brazing. A thorough water rinse followed by a chemical treatment is the most effective means of complete flux removal.

As much flux as possible should be removed by immersing the parts in an overflowing bath of boiling water just after the filler metal has solidified. If such a quench produces distortion, the parts should be allowed to cool in air before immersion, to decrease the thermal shock. When both sides of a brazed joint are accessible, scrubbing with a fiber brush in boiling water will remove most of the flux. For parts too large for water baths, the joints should be scrubbed with hot water and rinsed with cold water. A pressure spray washer may be the best first step. A steam jet is also effective in opening passages plugged by flux.

Any of several acid solutions (Table 6) will remove any flux remaining after washing. The choice depends largely on the thickness of the brazed parts, accessibility of fluxed areas and the adequacy of flux removal in the initial water treatment. A pitting or intergranular type of attack on parts can result as chlorides from the flux build up in the acid solution. Some solutions have a greater tolerance for these chlorides than others before parts are attacked. The degree of flux contamination tolerable for the five typical flux-removal solutions listed in Table 6 are given in the footnotes of the table.

The two chromium-containing solutions in Table 6 have the greater tolerance for chlorides and are preferred for thin-wall assemblies. In areas where disposal of chromates presents a problem, the nitric acid solution can be used if inhibitors such as 1% thiourea or triethanolamine salt of sulfolaurylalkylbenzoate are added. As a corrosion inhibitor, about 0.5% sodium or potassium dichromate is sometimes added to the final rinse water.

Agitation and turbulence improve the efficiency of any flux-removal treatment. Ultrasonic cleaning is effective for cleaning inaccessible areas, decreases the immersion time and reduces the possibility of attack on the aluminum.

Checking for complete flux removal should be a routine inspection procedure. To detect the presence of flux, a few drops of distilled water are put on the surface to be tested and left there for a few seconds. The water is then picked off with an eyedropper and placed in an acidified solution of 5% silver nitrate. If the solution stays clear, the metal is clean. If a white precipitate clouds the solution, flux was present on the surface. Flux-removal procedures must then be repeated until the brazed assembly tests clean. Complete removal of the flux is essential, because it is corrosive to aluminum in the presence of moisture.

Postbraze Heat Treatment

Brazing temperatures exceed the solution heat treatment temperatures used for aluminum alloys, and heat treatable aluminum alloys can attain full strength by aging after being quenched from the brazing temperature. After brazing of alloy 7005, a normal air quench for small parts of 5 F per second, or even a cooling rate as slow as 1 F per second, is adequate for precipitation hardening to occur at room temperature. Except as dictated by distortion problems, postbraze quenching and aging treatments are the same as for the base alloy. Typical treatment for artificially aging a heat

Table 6. Solutions for Removing Brazing Flux From Aluminum Parts

Type of solution	Amount	Concentration Component(a)	Operating temperature	Procedure(b)
Nitric acid	5 gal	58 to 62% HNO_3	Room	Immerse for 10-20 min; rinse in hot or cold water(c)
	34 gal	Water		
Nitric-hydrofluoric acid	4 gal	58 to 62% HNO_3	Room	Immerse for 10-15 min; rinse in cold water, rinse in hot water; dry(d)
	1 qt	48% HF (1.15 sp gr)		
	36 gal	Water		
Hydrofluoric acid	10 pt	48% HF	Room	Immerse for 5-10 min; rinse in cold water; dip in nitric acid solution shown at top of table; rinse in hot or cold water(d)
	40 gal	Water		
Phosphoric acid – chromium trioxide	1½ gal	85% H_3PO_4	180 F	Immerse for 10-15 min; rinse in hot or cold water(e)
	7¼ lb	CrO_3		
	40 gal	Water		
Nitric acid – sodium dichromate	4½ gal	58 to 62% HNO_3	140 F	Immerse for 5-30 min; rinse in hot water(f)
	32 lb	$Na_2Cr_2O_7 \cdot 2H_2O$		
	36 gal	Water		

(a) All compositions in weight per cent. (b) Before using any of the above solutions, it is recommended that the assembly first be immersed in boiling water to remove the major portion of the flux. (c) Flux contamination in acid should not exceed 5 grams per liter of chloride expressed as sodium chloride. Solution is not recommended for use on base metals less than 0.020 in. thick. (d) Flux contamination in acid should not exceed 3 grams per liter of chloride expressed as hydrochloric acid. Solution is aggressive, and not recommended for base metals less than 0.020 in. thick. (e) Tolerance for flux contamination is in excess of 100 grams per liter, and permissible limit will probably be governed by cleaning ability. If large pockets of flux are present, solution will promote intergranular attack at the pocket. Recommended for final cleaning of thin-gage parts, when most of the flux can be removed easily in water. (f) Exceptionally high flux tolerance. Recommended for cleaning thin-gage assemblies, if adequacy of water cleaning is doubtful. License required.

322

treatable alloy brazed assembly is 16 to 20 hr at 320 F, or 6 to 10 hr at 350 F.

Finishing

Because of the smooth, uniform fillets resulting from the brazing operation, little if any mechanical treatment is required before final finishing. If flux has been completely removed (or if fluxless brazing has been used), all chemical and electrochemical finishing treatments are effective when the brazed structures are aluminum throughout. Because of the high silicon content of the filler-metal fillets, any treatment that thickens the oxide or preferentially etches aluminum, leaving a residue of silicon, may cause the fillets to be a darker color than the remainder of the product.

Brazing fluxes containing chlorides of zinc or other heavy metals will deposit that metal on the surface of aluminum parts. These fluxes, as well as fluxes that cause severe etching of aluminum, should be avoided for highest quality in chemical finishing.

Mechanical Properties

At least a part of the base metal is heated above its annealing temperature during the brazing cycle. Torch brazing may anneal only a small region near the joint, whereas dip or furnace brazing anneals the entire assembly. Unless the completed part is quenched and aged, heat treated, or cold worked, the metal that was heated will have mechanical properties typical of the annealed alloy.

When the alloy is heat treatable, improved strength can be imparted by quenching directly from the brazing furnace or dip pot, then artificially or naturally aging according to regular procedures for the alloy involved. Another alternative is solution heat treating and aging as separate operations after brazing. Heat treating is not always possible, because the rapid quenching required for most heat treatable alloys can cause distortion. Alloy 7005 will age harden at room temperature to T6 properties after normal air cooling (1 to 2 F per sec) from brazing temperature. Table 7 lists typical properties of alloy 7005 air cooled from brazing temperature.

Resistance to Corrosion

The aluminum alloys best suited for brazing are also among those most resistant to corrosion. Corrosion resistance of aluminum alloys generally is unimpaired by brazing if a fluxless brazing process is used or if flux is completely removed after brazing. If flux removal is inadequate, the presence of moisture can lead to interdendritic attack on the filler metal at joint faces and to intergranular attack on the base metal.

When two aluminum alloys are brazed together, exposure to salt water or some other electrolyte may result in attack on the more anodic alloy. This condition is aggravated if the anodic part is relatively small compared with the other piece. It helps, therefore, to have the anodic aluminum alloy the larger of the two members.

Torch brazed alclad 3003 and alclad 3004 show excellent resistance to corrosion. Furnace or dip brazing, however, causes a certain amount of diffusion of the clad surface, which limits application of these methods with conventional alclad products. A brazing sheet with filler metal on one side and alclad with a special alloy on the other (see Fig. 2d) performs well in furnace or dip brazing.

Commercial filler metals of the aluminum-silicon type have high resistance to corrosion, comparable to that of the base metals usually brazed. Filler metals containing substantial amounts of copper or zinc are less resistant to corrosion, but they are usually adequate, except for service in severe environments.

Joints brazed with aluminum-silicon filler metals — BAlSi-2 (alloy 4343), BAlSi-4 (alloy 4047) and BAlSi-5 (alloy 4045) — all show a potential of −0.82 volt with respect to a 0.1N calomel reference electrode in an aqueous solution of 53 grams-per-liter of sodium chloride and 3 grams-per-liter of hydrogen peroxide. This potential is barely cathodic to the commonly brazed base metals, for which the value is −0.83 volt for 1100, 3003, 6061 and 6063. Therefore, there is little electrolytic action in assemblies of these base metals brazed with the usual filler metals.

The potential of joints brazed with filler metal BAlSi-3 (alloy 4145), which contains copper in addition to aluminum and silicon, depends on the cooling rate after brazing. For slow cooling, these joints have about the same potential as joints brazed with the aluminum-silicon filler metals (−0.82 volt). If the cooling is rapid enough to retain a substantial amount of copper in solid solution, the potential will be lower; a potential of −0.73 volt has been found for T-joints in 0.064-in. sheet brazed with BAlSi-3 filler metal and rapidly cooled.

Although considerable undissolved silicon-containing constituent is evident in brazed joints, it polarizes strongly (except in acid chloride environments) and has little influence on the potential of the brazed joint and its corrosion resistance.

Table 8 shows the results of long-time exposure in a highly corrosive environment of various sheet alloys that were furnace brazed with filler metal BAlSi-3 (alloy 4145). The good performance can be considered typical of a variety of brazing combinations.

Safety

Many of the safety considerations discussed in the articles on brazing processes (pages 593 to 660) are applicable to the brazing of aluminum alloys by the same processes. The principal hazard in brazing aluminum alloys that is not present in brazing steel or copper alloys arises from the use of molten fluorine-containing fluxes in dip brazing. Toxic effects may be produced by the inhalation of fumes from the fluorine compounds, and exhaust facilities are required for dip brazing. Furnace brazing with fluorine-bearing fluxes requires regular exhaust of the fumes generated, to prevent attack on exposed metals; the air changes necessary for this reason are adequate from the standpoint of health protection.

Selected References

M. A. Miller, Flow of Metal in Brazing Aluminum, *Welding Journal*, 20, 472s-478s (1941); Aluminum Brazing Sheet—Fundamentals of Metal Flow, *Welding Journal*, 22, 596s-604s (1943); Metal Flow and Fillet Formation in Brazing Aluminum, *Welding Journal*, 25, 102s-144s (1946).

M. F. Jordan and D. R. Milner, Removal of Oxide from Aluminum by Brazing Fluxes, *Journal of the Institute of Metals*, 85, 33-40 (1956-1957).

D. R. Milner, A Survey of the Scientific Principles Related to Wetting and Spreading, *British Welding Journal*, 5, 90-105 (1958).

J. R. Terrill, The R-260 Bonding Process for Joining Aluminum, *Welding Journal*, 41, 799-804 (1962).

Vacuum Brazing Honeycomb Panels, *Modern Metals*, 18, 54-56 (July 1962).

F. Bollenrath and G. Metzgar, The Brazing of Titanium to Aluminum, *Welding Journal*, 42, 442s-453s (1963).

G. Martin and W. W. Brandel, Aluminum Structures Joined by Fluxless Brazing, *Materials in Design Engineering*, 61, 122-123 (Mar 1965).

P. B. Dickerson, Working with Aluminum? Here's What You Can Do with Dip Brazing, *Metal Progress*, 87, 80-85 (May 1965); How to Dip Braze Aluminum Assemblies, *Metal Progress*, 87, 73-78 (June 1965).

Aluminum Alloy System Forms Vacuum Brazed Joints, *Steel*, 157, 66 (Nov 8, 1965).

J. H. Dudas, Joining New High-Strength Aluminum Alloy X7005, *Welding Journal*, 44, 358s-364s (1965).

R. H. Haines, The Dip Brazing of Aluminum and Its Alloys, *Revue de l'Aluminium*, 42, 209-212 (1965).

J. R. Terrill, Diffusion of Silicon in Aluminum Brazing Sheet, *Welding Journal*, 45, 202s-209s (1966).

E. C. Helder and J. F. Rudy, Dip Brazing 7005 Aluminum Fan Blades, *Metal Progress*, 97, 110-136 (Mar 1970).

O. R. Singleton, A Look at the Brazing of Aluminum—Particularly Fluxless Brazing, *Welding Journal*, 49, 843-849 (Nov 1970).

Table 7. Tensile Properties of 0.063-In.-Thick Alloy 7005 Heated as in Brazing(a)

Room-temperature aging treatment	Tensile strength, psi	Yield strength, psi	Elongation in 2 in., %
None	28,000	12,000	26
3 days	42,000	21,000	22
1 week	45,000	24,000	22
1 month	49,000	27,000	21
3 months	52,000	30,000	21
6 months	54,000	32,000	21
T63(b)	52,000	44,000	13

(a) Heated 10 min at 1090 F, air cooled, aged as designated. (b) Artificially aged (after solution heat treatment).

Table 8. Results of Microscopic Examination of Furnace Brazed Specimens Exposed Two Years to 3.5% Sodium Chloride Intermittent Spray(a)

Sheet alloy	Filler metal(b)	Sheet (base metal) — Type of attack(c)	Sheet (base metal) — Depth of attack, in. Maximum	Sheet (base metal) — Depth of attack, in. Average	Joint (filler metal) — Type of attack(c)	Joint (filler metal) — Depth of attack, in. Maximum	Joint (filler metal) — Depth of attack, in. Average
3003	4145	P	0.0098	0.0022	P	0.0014	0.0011
5052	4145	P	0.0182	0.0042	P	0.0042	0.0014
6053	4145	P + I	0.0126	0.0028	P	0.0012	0.0008
6061	4145	P + SI	0.0126	0.0033	P	0.0042	0.0014

(a) Specimens were small inverted T-joints of 0.064-in. sheet. (b) Filler metal 4145 corresponds to BAlSi-3. (c) P = pitting attack; I = intergranular attack; SI = slight intergranular attack.

Introduction to Aluminum Brazing

Brazing's Advantages

Strong, uniform, leak-proof joints without number can be made rapidly, inexpensively and even simultaneously by modern brazing techniques. Joints that are inaccessible and parts which may not be joinable at all by other methods often can be joined by brazing.

Complicated assemblies with thick and thin sections, odd shapes and differing wrought and cast aluminum alloys can be turned into one integral, all-aluminum component by a single trip through a brazing furnace or a dip pot. Metal as thin as 0.006 inch and as thick as 6 inches can be brazed.

Brazed joint strength is very high. The nature of the interatomic bond (metallic) is such that even a simple joint, when properly designed and made, will have equal or greater strength than that of the as-brazed parent metal.

As brazing is usually followed by quenching, heat-treatable aluminum alloys generally do not need solution heat treatment after brazing, but can be tempered by aging alone.

Brazed aluminum assemblies are all aluminum with excellent corrosion resistance when properly cleaned. Brazed aluminum joints generally resist corrosion as well as welded aluminum joints.

Brazed aluminum assemblies conduct heat and electricity uniformly. Brazed aluminum heat exchangers, evaporators and similar complex fabrications are therefore long lasting and highly efficient.

Brazing fillet shapes are naturally excellent. The meniscus surface formed by the fillet metal as it curves across corners and adjoining sections is ideally shaped to resist fatigue.

Complex shapes with greatly varied sections are brazed with little distortion. Aluminum's excellent thermal conductivity assures even distribution of the relatively moderate temperature required for brazing.

Precise joining is comparatively simple with brazing. Unlike welding, in which the application of intense heat to small areas acts to move the parts out of alignment, parts joined by furnace and salt pot techniques are heated fairly evenly. Part alignment is easier with brazing. Brazed joints with tolerances of $\pm$ 0.002 inch are commonplace in microwave component production.

Brazed joints are leak tight. A vessel, sealed by brazing and evacuated to 2×10^{-5} torr was observed for 100 hours. After that time, leakage increased internal pressure to only 1.6×10^{-4} torr which is excellent for any metal joint.

Finishing costs are negligible. The capillary action that draws the filler metal into the joint also forms smooth concave surfaces. Little mechanical finishing, if any, is required. The color match between parent metal and filler is generally good.

Personnel training is minimal. Production brazing equipment has been refined to where semi-skilled and non-skilled people suffice for most operations. Torch brazing is simple. Mechanically adept personnel can be trained in a few hours or less.

Basic Phenomenon

Bring two pieces of metal within 4 Angstrom units ($\mathring{A} = 10^{-10}$ meter) of each other and inter-atomic attraction will bind them together in permanent metallic bond. This is the basis of brazing and soldering and is accomplished by "wetting" the metals to be joined with molten metal, which on cooling forms the joint.

If the temperature of the wetting metal is above 800°F., the process, by accepted American Welding Society definition, is called brazing and the molten metal is called brazing filler metal. If the temperature is below 800°F., the process is called soldering and the molten metal is called solder. Welding differs in that the base metals to be joined are molten at the moment of joining.

Basic Techniques and Parameters

The basic techniques employed to braze and solder aluminum are similar to those used to join other metals. In fact, the very same equipment used for brazing and soldering aluminum may be used to join other metals in this fashion and is frequently done so commercially.

Aluminum and its alloys, however, have a number of physical properties that differ markedly from those of other metals commonly brazed and soldered. Aluminum's thermal conductivity is very high, it oxidizes rapidly, its coefficient of thermal expansion is greater than that of many other common metals, and aluminum doesn't change color as its temperature changes.

The oxide that forms on aluminum—just as quickly as the bare metal is exposed to air—has a very high melting point (3722°F.). Aluminum oxide is neither melted nor reduced by temperatures that melt the metal itself. When aluminum is brazed or soldered in our atmosphere, a flux is used to break up the oxide, float it away and protect the bare parent metal from further oxidation. Various mechanical means are also used to break up the oxide and expose the bare aluminum to the molten brazing filler metal.

These differing physical properties by no means limit the silvery metal's response to brazing, soldering and welding techniques. They merely require a bit of mental adjustment on the part of the engineer and designer who comes to aluminum fully trained and experienced in working with other metals.

The general procedure for brazing and soldering aluminum is as follows. The surfaces to be joined are cleaned, coated with suitable flux and spaced a few thousandths of an inch apart. A piece of brazing filler (or solder) is placed in or near the joint to be formed. Heat is applied. The flux reacts, displaces the oxide on the surface of the base metal and shields the bare metal from contact with the air. The brazing metal filler melts and is drawn into the joint by capillary attraction. As the "filler" flows, it displaces the flux and wets the hot base metal, adapting to sub-microscopic irregularities and dissolving the small high points it encounters. All this may take place in a few seconds. After cooling and cleaning the joint is ready for use.

As the fillers and solders used must melt at lower temperatures than the metals they join, their chemistries must be different. As a result, diffusion at the line of bond produces alloying in both the filler and base metal.

The resultant alloy is sometimes helpful, but most often undesirable. Diffusion can be controlled to some degree, but it cannot be eliminated. Because of this alloying, the resultant fillet (the cold, in-place solder or filler) always differs from its original composition, with most of the change occurring close to the filler base-metal interface.

Aluminum alloys are brazed with filler metals that are themselves aluminum alloys, fairly similar in composition to the parent metals they are joining. The brazing filler

metals commonly used have liquidus temperatures but slightly removed from the solidus temperature of the parent metals. Close temperature control is therefore very important when brazing.

Solidus and liquidus are terms used to define the melting zone of alloys. Whereas pure metals (and eutectics) melt and flow at the same temperatures, alloys begin to melt at one temperature, called the solidus, and are completely molten at a higher temperature called the liquidus. Below the solidus temperature the alloy is completely solid. Above the liquidus temperature the alloy is completely liquid. In between the alloy is mushy or slushy.

Aluminum Alloys That Can Be Brazed

All the nonheat-treatable aluminum alloys and many of the heat-treatable alloys can be brazed.

The heat-treatable alloys most frequently brazed are 6061, 6063 and 6951. The nonheat-treatable alloys that respond best to brazing are 1100, 3004, 3003 and 5005.

Casting alloys that are brazed include A712.0, C712.0, 356.0, 443, A356, 357.0 and 359.0.

Aluminum Alloys That Cannot Be Brazed

Alloys 2011, 2014, 2017, 2024 and 7075 are not readily brazed with existing fillers. The melting points of these alloys are too low for the fillers developed thus far. Alloys with a magnesium content of 2.0% are difficult to braze because present fluxes do not effectively remove the tenacious oxides that form on these alloys. Alloys with a magnesium content of more than 2.5% (found in the 5000 series) can only be brazed by vacuum techniques.

Brazing Aluminum to Other Metals

Aluminum can be brazed to many metals and alloys. A partial list includes the ferrous alloys, nickel, titanium, beryllium, Kovar, Monel and Inconel.

Aluminum cannot be brazed directly to magnesium. When this is tried, an alloy forms that is so brittle it fails under slight stress.

Aluminum can be brazed to copper and brass, but a brittle, intermetallic compound is formed that limits the joint's application. However, aluminum can be joined to copper and brass by means of a transition joint. Aluminum is brazed to steel, which is then brazed to the copper.

Brazing Methods

There are numerous brazing methods. They are described in detail in chapters following. All the methods include the same basic steps. The prime differences between the various methods lie in the way the parts are heated and in the way the flux and filler metal are applied. The only exceptions are vacuum and vibration or motion brazing, which require no flux.

Figure 1-1. *Giant, single manifold, brazed (and welded) aluminum heat exchangers are now manufactured with up to 500,000 square feet of exchange surface.*

Courtesy, South Wind Division, Stewart-Warner Corp.

Joint and Jig Design

Simple, strong and entirely satisfactory brazed joints can be made by lapping one clean, flux-covered piece of aluminum with another. Brazing filler metal is placed near the lap. The parts are heated until the filler melts and is drawn by capillary force into the space provided by the flux. The joint is cooled, cleaned and put to use. Thousands upon thousands of these simple "non-designed" brazed joints are produced every day in the course of manufacture, field construction and repair.

However, when maximum quality, tight-tolerance, distortion-free, complex aluminum assemblies are to be brazed, forethought—designing—is necessary.

Basic Design Considerations

Proper design normally begins with a full and careful study of the relationship between the brazed joints, the parts they are to join and the dimensional criteria of the completed unit. During this study and afterwards the designer should bear the following aluminum brazing parameters in mind.

1. The distance between faying surfaces, i.e., joint gap clearance, may be estimated on the basis of past experience, but the final dimension, as ascertained by testing, may differ.

2. Aluminum's coefficient of expansion is roughly a third greater than the metals commonly used for fixturing and jigging.

3. Aluminum is soft and barely self-supporting at brazing temperature.

4. Some distortion may be expected when a complex assembly is severely quenched after brazing.

Design anticipation can reduce the above considerations to negligible factors, for example:

1. Joint gap changes found necessary by testing and normal manufacturing variations in part dimensions both may be accommodated by placing the joint's plane of contact in line with expected or possible changes. Figure 2-1 illustrates this point. A change in joint clearance (from optimum) generally results in lowered joint quality and is usually avoided. Lap width, however, can be varied considerably with no penalty whatsoever.

2. The difference in expansion between aluminum and fixturing metals (steel for example) amounts to roughly no more than 0.005 inch/inch/1000°F. When small parts, or parts with curves free to expand are brazed, the difference in expansion is often ignored. When larger, non-flexing parts are brazed, light springs, weights and simple levers are used to hold parts in place. In many instances the fixture can also serve as an assembly and alignment aid. Figure 2-2 depicts a typical brazing fixture.

3. Small or fairly thick or vertical aluminum parts generally need no support during brazing. Long, thin, horizontal parts need support which may be provided in any of innumerable ways.

4. There are heat-treatable alloys which can be returned to their former temper without severe quenching. There are methods of quenching which reportedly eliminate distortion (proprietary quenching solutions and liquid nitrogen). However, when some distortion is anticipated and finished assembly tolerances are closer than ± 0.002 inch, slightly oversized parts may be used. The parts are machined to size after the assembly has been brazed. Figure 2-3 illustrates this approach. In this way it is possible to produce a

Source: Aluminum Brazing Handbook, 2nd Ed., Aluminum Assn., Inc.

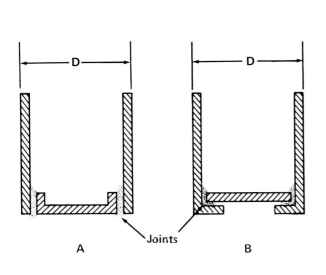

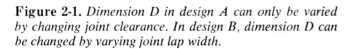

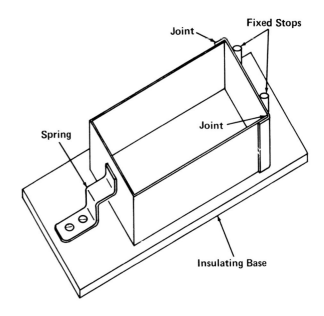

Figure 2-1. *Dimension D in design A can only be varied by changing joint clearance. In design B, dimension D can be changed by varying joint lap width.*

Figure 2-2. *Simple, spring-loaded fixture serves as an assembling and aligning aid. Fixtures of this type may be used for torch and furnace brazing.*

brazed structure with perfectly planed, highly accurate, finished angles and dimensions.

Joint Parameters

All the following conditions must be met if *maximum quality* brazed joints are to be formed.

1. The faying surfaces and a distance beyond are chemically clean, free of foreign adhesions and unwanted bumps and dimples. (In many instances the "as is" condition of the aluminum is satisfactory, and many commercial brazing shops merely vapor degrease their aluminum prior to brazing.)

2. The oxide, always present on aluminum, is thin on the faying surfaces and beyond for a half-inch or so.

3. The distance between mating surfaces is correct for the width of the joint, the filler and parent metals, brazing method and time/temperature used.

4. The joint is designed to permit flux and filler metal to enter easily and to permit flux, filler, oxide and heat-generated gases to exit just as easily.

5. The faying surfaces and the desired fillet surfaces are fluxed prior to brazing. Assemblies to be joined by flux dip and vacuum brazing excepted.

6. If one or both parts are not made of brazing sheet, the correct quantity of filler metal is covered with

flux and properly positioned prior to brazing or hand fed during brazing.

7. The assembly and furnace (if used) are vented to permit the escape of gases generated during brazing and the expansion of trapped air.

8. The joint is brought to proper temperature and held there long enough for brazing to be accomplished.

9. Parts are maintained in fixed relationship during brazing and cooling.

10. If brazing sheet is to supply filler metal, the clad (filler metal) surface of the brazing sheet touches the part it is to join for the length of the joint.

Joint Clearance

Joint clearance—the distance separating the two metal surfaces to be joined and the shape and relation of one surface to the other—is critical.

Joint clearance determines capillary force. And it is capillary force that makes thousands of simultaneous brazed joints possible, drawing the molten filler metal deeply into every crack and crevice, around corners, under touching parts, up vertical joints and overhead.

Capillary force acting on molten filler immersed in a salt-dip brazing bath is strong enough to draw the liquid metal into and up a vertical joint 24 inches high. It is this force that makes it unnecessary to place the filler metal in its final position. Aided and abetted by the molten flux

Joint Width	Suggested Clearance
Less than 0.250 inch	0.002 to 0.004 inch
Over 0.250 inch	0.002 to 0.025 inch

TORCH, FURNACE AND INDUCTION

Less than 0.250 inch	0.004 to 0.008 inch
Over 0.250 inch	0.004 to 0.025 inch

(When brazing sheet is used to supply the filler metal, the filler side or sides of the brazing sheet must be in firm contact with the part or parts to be joined.)

Table 2-1. *Suggested joint clearances for various brazing methods and joint widths.*

which reduces the filler's surface tension from about 850 dynes/cm in an inert atmosphere or in a vacuum to some 650 dynes/cm, liquid filler will follow a clean fluxed path or joint on hot metal to its end and into all clean, fluxed joints adjoining.

Capillary force is directly related to joint clearance. The smaller the clearance the greater capillary force. However, the smaller the joint gap the longer it takes molten metal to traverse the joint, the greater the possibility flux, oxide, gas and foreign matter will be trapped inside. Also the greater the possibility of filler stoppage by virtue of the filler alloying with the base metal to form a new alloy that is less fluid at that particular temperature.

On the other hand, overly large joint gaps pose difficulties of their own. Most important, capillary action is reduced. Flux and filler may not follow the joint to its end. More stress is placed on the fillet because of its larger cross section. The strength of the joint will be closer to that of the filler metal than the base metal. Gaps may appear in the joint. A smooth and even fillet may not form, and filler metal is wasted.

Fortunately, arriving at the correct or best joint clearance for a particular brazing job is not difficult. In practice, satisfactory joint clearance is quickly determined by means of a few test joints made under actual production conditions. Once gap dimensions have been established, they will hold true as long as the other factors involved—brazing method, time/temperature, flux and alloys—are not changed. Table 2-1 lists joint clearances suitable for most brazing conditions.

Establishing and Maintaining Joint Gap Clearance

For casual brazing, joint clearance may be established

by a layer of flux between the mating surfaces. If weight and pressure distribution is such that the assembly remains motionless, except for small thermal movement during the brazing cycle, a strong, useful joint will result without further care.

A simple but more positive method of establishing gap clearance consists of using correct-thickness shims of brazing filler metal to separate the parts to be joined. This technique is illustrated in Figure 2-4. As the brazing filler metal shims melt during the brazing cycle and shrink about 5% on cooling, shims alone cannot be relied upon for close-tolerance joint gaps. Additional support and fixturing means should be used. These are discussed and illustrated in following paragraphs and figures.

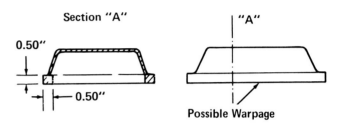

Assembly immediately after brazing

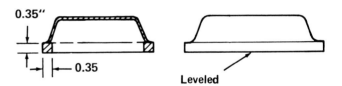

Assembly machined to fine tolerance after brazing

Figure 2-3. *Highly accurate final dimensions are easily obtained by using slightly oversize stock and machining the assembly after the parts have been brazed.*

Improving Brazing Filler Metal Flow

Molten metal flows best on clean, roughened or etched surfaces. Each scratch and pore acts as a capillary to pull the metal along. Metal surfaces should not be specular (mirror-like) if they are to be joined by brazing. (The chemicals used for cleaning aluminum quickly etch polished surfaces.)

Avoiding Flux Entrapment

Dry flux is chemically inert, but the fact that the flux is enclosed within a tight joint is no assurance that there is no moisture inside nor that moisture will never find its way into the joint to activate the flux and produce corrosion and damage.

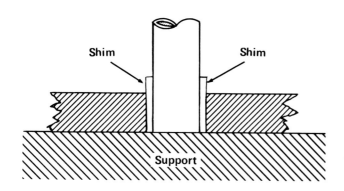

Figure 2-4. *How brazing filler metal shims may be used to center parts, and provide escape routes for gas and flux.*

Good design provides an escape route for molten flux, heat-generated gases and expanding air, and also provides easy access to the solidified flux that must be removed after brazing.

Long joints should be vented along their lengths. Joints should not be filled with filler metal from both ends, which could lock the flux and gas inside.

As mentioned previously, overly-small gap clearance can cause flux entrapment within the joint. Still other possible causes are low brazing temperature, insufficient filler metal and insufficient time at brazing temperature. If the filler metal doesn't more than fill the joint, some flux may be left inside.

Vessels Must Be Vented

At brazing temperature, flux releases hydrogen and other gases. At the same time, the air within the enclosed space expands. Together, they may produce sufficient pressure in a closed vessel to distort it, if it doesn't rupture or explode. Closed vessels must be vented. The small vent hole may be brazed closed in a separate operation afterwards.

Blind holes also must be vented. Solid members can be brazed into heavy pieces of metal, but if no vent hole is provided, gas pressure can drive the molten filler out of the joint. See Figure 2-5.

Joint Types

Lapped joints are very strong, easily brazed and require no special care other than the accurate determination and maintenance of joint clearance. Joints of this type, with 100% efficiency and even more strength than the parent metals joined, are easily produced by making the width of the lap two to three times the thickness of the thinner of the two pieces of metal to be joined.

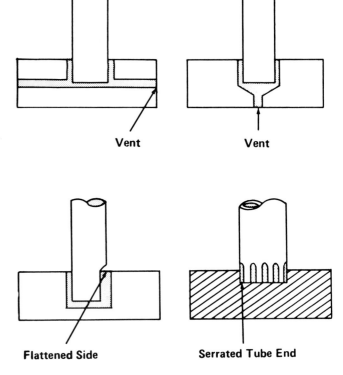

Figure 2-5. *Examples of how solid joints may be vented.*

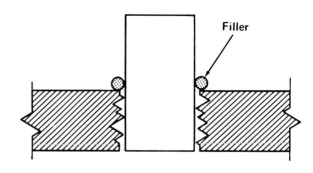

Figure 2-6. *How prick punch indentations and protrusions may be used to center and hold part in place.*

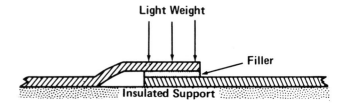

Figure 2-7. *A simple offset, formed in one of the parts, may be used to establish lap-joint clearance.*

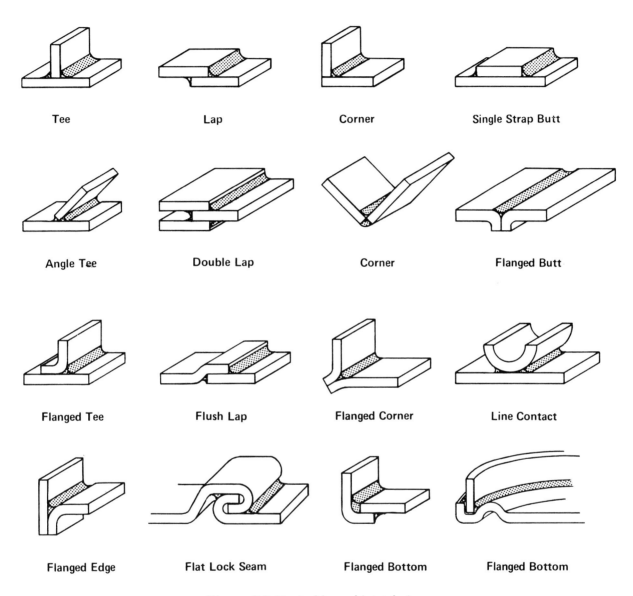

Figure 2-8. *Typical brazed joint designs.*

Lap-joint clearance can be established and maintained in any number of ways. A sharp prick punch can be used to dimple the thinner piece of metal. Or the punch may be employed to raise protrusions of the correct height on the heavier piece of metal. A piece of filler metal of the correct thickness may be placed between the two lapped pieces of metal and a light weight used to hold the sandwich immobile. Flat pieces of metal may be bent into offsets, which determine gap dimensions. Figures 2-6 and 2-7 illustrate these methods.

Where mating edges do not overlap, the edge may be turned or bent to provide a lap. Sometimes a flat or angular third piece of metal may be introduced to provide the desired lap.

Tee joints are easily made as there is usually no need for joint clearance when the butting member is of thin stock. Unless the pressure between parts is very high, the molten filler will flow under the edge of the metal, wetting and bonding to the butting edge and forming fillets on both sides of the tee.

Source: Aluminum Brazing Handbook, 2nd Ed., Aluminum Assn., Inc.

Line contact joints, such as are formed when a tube is placed on a flat surface, like tee joints, are easily made. If the curved contacting section is of relatively small radius and the line of contact is fairly narrow, clearance may be omitted between the two parts. Both surfaces must be fluxed, however.

The strength of line contact joints may be increased by increasing the width of the line of contact. Circular sections may be flattened to form oval sections with greater contact area. Sine-shaped corrugated sheets may be replaced by sheets with hat-shaped cross sections.

When this is done the joint must be treated as a lap joint and provisions made for establishing and holding joint clearance during brazing.

Butt joints can be made equal in strength to the parent metal, but they lack ductility and require so much care that designers avoid them whenever possible. To produce a 100% efficient butt joint the edges must be held in perfect alignment and the mating surfaces must be parallel. This usually requires machining. They are rarely used.

Typical recommended brazed joint designs, made with brazing filler metal and with brazing sheet, are shown in Figures 2-8 and 2-9.

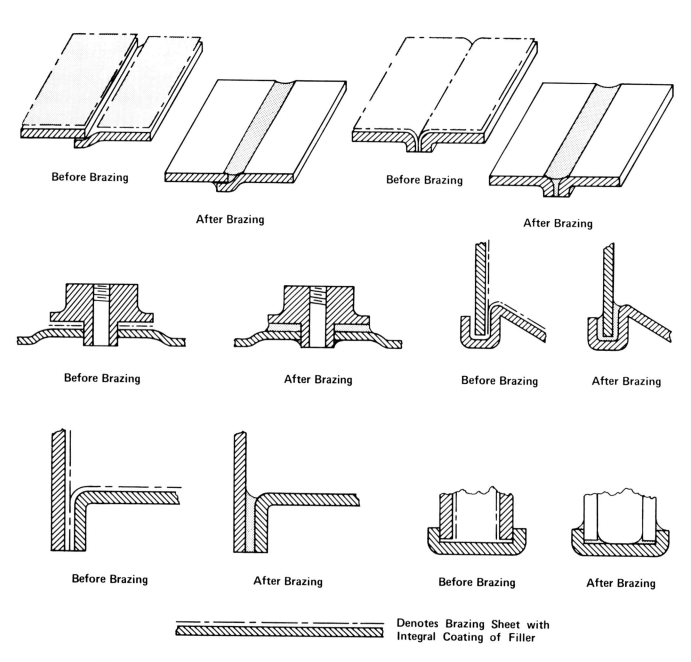

Denotes Brazing Sheet with Integral Coating of Filler

Figure 2-9. *Typical joints made with aluminum brazing sheet, before and after brazing.*

Thick-metal and Broad-lap Joints

When an ⅛ inch thick or thicker piece of aluminum is butted against a flat surface to form a tee joint, the butting surface (edge) should be reduced to promote the flow of filler metal. This may be done by roughing, serrating, rounding or angling the butting edge. See Figure 2-10. Serrations and corrugations cut into the contacting edge should never be so deep as to prevent the formation of fillets. Permissible depth will vary with brazing method. If the butting edge is curved, the radius should be large so that the space between the two pieces of metals is nowhere more than 0.010 inch or so. If the edge is angled, it is generally kept within 5 to 8 degrees of the plane.

When thick aluminum alloy plate is to be butt joined, the faying edges may be machined to an angle to produce a scarf joint thus increasing the faying surfaces. Or, the faying edges may be V'd or rounded, one edge concave

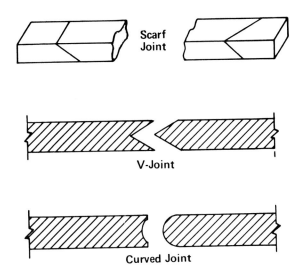

Figure 2-11. *Alternatives to use in place of butt joints.*

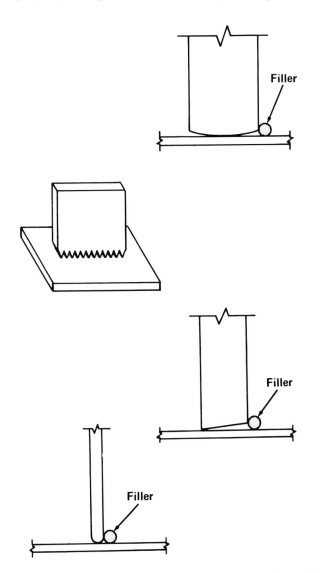

Figure 2-10. *How the contacting edges of thick sections may be rounded, serrated, angled or curved to promote the flow of filler metal into the joint.*

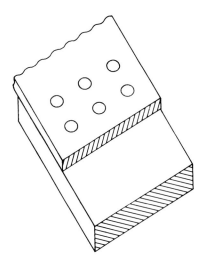

Figure 2-12. *Weep holes cut into one joint member are used to vent flux, gas and filler metal when making wide-lap brazed joints.*

the other convex so that one edge fits into the other. When the mating surfaces are wide, special means must be provided for the escape of fluxes and gases. Again, serrations, corrugations, dissimilar angles and curves to form narrow-angle faying surfaces can be used. See Figure 2-11.

Lap joints greater than ½ inch in width should be vented by means of weep holes. See Figure 2-12.

Pressed-fit joints are normally not used when brazing aluminum as there is always the danger of flux and gas entrapment and perfect contact areas which preclude the entrance of flux. Pressed fits can be used to position pieces and they can be brazed if the fillet is formed a distance beyond the tightly fitted pieces.

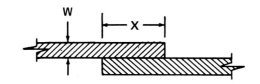

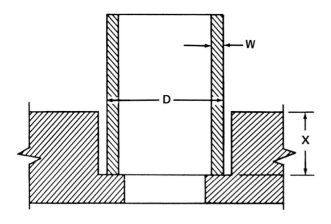

$$X = \frac{YTW}{L}$$

$$X = \frac{W(D-W)YT}{LD}$$

T   Tensile strength of thinner or weaker part in lbs/sq/inch

X   Length of lap in inches

W   Thickness of the thinnest part in inches

D   Diameter of the area of shear in inches

Y   Safety factor—this is usually 4 or 5

L   Shear strength of the braze alloy in lbs/sq/inch

Figure 2-13. *Calculating needed overlap by formula.*

Other Types of Joints

Tube-to-tube joints of aluminum are easily brazed when one tube end is tapered 10 to 12 degrees. The joint can be made with any of the brazing methods available.

Tube-to-fitting joints also are easily made. Two methods are commonly employed to insure satisfactory joints between thin wall tubing and cast or considerably heavier metal parts. One involves knurling the tube or fitting with the knurling lines or score marks cut parallel to length of the joint. The other method consists of tapering the hole.

Calculating Overlap

Joints should be overlapped sufficiently to provide the desired strength and possibly stiffness, but little more. There is nothing to be gained by indiscriminate overlapping.

The rule of thumb for overlapping is that the overlap be two or three times the thickness of the thinner member of the joint. When greater strength is wanted, or when an exact calculation of joint strength is needed, the formula given in Figure 2-13 may be used.

A formula is provided also for use in calculating the strength of a joint between a thin-wall tube and a fairly thick, solid member. Conversely, the formula may be used to find the required lap length in inches to produce specific joint strength.

Joints For Non-Constant Loads and Maximum Fatigue Strength

Brazed joints are naturally resistant to non-constant loads and vibration. A brazed assembly is an integral, single piece of metal. There is no possibility of inter-part motion developing as there is in a riveted or bolted assembly. In addition, brazing produces fillets that are ideally shaped to resist vibration—meniscus curves that sweep across the joints and up the sides of the parent metal.

The designer seeking to produce joints with maximum resistance to vibration and changing loads need but follow standard practice for joints of this type.

Joints should be as smooth as possible with no undercutting, cracks, porosity, flux inclusion, foreign matter and open spaces that might localize stress and provide the starting point for failure. Sudden changes in section should be avoided. Transitions from thin to thick members should be as gradual as possible. Joints loaded eccentrically should be supported by stiffeners to reduce secondary bending. Openings, fittings, baffles, brackets and other attachments should not be placed near highly stressed areas of the assembly.

Increasing a fillet's cross section generally increases the fillet's resistance to bending moments of force and vibration. However, there is an optimum fillet size beyond which strength may actually be lost and there is a maximum practical fillet size for a given joint configuration. Feeding additional filler metal into the joint will not increase fillet size beyond its natural limits. The fillet's base will increase, but its height will not.

Pressure Tight Vessels

Assemblies designed to withstand pressure from either within or without are best made with lap joints. The lap joint is the strongest joint and it provides the longest braze path, thus reducing the possibility of leakage through the joint. See Figure 2-14. All vessels must be vented while brazing.

Filler, Placement, Shape and Quantity

There are three ways in which filler metal is brought to the joint it is to fill. (1) The filler metal may be placed in or near the joint before brazing; (2) filler can be supplied by brazing sheet; (3) filler metal may be hand fed to the joint while brazing. When necessary, these methods may be combined.

If the designer selects the first method, he has hundreds of commercially prepared filler sizes and shapes to choose from. There are rods, sheets, washers, tubes, wires

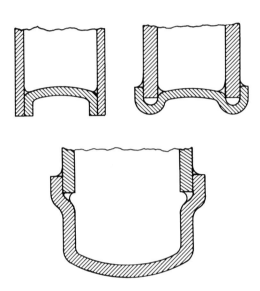

Figure 2-14. *Typical brazed joints that have proven suitable for pressure-tight containers.*

and rings. There are many companies that pre-form filler metal to specifications. Filler metal is also available in foil thickness, powder and paste form.

Filler metal may be cut, bent, shaped and drawn as desired. The only precaution necessary—other than not exceeding the limits of the ductility of the metal—is that no other metallic or undesirable substance be included with the filler by reason of its forming.

If the designer selects the second method he has a range of brazing sheet thicknesses to choose from, with filler cladding in a number of alloys and a number of thicknesses on one or both sides of the sheet.

Brazing sheets are also manufactured with a "barrier" layer between the base metal and the filler metal to reduce the amount of diffusion that may occur during the brazing cycle.

Brazing sheet can be spun and formed as severely as the parent metal without danger of loosening the filler cladding. While the use of brazing sheet increases the cost of filler metal in an assembly, brazing sheet can eliminate

the need to preplace filler metal and thus reduce labor costs.

As the clad surface of a brazing sheet does not emerge from the brazing operation with as finished an appearance as the unclad side of the metal—it is not as smooth—designers usually plan the assembly so that the filler-clad side of the sheet is out of sight on the finished part.

It is possible to compute the quantity of filler required to produce a particular fillet cross section in a particular joint configuration. (See Mike A. Miller, "Metal Flow and Fillet Formation in Brazing Aluminum," "The Flow of Metal in Brazing Aluminum," the Welding Journal Research Supplement Feb. 1946 and Oct. 1941, respectively, and "Diffusion of Silicon in Aluminum Brazing Sheet," J. R. Terrill, Welding Journal, May 1966.) However, the simplest and most accurate method of finding the quantity of filler metal needed is by test.

The filler supplied a joint need not be measured precisely—unless some special condition exists—but one general guideline prevails. It is better to supply a bit more filler than needed than a little less. However, an excessive quantity of filler should be avoided. In addition to the waste of metal, excess filler may be unsightly and may roll off to interfere with the assembly's working.

Maximum fillet height that can be achieved when dip brazing is roughly 0.5 inch. Maximum filler height with other brazing methods is roughly 0.3 inch.

Fillet height will be reduced if the assembly is accidentally shaken while the filler is molten, or if it is removed too rapidly from a dip tank.

Proper Filler Placement

Three factors should be considered when pre-positioning filler metal: (1) filler travel distance; (2) mass relation between filler and parent metal; and (3) heat source in relation to filler metal and parent metal.

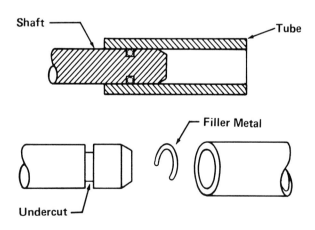

Figure 2-15. *One method of preplacement of brazing filler metal in wire form. This may be a preform.*

Source: Aluminum Brazing Handbook, 2nd Ed., Aluminum Assn., Inc.

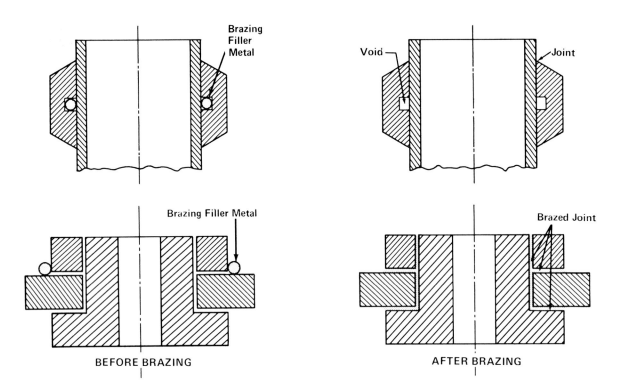

Figure 2-16. *Brazed joints after an internally and an externally positioned ring of filler metal has been used.*

1. Good design calls for the placement of the filler metal as close to its ultimate resting place as possible. The shorter the filler travel distance the less time there will be for the filler metal to alloy with the parent metal; the less chance the filler may encounter obstructions and the smaller the oxide load that has to be pushed out of the way.

2. When the mass of filler metal is small in relation to the parts being brazed, care must be taken to make certain the filler doesn't melt too early. If it does, it may ball up and roll off. One of the steps that can be taken to prevent this includes placing the filler in a groove within the part. Figures 2-15, 2-16 and 2-17 illustrate various possible filler placement treatments.

   When there is considerable mass difference between parts being brazed, the lighter or thinner part will reach brazing temperature first. It is therefore best, when possible, to place the filler metal in contact with the heavier part.

3. When brazing heat is supplied from one point or direction, as might be the case with an automatic torch or a cold-wall furnace, it is important that the filler be protected from the source of direct heat. Otherwise the filler may melt prematurely and may roll away before the parent metal comes to brazing temperature.

Dimensional Changes During the Brazing Cycle

When an aluminum plug is brazed within a hole in another piece of aluminum of relatively the same mass, the plug and hole expand and contract at approximately the same rate as the temperature goes up and down. If the joint's clearance is correct when the parts are cold, a good joint can usually be formed without difficulty.

If the external part is so large that it remains relatively cool throughout the brazing cycle, the inner part will reduce the joint's clearance as it heats up. If the inner part is small and a little additional clearance is provided, the loss in joint clearance may be inconsequential. If the inner part is large the joint may be unbrazeable unless the outer piece is thoroughly heated during the brazing cycle.

An inch of aluminum expands approximately 0.012 inch when it is brought to brazing heat (1000°F.). The metals normally used for jigging and fixturing expand considerably less. The approximate coefficients of thermal expansion for common metals over the temperature range

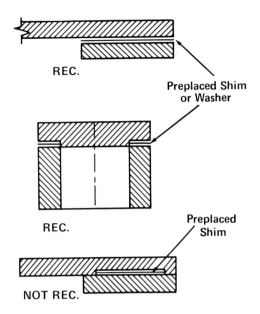

Figure 2-17. *Examples of correct and incorrect preplacement of brazing filler metal in shim form.*

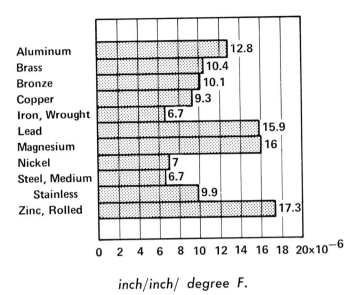

inch/inch/ degree F.

Table 2-2. *Approximate coefficient of thermal expansion for common metals over the range of 100°F to 1000°F.*

encountered while brazing aluminum are provided in Table 2-2. Its accuracy is sufficient for most brazing conditions.

Jigging and Fixturing

Except when flux-dip brazing, simple weights and levers frequently suffice to hold parts in alignment. Flux-dipped assemblies, however, require positive restraint. While the molten flux has a specific gravity close to that of aluminum and almost supports the immersed metal, the hot flux acts to separate the parts as they are dipped into and removed from the hot salt.

Although it may take more planning to design brazed assemblies that hold themselves together while being brazed, and more labor and material to fabricate self-jigging joints, in most instances self-jigged unit assemblies are far less costly to braze in the long run.

Jigs can be very expensive in more ways than one. There is the initial cost of design and fabrication. And there is the number of jigs required to be considered. The jigs themselves must be frequently cleaned: They pick up flux encrustations as readily as the assemblies. The jigs add to the heating and cooling load and increase space requirements in bath and furnace. As the jigs are in direct contact with the assemblies, the jigs lengthen the time needed to bring the assemblies up to brazing temperature, and this is always highly undesirable. Used for flux-dip brazing, jigs always increase the quantity of flux dragged out and thus wasted.

There is no limit to the variety of ways in which parts may be made self-jigging other than the limitations imposed by the designer's own imagination. Parts can be held together by tabs, pins, rivets, crimping, staking, tack welding, cold welding, springs, clips, folding, press fitting, tie wires and so on. Figure 2-18 presents a number of self-jigging ideas.

If the holding device is an alloy similar to the aluminum alloys being brazed, the holding element can be brazed right into the assembly and made integral. This can be done with tack welds, screws, wires, pins and bolts. Tabs and bolts may be deliberately positioned external to the brazed unit and later cut off and ground smooth.

If the holding device needs to be removed after brazing, it can be fabricated from oxidized stainless steel and other metals which are not readily wetted by the brazing filler metal. Or the part can be coated with a stop-off material.

As aluminum under heat expands more than the metals commonly used for jigs and fixtures, the designer has the choice of making his jigs from aluminum (which is rarely done) or incorporating some form of expansion relief in jigs and fixtures made from other metals.

Whatever arrangement of springs, weights or levers is devised, it must hold the aluminum parts lightly but positively. Parts must be allowed to expand and contract freely. If this is not done, the parts may be thrown out of alignment, strained or deformed during brazing. Figure 2-19 illustrates two fixtures incorporating springs.

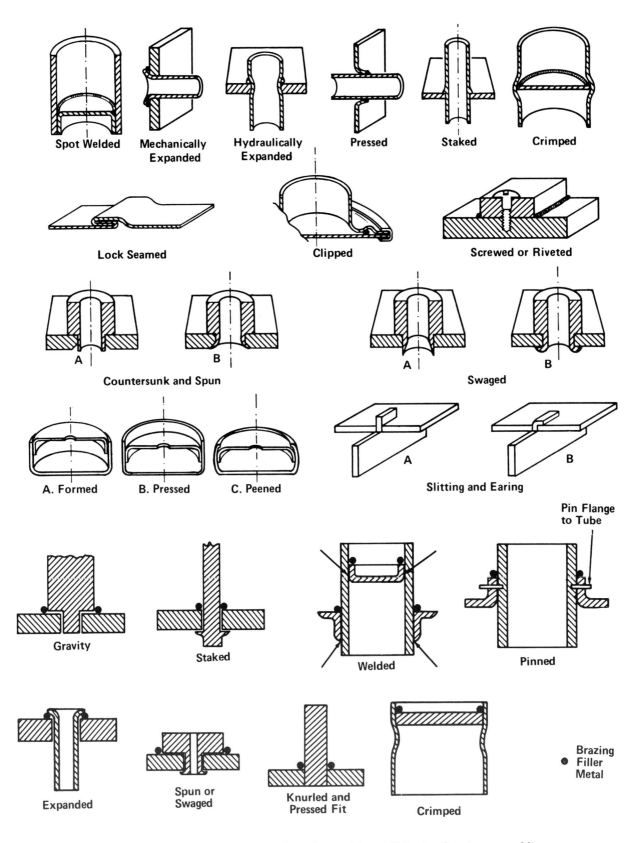

Spot Welded **Mechanically Expanded** **Hydraulically Expanded** **Pressed** **Staked** **Crimped**

Lock Seamed **Clipped** **Screwed or Riveted**

A B **Countersunk and Spun** A B **Swaged**

A. Formed **B. Pressed** **C. Peened** A B **Slitting and Earing**

Pin Flange to Tube

Gravity **Staked** **Welded** **Pinned**

Expanded **Spun or Swaged** **Knurled and Pressed Fit** **Crimped**

● Brazing Filler Metal

Figure 2-18. *Twenty-one suggestions for making self-jigging brazing assemblies.*

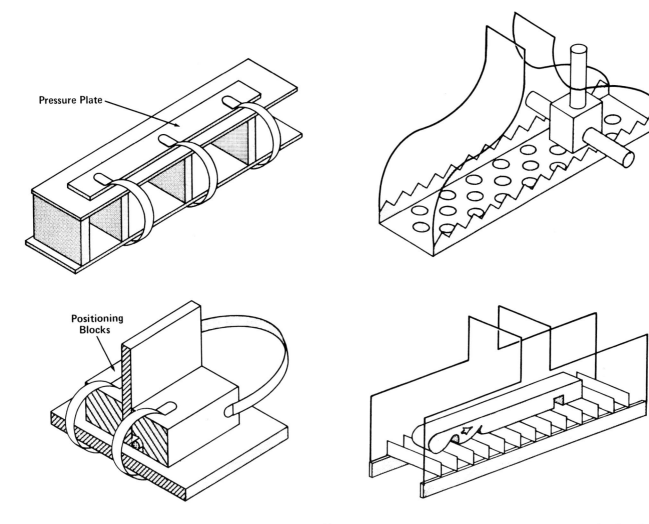

Figure 2-19. *How C-clamp springs may be used to hold parts lightly but dependably during brazing.*

Figure 2-20. *Two designs for dependable dip-brazing fixtures that can be fabricated in the shop.*

For furnace runs of several hundred units, low carbon steel without surface treatment is usually satisfactory as jig and fixture material. Longer life will be secured if the flux is removed each time the jigs and fixtures are used.

However, neither bare, low carbon steel nor coated carbon steel is recommended for flux-dip brazing. Steel and iron quickly contaminate the flux bath. Aluminum or nickel coating will protect the steel to some degree, but the action of the hot flux on the aluminum and nickel is very strong and the coating may not survive a dozen immersions in the hot bath.

When long furnace brazing runs are anticipated or when jigs and fixtures are to be dipped into hot flux more than a dozen times or so, it is advisable to use stainless steel or Inconel X-750. Of the two, Inconel keeps ts temper better under heat and when used for dip brazing. Reportedly, Inconel outlasts stainless several times over. Stainless steel is attacked by the hot flux which selectively

dissolves the nickel and eventually the alloy turns to crumbly black iron that falls apart.

The useful life of stainless steel jigs and fixtures can be extended somewhat and the unwanted effect of the iron contaminating the flux can be reduced by shot blasting the fixtures when they darken. This removes the surface iron and exposes fresh, high-nickel content stainless underneath. With repeated exposure, the hot flux selectively dissolves the nickel and peening is again needed.

Heat losses introduced by jigs and fixtures can be minimized by keeping the jigs and fixtures as small and as light as possible. Heat loss from the assembly into the fixture can be reduced by utilizing point and line contacts.

Dip brazing jigs and fixtures must be open to permit easy draining. Such fixtures are best fabricated from thin rods and bars set on edge. When a plate must be used, it should be pierced by large holes. Figure 2-20 shows typical dip-brazing fixtures.

Source: Aluminum Brazing Handbook, 2nd Ed., Aluminum Assn., Inc.

Unless one of the fluxless brazing methods is to be used, or the assembly is to be brazed by flux dipping, all surfaces that are to be wetted by the filler metal and the filler itself must be fluxed. Without flux, molten filler forms a ball even though the surface it contacts is clean and the temperature is high.

The flux should be applied to the cleaned parts and filler metal as soon before brazing as possible. Generally the time between fluxing and brazing is kept under 45 minutes. Flux is hygroscopic. The longer it is exposed to air the more it dilutes itself with water.

Both sides of the filler metal and both facing sides of the joint should be fluxed. This is best done prior to assembly and assures the presence of the flux within the joint.

When the filler is not placed within the joint but is positioned near the joint, it is necessary that the path the filler is expected to take be fluxed.

The means or method of applying the flux is unimportant. It can be brushed on, sprayed on or the part can be dipped into cold flux. Flux in powder form can be mixed with alcohol to form a thick paste. Glass, porcelain or porcelain-lined vessels should be used for mixing and holding flux. Steel containers will contaminate the flux. Containers should be tightly closed to prevent deliquescence. Generally, fresh flux is mixed every four to six hours and the old mixture discarded.

Sufficient flux should be applied to enable it to do its complex job. Insufficient flux leads to porous, weak, and incomplete joints. Excessive amounts of flux should also be avoided. The hot flux is corrosive and will attack and etch whatever metal it touches.

When using brazing sheet, the entire clad surface of the sheet is generally fluxed to aid the filler metal moving on. This also results in a smoother finish on the clad surface when the work is completed.

Stopping Filler From Flowing

Molten filler metal can be immobilized by omitting flux from the area on which the filler is not wanted. A more positive means consists of removing capillary attraction. A notch of one kind or another is cut in the line of capillary flow. For example, if only a portion of a tube's end is to be brazed to a flat, the not-to-be brazed section would be cut short so that it would not touch the flat surface. A distance of as little as 0.10 inch is usually sufficient to prevent filler metal flow.

Stop-off material, substances which literally block the flow of the filler much as an earth dam blocks the flow of water, is also frequently used to control the path of liquid filler metal. There are many excellent commercial stop-off compounds available. The only shop mixture worth making consists of colloidial graphite and water or alcohol.

The prime requisite of a stop-off material is that it block the flow of filler metal without adversely affecting nearby surfaces and that it be easily removed in hot water along with the flux. A few tests will quickly uncover the stop-off formula or product best for each brazing operation.

Sequential Joints

When it is desirable or necessary to fabricate an assembly from a number of sub units, or necessary to form a second, nearby joint after the first has solidified, the procedure calls for use of the highest melting point filler in the first brazing cycle. The next brazing cycle is accomplished with lower-melting point filler leaving the formed joints intact. As diffusion always accompanies brazing, the filler metal always loses a portion of its silicon to the base metal. This raises the melting point of the completed joint. Therefore a second joint can be brazed next to an already-cooled joint with far less danger of softening and damaging the entire assembly than listed temperatures indicate.

Brazed assemblies can also be welded. While welding temperatures are very high, welding speeds are equally high so that it is quite practical to weld brazed parts without disturbing the brazed joints.

Figure 2-21. *Applying flux to a bracket to be brazed to the inner cylinder of a Telstar satellite.*

Courtesy, Hughes-Treitler

Base Metals, Brazing Filler Metals and Fluxes

Heat-treatable and Nonheat-treatable Alloys

Various elements in differing ratios are added to aluminum to alter and improve its physical and chemical properties. Certain alloying elements produce a group of alloys which can only be strengthened and hardened by cold working. These alloys are classified as nonheat-treatable. The balance of the wrought aluminum alloys can be strengthened by heat treatment and to a much smaller degree by cold working. They are called heat-treatable alloys.

Both groups of alloys lose their strength at increasingly rapid rates as they are heated. At their respective annealing temperatures they part company. The nonheat-treatable alloys soften and return immediately to 0 Temper. The heat-treatable alloys must be held at annealing temperature for a minimum of 20 minutes before an appreciable portion of their temper disappears. The heat-treatable alloys can be returned to temper by heat treatment and aging. The nonheat-treatable alloys must be cold worked to be tempered.

Aluminum is brazed at temperatures betwen 1030°F. and 1195°F. Aluminum alloys are annealed at temperatures of 659°F. to 800°F. Obviously a certain amount of annealing cannot be avoided when brazing.

The exact amount of annealing that occurs depends on the alloy, time/temperature and mass of the area subjected to heat. As it is almost always impractical to strain harden an assembly after it has been brazed, the choice of a nonheat-treatable alloy results in a brazed assembly that is close to 0 temper. Loss of temper, however, is not undesirable in every design. In some instances it may be advantageous to shape and form the parts after they have been joined by brazing. And there are many brazed components that do not require the maximum strength available from aluminum.

In some cases, the choice of a nonheat-treatable alloy can reduce overall fabrication costs. With the exception of those alloys containing a high percentage of magnesium, oxides on the surface of the nonheat-treatable alloys are not as tenacious as those that form on heat-treatable alloys. Where maximum quality joints are not needed and an occasional reject is acceptable, nonheat-treatable aluminum is often prepared for brazing by vapor degreasing alone and is not chemically cleaned prior to brazing.

The composition and physical properties of all the brazeable aluminum alloys and the filler metals used with them are listed in Tables 3-1 through 3-6, which may be found at the end of this chapter. Figure 3-1 shows the maximum safe brazing temperatures for various aluminum alloys.

The nonheat-treatable alloys most frequently brazed are found mainly in the 1000, 3000 and low magnesium-content 5000 series of alloys. The major alloying elements in these series include manganese and magnesium. Some alloys contain but one alloying element. Others contain a number of elements. Filler metals are available for all present-day, commercial, wrought, nonheat-treatable alloys, so all of them can be brazed.

Heat-treatable alloys most frequently brazed are 6061, 6063, 6951 and 7005.

Heat-treatable aluminum alloys are tempered by solution heat treatment followed by quenching. This in turn is followed by natural or artificial aging, and with some alloys, a certain amount of cold working.

When the alloy leaves the quenching tank it is soft and workable. It can be kept in this condition for several hours by chilling it to below freezing temperature. Lower temperatures will hold the alloy in this soft condition for even longer periods of time.

This condition (W temper) is not stable. The alloy will of itself harden and gain strength with the passage of time.

The rate of change is temperature dependent, increasing with higher temperature.

When this process is complete or has reached an acceptably stable state the alloy is said to have aged. If aging has occurred at room temperature the alloy is said to be naturally aged. If aging has been accelerated by heating the metal to several hundred degrees and holding it there for a dozen hours or so, the alloy is said to have been artificially aged. Aging rate and final temper are closely related to time and temperature and vary considerably from alloy to alloy. Some alloys reach full strength at room temperature in months; others require years. Specific temperatures and time periods for aging aluminum alloys may be found in *Nonferrous Physical Metallurgy,* Pitman Publishing, *Aluminum,* Vol. II, *Fabrication & Finishing,* ASM, and standard heat-treatment reference works.

Brazing followed by quenching, followed by natural or artificial aging tempers heat-treatable alloys. Already tempered heat-treatable alloys lose little temper to brazing. Non-tempered, heat-treatable alloys are tempered by the brazing cycle. Specific temper gain or loss depends on the alloy, area involved (whether the entire assembly or only a portion is heated and quenched) and temperatures involved.

Quenching rate may be varied to match the alloy and the desired temper. Where economy of fabrication is paramount and some distortion is acceptable, the hot brazed parts are unceremoniously dumped into boiling water, which is the best water temperature for removing flux from the work pieces.

Slower quench rates may be secured with steam, fine water mists, blasts of cooled or ambient air, inversely soluble proprietary organic solutions and liquid nitrogen. The quenching rate and quantity of nitrogen lost is lower than might be imagined. The hot assembly is immediately surrounded by a shield of nitrogen gas, which insulates the metal from direct contact with the liquid.

A high quench rate is not necessary with all alloys. Alloy 7005 can be quenched as slowly as ½ to 1°F. per second through its 700° to 500°F. critical range and then aged at room temperature for three days to reach a tensile strength of 42,000 psi. Alloy 6061 can be quenched with a blast of ambient temperature air alone and reach a T4 condition after aging. In this condition its tensile strength is 32,000 psi. See Figure 3-2.

Brazeable Casting Alloys

High quality castings are no more difficult to braze than equally massive wrought alloys. Problems arise, however, when casting quality is low and the metal is porous.

Brazeable aluminum casting alloys include 443.0, 356.0, 406, A712.0, C712.0, D712.0 and 850.0. Alloys

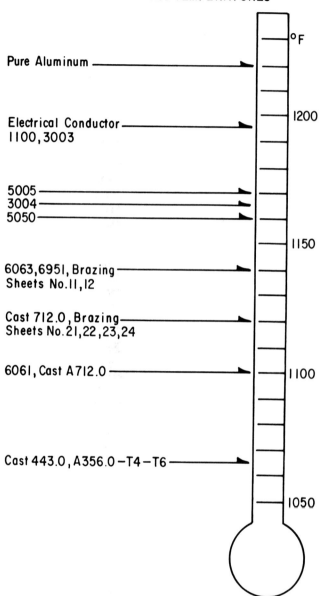

MAXIMUM BRAZING TEMPERATURES

If parent alloys are heated to a temperature higher than shown, excessive melting of the alloying constituents will occur.

Figure 3-1. *Maximum permissible brazing temperatures for various aluminum alloys.*

443.0, 356.0 and 406 are used for both sand and permanent-mold casting. Alloy A712.0 is primarily a sand-casting metal. Alloy C712.0 and 850.0 are used for permanent-mold casting. Alloys 443.0, 356.0 and 712.0 are the casting alloys most frequently brazed. The physical properties and composition of these alloys may be found in the tables at the rear of this chapter.

Alloys Difficult to Braze

High magnesium content alloys in the 5000 series such as 5154, 5083, 5086 and 5456 are difficult to braze. The filler wets the parent metal poorly yet penetrates and diffuses into it excessively.

Die cast alloys are also difficult to braze. The castings are not easily wetted by the molten brazing filler metal and tend to blister when brought to brazing heat because of their high gas content and entrapped lubricants.

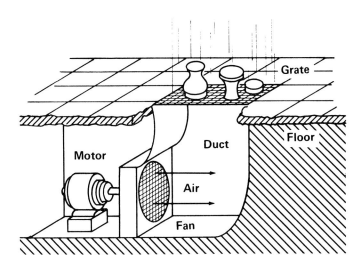

Figure 3-2. *Parts are frequently quenched by means of a blast of ambient temperature air.*

Alloys Presently Not Brazeable

So far, filler metals suitable for alloys 2011, 2014, 2017, 2024, and 7075 have not been developed. Fillers now on the market have melting points above the solidus points of these alloys; therefore brazing is not practical.

Filler Metals

To lower its melting point and give it other physical and chemical properties necessary and desirable for use as a brazing filler metal, silicon, copper, zinc and other elements are added in small quantities to commercially pure aluminum.

Silicon is an alloying element used in all standard fillers and in the largest quantities. Standard commercial fillers are 6.8 to 13% silicon. Silicon lowers the melting point of aluminum. However, ductility decreases as Si content increases and its use as an alloying element is self-limiting. Copper and zinc act to lower the alloy's melting point further still, but these elements increase the brazed joint's susceptibility to corrosion.

Tables 3-2 and 3-3, at the end of this chapter, list the composition and melting ranges of the more common, non-proprietary fillers. Figure 3-3 displays a chart which cross-references one manufacturer's product to another's so that the brazing engineer can quickly relate one trademarked filler to the others.

When and where a choice of filler alloys is possible, the following general guides may be found helpful.

1. When torch brazing, select a filler with a liquidus temperature as far below that of the parent metal as possible. As temperature control is difficult with a torch, a large temperature difference will reduce the chance of accidentally melting the parent metal.

2. When it may be necessary for the operator to push the molten filler into a far corner or to torch-braze a long joint, a filler with a wide spread between its solidus and liquidus will be found helpful.

3. When the importance of producing a "perfect" brazed joint is uppermost in the engineer's mind, fillers with a short melting range (minimum temperature spread between solidus and liquidus) should be selected. Alloy 4047, for example, is a filler metal with but 10°F. between its solid and liquid state. This filler is almost eutectic and will change quickly from a solid to a liquid, reducing the time to which the parts must be subjected to brazing heat, reducing filler-parent metal diffusion and reducing the possibility of the filler solidifying in the joint before it has reached all corners. When small-clearance joints are to be formed, the near eutectic filler is best.

4. When furnace and dip brazing, select a filler with a short melting range. High speed is most desirable.

5. When brazing by torch or induction, fillers with long melting ranges are advisable. The alloy starts to flow at a lower temperature and better control is possible.

Filler alloys 4043, 4343 and 4047 have good corrosion resistance. Filler alloys 4145 and 4245 have less corrosion resistance but are suitable for normal atmospheric exposure.

For maximum electrolytic protection, the pieces of aluminum that comprise the brazed assembly should be of the same alloy. Please refer to Chapter 11, Joint Performance, sub-section, *Corrosion Resistance* for more data on this subject.

A. A. Classification	4343	4145	4047	4045
AWS-ASTM Classification	BAlSi-2	BAlSi-3	BAlSi-4	BAlSi-5
Manufacturers				
Air Products	——	Air Products 4145	Air Products 4047	——
Airco Welding Products	——	——	Airco No. 718	——
All-State Welding Alloys Co., Inc.	——	All-State No. 716, No. 33	All-State No. 718, No. 31	——
Allweld Equipment Corp.	——	Allweld No. 716	Allweld No. 718	——
Aluminum Co. of America	——	Alcoa 716 (4145)	Alcoa 718 (4047)	——
American Brazing Alloys Corp.	Ambraze 356	Ambraze 716	Ambraze 718	——
Aufhauser Bros. Corp.	Aufhauser BAlSi-2	Aufhauser BAlSi-3	Aufhauser BAlSi-4	Aufhauser BAlSi-5
Canadian Liquid Air Ltd.	——	——	LA Aluminum 4047	——
Gases Agamex, S.A.	——	AGA-SUTEC Var 291	AGA-SUTEC Var 290	——
Handy & Harman	——	——	Handy Alumibraze	——
Marquette Corp.	——	——	No. 718	——
Pacific Welding Alloys Mfg. Co.	Pacific BAlSi-2	Pacific BAlSi-3	Pacific BAlSi-4	Pacific BAlSi-5
Super Tecnica, S.A.	——	SUTEC-VAR 291	SUTEC-VAR 290	——
United States Silver Corp.	Unibraze 356	Unibraze 716	Unibraze 718	——
United States Welding Alloys Corp.	——	US 716	US 718	——

Figure 3-3. *Cross-reference chart of popular brazing fillers by manufacturer and designation.**

* Source: AWS

Skulls and Skeletons

Skulls and skeletons found on the brazing fillet or the parent metal are generally the result of liquation. This occurs when the filler is kept at the lower edge of its melting range so long that the low-melting point elements leave solution and run off. The higher-melting point constituents remain and form rough, cracked surfaces when cooled. Liquation is most frequently caused by prolonged pre-heating. If pre-heat time cannot be shortened, switching to a lower temperature filler metal or a filler with a narrower melting range may solve the problem.

The appearance of liquation can sometimes be produced by inadequate cleaning and inadequate fluxing. Heavily oxidized brazing filler metal may also take on appearance of liquation.

Table 3-4 suggests parent metal, brazing alloy and flux combinations along with recommended brazing temperature ranges for torch, furnace and dip brazing. Figure 3-4, below, relates the recommended brazing temperature of the various parent metals and filler metals.

Filler Cleanliness

Filler metals as packed and shipped by their manufacturers are normally ready for use upon opening the package. If, however, the filler metal is exposed to the atmosphere for any length of time or handled during forming and placement, it is recommended that the filler metal be as carefully cleaned as the parent alloys before brazing. Filler metal may be cleaned by the same cleaning chemicals and methods as used with the parent alloys.

Flux

As stated previously, flux performs a number of important functions simultaneously during the brazing process. Flux displaces the oxide from the surface of aluminum

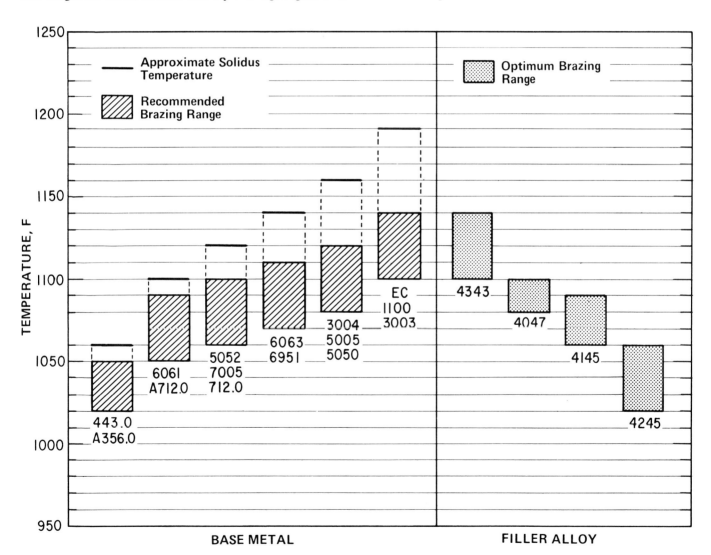

Figure 3-4. *Brazing temperatures of several aluminum alloys compared with melting range of aluminum filler alloys.*

and moves it away. Flux protects the bare metal from contact with the air. Flux lowers the filler metal's surface tension and promotes base metal wetting and filler flow.

Despite the number of years that have passed since aluminum fluxes were discovered, the action of flux in the removal of aluminum oxide from the surface of the metal is not fully understood. Experiments, however, lead to the hypothesis that aluminum oxide is almost insoluble in hot brazing flux. And that flux action actually begins when the metal is heated and the underlying aluminum expands slightly more than the surface oxide. The flux begins its attack at sites opened between the grains of oxide. The sites become linked by cracks and the flux, working its way underneath, lifts the oxide from the metal's surface, fragmenting and buckling it into tiny flat platelets of aluminum oxide. It is believed that these discrete particles are responsible for the thickening of molten flux in contact with aluminum.

Aluminum brazing fluxes are composed primarily of alkali and alkaline earth chlorides and fluorides, on occasion containing aluminum fluoride or cryolite. Fluoride is the more active agent and, without it, oxide removal would take hours. However, the presence of fluoride raises the flux's melting point and fluoride is mainly responsible for the etching action of the flux.

Some of the proprietary fluxes contain small quantities of chlorides of antimony, cadmium, chromium, cobalt, copper, lead, iron, manganese, silicon, tin, zinc, rare earths and precious metals in varying combinations and singly, in addition to the more or less standard chloride-fluoride mixture.

The purpose of all the mixing is a flux that (1) melts at a temperature slightly below that of the filler metal for which it is designed, (2) accomplishes the tasks previously listed, (3) produces a minimum of gas, (4) does not or but slightly attacks the metals it contacts, (5) is easily removed and (6) is inexpensive.

Flux formulation also affects the color and appearance of the finished joint. Some fluxes severely etch and roughen the surface of the fillet. Fluxes containing chlorides of zinc and other heavy metals tend to deposit these metals on the fillet, making the fillet darker than the adjoining aluminum.

Table 3-4 suggests fluxes for use with various brazing techniques and brazing alloys. Table 3-5 lists the major physical properties of two typical brazing fluxes.

It is no less important to match the flux to the brazing job than it is to select the correct filler metal or to determine optimum time/temperature relationships.

Fluxes have been developed to suit almost every individual brazing condition and brazing technique, but there is nothing cut and dried about the selection. The brazing engineer would do well to experiment with commercial fluxes and to call upon flux and filler manufacturers as well as aluminum producers when he requires aid.

Flux Storage and Handling

Flux may be stored for considerable time in tightly sealed, water-tight containers. Flux exposed to the atmosphere for several hours should be discarded. It is highly hygroscopic. Once moist it becomes active.

Some commercial fluxes have "built in" color codes. One such flux is light blue when it is dry and suitable for use. It turns a darker, different shade of blue when it has absorbed too much water from the air to be useful. In normal condition, it turns clear when it has reached its melting point and is close to its designed brazing temperature.

Flux should not be left exposed in "dirty" work areas. Specks of metal in the flux may cause pin holes in brazed joints. Dust and dirt will produce skips and holidays in the joint.

All aluminum brazing fluxes contain fluoride, which is a poison. *Flux must therefore be handled with caution at all times.* Please refer to Chapter 12 for more information on care in handling flux.

Preparing Flux for Application

Flux may be applied as a dry powder, or it may be mixed with clean, soft water to produce a paste. The less water used the better. If there is any doubt as to the suitability of the water, distilled or de-ionized water may be used. Alcohol may be used in place of water as a solvent. This will reduce the quantity of steam produced when the parts are brazed.

Alloy	Copper	Silicon	Manganese	Magnesium	Zinc	Nickel	Chromium	Lead	Bismuth	Approx. Melting Range °F	Relative Brazeability
EC				99.45% minimum Aluminum						1195-1215	A
1100				99% minimum Aluminum						1190-1215	A
3003	—	—	1.2	—	—	—	—	—	—	1190-1210	A
3004	—	—	1.2	1.0	—	—	—	—	—	1165-1205	B
4032	0.9	12.2	—	1.1	—	0.9	—	—	—	995-1000	D
5050	—	—	—	1.2	—	—	—	—	—	1160-1205	A
6951	0.25	0.35	—	0.6	—	—	—	—	—	1140-1210	B
6151	—	1.0	—	0.6	—	—	0.25	—	—	1025-1200	C
C5052	—	—	—	2.5	—	—	0.25	—	—	1100-1200	C
A6053	—	0.7	—	1.3	—	—	0.25	—	—	1105-1205	C
5154	—	—	—	3.5	—	—	0.25	—	—		D
5056	—	—	0.1	5.2	—	—	0.1	—	—	1100-1205	D
A6061	0.25	0.6	—	1.0	—	—	0.25	—	—	1140-1205	A
A6063	—	0.4	—	0.7	—	—	—	—	—	1140-1205	A
7072	—	—	—	—	1.0	—	—	—	—		B
7005	—	—	—	—	—	—	—	—	—	1125-1195	A-B
Cast 443.0	—	5.0	—	—	—	—	—	—	—	1065-1170	C
Cast 356.0	—	7.0	—	0.3	—	—	—	—	—	1035-1135	C
Cast 406	—	—	(99% min. Al.)	—	—	—	—	—	—	1190-1215	A
Cast A712.0	0.5	—	—	0.7	6.5	—	—	—	—	1105-1195	A
Cast C712.0	0.5	—	—	0.35	6.5	—	—	—	—	1120-1190	A

Per Cent of Alloying Elements—Aluminum and Normal Impurities Constitute Remainder

A—Alloys readily brazed by all techniques.

B—Alloys that can be brazed by all techniques with a little extra care.

C—Alloys that require special care and effort.

D—Alloys difficult to braze.

Table 3-1. *The nominal composition, melting range and relative brazeability of common parent alloys.*

Source: Aluminum Brazing Handbook, 2nd Ed., Aluminum Assn., Inc.

Product	Aluminum Association Designation	AWS-ASTM Class[2]	Per Cent of Alloying Elements—Aluminum and Nominal Impurities Constitute Remainder[1]							Approximate Temperature, °F		
			Silicon	Copper	Iron	Zinc	Magnesium	Manganese	Chromium	Solidus	Liquidus	Brazing Range
4043 Wire	4043	BAlSi-1	4.5-6.0	0.30	0.8	0.10	0.05	0.05	—	1070	1165	—
	4343	BAlSi-2	6.8-8.2	0.25	0.8	0.20	0.10	—	—	1070	1135	1110-1150
No. 714 Brazing Alloy[3]	4045	BAlSi-5	9.0-11.0	0.30	0.8	0.10	0.05	0.05	—	1070	1095	1090-1120
No. 716 Brazing Wire and Flattened Wire	4145	BAlSi-3	9.3-10.7	3.3-4.7	0.8	0.20	0.15	0.15	0.15	970	1085	1060-1120
No. 718 Brazing Wire and Sheet	4047	BAlSi-4	11.0-13.0	0.30	0.8	0.20	0.10	0.15	—	1070	1080	1080-1095
	4245	—	9.3-10.7	3.3-4.7	0.8	9.3-10.7	0.07	0.07	0.07	960	1040	—

[1] Single values are maximum percentages. [2] Tentative. [3] Cladding on Nos. 23 and 24 Brazing Sheet.

Table 3-2. *Composition and melting range of brazing filler alloys.*

Brazing Sheet Designation	No. of Sides Clad	Core Alloy	Cladding Composition % Si	% Cladding on Each Side for Sheet Thickness	Optimum Brazing Range °F
No. 11	1	3003	7.5%	10% for .063" and less 5% for .064" and over	1100-1140
No. 12	2	3003	7.5%	10% for .063" and less 5% for .064" and over	1100-1140
No. 21	1	6951	7.5%	10% for .090" and less 5% for .091" and over	1100-1120
No. 22	2	6951	7.5%	10% for .090" and less 5% for .091" and over	1100-1120
No. 718	—	718	12%	Not Clad	1080-1095

Table 3-3. *Composition and brazing range of clad aluminum brazing sheet and filler alloys.*

Parent Metal	Brazing Alloy	Optimum Brazing Range °F	Suggested Flux		
			Torch	Furnace	Dip
High Purity 1100 3003	4343 (713)[1]	1100-1140	Alcoa 33 Welco 10,700 Handy-Harmon Amco 4015, 2724	Alcoa 30, 53 Handy-Harmon Park E, D	Alcoa 34, 501 Amco 4024
	4047 (718)	1080-1095	Alcoa 33 Welco 10,700 Handy-Harmon Amco 4015, 2724	Alcoa 33, 105 Welco 10,700 Handy-Harmon Amco 4015, 2724	Alcoa 34, 501 Amco 4024
3004 5005 5050 6061 6062 6063 6951 A712.0 Cast C712.0 Cast	4047 (718)	1080-1095	Alcoa 33 Welco 10,700 Handy-Harmon Amco 4015, 2724	Alcoa 33 Welco 10,700 Handy-Harmon Amco 4015, 2724	Alcoa 34, 501 Amco 4024
443.0 Cast 356.0T4 Cast	4145 (716)	1060-1070	Alcoa 33 Welco 10,700 Handy-Harmon Amco 4040, 4056	Alcoa 33 Welco 10,700 Handy-Harmon Amco 4015, 4040	Alcoa 34, 501 Amco 4024
No. 11 Brazing Sheet No. 12 Brazing Sheet	4343 (713)	1100-1140	—	Alcoa 30, 53, 105 Park E, D	Alcoa 34, 501 Amco 4024
No. 21 Brazing Sheet No. 22 Brazing Sheet	4343 (713)	1100-1120	Amco 4015, 2724	Alcoa 33 Welco 10,700 Handy-Harmon Amco 4015, 2724	Alcoa 34, 501 Amco 4024
No. 23 Brazing Sheet No. 24 Brazing Sheet	4045[2] (714)	1080-1120	Welco 10,700 Handy-Harmon Amco 4015, 2724	Alcoa 33 Welco 10,700 Handy-Harmon Amco 4015, 2724	Alcoa 34, 501 Amco 4024
	4245	1040-1060	Amco 4056	Amco 4056	Amco 4024

[1] Old brazing filler metal designations in parentheses.

[2] Use alloy 4047 where additional filler metal is required.

The above relationships are approximate and are based in part on manufacturer's literature and field reports. Individual tests are necessary to establish performance.

This list is provided for the reader's convenience and is not to be considered all-inclusive nor does use here constitute an endorsement.

Table 3-4. *Parent metal, brazing alloy and flux combination suggestions for brazing aluminum.*

Source: Aluminum Brazing Handbook, 2nd Ed., Aluminum Assn., Inc.

	Flux A	Flux B
Solidus Temp., °F	900	660
Liquidus Temp., °F	1035	940
Density at 1130°F, lb/cu ft	104	103
Specific Heat, Btu/lb/°F (approx.)	0.2	0.2
Heat of Fusion, Btu/lb (approx.)	168	186
Heat Requirement, Btu to heat 1 lb of flux from solid at 70°F to liquid at 1150°F (approx.)	385	380
Resistivity, ohm-cm at 1030°F	0.43 ± 0.01	0.43 ± 0.01
at 1130°F	0.36	0.40
at 1150°F	0.33	0.40
at 1180°F	0.29	0.38
Solubility in boiling water (%)	94.3	95.7

Table 3-5. *Physical properties typical of dip brazing fluxes.*

Approx. Melting Range—°F	Principal Use
1010-1135	Furnace Brazing
915-1110	Torch and Furnace Brazing
900-1035	Dip Brazing
950-1090	Furnace Brazing
1025-1065	Furnace Brazing
660-940	Dip Brazing

Table 3-6. *Suggested flux melting ranges for various types of brazing.*

Pre-Cleaning, Oxide Removal, Post-Cleaning and Finishing

As stated previously, brazing aluminum requires that the metal be soil free and its oxide layer thin enough to be displaced by hot flux during the brazing cycle.

Most shops, to judge by volume of brazing work, find that both these conditions may be met by vapor degreasing alone. The oxide layer normal to mill-finished aluminum is generally no deterrent to satisfactory brazing.

Other shops find that aluminum as removed from its mill wrappings meets both brazing conditions with no treatment whatsoever.

Still other shops, working to tighter "specs" and seeking more nearly perfect brazed joints, or having to braze extensively shaped and formed aluminum, find that both cleaning and oxide removal (thinning the alloy's oxide layer) are necessary.

Pre-braze cleaning and oxide removal vary therefore with the parent metal, its surface condition and the joint quality desired. The brazing engineer may determine by test the degree of cleanliness necessary along with acceptable oxide thickness.

Pre-braze Cleaning

When maximum quality brazed joints are the design goal, the importance of cleanliness cannot be overstressed. The molten flux must make complete and perfect contact with the aluminum's oxide layer if the flux is to do its complex task.

A film of oil, for example, will insulate the flux from the oxide. Foreign material on the surface of the joining areas will divert the flow of flux and filler, producing skips and roughness. If the filler flows over foreign matter, gas may form and produce eruptions and voids in the filler. Copper particles between the faying surfaces may produce craters.

Pre-braze cleaning is a two-fold task: (1) removing all grease, oils and dirt from the base metal and filler; (2) preventing re-contamination once the parts have been cleaned.

When maximum joint quality is desired, it is best to clean the entire assembly and not to limit cleaning to the joint alone. Dirt and dust particles move under the influence of heat and heat-driven air. Grease and oil spread and run when heated, and the thinnest film of oil can be troublesome. It is for this reason that some shops teach their assemblers not to touch faying surfaces with their bare hands after the metal has been cleaned.

Greases, fatty acids and oils can be removed by vapor degreasing, using inhibited trichloroethylene or inhibited perchloroethylene or other commercial fluids. Petroleum solvents and chlorinated hydrocarbons also can be used for washing the parts clean. And the metal can be washed in hot detergents and water—hot alkaline baths made of water and trisodium phosphate or one of the many excellent commercial compounds made expressly for cleaning aluminum prior to brazing. This is always followed by a clear-water rinse.

Oxide Removal

Once grease and grime have been removed, the question of whether or not the oxide layer is thin enough to be displaced by the flux must be answered. This can be determined empirically with a number of test joints, which provide useful information only when all other factors are known. Or the thickness of the oxide may be measured electrically.

Oxide layers normally coating aluminum alloys range from one to five millionths of an inch in thickness and have resistances ranging in microhms (1×10^{-6}).

Figure 4-1. *Lint-free cotton gloves are often used to keep parts clean while they are assembled for brazing.*

Courtesy, Fairchild Hiller, Stratos Div.

Table 4-1 lists a portion of the range of surface resistances that may be expected when measuring a number of aluminum alloys. Resistance values will vary from sheet to sheet and from one point on the sheet to another. When the resistance values are within or below the range listed, surface oxide is sufficiently thin to permit dependably satisfactory brazing (low incidence of rejects).

Resistance measurements may be made with microhmeters used for electrical surface-resistance measurements when preparing aluminum for spot welding or by any other instruments designed for very low resistance measurements. As a general rule, alloys sufficiently free of oxide to be spot welded can be brazed.

It should be noted that the visual appearance of the metal under question is of little value. Some alloys appearing to be heavily oxidized are not. Other alloys may glow with cleanliness but may be too thickly oxidized to braze.

Overly thick oxide can be cut down by either mechanical or chemical means.

Mechanical means are practical when small areas are involved, as in the case of repairs. Sandpaper, Aloxite cloth, steel wool and files may be used. Stainless steel wool

or a stainless steel, motor-driven wire brush is preferred. With the latter there is little possibility of grit or steel particles being driven into the metal to later interfere with brazing and corrode.

When large quantities of metal have to be cleaned of oxide, or the shape and complexity of the parts preclude mechanical methods, chemicals are used. Chemical removal of oxide is comparatively inexpensive, rapid and dependable.

Both caustics and acids are used. Of the two, caustic is by far the most active and widely used oxide-removing agent.

An effective, rapid and relatively inexpensive caustic deoxidizer may be made by mixing a 5% solution of sodium hydroxide and water, generally kept at 150°F.

Figure 4-2 illustrates the action of a typical caustic solution upon aluminum. Notice how quickly solution A brought the oxide level down to approximately 100 microhms, and how quickly the caustic reversed its action and replaced the oxide.

Hot caustic will remove approximately 0.001 inch of immersed metal per minute, preferentially attacking the pure aluminum to leave the alloying elements behind in the form of a scum or surface smudge called smut. Alloys having greater quantities of added elements are most troubled by smut. By contrast, little or no smut forms on alloys 1100 and 1183. Smut must be removed as it interferes with brazing.

For these reasons, best results are obtained with strong caustic solutions when dip time is limited to 10 or 15 seconds and solution concentration and temperature are carefully controlled. Control requirements can be reduced by diluting the caustic or by using one of many commercial products made for this purpose. The horizontal portion of curve B in Figure 4-2 illustrates the change. To improve

Alloy	Resistance x 10^{-6}
1100	100-500
3003	300-1000
3004	500-3000
5052	1000-10,000
6061	1000-20,000
7039	2000-20,000

Table 4-1. *Alloys having higher surface resistances than listed cannot be dependably brazed. Values given are for two oxide layers in series (from one side of the sheet through to the other).*

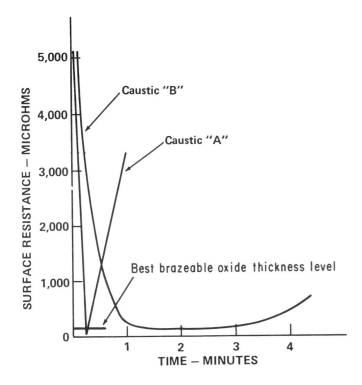

Figure 4-2. *Line A charts the rate of oxide removal and replacement when a caustic is used to remove oxide from aluminum in preparation for brazing.*

Line B charts the action of a diluted caustic solution or a proprietary cleaning solution used to remove oxide from aluminum. Note the two minutes during which the oxide is at a "safe" thin level.

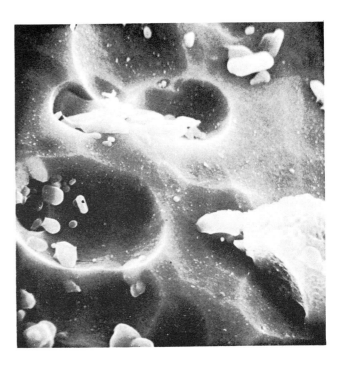

Figure 4-3. *Particles and pits on a caustically etched alloy 2014 aluminum surface as revealed by a scanning electron microscope. Magnification is 4800 X.*

Courtesy, ITT Research Institute

repeatability (with any solution) it may be advisable to pre-dip the metal in clear water to which a wetting agent has been added. This will negate the possibility of remaining degreasing solvent interfering with the action of the deoxidizer.

Whether a caustic composed of sodium hydroxide or one of the proprietary solutions is used, oxide removal must be followed by a rinse in clear water and desmutting. (Some manufacturers claim products that form no adhering smut.)

Smut is easily removed by dipping the metal into acid. The bath most frequently used is undiluted nitric acid at room temperature, or a chromic acid solution containing some dichromates. The aluminum is held under for 30 seconds or less. Some engineers find a mixture of nitric acid and hydrofluoric acid gives better results. Some shops add as little as 0.5 to 5% hydrofluoric acid. Others use as much as 20%.

The acid bath is always followed by a clear water rinse. The metal is then air dried. If the water used for rinsing is hot, the parts will dry more quickly. Wet metal parts should never touch when drying as water spotting—surface discoloration—may result.

An acid dip (not preceded by a caustic dip) is sometimes used to free aluminum of its oxide. The single treatment is used when little oxide is present on the aluminum. The bath may consist of nitric acid or a combination of nitric acid and hydrofluoric acid. This is always followed by a clear water rinse and drying. The acid bath also removes metal, as does the hot caustic, but at a far slower rate. The effect of a caustic is shown in Figure 4-3.

Forethought should be given to the removal of metal by the pre-braze baths when finely machined parts such as threads have to be deoxidized. In some instances the practical answer is the re-cutting or the cutting of threads and final dimensioning after the parts have been brazed. Allowance is made for the metal expected to be lost in the baths. There are, however, several proprietary non-etching solutions for oxide removal on the market which purport not to remove metal.

Some of the commercial deoxidants and desmutters are based on chromic acid, and some shops use chromic acid for desmutting. As a result, the desmutting bath will in time collect an excessive quantity of chromate. When this occurs the bath is said to be contaminated, and aluminum dipped into the bath will receive a chromate finish which is not brazeable. When the degree of contamination is very high or the metal is left in the bath for a long time, the chromate finish becomes visible as a color change on the aluminum. Chromate coatings sufficiently thick to interfere with brazing but too thin to be visible to the eye may be detected by electrical resistance measurements. Surface resistance values listed in Table 4-1 apply.

Keeping the Parts Clean

Contamination and oxide build-up can be greatly reduced by keeping the interim periods between cleaning, oxide removal and brazing as short as possible. Figure 4-5 depicts the rise of surface resistance (oxide built up) on aluminum alloys with the passage of time.

To maintain cleanliness during assembly, some shops tack-weld lengths of wire to the parts for use as handles when fluxing. Others provide lint-free cotton gloves. Still others depend on clean work fixtures and jigs for handling the parts.

To prevent recontamination during storage, cleaned parts are often stored in plastic bags. Some shops acid dip, rinse and dry all cleaned parts before brazing if they have been stored more than 48 hours. This is done as a precautionary measure.

Post-braze Cleaning

Flux adhering to the brazed assembly must be completely removed if corrosion by flux action is to be eliminated. Usually, the first post-braze cleaning step is the immersion of the still hot part into boiling water. This is the most rapid and efficient method of removing flux. Flux is highly soluble and boiling water will quickly remove most of it. If necessary, the part may be allowed to cool before it is placed in boiling or hot wash water. Washing will be just as effective, but somewhat slower.

Wash tank water must be changed constantly and either the parts or the water should be moved to force the water into all part corners and crevices. The parts may be moved by hand or mechanically. The water may be agitated by a pump or a stream of compressed air. Some shops use high pressure sprays of hot water. Others use steam jets and some shops have the workmen rub the part down with fiber scrub brushes.

Large ultrasonic transducers, sometimes with special proprietary cleaning solutions, also are being used successfully. Figure 4-4.

When the major portion of the adhering flux has been removed, the assembly may be rid of the balance of the flux by immersion in a second tank of agitated hot water, or by a dip into a chemical solution.

The use of a second water bath, as compared to a chemical bath, has several advantages and only one disadvantage—it is very slow. Complex parts with lengthy passages and small holes may have to be soaked for several days in the hot, constantly changing water. All flux that is not sealed off by brazing fillets can be removed if the soak period is long enough. The aluminum is usually not harmed by a lengthy submersion. Eventually, however, pitting will occur.

Residual flux is more often removed by chemical means. In addition to the solutions listed in Table 4-2, there are a number of proprietary solutions on the market.

All cleaning solutions must be followed by a thorough rinsing in hot or cold water (as directed) to make certain that none of the "cleaning" chemicals remain on the work piece. If some of the cleaning solution does remain on the brazed assemblies and the parts are left in the wash water or are subjected to moisture, there is a possibility that seeper leaks—small perforations—may develop in the thinner sections.

Some fabricators add 0.5% sodium or potassium dichromate to the final rinse water to prevent corrosion.

Figure 4-4. *Ultrasonic cleaning systems are especially effective for cleaning complicated parts.*

Courtesy, Branson

As a rule, brazed parts for every-day application are considered flux free when flux in quantities of less than 10 ppm (parts per million) remains in solution on their surfaces. Brazed assemblies designed for extended lifetimes, such as refrigeration system parts, are cleaned until the flux remaining is less than 5 ppm. Parts with flux in quantities exceeding 50 ppm should be re-washed as they will suffer corrosion in any application.

The silver nitrate test is popular for determining the presence of flux either in the wash water or remaining on the work piece after it has been washed and dried. A test solution is prepared by mixing 5 grams of silver nitrate with 100 grams of triple-distilled water to which a few drops of 20 to 50% nitric acid have been added. A few drops of distilled water are placed on the brazed assembly on an area likely to retain flux. After a few minutes an eye dropper is used to transfer the test water to a quantity of the test solution. If the solution clouds, chloride flux is present. As an alternate, a sample of the final wash water may be added to the test solution (assuming fresh wash water will not of itself cloud the test solution).

The silver nitrate test is extremely sensitive. Under controlled laboratory conditions, flux in quantities as small as 1 ppm can be detected. Chloride combines with the test solution to form silver chloride. Fluoride forms silver fluoride. Both are visible as white precipitates in the test solution. As chloride usually comprises 80% of common brazing fluxes, the silver nitrate test is essentially a test for chloride. But in practice, no distinction is made, and the combination of halides remaining is used as a measure of cleanliness. Under ordinary shop conditions, air borne contamination, chlorides in the wash water and similar impurities will mask the results, possibly producing turbidity without the presence of brazing flux. This test therefore requires judgment on the part of the user. The basis for judging the degree of precipitation can be established by the use of laboratory prepared samples and color charts.

Silver nitrate is extremely dangerous to the eyes; it will cause permanent blindness upon contact. Extreme care must be used.

The electrical resistivity of the test water also may be used to measure flux residue. Generally, when the resistivity of the sample is lower than 100,000 ohms per cc, as measured between platinum electrodes, flux residue is greater than 5 ppm. More exact estimates can be made by measuring test samples of clean water plus specific quantities of flux and using these resistivity figures as guides.

A) **Nitric acid** at room temperature, mixed 50/50 by volume with water is a very effective general purpose flux removing solution. It does its job in 10 to 20 seconds and the part can be later washed in cold or hot water. However, nitric acid reacts with flux to produce dangerous fumes which must be vented by a power fan and hood. Nitric acid also has a very low tolerance for flux. For these reasons, this solution is only used on small parts with little remaining flux.

When the chloride concentration in the nitric acid-water solution exceeds 5 grams per liter, thin gauge brazed assemblies may be perforated. Inhibitors such as 1% thiourea or 1% triethanolamine salt of sulfolaurylakybenzoate may be added to prevent chloride contamination from attacking the parts being cleaned.

B) **Nitric acid mixed with hydrofluoric acid** and water at room temperature will both etch the metal and remove flux in one immersion. Depth of etching is dependent on immersion time. Generally, 10 to 15 minutes is sufficient. Afterwards the parts are rinsed in cold water and then hot water. The hot water rinse, 168°F., should be limited to 3 minutes to prevent surface stains. The solution must be analyzed each week and discarded when its chloride content reaches 3 grams per liter, expressed as hydrochloric acid. The solution is made by mixing 1 gallon nitric acid, ½ pint hydrofluoric acid and 9 gallons of water.

C) **Hydrofluoric acid,** mixed with room temperature water in the ratio of 2½ pints of acid to 10 gallons of water, will remove flux effectively and rapidly. Dip time should not exceed 10 minutes as this solution dissolves the aluminum. This solution is not as quickly contaminated by flux as is nitric acid solution, but it does generate much more hydrogen gas, which must be vented. If the hydrofluoric acid discolors the aluminum it can be brightened with nitric acid.

D) **Nitric acid, sodium dichromate** and water mixed in a ratio of 4½ quarts of acid to 8 pounds of sodium dichromate and 9 gallons of water makes a solution useful for final cleaning of thin parts, and parts that must exhibit maximum resistance to corrosion. This solution is used at a temperature of 150°F. It does its job in 5 to 10 minutes and should be followed by a careful wash in hot water.

E) **2% chromium trioxide and 5% phosphoric acid** (both by weight) added to water at 180°F. is also used for very light-gauge metal. This solution can be used until chloride contamination reaches a maximum of 100 grams per liter, after which it should be discarded.

F) U.S. Patent 3,074,824 W. W. Binger and B. Ponchel describes an **alkaline phosphate-dichromate-fluoride** solution devised to both etch and remove flux from very thin gauge aluminum with a minimum of seeper leaks.

Table 4-2. *Flux removal solutions.*

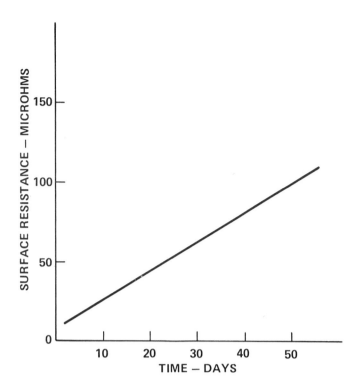

Figure 4-5. *Typical rate of oxide build-up on aluminum alloys with the passage of time as measured by electrical resistance.*

Figure 4-6. *Brazed heat exchanger is removed by travelling hoist from salt pot and dipped almost immediately into boiling water for cleaning.*

The spectrophotometer, tuned to the wavelength of the element it is to detect, is also used to measure flux residue. It can detect flux quantities as small as 1 ppm.

When the utmost in cleanliness is desired, fabricators subject the brazed assembly to 90% relative humidity at temperatures of 100°F. or more for 24 hours. This leaches the last few atoms of flux out of hiding and exposes areas that may require additional cleaning.

Tank Requirements

Nitric acid solutions can be held in stainless steel or mild steel tanks clad on the inside with a layer of type 304 stainless. If the tank is made by welding plates of 18-10 stainless, the joints should be annealed after welding. If stabilized stainless steel such as type 347, 321 or 304L is used, the welds need not be annealed.

Nitric-hydrofluoric and hydrofluoric washing solutions can be kept in fiberglas reinforced plastic tanks. Fiber glass or enameled steel tanks can also be used to hold hot solutions of nitric acid-sodium dichromate.

Finishing

When a brazing fillet has been properly formed, there is essentially no finishing required beyond flux removal and cleaning. Generally the fillet is a little darker in color than the parent metal. The difference in color depends on the choice of filler metal in relation to the parent metal and the choice of flux, which may stain the fillet's surface.

If necessary the fillet, like the parent metal, may be ground, filed or polished.

The fillet will darken if anodized and will weather when exposed outdoors. Again, color change difference in relation to the parent metal will depend on the alloys employed.

Careful design can minimize the unwanted effect of a darker fillet line across a fabricated assembly. The joint can be hidden behind other parts and sections. A piece of "trim" can be placed over the darker fillet, or the dark fillet line can be incorporated into the overall design.

The brazed assembly should not be cleaned in caustic. If it must be cleaned, a degreasing agent or solvent or a "soap and hot water" solution should be used. Caustic will attack the fillet preferentially making it rough and coarse. The finished, cleaned assembly may be treated as a single piece of aluminum for it truly is an all-aluminum structure. It can be electropolated, etched, anodized, painted or put to use without further treatment or attention.

Torch Brazing

Hand-held Gas-Torch Brazing

Hand-held torch brazing is the method most frequently used for repairs, one-of-a-kind brazing jobs, short production runs and as an alternative to fusion welding. Any aluminum joint that can be reached by a torch and brought to brazing temperature (by the torch alone or in conjunction with auxiliary heating means) can be readily brazed by this technique.

Although any source of heat can be used for torch brazing, commercial torch brazing is accomplished with the same type of torch, controls and gases used for fusion welding. Conversion to aluminum brazing merely requires a change in torch nozzles and goggle lenses.

Torch brazing technique is relatively simple and can be mastered by the mechanically adept in a short time. Those already experienced with torch welding and the brazing of other metals generally encounter no difficulty learning aluminum torch brazing.

All commercial gas mixtures can be used to fuel the torch: oxyacetylene, oxyhydrogen, oxy-natural gas, acetylene and air, hydrogen and air, propane, methane and natural gas and air. Oxyacetylene, oxyhydrogen and oxy-natural gas are the mixtures most often used commercially and are preferred in that order.

The oxyacetylene combination produces the highest temperature. The other gases are cooler and their flames are less concentrated. Thus they are easier to use and advantageous on light-gauge material.

The torch tip orifice used for brazing is usually larger than the tip selected for gas welding. Table 5-1, on page 42, relates tip orifice diameter to gas pressures recommended for various gauges of sheet aluminum.

Gas pressure should be kept low, no more than 4 psi, so that the flame can be readily adjusted by means of the controls on the torch.

Figure 5-1. *Torch brazing of aluminum can be learned by the mechanically skilled in a few hours.*

When oxyacetylene is used, the flame can be adjusted by visual inspection. The white cone produced by this mixture should be varied until it extends one or two inches from the tip of the torch. Its length should be roughly twice that of the inner cone.

The appearance of the other gases vary little with changes in oxygen/gas ratio and can only be adjusted by means of flow meters in the gas lines. Oxygen pressure is always half that of the accompanying gas. The aim with all gas mixtures is to produce a slightly reducing flame. A reducing flame tends to protect the heated aluminum from oxygen, as the flame itself consumes oxygen at a rate greater than the quantity of oxygen delivered. A reducing flame is also a softer flame; its heat is less intense and less concentrated.

Procedure

The parts to be brazed are cleaned and deoxidized as discussed in Chapter 4, and joint clearances are established by one means or another as discussed in Chapter 2. Generally,

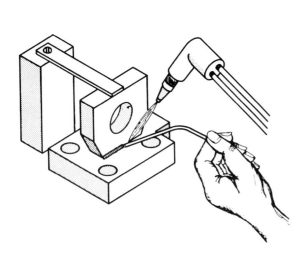

Figure 5-2. *Typical torch brazing set-up. A simple fixture holds the parts in place. The torch is moved around the work as necessary.*

joint gaps for torch brazing are held between 0.004 and 0.025 inch. In some joint configurations, as for example the joint shown in cross section in Figure 5-3, clearance may be omitted.

When possible, parts should be designed for self jigging and self-support. The assembly to be brazed will be subjected to the pressure of the gases emerging from the torch and the pressure of its own weight. Aluminum at brazing temperature is soft. Long horizontal sections, for example, must be supported along their length or they will sag.

Filler metal can be supplied to the joint by hand, as illllustrated in Figure 5-2, or preplaced. In the latter case, care must be exercised in the placement of the filler and the guidance of the torch to preclude premature melting of the filler metal. Flux is applied by any convenient method as discussed in Chapter 3.

Measuring Joint Temperature

There are three reliable and popular means for measuring the temperature of a joint while brazing. One means

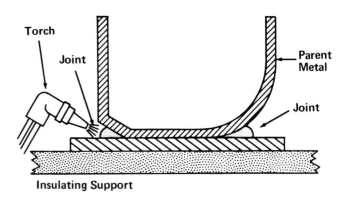

Figure 5-3. *Faying surfaces that meet at a small angle or a gentle curve may be brazed without joint clearance.*

is the flux. Applied to the joint, flux will indicate temperature in the following manner. As temperature increases the flux loses its moisture, turns white and dries out. As the temperature continues to increase the flux melts and turns grey. When the temperature for which that particular flux has been formulated is reached, the flux becomes transparent and the subsurface aluminum glows with a silvery sheen. The joint is now at brazing temperature. Some proprietary fluxes indicate brazing temperature by a show of color.

Temperature indicating "crayons" afford a second, reliable means of judging joint temperature. They are used to make a mark near the joint. The mark changes texture or color when the crayon's temperature has been reached. Sold under a variety of trade names, the crayons are produced in a wide range of indicating temperatures.

The third means of judging joint temperature is the brazing filler metal itself. The tip of the filler rod or wire is applied lightly to the work piece from time to time as the assembly is heated. When the filler's tip softens and melts, brazing temperature has been reached. Generally, the flame is then withdrawn a bit to prevent temperature overshoot.

Handling the Torch

Ignited and adjusted as directed in preceding paragraphs, the torch is held a few inches from the work, at any convenient angle—generally from 5 to 40 degrees to the plane of the aluminum's surface.

The flame is never permitted to rest on any portion of the assembly for more than a moment, but is played over the work from side to side or in a circle. For maximum heat, the outer edge of the cone is allowed to touch the work. Normally it is not brought any closer.

To bring parts of varying mass and surface area to the same temperature, the torch flame is moved rapidly over light, thin sections and slowly over heavier sections.

Heating unequal aluminum parts equally is not as difficult as it might appear. Aluminum, an excellent conductor of heat, is quick to correct major thermal differences in the assembly. Any or all of the three temperature estimating methods discussed may be used as aids to secure minimum temperature gradients across the assembly.

Whether the torch flame is directed on filler metal or parent metal depends on the thickness of the parts brazed. If the parts are very thin, it may be desirable to direct most of the heat onto the filler wire. If the parts are relatively heavy, most or all of the heat will be directed onto the parts and clear of the filler.

If the filler metal is preplaced, heat is applied as evenly as possible to the entire joint and the filler observed carefully. Fillet formation can be used as a guide.

If the joint is face fed (supplied by hand) and short, the usual practice is to "feed" the filler wire or rod directly into one end of the joint, letting the molten filler find its own way down the length of the joint. If the joint is long, it may be necessary to supply the filler metal from several points successively. Supplying the metal from one point is the better practice as there is less chance of flux entrapment.

To make certain the joint is complete, the operator should maintain heat until he clearly sees the bright metal flowing out of each end of the joint.

Filler metal tends to flow towards the hottest portion of the joint. It isn't necessary to push the molten metal along. If the joint is hot and clean and covered with flux, capillary action will draw the molten filler into every adjoining crack and crevice and form the fillet without any help from the operator.

When the joint is very long or when the operator has to remove heat from the joint, or when the joint has not been heated properly, irregular and unequal fillets may result. Some fillet correction may be obtained by reheating portions of the joint and supplying those portions with more filler metal. Generally, it is inadvisable to reheat an entire joint or to go over a fillet once it has formed and cooled in an effort to improve the fillet.

The operator must be very careful to bring both the filler metal and the parent metal to the liquidus temperature of the filler metal . . . but not to bring the parent

Metal Thickness In.	OXYHYDROGEN			OXYACETYLENE		
	Orifice dia. in.	Oxygen Pressure psi	Hydrogen Pressure psi	Orifice dia. in.	Oxygen Pressure psi	Acetylene Pressure psi
0.020	0.035	0.5	1	0.025	0.5	1
0.025	0.045	0.5	1	0.025	0.5	1
0.032	0.055	0.5	1	0.035	0.5	1
0.040	0.065	1	2	0.035	0.5	1
0.051	0.075	1	2	0.045	1	2
0.064	0.085	1	2	0.055	1	2
0.081	0.095	1.5	3	0.065	1.5	3
0.102	0.105	1.5	3	0.075	1.5	3
⅛	0.115	1.5	3	0.085	2	4

Table 5-1. *Tip orifice diameters and approximate gas pressures used for torch brazing.*

Source: Aluminum Brazing Handbook, 2nd Ed., Aluminum Assn., Inc.

metal's temperature above this point. Otherwise, the parent metal may collapse. Repeated heating of a formed fillet in an effort at perfection increases this danger.

When an assembly is too large to be brought to temperature by a single torch, a second torch, held at a safe distance by a second operator is useful. Multiple-head torches also are available. These are useful for brazing pipe and circular sections.

Assembly heat losses through radiation and convection can be reduced by insulating the parts from their fixture by strips or sheets of asbestos, using knife edges or points to reduce contact, and using a windbreak. This is very helpful outdoors on cold days and may be improvised from asbestos pipe insulation and asbestos cement when an asbestos blanket is not available.

When all the fillets have been formed, the torch is removed and the assembly is permitted to cool undisturbed until all the fillets have solidified.

If a number of small, quickly completed brazed joints need to be made, the prepared parts can be placed on a moving belt and brought automatically to the operator. A fan can be used to air quench the hot parts. After they have cooled, they can be dropped directly into a scrubbing tub for cleaning.

Hot flux generates toxic, irritating gases. Brazing should always be conducted in well ventilated areas. The operator should wear protective clothing, gloves and goggles. Goggles are a necessary protection for his eyes, and when properly tinted lenses are used, his view of the joint will be improved. Cobalt blue lenses may be used if aluminum-brazing lenses number 3 or 4 (AWS standard Z 49.1) are not available, but they are not as satisfactory.

Automatic Torch Brazing

Automatic torch brazing is similar to hand-held torch brazing in all respects save one: the assembly is moved automatically in relation to the torch, or vice versa.

The part may be rotated in front of the torch, or torches; the part may be slowly moved past the torch, or oscillated in front of the torches. Or the parts may remain stationary and the torches moved. The basic arrangement is illustrated in Figure 5-4.

Joint temperature is controlled by adjustment of time, torch-to-work distance and gas mixture. Once these parameters have been determined there is rarely any need to experiment further or to change adjustments on a production run.

Filler metal is, of course, preplaced with primary concern for the relation of the filler metal to the mass of the assembly and the flame or flames. Generally the filler is "buried" in the assembly so that the filler cannot be

Figure 5-4. *Simple automatic torch brazing set-up. The assembly is hand placed on the rotating fixture and later removed when it has cooled.*

brought to liquidus before the entire assembly reaches brazing temperature.

Any number of torches may be used in any number of positions and arrangements. Flames may surround the part, and successive flames may be applied to thicker parts to bring them up to temperature.

As filler metal is liquid during brazing, it is important that assemblies do not rotate too fast nor are shaken or tipped as they are moved through the flames. Molten fillets respond to gravity and shaking tends to reduce their height.

In the main, automatic torch brazing, or mechanized flame brazing as it is sometimes called, is best suited to high production runs of limited-joint assemblies. Assemblies that need but two or three brazed joints each; assemblies that cannot be flux-dip or furnace brazed for one reason or another, often can be economically brazed by this method.

Flux-Dip Brazing

Parts to be brazed by this method are cleaned, freed of excess oxide, assembled and jigged along with the necessary filler metal. The assembly is then heated to approximately 1000°F. in a pre-heat oven, removed and immersed in molten flux for a minute or two. Removed from the flux, cooled and cleaned, the assembly is ready for use or further treatment. One joint or a thousand can be formed during the few minutes the assembly is submerged in the hot salt.

The molten salt, at a temperature slightly above the liquidus of the filler metal, fluxes the joints, serves as a heat transfer and storage medium and partially supports the submerged metal parts.

Molten flux at brazing temperature has the consistency of water; it readily contacts and wets every inch of the assembly's surface and enters every joint and cranny not blocked by air or dirt. The molten salt's fluxing action is similar to that produced by a small quantity of flux placed on the faying surfaces alone. But its action is far more dependable as there is an unlimited quantity of moving flux in the pot.

The specific heat of molten flux is roughly the same as that of aluminum, about .02 Btu per pound per degree F. Flux temperature drop can be held to a negligible few degrees if some 16 to 18 lbs. of flux are placed in the pot for every 4 to 6 lbs. of aluminum to be brazed each hour and the aluminum assembly and jigging is preheated. Allowance in the form of increased flux volume must be made for the weight of the fixtures and jigs accompanying the aluminum assembly into the pot.

The specific gravity of molten flux is close to that of aluminum, reducing the weight of submerged parts to half or less. This makes it possible to dip-braze aluminum parts and assemblies that are too light to be self-supporting when brazed by other methods.

As molten flux is high in specific heat, low in viscosity and always in motion, its temperature can be held within ± 5°F. of a specific temperature with standard commercial equipment. This is considerably better than can be routinely accomplished with other types of heating equipment and allows the use of fillers with liquidus temperatures as close as 10°F. to the solidus temperatures of the parent metals.

Because flux and heat application are uniform and temperature can be precisely maintained, thick pieces and thin pieces, large pieces and small pieces can be dipped into hot flux without pause or adjustment. Parts that cannot be joined by any other technique can often be joined by dip brazing. Blind joints, inaccessible joints and complex joints without number can be brazed easily and simultaneously by this method. Even thin parts can be brazed to thick parts without problem or special concern.

The Salt Pot

Salt pots, or dip furnaces as they are called by their manufacturers, comprise steel reinforced vessels lined with high-alumina, acid-proof fire brick generally more than one foot thick. Pot covers are equally well insulated. Large covers may be mounted on rollers and power operated. The pots themselves last 10 to 20 years in normal service.

On starting, cold flux is placed in the pot and heated by temporary, external means, which may consist of a blow torch or a portable electric heater. Once molten, the flux becomes electrically conductive and is kept at brazing temperature by the passage of electric current flowing between electrodes immersed in the flux.

As aluminum is a much better conductor of electricity than molten flux, it is necessary that aluminum parts be kept from contacting the electrodes and out of the electrical

Figure 6-1. *More aluminum parts are brazed by flux dipping than all other brazing methods added together.*

Courtesy, Modine Mfg. Co.

Figure 6-2. *A large, submerged carbon electrode dip furnace installation at Hughes-Treitler Mfg. Corp. Furnace cover is power operated and is in the rolled-back position.* Courtesy, Upton Electric Furnace Co.

field around and between the electrodes in the molten flux. Otherwise, the parts may be overheated and damaged.

Minimum recommended work piece clearances are as follows: There should be at least 2 inches between the sides of the work (or its fixtures) and the sides of the pot. If the pot's electrodes are on the pot's sides a clearance of at least 3 inches on that side should be provided. Normal flux depth should exceed part height by some 8 inches. When the pot's electrodes are at its bottom, flux depth clearance should be increased to 10 inches.

Greater "bottom clearance" is desirable to keep the assemblies clear of sludge and unmelted salts which tend to collect at the bottom of the tank. Both can interfere with brazing.

Work-piece clearance is not the only dimensional criterion that must be satisfied when selecting a pot. Additional flux volume may be required if the work rate is high and if the flux drag-out rate is high.

Drag out can be approximated in advance. A minimum of 0.03 lbs. of flux can be expected to be lost for every square foot of flat metal surface dipped. Assemblies with catch corners, convoluted surfaces, complex fixturing and jigging will raise the figure. The temperature and composition of the flux involved are also important factors. Typically, an automotive radiator with an estimated 40 sq. ft. of surface will drag some 2 pounds of flux out of the pot when it is brazed.

Dip Furnace Heating Means

Commercially-manufactured dip furnaces are heated by AC current flowing between electrodes immersed in the flux. The electrodes in general use are carbon, wrought nickel or Inconel 600. These show less attack than copper and copper-bearing electrodes and cause far less bath contamination.

The carbon electrodes are the least costly. A pair, 16 to 24 inches in length, may cost $20 to $35. The electrodes are inserted into holders which are always water cooled. The holders are affixed to the sides of the tank and the "hot" ends of the carbon electrodes are always fully submerged beneath the flux, generally close to the bottom of the tank. As current passes through the electrode it erodes. Carbon particles leave the electrodes and collect on the surface of the salt. To compensate for electrode erosion, they are regularly given a turn and pushed inwards. At a given point of wear, a second electrode, provided with a male thread on one end and a female thread on the other, is screwed into the "in-place" electrode and both are moved inward. In this way an endless succession of carbon electrodes may be consumed without disturbing the flux. Each electrode lasts 3 to 6 months. A carbon electrode dip furnace is shown in Figure 6-2, above.

Carbon has half the electrical conductivity of nickel and therefore for a given current density the carbon electrodes must have twice the cross section of nickel electrodes of equal capacity. This may be an important con-

Figure 6-3. *Modern, dip-furnace installation with over-the top electrodes for heating salt. Note bus bars and transformers to right of furnace and travelling hoist used to move brazements. Some of the venting ductwork can also be seen. This is an Ajax furnace and preheat oven installation at Fairchild Hiller, Stratos Div.*

sideration in a small tank. Also, the higher resistance of the carbon forces the use of higher electrode voltages. While the nickel electrode voltages range from 15 to 30 volts, the carbon electrodes are usually powered with 30 to 60 volts. The power is always AC and is usually furnished by a step-down transformer stationed near the dip furnace. Single phase, two phase and three phase power supplies may be utilized.

The higher-voltage carbon electrode systems use less copper in the transformer secondary windings and less copper in the leads from the transformer to the electrodes. This can be an important savings. However, higher voltage necessitates greater insulation and, in the corrosive atmosphere of the brazing room, calls for better transformer sealing and more careful housekeeping.

Higher electrode voltage also increases the electrical field around and between the electrodes. Aluminum parts must be kept further away from the higher-voltage carbon electrodes and accidental contact is more likely to produce part damage.

On the other hand, nickel electrodes are far more costly. A single pair of electrodes, 4 inches square and 48 inches long, may cost $600 to $700. The metal is dense and costs a dollar or so a pound. Nickel electrodes are installed in one of three positions: over the top of the tank (see Figure 6-3), in the sides of the tank (a few inches below the surface) and in the sides of the tank, close to the bottom.

Nickel electrodes may or may not be water cooled; current density is the deciding factor.

Nickel electrodes wear most rapidly at their air/flux interface, and over-the-top electrodes generally need to be replaced in 3 to 6 months. They have the advantage of being easily removed. They are simply unbolted and lifted out of place with a fork lift or other power-lift equipment.

Over-the-top electrodes develop considerably more MHD (magnetohydrodynamic) force and therefore produce considerably more MHD flux circulation than sidewall and bottom-positioned electrodes. This is due to the greater length of electrode and its attendant magnetic field in the flux.

Submerged electrodes last much longer. Their average life is a year or two with some sets lasting three years. Bottom placed electrodes are more effective in producing convection currents in the molten flux and they are less likely to be accidentally struck by dipped parts.

On the other hand, submerged electrodes are difficult to replace. The pot has to be emptied of flux to a level below that of the electrodes, and the pot wall above the electrodes has to be disassembled. (Pot walls need also to be taken down when carbon electrodes stick in their holders or their holders develop leaks.) Bottom-positioned electrodes are troubled by sludge which tends to collect at the bottom of the salt pot and partially short circuit the electrodes. (Sludge removal methods are discussed in following paragraphs.)

Figure 6-4. *Modern pre-heat oven and dip furnace installations usually incorporate remote, temperature indicating and recording equipment.*

Electric power requirements are quite high and represent an appreciable portion of the cost of operating a dip tank, which is normally never shut down. It takes 385 btu to melt one pound of flux.

A 12″ by 12″ by 22″ pot draws about 15KW. A 36″ by 36″ by 30″ pot draws 55KW. The small pot is capable of brazing 100 lbs. of aluminum per hour at approximately 1100°F. The larger pot is rated at 225 lbs. per hour. In both cases, ratings are based on pre-heated work pieces.

There are two basic systems for controlling tank temperature. One is simply a temperature sensitive switch which calls for power when the temperature of the flux drops below a pre-set figure and shuts the power off when the temperature exceeds a certain figure. Its cost is low but it cannot provide the temperature accuracy possible with a "proportional power" system. This system senses temperature deviation also, but provides more power when the temperature is far from its desired setting and less power when the salt's temperature approaches the desired figure. With a proportional control system there is less "drag"—waiting for the temperature to come up and less "overshoot"—higher than desired temperature.

Pot temperature is usually controlled by a single knob. Actual oven and flux temperatures are usually displayed on large, direct-reading dials. The better-equipped brazing shops have both their pre-heat ovens and dip-furnaces connected to 24-hour recorders so that there is a permanent record of pre-heat and pot temperatures for every work shift. See Figure 6-4, above. Personnel involvement with oven and pot temperature is therefore extremely limited. In normal operation there is no need for temperature change once the equipment has been set for a production run.

Well maintained dip-furnaces and pre-heat ovens are temperature checked once a month. Calibrated thermocouples are used to make perhaps 36 temperature readings at as many different points in the pots and ovens, and the control system adjusted as necessary.

Ventilation

Salt pots must be forced vented. Hot flux produces a constant stream of irritating, toxic gases. The hot gases tend to condense on the nearest cool surface. If the gases and flux vapors are not removed, everything of metal in the brazing room will corrode and the health of those present will be endangered.

Venting can be accomplished by means of an over-the-pot hood system and/or a long, narrow, horizontal vent placed close to the surface of the molten flux.

The over-the-pot hood system is preferred. Opinion is that the side vent, hp for hp, is not nearly as effective, and that side vents tend to draw more air over the surface of the flux, thereby increasing the moisture content of the molten salt.

Aluminum is recommended for hood and ducting. Surprisingly, flux vapors attack the hood and leave the rest of the venting system virtually untouched.

Maximum fuming occurs when the pot is first fired up and when fresh flux is added.

Source: Aluminum Brazing Handbook, 2nd Ed., Aluminum Assn., Inc.

Choice of Flux

There is a fair range of commercial fluxes available and currently used in commercial brazing. Although one brand may be found most suitable for a particular product or condition, it is not incorrect to say that all fluxes work equally well, within their designed range, and that the choice of a flux for dip brazing is not so much a matter of joint quality as of other, important, but secondary considerations.

Commercial dip brazing fluxes are generally similar to fluxes used with other brazing methods. Their main ingredients include sodium chloride, potassium chloride, aluminum fluoride and lithium chloride. The proportions, methods of mixing and the various chemicals and elements added by the many firms manufacturing fluxes are highly proprietary. Salt manufacturers are nonetheless more than willing to aid the brazing engineer in selecting a flux and will in many instances develop special fluxes to suit individual brazing situations.

Commercial flux is sold in bulk quantities at prices ranging from 15 to 65 cents a pound. This is a considerable spread in flux cost when even a moderate-size pot can hold several hundred pounds of flux.

Flux price is based mainly on lithium content, plus manufacturing know how. Lithium, which sells for about $1.25 a pound, is the single most expensive ingredient in commercial flux.

Lithium lowers the melting point of flux. High-lithium-content fluxes melt and flow at lower temperatures than flux with lower lithium content. And at a given temperature, one at which both high and low-lithium content fluxes are liquid, higher-lithium content flux is less viscous. The higher priced fluxes are more stable and require less chemical adjustment. In one instance a tank of high-lithium content flux was operated for three years with nothing more added than make-up flux.

Maintaining the Salt Bath

A properly compounded, properly maintained salt bath will produce work pieces that are bright and shiny, with fillets well formed and complete. Such a bath will be found to be relatively free of sludge and surface film, slightly acidic with a ph of between 5.3 and 6.9, and its chemical composition will be relatively unchanged from its original formulation.

A poorly working salt solution will produce porous, pitted, ill-formed fillets with skips and holidays along their lengths. Fillets and parts will emerge dull and grey.

The poorly working salt solution may be alkaline with a ph somewhere above 7, filled with sludge or covered with surface film and possibly differing from its original and desired chemical composition. Any of these conditions may be severe enough of itself to cause brazing difficulties.

Of the three conditions described, alkalinity is by far the most frequent and troublesome. Alkalinity is caused by water in the bath which decomposes into oxygen and hydrogen and forms oxides and hydrides which react to turn the bath alkaline.

Water enters the bath in two ways. Dry salt, as received from the manufacturer in air-tight packages, contains a small quantity of water. If the water in the flux amounts to as little as ½ of 1% of the total volume of flux, the bath will turn alkaline, work pieces will be darkened, and fillets will be seriousy affected. A pot of freshly melted salt may require days of dehydration or rectification, as it is often called, before its water content is sufficiently lowered to permit satisfactory brazing. When fresh flux is added to a going bath in any quantity, work must be stopped and the bath dehydrated again.

New flux is not the only source of water in the bath. A pot of hot salt at 1100°F. can not only hold an objectionable quantity of water; the molten salt will actually draw additional water from the air. Flux is so hygroscopic that it is almost impossible to weigh an open sample of flux on a sensitive balance. The weight of the flux will increase as it absorbs water more rapidly than the scale can be balanced. It is therefore difficult to directly measure water present in molten salt. The sample's water content can change between the pot and the lab.

Excess water can be detected and removed with little difficulty. A sheet or coil or even a basket full of brazeable aluminum scrap is dipped into the hot flux. See Figure 6-5. Water in the salt reacts with the aluminum to re-

Figure 6-5. *Scrap aluminum sheets are used for salt dehydration and surface-scum removal. These plates will be washed, dried and then immersed in the flux again and again until they emerge reasonably clean.*

lease hydrogen which rises to the surface and bursts into puffs of yellow flame. When the flames stop, the water is effectively gone. Gas bubbles alone should be ignored as various gases are always being generated at the aluminum/flux interface. Some shops do not depend upon hydrogen flames alone, but braze a series of test joints until joint quality indicates the absence of water. (Test joints are discussed in a following paragraph.)

Aluminum for dehydration cannot be left indefinitely in the salt bath. The sheet is soon rendered inactive by oxide and sludge. It should be removed and cleaned or replaced at frequent intervals until either the absence of hydrogen flames and or satisfactory brazed joints are produced.

Raising flux temperature to 1300°F. or more is not recommended as a practical method of dehydration. The flux will fume excessively and there is a strong possibility some of the flux constituents will be destroyed.

On dry days, when a large volume of work is brazed, the need for dehydration is minimal; the clean aluminum work pieces remove water from the flux. On moist days, or when the bath is inactive, considerable dehydration may be required. Idle baths should be tightly covered to prevent moisture pickup.

When dehydration is believed complete, the salt's ph may be tested. This is accomplished with a standard ph meter and a 1% sample in neutralized, distilled water. The sample should be drawn from the pot at the time dehydration is completed.

It should be noted that some baths go alkaline and braze poorly because of contamination introduced by improperly cleaned assemblies.

In most instances, the removal of water (actually the hydrogen) is all that is necessary to turn the bath acidic. If this is not the case and the bath tests out above 7.0 ph, anhydrous aluminum fluoride, or one of the proprietary concentrates manufactured for this purpose, may be added. Aluminum fluoride reacts unfavorably with lithium chloride. The less added the better. At most, no more aluminum fluoride than 1% of the total flux volume should be added.

If a ph meter is not available, a test joint can be used to judge the condition of the salts. This is generally made in the form of a tee with a line of contact a foot or more in length. Filler metal is placed at one end of the joint, and that end is lowered vertically and first into the hot flux. If the bath is working properly the filler will run up the joint and form satisfactory fillets on both sides of the tee.

Undissolved contaminants in and on top of the hot salt interfere with brazing far less frequently and far less severely than alkalinity.

Contaminants that float to the surface are called scum and are composed mainly of iron oxide and carbon particles torn loose from the electrodes (when carbon electrodes are used). Surface contaminants are readily removed by skimming the salt's surface with a sheet of aluminum. There are a number of commercial preparations, which when added to the bath, cause the particles to coagulate, making their removal easier.

A simple rule of thumb test by which surface scum concentration may be evaluated comprises the immersion of a clean sheet of metal into the salt. If the scum forms no more than a ½-inch band around the top of the aluminum sheet, the bath may be used. If the black band is broader, the bath should be desludged.

Contaminants that sink to the bottom of the pot are called sludge. Sludge is composed of the oxides of dehydration, oxides from the brazed assemblies, insoluble fluoride complexes, and the results of the reaction of the flux with the ceramic sides of the pot. Sludge is all the heavy metal impurities that find their way into the salt: nickel, iron, copper, zinc and lead. Depending on flux formula, flux condition and brazing volume, a maximum of roughly 5 lbs. of sludge may be expected daily for every 1000 lbs. of salt in the pot.

There is no known way of preventing sludge, but by avoidance of iron-based alloys for the fixtures and springs, and by avoidance of steel-clad electric heating elements for initially melting the flux, heavy metal contamination may be reduced.

Some sludge is removed from the salt by brazing. The sludge adheres to the work in the form of dark stains. These stains may be removed by dipping the washed assemblies in hydrofluoric acid. Neither hot water nor nitric acid are particularly effective.

Some sludge is removed from the salt by dehydration treatment; the sludge adheres to the aluminum that is dipped into the pot for this purpose.

The major portion of the sludge collects at the bottom of the pot and is removed by ladling with a perforated tool. Some shops prefer to remove sludge the first thing in the morning, before the day's brazing activity has stirred up the collected contaminants. Dissatisfaction with this choice of time arises from the tendency of the sludge to "freeze" and form lumps during the preceding night. Sludging after work hours removes less sludge but reduces the incidence of salt freezing at the bottom of the tank.

The lumps of frozen salt on the bottom of the tank are called skulls. Most of the skull—some 90 to 95% of it—is composed of salt. The balance is sludge. It is extremely dangerous to the brittle ceramic lining of the tank to break the skulls free with bars and hammers. And it is a waste of salt to discard the pieces that are removed.

The far better, safer way consists of dissolving the frozen salt with the aid of a motor-driven impeller. The larger tanks have such impellers and motors built into their sides for just this purpose. See Figure 6-6. The small tanks can be stirred with stainless steel impellers mounted on portable electric motors.

Source: Aluminum Brazing Handbook, 2nd Ed., Aluminum Assn., Inc.

Figure 6-6. *Skulls should never be pried loose. A powered impeller should be used instead. Salt is conserved and the possibility of pot-wall damage eliminated.*

Figure 6-7. *When the bath is in proper working condition the brazed aluminum parts come out bright and shiny and are easily freed of flux.*

In small quantities, neither sludge nor surface scum adversely affect brazing. Large quantities of contaminants can, however, completely stop joint formation in portions of the brazed assembly.

The last and least frequent of the three general causes of poor brazing, attributable to the salt, itself is a major proportional change in flux formula.

The chemical composition or balance of a bath changes very slowly. Most slowly when the bath is active and fresh flux is added constantly to replace flux lost by drag out. The rate of change, even in inactive baths, is so slow that a once-a-month bath test is enough to forestall brazing difficulties. Companies manufacturing flux and others offer salt-bath testing service, and also sell the chemicals necessary to correct bath composition changes. These are merely added as and when needed.

Some changes in bath composition are fairly obvious. For example, a bath that is low in fluorides would be fluid at its operating temperature, but would braze poorly. Without fluorides, the chlorides are very slow to remove oxide from the surface of aluminum. If the bath's fluoride content were high, or its lithium content were low, the flux would be viscous at operating temperature, more salt would freeze out as skulls, but it would braze well.

The color of the molten flux is, however, only slightly useful in analyzing its composition. A desludged bath with carbon electrodes and sodium fluoride will be clear. The same bath with aluminum fluoride will be grey. A bath with nickel electrodes will be light blue in color when it is clean. As the quantity of metallic nickel in solution in-

creases, the bath's color becomes increasingly blue. When the blue is very dark or intense it is time to desludge the bath as the nickel may deposit out on the work in the form of a black sludge. A properly working bath is shown in Figure 6-7.

Bath Temperature

The temperature of the salt must match the alloys being brazed. The temperature should be high enough to bring the filler metal to liquidus without bringing the parent metals past solidus. Only within this range of temperatures is there room for experimentation.

Immersion Time

The time needed to completely form a joint or joints depends on the mass of the assembly and its temperature at the moment it enters the molten salt. Dip time varies from as little as a few seconds to as long as ten or twenty minutes. There is no formula by which immersion time can be calculated. It is a matter of trial and error. The better brazing shops keep careful work records so that a new "job" can be compared to the old and its immersion time estimated with considerable accuracy.

Immersion time is critical but not super-critical. A large wall-mounted clock with a second hand will provide all the accuracy needed. Some shops use a photographic timer. See Figure 6-8. Dip time variations of up to 20% are generally tolerable.

Excessive immersion is to be avoided. The longer the parts are subjected to brazing temperature, the greater the

Figure 6-8. *A photo-lab timer, connected to an electric bell, is used to time brazement immersion at the Fairchild Hiller, Stratos Div. plant.*

diffusion between parent metal and filler metal. However, diffusion is generally far less of a problem than that created by an incomplete joint. If there is any error in dip time, it is best it be on the plus-side.

Assemblies with incomplete joints and assemblies with new joints atop old can be re-dipped—frequently, but not always, without penalty. The deciding factors are the alloys and temperatures involved. Some silicon always leaves the filler metal and alloys with the parent metal, raising the filler's liquidus temperature and lowering the parent metal's solidus temperature. The extent of this change may be estimated if time and temperature are known. If the filler melts at the second dipping, it may very well complete the joint. If it doesn't flow, raising the bath's temperature to make the filler metal flow may soften the base metal beyond redemption and it may collapse.

In some instances, when the brazing assembly is massive, it is possible to face-feed (hand-fed) the filler metal into an open, visible joint. The joint is lifted clear of the flux, and filler metal is gently pushed into it.

Procedure

Parts are cleaned as discussed in Chapter 4 and assembled as discussed in Chapter 2. Dip brazing is more tolerant of joint clearances than other brazing methods. Joints with faying surface separations of 0.0020 to 0.025 inch are easily formed by dipping. Jigging requirements, on the other hand, are more stringent. The flux tends to float the assembly and spread the pieces apart. Gravity alone will not keep them together. All parts must be jigged by one means or another. Air pockets cannot be permitted. Sealed vessels cannot be dipped. They must be vented. The vent hole may be later brazed closed in a separate operation.

Filler metal is almost always prepositioned and is best "buried" within the joint or assembly. If the filler metal is a thin rod or shim and makes primary contact with the hot flux it may melt and drop off into the flux before the balance of the assembly comes up to temperature. Any form of filler metal may be used, including paste.

All assemblies should be preheated to approximately 1000°F. before dipping. There is less thermal shock to the parts and less heat is drawn from the flux. Small parts may be dipped without preheating but extreme caution is necessary to make certain no moisture is present on or in the parts. Water and alcohol turn to vapor at an explosive rate when they enter hot salt.

All dip-furnace brazing personnel should be forced to wear protective clothing and face shields. Hot flux spatters are extremely painful. In the event of a burn, cold water and ice are the best remedy. Applied immediately they can save pain and possibly life itself.

As pre-heating may take several hours and brazing just a few minutes, it is common practice to supply each dip furnace with several pre-heat ovens. The ovens and salt pots are best situated in a single room, close to each other and separate from the parts assembly and parts cleaning rooms or areas.

Dipping technique is straightforward. Hung from a wire or supported by a fixture (which has also been preheated and dried), the parts are gently lowered into the molten flux. If there is a mass differential, the heavier portion of the assembly may be lowered first into the salt and held partly submerged for a moment. Then the balance of the assembly may be dipped. In this way, reasonably equal heat distribution is attained.

After the fillets have been formed, the submerged assembly is slowly and carefully raised a short distance above the flux and held there until it cools to 900°F. or so. To encourage flux drainage, the assembly may be tilted slightly. The assembly should neither be raised too quickly nor tilted too sharply; rapid flux run off may "gutter" the fillets—reduce their size. When the fillets have solidified, the assembly may be moved on.

Source: Aluminum Brazing Handbook, 2nd Ed., Aluminum Assn., Inc.

Figure 6-9. *Well arranged brazing plant. Pre-heat furnace, salt pot and control equipment are at rear, wash tanks with large, power-vented hoods are to the sides. Workman is washing aluminum to be used for rectification of the salt bath.*

Furnace Brazing

Furnace brazing is the second most popular method of brazing aluminum in use today. Except for dip brazing, more assemblies are brazed in a furnace than by all other methods together.

Furnace brazing's popularity derives from the comparatively low cost of equipment, from the ease with which existing furnaces can be adapted to aluminum brazing and back again, and from the minimal jigging required. With many brazing assemblies, the weight of the parts alone is sufficient to hold them together. With other configurations, a rectangular block or two of metal is all the fixturing needed.

The furnace can be used to braze assemblies with pockets that might trap air or collect a troublesome quantity of flux when dipped, and to braze highly polished parts that might be unduly etched when immersed in hot flux.

Parts to be brazed in a furnace are cleaned and freed of excess oxide as discussed in Chapter 4. The faying surfaces are fluxed, filler metal is positioned and the parts are assembled and jigged as discussed in Chapter 2.

The assembly is then heated to approximately 300°F. to drive the moisture or alcohol out of the flux. This is generally accomplished in a pre-heat oven. Next, the assembly is placed in the furnace (which is already at brazing temperature) and permitted to remain some 3 to 5 minutes after it has reached brazing temperature. Brazing completed, the assembly is carefully removed, cooled or quenched and then cleaned as discussed in Chapters 3 and 4. Usually, the assembly remains no more than 15 minutes altogether in the furnace.

Two Furnace Systems

There are two basic types of furnaces used for brazing: the batch furnace and the continuous furnace. See Figures 7-1 and 7-2.

A batch furnace has a single brazing area into which a "batch" of assemblies is placed for brazing. Its initial cost is comparatively low and maintenance costs are low. It can be turned on and shut off at will. The batch furnace offers the manufacturer of brazed assemblies a practical, economical and flexible means of brazing up to several hundred work pieces a day. Batch cycling can be as rapid as 15 to 20 minutes, depending on the furnace, the physical mass of the parts and whether or not they are pre-heated in a separate furnace.

The batch furnace is suited to medium-to-large production runs and to shops that handle a large variety of brazing jobs. Unlike the automatic torch system where a change in the unit brazed requires a major change in the placement of the torches and possibly the associate machinery, any part that can be placed in the furnace can be brazed.

The continuous furnace may comprise one large unit or several units with differing temperatures through which the assembled parts are moved by means of a conveyor belt. Generally there is a minimum of three distinct temperature zones followed by a cooling zone. The continuous furnace can produce unlimited quantities of brazed assemblies. Base rates of 500 units and 500 lbs. of aluminum per hour and more are not uncommon with equipment of this type.

Neither the batch furnace nor the continuous furnace is suited to excessively massive parts. When furnace time approaches 30 minutes or more, braze quality falls off. This is caused by (1) flux change, (2) liquation and (3) diffusion. The scope of their detrimental effects are also in the same order and in decreasing magnitude.

Flux change begins when fresh flux is exposed to air and placed in the joint to be. The flux absorbs water immediately and reacts with contiguous metal. Brought to brazing temperature in normal time, neither are problems.

Source: Aluminum Brazing Handbook, 2nd Ed., Aluminum Assn., Inc.

Figure 7-1. *Front end of a continuous-belt furnace in operation.*

When heating is slow and prolonged, the flux may be too wet and too close to the completion of its reaction to be effective.

Liquation occurs when the temperature of an assembly is raised so slowly that some of the lower-melting point constituents of the filler melt and leave the filler before the balance of the filler metal reaches liquidus.

Diffusion is a problem mainly when assembly parts are considerably unequal in size: The filler may turn liquid in one portion of the assembly long before the entire assembly is brazed. Thus the time during which conditions favor diffusion is inordinately long in the lighter portion of the assembly.

The three problems notwithstanding, massive parts are satisfactorily brazed in furnaces. The actual determinant is the work piece itself and what is expected of it. Some parts are kept at brazing temperature for hours and the resultant joints are entirely satisfactory and within a design goal.

Furnace Selection

Any furnace capable of being brought to and held within ±5°F. of brazing temperature can be used to

furnace-braze aluminum. Any heating means may be employed: commercial gas, oil burner, electrical resistances, or infra-red heating lamps.

The simplest and least expensive furnaces are the "muffle" types in which combustion products pass through the brazing area. As moisture is always a by-product of combustion, and as moisture is a hindrance to good brazing, the muffle-type furnace is not first choice when optimum quality joints are sought. Muffle furnaces should not be oil fired. Oil combustion is never complete. The aluminum assemblies may be covered with soot.

Alloys 6061, 6063 and 6951 tend to oxide rapidly in the presence of combustion products. These alloys are usually not brazed in muffle furnaces.

The hot-wall furnace, in which the hot combustion gases are brought behind the furnace walls or through tubes or flues, provides for a cleaner, dryer brazing atmosphere and is much more desirable. Thermal efficiency is lower in hot wall and radiant tube furnaces, but thermal distribution is better.

Electrically heated furnaces for brazing are preferably of the hot wall type. Exposed electrical heating elements are susceptible to flux vapor corrosion and are not recommended. When the electrical elements are behind the

Figure 7-2. *Medium-size batch furnace. Note on-edge bars used to reduce contact between assembly and fixture.*

furnace wall or similarly protected, reasonably satisfactory service life may be expected.

Furnaces constructed expressly for brazing aluminum are generally lined with aluminum-coated steel or glazed fire brick.

Temperature gradients within a furnace can be reduced by installing air circulating fans and baffles. The baffles need not be mounted permanently. They may be partial shielding devices fastened to the fixtures to suit the needs of an individual assembly.

Standard annealing and heat-treatment furnaces can be used for brazing aluminum if they can reach the correct temperature, and if the temperature can be held to ±5°F. while the parts are brazed.

A number of secondary problems arise, however, when standard furnaces are used for brazing aluminum. The bare steel parts of the furnace are attacked by the flux that vaporizes from the brazing assembly's joints. Furnaces lined with unglazed refractory brick tend to absorb flux which later attacks other metals heated in the furnace when it is returned to its normal duty.

Assembly Temperature

When the parts to be brazed are comparatively small, or when there is little mass variation between parts of the

assembly, and heat is reasonably well distributed through the furnace, the "furnace-door" thermometer is sufficient guide to assembly temperature. When the assembly is large or composed of parts of unequal mass, no single-point temperature measuring means is satisfactory. A number of thermocouples or temperature sensitive probes should be mounted on different parts of the first assembly to be brazed. The assembly may then be moved, shielded or baffled as necessary until the temperature gradient across it is less than ±5 degrees at brazing temperature. When this has been accomplished, assembly placement and heat modifier positions are carefully noted. Similar assemblies following can then be brazed using a single thermometer as a guide.

Part temperature within a continuous furnace can be measured by fastening temperature probes to the assembly and noting assembly temperature as it passes through the different heating zones. The use of recorders will simplify the task. Some temperature variation across the work piece can be tolerated when the assembly is in the pre-heat area. But heat should be reasonably well distributed when the assembly reaches brazing temperature.

As with the batch furnace, small and regular assemblies can usually be satisfactorily brazed on the basis of past experience and single-point temperature readings in the continuous furnace heating zones. Complicated assemblies will require some manipulation and adjustment. Once ad-

Source: Aluminum Brazing Handbook, 2nd Ed., Aluminum Assn., Inc.

justed, succeeding assemblies can be brazed without further testing.

Preparing Joints to be Furnace Brazed

Joints to be furnace brazed require more care than joints to be dip brazed. There isn't the excess of hot flux to wash away the oxide and possibly dirt that may be present on the faying surfaces. Cleaning for furnace brazing must be done more thoroughly and carefully. Joints must be fully fluxed. Because there is less flux at the joint, a more active flux is generally selected for furnace brazing.

As considerable time may elapse between the application of flux and the completion of the brazing cycle, flux attack can be troublesome with very thin stock. This can be reduced by delaying the application of flux until the parts are ready to be placed in the pre-heat oven. Experimentation with various flux formulations is also suggested. Some fluxes are less active at room temperature and slightly above.

Joint clearance for parts to be furnace brazed is usually between 0.004 and 0.008 inch for laps less than ¼ inch wide. Greater overlap calls for clearances up to 0.025 inch. Tests should be made to determine the best joint clearances for work pieces to be furnace joined.

Brazing furnace jigging requirements are simple. In many instances, gravity positioning suffices to hold the parts in alignment. On occasion, rectangular blocks and other metal shapes may be used to support the parts or hold them in place. Any metal that won't melt or vaporize can be used as a weight or fixture material. Aluminum is not often used as it is easily brazed to the parts it contacts. However, if stop-off protection is provided, any aluminum alloy that will not melt at brazing temperature may be used.

When used, fixtures and jigs should be designed to permit the parts freedom of expansion and contraction. Temperature-test runs should be made with jigs and fixtures in place.

Mild steel, either bare or coated with aluminum or nickel, may be used as fixture material. Flux splatter is washed off after each using.

Springs should be of stainless steel or Inconel if they are to be used for long periods of time. For short runs, mild steel or spring steel springs are satisfactory.

Furnace Brazing Technique

The prepared and jigged parts, brazing filler metal and flux in place, are put into a pre-heat oven, which is usually preset, and heated to approximately 300°F. Higher pre-heat temperatures should not be used as the flux may boil and disturb the joints and filler metal. When the parts have reached this temperature, and/or when all the alcohol and/or water used with the flux has evaporated, the assemblies are moved to the brazing furnace, which too has been heated to the desired brazing temperature or a fraction above to counteract the admission of the cooler metal.

Lacking a pre-heat oven, the prepared assembly may be pre-heated in the brazing furnace, which has been heated to 300°F. Following pre-heat, the furnace is brought to proper brazing temperature.

The assembly is left in the furnace long enough to insure filler melting and complete forming of the joints. The time required for this may be found by test and by comparison with previously brazed assemblies of similar size and configuration.

Upon joint completion, the assembly is carefully removed from the furnace and permitted to cool until the filler solidifies, after which it may be further cooled and washed, or quenched and then washed. Alternatively, the brazed assembly may be permitted to cool and its joints to solidify in the furnace. But this lengthens the brazing cycle and slows production.

To speed production, the furnace may be set to a temperature considerably above brazing and the assembly's temperature controlled by carefully limiting the time the assembly is in the furnace. Reduced time at heat reduces the possibility of liquation, diffusion, flux change and flux attack.

In all cases, all pre-heat ovens and furnaces must be fully vented. Alcohol vapor and air, released during pre-heat, forms an explosive mixture. And hydrogen, generated during brazing, combines with air to form an even more explosive combination. Mixtures of hydrogen with air ranging from 4 to 75% hydrogen are explosive.

Vacuum and Controlled Atmosphere Brazing

Various techniques for reducing and eliminating flux in the brazing of aluminum continue to be developed. Many of these techniques and processes are patent protected. They are presented here as a review of the art. Permission to use these techniques must be secured from the patent holders prior to production.

Two approaches have borne fruit over the 20 or more years the problem of flux elimination has been studied. One limits or removes air from the surface of the joint to be formed by displacing the air with another atmosphere. With this technique, optimum quality joints can be produced with a minimum of flux. The other removes the air by means of vacuum. Generally, no flux whatsoever is needed for vacuum brazing.

Flux, Air and Joint Quality

As stated, flux performs two tasks during brazing. It undermines and displaces oxide from the surface of the aluminum and it protects the bare metal from contact with the air. Flux is highly hygroscopic and not completely devoid of water at brazing temperature. Flux therefore always introduces a minute quantity of water into the joint and never completely protects the joint from contact with the air.

Although the exact mechanism is not known, theory holds that bare aluminum beneath the layer of flux reacts with the oxygen in the water to form an oxide again. The remaining hydrogen is trapped beneath the filler metal and flux. Given time, it may bubble free. If not, the hydrogen remains permanently encapsulated within the filler. Some brazing engineers believe that hydrogen alone is responsible for most of the voids found in brazed aluminum joints.

The effects of water and air on a joint can be eliminated or severely reduced by brazing the joint under a protective blanket of dry, inert gas or in a vacuum. Joints so formed show "perfectly clear" under X-rays. These joints are free of voids, and both techniques, inert gas and vacuum are commercially used for the manufacture of aluminum RF waveguides, aerospace plumbing and assemblies for similarly stringent applications.

Brazing In Dry, Inert Gas

Parts to be brazed in dry, inert gas are prepared as usual. They are cleaned of soil and oxide, provided with filler metal, fluxed and jigged. Generally, considerably less flux than would otherwise be necessary is used. Next the assembly is pre-heated and placed in the controlled atmosphere furnace.

A number of different gases are used: argon, helium, nitrogen and carbon dioxide. The dew point is kept below $-70°$ F.

Any type of furnace that meets temperature requirements and can be satisfactorily sealed may be used for controlled atmosphere brazing. Obviously, combustion products cannot be permitted to enter the brazing area.

When argon is used, it is introduced through an inlet valve on the bottom of the furnace. A second valve on top of the furnace is opened. Argon is heavier than air. It remains on the bottom of the furnace as it enters and tends to displace the air which moves out through the top valve. When the furnace is filled, both valves are closed.

When helium is used, the reverse procedure is employed. Helium is lighter than air and is therefore introduced through the top of the furnace.

In addition to the usual heating and temperature control equipment necessary for the operation of a conventional brazing furnace, the controlled atmosphere furnace requires special valves for the admission and venting of

Figure 8-1. *Furnace brazing aluminum in ultra-dry air.*

the gases and generally a gas recovery system. In production, gas is too costly to be discarded after one using. Furnace sealing is complicated and usually requires skilled maintenance at frequent intervals. As a result, the overall investment and operating costs of a controlled atmosphere brazing furnace are considerably higher than its basic simplicity might indicate.

On the plus side, controlled atmosphere brazing greatly aids in the production of maximum quality joints. The absence of moisture and air in the controlled atmosphere furnace greatly eases the effort required of the flux. Water and air are present in the system, and they do react with the aluminum. But the quantity of air and water is small and limited; when they are finally depleted, the flux can and does remove the last of the oxide.

Not only is less flux required with controlled atmosphere brazing, making post-braze cleanup simpler by that amount, the inert atmosphere reduces the total amount of oxide trapped in the flux. As the oxide particles act like leafing pigment in paint, less oxide means easier dissolution of residual flux. The inert gas also substantially re-

duces the quantity of water-insoluble oxychlorides present, again making flux dissolution and removal easier.

Ultra-Dry Air Brazing

Workers in this field report all the advantages obtained with controlled atmosphere brazing—minimum flux, high quality joints and easier cleaning—can be secured by brazing in ultra-dry air. Work has progressed well past the pilot stage and at this writing plans are underway for the commercial production of heat exchangers by this technique. A view of a pilot plant is shown in Figure 8-1, above.

Vacuum Brazing

By brazing in a vacuum, both air and its attendant moisture are prevented from contacting the to-be-brazed joint. When this is done, the brazed joint can be formed without flux. The elimination of flux removes the major barrier to "perfect" brazed joints and higher quality joints are produced by fluxless vacuum brazing than any other known technique.

Figure 8-2. *An electrically heated vacuum furnace.*

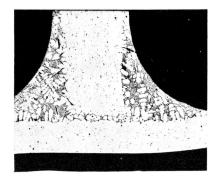

Figure 8-3. *Cross section of an aluminum joint, brazed in vacuum without flux. Magnified 50 X.*

Figure 8-4. *The first passenger car assembly to be produced by fluxless vacuum brazing. A brazed, aluminum, automobile air-conditioner evaporator manufactured by Philco-Ford.*

The savings effected by flux elimination is far greater than the cost of the flux alone. When a complicated assembly such as a radiator is brazed, the cost of cleaning, cleaning equipment, water and water purification after cleaning can together amount to 10 to 20 times as much as the cost of merely brazing. Vacuum brazing also obviates the need for an inert gas and its associate equipment.

Vacuum brazing is well past the laboratory and pilot plant stage. Automotive and home air conditioners are now mass produced by several companies using the vacuum type brazing process.

Successful vacuum brazing with alloys 1100, 2219, 6061, 3003, and 7005 and standard filler metals has been reported in the *Welding Journal,* May, 1967, *Materials Engineering,* December, 1967, *Materials in Design Engineering,* March, 1965, and in *Modern Metal Joining Techniques,* published by John Wiley & Son, N.Y.

Essentially the techniques described in the foregoing publications are identical to those used for furnace flux brazing. As reported, a high level of cleanliness is important and brazing is accomplished within 12 hours of cleaning. Filler metal No. 4047 in both wire and brazing sheet is used (4245 with 2219 core). Brazing temperature is held between 1080 and 1100 degrees Fahrenheit. Time at brazing temperature varies from 1 to 2 minutes. Joint clearances are held between 0.002 and 0.004 inches. The assembly is then placed in a vacuum furnace, which is pumped down to 10^{-4}—10^{-6} Torr. It is well known that high vacuum accelerates vaporization. The effect of heat and vacuum are not clearly understood, but certainly the rate of oxidation of the aluminum surface exposed during heating is held to a very low level. Inert gases (N_2 or CO_2) are used to return the evacuated furnace to normal pressure and to quench the hot assemblies. Figure 8-4 shows a vacuum brazed assembly. Similar brazements with ⅛ inch wide lap joints surpassed a helium leak test criterion of 10^{-6} cc/sec for 15 seconds.

A different production approach to fluxless vacuum brazing is reported in the December, 1969 issue of *Metal Progress.* The difference lies in the use of filler metals that have been slightly modified chemically (magnesium has been added). Cleaning is accomplished with vapor degreasing alone, the vacuum is 10^{-5} Torr. Heating and pumpdown proceeded simultaneously and require about 15 minutes. Brazing temperature is 1,120 degrees Fahrenheit, and is held for 1 minute in a typical cycle. Breaking vacuum requires another 1 minute. Cooling is done in ambient air external to the vacuum furnace. All the normally brazed alloys are successfully joined by this technique.

The report states that the inclusion of small quantities of magnesium and other elements in the filler results in more consistent joining and is better suited to high-speed commercial brazing than is so far possible with standard filler metals, and that less sophisticated pre-braze cleaning is necessary with modified filler metal.

Other Brazing Methods

Motion Brazing

In motion brazing, flux is not used to remove surface oxide from faying surfaces. Instead, joining surfaces are moved against and across each other to remove surface oxide from both parts to permit wetting and brazing.

The contacting surfaces may be moved slowly in relation to each other or rapidly or even oscillated at ultrasonic frequency. Abrasion is carried out at temperatures immediately below the liquidus temperature of the filler used. After the oxide has been displaced, temperature is increased until full liquidus is reached and held there long enough for brazing to take place. Subsequent cooling and further treatment of the joint follows standard practice. No cleaning is necessary as no flux is used.

There are a number of motion brazing techniques. The simplest utilizes two brazing sheets which form the parts or faying surfaces. The filler metal cladding on one sheet is placed in contact with the filler cladding on the second sheet. There is no joint gap. The parts are heated until the liquidus temperature of the cladding is almost reached. One part is then moved in relation to the other (the faying surfaces are rubbed against each other), and heating is continued until full filler metal liquidus is reached. The motion displaces the oxide "floating" on the liquid filler metal surfaces. The two liquids mingle and join. On cooling the joint is formed.

Another approach, sometimes called flow brazing, utilizes molten filler metal. The prepared parts are moved rapidly within a bath of molten filler metal. Conversely, the molten filler may be moved. This may be accomplished by means of a transducer driven at ultrasonic frequency. The relative motion between parent metal and filler metal displaces the surface oxide. The filler metal then wets the parent metals and forms the brazed joint on cooling.

Induction Brazing

Joints brazed by this method are brought to brazing temperature by high frequency electrical currents induced in the faying surfaces by an inductance (coil) positioned nearby.

Heating is localized, fast, and generally accomplished in less than one minute. There are no open flames and power is consumed only during the brazing cycle. Once brazing parameters have been ascertained, brazing by induction is a mechanically repeatable operation. It can be automated and it can be accomplished by untrained production help.

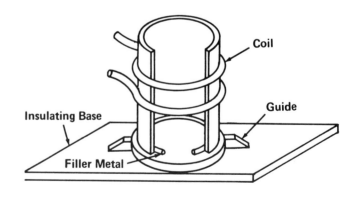

Figure 9-1. *Induction coil is shown external and clear of work piece, but it may also be designed to be positioned inside the work piece.*

Post-induction brazing cleaning is easier than post-torch brazing cleaning because there are no combustion products to react with the flux and form insolubles.

The equipment required is expensive compared to that necessary for other brazing methods. High production runs are needed to amortize the investment at a reasonable rate. However, the same equipment can be used for brazing and heat-treating other metals. Figure 9-1 shows the "working end" of a typical induction brazing installation.

Frequencies from 60 to 5,000,000 Hertz (cycles per second) are used for induction heating. A frequency of 530,000 Hertz has been found most satisfactory for a wide span of industrial heating applications, including aluminum brazing.

Energy transfer from the work coil to the aluminum parts to be brazed is directly related to the distance between the part and the coil. The shorter the distance the greater the quantity of energy transferred; i.e., the greater the coupling that exists.

The frequency selected has an important bearing on the manner in which the parts to be brazed are heated. The lower frequencies tend to penetrate more deeply into the metal, but power transfer from work coil to brazed part is less efficient than at higher frequencies, and the effect of coupling distance is more pronounced. The higher frequencies are transferred more efficiently from the output coil to the work and coupling distance effects are less noticeable. However, the higher frequencies are excluded

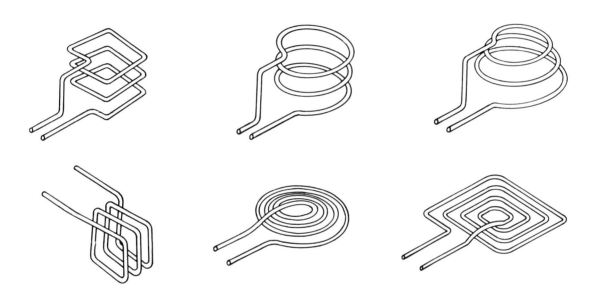

Figure 9-2. *A few of the many forms the work coil may take.*

Five types of power supplies are used. Motor-generator sets are used for frequencies up to 10 000 Hertz. Resonant spark gaps are used to supply middle-range frequencies, 20,000 to 300,000 Hertz. Vacuum tube oscillators are generally employed for frequencies from 300,000 to 5,000,-000 Hertz. Mercury-arc converters are also used for the middle range, and solid-state oscillators, the fifth type may be designed to produce any of the frequencies listed.

In operation, the work piece is placed in or near the output inductance or work coil. Or the coil is placed inside the work piece. No physical contact is necessary. The metal parts act as the shorted secondary of a transformer; the work coil is the primary.

from the depths of the metal by "skin effect" and time must be allowed for the inner portions of the metal to be heated by conduction. In some instances the selectivity of the higher frequencies may be used to advantage.

The work coil may be one turn or many. It may be shaped like a pancake, oval, helix, spiral or tube. Some examples are shown in Figure 9-2. Coils handling more than ¾ KW are generally water cooled. The coil is formed of a tube and tap water directed to run through its length. The voltage across the work is low and there is little problem with insulating it from the water pipe. Induction heating equipment suitable for brazing is available in power ratings to 100 KW.

Source: Aluminum Brazing Handbook, 2nd Ed., Aluminum Assn., Inc.

The work coil may be shaped to follow the contours of the assembly, and the coil's turns may be spaced to favor the heavier sections of the metal to be heated. If part-to-work variations are exceptionally large for a particular assembly, the use of a larger work coil will reduce individual differences. Heat will be less efficiently transferred but more evenly distributed. The higher frequencies are more effective over distance than the lower frequencies.

Portions of the work that must remain relatively cool throughout the brazing cycle may be insulated from the radiant energy by means of metal shields. They are interposed between the coil and the work. Generally they are constructed of copper, though aluminum may be used.

Work coils are simple to fabricate and are frequently made by brazing shop personnel as needed. One coil or a number may be used with one assembly. The work coil itself is not heated appreciably during the brazing cycle.

All conductors within the high frequency field act as shorted secondaries, absorb energy and heat up. Metal jigs and fixtures generally cannot be used for induction brazing. If they are, sufficient power must be supplied to heat the fixtures as well as the aluminum assembly. Magnetic metals such as steel absorb more energy (until they reach their Curie temperature) than better electrical conductors such as aluminum and copper and therefore are difficult to use for induction brazing.

Spring and clips can be used with the jigging. They will be heated along with the assembly to be brazed, possibly to higher-than-braze temperature because they may be closer to the work coils. Inconel and stainless hold up best. Ordinary spring steel may also be used although it will lose its temper rapidly.

Electrically non-conductive and heat resistant materials such as ceramics, steatites, asbestos and glass may be used as weights, supports and fixtures for induction brazing. The non-conductors will not absorb energy and will be heated by convection and conduction alone. Unglazed ceramics, such as bricks, must be dried before they are used as induction brazing fixtures. Water (plus salt) is a conductor. Water in a brick may absorb enough energy to turn to steam and cause the brick to explode.

Joint clearances for parts to be brazed by induction heating are similar to those used for furnace brazing; 0.002 to 0.004 inch. Joints designed for induction brazing are no different than joints designed for furnace brazing or other brazing methods. The prime guide in designing assemblies for induction brazing is the recognition of the limited heating area afforded by this method, and the neces-

sity of keeping all the joints to be brazed at one time within the heating area. Thought must also be given to the repulsion effect induced in the molten filler (and all metal within the range of the work coil) by the alternating current. The current induces a counter magnetic field, which acts to repulse the initial field. In some cases it may act to drive the molten filler out of the joint. This can be prevented by positioning the work coil properly in respect to the joint. For example, when the work coil is below a socketed tube-to-tube joint, the molten filler forms a closed metal ring above the magnetic field and is moved upwards and out of the joint. Raising the work coil above the filler tends to drive it down and into the joint.

Parts to be brazed by induction heating are cleaned, freed of oxide, fluxed and jigged along with the necessary preplaced filler metal. Then they are thoroughly dried. Heat generated by induced electrical currents is intense. Moisture turning to steam within the joint may drive the molten flux and filler out at high speed. The use of alcohol as a flux vehicle is advisable. It will dry more rapidly.

When the flux has dried, the assembly is placed on or within a non-inductive guide or work-locating fixture, which is in turn positioned within the work coil. Once the optimum assembly position has been defined, the locating device is permanently affixed to the supporting surface and subsequent assemblies can be positioned readily and with considerable accuracy.

Work piece temperature and time are established by varying the power delivered to the work coil, the relation of the coil to the work piece and the time interval. Although joints can be brazed by induction heating in as little as 5 seconds, it is generally better to reduce the power and extend the time period. Timing in seconds must be done automatically if it is to be consistent.

Once time, power and work-piece position have been determined, brazing by induction heating becomes simple routine.

After the joint has been formed the assembly must be permitted to cool before it is moved. Cooling and quenching may be accomplished by means of an ambient air blast provided by a nearby fan. The fan can be electrically connected to the induction equipment so that the fan is turned on a short time after the RF generator is turned off, and the fan is automatically turned off when the brazing cycle begins.

Treatment of an assembly after induction brazing is identical to that of assemblies brazed by other methods.

Brazing Aluminum to Other Metals

All the aluminum alloys that can be brazed can be brazed directly to other metals including steel, nickel, copper, cobalt, beryllium, columbium and their alloys, plus commercial alloys such as Inconel, Monel, Kovar and stainless steel. Some of these metals and alloys can be brazed directly to aluminum by conventional techniques and with conventional fluxes and fillers. However, stronger, more ductile and more satisfactory joints can be produced by using special brazing techniques and materials, some of which are patent protected. One metal, magnesium, cannot so far be brazed to aluminum. When brazing is attempted the two metals form an extremely brittle intermetallic at their interface, which severely limits the joint's usefulness.

Highly useful aluminum to steel joints can be made by dip brazing. The aluminum and the steel are both cleaned and freed of oxide, then jigged along with the necessary filler metal. The aluminum-steel assembly is preheated as quickly as possible to minimize oxide formation on the steel, and then it is dipped into a standard flux bath. This procedure is fast and dependable, but unfortunately tends to warp or distort the assembly. The joints are also somewhat heat and shock sensitive.

Distortion can be reduced by brazing the aluminum-steel combination in a controlled atmosphere furnace using dry, inert gas. Again standard fluxes and aluminum filler metals are used. The resultant joints, however, remain heat and shock sensitive. This is due to the brittle aluminum ferrite (Fe_3 Al) phase formed between the two dissimilar metals. Nonetheless, there are many designs which can incorporate aluminum-steel brazed joints made by flux-dipping or controlled atmosphere.

Stronger, more ductile steel-aluminum joints, less sensitive to heat and shock, can be produced by precoating the

Figure 10-1. *Liquid oxygen-liquid hydrogen flow to J-2 engines on the Apollo is controlled by 6061 aluminum and 304 stainless steel valve. Manufactured by Solar Div. of International Harvester, aluminum is treated with titanium in patented process prior to brazing. Arrows indicate bi-metal joints.*

steel with a protective layer of metal prior to brazing. See Figure 10-1. Brazing may then be accomplished by conventional means.

The protective metals may be applied by electroplating, hot dipping or metalizing. When copper or nickel are used, they are generally electroplated onto the steel. Zinc, silver and aluminum are usually applied by hot dipping. Tin is applied by either method. Zinc and aluminum are probably the plating metals most frequently used, but all the metals listed are known to improve wetting and produce stronger, more ductile aluminum-to-steel brazed joints.

Source: Aluminum Brazing Handbook, 2nd Ed., Aluminum Assn., Inc.

Figure 10-2. *Examples of brazed joints made with aluminum and stainless steel.*

Courtesy Bi-Braze

Using a hand-held torch and standard fillers and fluxes, aluminum-coated steel tubes have been brazed to aluminum tubes to form joints that exhibit shear strengths to 15,000 psi. Laps of 0.50 inch to 2.50 inches were used with a clearance of 0.010 inch. Pre-heat and brazing time were kept to a minimum.

Stainless steel is brazed to aluminum by first coating the hot stainless steel with Sn. The cleaned, deoxidized aluminum is assembled with the coated stainless steel and preplaced filler metal. The assembly is then dipped into hot flux, cooled and cleaned. When alloy 6061 is brazed to 304L stainless, filler No. 4047 (718) is used.

The aluminum brazing filler metals form an aluminum-tin alloy with the tin which in turn forms a continuous layer of metal on the stainless steel. Joints formed this way exhibit good resistance to cryogenic shock, vibration and pressure burst tests. Leak rates with helium are less than 10^{-8} cc/sec.

A patented process (Bi-Braze) is being used to "metallurgically bond" stainless steels, other ferrous alloys, beryllium, columbium, nickel, titanium and other metals to the brazeable alloys of aluminum. An aluminum-to-304 stainless steel joint produced by this process exhibits shear strength in excess of 6,000 psi and leak rates of less than 10^{-9} cc/sec as measured with helium and a mass spectrometer. Tubular transition joints are being fabricated in sizes to 24 inches in diameter. They have been operated in temperatures as low as 4.2°K and at vacuum pressure on the order of 3×10^{-12} Torr without failure. Examples are shown in Figure 10-2.

When aluminum is brazed to stainless steel by this process, the cleaned steel is soaked for hours in a bath of molten aluminum to which a proprietary quantity and mixture of alloying elements have been added. Afterwards, the stainless steel is brazed to the aluminum by standard flux dipping procedures.

Inconel, Kovar, Monel, nickel and beryllium can be wetted directly by standard aluminum brazing fillers with the aid of flux and can therefore be brazed directly to aluminum. Monel, however, forms a brittle inter-metallic compound with aluminum and is therefore preferably precoated with aluminum before brazing.

Copper can be satisfactorily brazed to aluminum if certain techniques are employed. Normally, copper and aluminum interdiffuse at brazing temperature to form a brittle, intermetallic. However, if brazing and cooling are accomplished quickly enough, a joint sufficiently ductile for limited applications can be formed. The above can be accomplished with standard filler metals and fluxes.

An alternative to the difficulty of joining copper directly to aluminum lies in the use of a transition joint. The aluminum is brazed to an aluminum-coated length of steel, which is then easily brazed to the copper.

Titanium may also be fairly easily brazed to aluminum if the titanium is first dipped into a molten alloy of silver and aluminum (67 Ag — 33 Al). This alloy forms a thin, uniform layer on the titanium with an intermetallic boundary less than 2 microns thick. A pre-coat of zinc and aluminum (50Zn — 50Al) can also be used, but strength and ductility will be less. Flux dip brazing has been found best with the above technique. Furnace brazing in air has so far not been satisfactory.

Joint Inspection, Testing and Performance

Inspection

Visual examination is the most commonly used means for rapidly assessing brazed joint quality. If the fillet is fully formed and smoothly curvilinear the joint may be accepted as being reasonably sound pending further, more detailed examination.

If the joint is not fully formed, smooth and sound, its appearance is usually a fair indicator of specific brazing errors or failures. Typical brazing failure causes and their characteristic appearances are listed following. Visual examination is best made before the cooled assembly has been cleaned as cleaning may remove pertinent clues.

If the surface of the fillet is broken and uneven, heat may not have been applied evenly to the length of the joint, the parts may have moved in relation to one another during heat or the fillet was reheated, as might be the case when the joint is made by hand-held torch brazing.

If the surface of the fillet is lumpy it is a possible indication that brazing temperature was too low or time at heat too short. The filler metal did not melt completely. Its original shape is still visible.

If the surface of the filler is rough with a texture somewhat similar to an alligator's skin—called a skeleton—the filler metal liquated; temperature was too low and applied too long.

If the surface of the filler is rough with sharp protrusions, and an uneven surface, the presence of dirt on the work piece is indicated.

If the surface of the fillet is pock-marked by tiny circular depressions, there is a possibility substances beneath the molten filler turned to gas during brazing. Gas, working upwards through the molten filler produced the craters. There is also the possibility that hydrogen was and is still trapped within the filler metal (voids).

If the joint is marked by skips, the faying surfaces may be out of alignment. Filler metal will not bridge an overly-wide gap. There is also the possibility that burrs on the edge of the joint may have stopped filler metal flow.

Long skips and the avoidance by the filler metal of large areas may indicate the absence of flux, insufficient flux and possibly surface contamination: dirt, oxide, oil.

If the filler does not arc smoothly across the joint, if the fillet's edges are clearly defined, rather than blended imperceptibly into the base metal (as they should be), the cause may be insufficient or ineffective flux, improper cleaning, insufficient heat, or area-limited heat.

If the fillets are undersized the cause may be insufficient filler metal, insufficient heat or time at heat, vibration, lack of flux and possibly lack of cleanliness beyond the joint proper. When brazing sheet is used, low temperatures and long brazing periods tend to reduce fillet size.

If the fillets are below normal height with wider than normal bases the cause may be vibration, uneven heat, dirt or lack of flux on the vertical member.

If the joint is cracked or open the cause may be overly-rapid quenching, lack of compliance in the supporting jig or fixture locking the parts in place, uneven heating, uneven cooling, excessive mass differences between parts producing uneven expansion and contraction.

Non-destructive Tests

Radiography, the exposure of a photographic plate to short wave-length radiation that has passed through the joint, is probably the foremost inspection test in use today. Thickness flaws amounting to as little as 1 or 2% of the

Source: Aluminum Brazing Handbook, 2nd Ed., Aluminum Assn., Inc.

Figure 11-1. *The display on the cathode ray tube is an indication of the homogeneity of the brazed joint.*

Courtesy, Krautkramer

total thickness of the material examined can be detected with X-rays. All joints that can be backed by photographic film can be X-rayed.

The thermal conductance of a brazed joint is also used as a measure of its quality. One side of the joint is heated as evenly as possible. The further side of the joint and the joint itself are covered with heat-sensitive, color indicating paint. If the joint is solid, the color change from the hot to the cool side of the joint will be smooth. Abrupt color changes at any point indicate voids or discontinuities at that point. This method is generally limited to simple configurations.

Brazed honeycomb panels are sometimes tested by another thermal-transfer test. Temperature sensitive, low-melting temperature powders or liquids are spread evenly over the assembly. It is then heated by an infra-red lamp. The liquid or the powder, which has turned to liquid, is repelled by warm areas and attracted to cool areas. Properly brazed joints in the structure are cooler than the balance of the metal and the liquid flows over them. Poor or defective joints remain covered and are therefore immediately obvious.

Sound waves at ultrasonic frequencies are also used to locate discontinuities and flaws in brazed aluminum joints. Test equipment has been developed that employs frequencies from ½ to 5 million Hertz. The sound is focused into a narrow beam and directed onto the joint. Homogeneous elastic materials, such as aluminum, propagate mechanical energy with little loss and little reflection. Discontinuities reflect energy. Reflected energy is picked

up by a quartz crystal transducer and displayed on a cathode ray tube. See Figure 11-1.

Both fluorescent and non-fluorescent dyes may be used to locate surface defects in brazed aluminum joints. The materials and techniques are similar to those used for locating cracks in ferrous material.

The non-fluorescent dye is applied to the surface of the joint by any convenient means. A few minutes are permitted to elapse to enable the dye to penetrate surface cracks, if any exist. Then the surface is wiped clean, whereupon the dye remaining within the cracks becomes highly visible.

The fluorescent dye is similarly applied and given some five minutes to find and enter any existing crack. Excess penetrant is then washed off and the metal's surface is air dried. A "developer" in the form of a dry powder is placed on the metal's surface. The powder draws whatever penetrant remains in the crack back to the metal's surface. The part is removed from normal light and exposed to high intensity ultra violet light. Any penetrant remaining in the crack, however small, becomes fluorescent and visible.

Testing for Leaks

As a brazed joint may be porous and still leak tight, a visual inspection followed by a leak test is frequently all that is usually necessary with assemblies of this type. However, to make certain no leaks exist, pressure vessels may be proof tested.

The choice of pressure medium will depend to some extent upon the maximum acceptable leak aperture. Oil, particularly a thin oil such as kerosene, or a heated oil will pass through holes that will hold water under equal pressure. Air leaks more readily than water and helium leaks and escapes where air will not.

From a safety point of view, water and oil are far safer as pressure mediums than gas. The two mentioned liquids are non-compressible and when pressurized vessels containing these liquids burst, there is no accompanying quasi-explosion.

Freon is often used for pressure testing as low-cost, simple Freon-detection equipment suitable for locating small leaks is commercially available. This type of equipment utilizes a flame which changes color in the presence of Freon. More sensitive and more expensive halogen leak detectors are also available. Figure 11-2.

Helium is the medium most often used for the detection of microscopic leaks. The vessel is pressurized with helium and placed in a vacuum. A mass spectrometer is used to detect any helium that may escape. Conversely, the vessel may be evacuated and helium flushed over its surface. The spectrometer is then preferably connected between the auxiliary diffusion pump and the mechanical

Figure 11-2. *Halogen gas detector is used by inspector to test high-pressure, brazed aluminum, aviation oil coolers manufactured by Fairchild-Hiller Stratos Division.*

backing pump. Figure 11-3 illustrates the use of helium as a leak test medium.

Proof Testing

Brazed aluminum joints and assemblies may be proof tested by subjecting them to loads slightly in excess of the loads expected during the unit's service lifetime. The standard means and method of applying such loads may be used.

Destructive Inspection

When joint configuration permits, the peel test is the simplest and quickest way of both testing the joint and inspecting its interior. One portion of the joint is locked in a vise while the other side is rolled back with pliers or a similar mechanical aid.

Peeling (rolling) the joint back on itself develops tremendous leverage at the point of metal separation. Therefore the force necessary to peel a joint cannot in itself be taken as a direct measurement of a joint's strength, but must be compared to the force necessary to peel similar joints pre-tested by other means. Surfaces exposed by ripping the metal apart will be bright. Unbonded surfaces may be dull, especially if some time has elapsed since the joint was brazed.

Unless the joint has been brazed in a vacuum or dry, inert gas, a number of voids should be expected. Joints that are 80% solid are considered satisfactory and entirely acceptable under Mil spec. 23362 and A.M.S. 2473.

Source: Aluminum Brazing Handbook, 2nd Ed., Aluminum Assn., Inc.

An even greater void percentage can be tolerated when nominal sealing and less than maximum joint strength are the design goals.

The visual aspects of the voids exposed by peeling are often indicative of their causes. Voids produced by flux traps would be filled with flux. Voids caused by hydrogen would be empty. Voids produced by air or flux pockets when the parts were dip-brazed would be characterized by their position and the finished surface of the fillet facing the sealed area.

Metallographic examination may be employed to evaluate porosity, filler metal flow, lack of wetting, filler-to-base metal diffusion and final joint clearance. Joint samples are obtained by sectioning. The sample is then polished, etched and examined under a microscope. Details on specimen preparation and etching reagents may be found in the ASM Metals Handbook. Data on microscopic preparation and examination of etched samples may be found in ASTM Standards, Part 31, May '69, *Physical & Mechanical Testing of Metals: Nondestructive.* Figure 11-4 shows a typical cross section taken from a brazed joint and prepared for metallographic examination.

Other tests to which brazed joints and assemblies may be subjected include all the standard tests applied to other metals and other joining techniques. These include tension and shear tests, fatigue, impact and torsion tests.

Joint Performance

The strength of a properly brazed joint is never less than that of the filler metal itself and never more than that of the parent metal. If filler metal is stronger than parent metal, joint failure will occur in the parent metal. If the parent metal is stronger than the filler metal the filler metal will give way—but the strength exhibited by the filler metal will be close to that of the parent metal and far in excess of the filler metal's inherent strength.

For example, pieces of alloy 6061, 1/8 inch thick, were lapped 1/8 inch and brazed with 4047 filler. After brazing, the assembly was quenched and aged to bring base alloy 6061 to T6. (The filler is nonheat treatable.) Alloy 6061 in T6 has a minimum ultimate tensile strength of 42 ksi. The filler has an approximate rating of 20,000 ksi. The joints developed 30,000 ksi in both shear and tension tests.

Similarly, brazed test joints were made of alloy 7005 and 4047 filler. The base metal was 1/8-inch thick. One joint was lapped 1/4 inch, the other was lapped 1/2 inch. After brazing, the joints were heat treated to bring them to a T6 condition. Tested in shear the two joints developed 35 ksi and 45 ksi respectively.

Aluminum alloy 7005, brazed and then air cooled exhibits tensile strengths of 28 ksi, immediately after cooling, 42 ksi after three days of aging and 54 ksi after 6 months of natural aging.

Figure 11-3. *Helium is often used to detect very fine leaks.* Courtesy, Stewart-Warner, South Wind Div.

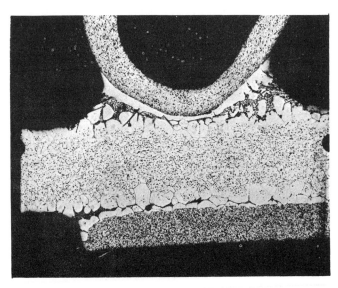

Figure 11-4. *Typical cross section of a brazed joint, polished, etched and magnified 75X. Joint is solid.*

| Sheet alloy | Brazing alloy | Type of attack | Base Sheet Depth of attack, in. | | Type of attack | Fillet Depth of attack, in. | |
			Maximum	Average		Maximum	Average
3003	716............	P	0.0098	0.0022	P	0.0014	0.0011
5052	716............	P	0.0182	0.0042	P	0.0042	0.0014
6053	716............	P + I	0.0126	0.0028	P	0.0012	0.0008
6061	716............	P + SI	0.0126	0.0033	P	0.0042	0.0014

Specimens were small inverted T-joints of 0.064-in. sheet.
SI=slight intergranular attack; P=pitting attack; I=intergranular attack.

Table 11-1. *Salt water exposure test results. Furnace-brazed aluminum joints were exposed for two years to intermittent sprays of 3.5% sodium chloride. Results of microscopic examination are shown above.*

In lap joints the thin layer of filler metal is placed under triaxial strain and joint strength exceeds filler metal strength. Material under triaxial tension is known to have higher breaking strength and lower elongation than when in simple tension.

Pores and voids that may be found in brazed joints are naturally sealed. A brazed joint is as pressure tight and leak proof as a welded joint in the same metal.

Typically, brazed joints are used in aluminum pressure vessels designed for working pressures to 1,000 psi. The vessels are hydrostatically tested to 150% of working pressure and to 500% of working pressure in burst tests. Sample units are subjected to pressure cycles 125% of working pressure, repeated over 1 million times.

Brazed aluminum containers are as vacuum tight as welded aluminum containers. A brazed vessel evacuated to 2×10^{-5} Torr increased in pressure to only 16×10^{-4} Torr after 100 hours.

Service temperature range for brazed aluminum joints is for all practical purposes the same as that of the parent metals. Brazed joints, like the parent metals, increase in ductility and lose strength with increasing temperature. Aluminum and aluminum joints increase in strength and toughness with no loss of ductility as their temperature drops. Typically, alloy 3003 in 0 temper has an ultimate strength of 16 ksi at room temperature, 8.5 ksi at 400°F. and 33 ksi at −320°F.

Brazed aluminum joints have found wide application in cryogenic service, operating continuously at liquid nitrogen temperature, −320°F. Both brazed aluminum-to-aluminum and aluminum-to-stainless steel joints are used in the liquified natural gas industry at temperatures of −452°F.

All the filler alloys used for brazing contain silicon which reduces their ductility. When the filler metal is "cast" between pieces of parent metal, a portion of the silicon leaves the filler and diffuses into the adjoining parent alloy. The final result may be likened to a casting with the highest silicon concentration in the center of the joint. The brazed joint is therefore less ductile than its equivalent thickness in parent metal.

Corrosion Resistance

The rate at which a brazed aluminum joint, completely free of flux, will corrode in the presence of moisture is directly related to the solution potential difference that may exist between the alloys involved. The lower the potential difference, the lower the rate of corrosion. Potential differences of less than 0.013 volt are usually considered insignificant.

A particular metal or alloy's solution potential is intrinsic and can only be changed by changing its chemical composition, as by alloying. As this happens to some degree in every brazed joint, the potential difference existing before the parts are brazed is always somewhat different from that which exists after brazing.

Fortunately, the aluminum parent alloys and filler alloys most frequently brazed have very slight potential differences. Joints formed with these alloys can be exposed to high-moisture conditions without protection and with excellent results. Table 11-1 shows the results of two years of exposure to intermittent salt spray. The four alloys so tested were negligibly affected.

Table 11-2 lists the more popular base metals and fillers in order of their solution potentials produced in respect to a 0.1N calomel reference electrode in a standard salt peroxide solution consisting of 53 gm/1 + 3 gm/1 H_2O_2 at 25°C. (Voltages produced by the same alloys in different solutions will vary somewhat.)

The greater the distance apart (voltage difference) on the solution potential scale of Table 11-2, the greater the potential for corrosion of the more negative alloy (lower end of scale).

Filler alloys 4343, 4045 and 4047 have minimal quantities of copper and zinc as alloying constituents, and produce a solution potential of −0.82 volt in the standard test solution. Commonly brazed alloys 1100, 3003, 6061, and 6063 show −0.83 volt. The difference in solution potential between these two groups of alloy is 0.01 volt, which is insignificant and is responsible for the excellent corrosion resistances these brazing combinations exhibit.

As all the base metals listed above are slightly more negative than the fillers used to braze them, the base metals form the anodes and thus protect the fillers.

The other popular aluminum brazing alloys in the 1000, 3000 and 5000 series also have little or no copper and zinc. And Alloy 6951, the popular heat-treatable alloy, has less copper than 6061 and no zinc at all. All these alloys are therefore highly corrosion resistant when brazed with fillers 4343, 4045 and 4047.

Certain Alclad products present problems when brazed slowly. Alloys 3003 and 3004, clad with 7072 are corrosion sensitive when furnace or flux-dip brazed. Brazing by torch, however, eliminates this problem as heating is area limited.

Joints in Electrical Conductors

The performance of a brazed aluminum joint forming a portion of an electrical circuit can be accurately predicted on the basis of the joint's DC resistance. This can be measured with standard electrical instruments.

When two electrical conductors are lap brazed the electrical resistance of the resultant joint can easily be made lower than that of the associate conductors by simply using a wide lap.

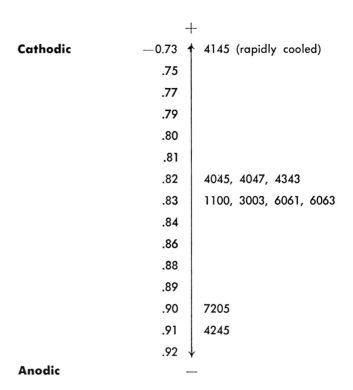

Table 11-2. *Listed alloys were tested against a 0.1N calomel reference electrode in a standard salt peroxide solution to produce the voltages given. The upper, less negative alloy in a couple is always the cathode and is protected in an electrolyte at the expense of the anode. The further apart the alloys are on the scale, the greater the galvanic difference and the greater the propensity for corrosion.*

Safety

Aluminum brazing is essentially a safe and danger free practice. There are few unpredictable factors. Brazing injuries are never true accidents in the sense of their being unavoidable. All brazing injuries can be traced to careless workmen and to lack of sufficient vigor and forethought on the part of the safety engineer in establishing and enforcing a complete safety program, or to a management that will not properly support the safety program.

Injuries can be eliminated and 100% safety records maintained by the careful development of a safe system for the handling of materials and tools and by proper and sincere safety motivation of the men engaged in brazing.

Brazing's constant, immediate danger is the presence of very hot metal and fluxes. Aluminum does not change color when heated. (Neither does iron glow when it's sufficiently hot to cause painful and dangerous burns.) Aluminum's color cannot therefore be used as a danger sign. Instead a system or pattern of metal handling must be established which eliminates the need for temperature sensing on the part of the workmen.

System Necessary

Perhaps the simplest of such systems is the development of a fixed and unchanging route by which the parts move in orderly fashion from preparation area to heating area to cooling area. Hot parts are confined to one location and are moved in one direction only.

Men assigned to the salt pots must be required to wear protective clothing, gloves and face masks. Men engaged in torch brazing should be given similarly protective clothing, plus tinted goggles for eye protection.

Figure 12-1. *Proper protective clothing is important to personnel safety. The man is wearing goggles, gloves and heavy clothing of wool, which is the preferred material.*

Source: Aluminum Brazing Handbook, 2nd Ed., Aluminum Assn., Inc.

Mechanical aid for lowering and lifting parts in and out of hot flux is advisable. The dangerous practice of having several men on one pole to handle a particularly heavy part should be avoided at all costs. There are many small, power-driven, mobile cranes available for this purpose.

Spatter caused by moisture in flux and by moisture in parts can be eliminated by a rigorous drying schedule long enough to overcome moisture variations in the flux and long enough to cope with day to day variations in ambient moisture, which affects drying rate.

Moisture in and on parts dipped into hot flux turns to steam and causes steam explosions. Moisture in flux used for induction brazing also explodes when turned to instant steam. In some cases, molten filler is driven out of a joint at bullet speed.

Spatter produced by parts accidentally dropped into molten flux can be prevented with properly designed supports, hangers and fixtures, and by the avoidance of overloading and crowding. Properly designed hangers and supports are self balancing and equiped with long handles. Indentations and hooks are provided to hold parts securely in place.

Constant Inspection

A constant inspection routine should be established in which each hanger and dipping fixture is severely rapped with a hammer to make certain the metal hasn't been eroded to the danger point by hot flux.

All pre-heat ovens and brazing furnaces must be ventilated. Alcohol, often used as a flux thinner and vehicle, forms an explosive mixture when it vaporizes. Hydrogen, released by flux action during brazing, also forms an explosive mixture when combined with air. Forced ventilation prevents the formation of such dangerous mixtures.

Oxygen, acetylene, propane, methane and other gases used for brazing aluminum are potentially dangerous and must be handled cautiously. The National Bureau of Standards Handbook H24 treats this subject in detail. Perhaps the most important single precaution is the complete removal of all oils and greases from and near the oxygen cylinder, its valves and gauges. Oil will explode in the presence of oxygen under pressure. A stream of escaping oxygen will ignite any oil it touches, forcing it to burn violently. Greasy gloves and rags are a potential danger near a brazing torch. Cylinders should always be fastened securely upright. Cylinder caps should be in place on all unused cylinders.

Men working with acids should be thoroughly instructed in the cleaning of spills. Acid spilled on the floor should be cautiously and slowly diluted with water and an alkaline neutralizing agent. Organic materials such as sawdust, mops, rags and clothes should not be used to clean up acid.

Acid will quickly decompose organics and produce highly toxic gases.

Extra Care With Caustic

Caustic cleaning solutions require two-fold precautions. Care must be exercised to prevent the caustic from dripping or splattering on personnel. Men must wear protective clothing and goggles. And secondly, the cleaning room must be well ventilated. Caustic combines with aluminum and liberates hydrogen which carries with it caustic vapors. Inhaled, the caustic vapors are painful and injurious to the respiratory system. And, if the hydrogen is permitted to accumulate, an explosive hydrogen/air mixture will form. Smoking should not be permitted in these areas.

All aluminum brazing fluxes contain fluoride which is toxic. Flux must therefore be handled with caution at all times. When a package or container of flux is first opened, care must be taken to make certain none is spilled. Flux is most dry at this time and can be easily blown about.

Keep Flux Away From Food

Workmen handling flux or working near others handling flux must not eat nor smoke in that area. Lunch should not be permitted in the brazing shop, nor should lunch boxes or open coffee containers be stored there at any time. Workmen should wash their faces, hands and arms thoroughly after each session in the brazing shop, before lunch and before going home. In this way the chance of some one accidentally ingesting flux will be completely eliminated.

The brazing shop must be well ventilated. Hot flux vaporizes and travels on thermals until it condenses on a cool surface. If that surface is metal, it will corrode. Inhaled flux vapors are both irritating and dangerous.

Hydrofluoric acid can produce particularly painful injuries upon contact. The burns it causes are very slow to heal. Extreme caution must be used with this acid. Sodium chromate may induce dermatitis when it contacts the skin. Again, caution and proper equipment, correctly used, are the best preventatives.

Silver nitrate, used for testing, is extremely dangerous. It causes permanent blindness upon contacting the eyes.

First Aid

All brazing shop personnel should be thoroughly trained in first aid. They should be taught the location and use of first aid equipment, the names and addresses of nearby doctors and the phone number of the local police, who are generally first to respond in an emergency.

A little training can stop panic and confusion and prevent the loss of all important time. Just teaching the secretary, for example, that upon hearing the word emergency, she is to stop all other activities and call the police and doctor, may save a life.

Burns

The instant an individual is burned, the burned area of his body must be cooled with water and ice. He is drenched as rapidly as possible without stopping to remove clothing. Cool water and ice will remove whatever heat remains in the body, stopping further burn damage. The human body is 98% water. When a portion of the body is brought above boiling or scald temperature, the body retains the heat of the burn for a long time unless it is chilled.

A number of high-volume, low-pressure showers should be installed at strategic points throughout the brazing shop. They should be close enough to be of immediate value, but not so close that water can splash into a flux pot or onto a brazing furnace. The showers should be controlled by foot or elbow treadles so that cold water can be turned on quickly and easily. Ice cubes and blocks of ice may be stored in standard freezers.

Ice numbs the body and reduces pain and shock. In many instances, it is the shock of pain as much as physical damage to the body that kills the victim. In many cases the quick application of ice to a moderate burn will prevent blisters and frequently prevent pain.

The use of ice—packing the body in ice—as a treatment for burns, is rapidly becoming standard hospital procedure.

The importance of applying cold water and ice as rapidly as possible cannot be overstressed.

A victim of serious burns should not be moved. No attempt should be made to remove his clothing: the skin may come off with it. This is a job for the doctor.

Acid Burns

Acid burns should be instantly flushed with volumes of cool water. This may be followed by the application of an alkaline such as baking soda.

Source: Aluminum Brazing Handbook, 2nd Ed., Aluminum Assn., Inc.

Section XII:
Soldering

Introduction to Aluminum Soldering

Soldering is an inexpensive and rapid means of permanently joining aluminum to aluminum and to other metals. Properly made joints are leakproof and strong. Soldering is used for joining aluminum wires, making heat exchangers, space-ship plumbing and thousands of other applications far too numerous to list here.

Aluminum soldering is relatively simple. Single joints are readily made in the field and shop with low-cost hand tools. Single and multiple joints, often numbering in the thousands, are automatically produced with comparatively low-cost equipment by untrained personnel.

The Advantages of Soldering

By accepted American Welding Society definition, soldering is a joining process wherein coalescence between metal parts is produced by heating to suitable temperatures generally below 800°F., and by using a filler metal having a liquidus not exceeding 800°F (427°C) and below the solidus of the base metals. The solder is usually distributed between the properly fitted surfaces of the joint by capillary attraction. Brazing, by the same definition, is a similar process accomplished at temperatures above 800°F., but below the melting point of the metals to be joined. Welding requires the parent metals be brought to or above their melting points.

As soldering is accomplished at lower temperatures than brazing (and at considerably lower temperatures than welding), it is often possible, by proper selection of alloy and solder, to solder aluminum with little loss of parent-metal temper. Brazing requires a following quenching and aging treatment to restore temper. (This is only possible with heat-treatable alloys.)

In contrast to welding, the heat of soldering (and brazing) is fairly evenly distributed. Part expansion and subsequent contraction associated with soldering is far less an obstacle to precise joining than the inter-part motion generated by the intense, concentrated heat necessary for welding.

As soldering does not need to be followed by quenching (to restore temper) and as soldering is accomplished at lower temperatures than either brazing or welding, assembly distortion due to soldering is generally nil. By the same token, soldered assemblies have lower temperature-induced stresses as compared to brazed or welded aluminum assemblies.

The temperatures employed in soldering, the nature of the process and aluminum's excellent thermal conductivity combine to make it reasonably easy to solder complex assemblies with varied sections.

The fluxes normally used to solder aluminum are easier to remove than the fluxes normally used for brazing aluminum. There is also a group of aluminum soldering fluxes which, in many applications, do not need to be removed. (Certain organic fluxes are non-hygroscopic and non-corrosive.)

Aluminum may be soldered with a wide range of solders, a wide range of temperatures and a variety of fluxes. Brazing aluminum is accomplished in a narrow range of temperatures just below the melting point of the parent metal. Only a limited variety of fluxes are presently available for brazing. Soldering therefore offers the designer greater flexibility within its scope.

Aluminum is brazed at temperatures no more than about 50°F. below the solidus temperature of the base metal and frequently closer. Aluminum soldering temperatures are, at a minimum, 200°F. below the solidus temperature of the base metal. Temperature control with aluminum soldering is therefore considerably less stringent and demanding than that necessary for brazing. Less skill is required on the part of the torch operator to keep from melting the base metal when soldering than when brazing. (The solidus temperature of a metal marks the onset of melting. Liquidus marks the thermal point at which the metal is completely liquid. Between its solidus and liquidus temperature points a metal is semi-liquid or slushy.)

As stated, soldering aluminum is relatively simple. Written instructions are all that is needed for casual forming of joints. Commercial-quality soldering can be quickly taught.

Basic Procedure

To solder, the surfaces to be joined are cleaned, coated with suitable flux and spaced a few thousandths of an inch apart. A third and differing piece of metal called solder is placed in or near the joint to be. The assembly is heated. The flux reacts. It loosens and displaces contiguous surface oxide and protects the bare metal so exposed from contact with the air and oxidation. The solder melts and is drawn into the joint by capillary force. As the molten solder flows it displaces the flux, dissolves sub-microscopic high spots in its path and fills the equally numerous, small depressions it encounters. This is called wetting and may take place within a few seconds. After the joint has cooled it is ready for use. The necessity for cleaning depends on the flux used and the joint's application.

Wetting is the crux of soldering (and brazing). It is a spontaneous phenomenon of nature and occurs between metals when their atoms come to within 4 Angstrom units of each other ($Å = 10^{-10}$ meters). At that instant, interatomic attraction takes hold. The atoms share electrons and lock in permanent metallic bond.

The strength of the joint is a function of the solder, the spacing between the faying (joining) surfaces and the area of bond. Surprisingly, joint strength may be considerably higher than the tensile strength of the solder.

The techniques and equipment used for soldering (and brazing) aluminum are essentially similar to those used for soldering and brazing other metals. The differences lie with the temperatures used for soldering aluminum and the nature of the silvery metal itself. Aluminum presents no particular problems in soldering. Rather it requires an understanding on the part of the engineer and designer accustomed to working with other metals.

Aluminum oxidizes with extreme rapidity; it is almost impossible to remove its ever present oxide coating more rapidly than it will reform. Aluminum oxide melts at $3722°F$. Aluminum oxide is neither melted nor reduced by temperatures that melt the metal. However, oxides normal to mill-finished aluminum alloys are removed during soldering by ordinary aluminum soldering fluxes.

Aluminum's specific heat is high and its thermal conductivity is excellent. Aluminum therefore requires more heat than other common metals to reach a particular temperature. By the same token, it is easier to heat a complex aluminum assembly evenly than it is to do so with many other metals.

Aluminum expands more with heat than many other common metals, notably, the metals frequently used to hold aluminum parts in assembly when aluminum is heated for soldering. The difference in expansion coefficients is absorbed by simple springing in the fixturing.

Aluminum does not change color with temperature. (Neither does iron glow though it may be much too hot to touch without injury.) Color-indicating crayons, solder and flux are used for convenient, in-the-field temperature indication.

Soldering With Flux

Many techniques are currently used to solder aluminum. Each has its own specific advantages and applications. Broadly, the techniques fall into two categories: flux and fluxless soldering.

Flux reduces and in some instances even eliminates the need for pre-solder cleaning. Flux aids wetting, thereby making all the alloys easier to solder. Certain fluxes (reaction types) can be used to solder aluminum without the addition of solder per se to the joint. Unfortunately all fluxes (excepting certain organic fluxes) must be removed after soldering. And the labor involved and the cost of equipment necessary to remove flux residue is usually a major portion of the total cost of soldering.

The problems attendant upon flux removal, especially that of removing flux completely from maximum reliability assemblies such as are frequently used in spacecraft, have led to increasing research and development of flux-free soldering. The latest to achieve success on a pilot plant scale indicating imminent commercial success is ultrasonic soldering.

Aluminum-to-aluminum or aluminum-to-other metal faying surfaces that are to be soldered with the aid of flux are cleaned, covered with the desired flux and spaced a few thousandths of an inch apart. Solder is placed in or near the joint to be and heat is applied.

Soldering Without Flux

Aluminum can be soldered without flux by removing the metal's oxide coat beneath a protective layer of molten solder. When this is done the solder bonds to the aluminum and a joint is formed upon cooling. A number of methods are used. The simplest, called abrasion or rub soldering, consists of forming a molten pool of solder on one faying surface and rubbing it with the second faying surface. Or, rubbing the surface of the aluminum beneath the molten solder with a glass brush or a length of solder or non-contaminating metal such as tungsten. This may be done to both faying surfaces, or one at a time, and then brought together. The bonded solder layers commingle and form a metallurgical joint on cooling.

The modern version of this technique is called ultrasonic soldering. A transducer, driven at above-audio fre-

Source: Aluminum Soldering Handbook, 3rd Ed., Aluminum Assn., Inc.

quency, is mechanically coupled to a pool of molten solder. Cleaned, pre-positioned faying surfaces to be joined are immersed in the rapidly vibrating, molten metal. Cavitation quickly removes all surface oxide from the submerged metal. The solder wets and bonds to the aluminum. This can be accomplished in seconds with the proper equipment. The assembly is then removed and cooled.

Soldering Without Solder

The reaction fluxes contain sufficient metal to form strong joints without the need of solder. The procedure is the same as if solder were pre-positioned or furnished to the joint during soldering. The technique, however, calls for close joint tolerances as there is no surplus of solder present to fill overly-wide joint gaps caused by manufacturing errors or field-damaged faying surfaces. Solderless soldering is not suitable for all joints.

Solder Heat

Heat for soldering by any technique may be supplied by any convenient and capable means. The soldering iron may be used for very small, light gauge material and low temperature solder. The hot plate (heated metal plate) is useful for small, simple assemblies. The torch (single or multiple) is used for field repairs, comparatively short production runs and in connection with automatic equipment for long production runs. The batch furnace is used for single assemblies and comparatively modest production runs. The continuous furnace is used for longer production runs.

Furnaces can be of the hot wall type. These may be heated electrically or by fossil fuel. Alternatively, cold wall furnaces may be used and the heat supplied by a radiant element inside the furnace. This may be a series of metal conduits through which the hot gases of combustion are carried, high-temperature electric lamps, or electric heating elements.

Assemblies to be soldered may be placed within a coil carrying alternating electric current and brought to soldering temperature by electric induction.

Final soldering heat (after pre-heating) may also be supplied by a pot of molten solder into which the assembly, or only the joints to be formed, are dipped.

Generally the source of heat or the equipment used for soldering establishes the designation common for that type of soldering, i.e., torch soldering, induction soldering, furnace soldering.

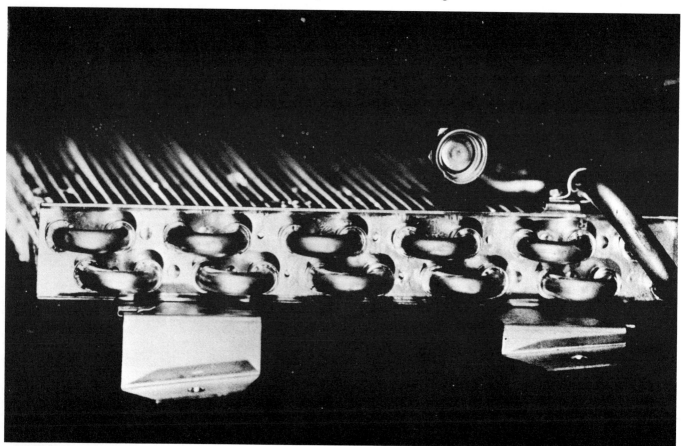

Figure 1-1. *Return bends on an automatically soldered all aluminum heat exchanger.*

Material for Soldering

Breadth of Choice

Almost all present-day wrought aluminum alloys can be soldered by one proven technique or another. Alloys that are not readily soldered can be made so by cladding or plating.

Table 2-1 presents the relative solderability of the various commercial alloys along with metallurgical problems that may be expected with some alloys. Table 2-2 does the same for casting alloys.

Solder, flux, temperature, time and base alloy are all interrelated and affect joint strength, corrosion resistance, appearance and assembly temper by virtue of their combination as well as their individual composition. No single element of a soldered aluminum joint is paramount—when one is seeking maximum quality joints—all the elements involved play an important part.

Alloy Temper and Solderability

So far as is known, an alloy's temper has no effect upon its solderability per se. Solder will wet an alloy in O-temper as quickly as it will wet the same alloy in T-6 or any other temper. The method or methods by which that temper was produced are, however, important factors in surface preparation, the retention of temper and intergranular penetration.

The Retention of Temper

There are two commonly used techniques to increase the strength of aluminum alloys: work hardening and precipitation hardening. The first method involves hardening or strengthening the metal by cold working. The second method consists of bringing an alloy to a certain temperature, holding it there a prescribed time, then quenching it. This is followed by aging at either room or an elevated temperature. Some alloys are further strengthened and hardened by cold working following aging. Alloys responsive to cold working only are classified as nonheat-treatable alloys. Alloys responsive to heat-treatment are classified as heat-treatable alloys.

Generally the method employed to temper aluminum is of small importance. To the soldering engineer, however, it is of considerable moment, because the heat-treatable and the nonheat-treatable alloys respond differently when raised to their annealing temperatures. Both the heat-treatables and the nonheat-treatables begin to show signs of annealing when they are heated to 350 or 400°F. As temperature is increased, both groups of alloys show increasing temper loss. When the individual alloys reach their respective annealing temperatures, they part company. The nonheat-treatable alloys, metals that have been hardened by cold working, soften quickly. As long as the temperature of the nonheat-treatable alloy is kept below its annealing temperature, the major portion of the strain-produced temper remains in the metal. Once exceeded, the temper flees.

On the other hand, when the heat-treated alloy is brought up to its annealing temperature nothing immediately happens. The heat-treated alloy must be kept at its annealing temperature for some 20 minutes before an appreciable portion of its temper disappears. The heat-treatables require more time to soften because the alloying elements must re-dissolve and re-enter solution. Complete annealing may require as much as two hours at heat. (Annealing temperatures and time periods for aluminum alloys may be found in *Nonferrous Physical Metallurgy*, Pitman Publishing, *Aluminum*, Vol. II, *Fabrication & Finishing*, ASM, and standard heat-treatment reference works.)

Assemblies therefore may be soldered without appreciable temper loss. When a heat-treated alloy is soldered, pre-heating and soldering time is kept under twenty minutes. A cold-worked temper may be maintained reasonably intact by using a soldering temperature that is safely below its annealing temperature.

Distortion Eliminated

As the temper of the base metal can be maintained to a considerable degree by matching temperature and time at temperature to the nature of the alloy joined, soldering eliminates the need for quenching with its attendant distortion. For all practical purposes, aluminum may be soldered without distortion.

Chemical Composition Limits, % (max unless shown as a range)

Alloy	Si	Fe	Cu	Mn	Mg	Cr	Ni	Zn	Ga	V	Other	Ti	Al Min.	Flux Recommended	Metallurgical Problem Encountered
Excellent Solderability															
1100	1.0 Si + Fe		0.20	0.05				0.10					99.00	Chemical & Reaction	None
1235	0.65 Si + Fe		0.05	0.05	0.05			0.10				0.03	99.35	"	
1200	1.0 Si + Fe		0.05	0.05				0.1		0.05		0.05	99.00	"	
3003*	0.6	0.7	0.20	1.0-1.5				0.10					Rem**	"	
Good Solderability															
3004	0.30	0.7	0.25	1.0-1.5	0.8-1.3			0.25					Rem		
5357	0.12	0.17	0.20	0.15-0.45	0.8-1.2			0.05					Rem	Reaction	
6003	0.35-1.0	0.6	0.10	0.8	0.8-1.5	0.35		0.20				0.10	Rem	Reaction(1)	Intergranular Penetration
6053	(4)	0.35	0.10		1.1-1.4	0.15-0.35		0.10					Rem	"	"
6061*	0.40-0.8	0.7	0.15-0.40	0.15	0.8-1.2	0.04-0.35		0.25				0.15	Rem	"	"
6063	0.20-0.6	0.35	0.10	0.10	0.45-0.9	0.10		0.10				0.10	Rem	"	"
6151	0.6-1.2	1.0	0.35	0.20	0.45-0.8	0.15-0.35		0.25				0.15	Rem	"	"
6253	(4)	0.50	0.10		1.0-1.5	0.15-0.35		1.6-2.4					Rem	"	"
6951	0.20-0.50	0.8	0.15-0.40	0.10	0.40-0.8			0.20					Rem	"	"
7072	0.7 Si + Fe		0.10	0.10	0.10	0.20		0.8-1.3					Rem	"	"
8112*	1.0	1.0	0.40	0.6	0.7			1.0				0.20	Rem	"	"
Fair Solderability															
2011	0.40	0.7	5.0-6.0					0.30			lead, bismuth 0.20-0.6 each	0.15	Rem	"	Intergranular Penetration(3)
2014	0.50-1.2	0.7	3.9-5.0	0.40-1.2	0.20-0.8	0.10		0.25			0.20 Zr + Ti		Rem	"	Corrosion Resistance Reduction
2017	0.20-0.8	0.7	3.5-4.5	0.40-1.0	0.40-0.8	0.10		0.25			0.20 Zr + Ti		Rem	"	
2018	0.9	1.0	3.5-4.5	0.20	0.45-0.9	0.10	1.7-2.3	0.25					Rem	Reaction(1)	Intergranular Penetration(3)
2024	0.50	0.50	3.8-4.9	0.30-0.9	1.2-1.8	0.10		0.25					Rem	Reaction(2)	
2025	0.50-1.2	1.0	3.9-5.0	0.40-1.2		0.10		0.25			0.20 Zr + Ti	0.15	Rem	Reaction(1, 2)	Corrosion Resistance Reduced
2117	0.8	0.7	2.2-3.0	0.20	0.20-0.50	0.10		0.25					Rem	"	
2214	0.50-1.2	0.30	3.9-5.0	0.40-1.2	0.20-0.8	0.10		0.25			0.20 Zr + Ti	0.15	Rem	"	Intergranular Penetration(3)
2218	0.9	1.0	3.5-4.5	0.20	1.2-1.8	0.10	1.7-2.3	0.25					Rem	Reaction	Corrosion Resistance Reduced
2225	0.50-1.2	0.30	3.9-5.0	0.40-1.2		0.10		0.25				0.15	Rem	"	Intergranular Penetration
5050	0.40	0.7	0.20	0.10	1.0-1.8	0.10		0.25					Rem	"	"
Poor Solderability															
5052	0.25	0.40	0.10	0.10	2.2-2.8	0.15-0.35		0.10					Rem	Reaction(2)	"
5652	0.25	0.40	0.05	0.01	2.2-2.8	0.15-0.35		0.10					Rem	"	"
7075	0.40	0.50	1.2-2.0	0.30	2.1-2.9	0.18-0.35		5.1-6.1				0.20	Rem	Reaction	"
7178	0.40	0.50	1.6-2.4	0.30	2.4-3.1	0.18-0.35		6.3-7.3			0.25 Zr + Ti	0.20	Rem	"	"
7277	0.50	0.7	0.8-1.7		1.7-2.3	0.18-0.35		3.7-4.3				0.10	Rem	Reaction	"
5055	0.30	0.7	0.25	0.30-0.80	4.0-5.0	0.25		0.25					Rem	"	"
5056	0.30	0.40	0.10	0.05-0.20	4.5-5.6	0.05-0.20		0.10					Rem	"	"
5083	0.40	0.40	0.10	0.50-1.0	4.0-4.9	0.25		0.25				0.15	Rem	"	"
5086	0.40	0.50	0.10	0.20-0.7	3.5-4.5	0.25		0.25				0.15	Rem	"	"
5154	0.25	0.40	0.10	0.10	3.1-3.9	0.15-0.35		0.20				0.20	Rem	"	"
5254	0.45 Si + Fe		0.05	0.01	3.1-3.9	0.15-0.35		0.20				0.05	Rem	"	"
5356	0.25	0.40	0.10	0.05-0.20	4.5-5.5	0.05-0.20		0.10				0.06-0.20	Rem	"	"

Legend:

* Alloys that are generally used to make assemblies where soldering is used. Rem**=Remainder

Reaction(1): The chemical fluxes can also be used to solder some but not all types of assemblies made using this alloy.

Reaction(2): Reaction fluxes can be used to solder some but not all types of assemblies made using this alloy.

Intergranular Penetration(3): The corrosion resistance of the parent aluminum alloy can be reduced by the soldering operation.

(4) 45 to 65 percent of Mg content.

Table 2-1. *Composition and solderability of commercial wrought aluminum alloys*

Solderability and Alloying Elements

Aluminum's solderability decreases as alloying elements are added in greater variety and quantity. The decrease is not a linear increment but is marked by exceptions. In general, commercially pure alloys, 1100 and purer, are most easily soldered. The highly alloyed, complex alloys are difficult to solder.

Two alloying elements are particularly inimical to soldering: magnesium and silicon.

nonheat-treatable alloys. In contrast, neither mild nor vigorous fluxes alone are "strong" enough to permit satisfactory wetting when soldering a heat-treatable alloy. For consistently satisfactory results, faying surface oxide must be removed from heat-treatable alloys prior to soldering. Actually, all aluminum oxide removal in air is an oxide thinning action as a thin film of oxide forms as quickly as it is removed. Oxide thinning or removal is often called deoxidizing in the trade. Oxide removal is discussed in paragraphs following.

CHEMICAL COMPOSITION LIMITS

AA Number	Silicon	Iron	Copper	Manganese	Magnesium	Chromium	Nickel	Zinc	Titanium	Aluminum	Solderability
213.0	1.0-3.0	1.2	6.0-8.0	0.6	0.10	....	0.35	2.5	0.25	Remainder	B
356.0	6.5-7.5	0.6	0.25	0.35	0.20-0.40	....	....	0.35	0.25	Remainder	A
443.0	4.5-6.0	0.8	0.6	0.50	0.05	0.25	....	0.50	0.25	Remainder	A
443.2	4.5-6.0	0.6	0.10	0.10	0.05	....	....	0.10	0.20	Remainder	A
A712.0	0.15	0.50	0.35-0.65	0.05	0.6-0.8	....	....	6.0-7.0	0.25	Remainder	B
C712.0	0.30	0.7-1.4	0.35-0.65	0.05	0.25-0.45	....	....	6.0-7.0	0.20	Remainder	B

Table 2-2. *Comparative solderability of various aluminum casting alloys. Alloys marked A are soldered most readily. Alloys marked B can be soldered with special effort. All other alloys are difficult to solder.*

The presence of magnesium in an alloy does not reduce the metal's wettability significantly until its percentage reaches approximately 1.0%. Alloys with less than this quantity of magnesium can be soldered with all the fluxes. When the alloy's magnesium content exceeds this figure, low-temperature organic fluxes do not work. With more than 1.5% magnesium, the alloy is difficult to solder with even the most active flux. However, the alloys can be easily soldered by abrasion techniques.

Silicon reduces aluminum's solderability by reducing the effectiveness of the flux. When an alloy's silicon content exceeds 4%, all the fluxes become increasingly less effective. However, the alloys can be soldered by an abrasion technique without recourse to plating.

Alloys and Surface Preparation

Pure aluminum and all its known alloys oxidize rapidly in the presence of oxygen. The oxide films so formed vary from alloy to alloy. The heat-treatables form the most tenacious and tough oxides, made even more refractory upon exposure to the heat of tempering. The oxides that form on the nonheat-treatable alloys are considerably less tenacious and less difficult to remove.

Generally the action of a mild or vigorous flux is sufficient to disrupt and displace surface oxide normal to

Alloying Elements and Intergranular Penetration

Like all metals, aluminum is crystalline. And like other common metals, its orderly spaced metallic atoms are gathered into small polyhedral cells called grains, typically about 0.01 inch across. It is at the boundaries between adjoining grains that intergranular penetration takes place. When aluminum is pure there is no chemical difference between the center of the metal grain and its boundaries. When aluminum is alloyed, a considerable difference may exist.

Many of aluminum's impurities, including elements deliberately added to produce a particular alloy, have higher melting temperatures than aluminum. When the aluminum is molten all the elements are in solution. As the metal cools the higher-melting point elements precipitate out first and act as nucleation sites for the grains of aluminum. When certain aluminum alloys and certain solders are placed in contact and heated, elements in the solder may exhibit a greater affinity for the non-aluminum elements present at the alloy's grain boundaries than for the aluminum atoms. A quantity of solder or one or more of its composing elements may therefore enter the interstices existing between the base metal's grains. This is known as intergranular penetration.

The degree of intergranular penetration in any given soldering situation depends on five factors: (1) the composition of the solder, (2) the composition of the parent metal, (3) the physical condition of the parent metal at the instant of soldering, (4) the length of time the metals are held at soldering temperature, and (5) temperature.

The degree of intergranular penetration suffered by parent metals varies from nil to serious; from zero for all practical purposes to where the metal is greatly embrittled, deep cracks are formed in thick sections and thin pieces are split in two. Penetrations less serious than this cannot always be seen by the naked eye nor always discovered by stressing the base metal. They can, however, be seen by sectioning and microscopic examination.

Intergranular penetration can be avoided by selecting a parent metal alloy which is non-susceptible. Table 2-1 lists these alloys. Generally the alloys containing the least quantity and variety of alloying elements are least prone to intergranular penetration.

Intergranular penetration can also be prevented by coating the parent metal with a barrier metal prior to soldering.

If neither of these two steps are possible or practical, penetration can be reduced by (1) matching the base metal with a solder that is less penetrating for that particular alloy, (2) soldering at lower temperature and (3) by reducing time at soldering temperature.

Specifically, binary aluminum alloys containing 0.5% or more magnesium should not be soldered with a tin-base solder nor coated or plated with tin. The purer the tin the greater the problem.

If the same binary magnesium alloy is coated or soldered with zinc in place of tin, the alloy's magnesium content can go to 0.7% before serious intergranular penetration ensues.

If the solder used with the aforementioned magnesium-aluminum alloy contains 4% or more aluminum, intergranular penetration will be reduced considerably as will solder-base-metal alloying in general.

Aluminum alloys containing other elements in addition to magnesium are not nearly as susceptible to intergranular penetration as the simpler aluminum-magnesium alloys. Alloys 6061 and 6063, the aluminum-magnesium silicide alloys, for example, contain as much magnesium as the binary Al-Mg alloys, have a general solderability rating somewhere between that of pure aluminum (the highest rating) and the binary Al-Mg alloys and are not troubled by intergranular penetration.

Other examples of this relationship include alloys 3004, 5005 and 5357. These alloys contain up to 1.3% magnesium and are not troubled by intergranular penetration. Alloy 5005 is used frequently for soldered assemblies.

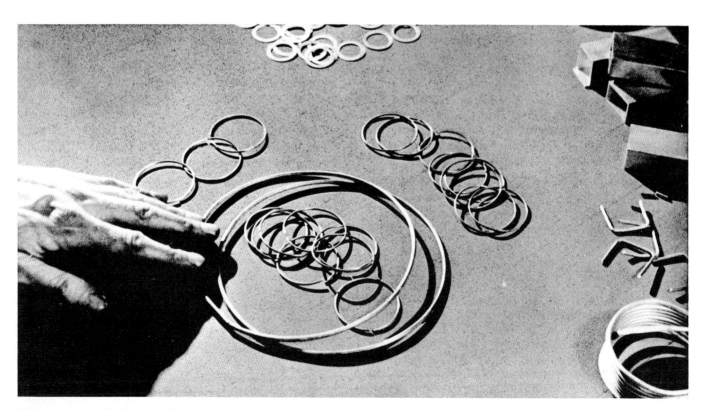

Figure 2-1. *Solder can be purchased in the form of rods, bars, wires, powder, flux-filled tubes and various shapes preformed to specifications. Some of the possible shapes are shown above.*

Unfortunately the presence of magnesium is not the only possible cause of intergranular penetration susceptibility. Alloy 7072, for example, never is more than 0.1% magnesium and yet it can be adversely affected by this phenomenon. The only generalization that can be made is that the highly alloyed, complex alloys are least resistant to penetration.

The physical condition of the parent metal at the time of soldering is the third factor affecting intergranular penetration. If the base metal is a susceptible alloy and it is in a stressed condition—as it would be if it were tempered by cold working, severely formed or quenched—intergranular penetration is accelerated.

Alloys normally not affected by intergranular penetration maintain their resistance to penetration though they may be stressed prior to soldering. The susceptibility of borderline alloys will be increased if they are stressed prior to soldering. Alloys normally subject to intergranular attack may crack upon soldering if they are stressed prior to soldering.

Base metal stress can be relieved by heating the alloy to 700°F. and holding it there a moment. This may be done before the part is soldered, in which case the heat-produced oxide layer must be removed before soldering. Stress relief can be performed simultaneously with soldering. A flux with a minimum reaction temperature of 720°F. is chosen. The joint is heated to 700°F., held there briefly and then brought up to reaction temperature. We are assuming, of course, that the alloy chosen will not oxidize sufficiently in the time at 700°F. to interfere with satisfactory soldering.

Flux is only obliquely involved in intergranular penetration: Its effect is related to the quantity and nature of the metal it deposits. The organic fluxes deposit very little metal and so have very little effect. The reaction fluxes have an adverse effect only when the metals they contain are troublesome.

Stressed or unstressed, of suitable chemistry or not, all the aluminum alloys may be easily soldered with any of the aluminum solders if the base metal is precoated with a metal that is easily soldered. Many metals, including pure aluminum, are used for this purpose. The metals are applied by electroplating, hot dipping, spraying, cladding, tinning, electroless plating and chemical reduction plating and other methods. These are discussed in paragraphs following.

Wrought Aluminum Alloys most frequently soldered

1060, 1100, 1145, 1200, 3003, 5005, 6061, 7072 and 8112 are the aluminum alloys most frequently soldered commercially. These alloys require no special surface preparation and are resistant to intergranular penetration. Alloys 1060, 1100, 1145, 1200 and 3003 are most readily joined by all soldering techniques and all standard solders. Wrought alloy composition and solderability are given in Table 2-1.

Solderable Casting Alloys

Casting alloys 443.0 (43), 443.2 (ingot) and 356.0 (356) are most easily soldered. Casting alloys 213.0 (113), C712.0 (C612) and A712.0 (612) have fair solderability. The balance of the aluminum casting alloys have so much copper or magnesium that they can be soldered only with difficulty, unless of course their surfaces are plated with another metal before soldering. Solderabilities of various casting alloys are noted in Table 2-2.

Flux

The fluxes used for soldering aluminum are as varied as the alloys they join. Each flux formulation is designed for a specific, limited temperature range and has its own special characteristics. Some fluxes are formulated for a specific solder and are sold together with the solder.

The purpose of soldering flux is to remove the oxide film on the aluminum, shield the bare metal from contact with the air and oxidation, and promote base metal wetting and solder flow. So far as these actions are concerned, all solder flux formulations work alike.

However, differing flux formulations do have differing secondary characteristics which are very important to the soldering engineer. These characteristics or parameters separate into two groups developing from the two basic flux formulas now used: organic and reactive. Characteristics of some typical fluxes for use in soldering aluminum are given in Table 2-3.

Organic Fluxes

The organic fluxes do not contain chlorides. When chlorides are added to an organic flux, some of the characteristics peculiar to organic fluxes are lost, and the resultant compound is more accurately labeled a reaction flux, or a mild reaction flux. With such mixtures, some of the properties later ascribed to reaction fluxes are to be expected.

The organic fluxes depend (1) on an organic fluoboride such as boron trifluoride-monoethanolamine to remove the aluminum oxide, (2) a heavy metal fluoborate such as cadmium fluoborate ($Cd(BF_4)_2$) to coat the bare metal, and (3) an organic vehicle, such as methyl alcohol and stearic acid to give the mixture body and plasticity.

When an organic flux is placed on aluminum and both are heated, the flux boils and melts. The alcohol and water, which may have been added as thinners, evaporate first. The heated aluminum expands more than the oxide covering it, thereby cracking the oxide. The active reagent, in the form of a gas, released by the heat, bubbles up through the molten flux and down through tiny cracks in the oxide, fragmenting the oxide layer and breaking it free of the base aluminum. Cadmium, or whatever metal may be incorporated in the flux, deposits out on the bare alumi-

Source: Aluminum Soldering Handbook, 3rd Ed., Aluminum Assn., Inc.

Flux characteristic	Chloride-free organic flux	Chloride-containing reaction fluxes	
Typical			
Composition	83% triethanolamine	88% $SnCl_2$	88% $ZnCl_2$
	10% fluoboric acid	10% NH_4Cl	10% NH_4Cl
	7% $Cd(BF_3)^2$	2% NaF	2% NaF
Form	Viscous liquid	Powder	Powder
Vehicle	Ethyl or methyl alcohol or water	Alcohol, water	n-propyl or n-butyl alcohol or methyl ethyl ketone
Fluxing range	350 to 525 F	630 F, and up	720 F, and up
Fume generation	Copious	Copious	Copious
Heavy-metal deposition	Slight	Heavy	Heavy
Corrosiveness:			
Of flux	Very slight	Severe	Severe
Of residue	Very slight	Severe	Severe
Electrical conductivity:			
Of flux	Moderate	High	High
Of residue	Low	High	High

Table 2-3. *Characteristics of typical soldering fluxes for aluminum.*

num. The solder then wets and bonds to the cadmium, not to the aluminum.

The bubbles that accompany organic fluxes make it difficult to produce void-free lap joints with this class of fluxes. However, line-contact joints and similar joints of narrow width can be made without voids as the gas has very little distance to travel to freedom.

Organic fluxes are less active than reaction fluxes. For equal results, organic fluxes require the metals they contact be cleaner and freer of oxide than do reaction fluxes.

Organic fluxes are effective on alloys containing up to 1% magnesium and 4% silicon. Organic fluxes are not used on alloys containing higher percentages of these metals.

Because organic fluxes react comparatively slowly when heated to their design temperatures, a major portion of the flux remains in place as a protective blanket over the joint during the soldering cycle. Organic fluxes therefore are well suited to hand-fed soldering operations.

Organic fluxes are usually manufactured and distributed as heavy syrups whose color may be anything from amber to deep brown. Organic fluxes may be diluted 50% with water or alcohol. Tap water, if used, must be soft, otherwise distilled or deionized water is advisable.

Organic fluxes are usually non-hygroscopic. Exposed to air, they tend to dry out. Heated, as when soldered, their residues are usually non-hygroscopic. If no moisture is present, and if the part is not to be subjected to high voltages, and if the part or parts are not particularly thin, the organic flux residue may be left in place.

If moisture is present, organic flux residue must be removed because it is corrosive when wet. If the residue shunts or contacts a high-resistance electrical circuit the

residue must also be removed because it is slightly more conductive.

Organic flux formulas are compounded for temperatures of 350 to 525°F. Above this temperature, the flux begins to carbonize at an ever increasing rate. At 600° F., deterioration and charring is so rapid that organic flux can only be used with ultra-rapid soldering techniques such as induction soldering. Heated and cooled quickly enough, organic flux can be used at temperatures slightly above 620°F.

The carbon produced by overheating organic flux is an effective stop-off material and will prevent the flow of solder. Care must therefore be used when soldering with an iron or torch to keep the flux from direct contact with the source of heat.

The price of an organic flux is considerably higher than a reaction flux and residue removal cost is also considerably higher. Reaction flux residues can be removed with hot water alone. Organic flux residues require an organic solvent such as ethyl or methyl alcohol for removal.

Reaction Flux

Reaction fluxes depend mainly on heavy metal halides to break up aluminum's oxide covering. Generally, reaction fluxes contain chlorides of zinc or tin plus smaller quantities of other halides which may contain lithium, sodium, or potassium. In addition the flux will generally contain a compound such as ammonium chloride to improve wetting, lower the mixture's melting point and cover the joint during heat to prevent the re-entry of air and oxidation of the bare aluminum before heavy metal deposition occurs.

During soldering, the chlorides react with the aluminum and not with the aluminum oxide (Al_2O_3), as the latter is not reduced, the temperature is far too low.

The basic zinc chloride or tin chloride—aluminum reaction is:

$$3ZnCl_2 \text{ plus } 2Al \longrightarrow 2AlCl_3 \text{ plus } 3Zn$$
$$3SnCl_4 \text{ plus } 4Al \longrightarrow 4AlCl_3 \text{ plus } 3Sn$$

The metallic portion of the halide or halides is deposited in a strong tight layer on the bare aluminum. The solder then flows into the joint, wets and bonds with the deposited metal and not with the parent metal.

The reaction fluxes are manufactured as both a heavy syrup and as a powder. Normal-propyl, normal-butyl, ethyl and methyl alcohol are all excellent vehicles for use with the reaction fluxes. They do not react with the chlorides and have relatively low vapor pressure. They burn clean when the assembly is heated, are inexpensive and easily wet slightly oily surfaces. They are also excellent for use with organic fluxes for the same reasons.

Water should not be used to dilute the reaction fluxes. Water reacts with heavy metal chlorides to form oxychlorides, which are stop-offs and impede the flow of solder and are difficult to remove.

Water may be used as a solvent on perfectly clean surfaces and when the mixed flux is applied immediately to a work piece that is quickly soldered. Water-thinned reaction fluxes often are used for high-speed automatic soldering processes. In most instances, only enough water is added to make a heavy paste.

All the reaction fluxes, including those called chemical fluxes and organic compounds that contain chlorides, are hygroscopic both before and after soldering. The reaction fluxes therefore must be tightly sealed when stored or they will dilute themselves with water to form undesirable oxychlorides. A freshly opened can of chloride-containing flux powder will clump up with moisture in fifteen minutes.

Reaction flux residues are electrically conductive—wet or dry—and cannot be left in contact with an electrical circuit. In short, reaction flux residues must always be removed.

Removal is fairly easy as much of the flux escapes into the air as a gas. Most of the chemicals remaining may be rapidly washed off in hot water by virtue of the chemical reaction $AlCl_3 \text{ plus } 3H_2O \longrightarrow Al(OH)_3 \text{ plus } 3HCL$. When the gaseous product of soldering (aluminum chloride) cools, it forms a powdery solid that is six times more soluble in water than sodium chloride ($NaCl$). However, such chloride that has combined with oxygen to form oxychloride by virtue of excessive heat (on the flux) is insoluble and difficult to remove.

The tin-based reaction fluxes usually are formulated to react at a temperature between 540 and 640°F. They may be used with any solder that is liquid at their designed reaction temperature. The zinc-based reaction fluxes react at a temperature between 620 and 720°F.

To minimize the number of elements within a joint, tin-base fluxes are generally preferred for use with tin-base solders and zinc fluxes with zinc solders.

Each flux mixture has its own useful but limited temperature range. If a particular flux is not brought to this temperature its reaction will be nil for all practical purposes. If its specified temperature is exceeded, its reaction may be so fast that the solder will be unable to flow into place and little soldering will be accomplished.

Overly high temperatures also tend to "dry" chloride fluxes, turning them to powder and flakes. When carried into the joint by convection currents and solder flow, these particles cause blockages and voids. The reaction or working temperature of the flux selected must be slightly below or the same as the flow temperature of the solder to be used with it.

The high-chloride content fluxes produce the greatest quantity of aluminum chloride gas and deposit the most metal, leaving very little molten salt to form a protective, oxygen-excluding blanket over the solder joint. The high-chloride fluxes therefore are difficult to use when the solder is hand-fed to the joint. With these fluxes the solder is best preplaced.

Reaction fluxes containing relatively small amounts of halides, sometimes called chemical fluxes or moderate reaction fluxes, do not react as rapidly as high-halide content fluxes. Moderate reaction fluxes can be used when the solder is hand fed to the joint.

Organic fluxes run through their cycle even more slowly and are therefore excellent for hand-fed solder joints.

It can be seen that accurate temperature control is important when soldering with all of the fluxes, but most important, even critical, when soldering with high-chloride content, reaction fluxes.

All fluxes deposit metal. The quantity deposited is naturally dependent upon the metallic content of the flux. The organics deposit very little. The moderate reaction fluxes deposit more and the high-halide reaction fluxes deposit the most metal; so much metal that joints can be formed by means of the flux alone. The deposited metal may be as much as 0.001 inch thick.

All solder fluxes generate large quantities of dense, white, irritating, corrosive smoke. The fumes produced by fluxes containing fluoride and/or cadmium are toxic as well. Power ventilation is mandatory when any quantity of work is to be accomplished indoors.

Flux and Intergranular Penetration

Solder flux of itself has no known effect on the intergranular penetration of base aluminum by an applied solder. However, all fluxes deposit metal, and it is this deposited metal that makes primary and for all purposes, singular contact with the parent aluminum. Therefore,

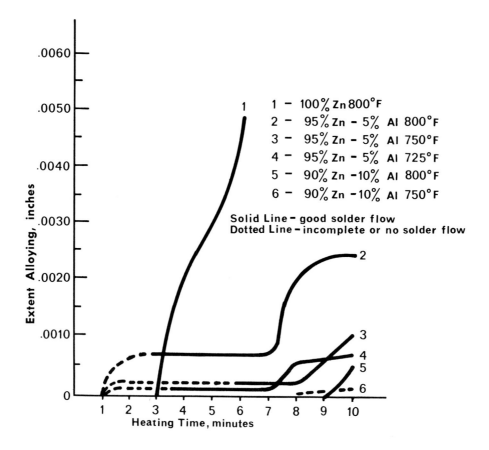

Figure 2-2. *Effect of composition of zinc solders, soldering time and soldering temperature on rate of inter-alloying between zinc solders and aluminum Alloy 6061.*

when a flux is used it must be chosen with a care to the metal contained, making certain that the metal is not deleterious to the alloy to be soldered.

An equally important factor to consider when selecting a "flux metal" is its electrolytic relation to the base metal and the solder. Minimum voltage difference is the goal as corrosion rates generally vary directly with potential differences. See Chapter 12.

Fluxes for Mixed-metal Soldering

All the fluxes used for soldering aluminum to aluminum may be used for soldering aluminum to other metals. However, better results are usually obtainable when a more active flux is used for soldering mixed-metals. Formulas for a number of such fluxes are provided in Table 2-4. Chapter 11 discusses mixed-metal soldering in detail.

Solder

For many engineers the selection of a solder is the natural starting point in designing a solder system, i.e.,

selecting the base metal alloy, solder and flux to comprise the soldered assembly.

Joint strength, exclusive of folds and interlocking parts, is established by the strength of the solder. Flux choice is limited to a great extent by the melting temperature of the solder. Corrosion resistance is determined by the joint's chemistry, which establishes the electric potential developed by the galvanic couple produced when moisture forms an electrolyte between the solder and the parent metal. Soldering ease is dependent on the solder's composition, and the cost of soldering itself is strongly related to the cost of the solder used.

Only four metals are used as the principal ingredients of all non-proprietary solder formulations. The metals are tin, lead, cadmium and zinc. The better known solder formulas and their major physical properties are listed in Table 2-5. The four metals used as the basis for aluminum solders and their alloying elements fall into three thermal groups. Those that melt below 500°F. are called low-melting point or soft solders. Those that melt between 500 and 700°F. are called intermediate solders and those

Paste fluxes for soldering aluminum

Stannous chloride	83 oz.
Zinc dihydrazinium chloride	7 oz.
Hydrazine hydrobromide	10 oz.
Water	10 oz.

Cadmium fluoboride	5 oz.
Zinc fluoboride	5 oz.
Fluoboric acid	6 oz.
Diethanol amine	20 oz.
Diethanol diamine	4 oz.
Diethylene triamine	10 oz.

Potassium chloride	45 oz.
Sodium chloride	30 oz.
Lithium chloride	15 oz.
Potassium fluoride	7 oz.
Sodium pyrophosphate	3 oz.

Chloride-free organic flux

Triethanolamine	25 oz.
Fluoboric acid	3 oz.
Cadmium fluoborate	2 oz.

(Fluxing range 350 to 525F. The viscous liquid can be dissolved with water or alcohol to any desired concentration.)

Reaction type flux for soldering aluminum

Stannous chloride	44 oz.
Ammonium chloride	5 oz.
Sodium fluoride	1 oz.

(Fluxing range 540 to 720F or higher. It may be used as a dry powder mixture or it may be suspended in alcohol.)

Reaction type flux

Zinc chloride	44 oz.
Ammonium chloride	5 oz.
Sodium fluoride	1 oz.

(Fluxing range 620 to 720F or higher. It may be used as a dry powder or mixed with water or alcohol.)

Table 2-4. *Special purpose corrosive fluxes suitable for soldering aluminum to stainless steel, alloy steel, nickel alloys, silicon and aluminum bronzes, zinc-coated stock, cast iron and aluminum to aluminum.*

that melt between 700 and 820°F. are called high-temperature solders. As nature would have it, the relative strength and corrosion resistance of the solders—when used with optimum gap aluminum joints—follow the same temperature pattern. The high-temperature solders are the strongest and most corrosion resistant, the intermediate solders are next, while the low temperature solders have the least strength and are least corrosion resistant.

The strength of the low temperature, soft solders in shear is a bit in excess of 5,000 psi. The melting points of solders in this group begins at 230°F.

Aluminum joints made with soft solders have relatively low corrosion resistance and therefore are rarely exposed to the weather or corrosive atmospheres.

The low temperature, tin-lead solders also suffer from a metallurgical phenomenon known as "creep," that is they extend. Under sufficient loading they may rapidly fail. Typically a 60-tin 40-lead solder joint loaded to 1400 psi in tension will give way in a few hours. If the initial stress is reduced to 600 psi the solder will resist for 22 hours. Reduced to 100 psi, failure during test occurred in 165 days. These solders are therefore useful only for bonding and sealing; holding twisted wires in place or folded and crimped metal edges in place.

The binary lead-tin solder combinations, such as are commonly sold for soldering copper, can also be used for soldering aluminum. But they are difficult to use. The joint formed is weak and therefore lead-tin solder is seldom used with aluminum. Lead alone is almost insoluble in aluminum and the addition of tin improves lead's wetting ability but slightly. Lead-tin solder combinations formulated for aluminum usually contain small quantities of zinc, cadmium and other metals to improve wetting and flow characteristics.

The tin-zinc eutectic mixture (91% Sn-9% Zn) that melts at only 390°F. and flows and wets aluminum readily is the most corrosion resistant of the low-temperature solders. Its strength approaches that of the intermediate solders.

The tin-zinc base intermediate solders exhibit shear strengths in excess of 7,000 psi. These solders are often used for exterior joints when protected from the weather by paint or similar means. Tin-zinc solders melt at 550°F. and higher.

Zinc-cadmium solders, which may contain 30 to 70% Zn, produce joints with shear strengths of more than 10,000 psi. Zinc-cadmium joints have intermediate corrosion resistance and are soldered at temperatures ranging from 510 to 750°F. Cadmium alone is only slightly soluble in aluminum and forms a limited diffusion zone.

The zinc-base solders may contain 90 to 99.99% zinc. They develop the highest strengths of all commercial solders, exhibiting shear strengths of 18,000 psi and more. Soldering temperatures are highest of all solders, ranging from 720 to 800°F. The zinc-base solders are most corrosion resistant; the greater the quantity of zinc in the solder the greater its corrosion resistance.

The zinc solders are most corrosion resistant when they are free of low-melting-temperature metal impurities like bismuth, cadmium, lead or tin. Small quantities of copper, silver, titanium and other metals sometimes are added to pure zinc to improve its flow and wetting capabilities.

These alloying metals do not appreciably reduce zinc's corrosion resistance when added in minute amounts.

To reduce zinc's tendency to penetrate certain aluminum alloys, aluminum is often added to zinc solder. While intergranular penetration is reduced, the addition of aluminum reduces zinc solder's corrosion resistance, melting point and ductility. Pure zinc is the most ductile and vibration-resistant solder known for use with aluminum.

Figure 2-2 illustrates the relationship between heating time, solder composition and alloying depth for a number of zinc-aluminum mixtures. At 800°F., pure zinc requires six minutes to penetrate alloy 6061 to a depth of 0.005 inch. Zinc readily alloys with aluminum to form a eutectic surface layer that is 5% aluminum. Aluminum addition slows down alloying markedly.

Close temperature control and short heating periods are necessary with zinc-base solders to minimize intergranular penetration by zinc. Typically the solder should not be heated more than 50°F. above its liquidus, and the time at soldering heat should be under one minute for optimum results.

Soldering Temperatures

In addition to the specific difficulties described, more general problems may be encountered if the heating cycle is not kept short and within the prescribed temperature range.

If too much time passes before a solder reaches liquidus temperature, liquation may occur to some degree. The lower melting point elements may leave a solder and thus change its composition. Excessive alloying may take place, which also acts to alter the composition of a solder, and flux composition may change unfavorably.

If the solder is not fully melted, solder flow will be sluggish. The joint may not be completely filled, wetting may be poor and incomplete and the solder fillet surfaces may not be smooth nor fully formed.

If the temperature is too high, the solder will oxidize and some of the elements may leave. Oxide particles will interfere with wetting and add to the dross the flux has to push out of the joint. Changes in solder composition are usually undesirable and lead to poor and incomplete joints.

Abrasion Solder

An abrasion solder is a solder that is firm enough just under its melting temperature to be used to abrade the surface of the aluminum. Some solders are formulated with this special characteristic in mind. Some abrasion solders contain non-interfering abrasive particles.

All high-temperature and some intermediate temperature solders may be used for abrasion soldering by the simple expedient of keeping the solder cool enough during the primary soldering steps to use the metal as a surface rubbing tool.

Available Solder Forms

High and intermediate temperature solders for use with aluminum are manufactured and stocked in the form of cast bars, rods, extruded tubes, powder, foil and a limited variety of preform shapes. The bars and rods are usually 18 inches long and vary upwards from 1/16 inch in diameter. The tubes are somewhat flexible: They are filled with flux and are available in various coil sizes.

Soft solders are produced in bars, rods and wire form, ranging upwards from about 1/32 inch.

Solder Clad Sheets

Sheets of alloy 1100 metallurgically clad with pure zinc on one or both sides are available. Though more expensive than the wrought metal and solder alone, the solder sheet greatly simplifies the fabrications of complex assemblies. Fluxed and in contact with one another, the solder-sheet parts need only to be brought to temperature to be joined. Tinned with zinc, aluminum can be as readily soldered as bare copper or nickel-plated steel. Additional solder is usually not needed, but when it is, the solder is pre-placed in the joint along with suitable flux.

Cladding the aluminum with zinc also provides a solder base amenable to lead-tin soft solders and ordinary fluxes.

Color Match

When selecting a solder for its color it is important to match the future color of the solder against the future color of the aluminum. Both the aluminum, assuming it will be finished bare, and the solder oxidize and weather with time. The color of the solder and the parent aluminum may draw closer as they age or further apart. For an accurate evaluation, sufficient time must be permitted for stabilization.

Several solders, including the eutectic (Zn17.5-Cd82.5) that melts at 509°F., match aluminum's color very well when they are freshly molten and still untarnished. If these solders are protected against oxidation by a clear lacquer coat or similar means the color match may be maintained indefinitely.

High-zinc content solders have weathered colors approaching aluminum's grey. The lead-based solders turn to dark grey quickly and have appearances least like that of aluminum. The colors of other solders fall somewhere between.

Wiping Solders

Wiping solders are solders that have a wide temperature spread between their solidus and liquidus states. The 30Sn-70Zn alloy with 320°F. between solidus and liquidus is one such solder. The 79.6Zn-10Al alloy is another. Its solidus is 527°F. and its liquidus is 750°F.

Solder Type	Composition, %						Melting Range °F Solidus-Liquidus	Wetting Ability	Flux Type	Corrosion Resistance
	Sn	Zn	Al	Cd	Pb	Cu				
Zn		100					787	Good	React.	V. Good
Zn		94	4			2	720-740	Good	React.	V. Good
Zn		95	5				710	Good	React.	V. Good
Zn		90	5			5	720	Good	React.	V. Good
Zn	2	79.6	10	0.4	3	5	527-750			
Zn-Cd		90		10			509 760	Good	React.	Fair
Zn-Cd		60		40			509-635	V. Good	React.	Fair
Zn-Cd		17.5		82.5			509			
Sn-Zn	20	15	0.8	64.2			230-530			
Sn-Zn	70	30					390-592	Fair	React.	Fair
Sn-Zn	30	70					390-710	Good	React.	Good
Sn-Pb	40				60		361-460			
Sn-Zn	60	39.4			.1	0.5	390-645	Good	React.	Good
Sn-Pb	63				37		361-420			
Sn-Zn	69.3	28	0.7		2.0		385-635			
Sn-Zn	80	20					390-530			
Sn-Zn	91	9					400	Fair	Org-react	Fair
Sn-Pb	36.9			3.8	59.3		290-450			
Sn-Pb	34	3			63		383-492	Poor	Org-or React	Poor
Sn-Pb	31.6	9		8	51	0.4	282-485			
Sn-Pb	40	15	0.8		44.2		335-675			
Sn-Cd	20	15	0.8	64.2			230-530			
Sn-Cd	50				50		360-420	Poor	Org-react	Poor
Sn-Zn	91	9					391	Fair	Organic	Poor

Note: Solders with but one temperature figure are eutectics.

Table 2-5. *Composition of typical solders for use with aluminum.*

Alcoa
    1501 Alcoa Building   Pittsburgh, Pa.

Alladin Rod & Flux Mfg. Co.
    1300 Burton St. S.E.   Grand Rapids, Mich.

All-State Welding Alloys Div.   Chemetron Corp.
    Hanover, Pa.

Amco
    19th and Willard St.   Philadelphia, Pa.

Bow Solder Products Co. Inc.
    25 Amsterdam St.   Newark, N.J.

Chemalloy Electronics
    Santee, California

Eutectic Welding Alloys
    170 2nd Street   Flushing, N.Y. 11358

Kester Solder Co.
    4201 Wrightwood Ave.   Chicago, Ill.

Lucas-Milhaupt Engineering Co.
    Cudahy, Wisconsin

Matthiessen and Hegler Zinc Co.
    La Salle, Ill.

Ney Metals Inc.
    269 Freeman St.   Brooklyn, N.Y.

Table 2-6. *Some solder and flux manufacturers.*

Source: Aluminum Soldering Handbook, 3rd Ed., Aluminum Assn., Inc.

Pre-Cleaning, Oxide Removal and Surface Preparation

As stated previously, soldering requires the aluminum be soil free and its oxide layer thin enough to be displaced by the hot flux during the soldering cycle.

Neither conditions are absolutes, but are satisfied in varying degrees, said degree being related to desired joint quality and joining dependability.

Most shops, judging by work volume, find that both conditions may be met by vapor degreasing alone. The oxide layer normal to mill-finished aluminum is generally no deterrent to satisfactory soldering.

Other shops find that aluminum as removed from its mill wrappings meets their soldering needs with no treatment whatsoever.

Still other shops, working to tighter specifications and seeking more nearly perfectly soldered joints, or having to solder extensively shaped and formed aluminum, or difficult to solder alloys, find that both cleaning and oxide removal are necessary.

Pre-solder cleaning and oxide removal varies therefore with the flux, solder, temperature, alloy to be soldered, alloy condition prior to soldering and joint quality desired. The degree of cleanliness and oxide removal necessary may be determined by the soldering engineer by test.

Soils and grease that may be present on the metal to be soldered can be removed by vapor degreasing using inhibited trichloroethylene or inhibited perchloroethylene or other commercial fluids. Petroleum solvents and chlorinated hydrocarbons can also be used for washing the parts clean. And the metal can be washed in hot detergents and water—hot alkaline baths made of water and trisodium phosphate or one of the many excellent commercial compounds made expressly for cleaning aluminum prior to soldering (and brazing). This is always followed by a clear-water rinse.

The presence of oil or grease on the work piece may be checked by means of the water-break test. The cleaned part is dipped into water and removed. It is then tilted in the light while the water runs off. If the metal is grease free, the surface of the water will be smooth and unbroken. If there is an oily spot, the water's surface will show a definite break there.

Something less than perfect degreasing can be tolerated if the flux incorporates a solvent rather than water alone as a vehicle.

The second condition for soldering aluminum, a manageably thin oxide layer, must be met only when a flux is to be used. If the oxide is to be removed mechanically, as by abrasion soldering, any oxide thickness short of a heavy encrustment can be handled.

The specific oxide thickness that can be removed by the flux during heating depends on the composition of the flux, the temperature at which it is used and the base alloy involved. The more active the flux, the thicker the oxide coating it will dispel. In this matter reaction fluxes are much more effective than organic fluxes, and certain flux mixtures are more effective than others on particular alloys. The organic fluxes, for example, are ineffective on alloys containing more than 1% magnesium or 4% silicon.

Aluminum oxide is more readily cracked and removed at high temperature than at low temperature. Initial oxide cracking is due to the base metal's greater coefficient of expansion. Higher temperatures naturally increase the effect of this difference.

Fluxes designed for high temperatures have greater oxide cracking ability than reasonably similar formulations designed for lower temperatures. Once the oxide is cracked, the flux penetrates the cracks and combines with the base metal to form a gas, aluminum fluoride or aluminum chloride. The higher the temperature, the more rapidly the gas is formed and the greater the pressure developed.

Figure 3-1. *A self-contained ultrasonic cleaning system.*
Courtesy Branson.

between flux effectiveness and the effectiveness of whatever oxide removal steps are being taken. Both parameters must be handled and measured together. A number of sample solder joints are made, then tested and examined. Test procedures are discussed in Chapter 12.

It should be noted that even heavily soiled and oxidized aluminum can sometimes be soldered. The mere fact of joining is no indication of joint quality or repeatability.

It should be also noted that the visual appearance of the metal in question is of little value. Some alloys appearing to be heavily oxidized are not. Other alloys may glow with cleanliness but are actually too thickly oxidized to solder (or braze).

Alloy	Resistance $\times 10^{-6}$
1100	100-500
3003	300-1000
3004	500-3000
6061	1000-20,000
7039	2000-20,000

Table 3-1. *Alloys having higher surface resistances than listed are difficult to braze satisfactorily. Values given are for two oxide layers in series. It is assumed these values are equally valuable in assessing aluminum oxide thicknesses prior to soldering.*

Measuring Oxide Thickness

Oxide layers normally found on aluminum alloys range in thickness from one to five millionths of an inch and more. The thickness of an aluminum oxide layer cannot be easily measured by direct means, but can be extrapolated from its electrical resistance. The electrical resistance of a layer of oxide varies with thickness and ranges from 50 to 20,000 microhms (1×10^{-6}) and more depending on the alloy and its condition. Resistance measurements may be made with microhmmeters such as are used for examining aluminum prior to spot welding or brazing, or any ohmmeter designed for very low resistance measurements.

Table 3-1 lists a portion of the range of surface resistances that may be expected with different aluminum alloys. Resistance values will vary from one sheet to another and from one point on the sheet to another. These figures were developed for use in brazing aluminum. When an alloy's surface resistance is higher than that given by the table, joint quality becomes erratic. A few joints may prove excellent, but the majority will be unsatisfactory.

Unfortunately no data have been published relating an alloy's oxide resistivity to its solderability as has been done for brazing. While it may be assumed that the acceptable oxide resistance values for soldering will follow more or less those values acceptable for brazing and listed in Table 3-1, exact figures will have to be determined empirically by the individual engineer. Once established, such data is invaluable, as they would enable a soldering engineer to quickly evaluate his cleaning and surface preparation schedule.

Without the aid of a microhmmeter to measure oxide resistance, and a set of values by which to judge the readings of different alloys, there is no way to differentiate

Oxide Removal

Overly thick oxide can be cut down by either mechanical or chemical means.

Mechanical means are practical when small areas are involved as in the case of repairs. Sandpaper, Aloxite cloth, steel wool and files may be used. Stainless steel wool and/or a stainless steel, motor-driven wire brush are preferred. With the latter there is less possibility of grit or steel particles being driven into the metal to interfere with soldering and corrode. When sandpaper or emery cloth is used the metal must be cleaned afterwards to remove adhering abrasive particles.

When large quantities of metal have to be freed of oxide, or the shape and complexity of the parts preclude mechanical methods, chemicals are used. Chemical removal of oxide is comparatively inexpensive, rapid and dependable.

Both caustics and acids are used. Of the two, caustic is by far the most active and widely used oxide-removing agent.

A very effective, rapid and relatively inexpensive caustic "deoxidizer" may be made by mixing a 5% solution of sodium hydroxide and water, generally kept at 150°F.

Figure 3-2 illustrates the action of a typical caustic solution upon aluminum. Notice how quickly caustic

Source: Aluminum Soldering Handbook, 3rd Ed., Aluminum Assn., Inc.

solution A brought the oxide level down to approximately 100 microhms, and how quickly the caustic reversed its action and replaced the oxide.

For the above reasons, best results are obtained with strong caustic oxide removal solutions when dip time is limited to 10 or 15 seconds and solution concentration and temperature are carefully controlled. Control requirements can be reduced by diluting the caustic or by using one of the many commercial formulas on the market. The horizontal portion of curve B in Figure 3-2 illustrates the change. To improve repeatability (with any solution) it may be advisable to pre-dip the metal in clear water to which a wetting agent has been added.

Hot caustic will remove approximately 0.001 inch of immersed metal per minute, preferentially attacking the pure aluminum to leave the alloying elements behind in the form of a scum or surface smudge called smut. Alloys having greater quantities of added elements are most troubled by smut. By contrast, little or no smut at all form on alloys 1100 and 1235.

Whether a caustic composed of sodium hydroxide or one of the proprietary oxide removal solutions is used, the deoxidizing step must be followed by a rinse in clear water and desmutting. (Some manufacturers claim deoxidizers that form no adhering smut.) Smut must be removed as it interferes with soldering.

Smut is easily removed by dipping the metal into acid. The bath most frequently used is undiluted nitric acid at room temperature, or a chromic acid solution containing some dichromates. The aluminum is held under for 30 seconds or less. Some engineers find a mixture of nitric acid and hydrofluoric acid gives them better results. Some shops add as little as 0.5 to 5% hydrofluoric acid to the nitric acid. Others use as much as 20%.

The acid bath is always followed by a clear water rinse. The metal is then air dried. If the water used for rinsing is hot, parts will dry more quickly. Wet metal parts should never touch when drying as water spotting—surface discoloration—may result.

An acid dip unpreceded by a caustic dip is sometimes used to free aluminum of its oxide coating. The single treatment is used when little oxide is present on the aluminum. The bath may consist of nitric acid or a combination of nitric acid and hydrofluoric acid. This is always followed by a clear water rinse and drying. The acid bath also removes metal, as does the hot caustic, but at a far slower rate.

Forethought should be given to the removal of metal by the pre-solder baths when finely machined parts such as threads have to be deoxidized. In some instances the practical answer is the re-cutting or the cutting of threads and final dimensioning after the parts have been joined. Allowance is made for the metal expected to be lost in

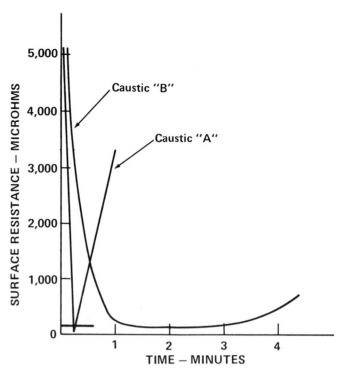

Figure 3-2. *Line A charts the rate of oxide removal and replacement when a caustic is used to remove oxide from aluminum.*

Line B charts the action of a diluted caustic solution or a proprietary cleaning solution used to remove oxide from aluminum. Note the two minutes during which the oxide is at a satisfactorily thin level.

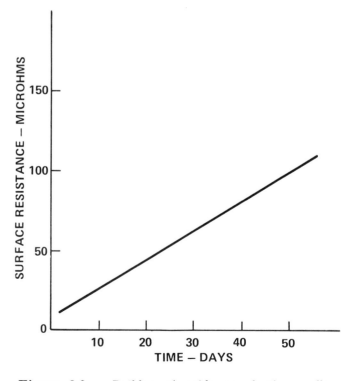

Figure 3-3. *Buildup of oxide on aluminum alloys.*

the baths. There are, however, several proprietary non-etching deoxidizers on the market which purport not to remove metal.

Some of the commercial deoxidants and desmutters are based on chromic acid, and some shops use chromic acid for desmutting, as a result the desmutting bath will in time collect an excessive quantity of chromate. When this occurs the bath is said to be contaminated and aluminum dipped into the bath will receive a chromate finish which is not solderable. When the degree of contamination is very high or the metal is left in the bath for a long time the chromate finish becomes visible as a color change in the aluminum. Chromate coatings sufficiently thick to interfere with soldering but too thin to be visible to the eye may be detected by electrical resistance measurements. Surface resistance values listed in Table 3-1 apply.

Mechanical or chemical removal of the parent metal's oxide layer does not eliminate the need for flux. (Except when a fluxless soldering technique is used.) For no matter how little time passes between scraping the aluminum bright and applying hot solder, oxidation will occur and without flux to remove the new oxide, little or no soldering will take place.

Keeping the Parts Clean

Recontamination and oxide buildup can be greatly reduced by keeping the interim period between cleaning, oxide removal and soldering as short as possible. Figure 3-3 depicts the rise of surface resistance (oxide buildup) on aluminum alloys with the passage of time.

To maintain cleanliness during assembly, most shops teach their workmen to avoid holding the parts by their faying surfaces. In some instances lint-free cotton gloves are issued and in other shops lengths of wire are tack-welded to the parts to be used as handles. Still other shops depend on clean work fixtures and jigs for parts handling.

To prevent recontamination during storage, cleaned parts may be stored in plastic bags. Some shops acid dip, rinse and dry all cleaned parts before soldering if the parts have been stored more than 48 hours. This is done as a precautionary measure.

Cleaning, Oxide Removal and Joint Quality

None of the aluminum soldering materials, techniques and equipment known today will produce perfect solder joints, i.e., joints that show perfectly clear under X-rays, joints with complete solder-to-base metal adhesion.

However, near perfect joints can be and are being produced by careful attention to cleaning and oxide removal. Perfect solder joints are not necessary for most applications. Joints containing voids are normally leak-proof and pressure tight because the voids are usually sealed.

Figure 3-4 is an X-ray of an all-aluminum heat exchanger with zinc-soldered return bends. A close examination of the bell joints—about ⅜ inch high—reveals very few and very shallow voids. The coils and the return bends were degreased and deoxidized before soldering. Heat was supplied by a radiant furnace which precluded the introduction of combustion products. The unit shown is one of a number produced on a pilot plant production line

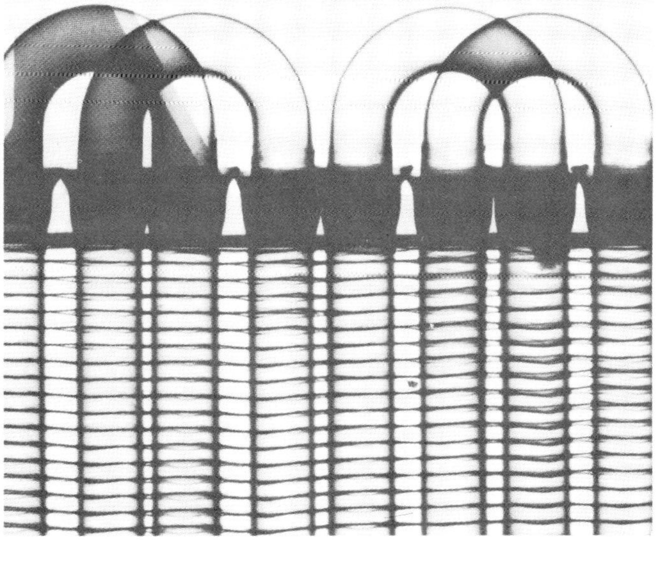

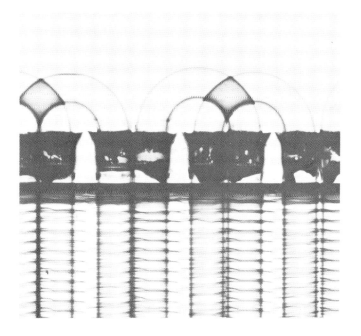

Figure 3-4. *X-ray of carefully cleaned and deoxidized solder joints comprising a heat exchanger.*

Figure 3-5. *X-ray of solder joints comprising a similar unit that were neither degreased nor deoxidized.*

Source: Aluminum Soldering Handbook, 3rd Ed., Aluminum Assn., Inc.

Figure 3-5 is an X-ray of a commercially produced all-aluminum heat exchanger with zinc-soldered return bends. Close inspection will reveal innumerable, deep voids. This core was neither degreased nor deoxidized. Heat was furnished by automatic gas torches and soldering was accomplished in about 20 seconds.

About 3% of the first group of cores were found to be leakers after soldering and were easily repaired by torch soldering. No figures are available on the percentage of leakers found in the second group.

Voids, lack of complete adhesion and post-soldering leakers not withstanding, the second group of cores remained leakproof, after repairs, in millions of instances (automotive air conditioners) for many years.

Surface Preparation—Precoating

Alloys that are difficult to solder, alloys that are prone to intergranular penetration, alloys that form highly galvanic couples with solder used or with neighboring metals, alloys forming assemblies that are best soldered dry—with little or no flux—are frequently coated with another metal or pure aluminum before soldering.

Aluminum can be coated with brass, cadmium, copper, gold, lead, nickel, silver, zinc or other metals. Silver plating eliminates the need for flux as molten zinc will immediately and completely wet and bond to silver. Intergranular penetration by the zinc through the silver and into the base aluminum is neligible.

When the base metal is coated with another metal and then soldered, the solder wets and bonds to the plating. Joint strength is therefore limited by the strength of the plating's bond to the base aluminum. For high quality joints, precoat or plating quality must be high.

Metal precoatings may be applied by chemical electroless plating, electroplating, reduction plating, hot dipping, spraying (hot), cladding, flux deposition and tinning.

Tinning

Tinning is a term that originated centuries ago with the literal application of tin or tin-lead solder to copper preparatory to soldering.

The applied metal is generally solder, and the tinning operations differ in but one respect from soldering: joining is not consummated. The base aluminum is cleaned, and heated. Solder is applied with the aid of flux, or a reaction flux alone is used to clad the aluminum or an abrasion technique with or without flux is used to "tin" the aluminum.

Hot dipping is useful when a number of aluminum parts need to be tinned. A quantity of flux is applied to both sides of the edge to be tinned and the metal is dipped into a pot of molten solder. This technique is discussed at greater length in Chapter 9.

Tinning can be accomplished without heat by loading a grindstone with solder and then pressing the base metal against the spinning stone. Actual contact is between solder and base metal. The heat and force of friction simultaneously melts the solder and removes the base metal's oxide layer. Fresh solder is repeatedly pressed into the rotating grindstone to replace the metal transferred onto the base metal.

In all tinning operations it is desirable to coat the base metal as completely as possible for the entire length and breadth of the joint area. And it is desirable that no specks or untinned spots be visible in the tinning as these "bare" spots will be bare of solder after the joint has been completed.

Molten solder will often "bridge" a surface depression or a particle of dirt. To preclude this possibility and check for complete tinning and adhesion, some operators add more solder to the tinned spot and then wipe the excess solder off with a clean cloth. Untinned places, as revealed by slight color differences, may be further abraded until tinning is complete.

Final tinning thickness should be fairly smooth and only a little thicker than needed to complete the joint. Too much solder may interfere with joint assembly.

Joints need not be completed immediately after the base metal's faying surfaces have been tinned. The prepared parts can be stored indefinitely so long as the solder's surface is not permitted to corrode excessively. Once tinned, two aluminum parts may be soldered by simply placing them in contact with each other and heating the joint area until the solder coatings melt and commingle. Any solder compatible with the tinned surfaces may be added to the joint.

Plating with Chemical Energy

As aluminum is chemically very active it may be plated with metal by chemical action produced by interaction between alloy and bath.

The two principal chemical plating processes in use today are chemical reduction plating and electroless plating.

Zinc is the metal most frequently applied by chemical reduction. The bath used may be either alkaline or acid. Table 3-2 provides typical formulas for both.

The metal to be plated must be thoroughly degreased and its oxide sufficiently thinned to permit the metal's surface to be uniformly dissolved in the bath. In an alkaline bath, the sodium hydroxide dissolves the remaining

Item	Alkaline bath	Acid bath
Bath composition	ZnO, 100 g per liter	ZnSO₄ 7 H₂O, 720 g per liter
	NaOH, 500 g per liter	HF (48%), 17.5 ml per liter
Bath temperature	Room temperature	Room temperature
Immersion time	30 to 60 sec	30 to 60 sec
Surface pretreatment	1 Degrease, if required	
	2 Deoxidize in hot H₂SO₄—CrO₃	
	3 Etch in 5% NaOH at 150 F	
	4 Desmut in HNO₃, or HNO₃—HF for high-silicon alloys	

Table 3-2. *Typical electroless baths for plating aluminum alloys with zinc. The alkaline bath is often called a zincating treatment.*

Composition or conditions	Alkaline bath	Acid bath
Nickel chloride, g per liter	30	30
Sodium hypophosphite, g per liter	10	10
Sodium hydroxyacetate, g per liter	....	50
Ammonium chloride, g per liter	50	11
Ammonium hydroxide	To pH	....
pH	8 to 10	4 to 6
Temperature, F	195 to 205	190 to 210
Plating rate (approximate), mil per hr	0.3	0.5

Table 3-3. *Alkaline and acid formulas for nickel plating of aluminum alloys by means of chemical reduction.*

aluminum oxide and the zinc "plates" out on the bare aluminum by galvanic displacement. Usually, the aluminum is removed from the bath when its surface is entirely covered with a film of zinc about 1 to 2 millionths of an inch thick. This treatment is referred to as zincating. For a more homogeneous coating the plated metal is stripped by means of nitric acid and plated a second time with either zinc or any desired metal.

Electroless plating is a fairly new process. It is often used to plate nickel on aluminum to improve aluminum's wear resistance, corrosion resistance and for soldering (or brazing) aluminum to stainless steel. With this process, nickel has been plated onto aluminum at rates of 0.2 to 1.0 mil per hour.

Electroless plating is accomplished by catalytic decomposition of the plating bath. Although aluminum is not inherently a catalyst, it initiates bath decomposition by precipitating nickel through a chemical sequence similar to that which occurs in the electroless plating process. Typical bath compositions are given in Table 3-3.

Clean aluminum may be immersed directly in a hypophosphites ion bath, but some fabricators pretreat the aluminum with a zinc layer applied by chemical reduction plating followed by a copper strike, especially when the aluminum alloy contains quantities of bismuth, cadmium, lead, manganese, tin or zinc, which are some of the elements known to poison the bath.

The nickel-phosphorous alloy commonly plated onto aluminum by electroless plating resists attack by chemicals normally troublesome to aluminum. The nickel plating may be soldered directly to many other metals with any compatible solder.

Alstan 70 Process

In recent years, methods have been developed by which aluminum is directly plated with thin films of chromium, nickel, copper, or bronze to form a base for subsequent electroplates or soldering. These have been applied by both electroplating and electroless techniques. These thin foundation films are generally applied in thicknesses in the order of 30-100 millionths of an inch. In the Alstan 70

M & T Chemical Co. process for example, the passivation is accomplished by deposition of an almost nondetectable film of a Stannate compound by electroless immersion in the Alstan 75 bath. Subsequent plating is carried out by electroplating a bronze flash, 40-60 millionths of an inch in thickness. This is followed by any plating desired or the bronze plating may be directly soldered.

Electroplating

Aluminum is frequently electroplated to improve its solderability and to reduce its electrical surface resistance. Most often the aluminum is preplated by the Alstan 70 process to produce 40 to 60 millionths of an inch of bronze, or preplated by the zincate process to produce a thin film of zinc 1 to 2 millionth of an inch thick. Either process is then followed by a top electroplate of 0.2 to 0.4 mil of tin or a top electroplate of 0.2 to 0.3 of copper which is again plated with 0.1 to 0.3 mil of silver. These four possible combinations of preplate and top plate comprise the plating systems used for the bulk of aluminum electroplate today.

For low temperature solders and fluxes, a thin electroplate of tin or silver is often used.

Local Plating

As stated, reaction flux heated to its design temperature will deposit a firm layer of whatever metal it contains upon an equally hot, clean, oxide-free aluminum surface. The plated surface may then be cleaned of flux residue. Two such plated surfaces may be soldered together without flux. They are placed in contact, and heated with or without suitable solder. The joint forms on cooling. This procedure can sometimes be used to produce flux-free assemblies that might otherwise be very difficult to clean after assembly.

Faying surfaces to be joined can also be pre-coated or tinned as it is sometimes called by rub soldering. This technique, discussed in Chapter 7, is used to coat the faying surfaces—one at a time without flux. Afterwards the surfaces may be joined with or without additional solder. No flux is used.

Post-Cleaning and Finishing

Post-soldering cleaning depends on the flux, solder and alloy used and soldered-assembly application.

Organic Flux Residue

The non-chloride containing organic fluxes are usually non-hygroscopic after soldering. When non-hygroscopic, these residues produce little or no corrosion if left in place. When possible corrosion is the only concern, non-hygroscopic organic flux residues are usually left in place on aluminum foil thicker than 0.005 inch and aluminum wire thicker than 0.010 inch. When appearance is of paramount concern, or when the flux residue may make contact with a high resistance or a high voltage electrical circuit, residue should be removed. When organic flux residue is hygroscopic, it is always removed.

Non-hygroscopic organic flux residues are commonly left on low-voltage transformer leads, speaker coil leads and similar electrical connections.

Organic fluxes are most easily removed when they have not been heated to their char point and have not been "cooked" by overly long exposure to soldering heat.

Organic flux residues are most easily removed directly after soldering, preferably while the solder-joint is still hot. Organic residues become increasingly difficult to remove with the passage of time; even a few hours can make a noticeable difference.

Organic residues respond poorly to hot water but are fairly readily dissolved and removed with a hydrocarbon solvent. Alcohol and trichlorethylene are frequently used.

The solder joint may simply be dipped into the solvent, but faster, more positive cleaning action can be secured by scrubbing the part with a fiber brush or by agitating the part or the solvent by mechanical means.

Chloride Flux Residue Removal

The soldered assembly must be cleaned quickly of flux residue when a reaction flux or a chloride-containing organic flux has been used for soldering. If this is not done, the joint will become moist and corrode no matter how dry the air may appear to be.

As solder flux manufacturers are loath to supply a list of contents with their products, the exact composition of a flux is often unknown. Under such conditions it is best to clean the soldered parts thoroughly. Although the flux residue may show no immediate signs of hygroscopic activity the flux may be hygroscopic, in which case it will deliquesce without fail. As it absorbs water, galvanic corrosion will start and continue until the reaction is fully completed.

Reaction flux and all other flux formulation residues containing chloride are most easily removed by washing in boiling water. However, when the residue incorporates a high percentage zinc chloride, different treatment is often necessary. This is discussed in following paragraphs.

Some shops dump the still hot soldered assemblies directly into boiling water. Other shops employ a hot water pressure hose or steam and still others use manually-powered scrub brushes and hot water.

When water temperature or parts volume makes manual scrubbing impractical, soldered parts may be moved mechanically or the hot water may be agitated by a pump or a stream of compressed air or even by an ultrasonic transducer. Agitation does not necessarily insure a cleaner end product but it does speed up the cleaning process.

Cleaning is generally not completed in a single tank. Instead, a series of tanks are used and the parts are moved from one to the other.

As all solders are susceptible to corrosion to some degree, soldered assemblies are usually not left for indefinite periods in tanks of hot water to secure perfect or near-perfect flux removal. Overly long water immersion discolors solder fillets.

Do Not Wash Soft-Soldered Joints in Water

Water should not be used for removing flux residue from a soft-soldered aluminum joint. Ordinary tap water is in itself an effective electrolyte. When mixed with flux residue, corrosion at the aluminum-solder interface is accelerated and the joint may quickly fail. The mechanism of this type of corrosion is discussed in Chapter 12. The need to wash the joint can sometimes be avoided by using chloride-free organic flux.

When cleaning speed and efficient flux removal are important, chemical treatments are incorporated into the cleaning schedule. Generally, the first wash consists of an alkaline solution. This may be followed by a clear water rinse, a mild acid water neutralizing bath, and another clear water rinse. Then the parts are dried.

Chloride-Containing Flux Residue Removal Formulas

The following cleaning solutions may be used in place of boiling or hot water, or they may be used following a hot water wash. The latter system requires more equipment and more handling but the working life of the chemical cleaning solution is greatly extended and chemical costs are reduced.

Steps:

1. A one minute soak in a 2% by weight solution of inhibited sodium hydroxide at room temperature
2. Rinse in cold water
3. A one minute soak in a 5% by weight phosphoric acid neutralizing solution at room temperature
4. Rinse in cold water
5. Dry.

----

1. Soak in a 2% sulfuric acid solution at 140 degrees F.
2. Dip in a 1% nitric acid solution at 140 degrees F.
3. Rinse in hot water
4. Rinse in cold water
5. Dry.

Flux residues containing high percentages of zinc chloride are particularly difficult to remove with water alone. The highly hygroscopic zinc chloride absorbs water and forms a white crust of zinc oxychloride, which is insoluble in water alone and acts to isolate the balance of the flux residue it covers.

The following formulas and cleaning procedure are effective with zinc chloride flux residues.

Steps:

1. Soak in a solution made of 2% concentrated hydrochloric acid per gallon of hot water.
2. Soak in a solution of crystals of washing soda (sodium carbonate) and hot water.
3. Rinse thoroughly in hot water.
4. Dry.

To prevent water staining after washing, parts may be given their final wash in hot water, which speeds drying, or they may be dried in a stream of hot air. Parts to be dried should not touch one another as water stains are

primarily caused by moisture trapped between pieces of aluminum.

Figure 4-1. *Workmen should be protectively clothed and provided with a face mask and gloves when working at the cleaning baths.*

Testing For Flux Traces

The silver nitrate test is the one most used for determining the presence of flux on the work piece after it has been washed and dried. A test solution is prepared by mixing 5 grams of silver nitrate with 100 grams of triple-distilled water to which a few drops of 20 to 50% nitric acid have been added. A few drops of distilled water are placed on the soldered assembly on an area likely to retain flux. After a few minutes an eye dropper is used to transfer the test water to a sample of the test solution. If the solution clouds, chloride flux is present.

The silver nitrate test is extremely sensitive. Under controlled laboratory conditions, flux in quantities as small as 1 ppm can be detected. Under ordinary shop conditions, airborne contamination, chlorides in the wash water and similar impurities will mask the results, possibly producing turbidity without the presence of chloride flux. This test therefore requires judgment on the part of the user. The basis for judging the degree of precipitation can be established by the use of laboratory prepared samples and color charts.

SILVER NITRATE IS EXTREMELY DANGEROUS TO THE EYES; IT WILL CAUSE PERMANENT BLINDNESS UPON CONTACT.

The spectrophotometer is also used to measure flux residue. It can detect flux quantities as small as 1 ppm.

The silver nitrate test is essentially a test for the presence of chloride and cannot be used with non-chloride containing organic fluxes. The spectrophotometer is tuned to the wavelength of the element it is to detect and can ostensibly be used to detect the elements comprising organic flux residues.

When the utmost in cleanliness is desired, fabricators subject soldered assemblies to 90% relative humidity at temperatures of 100°F. or more for 24 hours. This leaches the last few atoms of flux out of hiding and exposes areas that may require additional cleaning.

When it is impossible or impractical to remove all flux, the joint may be dried and sealed. This technique is frequently used when stranded cable ends are soldered. The soldered joint will remain corrosion free for as long as moisture is excluded.

Finishing

Aluminum solder fillets are similar to aluminum brazing fillets in that both naturally form smooth meniscus arcs between faying surfaces and both have naturally smooth, attractive surfaces when correctly formed. Except for flux removal, a soldered aluminum joint usually needs no further treatment.

However, if the need or desire arises, the exposed solder may be ground, filed, polished, painted or electroplated exactly like any other piece of metal. Aluminum solders cannot be anodized. Anodizing solutions attack the solder, darkening it and weakening the joint. In turn the solder tends to contaminate the anodizing solution. If a soldered assembly is to be anodized and colored, the solder joint is sealed off with paint or other coating.

Other chemical finishing treatments may be used with soldered aluminum assemblies when the chemicals used do not combine unfavorably with the solder. Nitric acid solution, for example, frequently used in diluted form to brighten bare aluminum, cannot be used with zinc-base solders. The nitric acid dissolves the solder, turning it dark and forming pits. Other solders are not attacked by this acid.

Soldered aluminum assemblies cannot be porcelainized. Vitreous enamels have fusing temperatures higher than those of aluminum solders.

Jig and Joint Design

Casual Soldering

The home mechanic or field repairman need not overly concern himself with scrupulous cleanliness and accurate joint clearance. Utmost cleanliness and exact joint gaps are important when maximum strength and joint quality are desired, and/or soldering is to be accomplished by automatic or semi-automatic means. Strong, useful aluminum solder joints can be made with little cleaning and no thought about clearances and joint widths.

Alloy 1100 and other easy to solder alloys are sometimes soldered as they come from the mill without cleaning and with ostensibly no joint clearance. A little flux is placed on one surface. The second piece of sheet metal is placed directly on top: The joining surfaces may be an inch or more in width. The solder is placed next to the joint edge, or fed during heating. When the parts are hot enough and the solder is molten, it will be drawn between the faying surfaces and form a reasonably strong joint. The flux layer holds the upper piece of aluminum just high enough to start capillary flow. There need be no fuss, measuring or testing. However, when maximum quality joints are the design goal, they must be carefully designed and executed.

Basic Solder-Joint Parameters

The decision to solder should come early in the planning of an aluminum assembly and should not follow the completed design as an afterthought. The nature and requirements of soldering must be fully realized and incorporated into the aluminum creation as it grows or the final results may be costly and unsatisfactory.

The first consideration is the exposure to which the solder joint and assembly will be subjected. The possibility of corrosive attack is a pivotal factor as the need for corrosion resistance will almost dictate the choice of solder which in turn will strongly influence the choice of flux, joint clearance and soldering temperature.

The second consideration is the required strength of the assembly and its individual solder joints. These needs will dictate solder choice, individual joint design, base alloy used, soldering method and temperature.

The third general consideration is assembly tolerance. If dimensional requirements are very tight, additional metal may be needed so that the assembly may be machined to accurate size after it has been soldered. In certain designs it may be advantageous to use a moderate temperature solder, thus eliminating any possibility of heat-induced distortion.

Solder Joint Requirements

Basic solder joint requirements are similar to brazing joint needs. If the following conditions are met, satisfactory soldered joints between aluminum and aluminum or aluminum and other metals will be formed.

1. The faying surfaces and a distance beyond are free of soil and grease. There are no foreign adhesions, bumps, burrs, dimples and grooves to interfere with the free flow of solder.

2. The oxide on the surface of the aluminum to be wetted and soldered is workably thin.

3. The distance between the mating surfaces is correct for the flux, solder, joint width, base metal, time and temperature.

4. The joint is correctly designed: Flux and solder can easily enter. Gas, dross, flux and solder can easily leave.

5. The aluminum surfaces to be wetted by the solder are covered with suitable flux; parts to be abrasion soldered, and tinned or clad parts excepted.

6. Tinned or solder-clad faying surfaces contact one another when soldering heat is applied.

7. Suitable solder is positioned in or near non-tinned aluminum solder joints, or the solder is fed to the joint during soldering.

8. If a reaction flux is to supply the solder, the correct type and quantity is positioned in the joint before soldering heat is applied.

9. The joint to be formed is brought to temperature and held there long enough for the solder to flow, wet the faying surfaces, fill the joint and drive the flux out.

Source: Aluminum Soldering Handbook, 3rd Ed., Aluminum Assn., Inc.

10. The parts are not moved during soldering nor while the solder hardens.

Joint Clearance

Solder joint clearance (the distance separating the two aluminum surfaces to be joined), the shape of these faying surfaces and their relationship to one another are critical.

Joint clearance determines capillary force, and it is this force that draws molden solder into the gap between the two pieces of metal and into every other contiguous gap and crevice.

Molten solder is not quite as liquid nor will it flow quite as readily as molten brazing filler metal. Molten solder will respond to capillary force and travel up a vertical joint and across an overhead joint; but conditions must be just right for this to happen. Whenever possible, joints to be filled are kept horizontal and the molten solder is not asked to travel against gravity.

Solder flow is dependent upon solder composition, temperature, base alloy composition, the presence of flux, flux composition and the condition of the base metal's surface. Solder flows best on slightly etched or slightly roughened surfaces: the tiny surface cracks act as capillaries and draw the molten metal along.

In general, narrow joint clearances promote capillary solder flow but are more prone to oxide slag or dross closure and alloying closure. This occurs when solder alloys with the base metal and the solder's composition changes. If as a result the solder's melting point goes up, the solder may harden sufficiently to block further flow through the joint. It is for these reasons that short joints are preferred to long joints and solder should be placed as close to its final position as possible.

Increasing joint gap clearance reduces capillary action along with the tendency of the joint to be blocked by oxide slag and alloying solder. However, there comes a point where capillary action is reduced to zero and the solder may divide into two streams, each stream coating one of the faying surfaces but leaving a void between. Figure 5-1 illustrates this point.

Increasing joint gap clearance also increases the strain placed on the solder when the joint is loaded. For maximum strength, minimum dependable joint clearance is desirable.

In practice the designer specifies a joint gap dimension based on experience. The engineer in charge of production modifies this figure by empirical means until an optimum distance is found. This dimension is used throughout the soldering run as it will remain valid so long as all the other soldering parameters—time/temperature, flux, solder and base alloy—aren't changed.

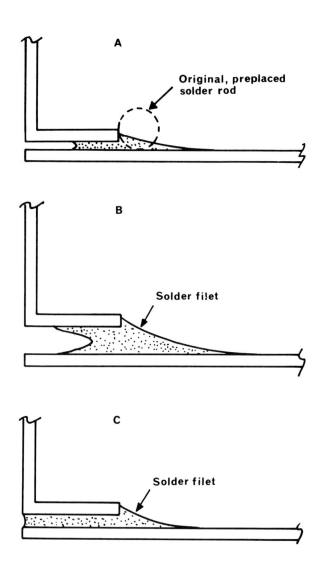

Figure 5-1. *A. The effect of an overly-narrow solder joint gap. B. An overly large gap. C. The results of proper joint clearance.*

Joint clearance is almost, but not quite a fixed dimension. Once it has been found it should not be changed to correct for errors in manufactured parts to be joined. The solder joint can be used for dimensional changes only if the change is parallel to and not across the joint. Figure 5-2 illustrates this point.

Suggested Joint Clearances

Faying surfaces of joints under ¼ inch in width and made with an organic flux and low temperature solders are usually spaced from 0.005 to 0.015 inch apart. When the same joints are formed with the aid of a reaction flux and high temperature solders, clearance is usually decreased to 0.002 to 0.010 inch. When the width of the joint is more than ¼ inch, clearances of up to 0.025 inch are often used.

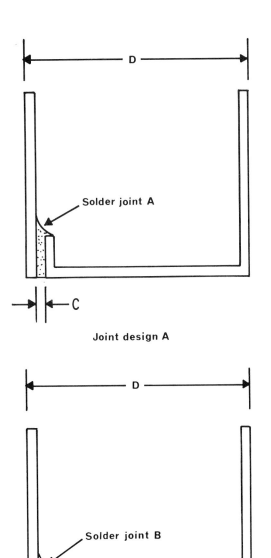

Joint design A

Joint design B

Figure 5-2. *Varying clearance C of joint A to alter D will result in poor joint quality. Joint design B allows dimension D to be altered without penalty. Joint lap width is not critical. Pool of solder formed at joint side acts as bank to keep joint itself filled with solder.*

When tubes are soldered within other tubes, overall diametral clearances of approximately 0.020 inch are used. Figure 5-3 illustrates a well designed socketed tube-to-tube joint incorporating an integral flange which is used to hold the flux and prepositioned solder ring.

The above joint clearances are by no means limiting. They are guides only and may be varied to suit individual soldering conditions.

Tee joints and line contact joints are generally not spaced though they are usually fluxed along the contacting edges. The molten solder is generally permitted to find its own way between the faying surfaces and to form the fillet on the further side.

Joints Must Be Vented

Solder joints as well as vessels to be soldered must be vented. If the white aluminum chloride and fluoride fumes generated by soldering heat are not released, sufficient pressure may develop to distort or burst a closed vessel and drive the molten solder out of the joint. Figures 5-4 and 5-5 show how different joints may be vented.

Joint Types

Joint designs frequently used for sheet aluminum are illustrated in Figure 5-6. Wide joint treatment use to prevent flux entrapment is shown in Figure 5-7.

Calculating Overlap

Joints should be overlapped sufficiently to provide the desired strength and possibly stiffness, but little more. There is nothing to be gained by indiscriminate overlapping except trouble.

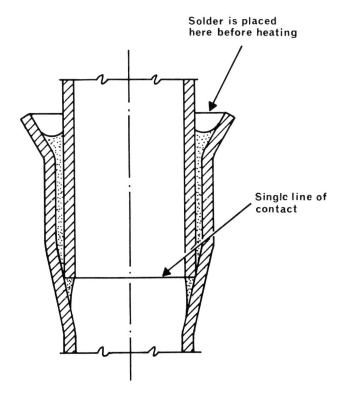

Figure 5-3. *Excellent socket joint design. Note flange which holds solder preform and the single line of contact between inner member and inner wall. The molten solder flows easily beneath the contact line to form a fillet on the other (lower) side.*

Source: Aluminum Soldering Handbook, 3rd Ed., Aluminum Assn., Inc.

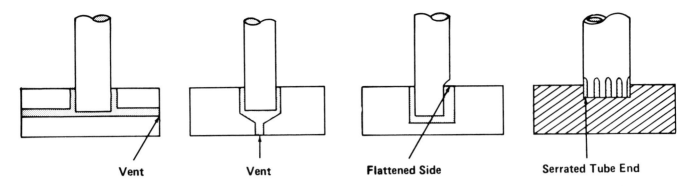

Figure 5-4. *Holes may be drilled into the solid member from one or more sides to vent the joint.*

Figure 5-5. *The shape of the internal member may be altered by flattening or serration to vent the joint.*

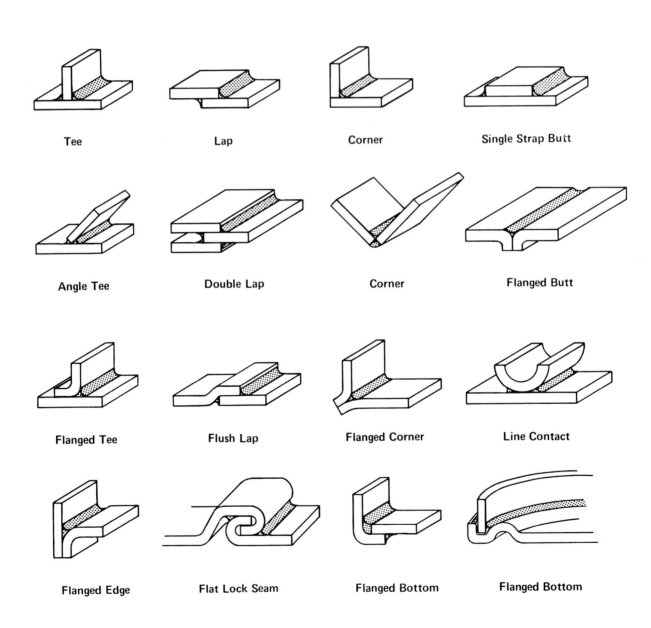

Figure 5-6. *Solder joint designs frequently used with aluminum.*

The rule of thumb for overlapping is that the overlap be two or three times the thickness of the thinner member of the joint. When greater strength is wanted, or when an exact calculation of joint strength is needed, the formula given in Figure 5-8 may be used.

A formula is also provided for use in calculating the strength of a joint between a thin-wall tube and a fairly thick, solid member. Conversely, the formula may be used to find the required lap length in inches to produce specific joint strength.

Solder joints as strong or stronger than their parent metals can be formed with the high temperature solders and some of the intermediate solders. Solder joints with 100% efficiency usually cannot be made with the soft solders, the required overlap is too great to be practical.

Locked Joints

To form locked joints, the mating edges of light gauge aluminum are turned under and folded back upon themselves to secure additional stiffness and strength. Typical examples of folded or locked aluminum joints are illustrated in Figure 5-9. Solder is frequently used to seal these joints and lock the mated edges together permanently.

No matter how carefully joints of this type are formed or how much pressure is used to close the folds, some flux will enter the joint when heat is applied. To eliminate the possibility of eventual flux corrosion, folded joints should be (1) sealed with non-chloride, organic flux and suitable temperature solder, (2) soldered without flux by abrasive techniques, or (3) the joints should be formed from pre-tinned or solder-clad aluminum.

Soft and intermediate solders are more than sufficiently strong for holding folded joints. The joint folds themselves provide the strength. The solder merely locks the parts in place and seals the cracks.

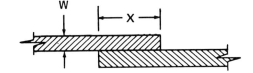

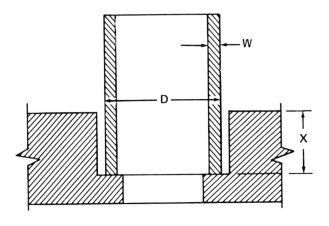

$$X = \frac{W (D-W) YT}{LD} \qquad X = \frac{YTW}{L}$$

X   Length of lap in inches

W   Thickness of the thinnest part in inches

D   Diameter of the area of shear in inches

Y   Safety factor—this is usually 4 or 5

L   Shear strength of the solder alloy in lbs/sq/inch

T   Tensile strength of thinner or weaker part in lbs/sq. inch

Figure 5-8. *Calculating needed overlap by formula.*

If accessible, folded joints may be abrasively soldered with excellent results. The base metal is cleaned prior to assembly. The metal leading into the crack and joint may be cleaned again with either a steel wire brush or a scraper shaped to fit the crack. The same tool or a glass fiber brush is then used to work the pool of molten solder along until the base metal is wet and the joint is formed. Chapter 7 discusses abrasive soldering.

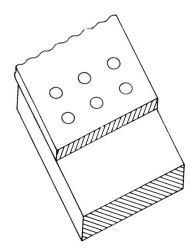

Figure 5-7. *Weep holes in one joint member are used to vent flux, gas and filler metal when making wide-lap joints.*

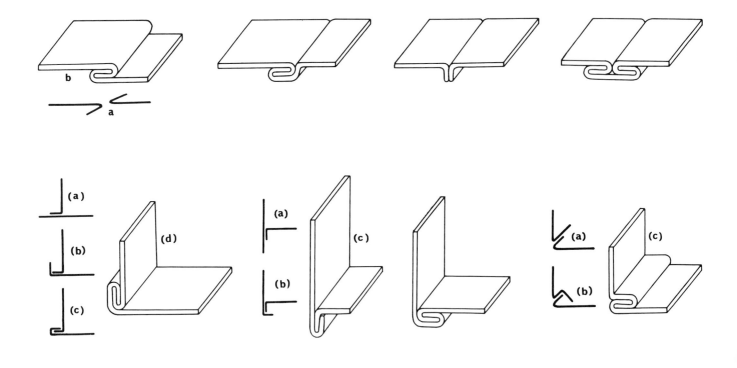

Figure 5-9. *A number of lock seam designs used in joining and soldering sheets of aluminum.*

Designing Corrosion Resistance Into a Joint

Assuming the extent and nature of the corrosive attack is fixed, two factors determine the service life of a soldered aluminum joint—its chemistry and design. Neither may be slighted without penalty.

Corrosion is generally the result of a potential difference between solder and base metal produced in the presence of moisture. The designer must therefore select the solder which generates the lowest voltage in relation to the aluminum alloy used. The joint itself is planned after the solder has been selected and should be designed to aid that particular solder.

Of all the solders commonly used with aluminum, the zinc-rich solders stand up best under the corrosive attack normally produced by moisture and sea air. The reaction of various solders to exposure is detailed in Table 12-3. The tremendous differences in service lives should be noted.

Zinc-rich solders are anodic to aluminum and in the presence of an electrolyte they corrode at a rate many times higher than that of the base metal.

When other than zinc-base solders are used the alum-inum becomes anodic to the solder in the presence of an electrolyte and corrodes most strongly.

As the corrosion products of solder are larger than the metal itself, corrosion tends to develop a separating pressure between the solder walls. Given sufficient time and the proper conditions, this pressure can force the joint apart. Corrosion product pressure is a problem only with the zinc-rich solders. Angling the walls of the joint, or angling the walls entering the joint and filling those areas with a fillet of solder (that in effect will be sacrificial) helps relieve corrosion-product pressure build-up.

An important facet of good anti-corrosion design is drainage. Good drainage can be provided in many instances by mere forethought. For example, if two lengths of pipe are to be soldered, one within the other and later exposed to the weather, the larger, outside pipe should be in the upper position. If the outer section is fairly thick, its exposed edge should be slightly rounded and smooth so as not to encourage condensation. See Figure 5-11.

Joints can also be protected physically from corrosion by painting with any suitable non-metallic paint or a paint that is compatible with the solder and aluminum used.

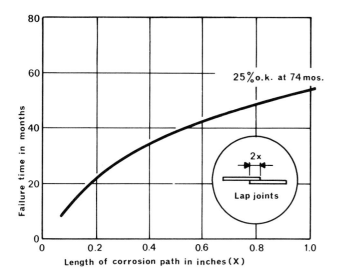

Figure 5-10. *Increasing the length of the corrosion path (lap width) increases the life of a soft-soldered joint.*

Corrosion Consideration When Soldering to Other Metals

When other metals are to be soldered to aluminum and both subjected to moisture, the value and polarity of the electrical potential produced by the other metals in relation to aluminum and the solder used must be carefully considered. The voltage produced by a number of metals in a standard solution are shown in Table 12-1. The most negative metal in any couple is always the anode and is most vigorously corroded. The larger the voltage difference, the higher the rate of corrosion.

In some instances it is possible to reduce the effect of high galvanic voltage difference by proper placement of the metals involved. When joining a copper tube to an aluminum tube it is best to place the copper tube on the inside. The voltage difference remains the same, but a considerable portion of the aluminum must be destroyed before the line is pierced. Placed in reverse relationship, less aluminum need be corroded before the line is fractured. This is illustrated in Figure 5-12.

Vibratory-Load Joint Design

While molten solder responds to capillary force to form fillets with cross sections ideally suited to non-constant loads, only zinc and zinc-rich solders are suitable for vibrating loads close to their maximum tensile ratings. Other solders may be used for such loads, but they are usually derated several times over. The soft solders are almost useless for direct vibratory application.

Designers seeking to produce joints with maximum resistance to vibration and changing loads need but follow standard practice for joints of this type.

Joints should be as smooth as possible with no undercutting, cracks, porosity, flux inclusion, foreign matter and open spaces that might localize stress and provide the starting point for failure. Sudden changes in section should be avoided. Transitions from thin to thick members should be as gradual as possible. Joints loaded eccentrically should be supported by stiffeners to reduce secondary bending. Openings, fittings, baffles, brackets and other attachments should not be placed near highly stressed areas of the assembly.

Increasing a solder fillet's cross section generally increases the joint's resistance to bending moments of force and vibration. However, there is an optimum fillet size beyond which strength may actually be lost and there is a maximum practical fillet size for a given joint configuration. Feeding additional solder into the joint will not increase fillet size beyond its natural limits. The fillet's base will increase, but its height will not.

Pressure Tight Vessels

Assemblies designed to withstand pressure from either within or without are best made with lap joints. The lap joint is the strongest joint and it provides the longest path, thus reducing the possibility of leakage through the joint. See Figure 5-13. All vessels must be vented while soldering.

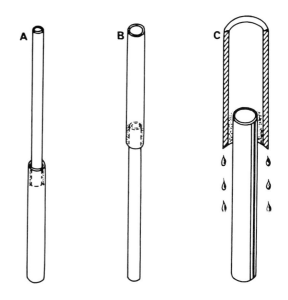

Figure 5-11. *Water tends to collect at A. Less water will collect at B. When the upper pipe is thick-walled, its end should be made concave to draw water from the joint, C.*

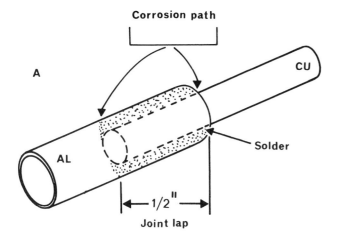

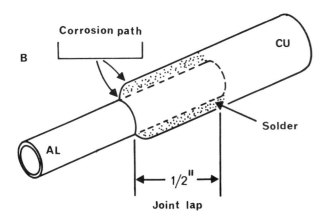

Figure 5-12. *In the upper configuration, with the copper on the inside, the corrosion path is longer than the length of the joint lap. In the lower configuration, with the copper on the outside, the corrosion path is shorter than the thickness of the solder. The upper is preferable.*

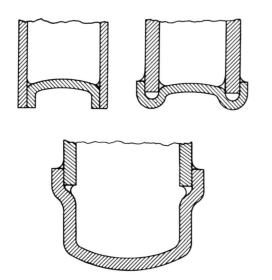

Figure 5-13. *Typical solder joint designs found suitable for pressure-tight containers.*

Solder Shape and Quantity

Solder may be cut and formed into any desired shape with no thought to the stresses that may be set up within the metal. All forming stresses are relieved immediately upon the solder melting. The only precaution is the careful avoidance of dirt and metal particle embedment during forming.

The quantity of solder supplied to a joint is important to economy, strength and appearance. The first is obvious, there is no point to wasting solder. For maximum strength, it is necessary that the joint be completely filled, therefore it is always better to supply a little more solder than needed to accommodate joint gap variations.

Too much solder, however, can cause difficulties. The excess may roll off to interfere with the workings of the soldered device or to mar a finished surface.

A slightly excessive quantity of solder is always desirable when flux entrapment is a possibility. The passage of a little extra solder through the joint aids in driving flux out. Additional time at heat sometimes helps, too.

Solder Placement

Solder can be brought to a joint in any of five ways. (1) Solder may be hand fed to the joint during soldering. (2) Solder may be preplaced before heat is applied. (3) Solder may be supplied by reaction flux positioned in and near the joint. (4) Solder may come from cladding on one or both of the faying surfaces. (5) Solder may be brought to the joint by tinning one or both of the faying surfaces prior to soldering.

So far as the completed joint is concerned, it makes little difference how the solder is brought to the joint as long as it is in sufficient quantity, clean and in or near the joint at the correct time.

When the solder is in the form of cladding or tinning, the parts must contact one another. The thickness of the cladding or tinning and their surfaces become important. There has to be enough solder present to form the joint, and the surfaces must be reasonably smooth. Bumps and protrusions can keep the faying surfaces sufficiently apart to prevent a joint from forming or keep the solder from completely filling the joint. Flux and additional solder may be added to help form the joint.

Pre-positioning Solder

Heat source, solder travel distance and solder-mass to base-metal-mass relationship should be analyzed when solder is prepositioned.

The solder should not be placed between the source of heat and the main body of the assembly. If the solder melts before the base metal is hot and the flux begins its action, the solder may ball up and roll away or wet an area outside the joint.

The solder should be pre-positioned as close to the joint as practical. This will result in a minimum time at heat and a minimum degree of alloying between solder and base metal. If the solder travel path is too long, the solder may spread out and fail to fill the joint.

If the pre-placed piece of solder is small compared to the total assembly, the solder may come to heat first and roll off. When the solder quantity is comparatively small it is good practice to bury the solder within the assembly if possible. See Figure 5-14.

Dimensional Changes at Soldering Temperatures

Aluminum's coefficient of thermal expansion is considerably greater than that of the metals to which it is commonly soldered and that of the metals with which aluminum is commonly jigged. Average coefficient values for many of these metals are given in Table 5-1. It should be noted that these values do not hold true over the entire temperature range encountered in soldering aluminum, i.e., 230 to 820°F. For exact dimensional change computation, coefficients for the specific temperature range and metal involved must be employed.

Dimensional changes accompanying low soldering temperatures are generally ignored. Changes accompanying middle range soldering temperatures may also be ignored when less than perfect joints are satisfactory. Dimensional changes produced by the higher soldering temperatures should not be ignored.

Provisions must be made for thermal expansions that may "lock" one piece of metal within another. If a comparatively light length of pipe is to be soldered within a massive section of plate, little expansion of the plate may be expected when torch soldering. Under such conditions the hot, expanded pipe will force the solder out of the joint. Upon cooling, a large void will develop between pipe wall and plate. The hole in the plate may be made larger to accommodate the inner member's expansion. Or, the heavy plate may be preheated so that the hole expands (and later contracts) with the pipe.

If both the inner and outer piece of aluminum have approximately the same mass and are subjected to the same heat, both pieces will expand and contract together. Such joints can generally be formed without difficulty.

When two dissimilar metals are to be soldered, one within the other, it is best to place the metal with the highest coefficient of expansion on the outside.

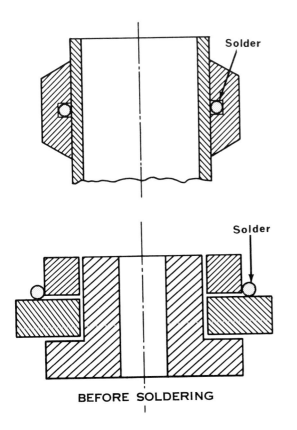

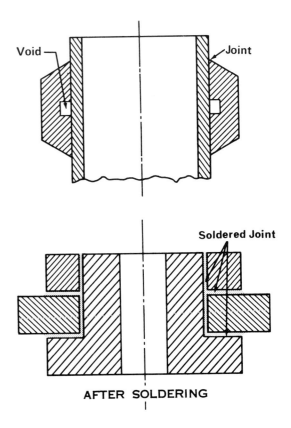

BEFORE SOLDERING

AFTER SOLDERING

Figure 5-14. *Soldered joints after an internally and externally positioned ring of solder has been used.*

Source: Aluminum Soldering Handbook, 3rd Ed., Aluminum Assn., Inc.

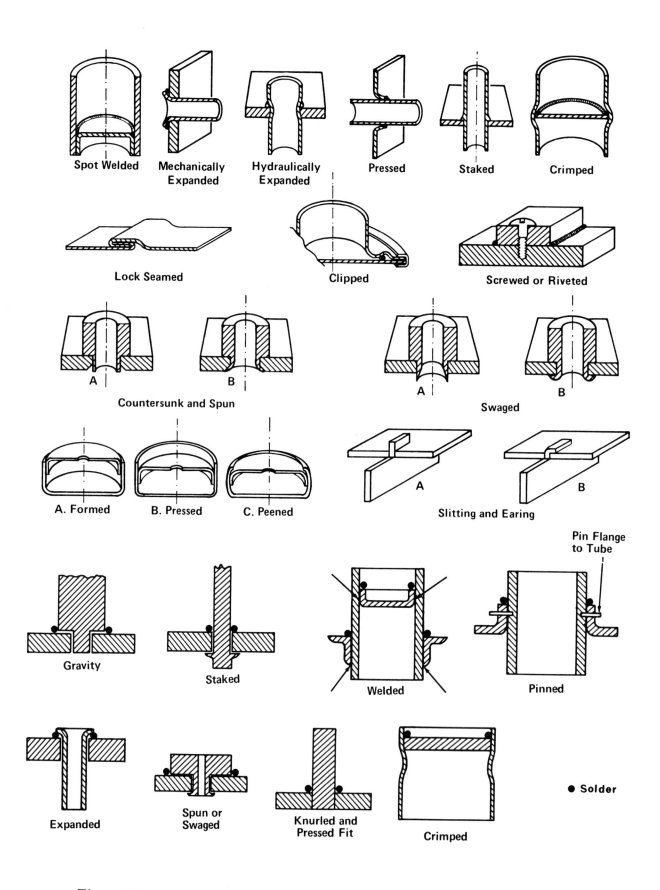

Figure 5-15. *Twenty-one suggestions for making assemblies to be soldered self jigging.*

Design for Self Jigging

The cost and effort of designing and constructing parts for assemblies that hold themselves in alignment during soldering is often more than repaid by higher production rates and lower overall soldering costs. A number of suggestions for making assemblies self jigging are provided in Figure 5-15.

Jig Design

As aluminum under heat expands more than the metals commonly used for jigs and fixtures, the designer has the choice of making his jigs from aluminum (which is rarely done) or incorporating some form of expansion relief in jigs and fixtures made from other metals.

Whatever arrangement of springs, weights or levers is devised, aluminum parts must be free to expand and contract. If this is not done, the parts may be thrown out of alignment, strained or deformed during soldering. Figure 5-16 illustrates a number of different jig and fixture designs incorporating springs.

For several dozen furnace runs, low carbon steel without surface treatment is usually satisfactory as jig and fixture material. Longer life will be secured if flux residue is removed each time the jigs and fixtures are used.

When long furnace-soldering runs are anticipated it is advisable to use stainless steel or Inconel X-750. Of the two, Inconel keeps its temper better under heat and does not wet easily.

Heat losses introduced by jigs and fixtures can be minimized by keeping the jigs and fixtures as small and as light as possible. Heat loss from the assembly into the fixture can be reduced by utilizing point and line contacts.

Establishing and Holding Joint Clearance

Joint clearance can be established and maintained by a number of methods. An off-set may be bent in one of the joint members. The parts may be placed on a stepped base or temporary platform. Solder in foil thickness is sometimes used. Dimples or protrusions may be formed in one of the mating surfaces, and flux alone may be used as previously suggested.

A stepped base can be made by machining the desired step in suitable metal. Two sheets of transite may be used to insulate the metal during soldering.

A temporary soldering platform can be made from oxidized stainless steel. The sheet of stainless is heated to 800 or 900°F. or until it shows a color change. Its surface is then heavily oxidized and almost impossible to wet with solder. It can therefore be used as a spacer or support when soldering without danger of adhesion.

When maximum joint gap accuracy is desired, care must be used to prevent flotation. Molten solder responds to surface tension by forming a ball. In doing so it tends to

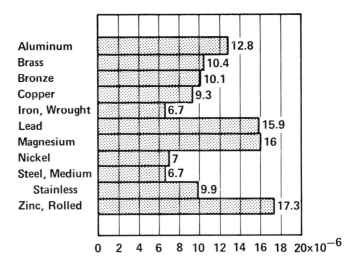

Table 5-1. *Approximate coefficients of thermal expansion for common metals over the range of 100°F. to 1000°F., in 10^{-6} inch per degree F. per inch length.*

Aluminum	12.8
Brass	10.4
Bronze	10.1
Copper	9.3
Iron, Wrought	6.7
Lead	15.9
Magnesium	16
Nickel	7
Steel, Medium	6.7
Stainless	9.9
Zinc, Rolled	17.3

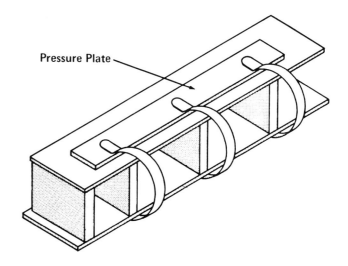

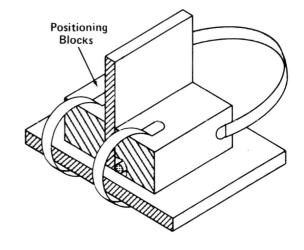

Figure 5-16. *How C-clamp springs may be used to hold parts lightly but dependably during soldering.*

Source: Aluminum Soldering Handbook, 3rd Ed., Aluminum Assn., Inc.

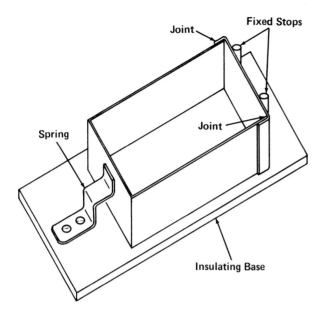

Figure 5-17. *Simple, spring-loaded fixture serves as an assembling and aligning aid.*

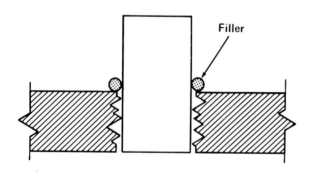

Figure 5-18. *How prick punch indentations and similar protrusions may be used to center and hold part in place.*

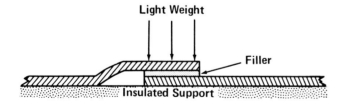

Figure 5-19. *Example of how an offset may be used to establish and hold joint clearance between parts while they are being soldered.*

float whatever aluminum may be resting on it. If the aluminum is heavy or held down by a weight or spring no flotation will take place. If not, the joint gap on cooling may be found larger than sought and only partially filled with solder.

Applying Flux

When solder is placed directly between the walls of the joint it is to form, only the faying surfaces need be fluxed. When solder is placed outside the joint, the solder's desired flow path must also be fluxed. Without flux (or rubbing) to encourage wetting, molten solder forms a ball that will roll down a slight incline much like mercury.

Flux may be applied by any convenient means including brushes, sticks, spray guns and eye droppers. However, a plastic or animal fiber bristle brush should never be used when the parts are hot. Heat will melt the brush into "gunk" that will interfere with soldering. An over-size eye dropper is best. With it, flux quantity can be controlled, the glass tube is not affected by the flux and its comparatively small opening limits air contact.

The part also may be dipped into flux. The use of a heated rod of solder to carry the flux to the joint is not advised. There is the strong possibility of overheating small portions of the flux. Overheated flux—both organic and chloride types—affects soldering adversely.

The chloride-containing, hygroscopic fluxes should be applied to the cleaned metal immediately before soldering. When not possible, time between fluxing and soldering should be kept to a minimum; never over 45 minutes.

Flux should be kept from base metal areas that are not to be soldered as the flux will attack the aluminum so soon as it makes contact and becomes moist. Even in the absence of heat, flux will stain or discolor a finished surface in a short time.

Sufficient flux must be applied to enable it to do its job. Insufficient flux leads to skips, incomplete joints, and weak joints. On the other hand, excess flux may lead solder away from the joint. Excess flux may contact and etch a finished surface, and, of course, overfluxing is a waste and a nuisance in increased fuming and cleaning.

Powdered flux may be sprinkled into a joint, or it may be made into a paste with the addition of a suitable vehicle.

Torch, Iron and Hot-Plate Soldering

Torch and Flux

Of all the means that can be employed to bring aluminum parts to soldering heat, the torch is the one most frequently used. It is low in cost, portable, suited to production work as well as single assemblies and repairs. Its flame is hot enough to be used readily with all solders and its output can be varied to accommodate small and large assemblies.

Although any source of heat can be used for torch soldering, commercial torch soldering is generally accomplished with the same type of torch, controls and gases used for fusion welding. Conversion to aluminum merely requires a change in torch nozzles.

All commercial gas mixtures can be used to fuel the torch: oxyacetylene, oxyhydrogen, oxy-natural gas, acetylene and air, hydrogen and air, propane, methane and natural gas and air. Oxyacetylene, oxyhydrogen, and oxy-natural gas are the mixtures most often used commercially and are preferred in that order for soldering aluminum.

The oxyacetylene combination produces the highest temperature. The other gases are cooler, their flames are less concentrated and are therefore easier to use and advantageous on light-gauge material.

The torch tip orifice used for soldering is usually larger than the tip selected for gas welding. Table 6-1 relates tip orifice diameter with gas pressures recommended for various gauges of sheet aluminum.

Gas pressure should be kept low, no more than 4 psi, so that the flame can be readily adjusted by means of the controls on the torch itself.

When oxyacetylene is used, the flame can be adjusted by visual inspection. The white cone produced by this mixture should be adjusted until it extends some one or two inches from the tip of the torch. Its length should be roughly twice that of the inner cone.

The appearance of the other gases vary little with changes in oxygen/gas ratio and can only be adjusted by

means of flow meters in the gas lines. Oxygen pressure is always half that of the accompanying gas. The aim with all gas mixtures is to produce a slightly reducing flame. A reducing flame tends to protect the heated aluminum from oxygen, as the flame itself consumes oxygen at a rate greater than the quantity of oxygen delivered. A reducing flame is also a softer flame; its heat is less intense and less concentrated.

A typical bench set-up for soldering with flux and torch is illustrated in Figure 6-2. The parts have been cleaned and deoxidized. A band of flux about ½ inch wide has been applied to the horizontal piece of metal. The vertical piece may simply be placed on the flux, which will provide the desired joint clearance. For a fillet of maximum height, the lower edges of the vertical piece are coated with flux.

If free-flowing solder is used, only one length of solder rod need be preplaced along one side of the joint: It will flow beneath the foot of the Tee and form a fillet on both sides of the joint when heat is applied. If the solder used does not flow freely the solder is preplaced on both sides of the joint.

Metal Thickness in.	Oxyhydrogen			Oxyacetylene		
	Orifice dia. in.	Oxygen Pressure psi	Hydrogen Pressure psi	Orifice dia. in.	Oxygen Pressure psi	Acetylene Pressure psi
0.020	0.035	0.5	1	0.025	0.5	1
0.025	0.045	0.5	1	0.025	0.5	1
0.032	0.055	0.5	1	0.035	0.5	1
0.040	0.065	1	2	0.035	0.5	1
0.051	0.075	1	2	0.045	1	2
0.064	0.085	1	2	0.055	1	2
0.081	0.095	1.5	3	0.065	1.5	3
0.102	0.105	1.5	3	0.075	1.5	3
⅛	0.115	1.5	3	0.085	2	4

Table 6-1. *Tip orifice diameter and approximate gas pressure used for torch soldering.*

Source: Aluminum Soldering Handbook, 3rd Ed., Aluminum Assn., Inc.

Figure 6-1. *Torch soldering is simple and rapid.*

it produces tend to travel upwards. This tendency is corrected when heating vertical parts by directing the flame somewhat downward.

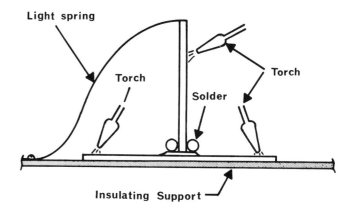

Figure 6-2. *Typical set-up for soldering a tee joint. The torch is shown in the three positions it will be held to promote even heating.*

To bring all parts of a joint evenly to soldering heat, the flame is constantly shifted from one part of the joint to the other. In the example shown in Figure 6-2, the flame is played alternately to the right and left side of the joint and occasionally on the vertical member.

Joint temperature is controlled by the position, angle and movement of the flame. Joint temperature is estimated from the appearance of flux and solder. It can be done this way: When using an organic flux, the first indication of rising joint temperature will be a bubbling of the flux followed by boil off of the flux vehicle. If it is not water the vehicle may burst into flame.

If solder and flux have been properly matched, the next indication of higher temperature will be the melting of the solder. At this point the torch may be backed off a bit to prevent overheating from temperature "overshoot."

When the solder begins to flow into the joint, the torch may be brought a bit closer and directed onto the remaining solder and joint—never onto the flux. The flame may then be played increasingly over the joint itself to speed soldering. This is continued until the solder has filled the joint or joints as evinced by the appearance of bright solder at the further edges. Heat is continued for a moment more to help clear the joint of flux. The torch is then removed and the joint is permitted to cool.

If a flame is directed onto organic flux, or if the melting point of the solder is too far above the working temperature of the flux, the flux will turn brown and char. No harm will occur if the flux is overheated after the joint has been filled with solder. If charring occurs before solder flow is complete, a poor joint will result.

If a reaction flux is used, vehicle boil-off will be followed by rapid gassing or fuming at soldering temperature. At

A joint prepared for soldering comprises three elements: parent metal, flux and solder. The three elements vary considerably in mass and specific heat. In addition, the two or more pieces of aluminum to be joined are separated from one another by flux and possibly an air gap.

For reasons discussed previously, base metal, solder and flux should be brought to soldering temperature, i.e., the liquidus of the solder, more or less simultaneously. Failing that, it is preferable to bring the aluminum, flux and then solder to soldering heat in that order.

A torch is selected suitable in size for the mass of the work pieces to be heated. If there is any doubt, it is safer to start with an undersized torch. For the same reason—avoidance of overheating—it is easier to work with propane and air than a hotter gas mixture.

As the temperature of the torch flame is many hundred degrees higher than that required for soldering, the flame is never played directly on the flux or the solder. Instead, the flame is directed onto the base metal a distance from the joint and at an angle leading away from the joint. This is done to prevent the moving stream of hot gas from carrying over onto the solder or flux. The flame and the hot air

428

this point the solder should begin to flow into the joint. Again the torch is withdrawn a bit to prevent overheating. As the solder flows, the flame is brought closer, but kept behind the solder to encourage its flow and on the joint itself to keep the joint hot. The heat is held on the joint for a moment after it is filled with solder.

If the solder does not melt immediately after the flux reacts, either the flame has been incorrectly positioned or the flux and solder temperature do not match. If the solder melts before the flux reacts, no joint or a poor joint will be formed. The flux must prepare a path for the solder.

If the flame is permitted to rest on the flux there is the possibility that water produced in the flame will combine with the salts in the flux to produce oxychlorides, which act as stop-offs and prevent solder flow. The oxychlorides also are difficult to remove after soldering. The presence of oxychlorides may be noted by the refusal of the molten solder to flow and wet the base metal and the absence of gassing. The flux will not react despite continued heating and high temperature. When this happens, further heating and the adding of fresh flux is a waste of time. Stop, cool, clean the joint and start over again.

If the joint is heated unevenly and a portion of the flux reacts before the rest of the flux does, the aluminum chloride (reaction flux residue) that is formed—white, flakey powder—may be blown into the joint and produce voids.

When solder is to be fed to the joint during heating, the torch is manipulated, as with preplaced solder, to bring the joint evenly up to soldering temperature. The tip of the solder rod or wire is gently touched to the joint or joint area from time to time to ascertain the temperature of the base metal. When the solder's melting point has been reached, as indicated by a softening or melting of the solder tip, the torch is backed off a bit to prevent overheating. The solder is gently pushed down into its tip or drawn along the accessible edge of the faying surfaces. Capillary action will draw the solder into the joint. To speed soldering, the flame is now brought to bear partially on the solder pool and partially on the joint. When the joint is filled the flame is played over the entire joint to aid the solder to push the flux out.

Melting solder into the joint is not recommended except for very light work. The joint is quickly filled this way, but in most instances a very poor joint results, even if the joint is heated afterwards.

When the base metal is very light gauge, however, this may be the only way of forming a joint without melting the parent metal.

Heating the solder directly will oxidize the solder and possibly separate the solder into its composite elements. Solder oxide will interfere with wetting and solder flow. A change in solder composition will prevent the solder from accomplishing the purpose for which it was formulated. A very poor joint or no joint at all may result.

Additional solder may be face-fed to a joint having insufficient preplaced solder. This can be done during heating or after the completed joint has been examined and found wanting. The cold joint is cleaned, fluxed and heated again.

Joint and associate metal temperature can also be ascertained by use of temperature indicating crayons. These may be purchased from solder, brazing and welding supply houses. A mark is made on the work piece near the joint to be. At the crayon's indicating temperature, the mark will either change color or change texture or both. Crayons are available for all temperatures.

Massive Parts and Castings

Joints as large and as massive as can be kept at soldering temperature may be produced with a single torch. When a single torch is incapable of keeping all the solder in the joint liquid at one time, additional heat must be supplied or a less than maximum quality joint should be expected. The tendency to hold the torch immobile while waiting for a heavy assembly to come to heat must be avoided. If the flame rests too long on one area the aluminum may melt. The onset of melting is preceded by a slight show of orange when a propane flame is used and a much stronger show of orange color when an acetylene mixture is applied.

To enhance color and to increase joint visibility, safety glasses of the type used for gas welding may be worn. Shades 4 or 5 are most often used for soldering.

When the parts to be soldered are overly massive for a single torch, additional torches may be brought to bear. Or the parts may be pre-heated in an oven and the soldering accomplished immediately thereafter. or just inside the oven. Or the parts may be heated on an electric stove or by infrared lamps. It doesn't matter how the parts are heated so long as base metal temperature doesn't rise too high above the melting point of the solder and combustion products do not enter the joint.

Heat losses into the air can be reduced with insulating blankets of asbestos and wind breaks.

Automatic Torch Soldering

The requirements and techniques of automatic soldering are similar to those of manual torch soldering. The difference lies in the means and methods used for moving the torch across the work or moving the work under the torch.

Joint temperature is controlled by the position of the flame on the work piece, gas pressure and gas mixture, torch to work distance and the length of time the work is beneath the flames. Gas pressure and gas mixture are held constant by automatic equipment.

Figure 6-3 shows an automatic torch set-up used for soldering return bends on an aluminum radiator. The pre-

Source: Aluminum Soldering Handbook, 3rd Ed., Aluminum Assn., Inc.

Figure 6-3. *An automatic torch soldering. Speed has been adjusted to match joint temperature needs to flame heat.*

pared assembly, with flux and solder preforms in position, is placed lengthwise in the center of the moving rollers. Speed is such as to expose the entire radiator for just 19 seconds to the flame; all that is needed to accomplish soldering with this particular set up.

Flux and Iron

Any type of soldering iron may be used. It may be heated electrically or by a gas or coal fire. However, the weight of the "copper" and its temperature is most important. It must be large enough and hot enough to bring the joint and much of the adjoining metal up to soldering temperature in a fairly short time.

The use of an iron is therefore limited by the size of practical, existing irons and the mass of the work pieces to be soldered. While the temperature of the standard electric soldering iron is high enough for all aluminum solders, ordinary 200 to 300-watt irons are not large enough for aluminum sheet more than 0.064 inch thick

or equivalent wire sizes. Generally, soldering irons are used only with soft and intermediate solders.

To secure maximum heat transfer and to prevent undesirable alloying, the tip of the iron should be tinned with the solder that is to be used. This can be done with flux or by abrasion alone. The hot iron is placed in a vice and the solder is rubbed against its tip until the solder wets the copper (or iron cladding). This is done most easily if abrasion is begun before the iron comes to full heat. The iron-clad soldering irons last about ten times longer than the copper tipped irons. Care must be used when cleaning not to cut through the comparatively thin iron coating.

Aluminum parts to be soldered with a hot iron are degreased and deoxidized. The surfaces to be joined and a distance beyond are coated with flux and the parts are positioned in any convenient manner. A practical set-up for soldering lap joints with an iron or torch is shown in Figure 6-4. The Tee joint set-up shown in Figure 6-2 can also be used with an iron.

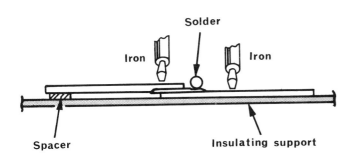

Figure 6-4. *Simple set-up for soldering a lap joint with an iron or torch. The iron (or torch) is moved from one side of the joint to the other to heat both pieces of metal.*

Figure 6-5. *Hot plate soldering.*

The parts to be lap joined have been placed on an insulating layer of Transite or similar material. A spacer of metal or insulation is used to hold the upper piece level.

Any means of providing the joint gap separation necessary to capillary flow may be used. For maximum joint quality, joint clearance may be established by methods suggested in Chapter 5. Less exact clearance may be effected by scoring or dimpling one faying surface with a sharp tool. For ordinary work, a layer of flux between the faying surfaces is all that is needed.

Solder may be preplaced or fed to a joint during heat. If the solder is preplaced, its position and the number of pieces used will depend on how well the solder flows when melted. Solder flow depends on formulation.

The soldering iron, like the torch, is not permitted to touch the solder nor the flux. The iron is placed in contact with the base metal at a distance from the joint and moved from one side to the other to heat the joint evenly.

Joint temperature is indicated by flux and solder response and/or temperature crayon. When the solder starts to melt and enter the joint the iron can be brought closer and may be placed on the remaining solder and joint after the flux has done its job.

It should be noted that only one of the above directions is an absolute. A good, strong solder joint can be formed despite a little too much heat, too much time at heat, some solder oxidation and some flux destruction. The one requirement that cannot be slighted is temperature. If the base metal isn't hot enough to melt the solder, no wetting and no bonding will take place.

Hot-plate Soldering

Any type of hot plate may be used to bring aluminum parts up to soldering temperature: thermostatically controlled electric units, non-controlled electric units and even metal plates set over gas jets. Grey cast iron plates work best.

Parts to be soldered are cleaned, fluxed and positioned. The solder may be preplaced or face fed. In the latter event the parts themselves must have sufficient weight to remain immobile while the solder is touched to them or they must be kept in position by suitable jigs.

Heat is applied. When the solder melts and flows through the joints, the heat is turned off. If the heat is not automatically controlled but is manually shut off, it is generally done a little before the joint is complete to prevent overheating.

Complex solder joints of excellent quality can be made with this method at a fair rate of speed. When the parts are self-jigging, they can be moved from the plate while the solder is still soft if care is used.

Source: Aluminum Soldering Handbook, 3rd Ed., Aluminum Assn., Inc.

Abrasion and Ultrasonic Soldering

If molten solder is placed on an equally hot piece of aluminum and the oxide on the aluminum beneath the metal puddle is detached, the molten solder will wet and bond to the bare metal. The oxide floats to the top. If this technique is repeated with a second piece of aluminum and the two tinned surfaces are placed in contact and heated, the solder layers coalesce and a joint is formed upon cooling.

When the oxide is removed from the aluminum to be soldered with a hand tool the process is called abrasion or rub soldering. When the oxide is removed by ultrasonic vibrations, the same basic process is called ultrasonic soldering.

Using this technique, it is possible to wet and tin all the aluminum alloys. Even the most stubborn alloy will wet if the abrasion is vigorous enough and prolonged for sufficient time.

The prime advantage of abrasion soldering, however, is that it is accomplished without flux. The cost and nuisance of applying flux and later removing its residue is entirely absent.

An additional advantage of this process is that deoxidizing is usually unnecessary and simple degreasing suffices to prepare most aluminum parts for soldering.

Abrasion soldering finds wide application where solder penetration control and the absence of flux residue and flux staining are important. Abrasion soldering, for example, would be useful to seal an interior joint: The exterior would remain perfectly clean and no solder would be visible.

On the minus side is the fact that abrasion soldering (as distinct from ultrasonic soldering) does not lend itself to mass production and generally requires two steps at heat for each joint—rubbing and joining.

In actual practice the first step in abrasion soldering is degreasing the parent metal. The oxide should be removed if it is overly thick. There is no rule of thumb on this matter. If the metal has been exposed for years, if it looks sandy and grey it should be deoxidized. Alternative to this, soldering may be attempted and if wetting is difficult, soldering may be stopped and the oxide removed by chemical or mechanical means. Or microhmmeter resistance tests may be made. In any case, oxide several times thicker than can be handled by flux alone can be removed by rub soldering.

Set-up for abrasion soldering is similar to that used for torch soldering with two important differences. The parts to be abraded must be "tied down" one way or another. Figure 7-1 depicts two practical methods for holding parts in position.

The second difference is that both joint surfaces must be abraded and wetted at the same time if the joint is to be made in one step. Non-abraded surfaces will not be wetted despite the possibility of capillary attraction drawing solder into a joint.

When this cannot be done, the faying surfaces are tinned individually, placed in contact with one another and heated until the solder melts and comingles. As neither the thickness nor surface of the solder on the faying surfaces can be controlled, it is not enough to simply place one tinned surface atop the other. Pressure must be provided to prevent flotation and control alignment. In most instances a simple weight and guide or a light spring is all that is necessary. This is illustrated in Figure 7-2.

Abrasion Tool

Almost any tool that is grease and dirt free—including the solder rod—may be used to abrade the surface of aluminum.

The best abrading tool is a glass fiber brush made for this purpose. Its bristles are closely packed, it is non-heat conductive, doesn't alloy with, nor contaminate the solder and if a fiber breaks off it floats to the surface of the solder.

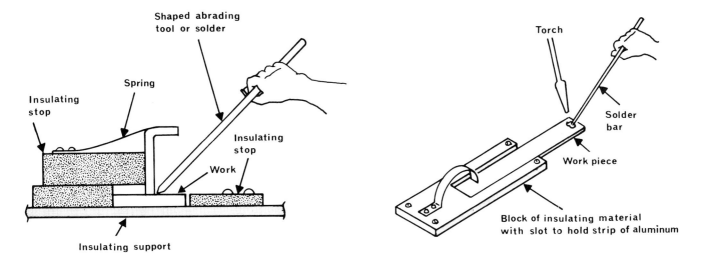

Figure 7-1. *Simple, table-top jigs for holding work pieces immobile when abrasion soldering.*

Tungsten and stainless steel welding rods are also useful as they do not alloy with the solder. If neither rods nor glass brush are available, a clean screwdriver, slim file, strip of aluminum or the tip of the hot soldering iron may be used to abrade the surface of the aluminum.

Solder

If the solder itself is not to be used as the abrasion or rubbing tool, any solder may be used. If the solder is to abrade the aluminum directly, "hard" and "intermediate" solders are best, in that order. The soft solders are useless for this purpose.

There are a number of solders specifically formulated for abrasive soldering. They differ from conventional solders in that they remain comparatively hard fairly close to their liquidus. However, any solder may be used for abrasive soldering by keeping it cool and therefore firm enough for abrasion immediately prior to soldering.

Technique

Assuming that abrasion is to be accomplished with a tool other than the solder, the parts are cleaned and positioned as discussed. A piece of solder is placed on or near the area to be tinned. The aluminum parts—not the solder—are heated with a torch, soldering iron or hot plate, and brought to the liquidus temperature of the solder. Care should be used not to exceed this temperature as the solder will oxidize and wetting will be delayed.

When the solder melts, the tip of the abrading tool is pushed down through the pool of metal and rubbed against the underlying aluminum surface. The pressure need not be great, but the entire surface to be wetted must be abraded. If the pool of solder is not large enough to cover the entire joint area at one time—and it doesn't have to be—the solder is pushed along with the abrading tool.

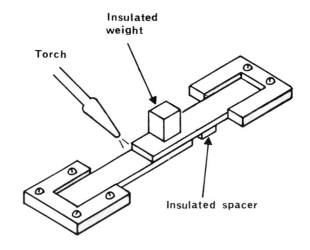

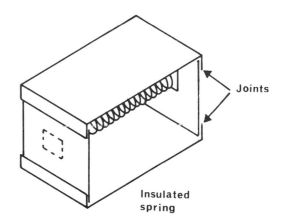

Figure 7-2. *Simple guide and weight arrangement to hold parts in alignment when tinned surfaces are heated for joining. Insulated spring holds box walls in place while tinned ends are heated for joining.*

Source: Aluminum Soldering Handbook, 3rd Ed., Aluminum Assn., Inc.

Wetting is accompanied by a spreading and flattening of the pool of solder. Wetting counteracts surface tension. To be certain of complete wetting, the solder may be wiped off with the glass brush or a rag and the joint's surface inspected. Unwetted areas may be scraped bright with a knife, more solder added and the process resumed.

When solder is to be used as the abrasion tool, the parent metal is heated carefully until it is close to the solidus of the solder. The end of the solder is rubbed back and forth across the base metal until the solder wets the aluminum. When the entire faying surface is coated, the temperature may be increased.

Ultrasonic Soldering

In rub soldering, aluminum's oxide is removed by physical force beneath a protective layer of molten solder. In ultrasonic soldering, the solder itself is vibrated at high frequency—from 15 to 50 kilocycles—and the vibrations dislodge the oxide by a process known as cavitation erosion.

High frequency alternating current may be produced by tube, solid state or spark-gap oscillator and by high frequency rotary alternators. The current is fed to a magnetostrictive transducer which comprises a coil of wire wound about a laminated nickel core. Nickel contracts about 3×10^{-7} inch for every inch of its length when it is magnetized, and the core expands and contracts two times with each current cycle.

The core's dimensional changes can be transferred directly to the molten solder, in which case the transducer might be mounted permanently on the bottom of a solder pot. Or the core may be extended with a metal rod called a sonotrode. In the latter design, the transducer and its vibrating extension are portable, the sonotrode is placed in a pool of molten solder and close to the aluminum work piece as needed. The sonotrode may also terminate in an electric soldering iron tip. The hot tip is then placed in a pool of solder on the work.

Ultrasonic soldering irons often are furnished with tips shaped for a particular task. For example, irons with cup-shaped tips are used for tinning the inside wall of tube ends.

No matter how the vibrational energy developed in the transducer is brought to the molten solder, the end result is the same; when the force is sufficiently strong and prolonged the oxide is dislodged and the base metal is wetted by the solder. Generally only a few seconds are required.

Cleanliness cannot be slighted but deoxidizing requirements are comparatively negligible. Anodized, alodized and iridized aluminum can be satisfactorily tinned with ultrasonic equipment.

Ultrasonic energy is not suited to small-clearance lap joints and tightly crimped joints: loosened oxide tends to remain in the joint. Similar difficulty is encountered when attempts are made to completely tin ends of stranded aluminum cable: all the oxide is loosened but some remains locked in the cracks between the strands. Subjecting the metal to continued ultrasonic vibrations results in excessive erosion.

The force that erodes aluminum suspended in molten solder also erodes the interior walls of the pot. Ultrasonic soldering iron tips are short-lived for the same reason.

Ultrasonic Solders

Low melting point solders are most frequently used for ultrasonic soldering. Typical formulations include: 96Sn-4Zn, 85Sn-15Cd, 97Sn-3Cu, 85Sn-15Zn, 35Sn-65Cd, 80Sn-20Zn.

Figure 7-3. *Typical ultrasonic soldering pot. The molten solder, vibrated at above sound frequency, dislodges the aluminum oxide, enabling the solder to wet the metal.*
Courtesy Blackstone Corp.

Furnace Soldering

Furnace soldering is essentially an unskilled operation. Once the parameters have been defined, each step in the cycle is simple and repetitious. Workman-training is comparatively limited.

Furnace soldering lends itself to both small-lot and high volume production. As many assemblies and joints as can be fitted into the furnace may be soldered at one time. If the batch furnace rate is too low, a semi-automatic continuous furnace is substituted.

Parts too large or massive to be evenly heated by other means may be soldered with minimum distortion in a furnace.

A furnace is also useful for soldering complex and intricate parts with joints that can not be easily neated—after assembly—by other techniques. Furnace soldering is excellent for long solder joints, for producing highly controlled solder fillets, neater joints and more efficient use of solder.

Any furnace capable of encompassing the assembly to be soldered, bringing it up to the melting temperature of the solder used and holding it there for the necessary time may be used. It may be heated by any means including infrared lamps. Combustion products should be prevented from entering the soldering chamber.

Soldering furnaces should be power ventilated. Flux vehicle vapors, such as are given off by alcohol, are highly combustible and explosive when mixed with air. These vapors can be eliminated by drying the flux assembly in air prior to soldering. Flux fumes, produced during soldering, cannot be as easily avoided. They must be vented outside the plant. In some localities anti-pollution laws require the installation of scrubbers.

Procedure

Parts to be furnace soldered are cleaned and prepared as discussed. Faying surfaces that are tinned or formed from solder-clad stock are assembled dry. All other faying surfaces must be fluxed and supplied with solder.

Preferably the parts should be self-jigging. If not, suitable jigs and fixtures are used as needed. Large or long parts, soldered at high temperatures, should be supported to prevent possible sagging at heat.

The aluminum assembly is placed in the furnace and left there for the required time. Afterwards it is carefully removed and cleaned as discussed in a previous chapter.

Time and Temperature

Temperature control requirements are not as stringent as those necessary for brazing. Permissible temperature variations depend on the solder and flux employed and the quality of work desired.

Optimum joints are produced by rapid soldering. The joints are brought up to temperature as quickly as possible and cooled as soon as the solder has completely filled them.

From a thermal point of view, furnace soldering is actually a three-step process: pre-heating, soldering and cooling.

Long pre-heat periods tend to produce liquation in some solders. Overly high temperatures and overly long periods at soldering heat tend to increase solder-to-base metal alloying and intergranular penetration of the base metal by the solder.

On the other hand, uneven soldering—incomplete joints, skips, slag and flux inclusions—may be caused by incomplete pre-heating, low soldering temperature and insufficient time at heat. Distortions may be produced by overly rapid cooling.

Pre-heat time will vary from as little as two minutes to more than thirty minutes, depending on the furnace and the mass of aluminum to be soldered. Soldering itself is generally completed in a minute or two.

Best results are obtained with a high heat-capacity furnace or a restricted quantity of aluminum in a lower heat-capacity furnace. In some instances the furnace is set

Source: Aluminum Soldering Handbook, 3rd Ed., Aluminum Assn., Inc.

100 or 150°F. above the desired joint temperature to speed pre-heat and soldering. Time then becomes the controlling factor.

Cooling rate is tied to metal mass and shape, ambient air temperature and whether or not the joints are removed from the furnace immediately. Some shops utilize a blast of air to speed cooling. When a three-stage continuous furnace is used, the chain belt carrying the aluminum assemblies is sometimes designed to drop the soldered parts directly into boiling water for flux removal.

Optimum soldering temperature and time at temperature can only be found by trial. But as a temperature of 80 or 90°F. above the given liquidus is the point at which many solders flow most readily, this temperature may be used as a starting point. All the aluminum solders may be used for furnace soldering.

Listed soldering temperatures refer to temperatures within the joint, which may differ markedly from other portions of the work piece; though this is not a desirable condition. When possible joint temperatures should be measured with a thermocouple or other direct-reading means. When this is not possible, joint temperature may be estimated from solder flow, flux behavior, temperature indicating crayons and radiant-temperature sensing instruments.

When testing is not possible, as might be the case when only one assembly is to be soldered, it is safer to extend the preheat and soldering periods and to up the temperature a bit rather than shorten the time and use a lower temperature. This gives the heat more time to soak through the metal and the solder more time to flow completely through the joints. Increased diffusion is less troublesome than an incomplete joint.

Figure 8-1. *Furnace soldering jigging.*

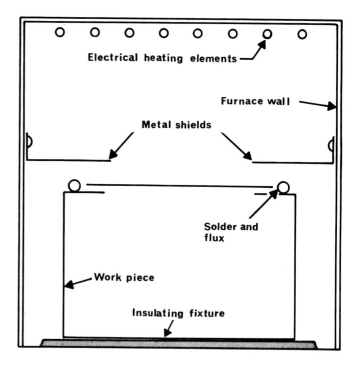

Figure 8-2. *Two temporary shields, fastened to the walls of the furnace, retard heating of the solder and flux.*

Heat Distribution Within the Furnace

Part and joint temperature depend on the source or sources of heat within the furnace and their relation and distance from the parts to be soldered. The assembly's trial position within the furnace should be carefully selected for repeatability so that following assemblies will reach the same temperature with the same furnace temperature setting.

The position of solder and flux relative to the source of heat within the furnace must be such that neither reaches soldering temperature before the base metal. If the flux reacts first, it will expend itself uselessly and no joint will be formed. If the solder melts and flows on relatively cold base metal, no joint will be formed.

Solder and flux therefore are best positioned—when possible—behind the aluminum assembly to be soldered. This may be accomplished by designing the solder joint within the assembly, i.e., burying it. See Figure 5-14. The same results can sometimes be achieved with baffles placed temporarily within the furnace or attached to the assembly to act as a heat shield or sink.

Other Soldering Techniques — Reaction, Wipe, Induction, Dip and Radiant Heat

Reaction Flux Soldering

Strong joints can be formed between aluminum and aluminum and aluminum and other metals by means of metal deposited by reaction flux alone. No metallic solder need be placed in or near the joint. The elimination of solder per se from the joint simplifies assembly and in some instances produces substantial overall cost reduction.

Reaction flux soldering is most often used for line contact joints such as are formed when a thin sheet abuts a plane surface or when a length of pipe rests on a plane surface. Flux is applied between the contacting metal surfaces.

Contrary to popular opinion, lap joints also can be made with reaction flux alone. The flux must be inside the joint before heat is applied and the joint must be self-spacing. This is illustrated in Figure 9-1. All mating surfaces are painted with liquid flux. The small weight holds the parts together and insures wetting of both the upper and lower mating surfaces. For optimum joint quality using liquid reaction flux, it is important that joints have accurately paralleled walls. If the joint walls are not reasonably flat, the quantity of solder deposited in the joint can be increased by using powdered flux, piling it high and installing a guide to keep the upper aluminum part aligned during heat.

Lap joints cannot be filled with solder by placing reaction flux beside the joint. Small quantities of flux will not produce a sufficient height of molten solder to wet both sides of the lap joint, a condition that must be met before capillary action will draw the solder into the joint. Large quantities of powdered reaction flux tend to disperse because of gases formed at reaction temperature, and a broader but no thicker layer of solder results.

Reaction flux solder content can be increased by adding powdered solder to the flux slurry or flux powder. As voids in reaction flux joints are more likely to be filled with flux than air, it is very important that lap joints made with this technique be cleaned especially carefully.

Wipe Soldering

Aluminum may be wipe soldered with the same technique used by plumbers for ages to wipe lead to lead and lead to cast iron pipes.

Wipe soldering is confined to forming joints between pipes or similar shapes. It may be used to join aluminum to aluminum, or aluminum to copper and other metals.

After cleaning and deoxidizing the aluminum and cleaning and deoxidizing the second metal, if necessary, both metal areas to be soldered are preheated by pouring hot solder over them. Immediately afterwards, flux is applied to the joint areas and more hot solder poured on. This tins the joint area. The solder in the pot is then permitted to cool to a slushy or semi-plastic condition. Using asbestos gloves and an asbestos cloth pad, the slushy solder is wiped over and around the two surfaces to form the joint. The pad is used to smooth the final results.

This basic technique may be varied somewhat. The flux is applied first and followed by very hot solder—as high as 750°F. The solder is poured over the joint area with a ladle. Excess is caught in a bucket. This is repeated until the joint surface is tinned. Wiping is done with solder at a lower temperature and in a slushy condition.

Flux used must be suited to the temperature of the solder that makes first contact. The wiping solder should have a wide spread between liquidus and solidus. A tin-lead mixture with a range of 282 to 485°F. might be used.

Tin-lead solders are normally not used to solder aluminum joints exposed to moisture.

Induction Soldering

Joints soldered by this method are brought to soldering temperature by high frequency electrical currents induced in the faying surfaces by an inductance (coil) positioned nearby.

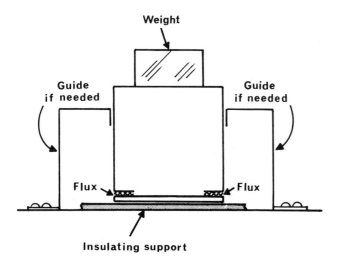

Figure 9-1. *Self-spacing lap joints soldered with reaction flux alone. Flux powder may be used.*

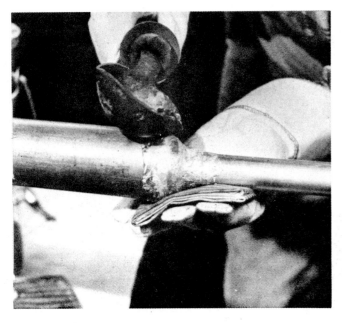

Figure 9-2. *Wipe soldering a splice between two aluminum cable sheaths.*

Heating is localized, fast, and generally accomplished in less than one minute. There are no open flames and power is consumed only during the soldering cycle. Once soldering parameters have been ascertained, soldering by induction is a mechanically repeatable operation. It can be automated and it can be accomplished by untrained production help.

Post-induction soldering cleaning is easier than post-torch soldering cleaning because there are no combustion products to react with the flux and form insolubles.

The equipment required is expensive compared to that necessary for other soldering methods. High production runs are needed to amortize the investment at a reasonable rate. However, the same equipment can also be used for brazing and heat-treating other metals. Frequencies from 60 to 5,000,000 Hertz (cycles per second) are used for induction heating. Five types of power supplies are used. Motor-generator sets are used for frequencies up to 10,000 Hertz. Resonant spark gaps are used to supply middle-range frequencies, 20,000 to 300,000 Hertz. Vacuum tube oscillators are generally employed for frequencies from 300,000 to 5,000,00 Hertz. Mercury-arc converters are also used for the middle range, and solid-state oscillators, the fifth type, may be designed to produce any of the frequencies listed.

In operation, the work piece is placed in or near the output inductance or work coil. Or the coil is placed inside the work piece. No physical contact is necessary. The metal parts act as the shorted secondary of a transformer; the work coil is the primary. See Figure 9-3.

Energy transfer from the work coil to the aluminum parts is directly related to the distance between the part and the coil. The shorter the distance the greater the quantity of energy transferred; i.e., the greater the coupling that exists.

The frequency selected has an important bearing on the manner in which the parts are heated. The lower frequencies tend to penetrate more deeply into the metal, but power transfer from work coil to part is less efficient than at higher frequencies, and the effect of coupling distance is more pronounced. The higher frequencies are transferred more efficiently from the output coil to the work and coupling distance effects are less noticeable. However, the higher frequencies are excluded from the depths of the metal by "skin effect" and time must be allowed for the inner portions of the metal to be heated by conduction. In some instances the selectivity of the higher frequencies may be used to advantage.

The work coil may be one turn or many. It may be shaped like a pancake, oval, helix, spiral or tube. Some examples are shown in Figure 9-4. Coils handling more than ¾ KW are generally water cooled. The coil is formed of a tube and tap water directed to run through its length. The voltage across the work is low and there is little problem with insulating it from the water pipe. Suitable induction heating equipment is available in power ratings to 100 KW.

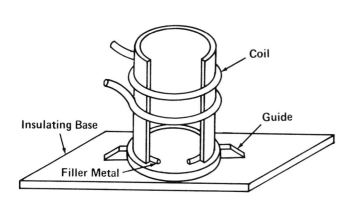

Figure 9-3. *Work may be placed inside or outside the inductor. Work is shown inside the coil.*

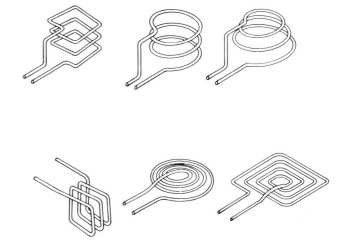

Figure 9-4. *The work coil may be shaped to suit the assembly that is to be soldered.*

The work coil may be shaped to follow the contours of the assembly, and the coil's turns may be spaced to favor the heavier sections of the metal to be heated. If part-to-work variations are exceptionally large for a particular assembly, the use of a larger work coil will reduce individual differences. Heat will be less efficiently transferred but more evenly distributed. The higher frequencies are more effective over distance than the lower frequencies.

Portions of the work that must remain relatively cool throughout the soldering cycle may be insulated from the radiant energy by means of metal shields. They are interposed between the coil and the work. Generally they are constructed of copper, though aluminum may be used.

Work coils are simple to fabricate and are frequently made by shop personnel as needed. One coil or a number may be used with one assembly. The work coil itself is not heated appreciably during the soldering cycle.

All conductors within the high frequency field act as shorted secondaries, absorb energy and heat up. Metal jigs and fixtures generally cannot be used for induction soldering. If they are, sufficient power must be supplied to heat the fixtures as well as the aluminum assembly. Magnetic metals such as steel absorb more energy (until they reach their Curie temperature) than better electrical conductors such as aluminum and copper and therefore are difficult to use for induction soldering fixtures.

Spring and clips can be used with the jigging. They will be heated along with the assembly to be soldered, possibly to higher-than-solder temperature because they may be closer to the work coils. Inconel and stainless hold up best. Ordinary spring steel may also be used although it will lose its temper rapidly.

Electrically non-conductive and heat resistant materials such as ceramics, steatites, asbestos and glass may be used as weights, supports and fixtures for induction soldering. The non-conductors will not absorb energy and will be heated by convection and conduction alone. Unglazed ceramics, such as bricks, must be dried before they are used as induction soldering fixtures. Water (plus salt) is a conductor. Water in the brick may absorb enough energy to turn to steam at an explosive rate.

Joint clearances for parts to be soldered by induction heating are similar to those used for furnace soldering: 0.002 to 0.004 inch. Joints designed for induction soldering are no different than joints designed for furnace soldering or other methods. The prime guide in designing assemblies for induction soldering is the recognition of the limited heating area afforded by this method, and the necessity of keeping all the joints to be soldered at one time within the heating area. Thought must also be given to the repulsion effect induced in the molten filler (and all metal within the range of the work coil) by the alternating current. The current induces a counter magnetic field, which acts to repulse the initial field. In some cases it may act to drive the molten filler out of the joint. This can be prevented by positioning the work coil properly in respect to the joint. For example, when the work coil is below a socketed tube-to-tube joint, the molten solder forms a closed metal ring above the magnetic field and is moved upwards and out of the joint. Raising the work coil above the solder tends to drive it down and into the joint.

Parts to be soldered by induction heating are cleaned, deoxidized, fluxed and jigged along with the necessary pre-placed filler metal. Then they are thoroughly dried. Heat generated by induced electrical currents is intense. Moisture turning to steam within the joint may drive the molten flux and solder out at high speed. The use of alcohol as a flux vehicle is advisable. It will dry more rapidly.

When the flux has dried the assembly is placed on or within a non-inductive guide or work-locating fixture, which is in turn positioned within the work coil. Once the optimum assembly position has been defined, the locating device is permanently affixed to the supporting surface and subsequent assemblies can be positioned readily and accurately.

Work piece temperature and time are established by varying the power delivered to the work coil, the relation of the coil to the work piece and the time interval. Although joints can be soldered by induction heating in as little as 5 seconds, it is generally better to reduce the power and extend the time period. Timing in seconds must be done automatically if it is to be consistent.

After the joint has been formed, the assembly must be permitted to cool before it is moved. Cooling and quenching may be accomplished by means of an ambient air blast provided by a nearby fan. The fan can be electrically connected to the induction equipment so that the fan is turned on a short time after the RF generator is turned off, and the fan is automatically turned off when the soldering cycle begins.

Dip Soldering

Dip soldering differs from ultrasonic soldering in that flux is used. Dip soldering is especially suited to assemblies incorporating a large number of joints to be filled by capillary action, as for example, cellular heat exchangers. The pot of molten solder insures sufficient solder to completely fill the joints, and complete immersion isn't always

Figure 9-5. *Small dip soldering pot in production use.*

necessary as the solder will travel at least one inch vertically in response to capillary attraction.

The dip process is also suited to rapid, one-at-a-time soldering of single or multiple joints such as twisted wire pairs and the like.

The process may be used with all the solders, matching fluxes and all the solderable aluminum alloys. Assembly size is limited only by the size of the solder pot and associate equipment.

Parts to be joined by dipping are degreased, deoxidized and assembled. If jigs or fixtures are needed, they should be of minimum mass and of a material, such as oxidized stainless steel, which will not be wetted by the solder.

Procedure at this point will depend on the assembly configuration, mass and joint location. If the parts to be joined are very small and relatively simple, the faying surfaces may be fluxed and the parts dipped directly (assuming there is no moisture in the joint) into the molten solder. Any of the aluminum solders may be used. Larger parts may be preheated with the flux in place, or preheated and then fluxed. With some configurations, it may be practical to preheat and then dip only the faying surfaces into hot flux and then into the solder. Sometimes preheating is accomplished by dipping the dry, unfluxed assembly into hot solder. Without flux no soldering will take place.

Assemblies preheated to the melting point of the solder used, or slightly higher to compensate for temperature drop between preheating and the solder pot, can be soldered in a matter of seconds with a minimum of "chewing" and intergranular penetration.

Chewing, the dissolution of aluminum by solder, decreases the solder's fluidity by virtue of changing solder composition. Raising solder temperature is a temporary answer which may be repeated until flux reaction temperature is exceeded or chewing and intergranular penetration are accelerated. At this point the solder in the pot must be replaced.

The surface of molten solder must be kept free of dross resulting from solder oxidation and flux residue. Dross, caught in a joint when the assembly is lowered, reduces joint quality. Dross remaining on the surface of the joint or assembly when the work piece is removed produces a rough and uneven solder-surface.

Solder and flux pots may be heated by any convenient means, though gas and electricity are most frequently used. The pots may be of cast iron, unlined or lined with a refractory material.

Solder and flux pots should be power vented to remove fumes. Overhead canopy systems are most efficient, but side vents about 6 inches above the bath are equally effective when sufficiently powered.

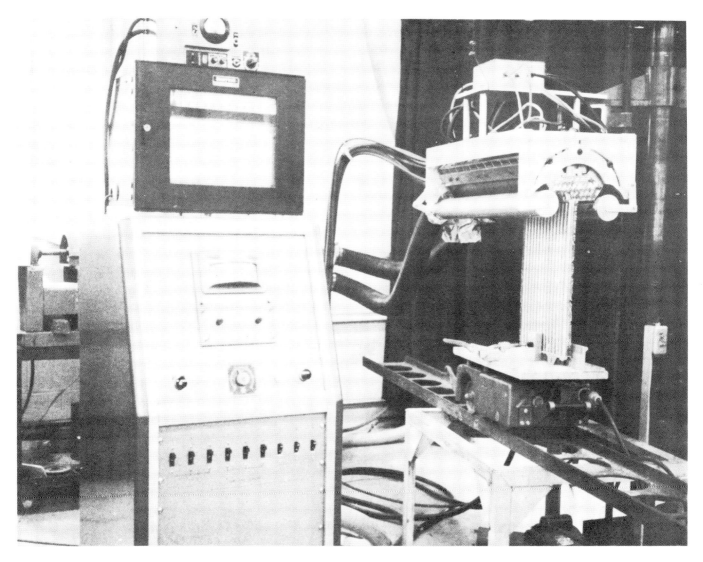

Figure 9-6. *Electrically powered radiant heat soldering equipment. Aluminum assembly shown in place can be soldered without preheating in some 20 seconds. Fumes are removed by pipes at top of elements.*

Radiant Heat Soldering

Electrically generated radiant heat is proving to be an excellent means for soldering complex aluminum assemblies. Infrared energy may be focused on the work pieces with little waste of heat. Time and temperature are controlled precisely. There are no combustion products to contend with nor any problems with moisture in the heat. The radiant energy source may be installed within a vented oven or in open air, indoors. Flux fumes, in the latter arrangement, are drawn off by vents placed close to the soldered assembly. Obtainable heat density is sufficient to solder a heat exchanger, for example, without preheating in less than one minute.

Figure 9-6 shows a pilot plant using 144, 1-KW heat lamps mounted in banks beneath a gold-plated heat reflector. The two parallel pipes to either side of the radiator are slotted and lead to a ventilating fan. Equipment with which time and temperature can be regulated by direct reading controls is visible to one side. The radiator shown can be soldered in less than 20 seconds.

The cost of radiant heating and control equipment is on par with similar capacity, automatic gas flame soldering equipment. The gas jet costs are nominal but the automatic gas mixing and gas pressure control equipment is costly.

Gas-fired radiant heating systems for soldering are under development. In a sense they are similar to the gas-fired space heaters which are operated at infrared temperature. At infrared temperature, gas heated elements radiate as effectively as electrically heated elements. However, at the present time, gas-fired radiant elements in this temperature range cannot be properly controlled, or controlled as well as electrical units.

Source: Aluminum Soldering Handbook, 3rd Ed., Aluminum Assn., Inc.

Soldering Castings

In theory the soldering of castings presents no more problems than the soldering of similar but wrought aluminum shapes. In practice, this particular theory is somewhat inaccurate. Alloys normally produced in wrought form are not normally produced in cast form. The act of casting aluminum produces three physical conditions which are barriers to good soldering: a thick, heat-produced oxide coating, a rough surface and porosity; in addition, castings by their very nature are generally considerably more massive than their wrought aluminum counterparts.

However, there are three aluminum casting alloys— 443.0, 443.2 and 356—which are relatively easily wetted by solder. Other casting alloys less responsive but still solderable are listed in Table 2-2. Alloys difficult to solder can be made easily solderable by surface preparation. This is discussed in Chapter 3.

Surface oxide may be removed by chemical or physical means. A rough surface may be made smooth by filing or machining. Porosity is at a minimum in high-quality castings, and can often be ignored or reduced by machining down to a denser layer of metal. In many instances, machining a flat is all that is needed to prepare a casting for soldering—after degreasing.

Files and power-driven wire brushes are not recommended for preparing castings unless the surface to be soldered is reasonably flat and care is used to keep it so. It is necessary that the surface of the casting to be soldered be relatively parallel with the surface to be joined, so that joint clearance will be equal for its entire length and width. Hand held tools follow local surface variations rather than level them.

Pits and similar small holes in faying surfaces can be ignored if the surface has been recently produced by cleaning or machining. In such cases it may be assumed that nothing but slag and similar inert material lies in the holes. If considerable time has passed between machining and soldering, open holes must be cleaned to make certain gas-forming matter and oils are not present.

If exposed holes represent a considerable area, the joint is made larger to accommodate the loss of lap.

If the alloy to be soldered is not readily wetted the prepared surface may be plated. Again the open holes are ignored if clean.

The faying surface may also be tinned as an aid to soldering. The fluxless, abrasive techniques are well suited to this purpose as hard rubbing can be used to offset wetting difficulty. The presence of pit holes and pores makes the use of flux inadvisable.

If the casting is to be tinned or soldered directly, high temperature solders are best. If the casting has been plated or tinned, any of the solders may be used. However, because of the possibility of entrapment, it is best to use no flux or only a non-chloride flux.

If the casting is large, tinning may require as much heat and time as soldering and is perhaps best done just before soldering.

Castings may be heated by any convenient means. When the castings are too large for a single heat source, multiple sources may be used including preheating in a furnace, multiple torches, induction heating, and hot plates. Insulating bricks and asbestos blankets are used to shield the parts from the wind and contact with cooling surfaces.

Joint temperature may be checked by abrading the tip of the solder bar against the joint surface. When the tip melts or softens, heat may be reduced somewhat to prevent overshoot, but should be continued to make certain that the solder is truly molten and not in a slushy condition. In the latter case the solder may adhere by virtue of locking to the pores. If heat is reduced or removed prematurely the base metal may not be wetted and a poor joint or no joint will be formed. In the absence of flux and in the presence of massive metal parts, a little more heat or a little more time is far better than too little. The entire joint must come to solder liquidus temperature.

Die castings of aluminum can be soldered without blistering by using intermediate solders with temperatures below 600°F. Again, care must be used to deoxidize the base metal and wetting difficulty can be expected with the hard-to-solder alloys. In such cases abrasion soldering is most helpful.

Solder can be used to plug holes in aluminum castings. The hole is undercut severely, leaving a fairly thin lip at the upper edges of the hole. The underside of the lip need only be wetted; the solder is melted into the hole itself and only soldered at the upper edges. While this confers little strength on the "plug," little strength is needed. The soldered edge seals the plug against moisture. Figure 10-1 illustrates this technique.

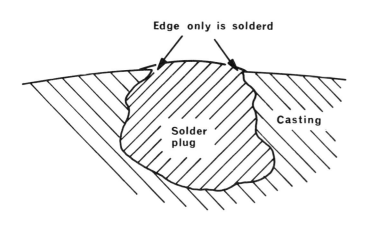

Figure 10-1. *Molten solder is poured into under-cut hole in casting. Only the thin lip of the hole is soldered.*

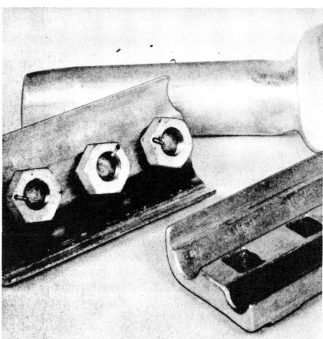

Figure 10-2. *Examples of castings that have been soldered. These are used in the electrical industry.*

Source: Aluminum Soldering Handbook, 3rd Ed., Aluminum Assn., Inc.

Soldering Aluminum to Other Metals and Non-Metallics

Aluminum may be soldered directly to all common metals and many common alloys including Kovar, stainless steel and others using standard aluminum soldering techniques, fluxes and solders. Aluminum may be soldered to magnesium and the refractory metals if one or preferably both are first plated. Aluminum may also be soldered to many non-metallics including glass, ceramics and cermets.

Table 11-1 lists various commercial metals and the relative ease with which they may be soldered to aluminum with high and low temperature aluminum solders. Obviously, when aluminum is soldered to a dissimilar metal, the resultant joint is more susceptible to corrosion than an aluminum-to-aluminum solder joint. Proper precautions should be taken to exclude moisture.

The high-temperature solders and suitable fluxes may be used to solder mild steel, stainless steel, nickel, magnesium, copper, silver, brass and zinc directly to aluminum.

The low-temperature, soft solders work well with some metals and other commercial metals and alloys including cast iron, Kovar and Alnico.

Magnesium, titanium, zirconium, columbium, tantalum, molybdenum and tungsten can be soldered if they are first electroplated, clad or tinned with a solderable metal or alloy including pure aluminum. These, so called, refractory metals are sometimes hot-dipped in aluminum or coated with silver solder alloy to provide a suitable soldering surface for aluminum.

Conversely it is sometimes advantageous to pre-plate or clad the aluminum when soldering it to other metals. This may be done on a small scale by local tinning as well as by hot dipping, cladding or electroplating the entire part.

Aluminum is frequently plated before soldering when the alloy is one that is difficult to solder. The plated or tinned aluminum may then be soldered with any of the fluxes and solders suited to the plating metal. Copper, brass, nickel, silver, cadmium, lead and zinc are the metals most often used for plating aluminum. By coating the aluminum with copper, for example, copper wires and nickel-plated copper wires can be easily soldered with soft solder and non-corrosive rosin flux. Copper-plated aluminum in wire and strap form is finding increasing application for the conduction of electricity.

Silver is particularly advantageous as a plating metal. Molten zinc will instantly wet silver without the aid of flux. And silver plating, no more than 0.01 mil thick, reduces intergranular penetration of aluminum by zinc.

Choice of Flux and Solder

Primarily the flux and solder chosen for mixed soldering should be suited to the aluminum alloy that is to be wetted. This is discussed in Chapter 2. However, there is considerable latitude of choice within this rule.

It is sometimes possible to select a flux and solder combination that readily wets the second metal as well as the aluminum and which is beneficial to the service life of the entire joint.

For example, if a length of galvanized pipe were to be soldered to a section of aluminum plate, it would be better to use a zinc-rich flux and a zinc-base solder rather than a tin-bearing flux or a tin or cadmium-base solder. To further reduce the varieties of alloys in the joint the galvanized pipe might be soldered to the aluminum with reaction flux alone.

Technique For Mixed Metal Soldering

The aluminum is prepared exactly as it would be if it were to be soldered to aluminum. It must be degreased and deoxidized, and depending on the alloy, possibly plated. The second piece of metal must at a minimum be degreased. Whether or not it needs to be deoxidized and how this is best accomplished depends on the second metal. Oxidized copper, rusted iron, etc., must be brightened. Steel wool, sandpaper and similar abrasive means are possibly best for small work pieces.

Materials	Low-temperature soldering	High-temperature soldering
Steel (low-carbon)	Satisfactory	Satisfactory
Stainless steel	Possible	Possible
Copper alloys	Satisfactory	Satisfactory
Nickel alloys	Satisfactory	Possible
Magnesium alloys	Possible	Possible
Silver alloys	Satisfactory	Possible
Precious metals	Satisfactory	No experience
Zinc alloys	Satisfactory	Possible
Lead alloys	Satisfactory	No experience
Tin alloys and tin plate	Satisfactory	No experience
Commercial electroplates or hot-dip coatings	Satisfactory	Possible
Bronze	Possible	Possible
Sintered graphite bronze	Not recommended	Not recommended
Titanium	Possible	Possible
Ceramics, cermets, glass	Possible	Possible

Table 11-1. *Solderability of aluminum to other metals and non-metals. "Satisfactory" indicates combinations easy to solder. "Possible" indicates limited experience.*

The parts are then assembled and soldered by any convenient technique. Most often, furnace and torch soldering are used for mixed-metal soldering. When the aluminum faying surface has been tinned, the second metal may be soldered with fluxes and solders suitable to the tinning and second metal.

When zinc is used to solder aluminum to a dissimilar metal such as copper or brass a brittle intermetallic interface forms between the second metal and the solder. See Figure 11-1. The formation of the intermetallic layer is time and temperature dependent. It is therefore good practice to complete mixed metal soldering as quickly as possible using the lowest practical temperature.

Soldering Aluminum To Non-Metallics

Non-metallics which can be wetted by solder or plated with a metal can be soldered to aluminum or another metal.

Glass can be wetted by solder composed approximately of equal parts of tin and indium. The glass is cleaned and heated to the melting temperature of the solder which is then rubbed over the surface of the glass, tinning it. Aluminum pre-tinned with tin-lead-zinc solder can be soldered directly to the tinned glass using the same solder with no flux. Made properly, aluminum-glass solder joints are vacuum tight. Other solders may also be used to solder

Source: Aluminum Soldering Handbook, 3rd Ed., Aluminum Assn., Inc.

Figure 11-1. *Magnified cross-sectional view of aluminum soldered to steel with a zinc solder.*

aluminum directly to the tinned glass, but they usually require flux.

Glass may be coated with copper, silver or aluminum by first roughening the surface of the glass by sand or grit-blasting. The glass is then heated and sprayed with the desired metal, in a molten state. Upon cooling any suitable solder and flux may be used to solder aluminum

Glass and other non-metallics can be coated or tinned by abrasion. This is done with a grinding wheel. The grinding wheel is loaded with soft solder by rubbing the solder into the rotating wheel. Heating the wheel is reported to speed loading. The surface to be tinned—ceramic, metal or glass—is pressed against the loaded, rotating wheel. Friction melts the solder which flows onto the hot, abraded surface, wetting it. Once tinned, the non-metallic or metal may be soldered with standard soft solders and fluxes.

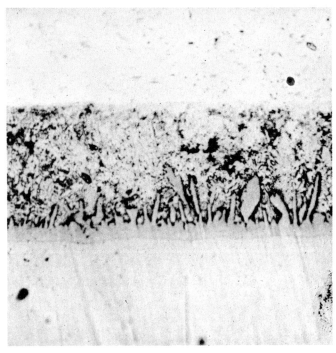

Figure 11-2. *Intermetallic interface layer can be clearly seen between the alloy 3003 aluminum and the 70-30*

Joint Inspection, Testing and Performance

Visual Inspection

For many applications visual inspection is all that is needed to accept or reject a solder joint. Strong, properly made solder joints are easily recognized. They have definite appearances typical of the solder, flux and temperature used to make them. Appearance variations are usually indicative of less than satisfactory soldering and can often be traced to specific errors or failures in the steps leading to the finished joint. Solder joints should be inspected before and after washing because flux residue is also an important indicator of joint conditions during soldering.

Improperly made solder joints frequently exhibit the following tell-tale signs:

If the solder's surface is strongly crystalline in appearance the joint is "cold," meaning there was inter-part movement while the solder was solidifying.

If the fillet's surface is sharply broken or uneven, heat application may have been uneven, solder may have been added after the original joint was formed or there may have been considerable inter-part movement during cooling.

If the fillet's surface is lumpy, solder temperature may have been too low, or time at heat too short. The solder failed to melt completely and a portion of its original shape is still visible.

If the fillet's surface is very rough, with a texture similar to that of an alligator's skin, liquation has occurred. Kept overly long at a temperature just below its liquidus, the lower melting point constituents melted out of the solder, leaving a skeleton of high-melting point metals behind.

If the joint is marred by skips and holidays, the cause may be ineffective degreasing and/or deoxidizing, burrs and dirt particles on the faying surfaces.

If the skips are long, or if large areas show no signs of solder wetting the cause may be excessive joint clearance, uneven joint clearance, the absence of flux, insufficient flux, the wrong flux (for solder and temperature used) or grease run-down (from a nearby, uncleaned portion of the work piece).

Poor or uneven solder-to-base metal wetting (as evidenced by a strong line at the fillet's edge) may be traced to insufficient or ineffective flux, improper degreasing and deoxidizing, insufficient heat, or area-limited heat.

Excessive porosity (not always visible from the surface of the joint) may be caused by too much flux, overly high temperature, or insufficient time at heat.

Undersized solder fillets may be due to lack of solder or misdirected heat resulting in solder run-off.

Low solder-fillet height may be caused by vibration, excessive application and spread of flux or excessive temperature and time at heat encouraging solder spreading.

Cracked joints may be caused by overly-rapid cooling, lack of compliance in the jig or fixture, excessive mass difference between joined parts resulting in uneven expansion and contraction.

Cracks in the base metal are almost always produced by intergranular penetration. Light or small cracks may be due to slightly incompatible material held too long at too high a temperature. Deep cracks are caused by highly incompatible metals, possibly in a stressed state.

Black, charcoal-like organic flux residue on a poor joint indicates misdirected heat. The flux was brought to temperature before the solder and base metal. Burnt organic flux is in itself no indication of a poor joint.

A dark brown or black viscous liquid on the work piece indicates a very poor joint. The torch flame struck the reaction flux forming an oxychloride which is a stop-off material. Normal reaction-flux residue is a grey-white powder.

Solder fillet surface is also a guide to internal conditions.

Source: Aluminum Soldering Handbook, 3rd Ed., Aluminum Assn., Inc.

However, unlike brazing, no general or broad guideline can be laid down for assessing solder joint quality by surface texture. Each solder and flux combination exhibits a different texture. The soft solders produce the smoothest surfaces, The intermediate solders may show fine pores. The high temperature solders are often marred by ridged circles much like flattened volcanos, produced by the violent passage of reaction flux gases. However, under favorable conditions, both the intermediate and high-temperature solders may form smooth-surface fillers.

Surface texture is, however, a useful indicator of change after the trial and error stage is passed. For example, the absence of craters on a fillet surface normally pock-marked could indicate an increase in soldering temperature, an increase in time at heat, a change in solder composition (wrong solder), an increase in solder quantity, a decrease in flux quantity or flux activity (wrong flux) or too much time between the application of flux and heating.

Solder color is not a useful criterion for joint evaluation; it remains fairly constant under a variety of soldering conditions.

"Flux staining" is an erroneous or poor description of metal deposited in varying quantities by all fluxes. Flux staining can only be avoided by soldering without flux. Changing flux quantity and composition (a different halo-

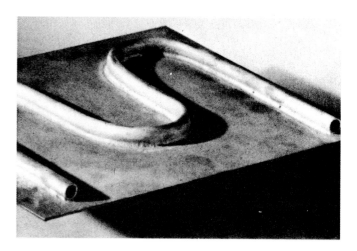

Figure 12-2. *An example of a good galvanized steel to aluminum plate solder joint.*

gen) will alter the color of the stain and possibly reduce its intensity or size. More careful flux application may also help.

Non-destructive Tests

Radiography, the exposure of a photographic plate to short waves that have passed through the joint, is probably the foremost inspection test in use today. Thickness flaws amounting to as little as 1 or 2% of the total thickness of the material examined can be detected with X-rays. All joints that can be backed by a photographic plate can be X-rayed. Figures 3-4 and 3-5 illustrate the results obtainable with X-rays.

The thermal conductance of a soldered joint is also used as a measure of its quality. One side of the joint is heated as evenly as possible. The further side of the joint and the joint itself are covered with heat-sensitive, color indicating paint. If the joint is solid, the color change from the hot to the cool side of the joint will be smooth. Abrupt color changes at any point indicate voids or discontinuities at that point. This method is limited to simple configurations.

Soldered honeycomb panels are sometimes tested by another thermal-transfer test. Temperature sensitive, low-melting point powders or liquids are spread evenly over the assembly. It is then heated by an infra-red lamp. The liquid or the powder, which has turned to liquid, is repelled by warm areas and attracted to cool areas. Properly soldered joints in the structure are cooler than the balance of the metal and the liquid flows over them. Poor or defective joints remain covered and are therefore immediately obvious.

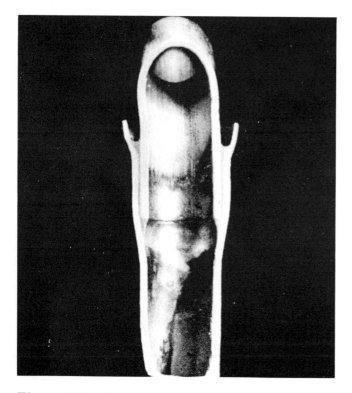

Figure 12-1. *Example of a good socketed tube joint.*

Sound waves at ultrasonic frequencies are also used to locate discontinuities and flaws in soldered aluminum joints. The test device employs frequencies ranging from ½ to 5 million Hertz (cycles per second). The sound is focused into a narrow beam and directed onto the joint. Homogeneous elastic material, such as aluminum, propagates mechanical energy with little loss and little reflection. Discontinuities reflect energy. Reflected energy is picked up by a quartz crystal transducer and displayed on a cathode ray tube. See Figure 12-3.

Both fluorescent and non-fluorescent dyes may be used to locate surface defects in soldered aluminum joints. The materials and techniques are similar to those used for locating cracks in ferrous material.

The non-fluorescent dye is applied to the surface of the joint by any convenient means. A few minutes are permitted to elapse to enable the dye to penetrate surface cracks, if any exist. Then the surface is wiped clean, whereupon the dye within the cracks becomes highly visible.

The fluorescent dye is similarly applied and given some five minutes to find and enter any existing crack. Excess penetrant is then washed off and the metal's surface is air dried. A "developer" in the form of a dry powder is placed on the metal's surface. The powder draws whatever penetrant remains in the crack back to the metal's surface. The part is removed from normal light and exposed to high intensity ultra violet light. Any penetrant remaining in the crack, however small, becomes fluorescent and visible.

Testing for Leaks

As a soldered joint may be porous and still leaktight, a visual inspection followed by a leak test is all that is usually necessary with assemblies of this type.

The choice of pressure medium will depend to some extent upon the maximum acceptable leak aperture. Oil, particularly a thin oil such as kerosene, or a heated oil will pass through holes that will hold water under equal pressure. Air leaks more readily than water and helium leaks and escapes where air will not.

From a safety point of view, water and oil are far safer as pressure mediums than gas. The two mentioned liquids are non-compressible and when pressurized vessels containing these liquids burst, there is no accompanying quasi-explosion.

Freon is often used for pressure testing as low-cost, simple Freon-detection equipment suitable for locating small leaks is commercially available. This type of equipment utilizes a flame which changes color in the presence of Freon. More sensitive and more expensive halogen leak detectors are also available.

Helium is the medium most often used for the detection of microscopic leaks. The vessel, pressurized with helium, is placed in a vacuum. A mass spectrometer is used to detect any helium that may escape. Conversely, the vessel may be evacuated and helium flushed over its surface. The spectrometer is then preferably connected between the auxiliary diffusion pump and the mechanical backing pump.

Proof Testing

Soldered aluminum joints and assemblies may be proof tested by subjecting them to loads slightly in excess of the loads expected during the unit's service lifetime. The standard means and method of applying such loads may be used.

Other tests to which soldered joints and assemblies may be subjected include all the standard tests applied to other metals and other joining techniques. These include tension and shear tests, fatigue, impact and torsion tests.

Destructive Inspection

When joint configuration permits, and the joint is not stronger than the parent metal, the peel test is the simplest and quickest way of both testing the joint and inspecting its insides. One portion of the joint is locked in a vise while the other side is rolled back with pliers or a similar mechanical aid.

Peeling (rolling) the joint back on itself develops tremendous leverage at the metal interface. Therefore the force necessary to peel a joint cannot in itself be taken as a direct measurement of a joint's strength, but must be compared to the force necessary to peel similar joints pre-tested by other means. Surfaces exposed by ripping the metal apart will be bright. Unbonded surfaces may be dull, especially if some time has elapsed since the joint was soldered.

Figure 12-3. *Cathode ray tube displays solder joint homogeneity.*
Courtesy Krautkramer

Source: Aluminum Soldering Handbook, 3rd Ed., Aluminum Assn., Inc.

Unless the joint has been soldered in a vacuum or dry, inert gas, a number of voids should be expected. Joints that are 60% solid are considered satisfactory for many applications. An even greater void percentage can be tolerated when less than maximum joint strength and nominal sealing are the design goals.

The visual aspects of the voids exposed by peeling are often indicative of their causes. Voids produced by flux traps would be filled with flux. Voids caused by hydrogen would be empty.

Metallographic examination may be employed to evaluate porosity, filler metal flow, lack of wetting, filler-to-base metal diffusion and final joint clearance. Joint samples are obtained by sectioning. The sample is then polished, etched and examined under a microscope. Details on specimen preparation and etching reagents may be found in the ASM Metals Handbook. Data on microscopic examination of etched samples may be found in the ASTM Standards, Part I, Metals.

Joint Performance

The low-temperature solders develop a little over 5,000 psi in tension. The intermediate solders develop upwards of 10,000 psi in tension and the hard solders develop up to 18,000 psi in tension.

These figures relate to solder alone. Sound solder joints exhibit far greater strength by virtue of triaxial strain and solder-to-aluminum bonding. All the high temperature solders and some of the intermediate solders produce joints that are as strong or stronger than the parent metal. When conditions are near perfect, high temperature solder joints can develop up to 40,000 psi in shear.

Zinc soldered aluminum pipe joints can withstand pressures high enough to rupture the pipe itself. Soldered pipe joints made of 3/8 inch O.D. x .035-inch wall, alloy 1200 extruded aluminum can withstand internal pressures of 2200 to 2500 psi. Rupture pressure is even higher when alloy 3003 is used; the pipe will give way before the soldered joint.

Solder may be used to form vacuum-tight joints between aluminum and aluminum, aluminum and other metals and aluminum and non-metals such as glass. Should the mixed metal or mixed material solder joint be subject to thermal change during its service life, provisions to accommodate differential thermal expansion should be incorporated within the joint design.

Solder joints, however, are not well suited to vibration, intermittent loads and shock. When such loads are expected, a zinc solder should be used.

Because of the brittle intermetallic layer formed when aluminum is soldered to another metal, mixed-metal solder joints are less resistant to shock and vibration than aluminum to aluminum soldered joints. Copper-aluminum and cadmium-aluminum joints are most brittle, with steel-aluminum joints somewhat less brittle and less susceptible to failure by shock loads. Good design, however, can often reduce the effect of vibration on joint loading. A tube to tube joint, for example, is far less prone to shock failure when the inner member is under compression.

Service Temperatures

Soft, low temperature solders retain a good portion of their strength up to 180° F. The high temperature, hard solders are fully effective up to 212°F. and can be exposed briefly to 350°F. without strength loss. The service range of the intermediate solders fall in between.

Solders containing a high percentage of lead retain their ductility and impact strength at low temperatures. When tin content reaches 50%, there is considerable loss of ductility and impact strength at low temperature. The tin-lead solders having 15% or less tin retain their room temperature properties at low temperature.

Corrosion Resistance

Aluminum solder joints, like all other solder joints, corrode when two or more parts of the joint are in contact with an electrolyte. The corrosion process is essentially electrochemical in nature. The metals joined by the electrolyte form a galvanic couple. The negative (or most negative) cell element corrodes most rapidly: The rate of corrosion depends on the voltage difference existing between elements, their distance apart and the composition of the electrolyte.

The voltage developed across the parts forming a galvanic couple and the areas of maximum galvanic attack and corrosion are dependent upon the metals forming the joint. Except for magnesium and zinc, aluminum has a higher negative solution potential than all other commonly soldered metals. The voltages are given in Table 12-1. The polarity relationship and voltage differences between different aluminum alloys is given in Table 12-2.

When identical aluminum alloys are soldered, there is no appreciable voltage across the joint proper, but a voltage will exist (assuming the presence of an electrolyte) between the joint walls and the solder. The polarity of the voltage and direction of current flow will depend on the solder.

If the joint is formed of soft solder, the intermetallic interface between the solder and aluminum will be most negative and anodic to the balance of the assembly. The voltage potential developed across such an interface is shown in Figure 12-9(A). As the interface is most negative it corrodes far more rapidly than any other element of the galvanic cell (joint).

As the interfacial, fusion layer is very thin, soft solder joints do not withstand hostile environments very well. And when such joints fail they tend to fail catastrophically; the solder separates from the aluminum as if cut by a knife. The solder shows very little evidence of galvanic attack. The aluminum may be pitted slightly.

When a joint is formed with zinc solder, which is negative and anodic to aluminum, galvanic corrosion is spread over the face of the zinc. As the exposed surface of the zinc solder is far greater than the forementioned interfacial layer, zinc solder joints withstand corrosive attack far longer than soft solder joints. The voltage potential developed across a zinc solder joint is shown in Figure 12-9(B).

The second factor of joint corrosion, the distance between the elements forming the galvanic cell, is a function of design. While it is physically impossible, to separate two parts of a joint by more than the thickness of the solder holding them together, it is sometimes possible to wrap one joint member around the other (folded joint) to reduce the solder area exposed, and to use other techniques. This is discussed in Chapter 3.

Designing Corrosion Resistance Into a Joint

The third factor of joint corrosion, the presence and composition of the electrolyte, is, of course, joint exposure. If the joint is not exposed, i.e., the joint is kept dry as it would be if it were installed indoors, for example, no corrosion would take place. In one test, soft solder joints kept dry for some 13 years showed no corrosion. In the absence of moisture, the life expectancy of solder joints is unlimited.

Exposed to the weather, locale and joint composition become highly important. Installed outdoors in another test, soft solder joints in an industrial area lasted 4 to 5 years before corrosion necessitated replacement.

Subjected to intermittent salt spray, similar soft-soldered aluminum joints lasted no more than 30 days.

Zinc-soldered joints, exposed to a marine environment, have so far provided 10 years of service and appear to be in good condition still. Zinc solder joints are used in refrigeration equipment and are compatible with most freon-type refrigerants dried to refrigeration industry standards.

Table 12-3 lists the results of exposing four different solders, various fluxes and base metals to salt spray for various periods of time.

Metal	Voltage
Magnesium	—1.73
Zinc	—1.10
1100 Aluminum	—0.83
Cadmium	—0.82
Iron	—0.67
Lead	—0.55
Tin	—0.49
Copper	—0.20
Bismuth	—0.18
Silver	—0.18
Nickel	—0.07

Measured in a 1 normal (5.85%) sodium chloride solution containing 0.3% hydrogen peroxide (N/10 Calomel Scale).

Table 12-1. *Solution potential in volts of commonly soldered metals. Note voltage of aluminum.*

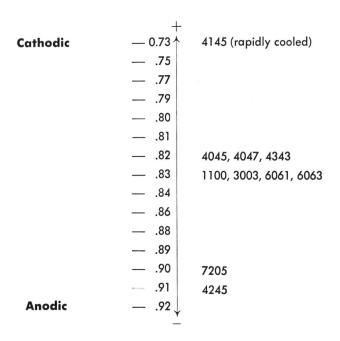

Table 12-2. *Listed alloys were tested against a 0.1N calomel reference electrode in a standard salt peroxide solution to produce the voltages given. The upper, less negative alloy in a couple is always the cathode and is protected in an electrolyte at the expense of the anode. The further apart the alloys are on the scale, the greater the galvanic difference and the greater the propensity for corrosion.*

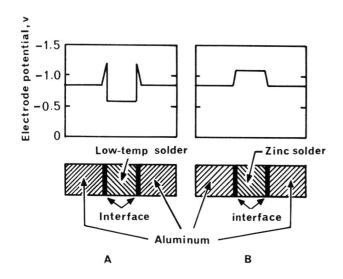

Figure 12-9. *Approximate electrical potential developed across low-temperature solder joint and a zinc solder joint. Note high anodic voltage at soft solder interface.*

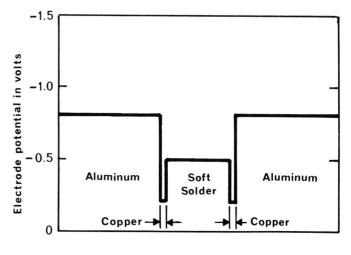

Figure 12-10. *Copperplated joint walls have a more positive potential than the aluminum. The aluminum becomes anodic and corrodes preferentially.*

Flux and Corrosion Resistance

Assuming complete removal after joint completion, flux in itself—exclusive of the metal it deposits—has no effect upon a joint's corrosion resistance. Complete removal is not always possible, however. Therefore, flux choice is of prime importance in the corrosion resistance of certain joint configurations and joints made in the field. Figure 12-11 shows the deterioration of a copper-to-aluminum joint resulting from the presence of chloride within the joint. If the joint had been completely cleaned, the chloride line would parallel the organic flux line.

The importance of complete removal of all chloride flux traces cannot be overstated. Chloride residues exposed to air always deliquesce. Once wet an essentially chemical reaction starts:

1. Chloride + H_2O → hydrochloric acid + an oxide of the flux.

2. 6HCl (hydrochloric acid) + 2Al → $2AlCl_3$ (aluminum chloride, a corrosion product) + $3H_2$ (hydrogen). The hydrogen forces its way out of the joint, forming a new entrance path for moisture.

3. $2AlCl_3 + 3H_2O$ → $6HCl + Al_2O_3$.

When the chloride solution contacts aluminum and another metal (or alloy) having a different solution potential a galvanic couple is formed. Driven by the voltage thus generated, the rate of corrosion increases markedly. The most negative element in the galvanic cell begins to dissolve and continues to do so until moisture is no longer present or the reaction is complete.

Protected Joints

When aluminum is plated prior to soft soldering the intermetallic interface layer becomes more positive than the soft solder and both are more positive than the aluminum joint walls. The aluminum therefore corrodes most rapidly, and the life of the joint is lengthened considerably. Platings of copper, nickel and iron are used. For maximum corrosion resistance, the plating should not extend beyond the edge of the solder. The potential across a soft-soldered, copper-plated aluminum joint is shown in Figure 12-10. Compare this with the potential relationships illustrated in Figure 12-9.

The service life of soldered aluminum joints can also be extended by exterior joint protection in one form or another, for example:

The life of soft-soldered joints exposed to marine atmosphere can be increased by coating the joints with a thin layer of aluminum-pigmented zinc-chromate paint. The life of soft-soldered joints on copper-plated aluminum was multiplied five times by using this paint.

Unpainted soft-soldered, aluminum to aluminum joints last no more than 5 years when exposed outdoors to severe industrial atmospheres. Painted, soft-soldered, lug-to-cable aluminum joints have withstood 14 years of exposure with no sign of corrosion.

A protected, aluminum-cable to copper-cable soft-solder joint forming a part of the underground power system of the Transit Authority of Chicago has given 38 years of trouble-free service.

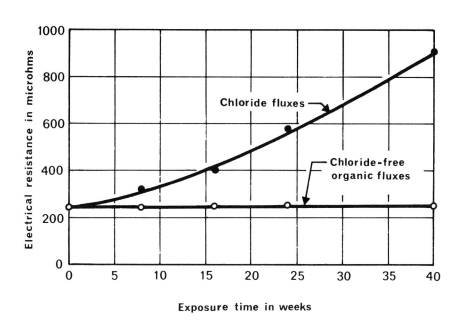

Figure 12-11. *Effect of flux residue over a period of time on the electrical resistance of an aluminum-to-copper joint exposed to an industrial atmosphere. There is little change with chloride-free flux.*

Corrosion Resistance of Dissimilar Metal Joints

The corrosion resistance of dissimilar metal joints made with soft solder is approximately equal to that of aluminum-to-aluminum soft-soldered joints.

The corrosion resistance of dissimilar metal assemblies joined with high temperature solder is generally inferior to that of all-aluminum assemblies joined with high temperature solder.

	Solder System			
	1	**2**	**3**	**4**
Solder Composition	95 Zn - 5 Al	90 Zn - 5 Al - 5 Cu - 0.1 Mg	90 Sn - 9 Zn - 1 Ni	83 Cd - 17 Zn
Melting Point	720°F	717°F	390°F	509°F
Flux Type	Zinc Chloride	Zinc Chloride	Organic Base	Metal Chlorides and Fluorides
Reaction Range	700-730°F.	700-730°F.	350-500°F.	450-530°F.
Base Metal	3003-H14 (1100-H14)[1]	3003-H14 (1100-H14)[1]	1100-H14 1) Zn-Sn Plate 2) Sn Plate	3003-1114 (1100-H14)[1]
Base Metal Pre-cleaning	Etched, Rinsed, and Dried	Etched, Rinsed, and Dried	Degreased and Dried	Etched, Rinsed, and Dried
Solder Flow	Good - V. Good	Fair - V. Good	Very Good	Good - V. Good
Wetting	Fair - V. Good	Fair - V. Good	Good - V. Good	Good - V. Good
Soldering Fumes	Heavy, Not Toxic Corrosive	Heavy, Not Toxic, Corrosive	Light, Toxic Corrosive	Medium, Toxic, Corrosive
Residues, and Post-Cleaning Required	V. Corrosive, Hot Water Rinse	V. Corrosive, Hot Water Rinse	Corrosive, Hot Water Rinse	V. Corrosive, Hot Water Rinse

Exposure and Results

	1	**2**	**3**	**4**
Salt Spray Test Hours to Failure and Appearance of "T" Joint	No Failure at 500 Hr. - Light Attack of Solder	No Failure at 500 Hr. - Attack of Solder	Perforation of Base Material 1) 236 Hr. 2) 500 Hr.	Failure Av. 30 Hr. - Interfacial Attack of Joint
Strength of Lap Joint as Soldered (Tension Pull Test)	Est. 30 KSI Shear Strength for 0.050" Lap	28 KSI Shear Strength for 0.050" Lap	1) 6.2 KSI for 0.050" Lap 2) 7.6 KSI for 0.050" Lap	12.3 KSI Shear Strength for 0.050" Lap
Strength of Lap Joint After 48 Hrs. in Flowing Tap Water	25 KSI Shear Strength for 0.050" Lap	24.6 KSI Shear Strength for 0.050" Lap	1) 6.9 KSI for 0.050" Lap 2) 9.2 KSI for 0.050" Lap	Failed in Test (Interfacial Attack of Joint)
Strength of Lap Joint After 720 Hrs. in 100% Rel. Hum. at 150°F.	13.6 KSI Shear Strength for 0.050" Lap	15.5 KSI Shear Strength for 0.050" Lap	1) 4.3 KSI for 0.050" Lap 2) 7.8 KSI for 0.050" Lap	1.0 KSI Shear Strength for 0.050" Lap
Corrosion Mode	Corrosion Attack in Body of Solder	Corrosion Attack in Body of Solder	"Alstan 70" Plating - Subj. to Heavy Pitting Attack	Corrosion Attack at Interface

[1] Although all unplated aluminum was 3003, the results are also applicable to 1100.

Table 12-3. *Solder systems vs. exposure to salt spray. (All joints formed by acetylene torch.)*

Safety Measures

Aluminum soldering is essentially a safe and danger free practice. There are few unpredictable factors. Soldering injuries are rarely true accidents in the sense of their being unavoidable. Most soldering injuries can be traced to careless workmen and to lack of sufficient vigor and forethought on the part of the safety engineer in establishing and enforcing a complete safety program, or to a management that will not properly support the safety program

Injuries can be eliminated and 100% safety records maintained by the careful development of a safe system for the handling of materials and tools and by proper and sincere safety motivation of the men engaged in soldering.

System Necessary

Soldering's constant, immediate danger is the presence of very hot metal and fluxes. Aluminum does not change color when heated. (Neither does iron glow when it's sufficiently hot to cause painful and dangerous burns.) Aluminum's color cannot therefore be used as a danger sign. Instead a system or pattern of metal handling must be established which eliminates the need for temperature sensing on the part of the workmen.

Perhaps the simplest of such systems is the development of a fixed and unchanging route by which the parts move in orderly fashion from preparation area to heating area to cooling area. Hot parts are confined to one location and are moved in one direction only.

Men assigned to solder dip pots must be required to wear protective clothing, gloves and face masks, even though the pots may be small. Men engaged in torch soldering should be given similar protective clothing, plus tinted goggles for eye protection.

Spatter caused by moisture in flux and by moisture in parts can be eliminated by a rigorous drying schedule long enough to overcome moisture variations in the flux and long enough to cope with day to day variations in ambient moisture, which affects drying rate.

Moisture in and on parts dipped into hot solder turns to steam and causes steam explosions. Moisture in flux used for induction soldering also explodes when turned to instant steam. In some cases, molten solder is driven out of a joint at bullet speed.

Spatter produced by parts accidentally dropped into molten solder can be prevented with properly designed supports, hangers and fixtures, and by the avoidance of haste and crowding.

Constant Inspection

A constant inspection routine should be established in which each piece of equipment is regularly inspected. Supervisors must make it their business to make certain the workmen follow established safety practices.

All pre-heat ovens and soldering furnaces must be ventilated. Alcohol, often used as a flux thinner and vehicle, forms an explosive mixture when it vaporizes. Hydrogen, released by flux action during soldering, also forms an explosive mixture when combined with air. Forced ventilation prevents the formation of such dangerous mixtures.

Oxygen, acetylene, propane, methane and other gases used for soldering aluminum are potentially dangerous and must be handled cautiously. The National Bureau of Standards Handbook H24 treats this subject in detail. Perhaps the most important single precaution is the complete removal of all oils and greases from and near the oxygen cylinder, its valves and gauges. Oil will explode in the presence of oxygen under pressure. A stream of escaping oxygen will ignite any oil it touches, forcing it to burn violently. Greasy gloves and rags are a potential danger near a torch. Cylinders should always be fastened securely upright. Cylinder caps should be in place on all unused cylinders.

Men working with acids should be thoroughly instructed in the cleaning of spills. Acid spilled on the floor should be cautiously and slowly diluted with water and an alkaline neutralizing agent. Organic materials such as sawdust, mops, rags and clothes should not be used to clean up acid. Acid will quickly decompose organics and produce highly toxic gases.

Source: Aluminum Soldering Handbook, 3rd Ed., Aluminum Assn., Inc.

Caustic cleaning solutions require two-fold precautions. Care must be exercised to prevent the caustic from dripping or splattering on personnel. Men must wear protective clothing and goggles. And secondly, the cleaning room must be well ventilated. Caustic combines with aluminum and liberates hydrogen which carries with it caustic vapors. Inhaled, the caustic vapors are painful and injurious to the respiratory system. And, if the hydrogen is permitted to accumulate, an explosive hydrogen/air mixture will form. Smoking should not be permitted in these areas.

Many aluminum soldering fluxes contain fluoride which is toxic. Flux must therefore be handled with caution at all times. When a package or container of flux is first opened, care must be taken to make certain none is spilled. Flux is most dry at this time and can be easily blown about.

Keep Flux Away From Food

Workmen handling flux or working near others handling flux must not eat nor smoke in that area. Lunch should not be permitted in the soldering shop, nor should lunch boxes or open coffee containers be stored there at any time. Workmen should wash their faces, hands and arms thoroughly after each session, before lunch and before going home. In this way the chance of some one accidentally ingesting flux will be completely eliminated.

The soldering area must be well ventilated. Hot flux vaporizes and travels on thermals until it condenses on a cool surface. If that surface is metal, it will corrode. Inhaled flux vapors are both irritating and dangerous.

Hydrofluoric acid can produce particularly painful injuries upon contact. The burns it causes are very slow to heal. Extreme caution must be used with this acid. Sodium chromate may induce dermatitis when it contacts the skin. Again, caution and proper equipment, correctly used, are the best preventatives.

SILVER NITRATE, USED FOR TESTING, IS EXTREMELY DANGEROUS. IT CAUSES PERMANENT BLINDNESS UPON CONTACTING THE EYES.

First Aid

All brazing shop personnel should be thoroughly trained in first aid. They should be taught the location and use of first aid equipment, the names and addresses of nearby doctors and the phone number of the local police, who are generally first to respond in an emergency.

A little training can stop panic and confusion and prevent the loss of all important time. Just teaching the secretary, for example, that upon hearing the word emergency, she is to stop all other activities and call the police and doctor, may save a life.

Burns

The instant an individual is burned, the burned area of his body must be cooled with water and ice. He is drenched as rapidly as possible without stopping to remove clothing. Cool water and ice will remove whatever heat remains in the body, stopping further burn damage. The human body is 70% water. When a portion of the body is brought above boiling or scald temperature, the body retains the heat of the burn for a long time unless it is chilled.

A number of high-volume, low-pressure showers should be installed at strategic points throughout the shop. They should be close enough to be of immediate value, but not so close that water can splash into a solder pot or onto a furnace. The showers should be controlled by foot or elbow treadles so that cold water can be turned on quickly and easily. Ice cubes and blocks of ice may be stored in standard freezers.

Ice numbs the body and reduces pain and shock. In many instances, it is the shock of pain as much as physical damage to the body that kills the victim. In many cases the quick application of ice to a moderate burn will prevent blisters and frequently prevent pain.

The use of ice—packing the body in ice—as a treatment for burns, is rapidly becoming standard hospital procedure.

THE IMPORTANCE OF APPLYING COLD WATER AND ICE AS RAPIDLY AS POSSIBLE CANNOT BE OVERSTRESSED.

A victim of serious burns should not be moved. No attempt should be made to remove his clothing: the skin may come off with it. This is a job for the doctor. Keep the victim cold until the doctor arrives.

Acid Burns

Acid burns should be instantly flushed with volumes of cool water. This may be followed by the application of an alkaline such as baking soda.

Mechanical Fastening and Adhesive Bonding

Riveting Aluminum

This reliable joining method still has considerable application to joining aluminum in spite of the fact that many structures, at one time joined by riveting exclusively have for many years been welded. The choice is governed by alloy, type of service, design of structure, location of joints and other factors.

Riveting is still used, for example, to make joints in aircraft, small boats, and van trailers, Rivets produce high-strength joints without distortion, and less skill is needed to make a riveted than a welded joint. The edges of a riveted structural aluminum joint should never be welded, either with the aim of making the joint watertight or of increasing the strength.

Strong riveted joints are obtained by driving rivets of the correct diameter and length in properly located and dimensioned holes. Watertight joints are best made by inserting a jointing compound.

Various types of manufactured heads for aluminum rivets are shown in Figure 10-1. Rivet holes may be drilled, punched or subpunched and reamed to size. Some specifications prohibit the placing of rivets in holes which have not been either drilled or reamed, but the practice of punching is becoming increasingly common, especially when automatic riveting machines are used with thin plate. It is not recommended for highest quality fabrication or critical applications, however, because it tends to reduce the strength of the joint.

The diameter of the finished hole should not exceed the nominal rivet diameter by more than 4% when driving aluminum rivets cold.

Squeeze riveters are ideal for closing aluminum rivets because there is greater certainty of filling the

Fig. 10-1. *Manufactured heads for aluminum rivets.*

holes and of producing properly formed points. While all types of points may be formed with a squeeze riveter, cone points are particularly well suited to this method of closing. The pressures required to close cone-pointed rivets with a squeeze riveter are given in Table 10-2.

Source: Metalworking With Aluminum, 2nd Ed., Aluminum Assn., Inc.

TABLE 10-2

Squeeze Riveter Pressures
Approximate Forces Required to Close Cold Rivets (Cone Points) in Tons

Rivet Diameter	Rivet Material				
inches	Alloy 1100-F tons	Alloy 2017-T31 [a] tons	Alloy 2117-T3 tons	Alloy 6053-T61 tons	Annealed Steel, tons
3/16	1	—	3	2	—
1/4	2	5	5	3	6
3/8	5	11	10	7	13
1/2	9	20	18	12	23
5/8	13	31	28	19	35
3/4	18	44	41	28	51
7/8	28	60	56	38	69
1	34	78	73	50	90

[a] Driven immediately after quenching.

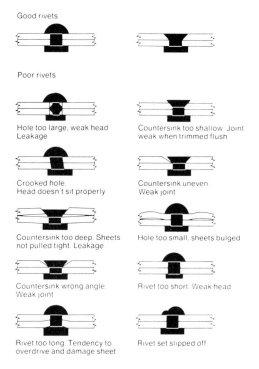

Fig. 10-2. Results of good and poor practice in riveting aluminum.

Where squeeze-riveting equipment is not available pneumatic hammers may be used. Small rivets (up to ¼ inch) can be driven with ease. In larger sizes, the high resilience of the cold aluminum alloy causes a light hammer to bounce off the rivet point instead of deforming it. Hammers must therefore be heavier than for an equivalent steel rivet and preferably of the slower-hitting long-stroke type.

The bucking tools should also be heavy, and should be held tightly against the manufactured head of the rivet. Aluminum alloys should be joined with aluminum alloy rivets, supplied as-fabricated or heat treated, and having sufficient ductility to enable them to be driven cold. Heat decreases the strength of the rivets and, for some alloys, the corrosion resistance.

In a joint between different alloys, the rivet alloy should not be appreciably stronger than the softer alloy. Steel rivets are used only when aluminum is to be joined to steel.

As a common rule, the diameter of a rivet should not be less than the thickness of the thickest member being joined or more than three times the thickness of the thinnest member. Rivet length, which depends on total joint thickness, clearance between the rivet and the hole, and the type of driven head, is best determined by driving tests.

Characteristics of aluminum rivet alloys are given in Table 10-3 and examples of both good and bad joints are shown in Figure 10-2. A blind rivet, Figure 10-3, is used where only one side of the work is accessible.

Blind rivets are all of patented design. As well as allowing a joint to be made from one side only, blind riveting is often economical because the high rate of production, and the need for only one operator, more than compensate for the higher rivet cost.

Recommended alloy combinations for blind rivets composed of a sleeve and mandrel are: 1100 sleeve, 5056 mandrel; 5050 sleeve, 5056 mandrel; 5052 sleeve, 5056 mandrel; and 5052 sleeve, 7178 mandrel. Blind rivets are not recommended when maximum watertightness, strength or corrosion resistance are required.

Stitching and Stapling Aluminum

Relatively thin sheets of aluminum are rapidly joined to each other, or to other materials by either stitching or stapling. Stitching forms its fasteners by bending and clinching wire fed from a roll. Stapling uses pre-formed fasteners and is more costly than stitching.

Stainless steel or galvanized steel wire is recommended for joining aluminum with either of these methods. Aluminum wire is not commercially suitable for this purpose. The most commonly used steel wire size used for joining aluminum is 18 gage (0.047 in. dia.).

Work-hardened alloys in sheet thicknesses totaling 0.08 to 0.09 in., or softer alloys totaling ⅛ to ³⁄₁₆ in. thickness, can be stitched. Stitching and stapling equipment is available in fixed portable types.

TABLE 10-3
Characteristics of Aluminum Rivet Alloys

Rivet Alloy	Typical Shear Strength, psi	Corrosion Resistance	Uses
1100-F	11,000	Excellent	Joining alloys 1200 and 3003 where only low strength is required.
6053-T61	22,000	Excellent	A heat-treatable alloy for general work requiring medium strength and excellent corrosion resistance.
2117-T4	28,000	Fair	A heat-treatable alloy for general structural applications. More difficult to drive in large sizes than alloy 6053-T61.
5154-F	23,000	Excellent	Relatively strong non-heat-treatable alloy used for joining olloys 5052 and 6061 when particularly good corrosion resistance is required for marine applications.
5056-F	29,000	Excellent	The strongest non-heat-treatable rivet alloy, used for joining alloys 5052 and 6061 when high strength is required.
2017-T4	36,000	Fair }	Rivets in these alloys should be stored in refrigerator after heat treatment, or be driven immediately. Use mainly in aircraft structures for joining alloys 2024, 2014 and 7075.
2024-T4	41,000	Fair }	

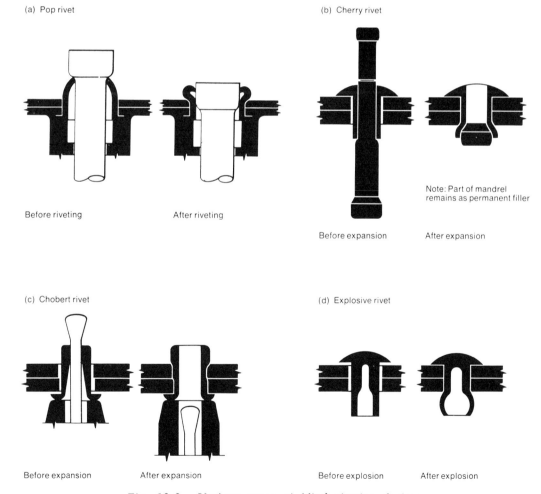

Fig. 10-3. *Various types of blind riveting devices.*

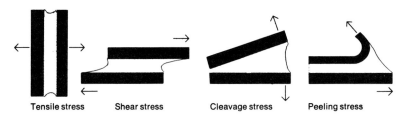

Tensile stress   Shear stress   Cleavage stress   Peeling stress

Fig. 10-4. Main types of stress encountered in adhesive bonding. Shear or tension type joints are best.

Other Standard and Special Fasteners for Aluminum

Mechanical fasteners are divided into two broad categories: standard and special. Almost all specific types have representatives in both of these divisions. For example, rivets, previously discussed, are for the most part standard fasteners; however, some rivets are special in size and/or design, or in the particular method which they are driven.

In general, standard fasteners include, besides rivets and staples, bolts, nuts, screws, clips, and nails, all manufactured to generally accepted, industry-wide specifications and used by a large number of fabricators and other consumers.

Special fasteners, which nearly always cost more than standards, either because they are more expensive to produce or because they are used in limited volume, greatly outnumber standard fasteners, being widely varied in design, function and size.

Threaded Fasteners—Bolted joints offer such advantages as high joint strengths and efficiencies, elimination of heat effects, ease of assembly and inspection, and the option to disassemble and reuse components.

Aluminum parts may be joined with either steel or aluminum fasteners—steel for high performance structural connections and aluminum for moderate strength connections where good appearance and freedom from corrosion are important. For joining aluminum to steel, galvanized or cadmium-plated steel bolts are recommended for all but severe marine environments, in which stainless steel is recommended. In aluminum-steel joints, bare steel fasteners should be used only where rust stains on the aluminum can be tolerated and aluminum fasteners only where the environment is non-corrosive.

With aluminum fasteners, care must be exercised in the choice of alloy. For superior resistances to stress corrosion, alloys 6061-T6 and 6262-T9 are preferred. Alloy 2024-T4 has higher strength but it should not be used in corrosive industrial or marine environments.

To tighten aluminum bolts on structural joints, it is advisable to use a torque wrench to avoid over tightening. For subsequent unfastening, the threads should be lubricated with one of the anti-seize compounds available for aluminum.

Nails—Because of their freedom from corrosion and staining, aluminum nails are popular fasteners for roofing and siding made of aluminum, or of non-metallic materials. The nails are manufactured from alloys 6061 and 5056 which, in this form, have tensile strengths in excess of 60,000 psi. Nevertheless aluminum nails are not as strong or as tough as steel nails and, therefore, industry standards specify a larger diameter for aluminum than for steel of the same size number.

Adhesive Bonding Aluminum

Many types of adhesives will bond aluminum to itself, to other metals and to wood, cloth, and plastics.

Principal requirements of the adhesives are that they must wet the aluminum; must not produce high internal stresses on solidification; must have strength and ductility over a wide temperature range; and must not be damaged by ultra-violet light, water or whatever else they may be exposed to in service.

Finished joists are generally neat, strong, pressure-tight and corrosion resistant, special jigging and equipment and careful control of procedures are generally required. Adhesives perform best under shear stress, which should be uniformly distributed over the largest possible area.

Failure of adhesive bonds is usually due to cleavage or peeling stress (see Figure 10-4). For structural applications, the adhesive bond should be 3-6 mils thick, and uniformly spread. The aluminum surface must be clean and most adhesives manufacturers recommend chemical pretreatments to improve the strength and reliability of the bond. Preferred procedures for cleaning aluminum include the sodium dichromate-sulfuric acid method, the alcohol-phosphoric acid method, and the chemical conversion coating method. Adhesives are applied either by hand (liquid, paste or sheet form) or with spray equipment.

High-strength adhesives such as the epoxies, with shear strengths of 3,000 psi and higher, have been used for some years to join aluminum to aluminum in the stressed parts of aircraft structures; this bonding technique has now been extended to many other types of applications. Adhesive manufacturers should be consulted about the most suitable adhesive for a particular application and for instructions in its use.

Evaluating Adhesives for Joining Aluminum

J. DEAN MINFORD

WHILE the chemical and physical properties of new adhesives are determined by the adhesive manufacturer, it usually remains for the customer to establish the anticipated service life. This requires careful consideration of a variety of factors that can affect the integrity of the bonded joint in service.

FACTORS AFFECTING BOND LIFE

The most accurate determination of service life would involve measurement of the changes in bond strength that occur in the service environment. Although these conditions can rarely be completely duplicated in the laboratory, certain tests will provide data relevant to most environments. Furthermore, exposure in selected natural environments provides additional information.

Test conditions used in the laboratory are fluid immersion, varying humidity, salt spray, and elevated or cryogenic temperatures. While an adhesive bond may fail due to any one of these conditions, more than one of these factors is usually operating at the same time in a service environment. It is also possible to obtain different degrees of bond deterioration. For example, elevated temperature can accelerate the oxidation rate of an organic adhesive. Also, as the joint is cooled below the ambient temperature, the peel and impact strengths of many adhesives will drop sharply. Water, as liquid or vapor, can disrupt the bond too.

To this complicated set of environmental factors must be added the fact that individual metals, plastics, and other materials will develop variable bond strengths and durability levels with each different class of polymer adhesives. Further variations in bond properties arise when polymers are modified. Also, each bonding surface has different bond durability properties, depending on surface preparation.

Finally, the service environment always includes some stress, which may be constant or intermittent, on the bond. (Sharpe[1] has shown that catastrophic and early bond failures can occur when stress and exposure are acting simultaneously.) Few studies in the literature have considered combined effects, and most published data do not permit good predictions of service life for bonded structures with built-in stresses.

TESTING BONDED JOINTS

A relatively small, durable fixture, light in weight, was developed by Alcoa, Fig. 1. More than 5 years of satisfactory testing has now been accumulated with this fixture with only minor refinements.[2]

Three laboratory tests have been selected for general evaluations of adhesives at the Alcoa Research Laboratories. In order of decreasing severity, they are:

1) Wet-Free-Thaw Cycle Test. This is a repeated

Dr. J. DEAN MINFORD is Group Leader, Adhesives and Cleaners Group Chemical Metallurgy Div., Alcoa Technical Center, Aluminum Co. of America, Pittsburgh, Pa.

3-day cycle consisting of exposure to 165°F water for 24 h, −30°F air for 24 h, and 170°F air for 24 h. Factors of water degradation, resin oxidation, and thermal shock are all present. Exposure for 2 years, which is standard procedure, helps to predict the effect of much longer natural exposures to water, elevated temperature, and free-thaw conditions. Only superior adhesives show no change.

2) High Humidity Test. In this test, the bonded joint is exposed to continuously condensing 100 pct humidity at 125°F for a minimum of two years. This exposure permits estimation of the effect on bond strength of water vapor trapped in a bonded structure, or the effect of a tropical environment over long periods of time. Excellent adhesives show no significant change.

3) Room Temperature Water Immersion. Continuous soaking in distilled water for two years is standard procedure. Fair adhesives show little change, and good adhesives show no change.

Figs. 2 to 5 show some typical shear strengths for

Fig. 1—Alcoa stressing fixture.

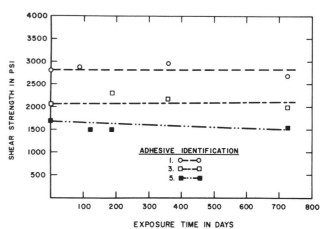

Fig. 2—Room temperature cured paste-and-liquid structural adhesives tested in room temperature water. Adhesives: (1) Polyamide-epoxy filled with china clays; (3) polyamide-epoxy mixed with mineral filler; and (5) polyamide-epoxy without filler.

aluminum bonded with two-part room temperature curing epoxies, and exposed to these "accelerated weathering" environments. As shown in Fig. 2, it is common for shear strengths of many two-part epoxy bonded joints to remain fairly constant for several years when immersed in room temperature water, providing that the aluminum surface has been deoxidized with an etchant (such as a mixture of chromic and sulfuric acids) preparatory to bonding. However, it is also possible for the bond shear strength of an epoxy adhesive to increase or decrease during such a test.

Fig. 3 summarizes some typical results when two-part epoxy bonds were exposed for two years to the high humidity test. No bonds deteriorated significantly, and bond strength increased appreciably in some instances because of additional curing at 125°F.

As anticipated, exposure to more severe conditions of the wet-freeze-thaw cycle test, Figs. 4 and 5, caused greater deterioration. Epoxies developing bond strengths under 2000 psi shear strength at room temperature, Fig. 4, had initial increases in shear

strength because of the high temperature conditions. After rising to a maximum in a few months, some of these bonds dropped to very low strengths or failed completely in 2 years.

Bonding strengths of other epoxy adhesives, Fig. 5, either remained constant throughout exposure, or significantly increased or decreased initially, and then held at a relatively constant level after the first three months of exposure. These varying responses to this aggressive environment indicate the wide latitude in performance of commercial two-part epoxies.

NATURAL ATMOSPHERIC EXPOSURES

In addition to making "accelerated weathering" tests, as described above, Alcoa engineers have exposed specimens in two natural environments: the industrial atmosphere at New Kensington, Pa., and the seacoast atmosphere at Point Judith, R. I. Fig. 6 shows the excellent durability of two-part epoxies in the New Kensington atmosphere. Checks of bonds

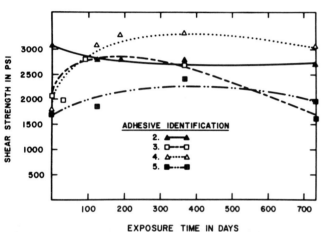

Fig. 3—Room temperature cured paste-and-liquid structural adhesives tested in 100 pct humidity at 125°F. Adhesives: (2) Polyamide-epoxy filled with aluminum powder; (3) polyamide-epoxy mixed with mineral filler; (4) amine-cured epoxy mixed with mineral filler; and (5) polyamide-epoxy without filler.

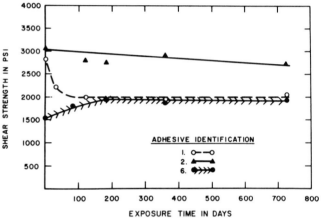

Fig. 5—Room temperature cured paste-and-liquid structural adhesives tested in wet-freeze-thaw cycle. Adhesives: (1) Polyamide-epoxy filled with china clay; (2) polyamide-epoxy filled with aluminum powder; and (6) polyamide-epoxy mixed with mineral filler.

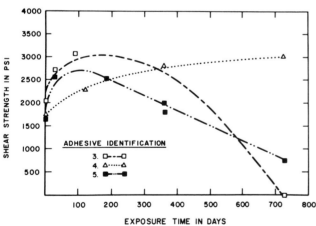

Fig. 4—Room temperature cured paste-and-liquid structural adhesives tested in wet-freeze-thaw cycle. Adhesives: (1) Polyamide-epoxy mixed with mineral filler; (4) amine-cured epoxy mixed with mineral filler; and (5) polyamide-epoxy without filler.

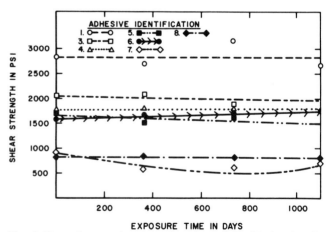

Fig. 6—Room temperature cured paste-and-liquid structural adhesives tested in industrial atmosphere (New Kensington, Pa.). Adhesives: (1) Polyamide-epoxy filled with china clay; (3) polyamide-epoxy mixed with mineral filler; (4) amine-cured epoxy mixed with mineral filler; (5) polyamide-epoxy without filler; (6) polyamide-epoxy mixed with mineral filler; (7) amine-cured epoxy filled with aluminum powder; and (8) polyamide-epoxy without filler.

tested beyond the 3 year exposure reveal that they retain initial strengths.

The seacoast atmosphere, however, is much more aggressive, as Fig. 7 shows. Bonded joints are adversely affected, usually because of interfacial metal corrosion. In most instances, there is an initial period, varying from six months to one year, during which no effect can be noted. This variability presumably reflects differences in the adsorption of the adhesive polymers to the etched aluminum surface. While no evidence of the chemical deterioration of the epoxy exists, there is clear evidence that metal surface corrosion proceeds progressively inward from the bond edge. For this reason, it is recommended that bond edges in seacoast exposures be protected, either by some compatible organic sealer, or by use of a primer prior to bonding.

Although the curves shown in Fig. 7 indicate the relative resistance of the epoxy bonds to the marine environment, they require, to be properly interpreted, supplemental data about the number and time span of the spontaneous bond failures. As Table I reveals, no

bonded joints spontaneously failed during the first 6 months. After 1 year, however, there were variations in performance ranging from no failures to ten failures out of 15 specimens. After 18 months exposure, 11 of the 15 aluminum filled polyamide-epoxy specimens were intact, while none of the mineral filled polyamide-epoxy specimens remained. After 24 months, only the aluminum-filled polyamide-epoxy joints had resisted the marine environment enough to furnish three intact specimens for shear strength evaluation.

SIMULTANEOUS STRESS AND ENVIRONMENT EXPOSURES

Figs. 8 and 9 show how bond deterioration is speeded by stressing. Although some properties of two-part epoxies and vinyl-phenolic adhesives may be quite different, they respond similarly when stressed or unstressed during exposure to the high humidity test. Fig. 8 indicates that bond shear strengths of unstressed specimens changed little during two years exposure. However, all specimens failed within 6 h when stressed to 1000 psi, about 30 pct of initial shear strength, Fig. 9.

A similar effect occurred with a one-part heat cured epoxy, modified with nitrile rubber to increase resistance to impact and raise peel strength. A number of

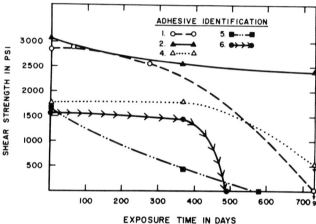

Fig. 7—Room temperature cured paste-and-liquid structural adhesives tested in seacoast atmosphere (Point Judith, R. I.). Adhesives: (1) Polyamide-epoxy filled with china clay; (2) polyamide-epoxy filled with aluminum powder; (4) amine-cured epoxy mixed with mineral filler; (5) polyamide-epoxy without filler; and (6) polyamide-epoxy mixed with mineral filler.

Table I. Bond Failures in A Marine Environment

	Exposure Periods*							
	0 to 6 Months		6 to 12 Months		12 to 18 Months		18 to 24 Months	
Adhesive	A	B	A	B	A	B	A	B
Polyamide-epoxy filled with china clay	15	0	12	2	7	0	7	7
Polyamide-epoxy filled with aluminum powder	15	0	15	0	12	1	11	8
Amine-cured epoxy mixed with mineral filler	15	0	15	3	9	3	6	5
Polyamide-epoxy without filler	15	0	15	9	3	2	1	1
Polyamide-epoxy mixed with mineral filler	15	0	15	10	2	2	0	

*Numbers under "A" indicate number of specimens remaining in exposure at the beginning of the time period. Numbers under "B" indicate total number of specimens which had spontaneously delaminated during the time period.

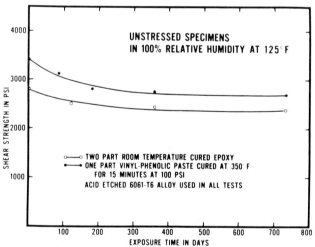

Fig. 8—Performance of unstressed bonded joints made with two-part epoxy or vinyl-phenolic pastes in 100 pct humidity at 125° F.

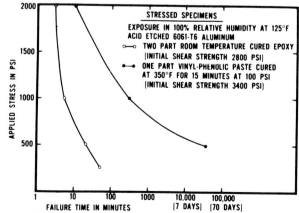

Fig. 9—Performance of stressed bonded joints made with two-part or vinyl-phenolic pastes in 100 pct humidity at 125° F.

Source: Metals Engineering Quarterly, Nov 1972

stressed specimens consistently exhibited longer bond life than did the adhesives of Figs. 8 and 9 when stressed to similar percentages of initial bond strength. Even at 2000 psi stress (37 pct of initial strength), specimens of this adhesive bond lasted averages of 10 days before failing. When the stress was lowered to 1000 psi, bond life increased to an average of 50 days. Times to failure continued to rise to about 170 days as the prestress level was lowered to 500 psi. Finally, at 250 psi stress (5 pct of initial), no bond failure had occurred after 960 days exposure. Why the bond did not fail is unclear; unstressed control specimens held in the same environment for the same time had fallen to a shear strength of less than 500 psi.

Figs. 10 and 11 show how stress and environment interact in tests of this one-part epoxy adhesive. Of those test environments used at the Alcoa Laboratories, the mildest is the New Kensington atmosphere and the next mildest is immersion in water at room temperature. Test results in these environments with unstressed specimens are shown in Fig. 10. It might be expected that applied stress would show the least effect on bonds in the New Kensington atmosphere, and Fig. 11 shows that this was the result. Our latest results reveal that no bond failures have occurred in the New Kensington atmosphere at 1000 psi stress or lower after five years exposure. Even at 2000 psi, bonds lasted 2 to 3 years.

With room temperature water immersion, no bond failures have occurred at 500 psi or lower after 840 days exposure. At 1000 psi, the failure time dropped to about 300 days, and at 2000 psi, to only 30 days.

Two generalizations follow from these results. First, as the stress on a bond is increased for specimens in a given environment, the time until bond failure decreases. Second, at a given stress level, the bonds will fail faster as they are placed in successively more aggressive environments.

CONCLUSIONS

1) Individual environmental conditions that can reduce the service life of aluminum-to-aluminum adhesive bonded joints include water, water vapor, or elevated temperature. When these factors act together or in exposure cycles, the rate of bond degradation usually accelerates.

2) Resistance to long-term exposure tests in natural industrial atmosphere would indicate long service life for most adhesive-bonded aluminum joints exposed to ordinary inland weather conditions.

3) Bonded aluminum joints exposed to seacoast weathering show significantly less endurance than in

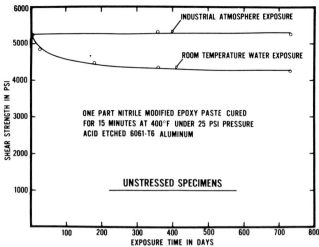

Fig. 10—Performance of unstressed joints made with a one-part nitrile-modified epoxy paste tested in room temperature water or the New Kensington (Pa.) industrial atmosphere.

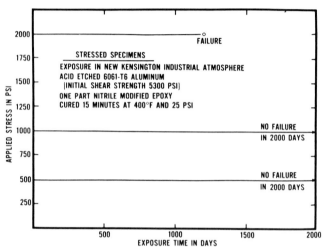

Fig. 11—Performance of stressed joints made with a one-part nitrile-modified epoxy paste tested in industrial atmosphere (New Kensington, Pa.).

nonseacoast exposures. This is attributed to interfacial metal corrosion.

4) Increasing the stress level on a bonded joint or increasing the aggressiveness of the exposure conditions at a given stress level act to decrease the potential service life of bonded joints.

REFERENCES

1. L. H. Sharpe: *Applied Polymer Symposia*, 1966, vol. 3, p. 353.
2. J. D. Minford: *Durability of Adhesive Bonded Aluminum Joints*, unpublished data, Aluminum Company of America.

INDEX